D3

574.5
EW3

D1276928

Ecological Biology 2

for A-Level and Intermediate Students in Africa

The Inter-relations of Organisms

Ecological Biology 2

for A-Level and Intermediate Students in Africa

The Inter-relations of Organisms

Editors:
Dr D. W. Ewer, *formerly Professor of Zoology, University of Ghana*

J. B. Hall, *Dept. of Botany, University of Ghana*

Contributors to this book:
Dr W. Z. Coker, *Dept. of Zoology, University of Ghana*

Dr M. Edmunds, *School of Science and Technology, Preston Polytechnic, U.K.*

Dr D. W. Ewer

J. B. Hall

Dr J. M. Lock, *Dept. of Botany, University of Ghana*

Dr J. Owen

Longman

Longman Group Limited
London

*Associated companies, branches and
representatives throughout the world*

© Longman Group Ltd 1978

First published 1978
Reprinted 1980

ISBN 0 582 60648 9

Printed in Hong Kong by
Yu Luen Offset Printing Factory Ltd

Contents

Acknowledgements

The publishers are grateful to the following for permission to use and adapt copyright material.

Academic Press Inc. (London) Ltd: Fig. 3.1 from *The Bird Faunas of Africa and its Islands* (1966) by R. E. Moreau; Fig. 5.12 from 'Root adaptations in West African trees' by J. Jeník in *Journal of Linnaean Society* (1967), **60**; Fig. 6.32 from *Journal of the Linnaean Society (Zool.)* (1939), **40**, by Stephenson; Fig. 23.18 from *J. Molecular Biology* (1971), **61**, by C. D. Lane, G. Marbaix and J. B. Gurdon. American Association for the Advancement of Science: Fig. 16.35 from *Science* (7 July, 1972), **177**, 19–27, by M. Beroza and E. F. Knipling, copyright © 1972 by the American Association for the Advancement of Science; Fig. 26.26 from 'Breakup of Pangaea and isolation of Relist mammals in Australia, South America and Madagascar' by J. Fooden and *Science* (25 February, 1972), **175**, copyright © 1972 by the A.A.A.S. The American Museum of Natural History, New York: Figs. 9.2(c) and (d) from *Evolution Emerging, Vol. II* by Gregory. The American Society of Plant Physiologists: Fig. 8.15 from 'Ipomeamarone and chloragenic acid in sweet potato roots infected by *Ceratocystis fimbriata*' by T. Akazawa and K. Wada in *Pl. Physiol.* (1961), **36**. American Society of Zoologists: Fig. 10.8 from *American Zoologist* (1969), **9**, by Wilson. Association of Applied Biologists: Fig. 8.16 from *Annals of Applied Biology* (1962), **50**, by Cole and Howard. Baillière Tindall: Figs. 10.2 and 10.3 from 'The behaviour of free-flying moths in the presence of artificial ultrasonic pulses' by K. D. Roeder in *Animal Behaviour* (1962), **10**. Ernest Benn Ltd: Figs. 9.6(a), 10.6 and 10.11 from *A History of Fishes* (1963) by J. R. Norman and P. H. Greenwood. Birkhaüser Verlag, Basel: Fig. 2.20 from *Z. Hydrobiol.* (1959), **21** by Ambul Schweiz. Blackwell Scientific Publications Ltd: Figs. 1.13 and 1.14 from 'The seed biology of *Themeda triandra* in relation to fire' by J. M. Lock and T. R. Milburn in *The Scientific Management of Animal and Plant Communities for Conservation* (1971), by Duffey & Watt; Fig. 1.17 from *New Phytologist* (1971), **70**, by Spence et al; Fig. 4.2 from *E. Afr. W. Life J.* (1963), **1**, by Lamprey; Fig. 14.7 from *E. Afr. W. Life J.* (1968), **6**, by Laws; Fig. 14.17(a) from *The Biology of Weeds* (1960) by Harper; Fig. 21.11 from 'Changes attributable to pesticides in egg breakage frequency and eggshell thickness in some British birds' by D. A. Ratcliffe in *Journal of Applied Ecology* (1970), **70**. E. J. Brill, Leiden: Fig. 9.35 from *Behaviour* (1971), **38**, by Guthrie; Fig. 10.9(h) from *Behaviour* (1952), **4**, by Witt. British Lichen Society: Fig. 12.18 from *The Lichenologist* (1961), **1**, 218 by D. C. Smith. Trustees of the British Museum (Natural History): Fig. 26.9(a) from *The Succession of Life through Geological Time* (1956); Fig. 27.14(c) from *Man the Toolmaker* (1950) by Oakley. Butterworths, London: Fig. 17.10 from *Progress in the Physiology of Farm Animals, Vol. 2* (1955) ed. Hammond. Cambridge University Press: Fig. 12.29 from *The Invertebrata* (1958) by Borradaile, Eastman et al; Fig. 17.9 from *Physiology of Farm Animals* (1946) by Marshall and Halnan; Fig. 23.3 from *Experimental Basis of Modern Biology* (1965) by Ramsey; Fig. 23.35 from *Genetics* (1971) by Cove, original photograph by Dr Ashburner. Carnegie Institution of Washington: Fig. 22.29 from *Experimental Studies on the Nature of Species* (1940), **520**, by Clausen, Keck and Hiesey. Centre for Overseas Pest Research: Fig. 9.25 from *The African Genera of Acridoidea* (1965) by Dirsch. Chapman and Hall Ltd: Figs. 9.19, 9.21, 9.23(b) and (c), 9.24(a) and (b) from *Adaptive Colouration in the Animals* (1957) by H. B. Cott; Figs. 9.34(a), 11.25 and 12.2(a) from *Textbook of Entomology* (1957) by A. D. Imms; Figs. 13.8 and 13.16 from *Ecological Methods* (1966) by Southwood; Fig. 23.26 from *Principles and Processes of Biology* (1972) by Hollingsworth and Bowler. Clarendon Press: Fig. 27.16 from *Introduction to the Study of Man* (1971) by Young. E. W. Classey Ltd: Fig. 9.9(a) from *A Practical Handbook of British Beetles, Vol. 2* (1932) by Joy. Wm. Collins Sons and Co. Ltd: Fig. 6.8 from *The Open Sea—The World of Plankton* (1956) by A. Hardy; Fig. 12.24 from *Butterflies* (1945) by E. B. Ford; Fig. 14.8 from *The Trout* (1967) by Frost and Brown. Commonwealth Agricultural Bureaux: Fig. 12.10(a) from *The Cyst-forming Species of* Heterodera (1951) by M. T. Franklin; Fig. 16.8 from *The Soil under Shifting Cultivation* (1960) by P. H. Nye and D. J. Greenland. Commonwealth Institute of Entomology: Figs. 11.6, 12.3(b) and (c) from *Bull. Ent. Res.*

viii

Hill Book Company: Fig. 9.6(c) from *Principles of Insect Morphology* (1935) by Snodgrass. Methuen Publishing Ltd: Fig. 14.15 from *Introduction to the Study of Animal Populations* (1970) by Andrewartha. John Murray (Publishers) Ltd: Fig. 23.17(b) from *Microstructure of Cells* (1965) by S. Hurry. Musée Royale de l'Afrique Centrale: Figs. 11.12, 11.13, 11.14 from *Ann. Mus. Roy. (Congo Belge)* (1955), **2** by Raignier and van Boven; Fig. 21.3 from *Rev. Zool. Afr.* (1966), **74** by Sikes. Natal Museum: Fig. 4.14 from *The Biology of the Cryptic Fauna of Forests* by R. F. Lawrence. National Central Bureau of Statistics, Sweden: Fig. 14.23 from *Historical Statistics of Sweden, Part 1, Population, 1720–1967*, 2nd ed. (1969). New York Academy of Sciences: Fig. 26.24 from *Introduction to Evolution*, 3rd ed. (1970) by Moody, published by Harper and Row. Oliver and Boyd Ltd: Fig. 21.8 from 'Affluence and the air' by R. E. Waller in *Biology of Affluence* (1972) by Smith and Smyth (eds.). Oxford University Press (E.A.): Figs. 3.3, 3.7 and 3.8 from *The Climate of Africa* by B. W. Thompson. Oxford University Press, Oxford: Fig. 4.13 from *West African Soils* (1970) by P. M. Ahn; Fig. 22.30 from *Living Organisms* (1924) by Goodrich; Fig. 27.1 from *Primates and their adaptations* (1972) by Napier; Figs. 27.4, 27.7 from *Fossil History of Man* (1972) by Day; Fig. 28.2 from *Chemical Evolution* (1967) by Calvin. Paul Parey, Germany: Fig. 9.37 from 'The behaviour of the Meercat, *Suricata suricatta* (Schreber)' by R. F. Ewer in *Z. Tierpsychol.* (1963), **20**, 570–607; Fig. 25.8 from 'Variation and incipient speciation in the African buffalo' by P. Grubb in *Z. Saügetierkunde* (1972), **37**, 121–144. Penguin Books Ltd: Fig. 21.7 from *Penguin Science Survey 2 of 1961* by E. M. Backett; Fig. 25.11 from *The Theory of Evolution* (1958) by J. M. Smith taken from *Darwin's Finches* (1947) by D. Lack, published by Cambridge University Press. Plenum Publishing Co. Ltd: Fig. 16.31(a) from *Biological Control* (1971) ed. Huffaker, by Wood; Fig. 16.31(b) from *Biological Control* (1971) ed. Huffaker, by Debach, Rosen and Kennett. Prentice-Hall, Inc., Englewood Cliffs, New Jersey, USA: Fig. 22.22 from *Human Genetics* (1969), p. 8 by V. A. McKusick. L. Reeve & Co. Ltd: Fig. 1.1 from *Dispersal of Plants throughout the World* (1930) by H. N. Ridley. Rothamsted Experimental Station: Fig. 16.25 from 'Cereal foot and root rots' in *Rothamsted Experimental Station Report for 1953* by M. P. Glynne, G. A. Satt and D. B. Slope. Royal Entomological Society of London: Figs. 4.10, 6.12 from *Trans. R. Ent. Soc.* (1961), **113** by Haddow; Fig. 9.34(b) from *Proceedings* (1969), **44** by Youdeowei and Calan; Fig. 12.25 from *J. of N.Y. Ent. Soc.* (1968), **76** by Kistner; Figs. 14.13(a) and (c) from *J. Ent. Soc. S. Afr.* (1949), **12** by Snyman; Fig. 16.30 from *J. Ent. Soc. S. Africa* (1969), **32** by Strude. The Royal Society: Fig. 9.27 from *Proceedings* (1931), **108** by Hogben and Slome. SERDAT, Brussels: Fig. 5.20 from 'Une classification ecologique des forêts du Congo' No. 63 *Serie Scientifique* (1954) by J. Lebrun and G. Gilbert, published by INEAC. Societé Entomologique de France: Fig. 11.9 from *Bull. Soc. Ent.* (1965), **70**, Nov.–Dec. by Lévieux. The Society for Promoting Christian Knowledge: Fig. 9.15 from *Butterflies and Moths* (1926) by Kirby. Springer-Verlag, Heidelberg: Fig. 12.26 from *Z. vergl. Q.* (1967), **56** by B. Hölldobler. Taylor and Francis: Fig. 12.1 from *Fauna of British Indian Fishes, Vol. II* (1889) by Day. Thames and Hudson Ltd: Fig. 27.13 from *The Evolution of Man* (1970) by Pilbeam. Transvaal Museum: Fig. 27.12 from *Memoir 4* (1950) by Broom & Robinson. University of Chicago Press: Fig. 9.33 from *The Spotted Hyena* (1972) by Kruuk, copyright © 1972 University of Chicago Press; Fig. 14.19 from *The Distribution and Abundance of Animals* (1954) by H. G. Andrewartha and L. C. Birch; Figs. 26.13(b) and (c) from *Osteology of the Reptiles* (1956) by Romer; Figs. 27.5, 27.11 from *The Fossil Evidence for Human Evolution* (1955) by Le Gros Clerk. University of Toronto Press: Fig. 15.6 from *Biological Series* (1937), **No. 43** by D. A. MacLulich. University Tutorial Press Ltd: Fig. 22.27 from *Animal Biology* 5th ed. (1957) by Grove & Newell. VEB Gustav Fischer Verlag: Fig. 4.12 from *Pedobiologia* (1965), **5** by Madge. Weidenfeld and Nicolson Ltd: Fig. 10.10 from *Life of Insects* (1964) by Wigglesworth; Figs. 10.14, 10.15, 10.16, 10.17 from *Life of reptiles, Vol. 1* (1969) by Bellaires; Figs. 26.8(b), 26.14 from *The Procession of Life* (1968) by A. S. Romer; Figs. 27.2, 27.3, 27.14(a) and (b) from *Man's Natural History* (1971) by J. S. Weiner. John Wiley and Sons Inc: Fig. 8.9 from *Plant Anatomy*, 2nd ed. by K. Esau; Fig. 9.22 from *Mechanisms of Animal Behaviour* (1966) by Marler and Hamilton; Fig. 9.36 from *Mechanisms of Animal Behaviour* (1966) by Marler and Hamilton, originally published by Cambridge University Press in *Darwin's Biological Work* (1959) ed. Bell; Fig. 15.7 from *The Biology of Populations* (1966) by MacArthur and Connell; Figs. 26.11, 26.12, 26.13(a) from *Evolution of the Vertebrates* (1969) by Colbert. The The Zoological Society of London: Fig. 25.12 from 'Intergrading between members of the *regularis* group of toads in South Africa' by N. I. Passmore in *J. Zool. Lond.* (1972), **167**, 143–151. Zoological Society of Southern Africa: Fig. 15.10 from *Zool. Afr.* (1971), **6** by Branch.

Fig. 3.43 is a drawing taken from a transparency by A. Smith, Department of Archaeology, University of Ghana, Legon.

Fig. 27.10 is an original drawing by Robert Broom, reproduced by courtesy of Transvaal Museum, Pretoria.

The Publishers regret that they have been unable to trace the copyright and obtain permission to use source material for the following figures: 2.16, 3.5, 3.44, 3.45, 9.6(b), 12.30, 16.22, 21.9, 23.6, 23.31, 26.15, 26.19. The publishers apologise for any infringement of copyright and will be grateful for any information concerning these figures.

Photographs

The publishers are grateful to the following for permission to reproduce photographs.

Prof. P. M. Ahn: Fig. 7.3; Heather Angel: Figs. 8.20(a) and (b); Ardea Photographics: Figs. 8.13 (P. Morris), 9.21(a) (I. Beames); Dr. E. S. Ayensu, Smithsonian Institution: Figs. 3.46, 8.2, 8.3(a), 12.27; Prof. C. H. Bornman and Dr C. E. J. Botha: Fig. 12.3(a); Dr C. K. Brain: Fig. 10.12; British Museum (Natural History): Figs. 26.2(b), 26.10; British Museum (Palaeontology): Fig. 26.2(a) (G. Colquhoun, Centre for Overseas Pest Research); Dr L. P. Brower: Fig. 9.11(b), (first appeared in *Scientific American*, February 1969, **220**, 24); Prof. D. T. Cole, University of Witwatersrand: Fig. 8.1; Dr G. C. Clerk: Figs. 16.24, 16.27(a), 16.28(a), reproduced by courtesy of Ghana Publishing Corporation; Bruce Coleman Ltd: Figs. 6.31, 9.32 (Sdeuard Bisserot); G. Colquhoun, Centre for Overseas Pest Research: Fig. 25.1(e); Prof. J. V. Dacie: Fig. 22.14(b); P. J. Dart, Rothamsted Experimental Station: Fig. 12.22; Faber and Faber Ltd: Fig. 12.19 (M. C. Rayner); R. Foli: Fig. 22.1; Prof. S. Fox: Figs. 28.3, 28.4; R. A. Francis: Figs. 17.2, 18.15; Ghana Information Services: Figs. 3.22(a), 16.10; Ghana Ministry of Agriculture, Fisheries Research Unit: Fig. 6.11; Dr R. W. Gibson, Rothamsted Experimental Station: Figs. 8.7(a) and (b); Prof. J. L. Harley: Fig. 12.20 (G. Woods); A. R. Hughes, by permission of Prof. P. V. Tobias: Fig. 27.8; Alan Hutchinson Library: Fig. 18.16; Dr Inman: Fig. 23.29, (previously published in *J. Mol. Biol.* (1967), **25**); Jacana: Fig. 6.16; Dr J. Jeník: Figs. 1.2, 1.3(a), 3.24, 3.26(a), 3.27, 3.29, 3.32, 3.35(b), 5.3, 5.4, 5.9, 5.15, 8.2, 8.3(a); D. John: Figs. 21.10(a) and (b); Dr H. B. D. Kettlewell: Fig. 25.5; S. Kemp: Figs. 25.1(a) and (b); Methuen Ltd., previously published in *Biochemistry of Nucleic Acids* (1950) by Davidson: Fig. 23.14; National Motor Museum, Beaulieu: Figs. 25.2(a), (b), (c), (d) and (e); Natural History Photographic Agency: Fig. 9.12 (A. Bannister); NERC copyright, reproduced by kind permission of The Director, Institute of Geological Sciences: Fig. 7.1; Dr L. Newton: Fig. 8.10; Prof. T. Pócs: Figs. 3.30, 3.34; Dr J. C. F. Poole: Fig. 23.17(a); Popperfoto: Figs. 9.30; 25.1(c), 25.1(d); Postgraduate Medical School of London, Pathology Department: Fig. 22.14(b); Radio Times Hulton Picture Library: Fig. 16.9; I. L. Rautenbach: Fig. 6.29; Robert, S. Peabody Foundation for Archaeology, reproduced by permission of University of Texas Press, from *Prehistory of Tehuacan Valley, Vol. 1*: Fig. 16.3; Dr D. M. Ross, reproduced by permission of the National Research Council of Canada, from *Canadian Journal of Zoology* (1970), **48**: Figs. 12.31(a) and (b); W. Sakai: Fig. 8.5(b); R. L. Story and R. A. Pullen, Institute for Agricultural Research, Samaru: Fig. 7.7; Dr M. Swain: Figs. 3.40, 11.10; H. C. Taylor, Botanical Research Institute, Pretoria: Fig. 3.41; United Africa Co. Ltd: Fig. 3.22(b) (Tom Smith, London); United States Information Service, Accra: Fig. 3.9; Prof. G. C. Varley: Fig. 9.16; W.A.S.A.: Fig. 19.6; C. James Webb: Fig. 22.14(a); Weed Research Organisation, Ghana: Fig. 16.20(a); Douglas P. Wilson: Fig. 9.4; Fergus B. Wilson: Figs. 5.18, 5.25, 16.16, 16.17, 16.18, 16.19, 16.21(b).

Figure 1.11 was first published in *Nigerian Field* (1969), **34**(1), by J. Jeník and J. B. Hall.

Figure 23.25 was previously published in *Science* (1970), **169** by Miller et al.

Front cover photograph by Peter Ward (Natural Science Photos). Back cover photographs: 1 by kind permission of the Plant Protein Institute, Ministry of Agriculture, Rhodesia; 2 and 3 by Dr Malcolm Edmunds; 4 by M. A. Fraser and K. Morgan, Centre for Science Education, Chelsea College.

Preface

It has been our aim in writing Ecological Biology to produce an integrated course of biology in which the structure and activities of organisms are considered not in isolation, but in relation to their conditions of existence. As the title suggests, we have not sought to produce a textbook of ecology so much as a book which regards biology from an ecological viewpoint.

In Book 1, subtitled 'Organisms and their Environment', we reviewed the ways in which the structure and physiology of organisms are determined by their positions in the food web, and by the prevailing environment; emphasis was on that part of biological science which is often called 'physiological ecology'. In this book we take the enquiry further to examine, in Chapters 1 and 2, those activities of organisms which enable them to find suitable habitats and then continue, in subsequent chapters, to consider the many different ways in which organisms interact.

It has long been recognized that certain groupings of organisms are commonly found together. Viewed globally, major groupings or biomes can be distinguished, while within these biomes are smaller units, the communities. The most important terrestrial biomes and communities are discussed in Chapters 3 to 6, while Chapter 7 examines the less conspicuous but equally significant communities of decomposers found in soil.

Even today, much community study is still at the stage of empirical description, but recent studies have increasingly shown that communities are more than mere random assemblages of those organisms which can tolerate a particular environment. Evidence of intricate lines of interdependence within a community, some of which is presented in Chapters 8–12, suggests that the species within communities have co-evolved over considerable periods of time.

Communities are not static: reproduction and mortality result in changes of population size; these are the subjects of Chapters 13–15.

Far from being a merely abstract study, ecology is of immediate importance to all countries, both developed and developing. Many biologists believe that unless a deeper understanding of ecological problems and principles guides the policies of the governments of the world, a human crisis of unprecedented dimensions lies ahead. In Chapters 16 to 21 we attempt to relate many of the ideas developed in earlier chapters to the problems of ensuring that all men are well fed and healthy, while indicating some of the difficulties which are likely to be encountered in the pursuit of this goal.

In discussing the control of pests and parasites, we introduce the important discovery that species are not fixed and invariable in their characteristics. Not only may individual disease-causing organisms of the same species differ in their resistance to chemical pesticides, but these differences may be heritable. The phenomena of heredity are examined more closely in Chapters 22 to 24 and, using the earlier-mentioned principles of population dynamics, we show that the genetic characteristics of a population may change with time in response to environmental pressure mediated by selection. This idea of evolution as a necessary consequence of variation is introduced in Chapters 25 and 26. The final chapters explore some of the wider implications of evolutionary change.

We have taken our illustrative material, where possible, from Africa and from African organisms which are familiar or of economic importance. In some cases, however, we have been compelled to look further afield. We hope that readers will draw our attention to African examples that we have overlooked and which ought to have been included, as well as to any misinterpretations and errors of fact.

In preparing this second volume, we have depended upon the kindness of many people who have most patiently answered our questions, but we are especially grateful to Mr. P. M. Ahn, Prof. G. C. Clerk, the late Dr. R. F. Ewer, Prof. P. Greig-Smith, Dr. P. Grubb, Dr. K. A. Haizel, Prof. J. K. M. Hodasi, Dr. D. M. John, Prof. R. Kumar, Mrs. M. L. Kumekpor, Dr. P. Lamptey, Dr. R. E. Larsen, Dr. D. Leston, Dr. D. U. U. Okali, Dr. R. Orraca-Tetteh, and Dr. M. D. Swaine, who read various chapters in draft and contributed many useful comments. Our thanks are due once again to the skilful assistance of Mr. R. Foli and Mr. T. Akoto, and also to Mr. G. K. Abokwa who typed the final chapters in conditions of great pressure. Finally one of us (D.W.E.) would like to record his sincere thanks to Professor G. C. Williams of the University of Reading and to the Warden and Fellows of Saint Patrick's Hall of that University where he did much of the reading for the preparation of certain chapters while on sabbatical leave from the University of Ghana to which his thanks are also due.

To the Reader

The Reader is assumed to be already familiar with the content of GCE O-level Biology, or with the Biology covered in General Science and Advanced General Science in the same examination. He is recommended to revise his knowledge in certain areas by reading the appropriate sections of an O-level textbook before starting to read some of the chapters. To assist, a section on 'Revision Reading' will be found at the end of certain chapters of the present volume.

Each chapter ends with a series of problems. Some of these arise directly from the material in the chapter; some are extensions of the ideas developed. If the Reader is to acquire a full understanding of what he has read, he should attempt to solve these problems.

Each chapter ends with suggestions for 'Further Reading' which will permit the Reader to follow certain topics if he should find them of interest. Some of the works recommended give more detailed treatment of the same problems; others deal with specific issues which may be of interest to the Reader.

At the end of the book there is a detailed index which will assist the Reader both to locate the meaning of unfamiliar terms and to bring together information on such topics as 'desert' or 'grasshopper' to which scattered references are made in the text. At the same time, it is desirable in certain matters such as 'mosquito' or 'ribosome' to refer to the indexes of both volumes.

Part 1
Autecology—the study of single species

1 The dispersal and distribution of producers

Distribution

If you look through the laboratory window it is likely that you will see several different kinds of plant. A walk round the school compound will reveal the presence of many others. In fact, the vegetation of the typical school grounds is likely to include several hundreds of species of plants.

When we come to examine where these plants grow, that is, their distribution, we find that most of them are not scattered at random over the compound, but tend to be restricted to certain kinds of habitat. Some of the distribution patterns are entirely man-made, for example, a row of evenly-spaced royal palms down either side of the main entrance road, or the restriction of cassava to the school farm; but even the wild plants are likely to be distributed in a non-random way.

We could study the distribution of a plant, such as *Tridax procumbens* (Book 1 Fig. 3.7), as follows. Firstly, we make a list of the main habitats near the school: these might be, for example, flower beds, exposed lawns, shaded lawns, path verges, rubbish dump, cassava farm, cocoa farm, forest. We could then simply note in which of these habitats *Tridax* occurs, but this would be a crude method as we would not distinguish habitats where it is abundant from those where it is rare. We can estimate relative abundance by sampling with a quadrat frame measuring 50 cm × 50 cm. This is dropped at random a number of times, say ten, within each habitat and the number of *Tridax* plants included in each sample is recorded. From the mean count per unit area, that is the density, we can draw conclusions as to the distribution of *Tridax* around the school (Table 1.1).

If instead of *Tridax* we had chosen the carpet grass *Axonopus compressus* or the shrub *Lantana camara* we would probably have found quite a different pattern of distribution; each species, in fact, will be found to have its own pattern. The determination of its pattern of distribution is a logical first step in the study of the autecology (the ecology of a single species) of *Tridax procumbens*, as it indicates the preferences of the species, which we may then attempt to explain.

It is possible to study distribution at different scales. *Tridax* has a distribution within the school compound, a smaller-scale distribution (sometimes called 'dispersion' or simply 'pattern') within any one of its habitats, and a larger-scale distribution within a district, country, con-

Table 1.1 Density of *Tridax procumbens* in different habitats near the University of Ghana, Legon; 15 December 1973. Each value is the mean number of inflorescences per 50 cm × 50 cm quadrat after ten throws of the quadrat (*Hall, unpublished data*)

Habitat	Tridax *density* (inflorescences per 0·25 m²)
Newly-sown lawn; unshaded	6·6
Road margin	5·9
Established lawn; unshaded	1·4
Established lawn; shaded	0·1
Cassava farm	0·0
Cocoa farm	0·0

tinent, or the world as a whole (Fig. 1.1). Distribution at the smallest scale may be the result of such factors as small irregularities in the ground surface, or of chance. At the largest scale, climate is important—*Tridax* is restricted to warm countries—as is also historical accident. *Tridax* until about seventy years ago was absent from West Africa, not of course because the climate is unsuitable there, but because it had not then been introduced. We do not know exactly how it got there but it may have been as seeds mixed with imported grain. *Tridax procumbens* came originally from South America.

Every mature growing plant has a history, in that it

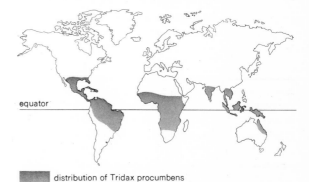

equator

▰ distribution of Tridax procumbens

1.1 Approximate world distribution of *Tridax procumbens*. This species is indigenous in South America and introduced elsewhere. (Data from Ridley)

must have arisen from a living seed or other propagule which reached its present site, germinated, and gave rise to a young plant which was able to establish itself under the conditions prevailing there. Thus the distribution pattern is built up by large numbers of individual cases of successful dispersal, germination and establishment. We shall consider the three aspects in turn.

Dispersal

When a plant reaches maturity it passes from a vegetative to a reproductive phase of growth (Book 1 p. 48). If there were no wastage, and if the number of individual plants in a species remained constant, each plant would need to produce only a single seed within its life-time to replace itself. Actual reproductive capacities are much in excess of unity. For example, a plant of *Tridax*, which is an annual or a short-lived perennial, may produce from 200 to 500 seeds; a silk-cotton tree during the course of its life will produce many millions.

The reason for this apparently excessive over-production is that each seed has only an infinitesimal chance of producing a mature plant. The parable of the sower in the Bible lists the main factors which may militate against establishment – unsuitable soil, competition from other plants, shortage of water, predation. Small as it is, the probability of success would be much less were it not for the various adaptations shown by the propagule for dispersal and germination.

Why is dispersal necessary? It may be argued that the very fact that a plant is growing and fruiting successfully proves the locality to be suitable also for its offspring, whereas many places farther off may be unsuitable. There is much truth in this argument, and in most species the majority of propagules are in fact deposited close to the parent. On the other hand the parent plant may cast shade too deep to allow its own seedlings to develop beneath it. This is especially true of so-called 'light-demanding' species such as the silk-cotton tree, which can become established only in clearings. In general, however, the main problem faced by seeds is that almost all the suitable land surface is, at any given moment, already fully occupied by plants. Space is created when plants die, are eaten, or are otherwise removed, and this space can be utilized only by a propagule which is already there. Such gaps arise in a more or less random way, and there is no guarantee that one will occur adjacent to any particular plant. The propagules must be widely dispersed to have a reasonable chance of finding such a gap. Also, the habitat required by many species is discontinuous: for example, the ponds in which an aquatic plant can grow may be small and widely scattered, separated by unsuitable dry ground.

We can make an analogy with the son of the family who wishes to live in his own house. If he insists on staying in the same place, he may have to wait a long time before his father leaves, or dies. There is only a small chance that one of the adjacent houses will fall vacant within the near future. If he requires a house quickly, he must 'disperse' himself, and hunt for a house over a wide area. Of course in the case of the plant, it is not a question of a single seed 'finding' a place, but of a large number of seeds being more or less randomly dispersed so that some will be available to make use of 'vacancies' as these arise.

Propagules should thus ideally be widely dispersed, but at the same time provided with a food store adequate to secure their establishment. These two requirements are, however, mutually opposed. If a plant has a certain amount of food material available for seed production, this can be devoted to making either a small number of large seeds with bulky food stores, or a larger number of smaller, less well-provided seeds, which are more readily transported and dispersed than large ones. Which of these strategies is adopted by a species depends on its ecological nature. We may contrast a plant of mature high forest with a weed of forest farms. High forest presents an essentially continuous habitat, in which one part is very much like another. Light intensity on the forest floor is critically low and close to the compensation point. It follows that seeds must be well-provided with food to enable seedlings to grow to a size at which they can compete with other plants and thus become established despite the adverse conditions for photosynthesis, but there is no over-riding necessity for wide, efficient dispersal. On the other hand, the weed requires openings which may be small and widely scattered, but where light and nutrient conditions are optimal immediately after clearing. It is evident that efficient dispersal is necessary in this case, but that the abundant light makes a large seed size unnecessary. As extreme examples, we can cite on the one hand a tree of mature forest *Omphalocarpum* (Fig. 1.2) whose large, heavy fruits grow on

1.2 *Omphalocarpum* sp. growing in West African forest. Note the large fruits, reaching a diameter of 15 cm, which are attached directly to the trunk.

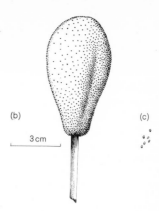

1.3 *Musanga cecropioides*, the umbrella tree; a fast-growing, 'weedy' tree of clearings in forest. (a) Dense stand of *Musanga* at the edge of newly-made road. (b) Ripe compound fruit, consisting of fleshy receptacle bearing the tiny individual fruits. (c) One-seeded fruits, drawn to same scale as (b).

the trunk and crash down to the ground below the parent tree, perhaps rolling a little way, and on the other hand *Musanga* the umbrella tree (Fig. 1.3), which springs up when forest is cleared, and whose tiny seeds are efficiently distributed by birds and bats.

Some plants produce both kinds of seeds—larger ones with a plentiful food store which are not adapted for dispersal, and smaller ones which are dispersed. In the dwarf annual herb, *Gymnarrhena micrantha*, which occurs in the semideserts of North Africa, there are two types of inflorescence, one at the soil surface and one below it. The two inflorescences produce different types of fruit. The underground fruits are large (mean fresh weight 6·5 mg), and lack the tuft of long hairs which assists in wind dispersal of the aerial fruits, which are much smaller (mean fresh weight 0·4 mg). The large fruits produce larger seedlings than the small fruits, and if the seedlings are exposed to a period of drought after germination, the seedlings from the large fruits survive much better (Table 1.2).

Table 1.2 Mortality of *Gymnarrhena micrantha* seedlings with increasing periods of drought; each figure is the number of dead seedlings from sets of 24 at the start of the experiment. Note that the seedlings from the larger subterranean fruits are more drought resistant than those from the smaller aerial fruits.

| | Duration of drought (days) | | | |
	1	3	5	7
Seedlings from aerial fruits	7	17	21	24
Seedlings from subterranean fruits	0	0	0	9

Some sedges in the genera *Scirpus* and *Bulbostylis* which grow on seasonally wet pool margins in tropical Africa show similar behaviour to that of *Gymnarrhena*. In *Scirpus*

articulatus the aerial fruits weight about 1·7 mg, while the large fruits which are produced at the base of the aerial stems weigh about 7·7 mg each (Fig. 1.4).

Dispersal of propagules away from the parent plant may have an additional function, as the neighbourhood of a parent plant may be a relatively dangerous place for both young individuals and propagules. Predators of the parent plant will of course be most abundant in its immediate vicinity. These predators may feed on the established parent plant, removing a proportion of the material which it produces, but not seriously affecting its vigour. The adult individuals of the South American forest climber *Dioclea megacarpa* are attacked by moth larvae which eat the shoot tips. This is not serious for the adult plant as it can afford to lose a proportion of its shoot tips, but moth larvae are constantly falling from the foliage of the climber to the ground below. There they search for alternative food sources, and if they encounter a seedling of *Dioclea* they will eat its shoot tip. The seedling has of course only one of these; moreover, its regenerative powers are strictly limited, as it has only two buds, in the axils of the cotyledons, from which regeneration can take place. If these are subsequently eaten, the seedling will be killed. Thus

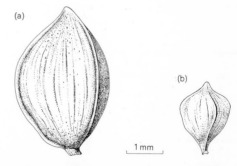

1.4 *Scirpus articulatus*. (a) Fruit taken from within a leaf sheath at the base of the plant. (b) Fruit from aerial inflorescence; drawn to same scale as (a).

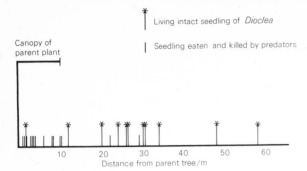

Canopy of
parent plant

Living intact seedling of *Dioclea*

Seedling eaten and killed by predators

10	20	30	40	50	60

Distance from parent tree/m

1.5 Diagram showing the survival of seedlings of *Dioclea megacarpa* at different distances from the parent plant. (After Janzen).

seedlings which take root close to the parent have a very poor chance of survival: Fig. 1.5 shows the distribution of damaged and undamaged seedlings along strips of ground, starting at the parent plant and moving away from it. Clearly there is an advantage here in dispersing the seeds away from the parent plant.

A further advantage of dispersal lies in the avoidance of seed predators. Seeds are extremely rich in food materials, and are fed upon by large numbers of predators. If large numbers of seeds all occur within a small area, it is very easy for a predator to move from one seed to the next without undue effort. If, however, the seeds are scattered widely, it may be extremely difficult for a predator to find them. Thus a seed which is dispersed to a considerable distance from its parent is more likely to survive: firstly, because it is likely to be well separated from other seeds and thus

missed by predators which are attracted to concentrations of seeds, and, secondly, because it is well separated from its parent, which may harbour predators which kill the seedling. Plants which are artificially introduced to areas far from their normal range may thrive because their predators are not introduced with them. For example, the shrub *Leucaena leucocephala* loses 95 percent of its seeds to predation by beetles in its original home area in Central America. However, in both Puerto Rico and West Africa where it was introduced as a cover crop, it sets abundant seed which is hardly attacked by predators, and consequently seedlings grow in profusion (Fig. 1.6).

The seeds of the silk-cotton are dispersed widely by the wind, but once on the ground they are rapidly attacked by the plant bugs *Dysdercus* (Fig. 9.34a) which destroy the seeds. Seedlings are normally very rare. However, numbers of seedlings appear on the mud around a drying pond: the seeds float on the water, where they are presumably immune from attack by plant bugs, and are then subsequently deposited in a place suitable for germination, thus evading the seed predators.

We have now seen some of the reasons why dispersal is necessary, and must next consider the ways in which it is brought about. Many agents participate in the dispersal of propagules; the most frequent of these are wind, water and animals. Other seeds are dispersed by the activity of the plant itself.

Wind dispersal

The simplest means of facilitating wind dispersal is to be very small. In all wind-dispersed propagules (Fig. 1.7), the

1.6 Seedlings of *Leucaena leucocephala* growing among old fruits.

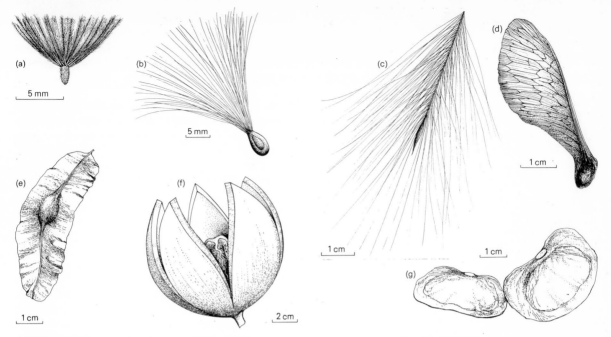

1.7 Wind-dispersed propagules. (a) Fruit of *Tridax procumbens*; the one-seeded fruit carries a parachute of hairs representing the calyx. (b) Seed of the shrub *Calotropis procera*; the fruit is many-seeded and dehiscent; each seed carries a tuft of long hairs to aid wind dispersal. (c) Seed of the forest tree *Funtumia elastica*; hairs are attached to a slender beak on the seed, and because of the direction of their attachment tend to spread more widely as the seed falls. (d) Fruit of the forest tree *Triplochiton scleroxylon*; the wing is formed by the pericarp. (e) Fruit of the savanna tree *Terminalia glaucescens*; the wing is part of the pericarp here also. (f) Capsular fruit of the West African mahogany tree, *Khaya ivorensis*, after the seeds have been shed. (g) Seeds of *Khaya*; the wing is formed by the testa.

surface area is large in relation to the weight, and thus the rate of sinking in air is relatively slow. Seeds like those of orchids, which weigh only 2 to 8 μg, and the spores of bryophytes and many pteridophytes, as well as the propagules of fungi and algae, are all small enough to remain suspended in air long enough to be dispersed significant distances. Quartz grains of similar weight have been found more than 1 000 km from land, and seeds, because of their lower density, could easily be carried much further.

Other fruits have hairs, plumes, or wings on them, which increase their surface area and decrease their rate of fall. The minute plumed seed of the cat-tail *Typha latifolia* falls 4 m in 34 seconds. If such a seed fell from an inflorescence 4 m high in a breeze of 3 m s^{-1}, it would be carried over 100 m, and nearly 700 m in a gale of 20 m s^{-1}. (These figures assume the airflow is smooth and without turbulence.) In nature seeds may frequently be carried up in rising currents of air, and thus be transported much further than they would otherwise have travelled. This can be readily observed if any light, plumed seeds are released upwind of a hot tarmac road. As they drift across it they will suddenly rise several metres before continuing onwards.

Propagules with wings or flanges on them are not carried as far as plumed or minute propagules but the seed may be larger. Many winged propagules have the seeds at one end; the whole unit spins like a helicopter rotor as it falls.

Such seeds are usually found on trees or climbers rather than on low-growing plants.

Water dispersal

Just as wind-dispersed propagules are buoyant in air, water-dispersed propagules must be buoyant in water. This buoyancy can be achieved by the inclusion of air spaces within the propagule (Fig. 1.8): in a corky pericarp as in *Pterocarpus santalinoides*, in a fibrous pericarp as in the coconut (*Cocos nucifera*) or between the embryo and the seed-coat as in the wild riverbank-dwelling form of the sponge plant *Luffa*. The outer covering of the propagule must be waterproof to prevent the flooding of air spaces, and also to avoid the premature wetting of the embryo which would cause it to lose its dormancy. Adaptations to dispersal are particularly impressive in seashore plants, many of which have a pantropical distribution. Fig. 1.9 shows the result of an experiment in which seeds of the shore plant *Canavalia rosea* collected on the coast of Ghana were floated on seawater in the laboratory and the number still afloat and unsaturated recorded at intervals. Table 1.3 gives survival times in seawater for the propagules of various other maritime plants. It would be possible for some of these seeds to be carried several thousand miles by ocean currents and still be able to germinate. In

5

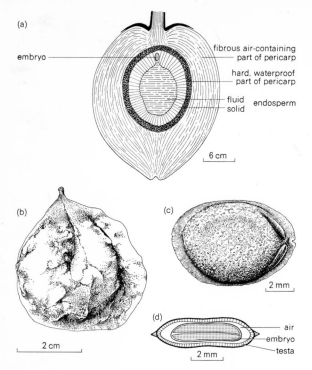

1.8 Water-dispersed propagules. (a) Vertical section through fruit of *Cocos nucifera* (coconut); buoyancy is provided by air within the fibrous pericarp, seawater is excluded from the embryo by the hard part of the pericarp, germination in rather dry sand is possible because the fruit carries its own supply of water. (b) External view of fruit of *Pterocarpus santalinoides;* the pericarp is corky. (c) External view of seed of loofah (*Luffa aegyptiaca*). (d) Transverse section through seed of *Luffa aegyptiaca* to show air space between testa and embryo.

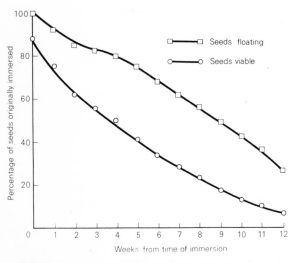

1.9 Survival of seeds of *Canavalia rosea* when floated on seawater in the laboratory. When seawater penetrates the testa the seeds swell and sink, and the embryo loses its viability. Some seeds die before sinking.

fact seeds of the genera *Mucuna*, *Entada* and *Ipomoea* are regularly carried in a viable condition by the Gulf Stream current from their home in the West Indies to the shores of north-western Europe, although they cannot grow so far north.

Table 1.3 Length of viability in seawater of some sea-dispersed fruits and seeds (*Data from various sources*)

Species	Time/months
Caesalpinia bonduc (oware seed)	30
Ipomoea tuba (a moonflower)	12
Thespesia populnea	12
Cocos nucifera (coconut)	4
Canavalia rosea	3

Animal dispersal

The seeds of many kinds of plants are dispersed by animals, either by adhering to their skin (Fig. 1.10) or because they are embedded in edible fruits. A walk through weedy farmland will quickly provide a sample of the adhesive propagules of an area; the mechanism of adhesion may be hooks, as in *Urena*, *Pupalia* or *Desmodium*, or sticky hairs as in *Boerhavia*. Spiny fruits such as those of *Alternanthera pungens* become attached to the hooves of animals or to the wheels of cars and aeroplanes.

Many of the grasses, sedges and other herbs which grow on muddy pond margins have small seeds which may have a rough surface but which have no other obvious adapta-

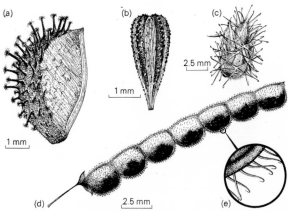

1.10 Adhesive propagules. (a) Mericarp of *Urena lobata*, consisting of hook-bearing pericarp surrounding a single seed; each fruit splits into five such mericarps. (b) 'Fruit' of *Boerhavia diffusa*; the true fruit is covered by the persistent base of the perianth, which bears droplets of sticky fluid. (c) Part of inflorescence of *Pupalia lappacea*; the star-shaped clusters of hooked bristles are attached to the bracts surrounding the fruit. (d) Fruit of *Desmodium gangeticum*; it breaks up transversely into one-seeded mericarps. (e) Margin of mericarp of *Desmodium*, magnified to show the hooked hairs.

tions to dispersal. Many of these species are very widely distributed, however, and it is likely that they are habitually dispersed in mud stuck on birds' feet. Human feet and cars may also serve. Plants of *Eragrostis superba* appeared at a car-washing site in western Uganda 600 km from the nearest known locality for this species.

When a fruit is eaten by a mammal or bird a proportion of the seeds may pass unharmed through the gut to be expelled in the faeces, perhaps some distance from the place where the fruit was taken. Elephants, monkeys and apes might be expected to be particularly good dispersers, since they are non-ruminants, and more seeds are likely to pass through their bodies undamaged (Fig. 1.11). However, many ungulates are also dispersers of seeds. A brief survey of the dung of various mammal species in northern Tanzania gave the results shown in Table 1.4. Within the genus *Acacia* there are species with dehiscent pods and others with indehiscent fruits. The ripe pods of the indehiscent-fruited species fall unopened to the ground, where they are eaten by animals, such as elephants, cattle, gazelle and baboons. The seeds are surrounded by a toffee-like flesh, which has a rich, sweet smell that may assist animals in locating the pods. The seeds have a very hard seed coat, and by sampling directly from the oesophagus of cattle through a fistula it has been found that less than 2 percent of the seeds were damaged during the initial chewing. Even if one allows for a further loss during remastication, the total seed loss is unlikely to exceed 20 per cent. There are many observations of seeds of species of *Acacia* germinating from animal dung.

The germination of some seeds is enhanced or accelerated by their passage through the gut of an animal. For example,

1.11 A seedling of *Detarium microcarpum* germinating in elephant dung which has been moistened by rain.

Table 1.4 Number of plant species whose seeds were found in the dung of various species of mammal in northern Tanzania (*Data from Burtt*)

Mammal	Number of plant species in dung
Elephant	12
Civet	10
Eland	7
Thomson's gazelle	4
Impala	3
Black rhinoceros	2
Giraffe	2

the time required for germination of seeds of two South African species of *Olea* (the genus including the olive tree), normally twelve months, is only four to six months after they have passed through the gut of a pigeon.

Edible fruits when ripe, like insect-pollinated flowers, attract animals by their bright colours, scent and taste. Such fruits usually change colour at maturity, from green shades which blend with the surrounding foliage, to yellow, red, blue or black colours which contrast with the leaves and render the fruit easily visible. The contrast may be enhanced by differences in colour between fruit and seeds, or within the fruit itself. Wind-dispersed and explosively dispersed fruits, on the other hand, are generally brownish at maturity; this is true of *Millettia*, *Khaya* and *Ceiba*, for example. Fruits with adhesive devices may be brownish, or green as in *Boerhavia*.

While contrasting colours are of particular importance in attracting birds, mammals, particularly nocturnal ones, may rely more on smell for locating ripe fruit. Thus it is not surprising that the unripe fruits of most species smell much less strongly than ripe ones; they also smell differently. The precise study of such changes is complicated by the large number of volatile compounds in fruits—152 have been found in oranges—and by the small quantities which may be present, as well as the extreme sensitivity of sense organs to certain compounds. Ethyl 2-methylbutyrate, an important scent constituent of ripe apples, is detectable by man at a concentration of 0·0001 parts per million. There is no reason to think that other animals are any less sensitive. In addition to changes in scent and flavour, the chemical composition of the fruit changes, with sugars often increasing and acidic components declining. Tannins and phenols which often give an astringent taste, also decline with age.

Explosive dispersal

Some plants have explosive fruits (Fig. 1.12), which expel the seeds to considerable distances from the parent plant. The mechanisms of action can depend either on the build-

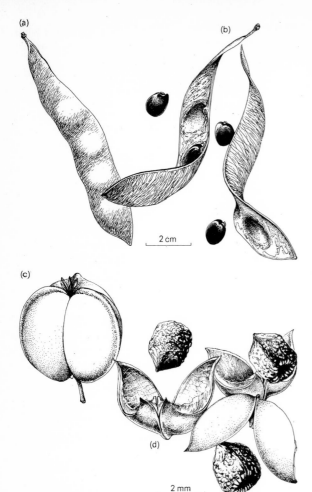

1.12 Explosively dispersed propagules; tensions develop in the fruit wall as a result of drying, and result in the twisting of the wall fragments when these separate along lines of weakness. (a) *Millettia thonningii;* intact fruit. (b) *Millettia* at time of dehiscence; the fruit opens along both margins, the fruit walls twist violently and the seeds are scattered. (c) *Euphorbia heterophylla;* intact fruit. (d) The *Euphorbia* fruit splits suddenly into three parts, each of which breaks open to eject a seed.

ing up of high turgor pressures within part of the fruit, followed by rupture along a line of weakness, or on the development of tensions consequent upon differential shrinkage of parts of the fruit during drying, again followed by rupture along a line of weakness and the violent ejection of the seeds. Such dispersal mechanisms are often thought of as rather inefficient, but seeds may be thrown to considerable distances. The discus-shaped seeds of the small tree *Millettia thonningii* may travel up to twenty-two metres from the crown when the pod dehisces, and each weighs about 300 mg. The common weed *Euphorbia heterophylla* has an explosive capsule which dehisces on drying and projects the three seeds it contains up to three metres from the plant.

Dispersal efficiency over long distances

It is of interest to compare the efficiency of these various methods in dispersing propagules over long distances. In 1883 an instructive 'experiment' was performed for us when a great volcanic explosion devastated the island of Krakatau in the East Indies, apparently killing all forms of life on it. When the lava cooled, the island presented a sterilized but moist and fertile soil to all propagules which could reach it, the nearest land being Java and Sumatra, both about 30 km away. In 1884 there was still no visible vegetation but by 1886 plants had started to grow, the most conspicuous being maritime species along the shore and blue-green algae and ferns inland. Table 1.5 gives the dispersal mechanisms of the species of seed plants recorded at different dates after the eruption. Clearly, wind dispersal

Table 1.5 Numbers of plant species, grouped according to dispersal mechanism, which were recorded on the island of Krakatau at various intervals after its devastation by volcanic explosion; dispersal data expressed as percentages of column totals (*Data from Docters van Leeuwen*)

Dispersal agents	Number of years after explosion				
	1	3	14	25	45
Wind	0	62	44	28	42
Sea	0	38	47	52	33
Animal	0	0	9	20	23
Man	0	0	0	0	2
Total number of plant species	0	26	64	115	214

was most efficient; the proportion of wind-dispersed species would have been even higher if non-flowering plants had been included. Sea dispersal also proved efficient; the eventual decline in percentage of sea-dispersed species as the total flora increased is presumably due to the relatively small number of such species. Figures for the proportion of animal-dispersed species in Java are not available, but they are probably roughly similar to those estimated for the forests of Ghana (Table 1.6); and thus much higher than for Krakatau. Explosively-dispersed fruits were not represented at all on Krakatau.

In addition to adaptations for dispersal, the propagules of many species have adaptations ensuring dispersal at the best possible season, and promoting dispersal to the most suitable position within a habitat.

Timing of dispersal

The best time for germination is the early rainy season; consequently the best time for dispersal is the late dry season, and as Table 1.7 shows, most West African forest trees do in fact disperse their fruits at this time. In the

Table 1.6 Dispersal mechanisms of a sample of 207 vascular plant species, of various life-forms, recorded in Ghana forests; dispersal data expressed as percentages of column totals (*Hall and Swaine, unpublished data*)

Dispersal agents	Tall trees	Understorey trees	Ground herbs	Epiphytes	Climbers
Wind	17	3	34	100	23
Animal (adhesion)	0	0	6	0	0
Animal (swallowing)	70	84	40	0	69
Explosion	9	13	17	0	5
Doubtful	4	0	3	0	3
Total number of species	54	37	35	3	78

Table 1.7 Months during which ripe fruit has been recorded for 157 species of forest trees in Ghana. More species fruit in the late dry season, i.e. February and March, than at other times of year (*Data from Taylor*)

	July	Aug.	Sept.	Oct.	Nov.	Dec.	Jan.	Feb.	Mar.	Apr.	May	June
Number of species fruiting	7	16	25	27	34	35	36	59	56	40	24	10
Percentage of species fruiting	4	10	16	17	22	22	23	38	36	25	15	6

savanna, grass fruits are dispersed rather early in the dry season, thus avoiding fire. As fruit development results directly from successful pollination of flowers, seasonality of fruiting depends on the same factors as those regulating flowering, discussed in Book 1 chap. 24, namely daylength, rainfall and temperature changes. To produce fruits in the late dry season, a tree should flower in the early dry season, that is, in tropical Africa, when days are shortening. This is probably why more tropical daylength-sensitive plants are short-day than long-day.

A species may secure advantage from the simultaneous dispersal of seed by plants over a wide area. There may be so many seeds that predators are not able to eat them all before germination starts. Many rodents in particular show hoarding behaviour in these circumstances and store large numbers of seeds by burying them either concentrated in a single pit, or dispersed in smaller, scattered pits. These rodents are able to find only a proportion of the buried seeds, and the remainder are favourably placed for germination provided they have no light requirements. We may suppose that the risk of damage by other predators will be less for seeds buried in small scattered caches.

Simultaneous dispersal is secured in some pod-producing species in which dehiscence requires exceptionally low humidity. In the coastal areas of West Africa relative humidity does not normally fall below 60 percent except during brief periods of 'harmattan' weather in December and January, when it may drop to 20 percent. At such times, the bursting of the pods of trees such as *Millettia*

thonningii (p. 8) produces an effect like the rattle of gunfire.

Precision in dispersal

Several of the dispersal mechanisms mentioned above result in the propagules being deposited in places suitable for germination and growth. Seeds deposited in animal dung are provided with a conveniently manured soil. Water-dispersed seeds washed onto the shores of a river or drying pond are left on moist earth. Particularly elegant examples of adaptations to ensure dispersal to the correct part of a habitat are shown by many savanna grasses, such as *Themeda triandra* (Fig. 1.13) which occurs throughout tropical Africa, being especially common in the east and south. The propagule consists of a fruit surrounded by bracts, one of which bears a long bristle, or awn, which twists and untwists in response to daily changes in

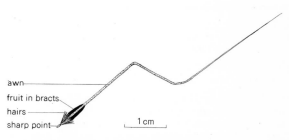

1.13 Propagule of the savanna grass *Themeda triandra*.

atmospheric humidity. The tip of the propagule is very sharply pointed and is covered with stiff hairs directed away from the apex, forming a barb; these features cause fruits to adhere to a person's clothing or to an animal's hair. After dispersal, once this sharp point enters a crack in the soil, the hairs prevent its withdrawal. The awn then twists and turns, and because of the hairs, any movement transmitted to the seed will push it further into the soil. Furthermore, if the awn encounters an obstruction which prevents it from turning, the twisting force is transmitted to the seed, actively screwing it into the soil. Once buried in the soil, the seed is protected from the heat of the annual grass fires, which pass so quickly that they do not heat the soil significantly to any depth, and certainly not to one cm, which is the average depth of burial of the *Themeda* seed. Burial beneath as little as one cm of soil also protects the seed from the very large fluctuations in temperature which occur each day at the surface after removal of the plant cover by fire (Fig. 1.14).

As an example from forest we may cite the 'mistletoe' parasite *Loranthus*, which obtains water and food from the branches of trees (Fig. 1.15). To be effective, seeds must germinate on the bark of a branch, which they penetrate by the production of a haustorium. The fruit of *Loranthus* is a berry containing a single seed surrounded by pulp which is attractive to birds, but very sticky, causing the seed to adhere to the bird's beak. A bird will often attempt to get rid of the unpalatable seed by wiping it off into a crack of the bark of the branch on which it is sitting, thus placing the seed in a suitable position. Less fortunate are those seeds which a bird wipes onto a telegraph wire— a frequent occurrence.

Germination requirements

Many kinds of seed require more than the presence of water, air and suitable temperature for germination; they

(a)

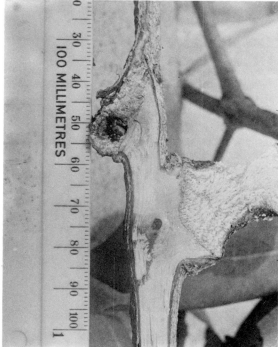

(b)

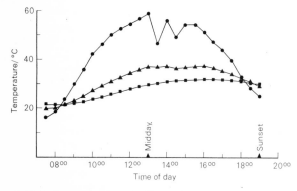

1.14 Soil temperatures in *Themeda* grassland burnt several days previously in Ruwenzori National Park, Uganda, measured on 28 June 1966. —●—●— at surface; —▲—▲— 1 cm below surface; —■—■— 5 cm below surface. (After Lock and Milburn).

1.15 (a) The partial parasite *Loranthus* (with broad leaves) growing on a branch of the shrub *Lawsonia inermis* (with small leaves). Note the swollen attachment of the parasite (towards the right of the photograph). (b) Vertical section of junction between parasite (right) and host (left); the haustorium is the part of the parasite which is in contact with the host and through which the parasite obtains food and water.

remain dormant until some additional requirement is supplied (Book 1 chap. 2). In some species the effect of dormancy is simply to slow down the rate of germination, ensuring that all seeds do not germinate simultaneously. In others, dormancy has a more specific function in ensuring that germination occurs only when conditions for establishment are favourable.

Weeds have been called the opportunists of the plant world; when a clearing is made they quickly colonize it. Frequently, when a road is cut through forest, the verges are quickly covered by a dense growth of the fast-growing umbrella tree, *Musanga cecropioides* (Fig. 1.3), although this tree is almost absent from mature forest. One may wonder how the seeds from which the trees grew arrived so soon after a suitable habitat was made. Experiments have been performed in which soil was collected from the ground below closed forest, placed in pans in a greenhouse and watered; the soil yielded abundant *Musanga* seedlings, showing that in fact *Musanga* seed was almost universally present in the sampled soil even far from parent trees. The tiny seeds are contained in fleshy fruits, and are presumably dispersed widely in the droppings of the birds and bats which feed on them. Although experimental work has not yet been performed, it is probable that the stimulus for germination of *Musanga* seed after the forest cover has been removed is the increase in light intensity reaching the ground, and particularly the change in light quality. The seeds of various varieties of lettuce are known to be stimulated to germinate by red light, with a peak at 660 nm, and inhibited from germinating by far-red light with a peak at 740 nm. Recently many other seeds have been shown to possess this property, which depends on the presence of a bluish pigment called phytochrome (Book 1 p. 24). Leaves absorb red light strongly because of their chlorophyll content, but transmit much of the incident radiation in the far-red region; the light beneath plants is thus relatively rich in the inhibitory far-red wavelengths. The diagram of transmission through a forest canopy in Fig. 1.16 demonstrates this clearly. The removal of the plant canopy alters the balance between stimulatory and inhibitory wavelengths, and allows germination to take place at a time when competition from other plants is at its lowest. The large flush of germination which is often observed after the burning or cutting of grassland probably results from the same phenomenon.

The fruits of the submerged freshwater plant *Potamogeton* (Fig. 1.17a) are adapted in a complex way for dispersal across the surface of lakes and ponds and for germination in shallow water. The fruit-coat is three-layered. The outer layer is one cell thick and cuticularized, the middle one is spongy and contains much chlorophyll, and the innermost is hard and stony. As long as the middle layer remains green, it photosynthesizes and produces oxygen which maintains the buoyancy of the fruit. In darkness, fruits sink much more rapidly than in light (Fig. 1.17b), and if previously illuminated fruits are cut under

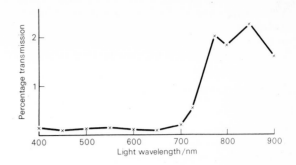

1.16 Light reaching the floor of temperate forest as a percentage of that falling on the canopy. Note that far-red light of long wavelengths of 700 to 900 nm is transmitted by the canopy far more readily than light of shorter wavelengths.

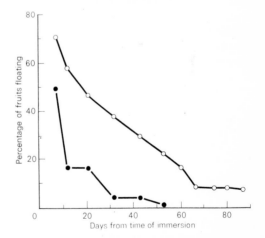

1.17 (a) Section through fruit of *Potamogeton*. (b) Rate of sinking of *Potamogeton* fruits; —○—○— in light, —·—·— in continuous darkness. (After Spence *et al.*).

water, a gas bubble is released and the fruit sinks. Although the seeds of *Potamogeton* require light for germination, no germination takes place while the fruits are floating, probably because the intact green outer layers absorb the germination-promoting red wavelengths while transmitting the inhibitory far-red wavelengths. Eventually the outer coat is damaged or decays, and the seed loses its buoyancy and sinks; germination then follows rapidly if the depth of water is small enough to transmit a sufficient intensity of red light. This may limit germination to

11

shallow water, particularly if the water is not very clear. Mechanisms such as this may at least in part be responsible for the rather precise zonations in relation to water depth common in aquatic plant communities.

Distribution in relation to dispersal

The mechanisms and adaptations discussed above result in the more or less wide dispersal of propagules and in their germination at a more or less appropriate time and place. The seeds of the majority of seashore flowering plants are dispersed by the sea, just as those of most freshwater species are dispersed by freshwater. In forest (Table 1.6) the propagules of most epiphytes are dust-like and readily dispersed by the wind; the fact that bryophytes, ferns and orchids produce this type of propagule must be one of the important reasons for their great success in this mode of life. Wind dispersal is less widespread among understorey trees than among taller forest trees; the crowns of the latter are exposed to wind and even a moderate angle of fall will carry propagules far from the parent. Weeds often have more efficient methods of dispersal than non-weedy species.

In some cases, however, distribution is more closely related to dispersal mechanism. A large-scale example is provided by the mangrove *Rhizophora* (Book 1 p. 245–7), which grows in tidal estuaries. The seed germinates while still attached to the tree, and the propagule which falls into the water (Fig. 1.18) consists of a long buoyant hypocotyl bearing a small plumule at its end. This seedling can float in the sea for many months without further development, but when it is washed up, branch roots develop rapidly from the tip of the radicle, and the seedling is anchored before the next tide. Three species of *Rhizophora* occur on the coast of West Africa: *R. mangle*, *R. harrisonii* and *R. racemosa*, the same species also occurring in tropical America. The only species of *Rhizophora* on the East African coast is *R. mucronata*, otherwise known from the shores of tropical Asia. This distribution pattern is readily explained in terms of dispersal by marine currents. West Africa and tropical America share the species whose propagules are readily carried across the Atlantic Ocean. The cold waters of the southern tip of Africa provide an impassable barrier to the spread of mangroves, so the East African mangroves are isolated from those of the west coast.

The following are small-scale examples. Lines of bird-dispersed trees and shrubs often appear along fence-lines, where birds have perched and defaecated seeds (Fig. 1.19). On Lolui Island, in Lake Victoria, the thicket clumps which occur in the grassland may well owe their origin to the habits of the Green Monkeys (*Cercopithecus aethiops*) which are abundant on the island. All woody species in the thicket clumps have seeds which are potentially animal-dispersed, in contrast to the woody species in the relict

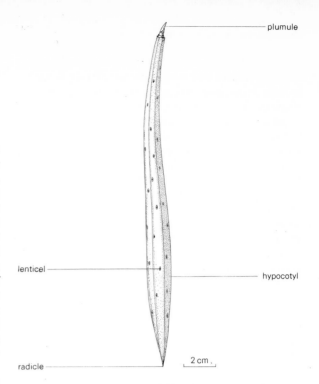

1.18 Seedling of *Rhizophora* at time of dispersal.

1.19 Young tree of *Fagara zanthoxyloides* which has grown from seed dropped by birds which roosted on the fence in the foreground.

forest patches, some of which have explosive fruits or wind-dispersed seeds. Thickets arise from a nucleus which is usually either a termite mound or a rock. Such eminences are much used by the monkeys and frequently there are large dung accumulations around them; the dung is largely composed of undigested seeds.

It would, however, be a mistake to suppose that plants become established wherever their propagules are dispersed. The example of the seeds of tropical seashore plants, profitlessly dispersed in ocean currents to the shores of northern Europe, has been mentioned above (p. 6). It is probable that the seeds of tropical swamp species are similarly carried to Europe by birds returning from migration. Any garden contains a large number of introduced species of plants which grow there successfully, but whose seeds, with few exceptions, are incapable of successfully establishing new plants beyond the limits of cultivation. Their lack of success may in part be due to their inability to produce a sufficient number of propagules to have a reasonable chance of producing daughter plants against the great odds which all seeds face. An additional and often more important reason is that they may be less well-adapted than indigenous species to the conditions outside the garden. In other words, they cannot compete successfully without the gardener's assistance.

We should not therefore expect to find a close correlation between mechanisms and areas of dispersal, and distribution. Dispersal provides species with the possibility of a wide distribution. The distribution which they in fact achieve depends largely on their ability to grow to maturity in competition with other species. For example, of the species of mahogany found in West Africa, *Khaya senegalensis* occurs in savanna, often along river banks, while *Khaya ivorensis* grows in forest. The fruit of both these species is a capsule of similar form, which splits to release winged seeds that are dispersed for relatively short distances by wind (Fig. 1.7). The seeds remain viable for only a few weeks; they have no period of dormancy. The characteristic distributions of these two mahogany species do not depend on their dispersal or germination mechanisms, but on features of growth habit and structure. The roots of the *K. senegalensis* seedling grow more rapidly than those of *K. ivorensis*, possibly enabling it to reach the deep savanna watertable quickly while the soil is moist. The leaves of *K. senegalensis* are better adapted to drought. For example, their stomata are more sensitive to water stress, closing before too great a proportion of their water content has been lost (Fig. 1.20). The interrelationships between the processes described in this chapter are summarized in Fig. 2.32.

Problems

1 From Table 1.1 it would appear that *Tridax procumbens* is absent from cassava farms in the vicinity of

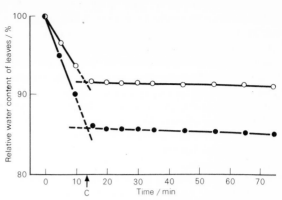

1.20 Results of an experiment in which detached turgid leaflets of two species of mahogany were repeatedly weighed while drying. The relative water content $\left(\dfrac{\text{actual weight}}{\text{turgid weight}} \times 100\right)$ fell steeply at first while the stomata were open, and then decreased rather abruptly as the stomata closed. Note that stomatal closure occurred at a higher relative water content in the savanna species, *Khaya senegalensis* —○—○—, than in the forest species *K. ivorensis* —●—●—. (After Okali and Dodoo).

Legon. Suggest possible explanations of this finding, in each case indicating what investigations you would carry out to test your suggestions.

2 Using Fig. 1.9, estimate the time after which all the *Canavalia* seeds would have lost their viability. Would you expect seeds to remain alive for a longer or a shorter time in the open sea than in the laboratory conditions under which they were studied? Given that the average speed of the west-to-east current across the Atlantic Ocean is 26 km per day, what conclusions can you draw as to the possibility of transatlantic dispersal of this species?

3 Table 1.3 shows that coconuts can survive immersion for several months in seawater. Coconut is also one of the most widely distributed tropical crops, being one of the very few to have occurred in both Old and New Worlds before the time of Columbus. Nevertheless in some areas, including West Africa, it seems to have been introduced relatively recently. What kinds of evidence would you try to obtain in order to decide whether the presence of coconut on a particular tropical coast is a result of natural dispersal or of deliberate introduction by man?

4 From Fig. 1.5 estimate the percentage survival of *Dioclea megacarpa* seedlings at the following distances from the parent plant: (a) 0–15 m; (b) 15–35 m; (c) 35–60 m. Janzen has suggested that the richness in species of tropical forest may be explained by the results of experiments such as the one whose results appear in Fig. 1.5. What do you think may be his reasoning? What further investigations would be needed to substantiate his theory?

5 Two proposals have been made to account for the

recolonization by vegetation of the volcanic island of Krakatau (see Table 1.5). The first hypothesis suggests that, although growing plants were killed by the explosion, some seeds remained viable, because they were buried in soil, and that the plants derived from these were responsible for recolonization. The second hypothesis suggests that all seeds were killed by the explosion, and that recolonization was entirely dependent on propagules which subsequently reached the island.

Which hypothesis is best supported by the evidence? Give your reasons.

6 Comment on interesting features of dispersal mechanisms in various categories of forest plants, summarized in Table 1.6.

7 How would you investigate experimentally the reasons for the dormancy (see p. 11) of *Musanga* seeds in the soil under intact forest?

8 What do you notice about the relation between soil temperatures at different depths (Fig. 1.14): (a) in the daytime, (b) at night? How can you explain these relationships? Assuming that the maximum temperature which dry *Themeda* seeds can withstand uninjured is 70°C, can we conclude from Fig. 1.14 that burial is not necessary for their survival in savanna? Explain your answer.

9 What happened at time C in Fig. 1.20? Comment on the fact that the relative water content of *Khaya senegalensis* was higher than that of *K. ivorensis* (a) before time C and (b) after time C.

10 Ferns occur not only as epiphytes, but also abundantly on the forest floor. How does this fact affect your interpretation of the figures for wind dispersal in Table 1.6?

Bibliography

Revision reading

Hall, J. R. *Senior Tropical Biology*, Longman, 1970, Chap. 7

Stone, R. H., *New Biology for Tropical Schools*,
Cozens, A. B. Longman, 1969, Chap. 12

Further reading

Ridley, H. N. *The Dispersal of Plants throughout the World*, Reeve, 1930

Salisbury, E. *Weeds and Aliens*, Collins, 1961, Chaps. 5 and 14

Taylor, C. J. *Synecology and Silviculture in Ghana*, Part 3, Nelson, 1960

2 The dispersal and distribution of consumers

Because they are consumers, most animals must be able to move. Some are indeed sessile as adults: for example, the sponges and barnacles on the rocky shore and many mealy-bugs which live upon trees and shrubs sucking in the fluid in the phloem vessels of the plants. Nevertheless, at least at some stage in their life, almost all animals have the ability to move.

On the other hand, the seeds of a flowering plant such as *Scirpus* will, when ripe, be scattered from the parent plant by some relatively simple mechanical means, or perhaps be carried away by animals. Where the seed finally falls to the ground, there it will remain. If conditions are suitable, it may germinate and form a new plant; if conditions are unfavourable, sooner or later the seed will die. Dispersal of seed is generally a passive process.

Dispersal of eggs

Just as plants' seeds are dispersed, so too the young stages of animals disperse. This may occur in different ways. Many sedentary marine invertebrates, such as some of the polychaetes, the bivalve molluscs and the sea urchins, shed their eggs into the water and the embryos are carried passively by water currents until they develop into swimming larvae. In other species the eggs are dispersed by the female parent. For example, the female of the mosquito *Anopheles gambiae* (Diptera) which transmits *Plasmodium*, the causative organism of malaria, will fly out from shelter about dusk to oviposit (Fig. 2.1). Then that same night she will go in search of a fresh meal of blood; two days later, when she has developed a new batch of eggs, she will fly off again to oviposit, quite probably in some different place. Experiments in Tanzania using *Anopheles* marked with radioactive isotopes of phosphorus or sulphur have shown that the females may live for more than three weeks and during that time they will have moved, on the average, about 5 km from where they first emerged. During this period each female will have laid about ten batches of eggs, so that her progeny will be fairly widely dispersed before she dies. A far more extreme example is to be found in swarms of locusts, such as the Desert Locust, *Schistocerca* (Orthoptera). A female may bury an egg pod containing 60 or more eggs and then move off with the swarm, to oviposit again some five or more days later at some other place which may be hundreds of kilometres away.

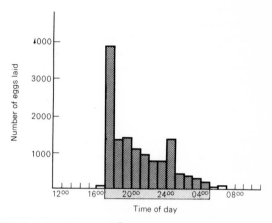

2.1 Number of eggs deposited during hourly intervals by females of *Anopheles gambiae*. Note the sharp onset of oviposition at dusk and the absence of egg laying during the hours of daylight. (Data from Haddow, Ssenkubuge and Ssenkubuge).

Dispersal of young

While some animals disperse their eggs, others may lay all the eggs of one brood in one place. Thus a bird lays a clutch of eggs in a single nest. Similarly rats and cats will litter in a nesting site and the family remain together at least until the young have been weaned. Dispersal in these species depends upon the activity of the young; when they can fly, young birds leave the nest. The young of the Black Rat, *Rattus rattus*, remain near the mother's nesting site until they are about twelve to sixteen weeks old and starting to mature sexually; the young will then disperse. Young male lion cubs remain with the family pride until they are about three years old; by then they have become independent of their mother for their supply of food and are driven away from the pride to hunt for themselves.

Like the seeds of plants, the eggs or the young of animals become dispersed. The subsequent survival and germination of seeds depends upon chance, upon where they were carried in being dispersed; we may ask whether this is true also of animals. Does their survival after dispersal also depend mainly on chance?

The answer to this question is not likely to be simple. A grass seed is influenced by the immediate conditions of the place in which it falls. Successful establishment may require the soil to have some limited range of pH or salinity, or it may depend upon the supply of water, the humidity or the light intensity; all these may vary within a distance of a few metres or even centimetres. The case of a young elephant, a young eland or a young cattle egret is clearly very different. Small, highly localized differences in environmental conditions are not likely to affect them, partly because of their greater size, partly because of their ability to move. Whether they survive or not will depend upon very different kinds of factor. They may die because their parent has been killed; they may themselves fall prey to some carnivore or die because they fail to find an adequate supply of food. The rains may fail and in such conditions young herbivores may die in large numbers (Fig. 2.2), while young lions and other young carnivores commonly die because they fail to make a kill. They are,

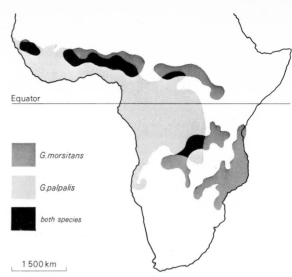

2.3 Geographical distribution of two species of tsetse fly. Note that *Glossina palpalis* occurs in the forest zone of West Africa and the Congo basin, while *G. morsitans* occurs in East and Central Africa. Both species occur in the northern West African savanna region but *G. palpalis* is limited to the rivers. (Simplified from Buxton).

however, unlikely to die because of unfavourable localized environmental conditions: they can move away.

Patterns of distribution

As we descend in the scale of size, the influence of local environmental conditions becomes more significant. A herd of migrating wildebeest may move as much as 10 km in a day, but clearly movements on this scale are impossible for most smaller animals. Nevertheless marked specimens of the tsetse fly *Glossina palpalis* (Diptera), released one afternoon, were collected the following morning as far as 8 km from their release point. Environmental factors do, however, restrict the places in which different species of tsetse fly are found. Those species which are of economic importance to man and his cattle can be roughly divided into riverine-forest species and savanna-living species. Fig. 2.3 shows the distribution of two of these in Africa. Even where both occur within a particular geographical area, the distribution of the species remains distinct. Thus *G. palpalis* is found only in forest fringing the banks of rivers and is normally never caught more than 50 m from a river. A second example of the action of environmental factors is illustrated in Fig. 2.4 which shows the distribution of reports of a grasshopper *Oedaleus* (Orthoptera) which occurs in the savanna zone and may attack crops. It occurs almost exclusively within an area where annual rainfall is greater than 25 cm but less than 100 cm.

Observations of this type are not limited to insects. Fig. 2.5 shows the distribution of two species of the small

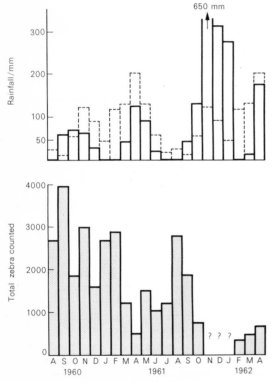

2.2 Number of zebra counted in monthly censuses in Nairobi National Park. No data are available for November 1961 to January 1962 when torrential rains prevented counting. The upper histogram shows the mean monthly rainfall in Nairobi (broken line) and the actual monthly rainfall recorded at a station in the Park (full line). Note that the rains in the early part of 1961 were below expectation and in 1962 far greater than normal. There had been drought early in 1960 and this forced animals to migrate northwards into the Park. The poor rains in 1961 resulted in lack of forage and many deaths with a resulting fall in the size of the population. The increase in August and September 1961 is probably due to further immigration. The torrential rains which followed were accompanied by still more deaths as the forage did not recover sufficiently rapidly to sustain the population which was further reduced. (Data supplied by Dr M. J. Coe).

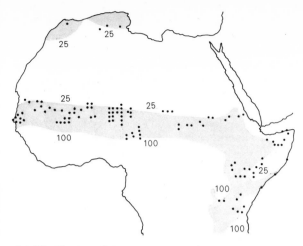

2.4 Distribution of the grasshopper *Oedaleus*. Each spot represents a report of its occurrence within a grid square; this method of recording accounts for the regular pattern of spots in some areas. The stippled areas are regions in which the mean annual rainfall lies between 25 and 100 cm. (Simplified from Batten).

2.6 A genet, *Genetta*. Adult body length is about 50 cm.

2.5 Distribution records of two species of genet in Kenya and northern Tanzania. The shaded area indicates regions in which the mean annual rainfall exceeds 63·5 cm (25 in.). Note that while one species, indicated by circles, is found normally within the high-rainfall area, the other, shown by triangles, is found typically in drier country. The shaded area in the small map of Africa indicates the approximate area included in the larger map. (Simplified from Taylor).

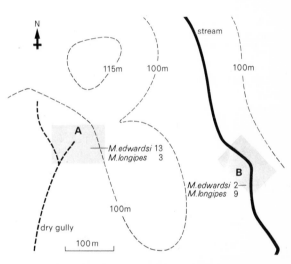

2.7 Records of trapped specimens of two species of the rat *Malacomys* in rain forest in Ghana. Area A was on high, dry ground; B lay in the valley of a small stream. Note that although the two areas are separated by less than 300 m, the relative abundance of the two species is quite different. (Data supplied by Dr L. R. Cole).

carnivore *Genetta* (Fig. 2.6) in East Africa: it will be seen that there is a close correlation between the annual rainfall in different localities and which species of genet is to be found there. A different type of relation is shown in Fig. 2.7, which displays the results of trap samplings of two species of rat in a small area of West African forest. One species tends to keep closely to the immediate vicinity of streams, while the other is to be found on adjacent higher ground.

Such observations lead us to various questions. We may ask what factors in an environmental complex determine

17

the distribution of a particular species. We can obtain some information upon this point by mapping the distribution both of the animal and of various environmental factors (Figs. 2.4 and 2.5). But this type of correlation does not tell us what are the actual environmental signals to which the animals are reacting. Thus, in the case of the two species of *Genetta* it seems probable that it is certain features of the environment resulting from different quantities of rainfall that are determining the animals' choice of habitat, not the actual mean rainfall itself. The precise factors involved have not been analysed in this case and are indeed not easily determined for most large animals. A considerable number of studies of this character, however, have been made upon smaller animals, especially the terrestrial insects.

Distribution, dispersal and dispersion

These terms will be used in the same way as in Chapter 1. We have seen how young animals normally scatter. These activities we speak of as dispersal movements; they result in a dispersal of the animals concerned. We have also seen that some animal species occur in one locality, some in another. We can plot such information on a map, as in Fig. 2.4, and what we have recorded is the distribution of the animal.

If, however, you go out into the school compound and make a very detailed map of where you find individuals of some particular species of insect, you will find that the animal concerned occurs only in certain limited places. Fig. 2.8 relates to the common Red Tree Ant, *Oecophylla* (Hymenoptera) (Fig. 11.6) and shows in which one-metre-square quadrats this ant occurred in part of a particular

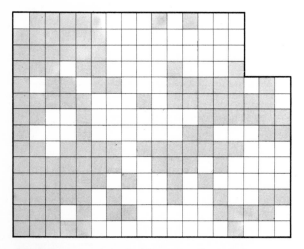

2.8 Occurrence of the Red Tree Ant, *Oecophylla*, in metre-square quadrats in a cocoa farm in Ghana. The shading indicates those quadrats in which the ants were found. Note that the distribution is discontinuous. (Simplified from Majer).

cocoa farm. You will notice that it is not found in all quadrats. Compared with Fig. 2.4, this is a much more detailed statement of where the animal occurs, and allows us to study whether it is spread within an area at random or whether individuals (or colonies in the case of ants) tend to clump together or possibly spread themselves out more evenly than would be expected by chance. This is a study of the dispersion of the individuals within a particular part of the normal habitat of the species and is a matter we will consider in detail later (p. 29f).

Selection of oviposition sites

In considering what factors determine the distribution of animals and how this distribution is maintained, we will start with what is often a clear-cut observation, namely that the larvae of certain butterflies (Lepidoptera) are found on only one or perhaps a few species of plant. That is, they have a definite pattern of distribution. This is a consequence of the fact that the adult females do not lay their eggs at random, but select certain plants as oviposition sites. Thus, the Citrus Swallowtail Butterfly, *Papilio demodocus* (Lepidoptera), oviposits most commonly on citrus, while the common brown *Acraea encedon* oviposits either on *Commelina benghalensis* or, in some localities, on the legume *Pseudarthria*. An analysis of the mechanism underlying this type of choice of oviposition site has been made using a butterfly common in England, the Cabbage White. Experiments with coloured papers show that hungry males and females are attracted to objects which are red, yellow, blue or violet; but they are not attracted to green. That is, they are attracted to typical flower colours and this response will lead them to sources of nectar. But when the females are about to oviposit, their behaviour changes. They are now attracted to objects which are green or blue-green: that is, to the colour of leaves. Such females fly about, alighting on leaves upon which they make alternate stepping movements with the fore-legs: this is called 'drumming'. On the terminal joints or tarsi of the fore-legs are sense organs of taste. It can be shown that if a particular chemical which is found in cabbage is present, the female may then oviposit. She will do this on leaves of plants other than cabbage if they are painted over with this substance; she may even oviposit on coloured paper if it is impregnated with the chemical. There are thus two factors involved in the females' selection of an oviposition site: a 'long-distance' visual response to colour and a 'local' response to the 'taste' of the leaf.

In an Indian butterfly which is closely similar to the Citrus Swallowtail, females which are about to oviposit are similarly attracted to green objects. But in this case there is an attraction only when the characteristic scent of a citrus tree is in the air: the location mechanism is more precise than in the Cabbage White. Whether the 'taste' of a citrus leaf is also involved has not been investigated.

Very different is the mechanism determining the choice

of oviposition sites by female locusts which excavate deep holes in the ground; in these the eggs are laid (Book 1 Fig. 25.3). Experiment with the Migratory Locust, *Locusta migratoria* (Orthoptera), shows that although the female may excavate a hole, she does not invariably oviposit. Several requirements have to be satisfied. She prefers a sandy soil which is well compacted and will reject loose sand; she also prefers soil which is damp, but not sodden with water. Table 2.1 shows the number of egg pods laid in sandy soils of different moisture contents; these were offered all at the same time to batches of 40 gravid female locusts. Waterlogged soil was rejected, as was totally dry soil. This selection of a damp soil correlates with the water requirements of the developing eggs. Locust eggs fail to develop in both dry and waterlogged soil.

Table 2.1 Number of egg pods deposited in sandy soils of different water content by females of *Locusta migratoria* (*Data from Choudhuri*)

Water added to 80 g soil(cm³)	0	2	4	6	8	10	12	14	16*
Number of egg pods deposited	0	1	2	11	18	17	25	17	0

*Soil with 16 cm³ of added water was completely water-logged

Another, rather different example of selection of an oviposition site is provided by female insect parasites seeking their host. Insects which are 'parasitic' on other insects are sometimes called 'parasitoids' rather than parasites. This is because the developing 'parasite' is effectively a predator on its 'host', eating it almost completely. One such parasitoid is a tiny wasp, *Nasonia* (Hymenoptera), which oviposits in the pupal cases of houseflies and blowflies. The female wasp flies about at random until she meets the characteristic odour produced when fly maggots are feeding on decaying material. This stimulus alters her behaviour. She alights and walks about, making frequent turning movements which serve to keep her near the place where fly pupae may be. If she comes within a few millimetres of a pupal case, she turns towards it, climbs on to it and presently bores a hole through the case with her ovipositor (Fig. 2.9). We find here the same pattern of long-distance and short-distance signals which we have already seen with the Cabbage White Butterfly. In *Nasonia*, however, a chemical rather than a visual signal is used initially in locating a suitable site for oviposition and the final identification of the pupa is at least partly visual, not simply a response to a chemical stimulus.

Finally we will consider insects which oviposit in water, taking as an example certain species of the mosquito genus *Anopheles* (Diptera). We still do not know precisely what determines their choice of oviposition sites. There are certain factors which to the human observer obviously

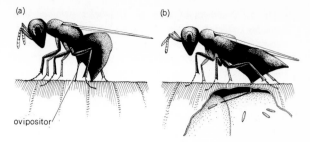

2.9 The wasp *Nasonia* on a housefly pupal case. The insect is about 2·5 mm long. In (a) the female is boring through the pupal case with its ovipositor. In (b) she is laying eggs; the pupal case has been cut away to show the long ovipositor and several eggs. (After Edwards).

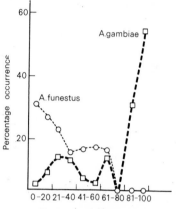

2.10 Abundance of larvae of two species of *Anopheles* in pools in Uganda and Tanzania in relation to light intensity. The horizontal axis indicates light intensity at the collecting sites expressed as a percentage of the light intensity in the open. The vertical axis shows the percentage of sites in each light-intensity class which contained one or other species of mosquito. Larvae did not occur in all the sites sampled. Note that while *A. funestus* is not found at sites with a high light intensity, *A. gambiae* occurs most frequently in such places. (Data from Leeson).

correlate with this choice in the field. Experimental studies suggest, however, that these are not of significance to the mosquitoes.

A. gambiae typically oviposits in pools with banks clear of vegetation and exposed to direct sunlight, while the larvae of *A. funestus* are most commonly found in shaded situations (Fig. 2.10). It might therefore be expected that *A. gambiae* would not oviposit in pools which were shaded artificially from above. This does not, however, prove to be the case. There is some evidence that the female is repelled by dense vegetation and this will incidentally provide shade. Closely related to *A. gambiae* is *A. melas*, whose eggs are found in brackish pools in the tidal zone and in mangrove swamps. Table 2.2, showing the total number of eggs of the two species collected from a large number of pools, illustrates this point. We might therefore expect that if we

Table 2.2 Numbers of eggs of *Anopheles gambiae* and *A. melas* collected from pools containing fresh or brackish water (*Data from Muirhead Thompson*)

Habitat	A. gambiae	A. melas
Rain-filled pools	2 316	20
Brackish pools in coastal swamps	16	1 998

offered adults of the two species the choice of different dilutions of seawater in which to oviposit, *A. gambiae* would select freshwater and *A. melas* a somewhat saline water. This expectation is also not fulfilled. With experimental pools in suitable localities, *A. gambiae* does not discriminate between freshwater and seawater diluted to 30 per cent. In similar experiments, *A. melas* was found to oviposit in water of all salinities from 0·1 to 100 percent seawater. Thus with neither of these two species are the obvious environmental correlates of light and salinity the significant factors determining the selection of oviposition sites.

The distribution of woodlice

The behaviours of the ovipositing female may be one factor which determines the distribution of the immature stages of certain insects. But many animals are less mobile than insects and in some species all the different developmental stages may be found together. There is normally no dispersal. This is true for example of woodlice (Crustacea: Isopoda) (Book 1 Fig. 18.56). There are probably many places around the school compound where you can find woodlice: under a rotting log, in a pile of rotting leaves swept up to keep the compound clean, beneath large stones and so on. One rarely finds just one woodlouse; where they occur they are in fairly large numbers. So the first observation we may make relates to their dispersion; they are clumped, not evenly spaced or scattered at random. The next thing that you will notice is that the various places in which you find woodlice share a number of characteristics which are absent from the rest of the compound. They are sheltered, dark, damp and probably cooler than the surface of the soil a short distance away. Since the places where these conditions prevail are limited in extent we emphasize the point by speaking of them as forming the microhabitats of the woodlice and, within each microhabitat we can recognize and describe a distinct microclimate.

Measurement of microclimates

If we are fully to describe the characteristics of a microhabitat, we must be able to measure the relevant parameters of its microclimate. We know from what we have already learnt of the life of animals on land (Book 1 p. 288) that there are at least two important things to measure: one is

temperature, the other humidity. How can this be done? It obviously is not satisfactory to try and measure the temperature within a small crevice using a mercury-in-glass thermometer. Two other methods are available. One depends upon the fact that if two wires of different metals are joined together at their free ends and the two junctions so formed are kept at different temperatures, then an electric current will flow along the wires. This is the thermoelectric effect and the pair of wires forms a thermocouple. Since the junctions are very small and the wires flexible, one junction can be inserted into the crevice, while the other is kept at a known constant temperature; a vacuum flask containing ice is commonly used. The current flow has then to be measured. A thermocouple can produce only a very small current, so a very sensitive galvanometer is required. Although this method has been used in the past, it is clearly not convenient for field work. A more useful technique depends upon the fact that the electric resistance of any metal varies with temperature. This is the principle of the thermistor which contains a small bead of a metal alloy whose resistance can be measured using a dry cell as a source of current and a normal Wheatstone bridge circuit (Fig. 2.11). Very tiny thermistors are available and these can be used to measure the temperatures of microhabitats in the field.

The measurement of humidity provides a more difficult problem. One method is to utilize the fact that the colours of cobalt(II) salts change with their degree of hydration, just in the same way as anhydrous copper(II) sulphate is a white powder while copper(II) sulphate heptahydrate is blue. A small piece of filter paper impregnated with a cobalt salt is placed within the crevice and left there for some time. The paper is then removed, using a pair of forceps, and placed in a tube containing liquid paraffin. It is then mounted between two glass slides and its colour matched against a set of calibrated standards. With this method an accuracy of about 5 percent relative humidity can be obtained.

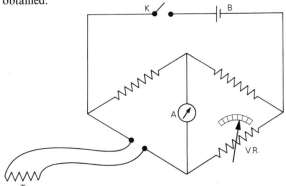

2.11 Bridge circuit for temperature measurements with a thermistor, T. A, milliammeter; B, dry cell; K, key; V.R., variable resistor with scale. By moving the setting of V.R. until the ammeter shows no current flow, the temperature at T can be read off the previously calibrated scale.

Relative humidity (R.H.) (Book 1 p. 64) is one way in which the 'dampness' of the atmosphere may be expressed. It is defined as the ratio of the mass of water vapour present in unit volume of air to the mass of water vapour required to saturate that volume at the same temperature: the greater the R.H. the more water vapour in the atmosphere. It is, however, often desirable to express the 'drying power' of the atmosphere, as this will give a measure of how rapidly water may be lost from an organism. This is expressed by the 'saturation deficit' (S.D.) which is the difference between the vapour pressure required to saturate a volume of air at a particular temperature (S.V.P.) and the vapour pressure of water actually present (V.P.). That is,

$$S.D. = S.V.P. - V.P.$$

Like other measures of vapour pressure, S.D. has in the past been expressed in mm Hg. In SI units S.D. is expressed as $N\ m^{-2}$ or pascals (1.0 mm Hg $= 133.32$ pascals or 0.00133 bars). At any one temperature there is a linear relationship between R.H. and S.D., but at constant R.H., S.D. increases with increasing temperature.

Woodlouse distribution and behaviour

Reverting to the woodlice, we find, using these techniques, that the characteristics of the microhabitats of any one species of woodlouse vary within only relatively narrow limits. So we may ask: why are these animals not found elsewhere? Clearly we can erect several different hypotheses in answer to such a question; one might be that 'they die elsewhere, since they lose water very rapidly'. This might imply that woodlice are constantly moving away from the microhabitats where we find them, only to die of desiccation. It is, however, possible that they have some behaviours which normally serve to restrict them to a microhabitat where they can survive.

We can examine this latter possibility experimentally, by offering the animals choices of different conditions. We noted that woodlice are normally found in sheltered places where it is dark: do they then avoid light? We can study this in a relatively simple way by covering the floor of a petri dish with damp filter paper, putting some woodlice in the dish, replacing the cover and then, after placing black paper over one half of the dish, illuminating the dish from above (Fig. 2.12).

In such an experiment we are trying to study one variable only and others must be kept constant as far as possible. This is one reason why damp filter paper was put on the floor of the dish; it will ensure a uniform, high humidity. A heat screen should be placed between the lamp and the petri dish; otherwise the unshaded portion of the petri dish may get relatively warmer. After, say, ten minutes we note where the animals are; how many are in the dark, how many in the light. Suppose we started with 10 woodlice; we may find 8 in the dark and 2 in the light. We want to confirm this observation; so we remove the lid, scatter

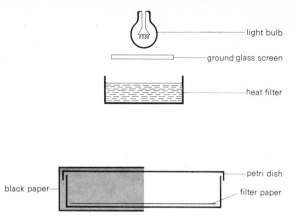

2.12 Simple light–dark choice chamber. Light from the bulb is diffused by a ground-glass screen and passed through a heat filter such as a dilute solution of copper(II)sulphate.

the animals gently with a paint brush and then repeat the experiment. After perhaps five such observations, we move the shade to the other side of the dish and make a further set of five observations. This will balance the effect of any directional influence which we have neglected or failed to eliminate. At the end, by summing all the observations, we are able to say that in these conditions x percent of some particular species of woodlouse go to the darker side of the dish. The behaviour of individual animals normally differs slightly one from another, so to obtain more meaningful results, the experiment should be repeated several times using different batches of animals. If one further variable, such as humidity, light intensity, time of day or species of woodlouse is now changed, a quantitative comparative statement can be made.

With most species of woodlouse, 70 percent or more will be found on the dark side in such an experiment. We learn two things: firstly, that one factor which may prevent woodlice from straying from their normal microhabitat is a behavioural response which tends to take them into dark places; secondly, that if we are to experiment further, we must be certain that the lighting conditions are completely uniform, a condition most readily attained in practice by doing all experiments in the dark.

We can now ask whether the woodlice have any response to humidity. This can be done in a suitable humidity choice chamber (Book 1 Fig. 23.9). Experimental precautions must be taken to eliminate any bias in the apparatus. As with the experiments on light and dark choice, we can express the result as the percentage of animals in one half of the dish, but various other expressions for the 'intensity of reaction' (I.R.) are also used. In one of these, all animals within a defined zone on either side of the mid-line are neglected, since they are not displaying any preference; the I.R. is then expressed by the ratio of the animals in the damper part to those in the drier part of the chamber. If the animal shows a preference for more humid conditions, the I.R. will be greater than 1; if a preference for drier conditions, the I.R. will be less than 1. As a further precaution a series of experiments in uniform humidity conditions should be made to control for any bias which there may be. Both controls and experimental results are then finally checked statistically against the expectation of a random distribution.

Fig. 2.13 shows the results of a series of experiments of this type. From these data we can see two things. Firstly, the I.R. is always greater than unity: the animals show a preference for moist conditions. Secondly, the magnitude of the I.R. is not constant, but is affected by the precise experimental conditions. The value of the I.R. is, for example, affected by the choice of humidities offered to the animal. This is shown by the lower curve which connects points obtained in a number of gradients all with a range of about 20 percent R.H. There is a very strong reaction to gradients of about 40 to 60 percent R.H., but the reaction is less intense to gradients which cover higher humidities such as 63 to 89 per cent, as well as lower humidities such as 5 to 25 percent R.H. The upper line relates to experiments in which the humidity range was about 40 percent R.H.; it is clear that when the humidity range offered is greater, the I.R. is also greater.

We may summarize these observations by saying that the animals avoid low humidity; they are, however, less selective if the available choices are both tolerable, that is in the higher humidities, or if both are unsuitable for survival, that is in the lower humidities. Similar experiments with other species show that most woodlice tend to avoid dry conditions; this is a second behaviour tending to confine them to their typical microhabitat.

Activity patterns

Such experiments give us one answer to our question 'why are woodlice not found elsewhere?'; this answer is 'they respond to certain environmental stimuli in such a way as to prevent them moving into drier, brighter places'. At night, when it is dark and the humidity rises, woodlice are free to leave their daytime microhabitat in search of food. Clearly it would, in simple terms, be possible for a woodlouse to set out in search of food at any time of day, but its responses to light and humidity would prevent it from leaving its microhabitat. One might picture the woodlice 'trying' at intervals 'to see' whether it was yet possible to forage for food. To put the idea in more objective terms, we might expect a woodlouse to display periodic activity, perhaps once every hour or so, until conditions were suitable for it to move more freely. Experiment suggests that this is not what actually occurs.

The walking activity of a small animal can be recorded using an apparatus called an aktograph. One type is shown in Fig. 2.14. It consists essentially of a pivoted box carrying a writing lever. If an animal placed in the box moves about, the box will rock around the pivot and thus make a vertical mark upon the slowly rotating drum. If the animal remains stationary, there will be a horizontal line.

Using such apparatus, it is possible to show that many species of woodlouse are largely inactive during the day. Fig. 2.15a shows observations on a specimen of the woodlouse *Oniscus* kept in artificially alternating light and dark. The animal tended to become active during the period shortly preceding darkness, while activity fell to a low level during the last part of the dark period. Fig. 2.15b shows records of another individual which was first kept in naturally alternating light and dark and later in constant darkness. The very dark bars in the figure indicate the period of night outside. It will be seen that even in constant darkness, this animal still has a rhythm of activity which coincides fairly closely with the natural cycle of light and dark which it had previously experienced. The rhythmic behaviour of this woodlouse is to some extent independent of environmental clues and results in its becoming active

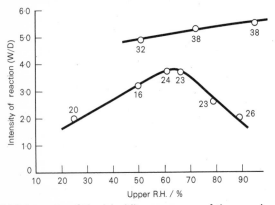

2.13 Intensity of the humidity responses of the woodlouse, *Porcellio*. Intensity of response is here expressed as the ratio of animals in the wet half of a choice chamber to those in the dry half. The figure by each point shows the humidity range of the gradient used in the experiment. (Simplified from Gunn).

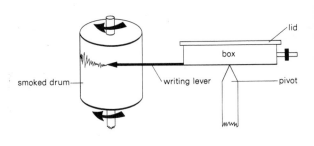

2.14 Principle of the aktograph. A pivoted box carries a writing lever whose movements are recorded on a slowly revolving drum. Movement of the animal up and down inside the box will cause it to rock upon the pivot.

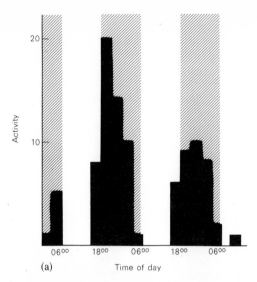
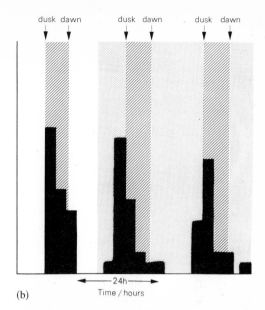

2.15 Activity patterns of the woodlouse *Oniscus*. Activity is expressed as total activity in arbitrary units in three-hourly periods. In (a) the animals were subjected to alternating artificial light and dark. Note that activity starts before 'dark', but occurs mostly during the dark period. In (b) the first record was made in conditions of naturally alternating light and dark. The apparatus was then covered so as to produce conditions of continuous dark, indicated by the medium dark tint. The periods between 'natural' dusk and dawn are indicated by darker vertical bars. Note that there is continuing alternation of activity and inactivity and that the activity periods correlate with the natural periods of darkness. (Simplified from Cloudsley-Thompson).

during the time when conditions of temperature and humidity are likely to be most favourable for survival. It is not constantly or even frequently active during the day but has a rhythmic pattern of activity related to the rhythmic changes in its environment.

One final point. If conditions in their shelter become increasingly dry, do the woodlice not remain trapped and likely to die from desiccation? Can they exercise a 'choice' in such a situation? It seems likely that they can, since laboratory experiments provide some evidence that the light-avoiding response weakens as the animals lose water. In adverse conditions, they may therefore disperse

and be able in this way to find another more suitable place in which to live.

There are, of course, many different species of woodlouse. Some of these have been fairly extensively studied and it is found, not only that different species occur in microhabitats characterized by different prevailing humidities, but that the ability of the different species to withstand desiccation, the extent to which they are active at night and the intensity of their light and humidity reactions all correlate with the typical microclimate, and especially the humidity, of their habitats. Table 2.3 summarizes some of these observations, the species being

Table 2.3 Comparison of characteristics of five different species of woodlouse (*Data from various sources*)

Species	Philoscia musica	Oniscus asellus	Porcellio scaber	Armadillidium vulgare	Hemilepistus reaumuri
Rate of cuticular water loss (mg cm^{-2} h^{-1})	180	165	110	85	23
Survival time at 50% R.H. (h)	—	6·2	10·2	30·2	—
Percentage in dark side of a choice chamber	100	80	79	72	50
Intensity of humidity response (% in wet)	95	72	58	39	53
Percentage of total activity at night	92	77	71	60	34

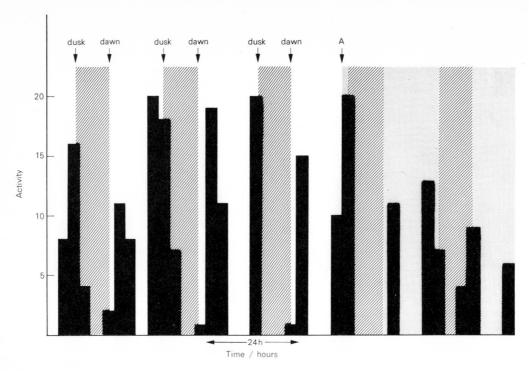

2.16 Activity pattern of the desert woodlouse *Hemilepistus*. Conventions as in Fig. 2.15. Note the bimodal daily activity pattern. From A onwards the recordings were made in continuous darkness: note the persistence of the bimodal rhythm. (After Cloudsley-Thompson).

arranged in the order of increasing dryness of their natural microhabitat.

Hemilepistus is a woodlouse which is found in the desert in North Africa. Its activity pattern (Fig. 2.16) is different from that of the species shown in Fig. 2.15, as it is characteristically active during the morning and again around dusk. The hottest hours of the day it spends in a

deep burrow which may be 30 cm or more below the surface. Here the temperatures are lower and the humidity greater. It also returns to the burrow at night. The figure shows also that this bimodal activity pattern persists in constant darkness.

Habitat selection in aquatic environments

These comparative observations show us the way in which the behaviours of different species of related animals cast some light upon their different patterns of distribution. *Armadillidium*, for example, is found in much drier country than *Philoscia* or *Oniscus*. The study of woodlice provides us with a particularly good example of this principle because, knowing that these animals have a poor ability to withstand desiccation (Fig. 2.17), we can surmise that humidity is likely to be an environmental factor of particular importance and we are indeed able to relate many of their behaviours to this fact. In some cases, however, although we may be able to recognize a particular factor as being involved in habitat selection, we cannot readily recognize its biological significance. Thus, for example, field observations show that the nymphs of the dragonfly *Paragomphus* (Odonata) are seldom found on river or stream bottoms composed of fine sediments. Experiments in the laboratory, in which the nymphs were offered a choice between coarse and fine sands, showed

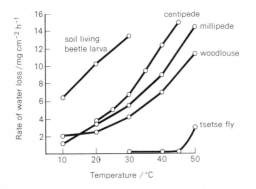

2.17 Rates of water loss in dry air at different temperatures of a soil-living beetle larva, *Agriotes*; a woodlouse, *Oniscus*; a millipede, *Glomeris*; a centipede, *Lithobius*; and a tsetse fly. Note the very low rate of water loss of the adult insect compared with that of the other animals. At 30°C the latter are losing water at least eight times as fast as the former. (From various sources).

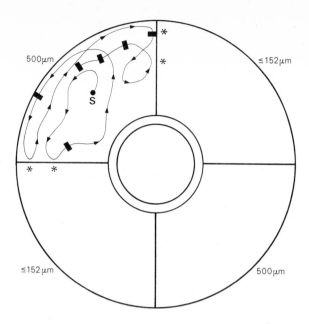

2.18 Tracks of a nymph of the dragonfly *Paragomphus* in a dish with quadrants of coarse (500 μm diameter) and fine (152 μm) diameter particles. The animal was released at S. The black bars indicate its position at successive hours. Note that each time the nymph approached the fine particles, as indicated by asterisks, it turned away from the boundary. (After Keech and Moran).

that more than 90 percent of the nymphs settled on the coarse sand. Fig. 2.18 shows the track of one nymph in such a choice chamber over a period of six hours. You will notice that whenever the nymph approached the fine sand it turned away, thus remaining on the coarse sand. In this instance, although the nymph's behaviour unquestionably contributes to determining its distribution, we do not know why it favours one sort of microhabitat rather than another.

Habitat selection determined by the characteristics of the substratum may also be seen in different species of the larvae of the chironomid midges (Diptera); many of these larvae (Book 1 Fig. 21.15) have haemoglobin in their blood and are obvious members of the fauna of water-filled cans and jars left in the open. They are abundant in the mud at the bottom of ponds. A considerable number of different species are often found in the same pond, but they occur in different parts of the pond: some in shallow water and some in deeper, some on coarse sediments and some on fine. The choice-chamber technique can be used to show that different species have different preferences, not only for the type of bottom sediment, but also for its organic content. Table 2.4 summarizes some results of two such sets of experiments using three different species which occurred in the same reservoir. The animals were offered a choice of coarse sand, silt and very fine clay. Subsequently they were offered a choice of whichever substrate they preferred and the same substrate with 5 percent or 50 percent of fine organic detritus added. You will notice that although two of the species prefer coarse sand, one preferred a higher organic detritus content than the other. Observations in the field of the characteristics of the bottom deposits where the larvae of each of these three species were most abundant agreed well with the choice-chamber results. Thus the distribution of these species within the water body was determined in part at least by their behaviour, by an active choice of habitat by the organisms concerned.

Table 2.4 Substrate selection by different species of chironomid larvae expressed as percentage occurrence on different substrates (*Data from Whyte*)

Species	Type of substrate			Number of specimens
	Coarse sand	Silt	Clay	
Tanytarsus zariae	6·4	18·6	**75·0**	172
Tanypus brevipalpis	**63·7**	25·0	11·3	168
Cladotanytarsus pseudomanchus	**67·9**	27·4	4·6	131

	Preferred substrate			
	No added detritus	+5% detritus	+50% detritus	
Tanytarsus zariae	20·4	**53·9**	25·7	152
Tanypus brevipalpis	33·6	**54·7**	11·7	137
Cladotanytarsus pseudomanchus	15·1	29·6	**55·3**	152

Another factor of importance in certain aquatic habitats is current speed. Experiments with stream animals show that, if offered a choice, they will select surfaces beneath water currents which lie within a fairly narrow range of speeds. Thus, for example, the larvae of the dipterous fly *Simulium* (Book 1 Fig. 18.34), the vector of *Onchocerca* (Nematoda), the causative agent of river blindness, are invariably found in fast-running waters. By placing suitable plastic devices (Fig. 2.19) in different positions in a river, it was possible to determine whether the larvae would settle on all surfaces or in fact only on those exposed to a limited range of current speeds. Such experiments showed that with one species the larvae settled only on surfaces exposed to current speeds within the range of 50–120 cm s^{-1}. Fig. 2.20 shows the similar influence of current speed upon selection of substratum by the nymphs

25

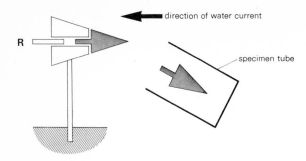

direction of water current

R

specimen tube

2.19 Device for studying settling patterns of *Simulium* larvae. The complete unit is set up in a stream and after an interval the larvae are collected. To do this the rod R is pushed forwards to displace the cone which is caught in a specimen tube. (After Phillipson).

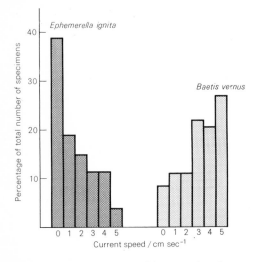

2.20 Selection of current speed by nymphs of two species of mayfly. A large number of specimens was introduced into a trough through which water was flowing at a constant speed. Blocks on the floor of the trough produced local variations in current flow. The numbers of nymphs in different regions corresponding to different current speeds were recorded. Note that while the majority of nymphs of *Ephemerella* preferred still water, those of *Baetis* tended to select the areas of high current speed. (After Ambühl).

of two different species of mayfly (Ephemeroptera). One species shows a clear preference for low current speeds, the other for faster currents.

Host selection by parasites

There is one type of microhabitat which might be regarded as one attained by chance rather than choice, namely that occupied by a parasite in or upon its host: the way in which *Nasonia* finds the pupae of flies in which to oviposit (p. 19) is one example. We will consider two further rather different examples, both of which also show the parasite

to play an active role in host finding, although the extent of this activity can be very different.

The first refers to the Blue Cattle Tick, *Boophilus decoloratus* (Arthropoda: Arachnida), which is the vector of redwater fever. The adult female, after she has been fertilized, drops off a cow and lays her eggs in some sheltered spot upon the ground. The young larvae which emerge from the eggs have to make their way back onto another cow to feed and develop. For about a week after hatching the larvae show a negative response towards light which keeps them close to the soil. Later their behaviour changes: they become attracted to light and also show a negative response to gravity. Both of these reactions result in their making their way to the tops of grass stems where they are more likely to be brushed by the legs of a passing cow and thus to reach the host. The larvae normally rest quite inactive with the forelimbs stretched out, but certain stimuli will cause them to make clutching movements of the fore-limbs. These stimuli include gentle air currents, sudden shade and the smell of sweat; all three are likely to be associated with the passing of a potential host. Clearly whether or not a host will pass is indeed a matter of chance; but the behaviours of the larvae are such as greatly to increase their chances of attaching to a host should one come near.

The second example relates to *Schistosoma mansoni* (Platyhelminthes: Trematoda), one of the two species which cause schistosomiasis or 'bilharzia' in man. A small ciliated larva, the miracidium, hatches from an egg which is passed out with the urine or in the faeces. This larva requires a snail host to carry forward its life cycle (Book 1 Fig. 18.29). Does this larva find a snail by chance alone? The vector snails commonly move about over the leaves of aquatic weeds close to the water surface. By putting miracidia larvae in half-shaded petri dishes, it is possible to show that the larvae are attracted to light. Further experiments, using deep measuring cylinders covered with black material, show that the larvae tend to swim upwards towards the surface of the water. Both of these responses will normally take the larvae towards the water surface where, as far as is known, they then move at random. If, however, they should come within a short distance of a snail, their behaviour changes; they either move directly towards the snail or swim around in tight circles (Fig. 2.21). This latter pattern will increase their chances of actually finding the snail as they will remain in its vicinity. This behaviour is a response to chemical substances produced by the snail, as can be shown by impregnating small agar blocks with an extract of the tissues of a snail. These will attract the larvae while agar blocks without the extract have no effect on larval behaviour.

The rocky shore

As a final example of habitat selection by an invertebrate determining its distribution, we will consider a barnacle

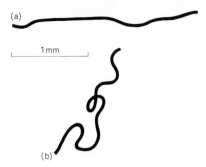

2.21 Tracing of photographic records of the paths of miracidium larvae (a) in clean water and (b) in water containing snail extract. Note the repeated turning movements in the latter track. Duration of each record is about 2 s. (After Davenport *et al.*).

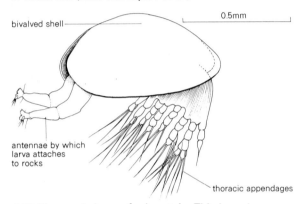

2.22 The cypris larva of a barnacle. This larva has a bivalve shell and looks rather like an ostracod (Book 1 Fig. 18.54c).

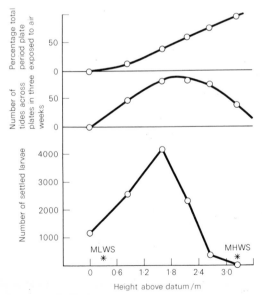

2.23 Settling of *Balanus* larvae on plastic plates set at different depths between tide marks. MLWS, height of mean low-water spring tides above datum, a standard reference point; MHWS, the same for mean high-water spring tides. (Data from Barnes and Powell).

(Book 1 Fig. 18.55) which is a crustacean with a sessile, filter-feeding adult. The distribution of the adult must therefore be determined by where the motile larval stage, the cypris larva, settles (Fig. 2.22). *Balanus balanoides* is a barnacle found between tide-marks and its settling has been studied by setting out a number of vertical plastic plates about 25 cm broad and 40 cm deep; these were fixed in the sea at various depths at and below the level of high spring tide. After three weeks the plates were examined and the number of young barnacles which had settled were counted. The results are shown in Fig. 2.23. It will be seen that most barnacles were found at a level between the mean of high spring tides (MHWS) and the mean of low spring tides (MLWS); that is in the intertidal zone where the adults normally occur. No barnacles survived on the top panel; if any larvae did settle, they were probably killed by the prolonged exposure. Few settled on the lowest panel, although larvae which did settle on this panel survived and grew well. The decrease of larval settling on the lowest panel appears to be related to the fact that it is below MLWS and therefore subjected to only limited wave action. As Fig. 2.23 shows, there is a correlation between the number of tides which have passed across a panel and the number of larvae which have settled on it. There is evidence that the larvae settle from thin films of moving water such as will occur as the water of each wave flows back; that is, in conditions which occur as the tide passes across. There is a critical range of water current over which the larvae will show their settling behaviour; at higher or lower values they will not settle. There is another species of barnacle which does not show this type of behaviour, but will settle even in still water. This species is found at depths well below the intertidal zone, where *B. balanoides* does not occur as the water movements there are insufficient to cause its larvae to attach. Once again there is a correlation between distribution and behaviour. Nevertheless other, purely environmental factors have an effect, as the animals which had settled on the plate at a depth of 2·6 m all died within three months.

Habitat selection in higher vertebrates

All the examples we have considered relate to invertebrates and the question arises as to whether habitat selection occurs in animals with more complex central nervous systems. A moment's consideration of your own behaviour on a hot day provides at least one answer: if possible you will move out of the sun into the shade. But it may be argued that this is a conscious action and thus perhaps something peculiar to man among the mammals. Small animals are the most convenient for experiments on habitat selection and with mammals this limits the choice of experimental material. Experiments have been made upon a small rodent which occurs in North America and is popularly called a Deermouse. Deermice are found both in the forest and the open fields. To the south of the Great Lakes the mice which live in the forest differ slightly but consistently in anatomy from those which live in the open fields. Nevertheless forest and field mice will breed together in the laboratory; we therefore regard them as members of a single species, *Peromyscus maniculatus* and recognize the slight differences between them by assigning the forest mice to one subspecies, *Peromyscus maniculatus gracilis*, and the field mice to another subspecies, *Peromyscus maniculatus bairdi*. In natural conditions the two subspecies do not interbreed, each being found only in its characteristic habitat.

We can now ask whether the mice of one or other subspecies will select its characteristic habitat or whether, say, mice of the forest subspecies are invariably killed if they move into the open fields, an event which might also account for their observed distribution.

This problem has been examined by making an artificial habitat in a room. The two halves of the room were separated by a low wall which could be crossed by a small bridge. One half of the room, of area about 9 m², contained nine short lengths of tree trunk, each about 1 m high and covered with a short plank to represent the canopy. The other half of the room contained tufts of 'grass' made by cutting stiff paper into suitable shapes (Fig. 2.24). Thus one half of the room was 'forest' and the other half 'grassland'. Specimens, first of one and then of the other subspecies, were liberated in the room and their behaviour observed. The time the animals spent in each half was recorded, as well as the quantity of food eaten and water drunk in each half. The results obtained in one of these experiments, using eight specimens of each type of mouse for a period of ten days, are summarized in Table 2.5. This shows that *P.m. gracilis*, the forest subspecies, divided its time about equally between the two habitats, while *P.m. bairdi* showed a marked preference for the 'grass'. Both species showed a marked preference for feeding and drinking in their normal habitat. Thus each subspecies displayed a characteristic-habit preference in its behaviour, even in the highly artificial conditions of this experiment. Pre-

Table 2.5 Behaviour of two subspecies of *Peromyscus maniculatus* offered a choice of two habitats. Experiments conducted in very dim light (*Data from Harris*)

| | P.m. gracilis | | P.m. bairdi | |
	'tree' habitat	'grass' habitat	'tree' habitat	'grass' habitat
Time in habitat (%)	53	47	14	86
Seeds eaten (%)	65	35	23	78
Water drunk (%)	76	24	23	78

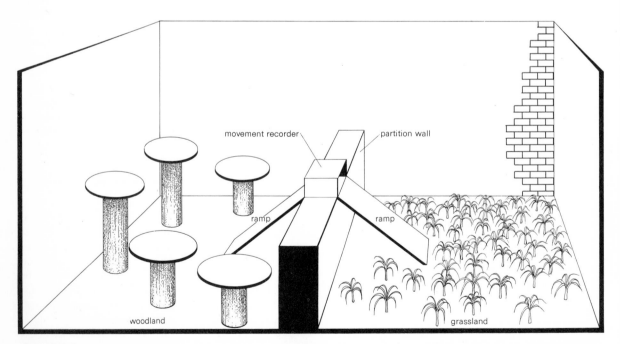

2.24 Drawing showing the arrangement of an experimental room for the study of habitat preference of Deermice. In one half of the room upright logs covered with planks represent woodland. In the other half stiff paper, suitably cut, represents grassland. The two halves of the room were separated by a low wall which could be crossed by using two ramps. On the top of the wall was a recording apparatus which registered movement of mice from one half of the room to the other. (Based on photographs by Harris).

cisely which features of its environment are recognized by *P.m. gracilis* as a token of 'forest' have still to be studied; the experiment does, however, show clearly that the observed distribution of the two subspecies is due, at least to some extent, to their behaviour; that is, their distribution is determined by choice not chance.

In a comparable experiment conducted with birds in a large cage, a group of ten sparrows was offered a choice between perching sites on pine branches and others on the Broad-leafed Oak. The birds, which are normally found perching upon conifers, spent on the average about 70 percent of the time among the pine branches; that is, they displayed in these artificial conditions a behaviour which would partly explain their distribution in the wild.

In all these examples the mobility of animals coupled with their behaviours allows them, at least to some extent, to select their habitats and this increases their chances of survival. If, however, you review the various examples we have considered, you will notice that there are two rather different types of mechanism involved. A nymph of the dragonfly *Paragomphus* can select, within the boundaries of its aquatic habitat, a suitable microhabitat (p. 24f). But the humidity and light responses of a woodlouse serve only to keep it within a suitable microhabitat, not to find one.

We know in fact relatively little about the behaviours of woodlice which assist them in finding a microhabitat, but one behaviour which may be of importance is worth mentioning. Imagine a cylindrical box whose walls are lined with white paper; over this white paper are laid four vertical stripes of black paper, equally spaced around the perimeter of the box (Fig. 2.25a). The box is lit from above and individual woodlice are set free in the middle of the box. What is observed is that they walk towards one or other of the black paper bands (Fig. 2.25b). Clearly this selection of a black object against a white background is a pattern which could lead a woodlouse, exposed by some disturbance of its habitat, back to shelter. It would not, however, be of value in keeping a woodlouse within the bounds of a suitable microhabitat.

There are then two different types of behaviours which can be involved in establishing the patterns of animal distribution. One is concerned with finding a suitable habitat or microhabitat, the other with keeping the individual within that habitat once it has been found. From the foregoing examples it can be seen that, in any study of animal distribution patterns, as we proceed from description to analysis, a knowledge of the characteristics of both these types of behaviours is likely to add to our understanding.

Dispersion

In attempting to analyse the factors which determine the distribution pattern of an animal, the first steps are to note the places in which we can find specimens of the species we are studying and to attempt to define the significant characteristics of these localities. But we have not con-

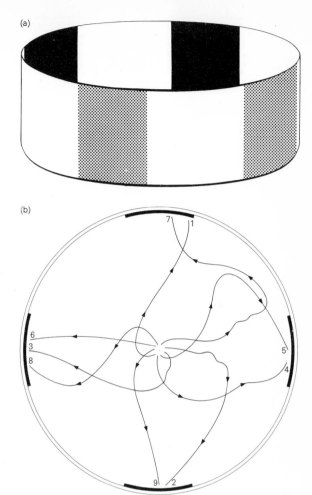

(a)

(b)

2.25 (a) Apparatus for the study of the responses of woodlice to a contrasting pattern of black and white vertical stripes. (b) Tracks of nine individual woodlice released in the centre of the arena. Note that each animal finally turns to move towards one of the black vertical stripes. (After Dietrich).

sidered how the individuals of a species are distributed within an area where they occur. We can, for example, prepare a detailed map of where specimens of, say, a limpet (Mollusca: Gastropoda) occur within a square metre of rock surface on a shore. This is relatively easy as limpets do not move very actively.

Fig. 2.26 shows three patterns of distribution which we might find, each dot representing the position of an individual specimen. In each case the individuals are scattered or 'dispersed' within the area and we can ask whether or not they are scattered in a completely random fashion. It is clear that the pattern in Fig. 2.26a is not a random one. The individuals occur in clumps or aggregations, this is described by saying that they are 'under-dispersed'. Similarly the pattern in Fig. 2.26b is obviously not random; the individuals are spaced out in a very regular manner so that the distance between one individual and

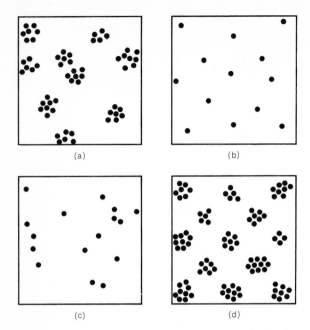

2.26 Possible patterns of distribution of individual animals in a uniform environment. In (a) the individuals are aggregated to produce a non-random pattern of distribution; this is an example of under-dispersion. In (b) the individuals are spaced out very evenly so that the pattern is non-random; this is an example of over-dispersion. In (c) the individuals are scattered at random. In (d) the individuals are aggregated so that they are under-dispersed, but the groups are spaced out fairly evenly, so that their pattern is over-dispersed.

its nearest neighbours is about as great as possible: such individuals are 'over-dispersed'. The pattern in Fig. 2.26c is indeed random. Clearly these three diagrams represent extreme examples. Suitable mathematical procedures can be used to test whether any pattern of points is random, under- or over-dispersed and to provide a measure of the extent to which the pattern may depart from being truly random.

Such a procedure is suitable for the study of plants or sedentary animals. It is less readily applicable to highly mobile animals. But obvious patterns of under-dispersion are familiar in flocks of small birds or in fruit bats which have communal roosts and feed together in noisy flocks at night.

Recognition of the occurrence of such patterns leads us to ask, firstly, what factors can result in a non-random distribution of individuals within an area and, secondly, what may be the biological significance of non-random distributions.

Let us consider a caterpillar which feeds upon the leaves of only one species of plant. The plant itself may be distributed at random within the area, but each plant may have on it many caterpillars. If we record the distribution of the individual caterpillars within the area, we will, as a result, have a pattern of clumping of individuals. This is

not a very useful observation. If, however, we analyse the details of the distribution of the caterpillars upon the plant we may find that they are scattered at random among the leaves, or that there are aggregations of caterpillars grouped together on particular leaves. Thus, depending upon the scale of our analysis, we may encounter both random and non-random distributions of individuals of one particular species (Fig. 2.26d).

The distribution pattern of members of a single species of animal is often directly determined by the fact that the area itself is not uniform and, since some resource required by the animal can be found only in a limited number of places, aggregations will form. This applies to our example of caterpillars. Similarly woodlice require shelter and, in an area such as the school compound, they will occur in aggregations wherever suitable shelter is available. Again, on a rocky shore at low tide, many species of animal are to be found sheltering in groups in crevices, or beneath rocks and stones. In these instances the individuals of a species are aggregated in a non-random pattern determined by the topography of the area.

Non-random patterns of distribution may also arise from the habits of the species or from the behaviour of individuals towards members of their own species. If the individuals are mutually aggressive and their numbers are high, we may expect to find a fairly regularly spaced pattern of distribution. Sometimes the individuals are positively attracted to each other and in such cases we will find aggregations or clumping.

Clumping and aggregations

Clumping may arise in different ways. In plants such as *Sansevieria* with vegetative methods of reproduction (Book 1 Fig. 6.4) individuals which have arisen from the same parent rhizome will be clumped together. Similarly among the sedentary animals on a rocky shore it is common to find clumps of certain anemones, such as *Palythoa* (Book 1 Fig. 20.19). These anemones can reproduce by budding off new individuals and, since the polyps are sedentary, a clump will form. Barnacles are also commonly found in dense clumps. This is because the larvae tend to prefer to settle where there are already others of their own species: the behaviour of the larvae thus leads to aggregation. We have already discussed the possible survival value of such behaviour (Book 1 p. 245). This situation has no parallel in higher plants.

Free-living animals may also aggregate. Herds of game and flocks of birds will be familiar. Dense crowding may be seen at the roosting or nesting sites of some species of bird. The Cattle Egret, for example, has separate communal roosting and nesting sites, although in some species of heron the same locality serves for both purposes. Groupings of fish also occur and are known as shoals or schools. Aggregation is seen also among the insects: clumps of ill-tasting butterfly larvae are common. In all these examples there is evidence (p. 107f) that such aggregates have protective value. We are concerned here only to emphasize that aggregation results in an uneven distribution of individuals within an area which provides them with suitable habitat.

Territories

The social habits of insects such as ants and termites result in aggregations of large numbers of individuals within a small area, but there is also a spacing out of colonies; clearly defined territories of separate colonies can be recognized (Fig. 11.8). Each territory is defended by the members of the colony and intercolony fights are not uncommon. Fighting between colonies of the ant *Oecophylla* is easily observed as the ants are large and active during the day. How can we account for the interrupted distribution pattern of colonies of the Red Ant shown in Fig. 2.8? The cocoa farm provides a fairly uniform environment, but the colonies are not distributed throughout the whole area. The individual colonies of *Oecophylla* have their territories, but between these colonies are others of different species of ants. These also defend their territories, so that neighbouring colonies of different species abut (Fig. 2.27). No single species is able to colonize the whole area and a broken pattern of distribution, described as part of an 'ant mosaic', is found.

Territorial behaviour is found in many other animals and can result in a fairly regular, non-random pattern of distribution, but it may also lead to aggregation. Territories sometimes reflect the division of the area into individual feeding grounds; sometimes they are concerned with reproduction, either in relation to mating or to raising the young; sometimes both factors are involved. Mating territories may be held for only a short while and thus have only a transient effect upon the distribution pattern; but feeding territories may be held for long periods and will then markedly affect the pattern of distribution. Sometimes the territory is held only during part of the life cycle of a species. One easily observed example is provided by the red, tube-building larva of the chironomid midge *Nilodorum* (Diptera). When many eggs are laid in a water tank, the larvae space themselves out very evenly over the bottom. Observation shows that each larva attempts to keep free as large an area around itself as it can reach without leaving its tube completely; adjacent larvae will bite at each other if they meet.

Territory among vertebrates

Temporary territorial behaviour in connection with breeding is found in fishes such as *Tilapia* (Fig. 6.23; Book 1 p. 265), as well as in some reptiles. Fig. 2.28 shows a map of a small lake in Central Island, Lake Rudolph. This lake supported more than 450 crocodiles but the shore line was divided into limited territorial stretches between 12 dominant males. Territorial behaviour occurs also in many

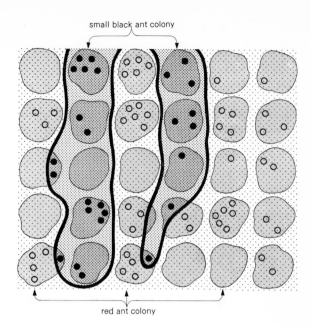

2.27 Detail of the distribution on cocoa trees in a plantation of the nests of a small black ant, *Macromischoides* (black circles), and the Red Tree Ant, *Oecophylla* (open circles). Note the way in which the territories of the two species interdigitate. In both species the members of a single colony occupy a large number of nests. The quadrat shown is about 15 m along each side. (After Majer).

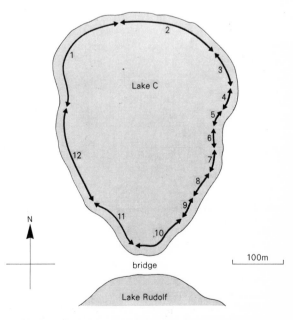

2.28 Map showing the territories of twelve dominant male crocodiles along the shore of a small lake on Central Island of Lake Rudolph. (After Modha).

31

species of birds. We have already noted the crowded roosting and nesting sites of herons; in some species the adult herons hold individual feeding territories away from the roosting and nesting sites. In other species of bird such as the Cape Wren-warbler a single area may serve as both a nesting and a feeding territory for a pair, so that the breeding pairs are spread out evenly over a considerable area (Fig. 2.29). Yet another pattern is found in some of the shrikes in which a nesting and feeding territory is held not by a pair, but by a permanent group of birds, although only one female in the group will lay eggs. Even in the crowded conditions of mass nesting sites, the individual birds nevertheless space themselves out so that both aggregating and segregating behaviours are displayed. This can often be easily recognized when large numbers of small birds assemble on a telephone wire before departure on migration. Although they flock together, nevertheless they perch at fairly uniform distances apart along the length of the wire.

Mammals may also establish temporary mating territories. Thus, for example, in the kob, *Adenota kob* (Fig. 2.30), each male holds a territory which may be as small as 15 to 30 m in diameter; ten to fifteen such neighbouring territories are closely packed together in favoured areas and are surrounded by larger territories (Fig. 2.31). Single females when on heat separate from the herds of females and young and move through the outer, larger territories to the densely packed dominant males; there mating will occur with a male chosen by the female, but within the male's own territory. Combined feeding and breeding territories also occur among mammals. For example, in Zululand, each dominant male White Rhinoceros, *Ceratotherium simum*, holds a territory of about 2 km². Here, along with subordinate males and females, he feeds, leaving his territory only to go for water. Aggressive encounters between neighbouring males do not normally lead

2.30 Male *Adenota kob*. Shoulder height is about 1 m.

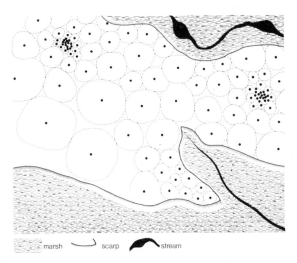

marsh ⌇ scarp ◣ stream

2.31 Diagram showing the distribution of the territories of the Uganda kob on a level area between two swamps. The approximate boundary of each territory is indicated by a broken line. Note that there are two concentrations of very small territories. These are occupied by dominant males and are the places where mating will occur. The subdominant males occupy larger territories around the mating grounds. (After Leuthold).

to fighting, and both courtship and mating by a bull can proceed undisturbed within the territory he defends.

It is clear that non-random distribution patterns in animals, unlike those in plants, are frequently a consequence of the behaviours of the animals. They serve a wide variety of different functions such as protection, freedom from disturbance during mating, freedom from disturbance of the young in the nest and the insurance of an

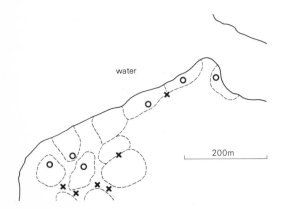

water

200m

2.29 Map showing the distribution of the nesting and feeding territories of the Cape Wren-warbler. The circles mark the sites of observed nests, the crosses places where fights between neighbouring birds were observed. (After Rowan and Broekhuysen).

adequate food supply for growing animals, as well as reduction of fighting between individual members of a species. Because of the mobility of animals, these non-random patterns may only be transient and thus less obvious than those occurring in plants. In a complete analysis of the distribution of any species, such patterns have to be considered. Thus, for example, the territories held by dominant male kob represent only a small fraction of the whole area occupied by the species in any one locality. Nevertheless, the same places are selected by the males as mating grounds each year. They must have certain distinctive features and an analysis of these would not only give us a clearer insight into the biology of kob, but might be of considerable practical importance in the successful management of the species within a game reserve.

The limits of distribution of plants and animals

Before leaving the subject of distribution patterns it is desirable to emphasize that the mechanisms which determine the normal areas of distribution of particular species of plants and of animals differ in one major respect. We have seen how the success of an individual seed depends upon the local conditions where it falls. If these lie within the range of physiological tolerance of both the seedling and the adult, the plant may be able to establish itself. But in natural conditions individuals of a particular plant species are rarely found to occupy the whole range of an area defined by their physiological tolerance (p. 13). As the limits of tolerance are approached, the plants appear to be unable to compete effectively with others better adapted to the prevailing environmental conditions (Fig. 2.32a).

With animals a comparable situation may exist. There is, for example, no evidence that the two subspecies of *Peromyscus* which we have considered (p. 27f) are in any way significantly different in their physiological tolerances; their distributions are largely, if not completely, limited by their behaviours. It is possible that very many species of animal do not usually spread to the limits of their physiological tolerances, but are kept within a narrower zone by their behaviours (Fig. 2.32b). The advantage of this, from the viewpoint of individual survival, is clear. There are relatively few environments which are perfectly stable in their physical and chemical characteristics. Apart from seasonal fluctuations, conditions differ from year to year, particularly in land environments where the heavy rains of one year may be followed by their partial or complete failure the next. The individuals of any species which spread to the limits of its physiological tolerances would, at least at the margins of this range, survive in some years; in other, unfavourable years, they would die. If, however, the behaviours of the animal restrict it to a narrower range

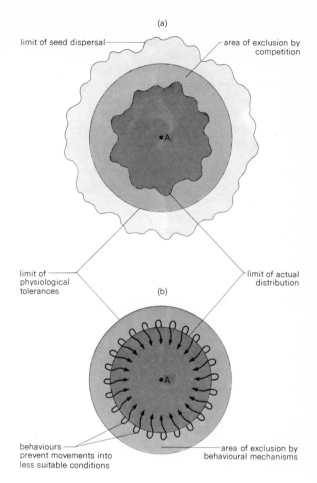

2.32 Diagram contrasting the factors tending to limit the distribution of (a) plants and (b) motile animals. Optimal conditions for a species are found at A; conditions become less suitable in all directions radially from this point until the limit of physiological tolerance is reached. For further explanation see text.

than that set by its physiological capacities, each individual enjoys a certain 'margin of safety' and its chances of survival are thereby increased. For this reason a study of the physiological tolerances of animals may be less important in attempting to understand the patterns of animal distribution than is a study of their behaviours. In the same way a study of competitive relations between different species of plants may also be of crucial importance in comprehension of the underlying factors determining distribution patterns of particular species.

Problems

1 You are required to investigate the humidity preferences of a small beetle using a choice-chamber type of apparatus. List all the experimental precautions which you consider necessary for the conduct of such an experiment.

2 What do you consider may be the practical value of a knowledge of the factors which determine the choice of oviposition sites by different species of mosquito? In an irrigation system, considerable trouble was encountered by the presence of large populations of *Anopheles gambiae* which bred in the irrigation canals. Other than the use of toxic materials, what recommendations for the control of this pest might be made?

3 The data in the following table show detailed information on the number of cypris larvae settling at different levels on panels exposed in the intertidal zone. They were obtained from the same investigation as the results summarised in Fig. 2.23.

Vertical distribution of cypris larvae on panels

Panel no.	Upper third	Middle third	Bottom third
II	50	154	159
III	1 077	670	565
IV	2 509	1 077	564
VI	1 837	555	148
VII	806	174	169

What hypotheses would you erect to account for these results? Explain your reasoning.

4 Outline a programme of investigations which might be undertaken to study factors involved in host-finding by the cercaria larvae of *Schistosoma*. Why might such information be of practical value?

5 On p. 19 and 20 results are given of experiments on the preferences of two different species of *Anopheles* for (a) shade and (b) salinity of water. Suggest, in detail, the way in which such experiments might have been carried out.

6 Why (a) are forceps used to handle a cobalt salt paper when the humidity of a locality is being measured, (b) is copper(II) sulphate a suitable salt to use in water to make a heat screen?

7 How could choice-chamber experiments be used (a) to determine the anatomical location of a sense organ known to respond to humidity, and (b) to study the possible function of a sense organ on the tips of the antennae of a beetle?

8 The responses to humidity of a small beetle were determined using a choice-chamber at 15°C and 25°C. In each series the beetles were offered a number of different gradients. The data below show the results obtained, intensity of reaction being expressed by the ratio of the number of beetles in the wet to the number of beetles in both wet and dry.

(a) Using these data describe qualitatively the characteristics of the humidity responses of this beetle.

(b) How can you account for the fact that while the intensities of reaction in a gradient of 1 to 10 percent

R.H. are nearly the same at the two temperatures, they are markedly different on a gradient of 50 to 90 percent R.H. Do the data justify your conclusion quantitatively?

Intensity of reaction (W/W + D)

Gradient (% R.H.)	15°C	25°C
1–10	0·86	0·85
10–20	0·70	0·69
10–30	0·72	0·70
20–40	0·54	0·55
40–60	0·51	0·50
50–90	0·76	0·97
70–90	0·63	0·74
80–90	0·57	0·62

(c) Do you consider that the same sense organs are responsible for the responses in a gradient of 1 to 10 percent R.H. and 50 to 90 percent R.H.? Give reasons for your opinion.

Saturated vapour pressure of water

15°C   1702·5 Pa   or   12·77 mm Hg
25°C   3163·7 Pa   or   23·73 mm Hg

9 The responses to temperature and humidity of mature female grasshoppers of two different species, A and B, have been studied using choice chambers. The intensity of reaction (I.R.) for temperature was expressed as $100(T_2 - T_1)/(T_2 + T_1)$ where T_1 is the number of individuals which selected the lower temperature and T_2 the number selecting the higher. For humidity, the I.R. was expressed as $100(W - D)/(W + D)$ where W is the number selecting the higher humidity and D the number selecting the lower.

The following results were obtained:

Temperature range (°C)	I.R. (%) Species A	I.R. (%) Species B
25–35	43	47
30–40	58	60
35–45	20	52
40–50	− 72	20
45–55	− 100	− 100

Humidity range (% R.H.)	I.R. (%) Species A	I.R. (%) Species B
50–100	46	− 32
60–100	38	− 26
70–100	25	− 21
80–100	0	− 19

Both species occur in the vicinity of Cairo in Egypt. One lives on the edge of the desert, while the other is most commonly found on the banks of streams and irrigation canals. Which is the species which lives at the edge of the desert? Explain the reasoning which led you to your answer.

10 The distribution of a common, large, plant-feeding, hemipteran living in the grass of savanna woodland was studied by dividing an area into 25 quadrats, each 5 m square. The number of bugs in each quadrat was determined by sweeping the grass with a net. The light intensity at the centre of each quadrat was measured daily at noon for a period of a week and the mean values given below are expressed in arbitrary units. The layout of the quadrats is shown in the accompanying figure.

1	2	3	4	5
6	7	8	9	10
11	12	13	14	15
16	17	18	19	20
21	22	23	24	25

←——25m——→

The following observations were made:

Quadrat	Mean light intensity	Number of specimens collected
1	3·1	137
2	1·9	164
3	3·0	141
4	4·3	125
5	3·2	146
6	5·7	97
7	4·1	119
8	5·3	87
9	6·6	72
10	4·3	134
11	5·5	68
12	3·6	151
13	4·7	129
14	6·1	78
15	7·6	64
16	2·5	155
17	0·9	192
18	3·4	129
19	5·6	106
20	5·1	132
21	3·8	111
22	2·7	168
23	4·3	103
24	3·9	156
25	2·1	179

(a) What is the relationship between light intensity and the number of specimens collected? Display the results suitably.

(b) Suggest three hypotheses which might account for the observed distribution and describe how you would attempt to check the validity of these suggestions.

11 Suggest a method by which it might be possible to measure current speed in a small stream.

Bibliography

Further reading

| Carthy, J. D. | *The study of behaviour*, Arnold, 1966, Chaps. 2, 5 and 7 |

Cloudsley-Thompson, J. C. — *Micro-ecology*, Arnold, 1967

Davis, D. E. — *Integral animal behaviour*, Collier-Macmillan, 1966, Chaps. 3, 4 and 5

Evans, S. M. — *Studies in invertebrate behaviour*, Heinemann, 1968, Chaps. 3, 4 and 5

Nash, T. A. M. — *Africa's bane: the tsetse fly*, Collins, 1969, Chap. 5

Wecker, S. C. — 'Habitat selection', *Scientific American*, 1964, Offprint no. 195

Part 2
Synecology—the study of biomes and communities

3 Biomes—producers in the forest and savanna

Autecology and synecology

In Book 1 (p. 2) we defined ecology as 'the study of organisms in relation to their environment'. So far we have been looking at the environmental requirements and reactions of individual species; this is autecology. A species occurs in a particular kind of habitat partly because of its physiological adaptations, which were discussed in Part 5 of Book 1, and partly because of its behaviour patterns, discussed in Part 1 of this book. We have seen that behaviour may be of greater significance than physiology in the autecology of animals, but that physiology which determines their ability to compete is of great importance to plants. Behaviour, in fact, is a term not generally considered to apply to plants, though some dispersal and germination phenomena may be considered to represent 'behaviour'.

Organisms do not usually live singly, but in communities where many species live together. This and the succeeding chapters will deal with the structure of such communities and the relationships between their constituent organisms, that is, with their synecology.

Biomes and communities

In discussing distribution we saw that patterns exist at the large scale of countries and continents, and also at the lower level of, for example, the school compound. The same is true of communities. A small number of major community types, for example, rain forest and savanna woodland, cover large areas. These community types are called biomes, and they will be considered in this and the next chapter. Within each biome may be discerned a variety of less extensive, more narrowly defined communities; these are the communities of Chaps. 5, 6 and 7.

The greater part of the biomass of any terrestrial biome is in its producers, the plants, which thus provide the framework of space and food on which the animals depend. The most obvious part of a forest is its trees. Although animals may be more abundant than plants in terms of species and individuals, their conditions of existence are determined by these bulkier plants. It is thus logical to consider the vegetation of biomes before proceeding to the animals.

Fig. 3.1 shows the distribution of the major biomes of Africa. Other African biomes exist, for example in aquatic habitats, but these cannot compare in importance on a continental scale with those shown on the map. Fig. 3.1 shows a considerable degree of symmetry about the equator. Closed forest lies in a belt within roughly 7° north and south of the equator. The belt of moist savanna lies outside the forest, and within 12°N and 20°S of the equator; outside this comes the dry savanna and steppe. Desert extends from 15° to 33°N and S, and finally come the small strips of xerophyllous scrub at the northern and southern extremities of the continent.

Climate

At the scale of Fig. 3.1, soil and human activity are relatively unimportant as factors determining vegetation type, though they are of great importance when we examine a smaller area more closely. The large-scale biomes are determined mainly by climate, and the most important aspects of this are temperature and rainfall. In fact similar conditions of these two factors are associated with similar vegetation types all over the world (Fig. 3.2).

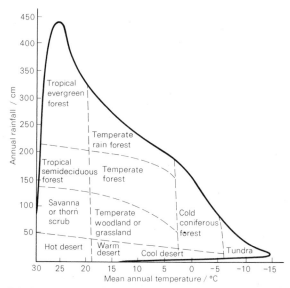

3.2 Approximate climatic limits of the major biomes of the world. (After Whittaker).

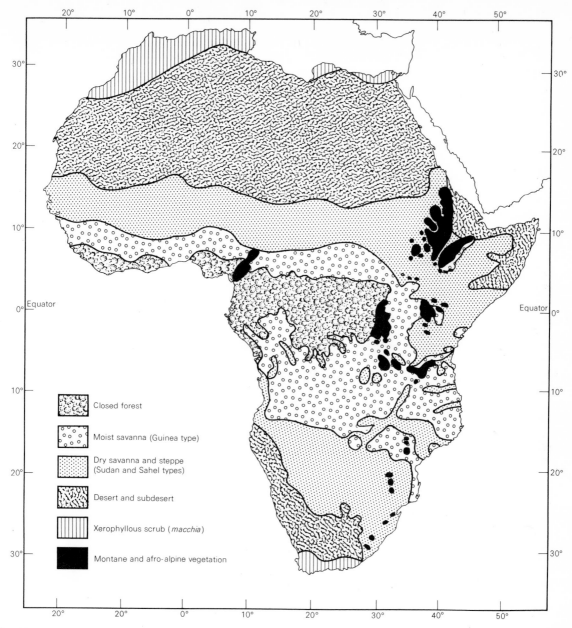

3.1 Major biomes of Africa. (After Keay modified by Moreau).

Legend:
- Closed forest
- Moist savanna (Guinea type)
- Dry savanna and steppe (Sudan and Sahel types)
- Desert and subdesert
- Xerophyllous scrub (*macchia*)
- Montane and afro-alpine vegetation

Temperature

In Africa near the equator, frost is restricted to mountains higher than 2 500 to 3 000 m; frosts at sea level occur only outside the tropics. Prolonged frost is fatal to the majority of tropical plants, including mangroves and most palms; it is thus the frost-limit which effectively separates tropical from temperate vegetation. It is noteworthy that the vegetation of high tropical mountains includes many plant genera which are absent from tropical lowlands, but wide-spread in temperate countries. In the tropics, the seasonal temperature range is usually much less than the diurnal range. For example, at Lagos the seasonal range of mean monthly temperature is 3°C, but the daily range may be 7°C.

Rainfall

As explained in Book 1 (p. 269), water relations are of over-riding importance in determining the vegetation type

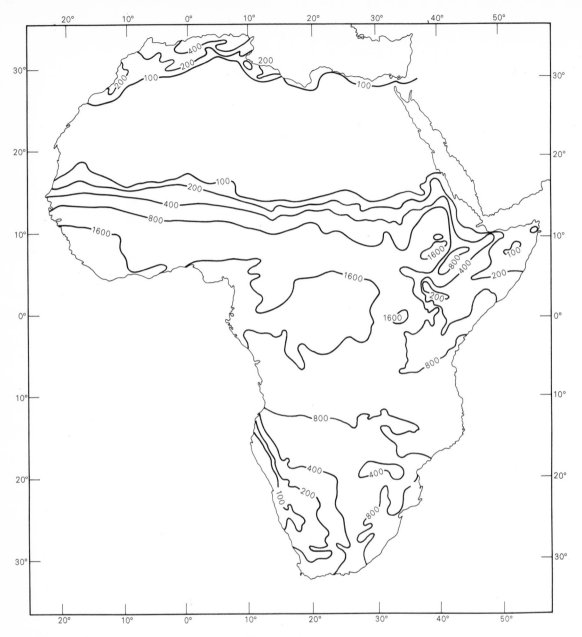

3.3 Mean annual rainfall of Africa in mm. (After Thompson).

within any climatic zone defined by temperature. Water available to the plant depends partly on rainfall (precipitation) and partly on evaporation. A place, or month, will be humid if precipitation exceeds evaporation, and dry if evaporation exceeds precipitation. Evaporation is higher at high temperatures; therefore a higher rainfall is needed near the equator than in temperate latitudes to provide the same water supply to plants.

The simplest expression of precipitation is mean annual rainfall, and although a map of this quantity (Fig. 3.3) gives a reasonable fit with vegetation, there are some notable discrepancies. For example, Conakry in Guinea has an annual rainfall of 4300 mm, and lies in savanna, whereas Aburi in Ghana has only 1170 mm, but lies in forest. The explanation is that forest requires not only a minimum annual total, but also a reasonably constant

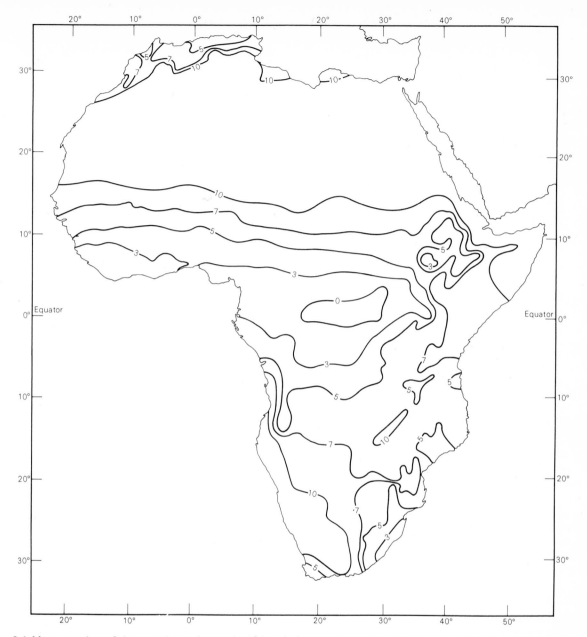

3.4 Mean number of dry months each year in Africa. A dry month is taken to be one in which the aridity index is less than 20. Aridity index (see Book 1 p. 274) is given by the formula $\dfrac{12 \times P}{T + 10}$ where P is mean monthly rainfall in mm, and T is mean monthly temperature in °C. (After Lauer).

supply of water throughout the year. If the soil is saturated by heavy rain, further rain can only run off the surface and be lost to plants; such surplus rain cannot compensate for deficiencies in the dry season. Thus the distribution of rainfall through the year may be almost as important as its total quantity; in other words, the length of the dry season may be of critical importance. In Book 1, we defined a 'dry month' in the lowland tropics as one with less than

60 mm rain, and stated that forest does not usually flourish where there are four or more dry months each year. Fig. 3.4, mapping the number of dry months in Africa, fits the vegetation map better than does the mean annual rainfall of Fig. 3.3.

A further complication is that these dry months may be successive or they may be divided between two dry seasons. Close to the equator there is not much seasonality

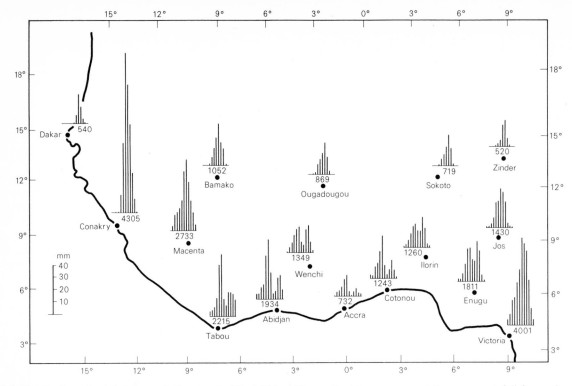

3.5 Distribution of rainfall through the year in West Africa. The vertical bars represent the mean rainfall for each month of the year; the scale is given in the bottom left-hand corner of the diagram. The left-hand end of the horizontal line below each set of bars represents January. The number below each horizontal bar is the mean annual rainfall in mm for that locality. (After Jackson).

in rainfall. Beyond 8° from the equator there is one rainy season and one dry season each year. Between 2° and 8° from the equator, some places have two rainy seasons separated by two dry seasons (Fig. 3.5). From the plant's point of view, dry months are least injurious if they are separated by a period of rain. Thus of two places at different latitudes, having the same total period of drought, the locality nearer the equator is more likely to carry forest.

Initiation of rain

Rain falls when a sufficient depth of moist air is cooled. Air becomes moist through blowing long distances over a moist surface, usually the sea, and may be cooled when it is raised by convection, by a range of hills or, more commonly, by convergence when winds blow into an area from different directions. In general, winds blowing from a continental interior are dry, whereas those blowing from the sea are more likely to bring rain. For reasons related to the direction of rotation of the earth, easterly winds are stable and not subject to much vertical mixing; though they may be moist in their lower levels when blowing across an ocean, the upper levels tend to remain dry so that they are not very effective in producing rain. Westerly winds on the other hand are unstable, and in them moist air tends to be carried to greater heights;

thus westerlies tend to bring rain. In most of Africa drought is associated with a northern air-mass with dry, north-easterly continental winds known in West Africa as 'harmattan', blowing from Asia across the Sahara Desert. Rain is associated with a southern air-mass with oceanic winds blowing from the south-east or south-west. North-easterly and southerly winds blow from zones of high pressure into the zone of low pressure called the equatorial trough (or the intertropical convergence zone),

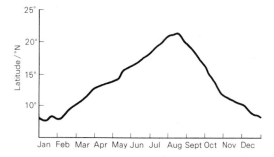

3.6 Mean position of intertropical convergence zone at ground level at 3°E, 1956–61. Note that the movement of the zone follows the apparent movement of the sun, but that the zone does not descend below the equator at this longitude. (After Ireland).

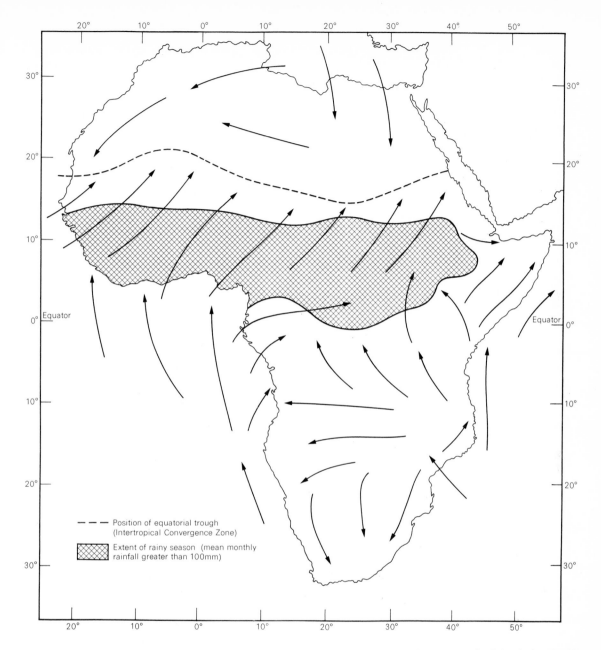

3.7 Directions of prevailing winds, and areas with mean monthly rainfall exceeding 100 mm in July, during the West African rainy season. The highest rainfalls occur where the southwesterly monsoon winds strike directly against the coast. The easterly winds between 10°S and 20°S do not bring rain. (After Thompson).

where they converge and consequently rise, producing rain as a result. The low pressure of the equatorial trough is caused by heating of the air when the sun is overhead; the trough therefore tends to move northwards between December and June, and south again from June to December (Fig. 3.6). In West Africa it is prevented from moving south of the equator by a high-pressure belt over the relatively cold waters of the Gulf of Guinea.

In June and July, the northern summer, when the trough is about 18°N, the south-easterly winds which have blown across Africa are deflected to a south-westerly direction as they cross the equator. As mentioned above, westerly winds are more likely than easterlies to cause rain, and these south-westerlies are the wet 'monsoon' winds of the West African rainy season (Fig. 3.7). Most of southern Africa has its rainy season during the southern summer

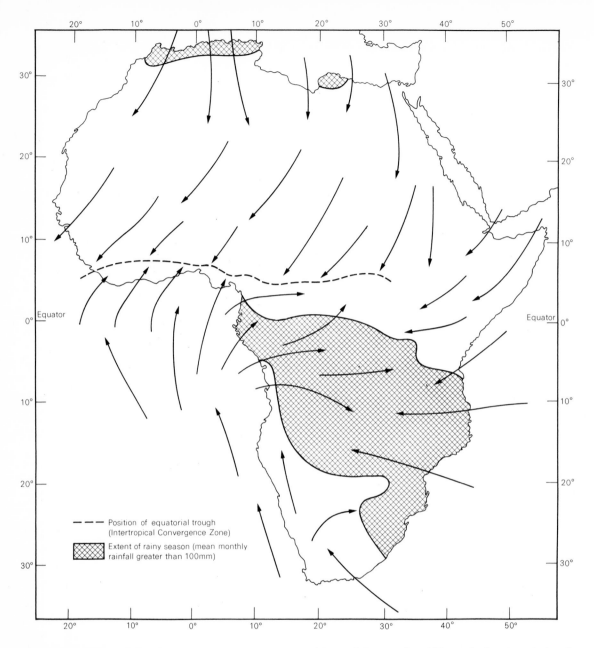

3.8 Directions of prevailing winds, and areas with mean monthly rainfall exceeding 100 mm in January, during the Southern rainy season. Note that at this time winds between 10°S and 20°S are generally westerly. Although the surface position of the intertropical convergence zone at this season lies north of the West African coast, there is no rain there because the moist southwesterly air mass is overlain by dry air at higher levels in the atmosphere. (After Thompson).

months of December and January when the trough reaches its southern limits (Fig. 3.8).

The shortest dry season is found along the equator, which is within the southern limit of the northern rainy season and the northern limit of the southern rainy season. The Sahara Desert is permanently covered by the dry continental air-mass, and has no rainy season. The 'Horn of Africa' including Somalia and eastern Ethiopia is too far north to benefit from the southern rainy season and too far east to be reached by the south-westerly winds of the northern rainy season; it is also in the 'rain shadow' of the Ethiopian highlands, and north-easterly winds which reach it have blown over the deserts of Arabia.

The highest rainfalls are recorded where the rain-bearing winds impinge directly on the coast as in Cameroun, Liberia and south-east and north-west of the Malagasy Republic. The highest annual rainfall in Africa, 10 000 mm, is at Debundscha Point in Cameroun where the rain-bearing winds strike the coast directly below the 4 000 m high Cameroun Mountain.

The area of land relative to sea is much greater in the northern than in the southern hemisphere. The more maritime nature of the southern hemisphere is reflected in the generally more favourable climate of southern Africa, and the very much smaller proportion of the land covered by desert as compared with Africa north of the equator.

The northern and southern tips of Africa receive their rain from air-masses other than those which supply the rest of the continent. The south-western part of the Cape Province of South Africa, unlike the remainder of southern Africa, receives its rainfall in July and August, that is, during the southern winter. The northern coasts of Morocco, Algeria and Tunisia receive rain in the northern winter from winds of a Mediterranean air-mass.

Evidently broad rainfall patterns, and hence vegetation patterns, have their origins in such features as the relative positions of seas, coasts, hills and land-masses, and the seasonal movements of wind-belts. In the past we have had to rely for our overall picture of weather on piecing together the records of very many surface meteorological stations, but with the coming of space travel and weather satellites, large-scale cloud and wind patterns can be photographed from space. Fig 3.9 shows cloud massed over the forest zone of Africa while the desert and savanna are largely cloud-free.

We must next look more closely at the various kinds of vegetation, the biomes themselves.

Saudi Arabia
Gulf of Aden
Somali Republic

Mozambique coast
Malagasy Republic
Indian Ocean

Atlantic Ocean

3.9 Earth as seen by the Apollo-17 astronauts during their return flight from the moon. Africa occupies most of the upper left-hand and central part of the photograph. The convergence zone where cloudless Saharan air meets clouds along an east–west line through West Africa can be clearly seen

Forest

It is logical to begin with the closed forest. Tropical forest is the most complex and highly developed type of vegetation on earth, and very probably the oldest. There is reason to think that other biomes have been derived from it. With the exception of tropical forest, all biomes are adapted to certain adverse factors. Savanna is adapted to fire, semidesert scrub to drought, temperate forest to seasonal frost, mangrove to high salinity, swamp to poor soil aeration and so on. It is only in tropical forest that conditions are favourable to plant growth throughout the year; consequently we find here the greatest diversity in species and life-forms, and also probably the highest productivity.

The figures in Table 3.1, obtained from a plot measuring only 25 m × 25 m (625 m²) in a Ghanaian forest, illustrate this diversity. A total of 57 tree species were recorded on the plot, and of these 15 had trunks measuring more than 10 cm in diameter; this figure may be compared with the total of only 30 or so indigenous species of tree in the whole of the British Isles. About 600 tree species are known from the Ivory Coast tropical forest. Although this seems a large number there are even more in other similar-sized areas of tropical forest—1000 in the state of Pará in Brazil, and 2500 in Malaysia.

The life-forms in tropical forest include all those shown in Table 3.1, and rarer ones such as saprophytes and parasites. The dominant life-form is, however, that of the tree; the other life-forms fit on, round or under the trees. Within the forest, however, although the lower parts of the trunks are easily seen, the crowns of the taller trees may be largely hidden by the shorter trees. It is impossible to get a complete view of the forest from any one point; a picture of forest structure must be built up from the glimpses seen from many angles. To get round this difficulty, ecologists have adopted the plan of constructing diagrams of sections through the forest. To make such a 'profile diagram' (Fig. 3.10) a strip of forest 7·6 m wide and at least 60 m long is measured out, pegs put into the corners, and the sides demarcated with strings. The position of each tree having a trunk exceeding 10 cm diameter is then measured and marked on the ground plan (Fig. 3.11). To find the height of each tree and the position

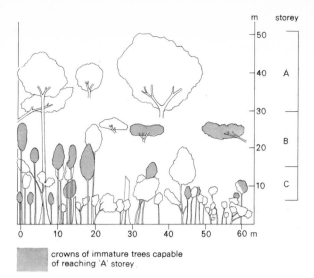

crowns of immature trees capable of reaching 'A' storey

3.10 Profile diagram of a strip of forest 7·6 m wide in Ghana. The tree crowns apparently floating in mid-air are in fact attached to trees rooted outside this strip. (After Lawson *et al.*).

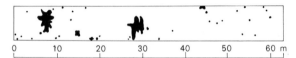

3.11 Ground plan of trees shown in profile in Fig. 3.10. (After Lawson *et al.*).

of the major branches, it is necessary to use an instrument such as a Haga altimeter, (Fig. 3.12) which can measure angles from the horizontal; the height can then be calculated if the distance from the tree is known (Fig. 3.13). The diameter of the tree crown can be found by noting the positions along the strip where you are just below the edge of the canopy as seen when you look vertically upwards. By taking one tree at a time, it is not too difficult to build up a complete diagram.

Stratification within the forest

The diagram will probably show that the trees are stratified, that is, they occur in distinct layers. In the profile shown in

Table 3.1 Species composition of a forest plot 25 m × 25 m in the Aiyaola Forest Reserve, Ghana (*Hall and Swaine, unpublished data*)

	Trees; > 10 cm diam.	Trees; additional species as seedlings and saplings	Shrubs	Herbs	Climbers	Total
Number of species	15	42	27	19	50	153
Percentage of total	10	27	18	12	33	100

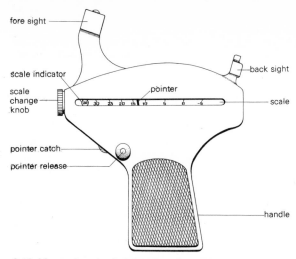

3.12 Measuring the height of a tree with a Haga altimeter. This instrument has several scales for use at different distances from the tree. Using the '20' scale, the scale will give a reading direct in metres at 20 m from the tree; at 40 m the scale reading is multiplied by 2, and so on. To obtain a reading, the pointer release button is pressed, the top of the tree aligned with the sights, and then the catch button pressed. The reading for the base of the tree is then deducted to get the total height.

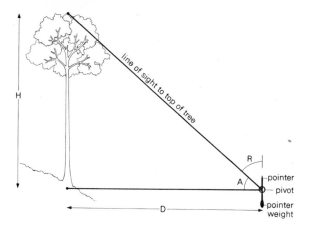

3.13 Diagram showing the principle of the altimeter. The pointer is pivoted within the instrument, and kept vertical by a weight at its lower end. Increase in the sighting angle A thus results in a corresponding decrease in the reading angle R. The distance D (distance to tree) is known. The height of the tree H is related to R as follows: $H = D \tan(90 - R)$.

Fig. 3.10 there are three layers, as is usual in undisturbed forest. The upper layer, or A-storey, consists of trees above 30 m. In some forests the A-storey may form a continuous canopy, but in tropical Africa the trees of this storey are usually isolated 'emergents' whose crowns protrude completely above the rest. The main canopy is generally formed by the middle storey or B-storey trees,

at about 30 m above the ground. Below this is the understorey, or C-storey with small trees up to about 15 m high. Some of the trees in the B- and C-storeys are young specimens of the species constituting the A-storey, but the majority are of species which never grow beyond these storeys. Not shown in the diagram are the two lowest storeys, the so-called 'shrub' layer (in fact consisting mainly of miniature trees or 'treelets') from 1 to 5 m high, and the herb layer below this.

The canopy forms the 'roof' of the forest but, compared with the roof of a building, the canopy is very irregular both in thickness and elevation. Where a group of tall trees stand close together the canopy may be 40 m high but in the gaps between the trees it comes right down to the ground. Inside a house, the rainfall, temperature, light intensity, wind speed and humidity are all quite different and less variable than they are outside; although the canopy has more 'leaks' than a roof, the same is broadly true of forest. We have already described the climatic conditions which are necessary for the development of forest, and these define the forest macroclimate. Within the forest is a range of microclimates determined by the forest itself. The leaves in the crown of a tall tree are exposed to whatever wind may be blowing, to full light intensity, high temperatures and low humidities; conditions for a seedling on the forest floor will be the opposite of these. Thus within forest there is a vertical gradient of environmental characteristics (Fig. 3.14 and 3.15). To

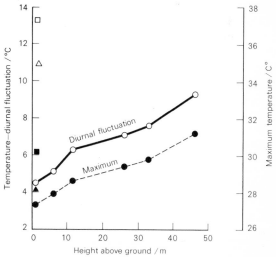

3.14 Vertical and horizontal temperature gradients in forest. Mean daily maximum temperature (—●—●—) and mean diurnal temperature fluctuation (—○—○—) at different levels above the ground on a tower in an Ivory Coast forest, 21–27 March 1960. The tallest nearby tree was 43 m high. (Data from Cachan and Duval). Isolated points show maximum temperature (▲) and diurnal temperature fluctuation (■) in the understorey as compared with an adjacent clearing (△, □) in a Ghana forest, 26–27 March 1968. (Data from Lawson et al.).

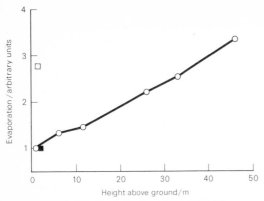

3.15 Vertical (—○—○—) and horizontal (■, □) gradients of evaporation as measured by Piche evaporimeter (see Book 1 p. 65) in the positions described under Fig. 3.14. Units are arbitrary, on a scale in which a value of 1 is assigned to evaporation at lowest end of vertical gradient and at inner end of horizontal gradient. (Data from Cachan and Duval, and Lawson *et al*.).

measure the gradient directly is difficult, as it requires the construction of a tower from the forest floor up through the canopy, but as the microclimate within a large forest clearing is rather similar to that above the canopy, we can more easily get an idea of the differences involved by studying a horizontal rather than a vertical gradient. Fig. 3.14 and 3.15 show the similarities between these gradients. To summarize: the canopy environment is optimal for photosynthesis, but canopy leaves are likely to be subject to water stress (Table 3.2), partly because conditions are favourable to high rates of transpiration and partly because they must withdraw water from the

Table 3.2 Leaf water stress, measured as diffusion-pressure deficit (D.P.D.), in leaves of plants of various life-forms in Indonesian forest (*Data from Blum*).

Life-form	Mean D.P.D. of leaves (Atmospheres)
Small herbs	5·4
Large herbs	6·1
Lianes	12·4
Small trees	13·0
Large trees	15·1

xylem which, in a tall tree, is under considerable tension (Book 1 p. 72). On the other hand, the forest floor environment is humid but dim, and the light which reaches it has largely been filtered through leaves and is therefore deficient in the red wavelengths useful in photosynthesis, in favour of useless green wavelengths (Fig. 1.16).

Form and function in the forest flora

The leaves of forest plants are usually smooth and hairless,

shiny and with entire, untoothed margins. The average size is about 20 cm², though a few such as *Thaumatococcus*, whose leaves are used for wrapping food (Fig. 3.16), are much larger; some species, such as *Piptadeniastrum* (Fig. 3.17), have leaves divided into very small leaflets about 1 mm wide. As would be expected, there are differences between canopy or 'sun' leaves and understorey or 'shade' leaves. Fig. 22.31 in Book 1 shows that the sun leaves of the forest tree *Cynometra ananta* are more xeromorphic than those of shade leaves of the same species, as they are smaller, thicker and have more layers of palisade mesophyll. This figure also shows that the understorey leaf has a long point whereas the tip of the canopy leaf is relatively blunt.

This differentiation of leaves is typical of tall trees. All the leaves of species of tree or treelet which never get above the C-storey are of the shade type, as are the leaves of many herbs. Fig. 3.18 shows the similarity in leaf-blade form of forest understorey plants which are quite unrelated to one another—a dicot tree with simple leaves, the leaflet of a dicot tree with compound leaves, a grass and a monocot herb. In view of its almost universal occurrence,

3.16 The monocot herb *Thaumatococcus daniellii* growing in forest understorey. The petioles of this plant may exceed 2 m and the leaf blade 50 cm in length.

3.17 Branch of the forest tree *Piptadeniastrum africanum*, which has bipinnate leaves. The leaflets are about 8 mm long and 1 mm wide.

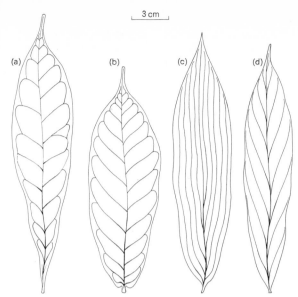

3.18 Leaf shapes of plants of forest understorey, all drawn to same scale. (a) *Cola reticulata*, a dicot tree, with simple leaves. (b) Leaflet of *Chytranthus villiger*, a dicot tree with pinnate leaves. (c) Leaf of the grass *Leptaspis cochleata*. (d) Leaf of *Aframomum stanfieldii*, a monocot herb.

3.19 *Celtis* tree uprooted during a storm. Note the shallowness of the root system.

it can scarcely be doubted that this leaf form has great advantages in this habitat. We would expect a leaf to be thin where light intensity is low, as one palisade layer may be sufficient to trap available light, while extra cell layers might respire without contributing to photosynthesis. Hair is not needed to reduce transpiration in an environment where humidity is high, and its presence would interfere with light reception by the mesophyll. The smooth margin and long leaf tip can be shown experimentally to facilitate the run-off of rain water from the leaf surface; the tip in fact is often called a 'drip-tip', as drops of water can be seen to fall from it after rain. Various opinions have been expressed as to the value to a leaf of rapid drying. It has been suggested that growth of forest-floor plants may be limited by poor inorganic nutrient supply resulting from low rates of transpiration, but the supply of ions to a leaf is more usually limited by rate of uptake in the root than by rate of translocation through the xylem (Book 1 chap. 8). It is more probable that a layer of moisture on the leaf surface may block the stomata and thus interfere with the gaseous exchange of photosynthesis.

The periderm of most forest plants is thin, presumably because the prevailing high humidity makes unnecessary the production of a thick waterproof layer. One consequence is that forest trees are readily damaged by fire, and even by the increased desiccation which occurs when surrounding vegetation is cleared away. Forest trees seldom grow well in isolation from each other or with the undergrowth removed, perhaps partly because of increased evaporation from the trunk, or perhaps because the bark becomes over-heated.

One important part of the forest is normally difficult to observe: the complex of root systems lying within the soil. When a tree is blown over in a storm, however, it can be seen that the bulk of the large roots lie horizontally not far below the surface, and that most trees do not develop thick tap roots (Fig. 3.19). A more exact method of studying root distribution is to dig a pit, isolating on one side of it an undisturbed vertical pillar, or 'monolith', of soil of known dimensions. This monolith is then removed layer by layer, and the roots washed from each sample in turn. Fig. 3.20 summarizes the results of an investigation of this kind in a Ghana forest soil, which showed that 80 percent of the roots occurred within the top 10 cm of soil. The explanation is that nutrients are similarly concentrated in the superficial layers of the soil (see Chap. 7).

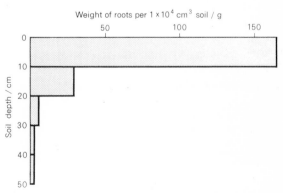

3.20 Distribution with depth of roots in a Ghana forest soil. (After Lawson *et al.*).

47

3.21 0beche tree (*Triplochiton scleroxylon*) growing in cocoa farm, showing well-developed buttresses.

The lower part of the trunk of many A- and B-storey trees is not cylindrical, but expanded into thin, flattened structures called buttresses (Fig. 3.21). A little digging will show that a buttress is formed by the upper side of a large horizontal root growing faster than the lower. Each buttress begins in a young tree as a slight ridge in the angle between root and trunk. As the tree grows, the buttress extends further along the root and also further up the trunk, splitting the bark as it goes. Almost all the wood production of the basal part of the trunk is channelled into the buttresses; the diameter of the central part of the trunk base remains small. Buttresses are a nuisance to the forester, as they reduce the volume of useful timber, make measurement of trunk diameter very difficult, and are an obstacle to felling. Until recently the tree feller had to build a platform above the buttresses on which to stand while cutting with an axe, but nowadays the buttresses can quickly be sliced away using a petrol-driven saw (Fig. 3.22). The widespread occurrence of buttresses in all tropical forests suggests that they must have some value to the tree. While there has been much speculation and disagreement on this point, buttresses probably give support to the tree trunk, and this may be of particular importance when the tree is large, and its roots mainly shallow. Outside the tropical forest, buttresses may be disadvantageous because their thin bark and large surface area would be too susceptible to damage by frost, fire or drought.

3.22 (a) Traditional method of felling a large forest tree. The axeman works from a platform lashed to the tree in order to be able to cut the trunk above the buttresses. (b) Modern method of felling using a power saw which can slice rapidly through the buttresses.

3.23 Cocoa tree (*Theobroma cacao*) bearing fruits on the trunk.

Flowers and fruit

The vast majority of plants produce their flowers and fruits among the leaves at the tips of their branches. Although this is also true of most forest trees and climbers, there are some, said to be 'cauliflorous', whose flowers are borne on the main trunk and large branches, below the leaves. The cocoa tree (Fig. 3.23) is perhaps the best-known example. An obvious limitation on this mode of flowering is that the bark must be sufficiently thin for the flower buds to grow through it; it is thus not surprising that cauliflory is almost completely restricted to the tropical forest. Cauliflory is advantageous to a plant pollinated by animals which normally live below the level of its crown—in cocoa these are tiny two-winged flies—or by bats, whose access might be obstructed by leaves. A fruit growing on the main branch is better placed to receive adequate supplies of water and organic food than a fruit on a small twig. If the fruit is very heavy, as in *Omphalocarpum* (Fig. 1.2) the trunk is also preferable as being mechanically stronger than a branch or twig.

Climbers

Forest includes climbers in great variety both of species (Table 3.1), and form. Some are slender 'shade' climbers, restricted to the forest understorey, others grow only on the edges of forest clearings, but the most conspicuous are the large lianes with stems up to 15 cm thick which climb right up into the canopy (Fig. 3.24). Climbers grow most rapidly in gaps where an old tree has fallen down, allowing light to reach the forest floor. The climbers soon form a curtain around the edge of the gap, attaching themselves to trees, shrubs and other climbers usually by twining but sometimes by tendrils, as in *Strychnos* (Fig. 3.25), or hooks,

3.24 Rope-like stem of a large liane (*Agelaea* sp.) in forest.

2 cm

3.25 Shoot of *Strychnos*, a liane with characteristic woody tendrils.

49

as in the climbing palms (Fig. 3.26). In forest which has been disturbed by farming or felling it is often difficult to distinguish the foliage of the trees from that of the climbers in the dense tangle. Trees left isolated may be so smothered in climbers that their trunks are invisible: these are the so-called 'climber towers' (Fig. 3.27). As trees grow in a gap, they carry the blanket of climbers up with them, the stems of the climbers as well as the trunks of the trees thickening with time. The branch or tree to which a climber is attached may die or break, resulting in a loop of the climber falling onto the ground or onto some other support; in this way the stem of a liane may have a total length of up to 100 m, much greater than that of any of the trees.

If it too is not to break, the stem of a liane must be flexible, and this is achieved by the dividing of hard xylem in which the vessels lie into layers or strands separated by softer tissue. Sometimes this softer tissue is phloem, and many lianes show in section unusual arrangements of their tissues (Fig. 3.28).

The crown of a large liane may be spread over several trees, and carry a larger leaf area than any of them. As the stem is relatively narrow, rates of water movement through the xylem must be very high to replace transpiratory losses, and the vessels are often unusually wide to reduce frictional resistance to water flow (Book 1 p. 70). When a liane is slashed with a cutlass, it is often possible to hear a hissing noise as tension is released and air is sucked into these large vessels. Some climbers are cauliflorous, for example *Pararistolochia flos-avis* (Book 1 Fig. 24.2).

Epiphytes

Epiphytes have no access to water stored in the ground and are therefore dependent on rain, fog drip, and whatever water their roots are able to obtain from the humus derived from decomposing bark of the supporting tree. A tree provides a range of microhabitats for epiphytes: the canopy branches are well illuminated but exposed to desiccation, whereas the trunk and lower branches of the tree are dim but humid. Accordingly we find xeromorphic species, sun-epiphytes, which prefer the canopy, and species of shade-epiphytes growing lower on the tree. When rain falls on a tree, some is retained by the leaves and some falls through the canopy, but quite a high proportion runs along the branches and down the trunk as stem flow. The large forks where major branches meet are thus well supplied by rain and are frequently occupied by masses of epiphytes (Fig. 3.29).

A long dry season is even more injurious to epiphytes than to other members of the forest biome; in really dry forest, epiphytes (apart from lichens) may be limited to a few liverworts and algae at the bases of the tree trunks. A high annual rainfall is not essential, provided there are frequent fogs and mists. The most luxuriant growth of epiphytes occurs in montane forests where humidity may

(a)

(b)

3.26 Climbing palm, *Ancistrophyllum secundiflorum*. (a) Photograph showing the long rhachis protruding beyond the leaflets, bearing recurved hooks which become attached to the other plants growing with *Ancistrophyllum* in thickets and forest margins. (b) Detail of part of a leaf.

3.27 Forest margin exposed by farm clearing. Notice how climbers are smothering the trunks of some of the trees.

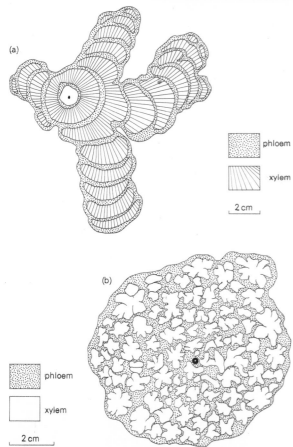

(a)

phloem

xylem

2 cm

(b)

phloem

xylem

2 cm

3.28 Transverse sections through stems of woody lianes showing anomalous secondary thickening. (a) *Agelaea;* the xylem is arranged in concentric hollow cylinders, which separate and join in a complicated manner (see Fig. 3.24). (b) *Flabellaria;* the xylem becomes divided up into separate strands.

3.29 Crown of forest tree with thick growth of epiphytes on the main branches.

Table 3.3 Occurrence of epiphytes in two forest localities in Ghana: Atewa, on a hill 780 m high, is subject to frequent fogs; Kade is in lowland forest at an altitude of only 150 m, and is much less foggy. A sample plot of 50 m × 50 m was demarcated in forest at each locality, and vascular epiphytes were assessed on all trees exceeding 30 cm girth in each plot (*Hall, unpublished data*)

	Atewa	*Kade*
Total number of trees exceeding 30 cm girth in plot	46	138
Percentage of trees carrying epiphytes	93	2
Mean number of epiphyte species per tree	2·2	0·04
Number of epiphyte species in plot:		
Ferns	9	3
Orchids	1	2
Others	10	1
Total	20	6
Total rainfall April 1966 to March 1967 (mm)	2182	1930
Total number of days on which rain fell, April 1966 to March 1967	225	163

seldom or never fall below 90 percent (Fig. 3.30), because they lie below an almost constant belt of clouds (Table 3.3).

As mentioned in Chap. 1, most epiphytes have very light seeds or spores which can be readily dispersed to branches by air currents; others are dispersed by birds. Bryophytes (Book 1 p. 165) are adapted to life as epiphytes because they can survive complete desiccation, resuming activity after rain. Orchids (Fig. 3.31) are another important group of epiphytes. They are monocotyledonous herbs in which the leaves are succulent and in which the roots are covered by a specialized tissue, velamen, which soaks up moisture after rain, but resists desiccation in drought. The other major group of epiphytes, the ferns, are intermediate between bryophytes and orchids, in that the leaves are often fleshy or leathery, but can also withstand considerable drying out (Book 1 Figs. 17.30 and 17.31).

Figs (*Ficus* spp.) differ from the epiphytes mentioned above in being woody, dicotyledonous plants. Some species start life, as do most other kinds of trees, as seedlings in the ground, but the majority require, for the germination of their small, bat- and bird-dispersed seeds, a high light intensity, which they most readily receive on the branches of trees. The fig seedling grows first as an epiphyte, generally obtaining its water from a major fork. In time, the roots grow down the trunk of the supporting tree until they reach the soil. These roots fuse with each other, forming a network which at first surrounds and

3.30 Montane forest in the Uluguru Mountains, Tanzania. The fruticose lichen *Usnea* can be seen hanging from the branches of many of the trees.

3.31 The orchid *Cyrtorchis arcuata* growing on the branch of a cocoa tree. The leaves are somewhat succulent.

3.32 Roots of an epiphytic fig surrounding the trunk of the tree on which it is growing.

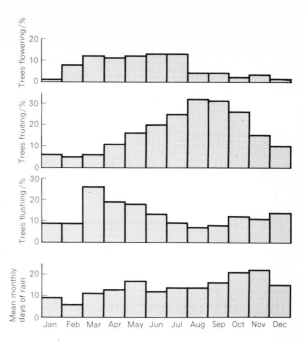

3.33 Flowering, fruiting and flushing of new leaves observed in 61 large trees of 45 species in Malaysian forest. Each bar in the top three histograms represents the mean of observations over about eight years. It can be seen that the main peak of flowering precedes that for fruiting, and also that leaf production is inversely correlated with fruit production. The bottom histogram shows that, on average, rain occurs on at least 6 days in each month, throughout the year. (After Medway).

may later cover the host trunk. Species of this habit are called 'strangling figs' (Fig. 3.32) and are hemi-epiphytes; they occur in the driest forests, and even in savanna.

Seasonality

On p. 44 we stated that in tropical forest, growth may be possible throughout the year. Nevertheless, in all forests, even those of Malaysia where there is no real dry season, the vegetation shows some evidence of seasonality (Fig. 3.33) and a few trees are sporadically deciduous. As a general rule the more severe the dry season, the more markedly seasonal is the vegetation and the higher is the proportion of deciduous species of tree. The attempt has sometimes been made to distinguish 'true rain forest', growing in places with a mean rainfall of at least 100 mm each month, from 'seasonal forest', growing where some months have less rain than this; but as the characteristic structure and life-forms of tropical forest are found in both, the distinction is hardly worth making. It is probably best to describe all forest of thin-barked trees with a complete canopy where fire does not normally occur, as 'closed forest', and to distinguish as subgroups 'wet' or 'evergreen' forest, 'moist' or 'semi-deciduous' forest and 'dry' or 'deciduous' forest, according to the prevailing

Table 3.4 Major differences between principal types of tropical forest

Characteristic	Wet, evergreen	Forest type Moist, semi-deciduous	Dry, deciduous
Tree layers	three; highest reaching 40 m or less	three; highest reaching 50–60 m	three, two or one; highest 40 m or less
Valuable timber trees	few	many	few to many
Epiphytes	many	many	few
Climbers	many	many	many
Ground herbs	many	many	few
Rainfall	>2000 mm	1500–2000 mm	<1500 mm
Soils	leached, acid, poor in nutrients	not much leached, fairly rich	not much leached, fairly rich

rainfall and proportion of deciduous species. The major differences between these forest types are set out in Table 3.4.

In dry forest, the rainfall may be only just sufficient to support the growth of large trees, and gaps may be very frequent. An extreme form of dry forest is thicket, in which there are very few or no large trees and the vegetation consists entirely of shrubs.

Finally we should mention montane forest, which occurs above 1500 m near the equator, and at lower elevations in higher latitudes. It differs from lowland forest in that its trees are shorter, not usually higher than 20 m, and lack buttresses, and also in the abundance of epiphytic mosses and liverworts (Fig. 3.34) and the hanging lichen *Usnea* (Fig. 3.30).

Savanna

In contrast to the vague, uncertain limits between the various types of closed forest, the boundary between forest and savanna is usually quite clear and sharp. Within the space of a few metres one can pass from typical forest with a closed canopy, lianes and epiphytes to savanna—in which the trees are shorter and have thick, fissured bark, from which perennial lianes and epiphytes are absent, and in which there is a continuous ground cover of grass.

The explanation for the suddenness of this change can be seen if one visits the boundary in the dry season. Fire is the key factor. The dry savanna grasses burn fiercely (Book 1 Fig. 22.35), charring the trunks of the trees and severely damaging any that lack sufficiently protective bark. In exceptionally dry years, fire may run from the savanna into the adjacent forest, smouldering among the dead leaves, but only rarely is the forest much harmed by fire unless it is first cleared by farmers.

The seasonally inflammable grass layer is the most constant and diagnostic feature of savanna. The grasses are mainly tussock-forming perennials, many of them in the genera *Andropogon* and *Hyparrhenia*. Closely spaced

3.34 Epiphytic mosses and liverworts in montane forest on the Uluguru Mountains, Tanzania.

(a)

(b)

(c)

buds at the lowest stem nodes are protected from fire by the old leaf sheaths and also by the soil surface; they are thus able to regenerate the tussock after burning (Fig. 3.35a). The tussock is enlarged by the development of leafy shoots from further buds during the early rainy season (Fig. 3.35b). At this time all the species of grass look very much alike, and it is only when the tall flowering shoots, often 3 m high, elongate towards the end of the rainy season (Fig. 3.35c) that they can be distinguished with certainty.

Among the grasses is a variety of herbs and undershrubs, many of them geophytes with perennating organs—tubers, corms, xylopodia and so on—buried in the ground and thus avoiding fire (Book 1 Fig. 22.17). A common geophyte in moist savanna in West Africa is *Aframomum latifolium* (Fig. 3.36), which possesses rhizomes lying about 15 to 20 cm below the soil surface. The rhizomes of the forest species of *Aframomum* lie either on the surface or at most 5 cm below it. There are also many annuals, which avoid the effects of fire as seeds in the soil.

The extent of woody vegetation in savanna is quite variable, and is in fact used to define the main savanna types (Fig. 3.37): grass savanna which is devoid of woody

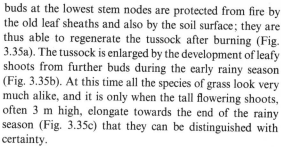

3.35 Seasonal changes in savanna grasses. (a) Leaves developing from old tussocks shortly after burning; old burnt stalks can be seen in the photograph. (b) Photograph taken during the rainy season; grass leaves form a complete cover, and flowering shoots are beginning to elongate. (c) Tussocks of the grass *Vetiveria nigritana* in flower towards the end of the rainy season.

3.36 The monocot herb *Aframomum latifolium* growing in savanna.

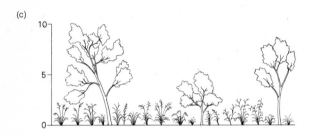

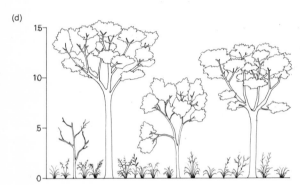

3.37 Profiles of principal savanna types: (a) grass savanna, (b) shrub savanna, (c) tree savanna, (d) savanna woodland.

plants, shrub savanna with scattered shrubs up to 3 m high, tree savanna with isolated trees to 10 m high, and savanna woodland in which the trees may reach a height of 20 m and the tree crowns touch, forming an open canopy.

Even in savanna woodland, development of woody plants is less in every way than in forest. The tallest trees are only half as high, the biomass is about 70 tonnes ha^{-1} as against 500 tonnes ha^{-1} for forest, and the number of woody species per 25 m × 25 m plot is up to 25 as compared with 130 for forest. Because the dead leaves are mostly burnt before they can be incorporated into the soil, savanna soils are less rich in humus than forest soils (p. 72), and consequently also in many nutrients, especially nitrogen. In many respects, then, savanna is a poorer environment for plants than is the forest.

Differences between forest and savanna plants

Bud position and life-form categories

The major environmental difference between forest and savanna is clearly the much greater severity of the dry season in the latter, mainly because of fires; the characteristic differences in appearance and life cycle between forest and savanna plants largely reflect this distinction. The protection of buds during the adverse season is of great importance, because the plant must regenerate from these buds when the growing season returns. We can, in fact, classify all plants with respect to their bud protection into the life-form categories defined in Table 3.5.

Once the categories have been defined we may readily assign each species within the community to one or other of them, and thus calculate the percentage of the total

Table 3.5 Major life-form categories (*After Raunkiaer*)

Life-form	Position of resting buds in relation to ground	Included plants
Megaphanerophyte	> 30 m above	large trees of forest A-storey
Mesophanerophyte	8–30 m above	trees of savanna and of B- and upper C-storey in forest
Microphanerophyte	2–8 m above	trees of savanna and lower C-storey in forest
Nanophanerophyte	0·25–2 m above	shrubs and treelets
Chamaephyte	0–0·25 m above	low shrubs and many perennial herbs of forest
Hemicryptophyte	at surface	perennial tussock grasses and some other perennial herbs
Geophyte	below surface	perennial herbs with rhizomes, bulbs, corms and tubers
Therophyte	in resting seeds	annual and ephemeral herbs

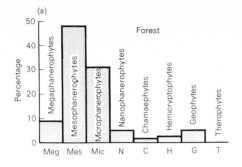

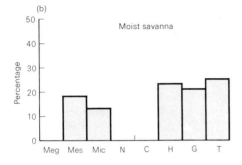

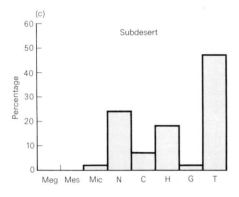

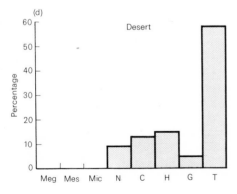

3.38 Life-form spectra of different vegetation types. (a) Forest, Nigeria. (b) Moist savanna, Nigeria. (c) Subdesert, USA. (d) Desert, Algeria. (After Hopkins, and Raunkiaer).

flora belonging to each category. The diagram thus obtained, the 'life-form spectrum', because it is based on characteristics which are of great ecological significance, summarizes many important aspects of the interrelations between a community and its environment.

Fig. 3.38a, a life-form spectrum for a humid forest community, shows the great predominance of phanerophytes. The buds of these plants are up in the air, not much protected by their position; this reflects the absence, or relative unimportance, of an unfavourable season in the tropical forest. Hemicryptophytes and geophytes with better protected buds are few, and therophytes (annuals) are completely absent. In the tropical forest phanerophytes and epiphytes achieve their greatest abundance and diversity. If we look at the spectrum for drier forest we find a tendency for the numbers of epiphytes to decrease with decreasing moisture; the trees of such forests are also characterized by lower stature and smaller leaves.

The spectrum of savanna (Fig. 3.38b) differs in many ways from that of forest. Although savanna does contain phanerophytes, the largest sizes are absent, perhaps because conditions are too dry, and the smallest, together with chamaephytes, are also absent because the zone 0 to 2 m above the ground is most strongly affected by fire, and buds here would mostly be killed in consequence. The soil surface protects the buds of hemicryptophytes and geophytes, and the seeds of therophytes, from fire; all these life-forms are therefore well represented.

Subdesert (Fig. 3.38c) may have many small shrubs. Desert (Fig. 3.38d) has a higher proportion of therophytes; seeds are more resistant to drought than even the best-protected bud.

Other differences between forest and savanna plants

In addition to their thicker bark and lower stature, savanna trees also differ from forest trees in having thicker leaves with blunt tips: in other words, all their leaves are sun leaves. The sapling leaves of the forest mahogany species *Khaya ivorensis* (Chap. 1) have very long drip tips, whereas those of the savanna species *Khaya senegalensis* are only shortly pointed (Fig. 3.39 and 3.40). Although rainfall may be seasonally heavy in the savanna, there is evidently no advantage in adaptations to increase the rate of drying of wet leaves!

Some, but not all, savanna trees are deciduous, much as in deciduous forest. In savanna, most leaves are killed by the annual fires, new leaves flushing shortly after the old are burned, so it is not always easy to say whether a species is naturally deciduous or not.

It remains to be discussed whether savanna is to be regarded as primarily fire-adapted or as a primarily drought-adapted biome. The abruptness of the forest-savanna boundary and its frequent lack of correlation with evident climatic parameters have led some ecologists

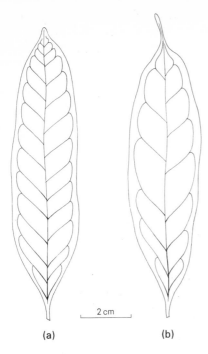

to state categorically that it is unnatural, and that savanna is largely the result of man's activity in causing fires. There is much evidence in support of this view. Where forest and savanna form a complicated mosaic of patches, both types of vegetation must clearly enjoy the same macroclimate. Undoubtedly the vast majority of bush fires are started by man; furthermore, savanna will often change to forest if protected against fire (Book 1 p. 286). Nevertheless it is also true that savanna, on the whole, occupies drier country than forest. Even if human activity were absent, the boundary between forest and savanna would still be abrupt, although climatic change across the boundary is gradual. The reason is that each of these vegetation types, developing where it has a slight environmental advantage, creates its own microhabitat in which it can flourish but which prevents the development of the other. The forest casts dense shade which prevents the spread of tall grasses, but which allows the development of its own plants. The savanna has grass which burns and thus kills forest plants. There is much evidence that fires occur naturally in savanna as a result of lightning. When the first ascent was made recently of a rock pillar 100 m high whose sides overhang all round (Fig. 3.40), the savanna on its summit was found to show clear signs of having burned, even though the rock itself is surrounded by forest and farms.

In Chap. 22 of Book 1 we dealt with some of the ways

3.39 Leaflets of saplings of two species of West African mahogany, (a) *Khaya senegalensis*, which grows in savanna; (b) *Khaya ivorensis* which grows in forest. Note the difference in the shape of the apex.

3.40 Buruku Rock in Ghana, whose summit grassland appears to be burnt as a result of lightning strikes. The photograph was taken from a local patch of savanna on shallow soil, but the Rock itself is surrounded by forest.

3.41 Macchia vegetation in the Cape of Good Hope.

in which savanna plants are drought-adapted; the thick bark of the trees and the subterranean positions of resting buds of grasses and geophytes are effective protection against drought as well as fire. The objection has been raised that transpiration rates of savanna plants are as high as those of forest plants. This may be true, but the experiments with *Khaya* (p. 13) show that the leaves of the savanna species are better able to reduce water loss as water becomes less available. In any case, rates of transpiration are calculated per unit area of leaf. Thus a plant community with a small total leaf area will lose less total water than a community covering a similar ground area but with higher total leaf area, even if the rate of transpiration is the same in both. During the driest part of the year, the total leaf area index (total leaf area ÷ total ground area) is of course much less in savanna, as the ground layer is dead or burnt off, and the trees are smaller and more widely spaced than in forest.

Fig. 3.1 distinguishes two major savanna zones in Africa, a moist zone adjacent to the forest enjoying an annual rainfall of 1 000 to 2 000 mm and $3\frac{1}{2}$ to 6 dry months, and a dry zone adjacent to the subdesert with an annual rainfall of 250 to 1 000 mm and 6 to 11 dry months (Fig. 3.3 and 3.4). We must now look briefly at the characteristics of these types.

The moist savanna zone includes a high proportion of savanna woodland (Book 1 Fig. 22.5), but the zone is not completely covered by this type of vegetation. In shallow flat-bottomed valleys that are temporarily flooded in the rainy season grass savanna may occur—such places are called 'dambos' in Central, and 'mbugas' in East Africa. Grass savanna also occurs on flat expanses, known as 'bovals' in West Africa, with, close to the soil surface a hard rock-like layer (or 'iron pan') in which the soil particles are cemented together by iron oxides (Fig. 5.3). On steep slopes and stony soils the vegetation may be shrub or tree savanna. Particularly close-canopied savanna woodland in favourable sites is sometimes called simply 'moist woodland'. On river banks, fringing forest is often found (p. 81). Moist savanna is known as 'Guinea savanna' in West Africa and 'miombo' in East and Central Africa.

In dry savanna, the predominant vegetation is tree or shrub savanna, and savanna woodland is restricted to moist situations near streams. Grass savanna occupies areas with soils unfavourable to tree growth. In the driest areas, with annual rainfall less than 600 mm, the grass cover may be sparse and very short, less than 80 cm high, consisting of species with narrow leaves whose margins roll inwards during dry weather. Such grass may not burn readily, or in every dry season. Such vegetation is sometimes called 'steppe' although it is not exactly comparable to the steppes of temperate Asia. Steppe is richer than savanna in annual herbs. The characteristic trees of the driest savannas are various species of *Acacia*, often with flat-topped crowns (Book 1 Fig. 22.7).

The steppe-like dry savanna is known as 'sahel savanna' in West Africa, and 'acacia steppe' or 'thorn scrub' elsewhere. The typical dry savanna is called 'sudan savanna' in West Africa and 'mopane' in South-central Africa.

Desert and subdesert occur in areas with less than 250 mm rainfall and 11 or more dry months. In the most extreme deserts of the Sahara no rain may fall for years on end, and vegetation may be almost non-existent. In 250 000 km² of desert north-west of Timbuktu, no more than half a dozen species of flowering plant have been found, and these are low shrubs and xerophytic grasses. The driest parts of the Namib desert in South-west Africa are similarly bare. On the other hand the South African Karroo, which is subdesert, has a very rich flora including enormous numbers of succulent species of genera such as *Euphorbia* (Book 1 Fig. 22.25) and *Aloe* (Book 1 Fig. 22.26), together with many geophytes and annuals. The Karroo has supplied very many decorative plants to world horticulture. Similar vegetation occurs in the 'Horn of Africa', Somalia and eastern Ethiopia, as well as in the subdesert to the south of the Atlas Mountains in Morocco and Algeria. The Kalahari Desert of Botswana is not desert at all, strictly speaking, but acacia steppe.

We are left finally with the evergreen sclerophyll thicket vegetation, macchia, of the northern and southern tips of Africa. The southern Cape macchia occupies a very small area but is possibly the most species-rich vegetation in Africa. The Cape macchia is very isolated geographically, and almost all of its typical species are endemic, that is, not known from other parts of the world. In contrast the North African macchia is in continuity with that of the northern shores of the Mediterranean, and shares many species with them.

We have now completed our broad survey of Africa's main biomes. It should be realised, however, that the distribution of these biomes has not always been what we see today. During the past two million years, known to geologists as the Pleistocene period, there have been major fluctuations in climate. During the coldest times, the Arctic ice-cap has extended to cover much of Eurasia and North America. There have been in fact four major ice ages, or glaciations, the most recent of which extended from 70 000 to 15 000 B.P. (before present), but in the intervening periods the climate has sometimes been warmer than it is today. The longest interglacial period lasted 300 000 years, and as it is only 15 000 years since the last retreat of the ice, it is quite possible that the ice may advance again at some time in the future.

There is every reason to think that temperatures in Africa dropped during the northern ice ages. Evidence for temperature change comes from study of the glaciers on tropical African mountains, particularly Ruwenzori. At present the Ruwenzori glaciers do not extend below 4 000 m, but extensive deposits of ice-borne rocks, moraines, exist down to 1 750 m. These were laid down 15 000 to

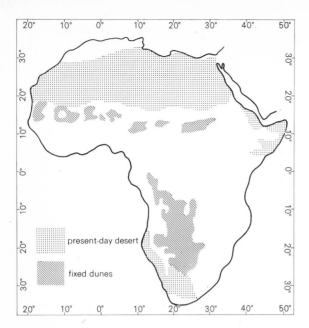

3.42 Map showing distribution of ancient sand dunes, formed at times of desert conditions, in relation to present-day desert.

3.43 Representation of a giraffe, chipped from a vertical rock in what is now bare desert in southern Algeria.

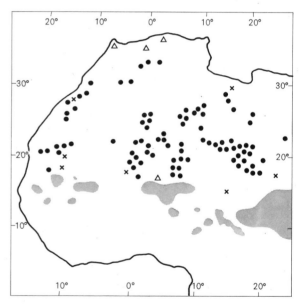

present-day distribution of giraffe

×   historical mention of giraffe

△   giraffe bones

●   rock drawings of giraffe

3.44 Distribution of giraffe in north-west Africa, now and in the past. Rock drawings, which are the most abundant finds, provide less direct evidence for giraffe distribution than do the bones, and written reports. Nevertheless they strongly suggest that giraffe must formerly have been widely spread through what is now uninhabitable desert. (After Mauny).

20 000 years ago, showing that the glaciation of Ruwenzori must have reached its greatest extent at the end of the last European ice age.

Rainfall was probably also affected by the ice ages, and until recently it was believed that in lowland Africa moist 'pluvial' periods coincided with the glaciations. Modern evidence suggests that the effect of glaciation on rainfall was not uniform throughout the tropics, but that it caused a southward shifting of the rainfall belts. At the height of glaciation equatorial Africa seems to have been much drier than it is now. There were great droughts in central Africa about 60 000 B.P. and again about 40 000 B.P. Between 30 000 and 15 000 B.P. the sand dunes of the Sahara came 500 km further south than they do at present (Fig. 3.42); at some time sand dunes covered most of what is now the forest land of the Congo basin. During all these arid periods, the area of forest must have been very much reduced in comparison with its present extent.

On the other hand, about 10 000 years ago moister conditions were widespread in what is now the Sahara Desert and many typical savanna animals such as giraffe were able to cross it (Figs. 3.43 and 3.44). Lake Chad was many times bigger than it is now (Fig. 3.45), reaching a size equal to the present Caspian Sea, and this must mean that rainfall onto surrounding watersheds was much higher than at present, and forest presumably more extensive. It seems that in the northern Sahara a pluvial period was contemporaneous with the last glaciation, in the southern Sahara the pluvial coincided with the end of the glacial and the early interglacial, while in the tropical areas there was a pluvial after the glaciation, about 10 000 to 7000 B.P.

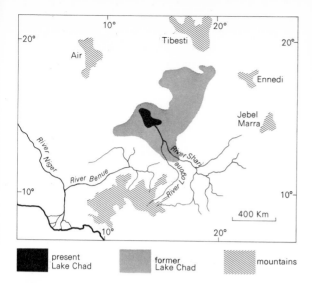

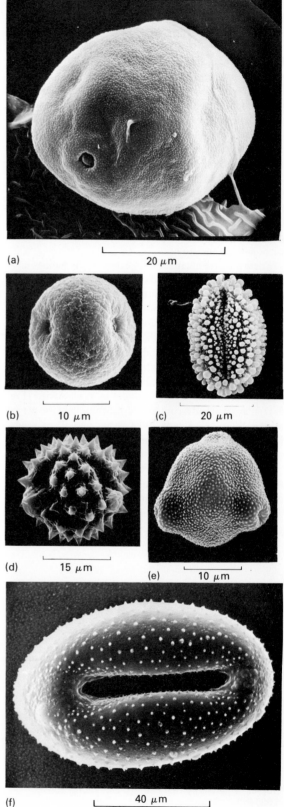

3.45 (Above) Former extent of Lake Chad. At its maximum, the area of the lake was some 30 000 km². At present, Chad is supplied by water flowing in rivers draining from the mountains to the south. The mountains to the north lie in desert and now lack permanent streams. The modern lake has no outlet, but at its maximum overflowed into the River Benue. (After Grove and Pullan).

3.46 (Right) Scanning electron micrographs of pollen grains of some genera frequently represented in Pleistocene pollen-bearing deposits in East Africa. (a) *Andropogon:* grasses. Note almost smooth surface and single pore, which are characteristic of all grass pollen. (b) *Celtis:* lowland forest trees. Two of the three pores are visible in the photograph. (c) *Ilex:* a montane tree. The club-shaped papillae are very distinctive. (d) *Senecio:* some members of this genus are afro-alpine trees. Note conical spines. (e) *Myrica:* a montane shrubby tree characteristic of relatively dry environments. Pores at the corners of the triangular pollen grain. (f) *Agauria:* a montane shrub of the heath family. The pollen grain is a flattened ellipsoid with a slit-shaped pore on each side.

Much of the evidence for these climatic changes has come from the analysis of pollen in cores of mud removed intact from the beds of East African lakes. Pollen grains are covered by a substance, sporopollenin, which is extremely resistant to decay provided the grains are preserved in anaerobic conditions, as on a lake floor. The pollen wall of each plant species bears a characteristic pattern by which it can be identified (Fig. 3.46). Wind-pollinated plants produce vast quantities of pollen which is blown all over the countryside, some onto the surface of adjacent lakes, there to fall to the bottom. Insect-pollinated plants produce lesser amounts of pollen, but some of this may also find its way into a lake. Thus each layer of mud on the lake floor contains a record of the species of plants which were growing near the lake at the time of its deposition. The age of the layer can be found by analysis of its radioactive carbon content (p. 466). For example, in a core from Lake Victoria it was found that mud deposited before 12 000 B.P. contained much grass pollen and no tree pollen, showing that the surrounding vegetation was savanna. The mud also contained insoluble carbonates which provide direct evidence for dry climatic conditions because they must have been precipitated as a result of high evaporation from the lake surface. Between 12 000 and 8 000 B.P. the relative abundance of grass pollen dropped very sharply while that of forest trees increased more than twenty times. The hypothesis that the change from savanna to forest resulted from increased rainfall is supported by the absence of precipitated carbonates in the mud.

These massive fluctuations in extent of the biomes have left their mark in present-day distribution patterns. For example, the Usambara Mountains of eastern Tanzania, over 1 000 km from the nearest part of the Congo basin forest, bear typical moist forest in which many Congo species occur. Presumably these forests were in continuity at some time in the past, and the Usambara forests have been left isolated as a result of subsequent desiccation. Many montane species and genera which are now restricted to 'islands' of high ground in West Africa (Fig. 3.47) may have had a continuous distribution at the height of the Würm glaciation 20 000 years ago if, as seems probable, the prevailing temperature in tropical Africa was 5°C lower than at present.

In the past 500 years or so the major changes in vegetation have been brought about by the increasing numbers of hunters, foresters and farmers who have been burning savanna and clearing forest at an ever-increasing rate.

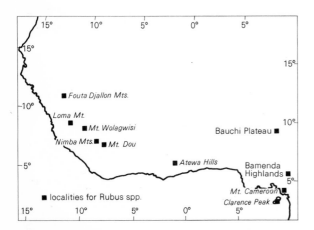

3.47 Distribution of the genus *Rubus* in West Africa. *Rubus* is abundant in temperate countries, but in the tropics is generally restricted to elevations above 1 000 m.

Problems

1 Fig. 3.2 is only an approximate representation of the distribution of vegetation types in relation to climate. What important environmental factors does it fail to consider?

2 If you were attempting to convince someone that length of dry season is a better guide to vegetation distribution than is total rainfall, to which features of Figs. 3.1, 3.3 and 3.4 would you draw his attention? What objections might he raise, and how would you attempt to answer them?

3 Using Fig. 3.5, summarize the distribution of double-peak rainfall in West Africa. In which of the localities do 'dry months' in the sense of Fig. 3.4 occur in mid-year?

4 What can you conclude from Figs. 3.7 and 3.8 as to the correctness of the opinion that rain will fall when winds reach land after travelling a long distance over the sea?

5 Comment on the fact (Fig. 3.33) that leaf production does not coincide with fruit production in Malaysian forest.

6 How could you investigate experimentally the hypothesis that possession of an elongated apex helps a leaf to dry more quickly after rain? What further experiments could you undertake to find whether faster drying is useful to the plant?

7 What problems can you envisage in attempts to obtain accurate data on forest microclimate using a tower such as that mentioned on p. 46? What precautions would be necessary in constructing the tower?

8 When the anatomy of a forest tree species is examined, it is commonly found that the vessels in the xylem of the root are much wider and more abundant than vessels in the xylem of the stem. Can you suggest any explanation for this difference?

9 Judging by the figures in Table 3.3, which group of epiphytes appears to be the more resistant to drought— ferns or orchids? How could you test your hypothesis? What other criteria might have been used to compare epiphyte abundance in the two forests?

10 The relative deciduousness of a tropical forest is difficult to assess. Only a proportion of species in any forest are deciduous; the deciduous period varies from tree to tree in timing and in length. Suggest ways of deriving an 'index of deciduousness' that would take such difficulties into account.

11 It has been suggested that forests in regions of high rainfall are evergreen not so much because water is abundant but because they must conserve inorganic nutrients. What kinds of evidence would help you to assess the reasonableness of this hypothesis?

12 Architectural buttresses are used to prevent the walls of a building from collapsing outwards; they resist compression. On the other hand, it has been claimed

that the buttresses of trees are developed to withstand tension rather than compression. It has recently been shown that buttresses of silk-cotton trees (*Ceiba pentandra*) planted in an avenue were better developed on the windward side of the trunks. Does this finding support the compression or the tension theory? What other explanations are possible?

13 In the analysis of pollen from a core taken from a lake bed, it was found that above a particular level the grass pollen (expressed as percentage of total pollen) increased, while the percentage of tree pollen decreased. The following suggestions were made to account for the changes: (a) Grasses became more abundant and trees less abundant. (b) Grass became more abundant, while trees did not change. (c) Grass did not change but trees became less abundant. (d) Both trees and grass became less abundant, but trees declined more than grass. What further information would have to be obtained from the core before a decision could be made between these theories?

Bibliography

Further reading

Grove, A. T.	*Africa South of the Sahara*, Oxford University Press, 1967, Chaps. 1 and 2
Hopkins, B.	*Forest and Savanna*, Heinemann, 1974
Lawson, G. W.	*Plant Life in West Africa*, Oxford University Press, 1966
Lind, E. M., Morrison, M.E.S.	*East African Vegetation*, Longman, 1974
Longman, K. A., Jeník, J.	*Tropical Forest Ecology*, Longman, 1974
Moreau, R. E.	*The Bird Faunas of Africa and its Islands*, Academic Press, 1966, Chaps. 2 and 3
Richards, P. W.	*The Tropical Rain Forest*, Cambridge University Press, 1952
Richards, P. W.	*The Life of the Jungle*, McGraw-Hill, 1970
Walter, H.	*Ecology of Tropical and Subtropical Vegetation*, Oliver and Boyd, 1971
Whittaker, R. H.	*Communities and Ecosystems*, Macmillan, 1970, Chaps. 2 and 3
Echlin, P.	'Pollen', Scientific American, 1968, Offprint no. 1105
Penman, H. L.	'The Water Cycle', *Scientific American*, 1970, Offprint no. 1191

4 Biomes—consumers and decomposers in the forest and savanna

The appearances of forest and savanna are as different as those of a giraffe and a lizard and we may reasonably ask how this difference affects both the consumers and the decomposers. Fig. 4.1 shows the food web of an open grassland savanna in highly schematic form. The primary producers are at soil level and form a carpet, upon which almost all the trophic events of the food web take place. It is here that the primary consumers, such as the herds of ungulates, the grasshoppers (Orthoptera) and plant-sucking bugs (Hemiptera), feed. Here too the secondary consumers, whether insect-eating or 'entomophagous' insects like mantids (Dictyoptera) or carnivores like cheetah, find their prey. Thus all the events which go to build up the food web occur on what is essentially a two-dimensional surface. Such a picture is valid for grassland savanna, but in the wooded savanna the fauna will contain species which will exploit the trees for food, as well as for the shade and shelter they provide. This may be illustrated

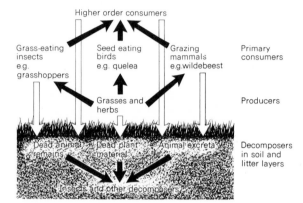

4.1 Schematic representation of the food web in open savanna. The producers form a carpet which grazing and seed-eating consumers exploit. The black arrows indicate the direction of flow of food materials, and the white arrows the movement of the products of metabolism and death. Contrast with Fig. 4.9.

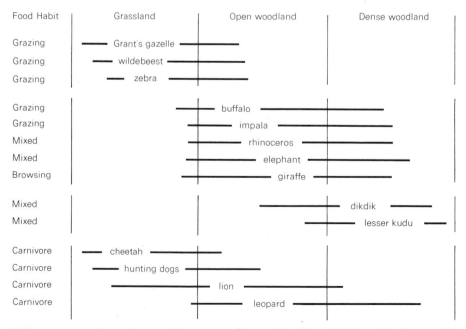

4.2 Range of different mammal species over three types of vegetational zone in Tarangire Reserve, Tanzania. The lines show the relative proportions of sightings of the different species in the three types of habitat. Thus, for example, wildebeest is more common in grassland than open woodland, while impala is common in open woodland, fairly frequent in dense woodland and occasionally seen in grassland. Further details of the feeding habits of the ungulates are given in Table 4.1. (After Lamprey).

4.3 A male dik-dik, *Madoqua*. The animal stands about 35 cm high at the shoulder.

by the distribution of different mammals (Fig. 4.2). In the open woodland occur browsers such as giraffe together with mixed feeders like elephant and rhinoceros, while the ungulates of the dense woodland may be grazing animals like the lesser kudu, and browsers on low shrubs, like the dik–dik (Fig. 4.3). Table 4.1 shows the different emphasis in feeding habits of animals found in these three zones.

Table 4.1 Relative importance of different types of food of ungulates in the Tarangire Reserve in Tanzania (*Data from Lamprey*)

| Habitat | Species | Type of food | | |
		Grass	Shrubs	Trees (leaves and fruit)
Open grassland	Grant's gazelle	91	1	4
	Wildebeest	94	2	0
	Zebra	93	2	0
Open woodland	Buffalo	94	5	0
	Impala	93	3	3
	Rhinoceros	36	41	11
	Elephant	13	30	56
	Giraffe	1	12	86
Dense woodland	Lesser kudu	67	14	14
	Dik–dik	17	56	23

Note: The data are expressed as percentage occurrence in stomachs of different types of vegetation by species. They do not represent percentages by weight. Not all categories originally recorded are listed above. The type of food taken will be influenced by its character and availability. For example, more than 85 percent of the food taken by elephant in the Murchison Falls Reserve is a tall grass not abundant in the Tarangire Reserve.

The species of carnivores also change. Cheetah and Hunting Dog are restricted to open country where they can chase their prey by sight, leopard to woodland where it can stalk its prey, while lion ranges more widely but rarely hunts in dense woodland.

The forest

The forest is completely different. While the dominant feature we usually associate with savanna is one of vast herds of game animals grazing or moving in a slow migration across the open country, within the forest the trees are the dominant feature. Even in savanna woodland the game move singly or in small groups, while in true forest the larger animals are rarely seen as they are mostly nocturnal and solitary. Almost all primary production occurs at a height of 25 to 40 m above the soil surface. If the canopy is dense, almost no light will reach the ground (Fig. 1.16) and primary production there will be relatively slight. Further, while in savanna dead and decaying vegetable matter lies in close contact with the sites of primary production, within the forest leaves and branches drop to ground level far below: there is a major spatial separation between the sites of production and of decomposition and between these lies a zone in which there is still lower productivity as well as relatively little decomposition.

In considering the consumers, it is convenient to recognize three major zones: the upper zone or canopy, corresponding to the A- and B-zones of the trees; the middle zone, including not only the understorey trees of the C-zone, but also the trunks of the trees of the A- and B-zones, and finally the lowest layers on or close to the ground, including both the shrubs and herbs and characterized by litter accumulation and decomposition.

In such a biome there is no ecological equivalent of the grazing flocks of ungulates which characterize the savanna. To exploit the productivity of the canopy, the primary consumers must be able either to climb or to fly. This is illustrated by the data in Table 4.2, which compares in very general terms the habits of the mammals of the forest and savanna in Ghana. It will be seen that while the

Table 4.2 Number of species of mammal found in forest and savanna in Ghana (*Data from Grubb*)

| | | Biome | |
		Forest	Savanna
Fruit bats		10	5
Other bats		36	32
Other species of mammal	Terrestrial	43	67
	Arboreal	33	7
Total species		122	111

number of species of bats is very similar in the two biomes, the number of tree-living or 'arboreal' species is far greater in the forest, where both monkeys and squirrels are especially common.

The food web in the forest

There is a further important difference; the forest plants produce far more large fruits and nuts than do those of the savanna and we may therefore expect to find more fruit-eating species in the forest. We can see this reflected in the types of food eaten by the birds found in the two biomes. Table 4.3 compares the feeding habits of the birds typical of the southern closed forest of the Congo basin with those of dry savanna to the north. While the percentage of purely insectivorous and flesh-eating birds is very similar in both places, the forest-living species which feed partly or wholly on vegetable matter are predominantly fruit-eaters, while small seeds play a far more important part in the diet of the savanna birds. In more open savanna this tendency is even more marked, as shown in Table 4.4 which gives comparative data on the feeding habits of birds from a variety of types of savanna and woodland. The changing importance of seeds and fruit in the diet is apparent.

Table 4.3 Typical diets of different species of bird from forest and savanna in Zaïre (*Based on data from Chapin*)

Diet	Percentage of species in	
	Forest	Savanna
Insects only	59	53
Vertebrates	9	13
Seeds*	5	17
Fruit*	25	13
Other plant material	2	4
Number of species	132	64

*Includes both pure plant feeders and mixed plant and insect feeders

The same sort of analysis shows us something of the sources of food in the three zones within the forest. Such data, again relating to the Congo forest, are shown in Table 4.5. You will notice that insects become increasingly important as a source of food below the canopy, that fruits are replaced by seeds at the lowest level and that vertebrates figure as an item of diet of birds both in the canopy and the mid-region.

Table 4.5 Percentage of bird species with different diets in different zones within the Congo forest (*Based on data from Chapin*)

Diet	Canopy	Understorey	Ground
Insects only	47	62	77
Vertebrates	12	11	0
Seeds	2	0	19
Fruit	35	25	4
Other plant material	4	2	0
Number of species	51	55	26

Analysis using numbers of species is thus one way in which we can study the major characteristics of the different zones within the forest. These data refer, however, only to numbers of different species, not to the numbers of individuals nor to their biomass; unfortunately data relating to Africa and expressed in these more useful parameters do not as yet exist.

Forest mammals

What are the other consumers in the forest, apart from birds and insects? They are mainly fruit- and leaf-eating mammals—monkeys (Primates), squirrels and rats (both Rodentia) and fruit-eating bats (Chiroptera). Of these, the habits of the monkeys have been studied in some detail. Table 4.6 summarizes the results of one such investigation. You will notice that, as with the birds, different species of

Table 4.4 Percentages of bird species taking different types of food in various localities in Africa (*From various sources*)

Locality		Type of food		Number of
	Invertebrates	Fruit	Seeds	species
Acacia steppe, N. Tanzania	54	13	32	78
Mopane woodland, Zambia	66	11	20	50
Miombo woodland, Zambia	77	10	9	89
Primary lowland evergreen forest, Uganda	76	19	3	127
Montane forest, Mount Kenya	53	34	10	43
Closed forest, Zaïre	67	28	5	117

Note: These data do not include various families of predominantly carnivorous birds, nor those which are semi-aquatic such as herons, ducks, ibises and pelicans.

Table 4.6 Habits and distribution of monkeys in the forest zone of south-west Ghana (*Modified from Booth*)

Species	Food		Feeding place				Sleeping place		
	Fruit	*Leaves*	*Upper*	*Middle*	*Lower*	*Ground*	*Upper*	*Middle*	*Lower*
Red Colobus (*Colobus badius*)		+	+ +	+			+		
Diana (*Cercopithecus diana*)	+		+	+			+	+	
Black Colobus (*Colobus polykomos*)		+		+	+		+	+	
Mona (*Cercopithecus mona*)	+			+	+			+	
Olive Colobus (*Colobus verus*)		+			+			+	+
Spot Nose (*Cercopithecus petaurista*)	+	+			+			+	+
White-crowned Mangabey (*Cercocebus torquatus*)	+				+	+		+	+

monkey live at different levels among the forest trees. Thus the leaf-eating Red Colobus is found typically in the canopy, the Black Colobus (Fig. 4.4a) feeds in the middle and lower zones, while the Olive Colobus feeds both in the middle zone and near to the ground. The same sort of pattern is repeated for the several fruit-eating species of *Cercopithecus*; *C. diana* (Fig. 4.4b) is found in the upper zone, while the Spot Nose, *C. petaurista*, lives in the lower layers of the forest. The White-crowned Mangabey (Fig. 4.4c) feeds in the lowest layers and on the ground. Here too may be found the two apes, the gorilla and *Pan*, the chimpanzee, which is mainly vegetarian but will take other sorts of food as well, while in the north-western part of the Congo forest region occur the drill *Mandrillus leucophaeus* and the mandrill *M. sphinx* (Fig. 4.4d), both closely related to the baboons of the savanna. There are two other forest Primates, the slow-moving pottos (Book 1 Fig. 18.79b) and the lively bush babies (Book 1 Fig. 18.79a): both of these are arboreal and feed upon insects as well as fruit.

(b) The Diana monkey, *Cercopithecus diana*. Body length is about 45 cm.

(c) The White-crowned Mangabey, *Cercocebus torquatus*. Body length is about to 60 cm.

4.4 Forest primates. (a) The Black and White Colobus monkey, *Colobus polykomos*. Body length is up to 60 cm.

The squirrels, like the monkeys, are characteristically arboreal and although their diet is mainly fruit and nuts, they may also eat insects, lizards and even young birds. While the common squirrels are omnivorous, the flying squirrels (Fig. 4.5) are purely vegetarian. They do not actually fly, but have a membrane of skin between the fore- and hind-limbs and, using this, can glide from tree to tree over distances as great as 100 m; these flaps of skin serve also as air brakes so they can land gently upon tree trunks. Another arboreal vegetarian is the Tree Hyrax, *Dendrohyrax* (Hyracoidea) (Book 1 Fig. 18.78), while the Palm Civet, *Nandinia*, is omnivorous although it belongs to the order Carnivora. Arboreal mammals which are predators include the carnivorous genets, the leopard, *Pardus panthera*, and various species of *Manis*, the insectivorous pangolins (Pholidota) (Book 1 Fig. 18.81) whose main food is ants and termites.

On the forest floor is a variety of browsing ungulates, including elephant, buffalo and the okapi (Fig. 4.6) which is related to the giraffe. Duikers not only browse but also feed on fruit, as does the tiny Royal Antelope, *Neotragus pygmaeus*. The Giant Pangolin is not arboreal but a ground-living insectivore.

The browsing forest ungulates are commonly said to be smaller than their grazing relatives in the open country. This is only very broadly true. If you draw a frequency polygon of adult weights of the various species of ungulate of forest and savanna in West Africa, you find that the weight class which contains the most species, that is the

(d) The mandrill, *Mandrillus sphinx*. The cheeks of the male are a brilliant blue, while the nose and lips are bright scarlet. Body length up to 1·0 m.

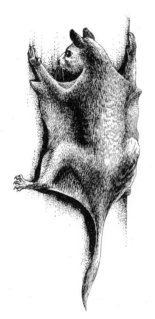

4.5 A flying squirrel, *Anomalurops*, climbing on the trunk of a tree. Note the membranes between fore and hind limbs and between the hind limb and the tail. Body length about 35 cm.

4.6 The okapi, *Okapia johnstoni*, a forest-living relative of the giraffe. The height at shoulder is about 1·5 m.

modal weight class, is the same for the two biomes. There are, however, two striking examples of this difference. Both relate to the larger species. One is the elephant, *Loxodonta africana*: just as there are forest and prairie subspecies of Deermice (p. 28), it is possible to distinguish forest and savanna subspecies of elephant. The savanna elephant, *L. a. africana*, stands when adult from 2·9 to 4·0 m high at the shoulder. The forest subspecies, *L. a. cyclotis*, stands only 2·3 to 2·7 m. The subspecific name 'cyclotis' refers to a second difference between the two subspecies; the ear of the forest elephant is smaller and rounder in shape than that of the savanna elephant (Fig. 4.7a and b). The second example is the buffalo, *Syncerus caffer*: here again there is a savanna subspecies, *S. c. caffer*, which may reach 1·7 m at the shoulder, and a forest subspecies, *S. c. nanus*, which is smaller, reaching only about 1·2 m. Correspondingly the horns of the savanna subspecies are longer, typically about 90 cm long; those of the forest subspecies are only about 50 cm on the average and never exceed 70 cm in length (Fig. 4.7c and d).

While there is a rich and varied mammalian fauna in the forest, little of it can be seen by day. Those mammals which are active in the daytime, including the apes and monkeys, move in groups, but most are both nocturnal and solitary, an exception being the pigs which, although nocturnal, move about in small herds.

As well as birds and mammals, there are also snakes, lizards and frogs. The frogs are insectivorous and many are tree-living, having special adhesive discs on the feet to

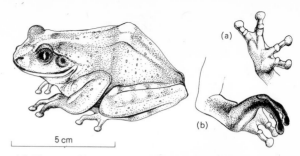

4.8 The tree frog *Chiromantis*. Note (a) the adhesive discs on the tips of the digits of the fore foot and (b) the way in which the hand can be flexed so that the tips of the digits can grasp a small branch. (After Stewart).

allow them to climb. In one genus the fingers of the hand are opposable; that is to say, their lower surfaces can be brought into contact, just as you can rub your thumb over your fingers. This frog is thus able to grasp the smaller branches of trees (Fig. 4.8). The lizards are also mainly insectivorous and many are arboreal. These include the geckos, which have adhesive tips to their toes, enabling them to run freely up walls and across the ceiling of a room. The snakes include both ground-living and arboreal species; some are nocturnal, others diurnal; they differ also in their feeding preferences (p. 102).

These various relations between the vegetation, the insects and the vertebrates are shown schematically in Fig. 4.9 which, when compared with Fig. 4.1, may serve to emphasize the way in which the difference in structure between forest and savanna affects the consumers. Vertical stratification within the forest is not limited to differences in productivity and types of food supply: microclimatic conditions also differ. Table 4.7 shows that, while there is no very marked temperature gradient within the forest,

Table 4.7 Comparative data on climatic conditions, expressed as the mean of 28 days without afternoon rain, at or close to the ground, in the canopy and at an intermediate level in the Mpanga Forest, Uganda (*Based on data from Haddow and Corbet and from Dirmhirn*)

	Height	Time of day			
	(m)	06.00	12.00	18.00	24.00
Temperature	2	17·3	24·3	21·5	17·4
(°C)	20	16·8	25·9	22·6	17·3
	40	17·4	26·2	22·6	17·9
Saturation deficit	2	0·9	8·5	3·6	1·0
(mm Hg)	20	0·9	11·9	5·6	0·9
	40	125·1	723·1	489·0	89·1
Light (% of	0		8·4		
overhead)	20		27·6		
	40		94·8		

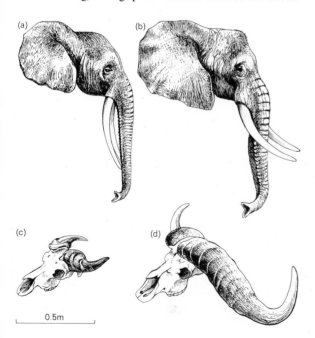

4.7 Drawing of the heads of (a) the forest and (b) the savanna subspecies of elephant, and the skulls of (c) the forest and (d) the savanna subspecies of the buffalo, *Syncerus caffer*. (Partly after Grubb).

0.5m

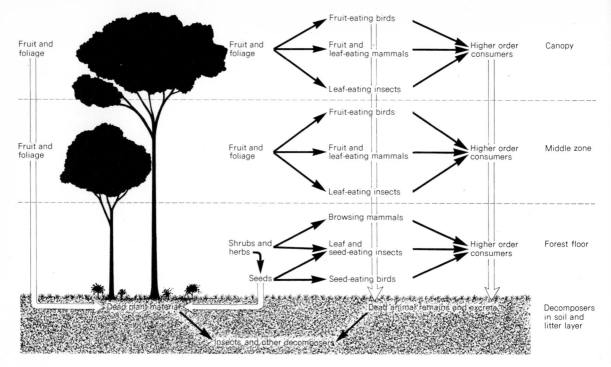

4.9 Schematic representation of the food web in forest. The producers occur at different levels above the soil surface, so that the fauna is distributed in three dimensions. Conventions as in Fig. 4.1.

both saturation deficit and wind speed are far higher in the canopy than on the ground; together these will increase evaporative water loss considerably. This difference in microclimate, together with the great difference in light intensity, may be expected to have a considerable effect upon the vertical distribution of insects within the forest. This has been studied closely as far as mosquitoes are concerned; Fig. 4.10 shows the different patterns of vertical distribution of four species of mosquito. Information on other insect groups is still lacking.

The fauna of litter and soil

The litter layer of forest differs from that of savanna, above all in being moist and protected by the canopy from extreme daily variations of temperature and light. This is shown in Fig. 4.11 where the daily and annual fluctuations of soil temperature in grassland and adjacent forest are compared. At the same localities the annual range of mean monthly R.H. beneath the canopy was from 70 to 90 percent, while in the adjacent grassland it varied between 60 and 70 percent. Thus, although the range was less in the open, the humidities were higher within shelter. As a result the

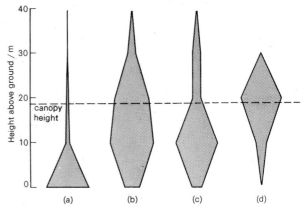

4.10 Vertical distribution of four different species of mosquito in the Mpanga forest in Uganda. (a) *Culex annulioris;* (b) *Aedes apicoargenteus;* (c) *Aedes ingrami;* (d) *Aedes longipalpis.* Samples were collected at ground level and at four stations up a 40 m high tower erected within the forest. The widths of each diagram show the relative abundance at different levels: each diagram has been adjusted so as to give the same value for maximal abundance. The canopy at the station was just less than 20 m high. (After Haddow).

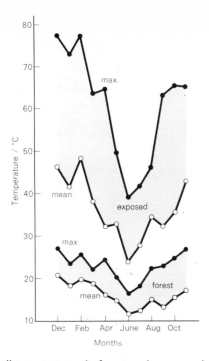

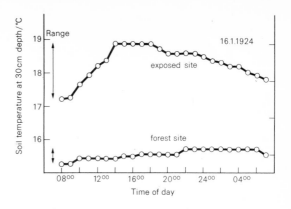

4.11 (b) Diurnal variation in soil temperatures at a depth of about 30 cm in the same exposed and forest sites during a summer day. Note the far greater daily range of temperature at the former than the latter. (Data from Phillips). The effect is, of course, more marked at shallower soil depths as can be seen from the following data (unpublished observations of N. J. Myers) on temperatures of exposed soil and soil beneath the umbrella-like crown of a citrus tree on a calm day.

| Depth (cm) | Daily temperature range (°C) | |
	Exposed site	Shaded site
0·7	42·8	8·0
30·0	4·0	0·8

4.11 Soil temperatures in forest and savanna. (a) Annual cycle of temperatures 6 mm below the soil surface in a forest site and in adjacent open land in Cape Province, South Africa. Note that not only are forest soil temperatures lower than those outside, but that the temperature range, expressed as the difference between the monthly mean temperature (mean) and monthly maximum recorded temperature (max) is less within the forest. (Data from Phillips).

soil beneath the protection of the canopy does not become baked hard as it may in open savanna during a dry season. These differences are reflected in the rate at which leaf litter is decomposed in forest and savanna woodland. In both litter accumulates during the dry season. In the forest litter decays rapidly during the rains (Fig. 4.12), but in woodland and open savanna the far smaller accumulations are commonly destroyed during fires before the rain. As a result the organic matter in the upper soil layers of savanna is markedly less than in those of forest (Fig. 4.13).

Such differences are reflected very strikingly in the characteristics of the invertebrate fauna of the soil and litter layer from the two biomes. Fig. 4.14 shows the abundance, by broad taxonomic groupings, of over 1 000 animals extracted from a sample of forest soil and litter. Table 4.8 compares the abundance of the arthropods in this sample with that in a sample taken from shrub savanna. These data show that, with the seeming exception of the mites and small, wingless insects, the arthropod fauna of the forest floor is much more abundant than that of savanna land. Apart from the greater food supply provided by the higher content of organic matter, it is possible for many arthropods which lack a water-impermeable

cuticle to survive in the forest environment. These include the millipedes and centipedes, the woodlice and many insect larvae (Fig. 2.17). Species found in savanna have a lower rate of water loss than related forest-living forms. For example, the rate of water loss of the savanna-living scorpion *Buthus hottentotta* (Arthropoda: Arachnida) was found to be about half that of the forest-living *Pandinus imperator*. Different species of tsetse pupae, which are buried in the ground, show analogous differences. As Fig. 4.15 shows, the pupae of the savanna-living *Glossina morsitans* are better able to survive exposure to low humidities than are those of *G. palpalis*.

Many other invertebrates which have water-permeable integuments, such as snails and earthworms, are common in the litter and upper soil layer of the forest; in savanna they are found on or near the surface only during the rains. There are indeed certain types of invertebrate which occur only in the forest; these include terrestrial ostracod crustaceans (Book 1 Fig. 18.54c), as well as flatworms and the soft-bodied, arthropod-like Onychophora (Fig. 4.16) of the forests of southern Africa and the Congo. The latter two are carnivorous and all require easy access to water for survival.

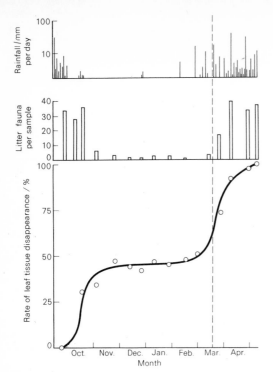

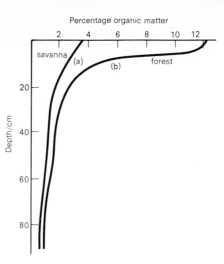

4.13 Profiles showing percentage organic matter at different depths in soil from (a) grassland savanna and (b) closed forest. Note the much greater organic content of the upper layers of the forest soil. (After Ahn).

4.12 Rate of decomposition of leaf discs set out in deciduous forest in Nigeria in early October. The upper bar chart shows daily rainfall (on a logarithmic scale) and the lower the relative abundance of litter fauna in approximately fortnightly samples. The graph shows the percentage decomposition of samples of leaf discs removed for inspection at intervals. Note that there is an initial high rate of decomposition correlated with an abundant litter fauna, which itself correlates with rains in late September and early October. Then follow dry months with almost no litter fauna and no decomposition. With the return of regular rain about the middle of March the litter fauna population builds up rapidly and the process of decomposition is also quickly completed. (Simplified from Madge).

Examination of Table 4.8 suggests that both mites and wingless insects are more abundant in the savanna than the forest; this is almost certainly misleading as different techniques were used to extract material from the samples. These give comparable results for the larger animals, but with the shrub savanna soil a method was used which is particularly effective in extracting the very tiny mites and the springtails or Collembola (Fig. 4.17) which form the bulk of the wingless insects. When the same extraction technique has been used, the abundance of these minute members of the soil fauna, the soil mesofauna, proves to be greater in woodland than in savanna, as Table 4.9 shows.

The bulk of these animals are decomposers. This is true

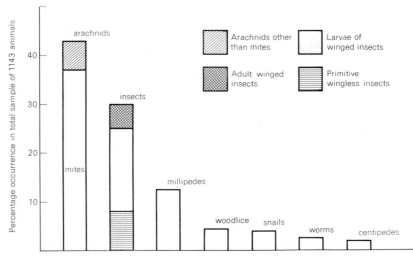

4.14 Composition by taxonomic grouping of a sample of forest litter. Note that the data do not include nematode worms. (After Lawrence).

Table 4.8 Number of arthropods per litre of soil and litter samples from forest and shrub savanna (*Data from Lawrence and from Graham*)

Taxonomic grouping	Number of specimens per litre of sample	
	Forest	Shrub savanna
Arachnids other than mites	25	16
Mites	183	282
Winged insects	68	25
Larvae of winged insects	81	12
Wingless insects	40	239
Millipedes	62	11
Centipedes	11	11
Woodlice	22	less than 1
Total except for mites and wingless insects	269	75

Table 4.9 Abundance of animals per m² in soil samples from two localities in Zaïre (*Data from Maldague and Hilger*)

Locality	Mites	Springtails	Total fauna
Savanna woodland	49 749	11 509	63 734
Grass savanna	18 038	4 517	23 437

of the worms and snails as well as of most of the springtails and insect larvae. Mites include both carnivorous species and species which feed upon fungi and decaying plant material. In forest soils, which have a high content of organic matter, species feeding upon plant material are more abundant than carnivorous species, forming more

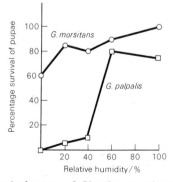

4.15 Survival of pupae of *Glossina morsitans* and *G. palpalis* at different relative humidities. Note that while about 60% of the pupae of the savanna species, *G. morsitans*, survived at 0% R.H., only 10% of the riverine forest species, *G. palpalis*, survived at 40% R.H. (After Bursell).

4.16 *Peripatopsis* an onychophoran found in South Africa. These animals, which are commonly placed in a distinct phylum Onychophora, have many anatomical characteristics in common with the Arthropoda but lack a chitinous, jointed exoskeleton. The animal when fully extended may reach a length of about 5 to 6 cm.

4.17 A collembolan or 'spring-tail'. Attached to the tip of the abdomen and held beneath it is a long spine which, when released, strikes the ground, throwing the animal into the air. The ventral tube is a structure by which the animal can absorb capillary water from the soil. (After Skaife).

than half the population. In savanna soils of lower organic content the situation is reversed; the majority of the population are very tiny carnivorous mites which feed upon bacteria and Protozoa. This balance between primary and secondary consumers is reflected also in the myriapods: millipedes, which feed on vegetable matter and soil rich in organic matter, are far more abundant in the forest than are the carnivorous centipedes; in savanna the two groups are about equally abundant. Further, just as many birds and mammals of the forest are fruit-eaters while those of the savanna are seed-eaters, this is possibly true also of millipedes. Laboratory studies show that the forest millipede *Spirostreptus* will accept a variety of fruits such as banana, pawpaw and mango as food; in contrast *Habrodesmus*, which occurs in open country, prefers detritus-rich soil to fruit, although it will eat freshly-germinated soft maize and ground-nuts. Similarly, the diet of the forest-associated grasshoppers differs from that of the savanna species in a manner recalling the difference between the grazing savanna and the browsing forest ungulates (Table 4.10).

Table 4.10 Feeding habits of different species of short-horned grasshopper in Nigeria (*Data from Phipps*)

Habitat	Number of species eating		
	Grass	Forbs*	Mixed
Thicket and woodland	4	16	5
Grassland	35	8	6

*Herbaceous plants which are not grasses are termed forbs'.

Termites in different biomes

There is one very significant group of decomposers which has so far not been mentioned. These are the termites, which are more abundant in woodland than in open savanna soils, but possibly less abundant in true forest. This is reflected in the relative rates of decay of wooden blocks of *Triplochiton* exposed in savanna woodland and in semi-deciduous forest: decomposition in the former habitat was markedly more rapid. The abundance of species correlates with the humidity, as shown in Table 4.11. Two other features distinguish the woodland termites from those of the open savanna. The first relates to the habit of mound building: Table 4.11 shows that mound-building species are relatively less common in open, drier areas. The significance of the mound-building habit of certain termite species is very far from clear: in some like *Trinervitermes* (Fig. 4.18) it serves to provide storage space for food in a place where it will dry out and is likely to be safe from flooding; in others like *Macrotermes* (Fig. 4.19) it is concerned, at least in part, with effective ventilation of the nest. Mounds in exposed positions are likely to reach very high temperatures and it is possible that these cannot be tolerated by certain species.

Table 4.11 Frequency and habits of termite species in different localities in Tanzania (*Data from Kemp*)

Locality	Number of species	Ratio of mound-building to subterranean-nesting species
Moist coastal plain	60	2·3
Savanna with *c.* 70 cm rain annually	36	1·5
Very dry acacia steppe	17	0·9

4.18 Vertical section through the nest of the termite *Trinervitermes*. Food material is kept in the upper chambers while tunnels run from the main nest both horizontally beneath the soil surface and also deep into the soil. (After Josens).

20cm

chambers used for food storage

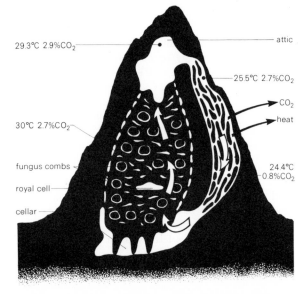

29.3°C 2.9%CO₂ — attic
25.5°C 2.7%CO₂
CO₂
heat
30°C 2.7%CO₂
24.4°C 0.8%CO₂
fungus combs
royal cell
cellar

4.19 Diagrammatic section through the nest of *Macrotermes* (Book 1 Fig. 23.10). The metabolism of the termites warms the air which rises to the 'attic' and then passes downwards beneath the relatively thin and porous outer wall of the nest. Here both heat and carbon dioxide are lost and the cooler air collects in the 'cellar' to be drawn up by the air currents once again into the nest. The arrows indicate the direction of flow of the air. The values for temperature and carbon dioxide at different points were obtained from a mound in Ivory Coast. Nest temperature was found to remain almost constant at about 30°C while outside temperature fluctuated between 22 and 25°C. Not all mounds of *Macrotermes* are of this pattern. The cellar may be open below and thin-walled chimneys connected with the attic are constructed on the summit of the mound; in such mounds the air conduits beneath the side walls may be unimportant. It is possible that young nests conform to the pattern shown in the diagram and that older nests in which openings have been made into the cellar construct chimneys. (After Lüscher).

Secondly, termites constitute a smaller fraction of the total soil arthropod fauna of open savanna than of woodland; thus their importance as decomposers is far greater in the latter type of habitat. Moreover the type of food available is different. In woodland, grass-eating harvester termites are relatively less abundant, while soil-living, humus-feeding species are more common than they are in the savanna.

The break between forest and savanna is less clearly defined by the fauna than by the flora, and some species of insect are to be found in both. Thus, for example, there are four species of the Cotton Stainer *Dysdercus* (Fig. 9.34) in Ghana. Only two are found in forest, but all four species may be found feeding in savanna. More commonly, different species of the same genus are to be found in forest and adjacent savanna. Such species probably differ in their adaptations to resist water loss, like the savanna and forest species of *Glossina* (Fig. 4.15). As we move away from the forest, conditions become increasingly arid and the fauna increasingly sparse until we reach the desert biome.

The desert

Within the desert the fauna, both in number and composition, is greatly influenced by local conditions. This is illustrated by the data summarized in Table 4.12 which shows the total number of surface-living arthropods of various types collected in two areas on the Erkowit Plateau, which lies to the south of Port Sudan and is cloud-covered for many weeks during the winter. As a result there is a heavy dew fall, forming a 'mist oasis' in the desert. This is highly localized so that, within a distance of 10 km, the flora changes from one dominated by small evergreen trees

Table 4.12 Numbers of arthropods collected from an area of 25 m^2 at two localities on the Erkowit Plateau. Locality II is the more arid with *Euphorbia* thicket as the dominant vegetation (*Data from Cloudsley-Thompson*)

Taxonomic grouping	Locality I	Locality II
Spiders	30·0	27·0
Scorpions	2·5	3·0
Millipedes	15·0	Absent
Centipedes	32·5	6·0
Orthoptera	12·5	8·0
Coleoptera	20·0	5·0
Isoptera*	10·0	4·0
Ants*	12·5	2·0
Number of 0·25 m^2 quadrats sampled	42	96

*Data expressed as number of quadrats out of 100 within which ants or termites were observed.
Note: The data have been standardized from the number of 0·25 m^2 quadrats actually sampled to 100 quadrats. This explains the fractional values recorded.

to one dominated by succulent *Euphorbia* as the area of oasis gives way to the still more arid inland plateau. This change in conditions of prevailing humidity is reflected in both the composition and abundance of the fauna.

The desert food web

While in the peripheral semidesert gazelles and oryx can be seen by day browsing upon the shrubs, in the more arid areas most animals, including small mammals, spend the daytime in burrows or in caves. If rain does fall, abundant food for primary consumers may be available for a short time, while some plants, by drawing upon reserves accumulated at such times, continue growth of new tissues for a longer period. The primary consumers include ants, beetle larvae, grasshoppers and crickets as well as small mammals such as the jerboas (Fig. 4.20) which are bipedal and move by jumping with their long hind legs: these various animals depend partly upon seeds, partly upon the dry remains of desert plants. Vegetable litter, carried by wind from surrounding, more productive regions or from scattered oases, adds to the organic matter available to form the basis of the food web.

Upon these primary consumers feed a remarkable diversity of higher-order consumers, although their actual numbers are low. They include centipedes, spiders and

4.20 The desert jerboa, *Jaculus*. The length of head and trunk is about 10 cm.

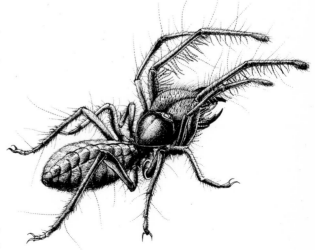

4.21 A carmel-spider, *Galeodes* (Arachnida: Solifugae).

4.22 Dung beetles, *Scarabaeus*, rolling a ball of dung. The dung ball will be buried and may then simply serve as food. Alternatively a female will bury a dung ball and then excavate a hollow in the ball in which she lays an egg. This is then covered and the larva which emerges feeds upon the dung, eventually pupating inside the dry and hardened outer case. The drawing shows two beetles: these are not necessarily male and female. The two animals are in fact competing for possession of the ball of dung.

scorpions as well as the camel spiders, arachnids of the order Solifugae (Fig. 4.21), while among the decomposers are scarab beetles (Fig. 4.22) feeding upon the dung of mammals. Predatory vertebrates, especially reptiles, also occur; they include lizards and geckos, skinks and vipers. The Desert Fox, *Fennecus* (Book 1 Fig. 23.4), feeds upon lizards but also on insects and even plant material.

Life in such arid conditions is possible only for animals which are able effectively to conserve water. Many groups which live in the better-watered savanna therefore do not occur. But the fauna of deserts, even though it includes many highly specialized species, is essentially an extension of the savanna fauna into conditions of extreme aridity.

The flora and fauna of forest and savanna

When we compare these two major biomes of Africa, the most outstanding feature is that while their floras are very markedly different, this is less obviously true of the fauna. The life-forms of the plants are so different that it is generally possible to tell from its appearance whether a plant is a forest or a savanna species. On the other hand it is not usually easy or even possible to decide upon the basis of structure whether a particular beetle, lizard or mouse is a savanna or a forest dweller.

Diversity

The flora of the forest is not only characterized by a greater biomass than that of the savanna, but also by a greater diversity of species (p. 44): these in turn provide a great diversity of potential microhabitats and sources of food for consumers. Moreover, the plants of the understorey commonly contain unpalatable chemical substances; in the prevailing low light intensity and the consequent low productivity, these protect them from general attack by plant-eating insects. One result is that many of the phytophagous forest insects are specialized in their feeding habits and, corresponding to the diversity of understorey plants, there is a great diversity of such insects; these in turn are preyed upon by a diversity of higher-order consumers. Finally, as we have already seen, the almost constantly humid conditions within the forest result in the presence of several groups of animals which cannot survive in the savanna. All these effects contribute to the characteristic high diversity of the forest flora being accompanied by an even greater diversity of forest fauna.

Fire

We have emphasized the occurrence of fire as a major factor differentiating savanna from forest. To survive, the plants must be able to resist the effects of passage of a fire: they cannot escape. Fire has much less effect upon the fauna which, by virtue of its mobility, can often escape unharmed (p. 110). Adaptations to resist the effect of fire are thus essential for the savanna flora and are one factor which distinguishes it sharply from that of the forest. No such distinction can be made for the fauna; indeed, apart from protective behaviours, animals appear to have no structural or physiological specializations which can be regarded specifically as adaptations to resist fire.

We have mentioned the way in which the grass cover will end abruptly at the margin of the forest, and that both types of biome may exist side by side within climatically uniform conditions (p. 58). The forest creates its own 'internal environment', while the destructive action of fire upon the forest flora serves to maintain the savanna. Both display what we might describe as 'ecological homeostasis' (cf. Book 1 p. 295). Except in so far as they require particular microhabitats, the fauna, especially the insects and the birds, are free to range widely within a climatically acceptable zone. As a result, the same or closely related species of birds, insects and small mammals may be found both in savanna woodland and in forest: the dividing line is less clear-cut. Similarly a clearing made within the forest is rapidly invaded by many species of animal which may be regarded as typically 'savanna forms'.

It is only at the extreme end of the range of vegetational types that the differences in fauna between forest and savanna become strongly marked and here it is a difference more especially of habit. The more open savanna offers wide areas over which large herds of grazing animals may move freely, migrating from one place to another with the changing pattern of the seasons (p. 105). Nothing comparable is to be found in the forest or even in savanna woodland, whose fauna is an intermediate between the two extremes.

In this way we may understand those factors which result in the difference between the two major biomes being very clear-cut as regards their flora and why the difference is less striking (unless we contrast closed forest with open grassland) as regards the fauna.

Problems

1 (a) The ears of forest elephant are smaller than those of their savanna relatives.

(b) The horns of forest buffalo are smaller than those of savanna buffalo.

(c) In both the elephant and the buffalo, the forest animals are smaller than individuals of the corresponding savanna subspecies. Suggest possible explanations for these differences.

2 In comparing the diet of forest and savanna birds, use has been made of the numbers of species of bird which have particular diets. It is stated (p. 66) that a comparison involving numbers of individuals or total biomass of different species would be a more useful parameter. Why should this be the case?

3 Diurnal forest mammals tend to move in groups while the solitary mammals are almost exclusively nocturnal. Suggest a possible reason for this difference.

4 What will be the main sites of water loss from (a) a millipede and (b) a tsetse pupal case or puparium? If you wished to determine the water permeability of a puparium, what experimental precautions would you take? In what units would you express your answer?

5 Many desert beetles have exceptionally long legs, so that they run with the body lifted well clear of the sand. What do you consider might be the advantage of this structural characteristic? Give reasons for your opinion.

6 Suggest ways in which you might measure the rate of (a) litter accumulation and (b) litter decay in forest.

7 Studies upon the grasshopper fauna of a savanna area in West Africa have shown that there are two characteristic patterns of annual reproductive cycle. These are illustrated by the data for two species in the table below. The adult grasshoppers of the species displaying the type of pattern shown by species A are all large with long abdomens. The grasshoppers showing the other pattern include many species which have relatively small adults. It is suggested that these two patterns allow the species to survive despite annual grass fires which normally occur in January.

Present the data in suitable graphical form and suggest the arguments which have been advanced correlating life-cycle patterns with annual fires.

Bibliography

Further reading

Cloudsley-Thompson, J. L. — *The Zoology of Tropical Africa*, Weidenfeld and Nicolson, 1969, Chaps. 3, 4 and 5

Kormondy, E. J. — *Concepts of Ecology*, Prentice-Hall, 1969, Chap. 5

MacArthur, R. H., Connell, J. H. — *The Biology of Populations*, Wiley, 1966, pp. 14–57

Odum, E. P. — *Ecology*, Holt, Rinehart and Wilson, 1963, Chap. 7

Whittaker, R. H. — *Communities and Ecosystems*, Collier-Macmillan, 1970, Chap. 3

Population data for two species of grasshopper which occur in savanna in West Africa. Eggs: the estimated number of eggs deposited by females per ha. Immatures and adults: estimated numbers per ha

| Month | Species A | | | Species B | | |
	Eggs	Immatures	Adults	Eggs	Immatures	Adults
Jan.	—	—	19	—	100	620
Feb.	—	60	—	1 344	20	310
March	—	490	—	5 487	120	320
April	—	775	—	2 160	1 900	100
May	—	580	—	1 395	4 000	20
June	—	660	—	—	7 000	10
July	—	460	11	—	6 200	10
Aug.	1 116	450	39	—	4 400	15
Sept.	1 890	400	82	—	5 800	10
Oct.	2 697	500	124	—	3 000	15
Nov.	2 790	400	117	—	2 700	100
Dec.	—	—	58	—	1 400	900

5 Communities—producers

In Chap. 3 we looked at the vegetation of the various biomes, the most important of which in tropical Africa are savanna and forest. We also stated that within each biome it is possible to distinguish subdivisions, which are the communities. The structure and development of such communities are the subject of this chapter.

Savanna communities

The existence of different communities within a biome is not obvious at first glance. In the savanna regions we can, for example, drive along a road for many hours through what appears superficially to be a monotonous, unchanging vegetation of smallish, gnarled trees and tussocky grass. Gently undulating country is typical of savanna; the road will go down a long, gradual slope into the valley bottom, cross a stream and then climb slowly back to the flat top of a broad ridge before descending again. The scenery is varied by an occasional steeper scarp or broad flood plain.

But if we alight from the lorry and walk over some of these slopes looking carefully at the plants and at the soil, we shall find that the vegetation is not as uniform as it appeared at first. Correlated with the different soils and the conditions of water supply and drainage in the various parts of the topography, we shall find different communities of plants.

A similar pattern of slope–soil–vegetation relationships, in which the same kind of community occurs repeatedly at corresponding positions in the topography, has been found in many parts of the moist savanna regions of Africa. The examples which follow are taken from savanna areas of south-west Sudan, northern Ghana and central Ivory Coast, but conditions in Central and East Africa are basically similar. We may profitably distinguish three main zones in the topography: ridge top, middle slope and valley bottom (Fig. 5.1).

Ridge tops

The ridge tops are often rather flat and, lying at a variable distance below the surface, there is frequently a layer, up to 2 m thick, of hard, rock-like iron pan or 'ferrocrete'. This material, whose origin is discussed on p. 124, is more or less impermeable to water and to roots, and is very poor

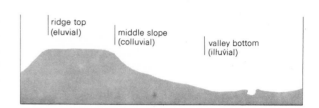

5.1 Diagrammatic section through savanna topography, showing the major zones.

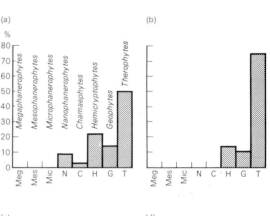

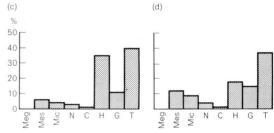

5.2 Life-form spectra of plant communities in different parts of the topography in Ivory Coast. (a) Dry iron pan with very shallow soil. (b) Seasonally flooded iron pan, desiccated in the dry season. (c) Flood plain in valley bottom. (d) Savanna woodland on middle slope. (After Adjanohoun).

78

(a)

(b)

5.3 (a) Bare iron pan at the end of the dry season; note the dense growth of trees in deeper soil beyond the edge of the pan. (b) View of a similar iron pan while flooded in the rainy season. Vegetation consists mainly of annuals.

in plant nutrients. Where it comes right to the surface and is not covered by soil, the iron pan may bear a community consisting only of a thin crust of lichens (Book 1 p. 229) and a few herbs in cracks. In other places there may be a shallow layer of gravelly soil in which the community is made up of low herbs and bulbous plants which grow up in the rainy season, but whose above-ground parts soon shrivel as the soil dries out again (Fig. 5.3a). These survive the dry season either as seeds if they are annuals, or as dormant buds at or below the ground surface if they are perennials. Fig. 5.2a shows that woody plants are few, and less than 2 m high.

Sometimes the iron pan is slightly saucer-shaped, and water collects on it in the rainy season, forming shallow pools and patches of marsh. The vegetation in such places (Fig. 5.3b) consists almost entirely of specialized annuals (Fig. 5.2b) which are tolerant of flooding. Because of the alternation of flooding with complete desiccation, woody plants are unable to survive and the proportion of perennial herbs is low.

Intact iron pan, however, is found at the surface only rarely; generally it is either much cracked or covered with fairly deep soil, in which case a more typical savanna vegetation is able to develop (Fig. 5.4) with a much higher proportion of woody plants (Fig. 5.2d), many of which exceed 10 m in height. As Fig. 5.5a shows, the greater the depth of soil, the greater the quantity of trees. The ridge-top soils are described as eluvial, because rainfall tends to wash out of them the smaller soil fractions such as clay and silt. They tend therefore to be rather gravelly and, where

5.4 Savanna woodland in Zambia.

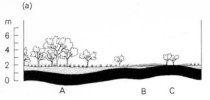

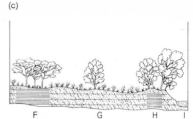

5.5 Profiles through savanna vegetation and soil in the major topographical zones. (a) Eluvial site on ridge top. Note that iron pan (shown solid black) underlies a variable depth of soil. At A the soil is fairly deep and woody vegetation is dense; at B the soil is shallow and supports annual grasses; at C, where the iron pan outcrops, the vegetation consists only of a few shrubs rooting in cracks. (b) Colluvial site on middle slope. Soils are fairly deep and loamy; at D they overlie a soft iron-rich material; at E they overlie clay. (c) Illuvial site in valley bottom. The levee (H) of the river (I) bears fringing forest on the riverward side, and savanna woodland on the side away from the river. The poorly drained soils of the flood plain (F has clay, and G has clay loam) bear tall perennial grass, but few trees. (After Morrison *et al.*).

there is no pan, free-draining. Shallow soils over iron pan may be unsuited to any form of agriculture other than poor rainy-season grazing for livestock.

Middle slopes

The middle-slope soils are described as colluvial, meaning that some material is washed from them to situations further down the slope but that at the same time other material is washed in from above; water cannot accumulate on slopes, so they are well drained. These factors together tend to make such soils suitable for the growth of trees. Different communities are found here, according to the steepness of the slope and conditions on the ridge top. A flat, bare iron pan on the ridge top behaves like a roof during rain, and sheds most of the water which falls on it. This water benefits the vegetation at the top of the slopes around the edge of the hard pan, allowing the development of well-grown savanna woodland or, in some places, woodland or even dry forest. A similar vigorous growth of woody vegetation may frequently be observed at the foot of bare rock inselbergs (Fig. 5.6).

The degree of steepness of the middle slope will, however, influence the community which grows on it. Water runs quickly from a steep slope and the proportion of rainfall soaking into the soil and thus benefiting the local vegetation is less than on flatter ground. Fast-flowing water also tends to remove soil, especially where the vegetation is sparse. The community on steep slopes is thus commonly a shrub or tree savanna with widely spaced tussocks of grass.

On gentler slopes, with deeper soil and better water penetration, trees are favoured by the well-drained but not impoverished colluvial situation. Here savanna woodland can develop which is similar in its physiognomy (that is, in its stratification, life-form spectrum and general appearance) to that in Fig. 5.4 and 5.2d. A colluvial profile is given in Fig. 5.5b. These colluvial soils on gentle slopes are also generally preferred for agriculture.

5.6 Sloping side of granite inselberg. The surrounding plains bear savanna vegetation, but a girdle of forest can be seen along the lower side of the exposed rock.

Valley bottoms

Soils in the valley bottom are of two main types. Material washed from the slopes collects in illuvial soils at their foot. Immediately along the stream bank may occur deposits of alluvial soil, deposited from the stream itself. The distance to which soil particles can be carried by water travelling at a particular speed is inversely proportional to their size. Illuvial and alluvial soils are therefore rich in small silt and clay particles, which are transported further than the sand and gravel.

In the rainy season a stream may overflow its banks and water runs out onto the surrounding land. The water in the stream bed rushes along at great speed, carrying a heavy load of silt. As it spreads over the bank, however, it is slowed down and silt is deposited. Each flood season, large quantities of silt are deposited in this way on the bank, whose level is thus raised; smaller quantities of silt are deposited on the flood plain further away. In a broad valley bottom there are three main habitats (Fig. 5.5c): the actual river bank, the area of deposition just beyond the top of the bank, and the flood plain itself.

The river bank, or 'levee', is a particularly favourable situation for tree growth. It is close to a more or less reliable water supply but, except during the flood season, it is well drained because it is raised above the stream surface and the flood plain. The soil is also enriched by nutrients contained in the alluvium. It is therefore not surprising that even in the heart of savanna country the river bank may often bear a narrow strip of 'fringing' or 'riparian' forest which has a closed canopy, no grass understorey and which is never burnt. Not all species of tree can survive the two or three months submergence of their roots and lower trunk which the fringing forest trees must tolerate. The specialized plants which grow here, such as *Berlinia grandiflora* (Fig. 5.7), lack aerenchyma or any other of the morphological features which characterize many hydrophytes (Book 1 p. 254); their adaptations are presumably biochemical.

If the levee is broad it may include a zone further from the river. This will have a less reliable water supply than the riparian forest, but will nevertheless be well drained and fertile. Vegetation here is often a 'riverain woodland' with a grass understorey and tall savanna trees. If well developed, this zone may provide the most fertile agricultural land.

The flood plain, like the saucer-shaped hard pan, suffers from extremes of wetness and dryness. During and immediately after the rainy season it is completely waterlogged, but during the dry season its clay floor bakes hard and dry. If we compare its life-form spectrum (Fig. 5.2c) with that of the better-drained savanna woodland we see that it has, as we should expect, a much higher proportion of hemicryptophytes (mainly perennial grasses) and a correspondingly lower proportion of phanerophytes (shrubs and trees). In fact trees may be virtually absent from flood-plain grass savanna; one of the few species which can withstand the most extreme conditions is *Mitragyna inermis* (Fig. 5.8).

Small-scale community pattern

This simplified account may perhaps have given the impression that the various communities form broad, well-defined zones, each extending uninterrupted over considerable areas. This may sometimes be so, but particularly where the slopes are very gentle, slight differences from place to place in soil depth and drainage may give rise to a complex patchwork or mosaic of the various plant communities. Characteristic of most savannas are large mounds constructed by the termite *Macrotermes*. sometimes reaching a height of 5 m. These are subject to erosion by rain, and gradually give rise to low hillocks of deep soil, which may be richer in clay than soil

5.7 *Berlinia grandiflora*, a typical tree of fringing forest in savanna. This small specimen, about 4 m high, was growing beside an inlet of the man-made Lake Volta in Ghana. The photograph was taken at the season of minimum lake level; the tree had already survived two seasons of almost complete submergence which killed all the surrounding trees.

5.8 *Mitragyna inermis*, growing in the flood plain of the River Volta, in the dry season. Blackish tufts of dried aquatic weeds caught in its branches show that at times of flood the tree stands in water up to 4 m deep.

of surrounding areas, and will also be better drained. For these reasons termite mounds generally bear a denser growth of trees and shrubs than the adjacent savanna woodland. In some areas, otherwise covered by grass savanna or grass steppe, there may be thickets on old termite mounds (Fig. 5.9); the vegetation thus consists of a mosaic of communities representative of two quite different biomes.

Density and basal area

From the above discussion we can see that the quantity of woody vegetation is an important character of the community and a useful indicator of environmental conditions. We must therefore consider the methods available for assessing the contribution of woody plants to the structure of plant communities. Differences between communities have been shown in profile diagrams (Fig. 5.5), but these cannot provide more than a qualitative picture. Life-form spectra (Fig. 5.2) are also useful, but their quantitative assessment is based mainly on the numbers of species rather than on the total biomass of the plants in each life-form category. In other words, the spectrum would be the same whether each species is represented by one small tree or ten large ones. A more direct way of comparing quantitatively the woody growth in two communities is to count all the trees of each species growing in sample plots laid out in each community; this will give us the density, that is, the number of plants per unit area, for each species. The girths of these trees can also be measured and converted to cross-sectional area, that is, basal area. Table 5.1 shows that in sample plots at Mole Game Reserve in Ghana the total basal area in middle-slope savanna was found to be the same as in riverain woodland, but that

5.9 Thicket occupying old termite mound, in West Africa. The trees are *Elaeophorbia drupifera;* in East Africa similar thickets often contain *Euphorbia candelabrum* which closely resembles *Elaeophorbia* in its habit and manner of branching.

Table 5.1 Density of trees and total basal area in six sample plots, each measuring 50 m × 50 m, in different types of savanna at Mole Game Reserve, Ghana (*Data from Lawson et al.*)

Species	Ridge top	Sample plots Middle slope	Middle slope	Middle slope	Middle slope	Riverain woodland
Pteleopsis suberosa	43	0	1	0	0	0
Detarium microcarpum	114	2	5	5	1	0
Terminalia avicennioides	4	50	61	93	64	2
Butyrospermum paradoxum	0	10	22	15	16	0
Piliostigma thonningii	0	28	3	0	3	87
Anogeissus leiocarpus	0	0	0	0	0	11
Burkea africana	25	85	44	31	94	0
Lannea acida	0	1	1	2	2	2
Other species	24	111	90	134	68	22
Total no. of trees	210	287	227	280	248	124
Total basal area (m^2)	1·2	2·4	2·5	2·3	2·2	2·4
Mean basal area per tree (cm^2)	57	84	110	82	89	194

the average tree was twice as large in the latter community. On the other hand the upper-slope savanna on dry, stony soil had the same number of trees as the middle-slope savanna, but they were much smaller, with only half the total basal area. These findings support the suggestion on p. 80 that middle slopes provide better conditions for tree growth than upper slopes with shallow soils, and also that optimum tree growth is found on the levees.

Floristic composition of communities

Communities differ not only in physiognomy but also floristically, that is, in the plant species of which they are composed. Whereas the number of savanna communities which can be distinguished physiognomically is quite small, the large number of species which may or may not be present in a particular community gives much greater scope for defining communities floristically. For example, Fig. 5.5 shows that the ridge-top savanna woodland has more or less the same physiognomy as the middle-slope savanna woodland and the riverain woodland. Nevertheless these are different communities as the species composition is different (Table 5.1).

What do such differences signify? Each plant species has a certain range of occurrence, in which it can not only tolerate the prevailing environmental conditions but also flourish sufficiently to establish itself in competition with other species (p. 13). Species differ in their breadth of range; in other words, some are narrowly restricted to particular habitats, whereas others are distributed more widely. Table 5.1 shows that in the Mole Game Reserve *Pteleopsis suberosa* and *Detarium microcarpum* are abundant in ridge-top savanna but virtually absent elsewhere, *Terminalia avicennioides* and *Butyrospermum paradoxum* are mainly or entirely middle-slope trees, whereas *Anogeissus leiocarpus* and *Piliostigma thonningii* are predominantly found in riverain woodland. On the other hand *Burkea africana* is equally at home on ridge top and middle slope, and *Lannea acida* is spread sparingly but evenly through middle slopes and riverain woodland. In view of the similarity between the four plots in middle-slope savanna, it is not likely that the differences from the

communities in other habitats are due entirely to chance.

Species of restricted distribution may therefore be taken as indicators of the environmental conditions of the preferred sites. In the case which we have described the indicators are not very useful because we can recognize the differences in conditions without identifying species, but where these conditions are less obvious, they may be recognized more readily from the presence of indicator species than by attempting to measure them directly. Thus, for example, some species are unusually tolerant of high concentrations of certain metals such as copper. Indeed, the presence of ore below the surface may be revealed by the existence of a particular plant community (Table 5.2).

Ecology and taxonomy

At this stage we will digress to examine the relationship of the ecology of plant species, that is the communities in which they occur, to their taxonomy, that is their overall affinities. We have seen, for example, that the life-forms of savanna plants are in general different from those of forest plants, and also that the species occurring in one biome are different from those in other biomes. The question then becomes: to what extent are the families and genera of plants similarly restricted in their ecological distribution?

There is no simple answer to this question. Grasses all belong to the family Gramineae which is extremely abundant and in fact dominant in savanna. The family is not absent from forest, but the grasses of the forest floor belong to genera such as *Leptaspis* (Fig. 3.18) which are restricted to this habitat. Grasses of paths and clearings and the edges of forest streams, on the other hand, mainly belong to genera which are also present in savanna. The vast majority of genera of orchids (family Orchidaceae, Fig. 3.31) consist exclusively of epiphytes of forest. A few genera are geophytes and of these some are confined to savanna, others to forest and yet others such as *Eulophia* (Fig. 5.10) include both forest and savanna species. Among trees and shrubs the distinction between forest and savanna genera and families is much less clear. Of the 33 species of tree occurring in savanna plots in the Mole

Table 5.2 Copper content of soils in which various species of grass were recorded near Mangula, Rhodesia. The last three species in the list are copper indicators in this district, though not necessarily so in other parts of Africa (*Data from Jacobsen*)

| Species | Copper content of soil (parts per million) | | |
	Minimum	Maximum	Mean
Themeda triandra	20	840	215
Andropogon gayanus	40	740	329
Eragrostis racemosa	320	25 270	5 912
Trachypogon spicatus	610	25 270	6 278
Monocymbium ceresiiforme	1 010	25 270	8 578

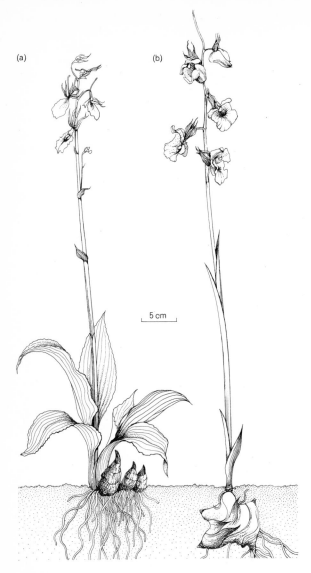

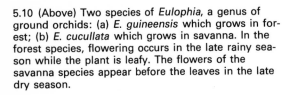

(a)   (b)

5 cm

(a)

(b)

5.10 (Above) Two species of *Eulophia*, a genus of
ground orchids: (a) *E. guineensis* which grows in forest; (b) *E. cucullata* which grows in savanna. In the
forest species, flowering occurs in the late rainy season while the plant is leafy. The flowers of the
savanna species appear before the leaves in the late
dry season.

5.11 (Right) *Cussonia*, a genus of trees which includes
closely related species in forest and savanna. (a) *C.
bancoensis*, a forest species with a slender trunk up to
20 m high, and fairly smooth bark. (b) *C. barteri*, a
savanna tree with very deeply fissured bark, and which
branches from near the base. These differences persist
even when the two species are grown under the same
conditions in a garden.

84

Game Reserve (Table 5.1) only 4 may be found in forest, but 24 belong to genera which include forest species, and all belong to families which are represented in forest. In many genera such as *Khaya* (Fig. 3.39) and *Cussonia* (Fig. 5.11) there are pairs of closely related species, one of which occurs in forest and the other in savanna. The members of such pairs frequently differ in those features which commonly distinguish forest and savanna trees; thus the savanna species may have blunter leaves and thicker bark than its forest relative.

The reason for this is that the most striking and consistent differences between taxonomic groups of plants are in the structure of their flowers and fruits, and are thus related more to their adaptations for pollination and dispersal than to their vegetative features. The implication for community ecology is that a floristic description in which the plants are identified only as far as genus or family is not likely to be very informative. Identifications should, as far as possible, be made to species although, for purposes of comparison, it may be sufficient to give code names to the species if their scientific names cannot be determined.

Communities in forest

The effects on vegetation of normal variation in topography and soil are easy to discern in savanna, where structure is simple and the number of species not too large, and where major variations in the biomass of trees and shrubs lead to obvious differences in the physiognomy of communities. Differentiation of forest communities on this basis is much less easy. For one thing a solid iron pan is usually absent, so that differences between the eluvial and colluvial soils, although recognizable by the soil scientist, do not always produce very marked changes in plant communities. Individual species, however, may respond to such changes; for example, in one West African forest 36 large trees of *Celtis mildbraedii* were recorded from 6 ha of ridge-top forest and only 5 from 4 ha of mid-slope forest. Differences greater than this become apparent only where ridges are high and narrow, and slopes steep and rocky.

The clearest distinction is between the communities of slopes and hill tops taken together, and those of broad, swampy valley bottoms. The soil in such valleys may be permanently waterlogged because, compared with savanna, seasonal differences in rainfall are less and the forest soils release water into the streams more gradually after rain. These soils are badly aerated, preventing most trees from growing in them, and because the soils are wet and unstable, trees tend to be blown over rather readily in storms and the canopy is broken and patchy as a result.

Many of the trees and even some of the herbs of these forest swamps have breathing roots, pneumatophores, similar to those of the mangroves (Book 1 Fig. 20.24). The pneumatophores of *Raphia* palm (Fig. 5.12), one of

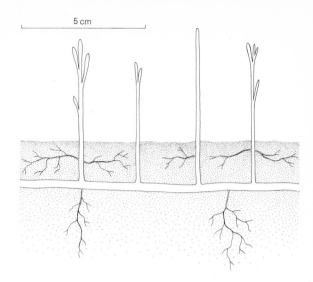

5 cm

5.12 Pneumatophores of *Raphia* palm; the pneumatophores protrude above the mud in which the horizontal roots grow.

5.13 *Halopegia azurea*, a monocot herb of swamp forest.

the most characteristic trees, are very narrow, partly because palms are monocots and lack secondary thickening. The epidermis at the tips of the pneumatophores breaks open to expose the air-conducting tissue which contains abundant air spaces. The pneumatophores of the herbaceous monocot *Halopegia* (Fig. 5.14) are essentially similar to those of *Raphia*. The forest species of *Mitragyna* (Book 1 Fig. 21.13) produce 'knee-roots' which have large lenticels on the upper surface at the top of the loop; the savanna species, *Mitragyna inermis* (Fig. 5.8), in common with other trees of temporary savanna swamps, lacks pneumatophores.

85

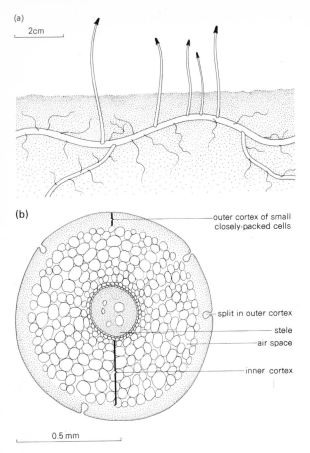

(a)

2cm

(b)

outer cortex of small
closely-packed cells

split in outer cortex
stele
air space

inner cortex

0.5 mm

5.14 *Halopegia azurea:* (a) Pneumatophores; similar to
those of *Raphia* except that they are unbranched. Each
is tipped by a persistent root-cap. (b) Transverse section through pneumatophore, showing the splits in the
outer cortex which allow gaseous diffusion into the air
spaces of the inner cortex.

5.15 *Xylopia staudtii* in West African forest. Stilt roots
are formed up to 3 m above the ground.

Stilt-rooted trees (Fig. 5.15) resembling the mangrove
Rhizophora (Book 1 Fig. 20.23) are also found in swamp
forest; they are usually not restricted to valley bottoms,
but may occur in slope forest also. The climbing palms
(Fig. 3.26) are especially characteristic of swamp forest,
forming impenetrable thorny tangles in the extensive gaps.
The abundance of palms is in fact one of the most striking
features of this vegetation.

Topography in relation to the forest–savanna boundary

It was mentioned on p. 81 that a narrow strip of 'fringing'
forest is very often found on river banks in fairly dry
savanna regions. The species of tree in this forest are
adapted to survive great fluctuations in the height of the
watertable, and normal forest trees may be absent or

scarce. As the boundary of continuous forest is approached, rainfall becomes higher, the dry season shorter,
and conditions in the valleys less subject to extremes. The
fringing forest strip may then widen to a broader belt in
which many typical forest species are present; the landscape bears a complicated pattern of forest in valleys, but
savanna on the slopes and tops. Eventually an area is
reached where the forest becomes continuous and the
savanna may be represented by isolated patches on
unfavourable soils. The boundary between forest and
savanna may still be abrupt, but it is far from straight
where a transition zone of this kind occurs.

Savanna patches also occur in some parts of Africa deep
within the tropical forest, under conditions of high rainfall. In south-west Ghana and southern Ivory Coast such
included savanna occurs in very gentle topography on
highly leached, nutrient-deficient soils. The hollows in

these areas are permanently wet and bear swamp forest with abundant *Raphia* palms. The highest parts are more or less permanently dry and carry rather low evergreen forest. The middle slopes, however, flooded in the rainy season and dry for the rest of the year, are covered by a poor savanna grassland community which often includes many of the species found in savanna regions on exposed iron pan.

Coastal communities

In Book 1 (p. 239) we described the zonation of communities on a rocky shore in response to variation in degree of exposure to desiccation, and on p. 247 the distribution of mangrove communities was discussed in relation to variations in salinity. Because of the greater variety of important ecological factors and the generally low diversity of plants and animals, coastal areas provide especially clear examples of the control of distribution of communities by the environment.

Fig. 5.16 shows changes in species composition and in soil along a transect taken from the edge of an *Avicennia* (Book 1 Fig. 20.24) mangrove swamp through the grass communities on the gentle slope behind it; *Avicennia* is evidently restricted to the saltiest clay soils where nothing else grows. Mangrove is a kind of swamp forest in which the ground is waterlogged for most of the year. The mangrove trees form a complete canopy which excludes grass and therefore mangrove is not subject to fires. There is a sharp boundary between this forest and the rest of the vegetation which is grassland savanna and regularly burnt. The grassland is of rather uniform physiognomy, as the grasses are all about 1 m high, and trees are lacking. The zonation of the soil, however, is reflected in the species composition of the grassland communities, as follows:

Zone 1: Soil with high salinity and high clay content; important species *Sporobolus robustus* and *Paspalum vaginatum*.
Zone 2: Salinity moderate and clay content high; important species *Cyperus articulatus*, *Panicum repens* and *Imperata cylindrica*.
Zone 3: Salinity moderate and soil loamy; important species *Panicum repens* and *Imperata cylindrica*.
Zone 4: Salinity low and soil sandy; important species *Imperata cylindrica* and *Andropogon gayanus*, together with various annual herbs.

Fig. 5.16 illustrates the point made earlier, that species differ in the range of conditions under which they can grow successfully. *Sporobolus robustus* is restricted to a very narrow zone, and is therefore a good indicator of highly saline soil. *Imperata cylindrica* on the other hand extends through all but the saltiest zone. In fact there are no two species which have exactly the same range. It is not possible to define our communities exactly and un-

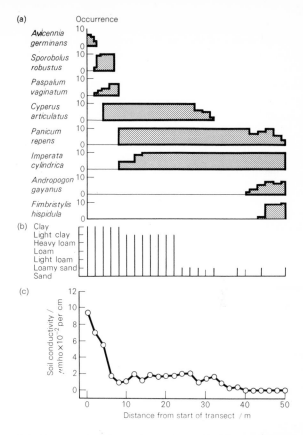

5.16 Transect from the edge of an *Avicennia* mangrove swamp through grassland near the coast of Ghana. The right-hand end of the transect has an elevation about 2·5 m greater than that of the left-hand end. (a) Frequency of important species, determined by placing 10 quadrats each 30×30 cm in a row at right angles to the line of the transect, and recording the number of quadrats in which each species occurred. (b) Soil texture. (c) Soil conductivity; this is proportional to salt content.

ambiguously, because of the existence of intermediate combinations of plants. If we were to make similar transects in other places with similar conditions of soil we should probably find slightly different groups of species.

Stability and change in communities

So far in this chapter we have looked at communities as if they were static, describing their composition and position in the biomes. This is only part of the story. Plants are continually growing, reproducing and dying; the vegetation which they constitute is therefore always undergoing change.

Seasonal change

Forest, as we shall see on p. 277, is much more productive than savanna; growth rates are high, and new leaves and twigs are produced almost throughout the year. Nevertheless, forest is the most stable kind of vegetation, as its appearance varies less than that of other biomes. The reason is that decay—loss of dead leaves, branches and so on—takes place concurrently with growth. A dynamic equilibrium is thus established between the two processes. There are no annuals, and plants of all life-forms, even the geophytes, have shoots visible above the ground throughout the year. Nevertheless even the wettest forest shows some seasonality (Fig. 3.33), with more or less distinct peaks in flowering, fruiting, flushing of new leaves and leaf fall. In semi-deciduous and deciduous forest seasonal changes are more marked (Fig. 5.17a), but nowhere are seasonal changes as striking as in savanna (Fig. 5.17b). Immediately after burning the landscape is coated with black ash and everything looks dead (Fig. 5.18). It soon appears that the fire, by removing old leaves, stimulates both trees and grasses to produce new ones and the savanna begins to turn green even before the rains come (Table 5.3). Geophytes generally require the stimulation of rain to break their dormancy, and their flowering spikes grow very quickly above the young grass leaves and often also before their own leaves develop. Through the rainy season the grass grows steadily until flowering occurs just before the next dry season. It is clear that such things as physiognomy, stratification, biomass, floristic composition and density do not have absolute values in savanna communities; rather their values change with the seasons.

Savanna therefore differs from season to season but the high proportion of perennials, both herbaceous and woody, ensures reasonable stability from year to year. Annuals however, die at the end of each growing season, and the number of seeds available to give rise to mature plants during the following season depends on the variable factors which affect the size of the seed crop, and on growing conditions in the following year. Because annuals (therophytes) are the most important life-form in many deserts and subdeserts (Fig. 3.38)—that is in the biome where rainfall shows the greatest unreliability and variation from year to year—desert vegetation may be particularly unstable, both density and species composition showing erratic fluctuations (Table 5.4 and Fig. 5.17c).

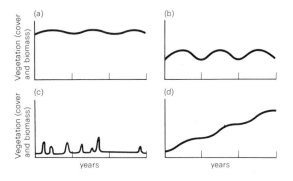

5.17 Diagrammatic representation of types of change in vegetation. (a) Semi-deciduous forest, with slight seasonal fluctuation in leafy cover. (b) Savanna woodland, with more marked seasonal change. (c) Desert vegetation, in which change is erratic, depending on rare rainstorms. (d) Successional change in forest; seasonal changes are superimposed.

Table 5.3 Effects of fire on times of sprouting of trees and grasses in sample plots in Nigerian savanna. Treated plots were burned on the dates shown; note that on some of the burned plots plants sprouted well before those on the unburned (control) plots. The first rains fell in early March (*Data from Hopkins*)

Plant species	Date of sprouting on unburned (control) plots	Dates of burning on treated plots	Dates of sprouting on burned plots	Number of days from burning to sprouting
Butyrospermum paradoxum (tree)	22 March	29 December	9 February	42
		12 January	9 February	28
		26 January	16 February	21
		9 February	23 February	14
		23 February	17 March	22
Daniellia oliveri (tree)	2 February	7 December	20 January	43
		29 December	2 February	35
		12 January	2 February	21
		26 January	9 February	14
Monocymbium ceresiiforme (grass)	2–16 February	7 December	6 January	29
		12 January	26 January	14
		26 January	2 February	7

5.18 Savanna immediately after burning. Note the blackened stumps of the grass tussocks, from which new shoots will soon grow.

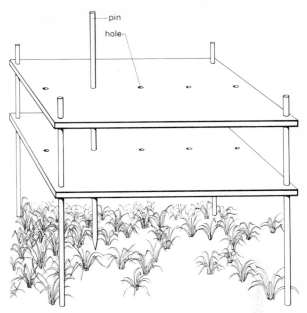

5.19 Point quadrat method for determining cover. The pin can slide freely in any of the five pairs of holes in the frame. The height of the frame will depend on the height of vegetation being sampled; 20 cm would be satisfactory for a well-mowed lawn.

Seasonal change can be well studied on a lawn or football field, particularly in a place where the rainfall is rather low and the water supply is not large enough to permit the watering of the grounds. In the dry season the ground may be almost bare, apart from a few tussocks of particularly drought-resistant perennial grasses and a few deep-rooted perennial herbs. The first heavy rains bring a flush of seedlings, and a growth of new shoots from the rootstocks of what had seemed to be dead or moribund perennials. If there is a dry spell before the next rains, the ranks of seedlings will be thinned as some dry up, allowing a few vigorous ones to become established. During the rainy season annuals and perennials alike grow, at first vegetatively, then producing flowers and fruit. With the return of dry weather the annuals disappear, and the perennials once more begin to lose most of their leaves. These changes can be studied in detail if quadrats are marked on the ground permanently, perhaps by nails at their corners, and the vegetation assessed repeatedly in the same areas. This may be done by counting individual plants to obtain density. Alternatively 'cover' can be determined using the point quadrat method in which slender pins are dropped downwards through holes in a frame (Fig. 5.19) and the name of any plant touched is recorded. Cover is simply:

$$\frac{\text{number of times the pin touched plants} \times 100}{\text{number of times the pin was dropped}}$$

Table 5.4 Year-to-year variation in frequency of annual plants in undisturbed subdesert steppe in north-western United States, mean rainfall 180 mm per annum. Frequency of each species was measured as percentage occurrence in 40 permanent sample plots, each measuring 20 × 50 cm (*Data from Daubenmire*)

	1958	1959	1960	1961	1962	1963	1964
Festuca pacifica	92	100	32	88	58	90	80
Festuca octoflora	92	85	40	88	30	98	47
Bromus tectorum	45	90	55	62	18	50	52
Descurainia pinnata	18	20	0	25	0	18	2
Cryptantha flaccida	12	10	4	0	0	0	0
Draba verna	2	0	0	0	0	12	0

and is a measure of the extent to which the leaves of each species cover the ground. Table 5.5 shows results obtained in this way on a golf course.

Succession

Seasonal change is essentially cyclic; at the end of the year, the vegetation returns to what it was at the beginning. The amplitude of change may be great as in savanna, or narrower as in forest. Provided, however, that the vegetation, whether stable or unstable, is in harmony with the environment, we have essentially a condition of dynamic equilibrium.

Where there is disequilibrium between vegetation and environment, the stage is set for change of a different kind —succession—in which cumulative adjustments, perhaps continued over many years, eventually restore the equilibrium or produce a new one as the case may be. A well-known case of succession is the development of vegetation which occurs when a piece of forest which has been cleared to make a farm is later abandoned. In the first year, the ground becomes covered by farm regrowth. This is a mixture of weedy plants—grasses, other herbs, soft-wooded shrubs such as *Solanum*, and saplings of such trees as *Musanga* (Fig. 1.3) and *Trema*. These weedy trees grow very quickly (Fig. 5.20) and suppress the herbaceous plants, forming secondary thicket which thorny climbers such as *Acacia* species make difficult of access. Under the thicket canopy, the shade-tolerant seedlings of longer-lived trees can establish themselves. Within 15 years most of the *Musanga* is dead and secondary forest has developed. If such forest remains uncleared more than 50 years, it comes increasingly to resemble the original primary forest. This succession, summarized in

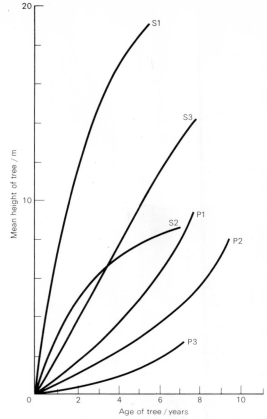

5.20 Rate of height growth of six species of tree in the Congo forest. S1 *Musanga cecropioides*, S2 *Caloncoba welwitschii* and S3 *Terminalia superba* are secondary forest species; P1, P2 and P3 are species of primary forest. (After Lebrun and Gilbert).

Table 5.5 Cover of grass species in a 3 m × 3 m sample plot on a golf course in Ghana. A pin was dropped 25 times in each of ten 0·25 m² subplots within the plot; the rows of results give the numbers of occasions on which the pin touched plants of each species. Total rainfall in the 20 days preceding 5 February was 0 mm, and in the 20 days preceding 15 May was 78 mm (*Swaine, unpublished data*)

Subplot no.	Cynodon 5 Feb.	Cynodon 15 May	Paspalum 5 Feb.	Paspalum 15 May	Dactyloctenium 5 Feb.	Dactyloctenium 15 May	Others 5 Feb.	Others 15 May	Bare 5 Feb.	Bare 15 May
1	7	23	1	6	0	7	0	2	17	0
2	6	17	1	10	0	5	0	10	18	0
3	7	15	1	10	0	5	3	2	14	3
4	9	18	0	8	0	6	0	3	16	0
5	9	20	1	9	0	5	0	9	15	0
6	9	14	0	0	0	14	1	7	15	0
7	9	21	4	6	0	15	0	12	12	0
8	8	24	2	2	0	15	0	13	15	0
9	5	19	0	4	0	12	4	5	16	0
10	3	18	1	18	0	4	0	1	21	2
Mean cover %	29	76	4	29	0	35	3	18	64	2

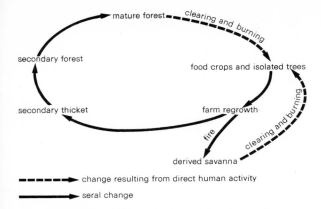

mature forest — clearing and burning

secondary forest

food crops and isolated trees

secondary thicket

farm regrowth

fire

clearing and burning

derived savanna

- - - - - ▶ change resulting from direct human activity

———▶ seral change

5.21 Outline of events in succession on cleared forest. Note that savanna may become established in drier parts of the forest if farm regrowth is repeatedly burned.

Fig. 5.21 and Table 5.6, thus consists of a number of temporary stages, each of which is unable to maintain itself in the face of competition from the plants of the subsequent stages. Succession is a general term for the phenomenon; a particular example of succession is called a sere, and the temporary communities of which the sere consists are called seral stages or seral communities.

The example we have chosen illustrates many of the commonly observed characteristics of seres.
(a) The earliest colonizers are weedy species which have good means of dispersal (p. 11) and grow very quickly in the sunlight but which are intolerant of shade. The first of these weedy species are commonly herbaceous; they therefore have a short life cycle and are able to reproduce themselves in their first year.
(b) Cover and biomass of the colonizing vegetation increase progressively, apart from slight decreases during the dry season; the changes are represented diagrammatically in Fig. 5.17d.
(c) Young secondary forest has a lower basal area and height, and lower species diversity, than primary forest, the storeys are often less distinct, and microclimate is less clearly differentiated.

Succession on an abandoned farm, lawn or football field leads to the return of vegetation which was previously there; it is called secondary succession and its seres are secondary seres. Primary succession and 'priseres' occur on a previously uncolonized substrate, such as a sandbank in a river, the mud of an estuary or cooling volcanic ash as on Krakatau (p. 8). During the course of a primary sere on land, the substrate is gradually converted to soil; because this process is slow, a primary sere is generally very protracted. A secondary sere can be completed more quickly, provided that the soil, with the seeds it normally contains, is not removed during the clearing of vegetation by which the sere was initiated. Hydroseres, on or in water, are often particularly rapid if the water is rich in nutrients. Fig. 5.22 shows two views of the same piece of floating vegetation taken just 11 months apart. On the first occasion the community consisted entirely of the water lettuce, *Pistia stratiotes*, but less than a year later this had been invaded by the aquatic sedge *Scirpus*

Table 5.6 Characteristics of the principal seral stages in succession from an abandoned farm to mature forest (*Data from various sources*)

Seral stage	Duration from abandonment of farm (*years*)	Canopy height (*m*)	Biomass (tonnes ha^{-1})	Important life-forms	Important plant genera
Farm regrowth	0–2	1–5	5–20	grasses; herbs, shrubs; young trees; slender climbers	*Setaria; Solanum; Musanga; Tragia*
Secondary thicket	2–10	8–20	15–100	shrubs, soft-wooded small trees; climbers	*Trema, Anthocleista, Macaranga, Musanga; Acacia, Mussaenda*
Secondary forest	10–80	15–50	100–150	large light-demanding trees; large lianes	*Ceiba, Funtumia, Terminalia; Acacia*
Mature forest	>80	40–60	100–150	large trees, many shade-bearing; large lianes	*Celtis, Khaya, Piptadeniastrum; Agelaea*

(a)

(b)

5.22 Succession in an aquatic plant community on the Volta Lake, Ghana. (a) October 1970. Floating mat of *Pistia stratiotes* with a few small patches of *Scirpus cubensis*. (b) September 1971. *Pistia* almost completely hidden by *Scirpus* which has spread rapidly.

5.23 Cat-tail (*Typha domingensis*) forming dense floating vegetation up to 2·5 m high. In the foreground can be seen *Pistia* and *Scirpus* which have not yet been invaded by *Typha*. The broad-leaved plant is the aquatic fig tree *Ficus congensis*.

cubensis whose creeping stems are supported at first by the *Pistia*, but whose leaves eventually reduce the *Pistia* by shading it out. The *Scirpus* may later be colonized by still larger aquatic plants such as *Typha* (Fig. 5.23).

Practical importance of succession

Succession is a phenomenon of general occurrence and a knowledge of seres is often of great practical importance. Any human activity which disturbs the natural equilibrium is likely to initiate a sere. For example, we may plant a lawn with Bahama grass (*Cynodon dactylon*), a narrow-leaved perennial species whose stems creep over the surface, forming a mat. If we are lucky a pure crop of this grass may turn out to be in equilibrium with the environmental complex, which will include soil type, rainfall, seasonality, frequency of mowing and so on. If, however, the rainfall is rather low, it is likely that the Bahama grass will die back in the dry season, and that in the following rainy season its growth will be restricted by self-sown

annuals which grow quickly, filling the gaps. When these die in the following dry season they will leave bare patches in the lawn. If mowing is too infrequent, tussock-forming perennial grasses will become firmly established, and the lawn surface will therefore be bumpy. Where tree branches overhang the lawn, Bahama grass may not grow well because of the shading, and give way to broader-leaved, shade-tolerant species.

From this point of view, weeding is an attempt to prevent succession from taking place. The less natural the crop, the more will be the weeding needed to maintain it. The labour of weeding is minimized when the crop is allowed to approximate as closely as possible, at least in structure, to a natural community.

We may cite examples also from the major biomes. If dry forest near the savanna boundary is subjected to repeated cultivation without being sufficiently fertilized or rested, the soil may become exhausted and the farm then be invaded by perennial grasses. If these are burnt

5.24 Elephant grass (*Pennisetum purpureum*) 5 m high which has invaded old farms in semi-deciduous forest, forming a derived savanna. Forest trees can be seen in the background.

5.25 Thorny *Acacia* scrub on heavily grazed farmland in Tanzania.

regularly, forest trees are killed and prevented from regenerating, and the erstwhile forest may be converted to 'derived savanna' (Fig. 5.24). The chief danger for dry grassland is over-grazing by cattle; this may lead to the killing of valuable perennial grasses and their replacement by inferior annuals and sometimes by unpalatable shrubs, which persist because they are no longer controlled by annual fires (Fig. 5.25). Even game reserves must be managed if the communities are to be conserved (p. 373).

Climaxes

In its early stages, a sere usually shows rapid change, but towards the end change is slower until eventually a relatively stable community is reached. This is called a 'climax' community, and represents the tallest, most massive, most highly organized vegetation that the environment is capable of supporting. In the desert environment, the low rainfall permits a climax vegetation consisting only of scattered bushes or clumps of grass and a temporary flush of annuals after rains. Where the rainfall is higher savanna or forest will develop.

The definition of the climax is, however, far from a straightforward matter. The climax is said to be reached when change has ceased, but what does this mean in practical terms? We know from work on East African lakes (p. 61) that climatic change has resulted in far-reaching changes in vegetation within the past few thousand years, and there is no reason to suppose that such processes have now ceased. In practice we cannot demand absolute finality for a climax, but must be content with the absence of succession during, say, the past twenty years or so.

Another problem, around which there has been much controversy, is this. We saw in our discussion of savanna earlier in this chapter that vegetation is not uniform over large areas. Of all the various communities of undisturbed savanna which, if any, is the climax? Some ecologists have refused to recognize any savanna woodland as climax vegetation on the grounds that all 'true' climaxes are determined by climate, and savanna woodland is usually prevented from developing into forest only by the action of fire. This, however, seems an excessively narrow view of the climax, in view of the undoubted stability over the years of many savannas. It seems preferable to recognize different kinds of climax: climatic climaxes are those where climate is the most important factor, and edaphic climaxes those where, as in savanna patches in evergreen forest, the substrate prevents the development of the climatic climax community. A lawn is a man-made climax, being prevented from developing further by the men who cut it. Savanna woodland is a fire climax; the other savanna communities are determined by factor complexes involving soil, termites, slope and fire. Grasslands close to certain lakes in Uganda are greatly influenced through grazing by the hippopotamus which live in them (Fig.

5.26), and here we may perhaps speak of a biotic climax.

The stability and uniformity of the climax should not, however, be over-emphasized. Apart from seasonal changes, there are fluctuations associated with regeneration. It may have occurred to you to wonder where *Musanga* lived before men began to burn and farm the forest. The answer is that it lived in the natural gaps in the primary forest. Every time a large forest tree falls, it drags down with it other trees to which it is attached by climbers, and also those in the line of fall. Elephants browse on the fallen crowns, and a gap as large as 0·5 ha may ensue. Forest regeneration within this gap follows a secondary sere similar to that on abandoned farmland. Climax forest is thus a patchwork of different phases or stages in regeneration (Fig. 5.27). Wherever close study is made, climax vegetation is found to be not strictly homogeneous, but patterned in some way. Although small patches of the climax may undergo change, a sufficiently large area, including all regeneration stages, will show overall stability.

Relationship between the species in a climax community

A climax community shows a considerable degree of organization, both physiognomic and floristic. Within a community, plants of the same life-form constitute a group whose members have similar size and structure and make similar demands on the environment. Such groups are the subcommunities or component parts of a community; they are often called *synusiae*. In forest, for example, the synusiae of trees are the more or less distinct storeys, which provide the scaffolding that supports the epiphyte and climber synusiae and give the shade which determines the shrub and herb synusiae. The synusiae are so interwoven that they cannot be considered to represent distinct communities. The community is also characterized by a fairly constant species composition; the species of one savanna community are different from those of another community (p. 83). Among the species characteristically present in a community, some are typically abundant and conspicuous while others are typically rare.

Observations such as these have led some ecologists to compare the community to an organism, suggesting that each component species plays an essential role comparable to that of an organ in the body, and that the species are therefore closely dependent on one another. It is now generally considered, however, that this view is exaggerated. A better analogy might be with a small town in which there is some degree of interdependence between the 'synusiae' of lorry drivers, market women, farmers and so on, but in which there is also competition between the individuals within each 'synusia'. To press the metaphor a little further, the different 'species' of trader also compete, and the 'species' composition may differ from place to place and from time to time without the working of the whole community being greatly affected.

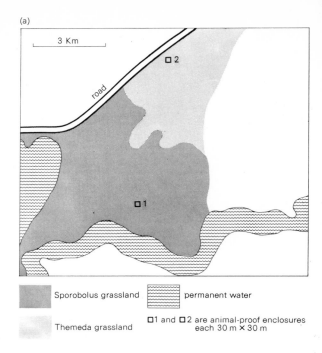

(a)

3 Km

road

□2

□1

| | Sporobolus grassland | | permanent water |
| | Themeda grassland | | □1 and □2 are animal-proof enclosures each 30 m × 30 m |

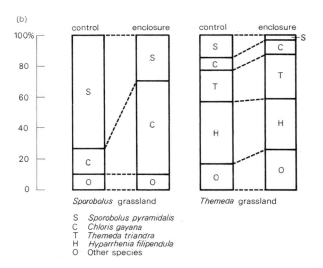

(b)

control   enclosure   control   enclosure

Sporobolus grassland   *Themeda* grassland

S   *Sporobolus pyramidalis*
C   *Chloris gayana*
T   *Themeda triandra*
H   *Hyparrhenia filipendula*
O   Other species

5.26 Effects of hippopotamus grazing on grasslands near Lake Edward, Uganda. (a) Map of the area studied. Hippopotamus live in the permanent water, coming on land at night to graze up to 3 km from the water. Notice that *Sporobolus* grassland, which is rather short, occupies the land closest to the water, whilst the taller *Themeda* grassland is further away. (b) Results of experiment to find the effects on the composition of vegetation of excluding grazing animals. Vegetation was recorded in the enclosures about 2 years after they were first fenced; the 'control' results were obtained in grassland adjacent to the enclosures which was exposed to grazing. (After Lock).

low thicket with many climbers

broken canopy; many gaps

mature forest; canopy mostly intact

5.27 Map of 72 ha of the Strict Nature Reserve in the Omo Forest Reserve, Nigeria, showing the distribution of the major forest phases. Mature forest with a high, intact canopy covers only a small proportion of the area. The remainder consists of various stages in forest regeneration, and thickets along streams. (After Baur).

As regards a plant community, this opinion sees each species as waging a solitary battle for establishment in competition with other species of similar physiological tolerance. Thus *Paspalum vaginatum* and *Sporobolus robustus* grow together in the salt-marsh community not because they need each other, but because they are adapted to grow under similar environmental conditions. The most important 'weapons' in this battle are aggressive roots which compete effectively for soil water and nutrients, and leafy branches which shade out competitors. Some species may also wage chemical warfare, liberating into the air and soil substances which prevent the establishment of other plants (Table 5.7). It might be thought that interspecific co-operation would be found in the relationship between epiphytes and the trees on which they grow, but here too it seems that although an epiphyte species may require rough bark for its establishment it will not need the bark of any particular species of tree.

Why are there so many species?

If it is true that competition is severe, and that some species are better adapted than others, we may well ask why it is

that one species does not always come out best in the struggle, so that a community consists of just one species in each synusia. As a matter of fact, a few communities are like this. The mangrove community mentioned on p. 87 has one tree storey, consisting entirely of *Avicennia germinans*, and a herb layer consisting of *Sesuvium portulacastrum*. At the other extreme, we have the forest analysed in Table 3.1 with large numbers of tree species growing side by side, none of them dominant. Can we suggest explanations for these differences? It is clear that the simplicity of the mangrove community is not a result of fierce competition, but of the opposite—*Avicennia germinans* is perhaps the only West African tree capable of growing under those conditions. There is in fact a general tendency for simple communities to occur under environmental conditions which are difficult or unusual, and in which the few 'specialist' species can flourish.

Two kinds of explanation have been offered for the great diversity of species in mixed communities, including most forests. The first depends on the fact that conditions are not uniform within a synusia; there are many microhabitats or 'niches' to which a species may have different degrees of adaptation. The concept of the 'niche' is explored further on p. 116. The second explanation is based on the existence of predatory insects which cause increasingly high mortality as the density of their host species increases (Fig. 1.5).

Adaptation

Adaptation is a central idea in ecology: nevertheless our knowledge of adaptation in plants is still very meagre. In the case of *Avicennia*, a variety of structural and physiological features (Book 1 p. 245) give us insight into its habitat preferences. But we are completely ignorant of the causes of the distribution of most plants, and if we say, for example, '*Detarium microcarpum* is adapted to ridge-top savanna' we are implying nothing more than that this is where we find it, without having the least idea of any morphological or physiological reasons leading to this distribution. Although an understanding of the causal relationships between plants and their environments

Table 5.7 Root lengths (mm) of 2-day-old *Euphorbia* seedlings grown in dilute aqueous extracts of various parts of the West African tree *Okoubaka aubrevillei*. All parts of the tree tested were found to contain growth inhibitors (*Armstrong-Mensah, unpublished data*)

| Replicates | Control (pure water) | root bark | Parts of Okoubaka extracted | | |
			stem bark	young leaves	mature leaves
1	8·72	6·00	3·42	3·42	2·58
2	9·00	6·12	3·42	3·52	2·70
3	8·24	5·98	3·40	3·20	2·64
Mean root length	8·65	6·03	3·41	3·38	2·64

remains the chief goal of ecology, there are few plants whose distribution could be accurately predicted from the results of anatomical studies and growth experiments. The complexities and difficulties are such that a very great deal of research will be required before this situation can be substantially changed.

Problems

1 In many savanna geophytes, including *Eulophia* (Fig. 5.10), flowers are produced in the dry season before the leaves. What advantage do you think might be conferred on the plant by such behaviour? Why do you think the tubers of *Eulophia cucullata* are formed below the soil surface while those of *E. guineensis* come above the surface?

2 (a) At what distances in Fig. 5.16 would you place the limits of the vegetation zones listed on p. 87?
   (b) Comment on the fact that salt glands are present in the leaves of *Avicennia germinans* and *Sporobolus robustus*.
   (c) What further observations would you make to discover whether the correlations between vegetation and soil suggested by Fig. 5.16 are widespread, and significant?

3 Compare Figs. 5.22a and 5.22b. On which occasion was the water level higher? How could you use photographs such as these to estimate the rate of decay of the dead trees? What other observations would be needed?

4 In what ways do the data presented in Fig. 5.26 support the view that differences in the intensity of grazing by hippopotamus are responsible for vegetational zonation in the area of study? What other factors might be responsible for the zonation? What further data would you need before deciding between the various theories? How may the following facts be assimilated by your theories?
   (a) Hippopotamus account for over 50 percent of the biomass of large herbivores in the area.
   (b) Warthog and buffalo, accounting for a further 25 percent, are seldom recorded within 1 km of permanent water.
   (c) *Sporobolus pyramidalis* is less palatable to cattle than is *Themeda triandra*.

5 Use a simple statistical test to find which of the species recorded in Table 5.1 are significantly more abundant in middle-slope savanna than in the other savanna types.

6 Coconut seedlings were planted in a high-rainfall area (2 500 mm per annum) which carried a mosaic of forest, thicket and grassland.
   The young coconut trees grew well in land cleared of forest and thicket, but completely failed to grow when planted in the grassland. What may have been the reasons for this difference in performance? What

investigations could you carry out to test your suggestions?

7 *Monocymbium ceresiiforme* is a common grass in West Africa on copper-free soils. How might we explain the finding (Table 5.2) that in Rhodesia this species is a good indicator of copper? What experiments could be performed to test this explanation?

8 The roots of many kinds of forest-swamp trees bear pneumatophores, but these structures are not formed by trees of savanna swamp. What differences between the two kinds of swamp might account for this distribution of pneumatophores?

9 Which of the species in Table 5.3 showed evidence that its sprouting was hastened by burning? What major difficulties would have to be faced in an experiment of this kind?

10 Why are therophytes absent from forest though abundant in savanna?

11 The fireball lily *Haemanthus multiflorus* has a well-developed bulb, and propagates itself vegetatively by creeping underground stolons. Its relative *Haemanthus cinnabarinus*, has a poorly-developed bulb and propagates by bulbils which develop on its leaves. Which of these species would you expect to live in forest and which in savanna?

12 Display the data of Table 5.4 in suitable graphical form. Assuming that annual rainfall was proportional to mean frequency for all species, arrange the years in order of increasing dryness. Is there evidence that any one species is more drought-resistant than the rest? Can we conclude that *Cryptantha* became extinct in 1960? Can we conclude that the seeds of *Draba* retain their viability for at least five years? What precautions would have to be taken in an experiment such as this if the data are to be meaningful?

13 The results for *Cynodon* in Table 5.5 suggest that this grass increased its cover between 5 February and 15 May. Apply a statistical test to find whether the increase was significant. Draw a graph to show the relationship between *Paspalum* and *Dactyloctenium*. How would you describe this relationship? What might account for it? Which of the three grass species is a therophyte?

14 Which part of the *Okoubaka* tree appears to have the strongest inhibitory effect on seedling growth (Table 5.7)? What further work would be needed to show that these inhibitory substances are of real value to the tree in its competition with other plants in the forest?

Bibliography

Further reading

Daubenmire, R. *Plant Communities*, Harper and Row, 1968

Hopkins, B. *Forest and Savanna*, Heinemann, 1974

Kershaw, K. A. *Quantitative and Dynamic Ecology*, Edward Arnold, 2nd ed. 1973, Chaps. 1 and 3

Langdale-Brown, I., Osmaston, H. A., Wilson, J. G. *The Vegetation of Uganda, and its Bearing on Land Use*, Government of Uganda, 1964

Lind, E. M., Morrison, M. E. S. *East African Vegetation*, Longman, 1974

Richards, P. W. *The Tropical Rain Forest*, Cambridge University Press, 1952

Wills, J. B. (ed.) *Agriculture and Land Use in Ghana*, Oxford University Press, 1962, Chaps. 9 and 10

Cooper, C. F. 'The Ecology of Fire', *Scientific American*, 1961, Offprint no. 1099

6 Communities—consumers and the concept of niche

Our knowledge of the relations within a food web would lead us to expect that different plant communities will have associated with them different primary consumers; these in turn will have their characteristic secondary consumers, and so on. Thus there will be communities of consumers—and also, of course, of decomposers—associated with particular communities of producers, although some of these, such as the consumers and decomposers on the sea floor, may be physically remote from the producers upon which they depend. So we may consider a community of consumers as being an association of animals exploiting some common food resource.

It would clearly be possible to describe the composition of a very wide variety of communities. Depending upon where your school happens to be, different communities will be available to you for study. Here we have attempted to describe some of the more significant characteristics of all or most communities and also some of the factors which may affect them.

The numbers of consumers

We may expect that the number of animal species associated with a plant community will far exceed the number of plant species within that community. There are two reasons for this. Firstly, different parts of a single plant may be exploited for food by different animals, especially insects; secondly, higher-order consumers, whether predators or parasites, will add to the total number of species exploiting the resource (Fig. 6.1). Thus although the total number of organisms may decrease as we pass from one trophic level to another, the number of species may increase. The extent to which this will be true depends partly upon where we elect to place the boundaries of the community under study, and partly upon how host-specific are the individual species of consumer (Fig. 6.2).

The area occupied by a community may be very small or of considerable extent, depending both upon the nature of the resource and the topography of the area. For example, the community of the forest canopy may extend over a vast area, while that of a fallen tree within the forest will, like the resource it provides, be limited in extent. Similarly savanna grasses provide a major resource, but within this area a dung heap or an abandoned termite mound will provide special but highly localized resources, each sup-

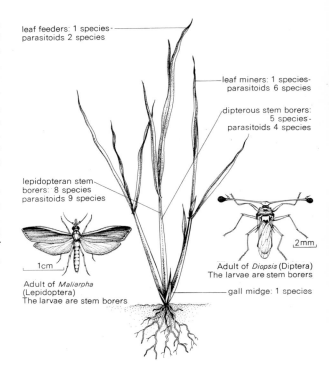

leaf feeders: 1 species-parasitoids 2 species

leaf miners: 1 species-parasitoids 6 species

dipterous stem borers: 5 species-parasitoids 4 species

lepidopteran stem borers: 8 species parasitoids 9 species

Adult of *Maliarpha* (Lepidoptera) The larvae are stem borers

Adult of *Diopsis* (Diptera) The larvae are stem borers

gall midge: 1 species

6.1 The numbers of different insect pests of rice plants and of their parasitoids so far reported to occur in Ghana. Note that the single species of plant has associated with it 37 consumer species of which 16 are first-order consumers and 21 are second-order. Much damage to rice is done by larvae which feed inside the stems of the plants. The adults of two of these are shown: one is a moth (Lepidoptera) and the other a two-winged fly (Diptera).

porting a characteristic community (Fig. 6.3a). Moreover, the boundary between one community and another is not always sharply defined. Thus, if we make a transect across a river, its topography, expressed by the depth of water and the nature of the bottom, will change as we move from one bank to the other. As a result the vegetation will change and there will be thus two or more animal communities, each supported by a different resource but usually without sharp boundaries between them (Table 6.1).

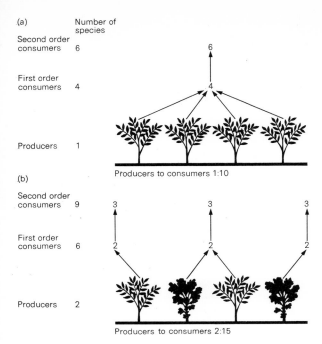

(a)

	Number of species
Second order consumers	6
First order consumers	4
Producers	1

Producers to consumers 1:10

(b)

Second order consumers	9
First order consumers	6
Producers	2

Producers to consumers 2:15

6.2 The effect of 'diversity' of producer species on the ratio of producer to consumer species. In (a) there is a single species of producer and the ratio is 1:10. In (b) with two species of producer, some consumers feed on both producers. Thus, although for each species the ratio is still 1:10, for the two species living in a single habitat, it has fallen to 1:7.5. The arrows indicate the direction of flow of material in the food web.

Table 6.1 Composition of fauna at three sampling points at a pollution-free station on a river in the Transvaal, South Africa. In each column the data are expressed as percentages of the total number of animals collected at each locality. The numbers in marginal vegetation were originally expressed as the number of animals caught with a water net in a sweep of 0·3 m length; for stones in current, the number in an area of bottom of 0·1 m² (*Based on data from Chutter*)

Taxonomic group	Marginal vegetation		Stones in current
	Sheltered	Exposed	
Flatworms	0·6	1·0	1·8
Nematodes	34·7	1·5	2·7
Oligochaetes	4·5	12·5	3·1
Ostracods	10·8	13·0	1·7
Mayflies	15·3	29·5	35·2
Caddis flies	0·0	0·0	22·4
Beetles	0·0	0·5	1·8
Simulium	0·0	0·0	8·0
Chironomids	34·0	42·5	23·3

Note the way in which the sheltered vegetation is dominated by nematode worms and chironomid larvae, while mayfly nymphs become increasingly abundant as current speed increases.

Diversity of species; indicator species

We have already seen (p. 44) that the diversity of forest trees is much greater in tropical than in temperate latitudes; this is true for plants in general. There is therefore a much greater variety of resources and thus a greater diversity of

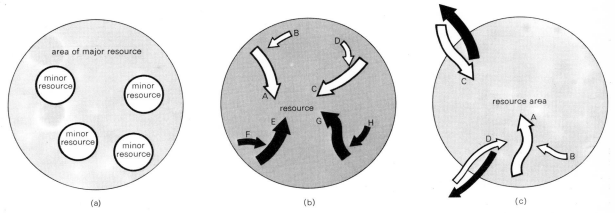

(a)　　　　　　　(b)　　　　　　　(c)

6.3 Diagrams showing three characteristics of animal communities. (a) Within an area occupied by a major resource and supporting a major animal community, there will be other smaller resources supporting small communities. (b) A primary resource may be exploited by two or more effectively separate groups of consumers. When A and C, together with their predators B and D, are exploiting the resource, E and G with their predators F and H are inactive. (c) While some consumers such as A and B may live within the area of the primary resource, other primary consumers such as C and secondary consumers such as D may visit the resource area without remaining permanently within it.

consumers in the tropics than in the temperate areas. This is illustrated in Table 6.2. The comparison between Ghana and Great Britain has been chosen because they both lie within a belt of about 8° of latitude and because they have almost the same surface area: that of Ghana is 23 787 km² and that of Great Britain 24 418 km². Such a comparison is open to the objection that Britain is an island and its fauna might perhaps be expected to be sparse, while the fauna of Ghana is part of that of the whole African continent. A precisely similar trend can, however, be seen also in continental America (Table 6.3).

If we count the numbers of individual specimens of each plant species within a sample community, we find that most of the community is formed from relatively few species. These most abundant species are sometimes described rather loosely as being 'dominant'; they will form the major resource of the community available to primary consumers. We may thus expect a similar pattern to be found among the animals, since the numbers of those consumers which feed upon the most abundant plant species will be greater than those of consumers which depend on some more limited food resource.

The relative abundance of different species in an animal community is illustrated by Fig. 6.4, which is an analysis

Table 6.2 Number of species of plants and animals of different groups known to occur in Ghana and Great Britain (*From various sources*)

Group	Ghana	Great Britain
Vascular plants	*c.* 3 500	*c.* 1 500
Grasshoppers	183	10
Ants	more than 400	36
Freshwater fishes	more than 174	22
Frogs	more than 54	5
Snakes	91	3
Nesting birds	more than 300	193
Mammals	207	41*

*Excluding marine species and those known to have been introduced within the last 2 000 years.

Table 6.3 Number of species of animals of different groups in temperate and tropical America (*Data from Kormondy*)

Group	Temperate region Locality	Number	Tropical region Locality	Number
Ants	Iowa	73	Trinidad	134
Snakes	U.S.A.	126	Mexico	283
Nesting birds	New York	195	Colombia	1 395

of the distribution by numbers of the animals taken in a series of standard samples from an area of stony bottom of the Vaal River in South Africa. 16 329 animals were collected in all and they belonged to at least 69 different species. Nevertheless more than half the animals belonged to four species only, and the six commonest species accounted for two-thirds of all the specimens collected. Of these six species the most abundant was a snail (Mollusca: Gastropoda), a primary consumer probably feeding upon encrusting algae on the stones. The next two most abundant were an oligochaete and a mayfly (Ephemeroptera). Both of these are probably detritus feeders, but differ in the coarseness of the material they take as food. Both are thus decomposers. The next most common was *Hydra* (Fig. 6.5), which is a small freshwater polyp and a carnivore; it catches small worms and crustacea by means of the nematocysts on its long tentacles. Finally there were two caddis larvae (Trichoptera); both build nets and feed upon material which is being carried by the water current

6.4 Relative abundance of different species of animals from an area of stony bottom of the Vaal River in South Africa. For further explanation, see text. (Data from Chutter and Nobel).

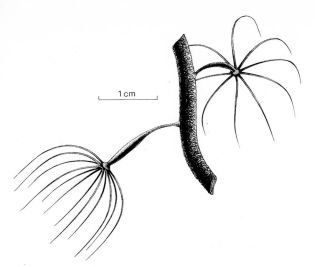

6.5 *Hydra*, a freshwater coelenterate of the Class Hydrozoa, attached to a plant stem. *Hydra* has no medusa stage; the polyp can reproduce asexually by budding, but drought-resistant eggs are also produced by a sexual process. Note the long tentacles. (After Trembley).

(Book 1 Fig. 21.31). One of these is a carnivore; the other is omnivorous but feeds largely upon algal filaments. Thus these six most abundant species include two primary consumers, two carnivores and two decomposers. Each is exploiting a rather different and important resource available within the boundaries of the community.

We have selected this example because the fauna of the streams and rivers of southern Africa is now fairly well known and a complete analysis of this sort can therefore be undertaken. But the result is typical of what is found in all communities. If one limits consideration to one type of animal alone, such as the species of snakes found in a forest area, the same type of hollow curve is obtained (Fig. 6.6). In this example 371 specimens were collected on a cocoa farm in one locality. These belonged to 36 different species. Nevertheless nearly half the specimens belonged to only 5 species and two-thirds to 8 species. 10 species accounted for 73 percent of all specimens caught.

A community of animals thus consists of a number of species, some abundant and some rare, which form a food web based upon the exploitation of an available resource within a limited range of environmental conditions. The species will, however, differ in their tolerances of environmental factors. Those which have narrow tolerances are said to be 'indicators' of the habitats in which they occur; they may either be completely restricted to such habitats or be relatively rare outside them. Thus, for example, the characteristics of temperate lakes, and especially the levels of nutrient salts in the water, can be predicted if the species of the most abundant chironomid midge larva (Diptera) is known. Similarly, distinct water bodies in the seas can often be characterized by the presence of a single 'indicator species' of plankter (Fig. 6.7). The most abundant species,

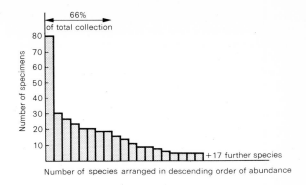

6.6 Relative abundance of 36 different species of snake collected in cocoa farms in eastern Ghana. Just as the relative abundance curve for different species of animal in a single habitat is a hollow curve, so too is the relative abundance of different species of a single taxon in an area offering many different resources. The total number of specimens was 371 and two-thirds of these belonged to eight species. (Data from Leston).

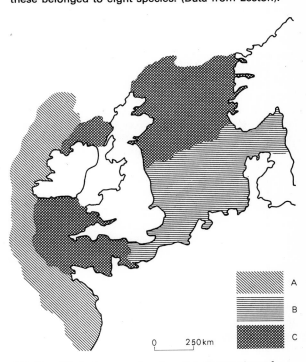

6.7 Simplified diagram showing the distribution of three different species of arrow worm (Book 1 Fig. 20.5) in the sea around the British Isles. The whole area was not surveyed when these data were collected; this is why the sea between England and Ireland has been left blank. Species A is characteristic of the open water of the Atlantic Ocean and is replaced by B in the highly productive water above the continental shelf around the south and east of England. Elsewhere the bottom is deeper and water from the Atlantic and North Sea mix, to produce conditions where a third species, C, becomes the indicator. (Simplified from Bainbridge).

whether of a plant or of an animal community, are not, however, always useful as indicator species since they may also be common in other communities or habitats. Species which are rare within a community are also of little value as indicators because they are likely to be absent from many samples taken even within their range of tolerance.

The dynamics of animal communities

So far we have looked at animal communities as if they were static assemblies of organisms, neglecting both the mobility of animals and the fact that many have alternating periods of activity and inactivity. We obtain a more useful and dynamic concept if we think of an animal community as an assembly or set of animals which together form a food web dependent upon some particular local primary food resources. Such an idea allows for the co-existence within one locality of two largely independent groups of animals, both dependent upon the same ultimate food resource, but exploiting this resource at different times, one being a diurnal community and the other a nocturnal one (Fig. 6.3b). Furthermore, if we regard a primary food resource as being part of the bond uniting the members of a community, we must recognize that some species may be physically present only temporarily, migrating to join the community either at certain times of day or at certain times of year (Fig. 6.3c). Within any one locality some members of the community may be always present while others have a limited seasonal occurrence, so that the structure of the food web also changes during the year.

Changes of these sorts commonly are regular happenings, but other types of change may also occur. The fauna may modify the nature of the primary resources by its own activities, so that there will be a succession of animal communities; other natural agencies, such as fire and prolonged drought, may also modify the composition of the fauna, as may also epidemic disease, the introduction of new species or the extermination of others.

Thus no assembly of animals in a single locality should be regarded as a static structure; a diversity of influences affect it on varying time scales. We will describe some specific examples of these different influences and, where the data are available, examine their further ecological consequences.

Diurnal activity patterns

Let us return to the snakes of the cocoa farm: Table 6.4 presents data relating to the habits of nine common species. You will see that less than half the species are active by day, the others only by night. The snakes on the farm thus belong to two distinct communities—some to a diurnal community, others to a nocturnal one. Even within these we can also regard certain species as being

Table 6.4 Activity times, habitat and food of the common snakes found in a cocoa farm in Ghana (*Data from Leston*)

Habits	Food
Diurnally active species	
Terrestrial species	
Psammophis phillipsii (Olive grass snake)	mammals and lizards
Natriciteres variegatus (Marsh snake)	frogs and toads
Arboreal species	
Dendroaspis viridis (Green mamba)	mammals
Gastropyxis smaragdina (Emerald snake)	lizards, frogs and toads
Nocturnally active species	
Terrestrial species	
Boaedon virgatum (House snake)	mammals
Arboreal species	
Naja melanoleuca (Black cobra)	all vertebrates except snakes
Boiga pulverulenta (Tree snake)	mammals and lizards
Boiga blandingii (Tree snake)	birds and lizards
Causus rhombeatus (Night adder)	frogs and toads

Note that both the tree snakes active in the day are coloured green.

members of a terrestrial community and others of an arboreal community, just as the different species of monkeys in the forest are members of a canopy community, a mid-level community or a lower-level community (p. 67). Thus within this one locality we have in fact several distinct groups, members of largely distinct food webs: to treat them as a unit is to obscure the different biological relations which exist.

Diurnal migratory movements

The existence of distinct diurnal and nocturnal communities is not peculiar to life on land. It is found in aquatic environments as well. Many marine zooplankters (Book 1 p. 234 ff) do not remain at a single depth, but perform a complex diurnal vertical migration: they are found in deep water during the daytime and then actively swim upwards towards the surface layers at sunset, as the light intensity falls (Fig. 6.8). Such migrations are also shown by many deep-sea fish which spend the day at depths of 250 m or more, and then move into the surface waters at night where some feed upon the zooplankton and others upon the smaller fishes. We have, thus, in the sea the strange situation that the area of primary production, the euphotic zone, is invaded every night by primary consumers, as well as by those of higher orders. The complete community which forms the food web of the euphotic zone is not there constantly but only during the hours of darkness. The biological significance of this major migration is far from clear. Perhaps one advantage is that by avoiding the surface layers in daylight both zooplankton and small fish obtain some protection from their predators. Such migrations of zooplankton and of fishes are not limited to the sea: the same type of diurnal migrations of plankton and fishes occur in the African lakes. Thus, for example, one of the small, sardine-like fishes in the Volta Lake in Ghana stays in deep water during the day, but comes to the surface in shoals towards sundown. These shoals then scatter in the surface waters to re-form at first light and sink once more to the bottom.

One method by which the diurnal migration of bony fishes has been studied involves the use of an 'echo-sounder'. This instrument is normally used to determine the depth of water beneath a ship; this is the process called 'sounding'. The instrument makes a brief, strong noise, and an underwater microphone is used to detect the echo of the sound from the sea floor (Fig. 6.9). The deeper the water, the longer the time interval between the start of the noise pulse and the return of its echo. Many bony fishes have a gas bladder lying over the gut (Fig. 6.10 and Book 1 p. 236). One characteristic of this gas bladder is that it will reflect sound waves. If a shoal of fishes passes beneath a boat whose echo-sounder is in operation, the echo-sounder

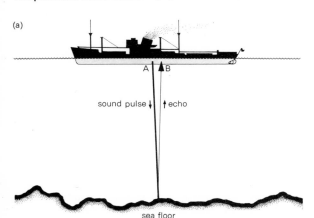

6.8 Diagram showing the relative numbers of a marine copepod at different depths at different times of day. Sunset was at about 2000 hours and dawn about 0400 hours. At noon, the greater part of the population is below 15 m. As light intensity falls, the population rises, spreading out in the surface water at 2100 hours and becoming uniformly distributed at midnight. Towards dawn the population concentrates again near the surface and then moves deeper as light intensity increases. In different places this migration pattern may be modified by temperature gradients in the surface water or by vertical mixing which distributes the zooplankton more uniformly. (After Russell).

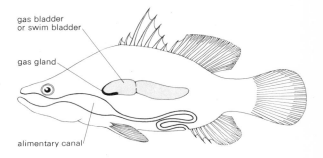

6.10 The gas or swimbladder of a bony fish lies dorsal to the alimentary canal. Details of shape are variable and in some fishes the bladder is connected to the oesophagus by a duct. The gas gland is the organ responsible for secreting gas into the bladder. Not all bony fish have swimbladders. They are absent in fast-moving predators such as mackerel and also in many deep-sea fish.

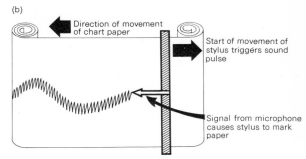

6.9 Principle of echo-sounding. (a) A sound pulse of about 1 ms duration and frequency of about 200 kHz is emitted from A and its echo detected by a microphone at B. The time between the start of the pulse and the return of the echo is a measure of depth. (b) Simplified diagram of recorder. A writing point or stylus is moved downwards across a sheet of recording paper. As the stylus starts to move downwards it triggers off a sound pulse. Pulses are emitted at intervals of about 0·5 s and the stylus takes about 0·1 s to traverse the sheet. The echo detected by the microphone operates an electric circuit which causes the stylus to make a mark on the recording paper. Thus there is a vertical time scale which can be calibrated in depth units. The recording paper is moved forward at a rate of about 5 mm per min so that there is a horizontal 'distance scale'. In this way the profile of the sea floor is drawn. Any shoals of fish below the vessel will also produce echoes which will show, at the appropriate depth, upon the chart.

recording chart will show not only the echo from the bottom but also one from the fish (Fig. 6.11). It is thus possible to follow the vertical migrations of shoals of fish both at sea and in lakes; the technique is also used in commercial fisheries to locate shoals of fishes, so that nets can be lowered to the correct depth to catch the fish and only at such times as there are fish available to be caught.

Such diurnal vertical migrations are not limited to aquatic organisms. They are made also by forest-dwelling mosquitoes (Diptera) which are common near the ground during the day, but which can be seen rising upwards in

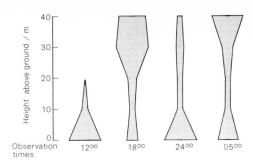

6.12 Diurnal vertical migration of the mosquito *Mansonia fuscopennata* in the Mpanga forest in Uganda as reflected by biting activity at different levels on a tower within the forest and reaching above the canopy. Conventions as in Fig. 4.10. (After Haddow).

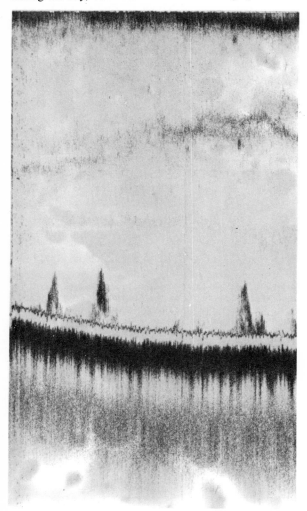

6.11 Record from an echo-sounder showing three shoals of fish. The sea bottom is sloping gently. Note that the recorder is so designed that a clear line is left immediately beneath the record of the bottom. This makes detection of fish shoals resting close to the bottom easier. The trace records the echoes obtained from a depth of about 80 m above the sea floor which was at a depth of about 100 m. The horizontal distance shown is about 1 km. (Courtesy of the Fisheries Research Unit of Ghana).

swarms above the canopy at dusk, probably scattering at night and then aggregating again at dawn before descending to ground level once more. Fig. 6.12 illustrates this movement, biting activity being taken as an index of population density. The significance of this diurnal migration is still not known.

These diurnal vertical migrations are but examples of more familiar phenomena. Cattle Egrets scatter widely to feed during the day, but spend the night in communal roosting places. Similarly fruit bats will emerge from their daytime roosting sites to fly to different trees to feed during the night. Both these animals are only temporary members of the communities in which they find their food.

Seasonal changes

Communities of animals, since they depend upon the resources provided by the producers, will show seasonal changes reflecting changes in the plant communities. One such important change is the annual cycle of wet and dry periods, on which may be imposed differences in temperature and insolation. This will produce a complex seasonal pattern which, in some places, may result in there being more than four annual seasons, a number adequate to describe events in temperate latitudes. Such changes will be especially marked in grass savanna, but occur also in deciduous forest. As a result animal communities may show an annual cycle in species composition. Particular species may occur in the community only at certain times of year (Book 1 Fig. 1.14), or the relative proportions of different species making up the community may alter.

Such changes are illustrated in Fig. 6.13 which shows the relative abundance at different months of the year of the adults of three species of grasshopper (Orthoptera) in shrub savanna. The times of rain are also shown. While adults of all three species do occur during the wetter months, only *Heteropternis* is at all abundant during the

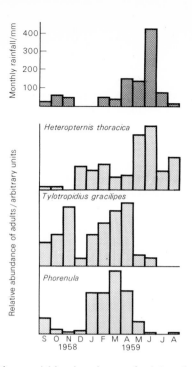

6.13 Relative monthly abundance of adults of three species of grasshopper in shrub savanna near Accra, Ghana. Note that for ease of comparison the data for all three species have been scaled so as to give the same maximal value. To follow the cycle of events, imagine the pattern of rainfall and abundance being repeated on the right hand side of the diagram. The numbers of *Heteropternis* will fall, while those of *Tylotropidius* will immediately increase. (Data from Chapman).

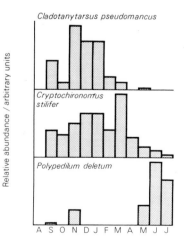

6.14 Relative monthly abundance of larvae of three species of chironomid flies in a small reservoir near Accra. (Unpublished data of S. A. Whyte).

rains of May and June; after the rains *Tylotropidius* becomes common, to be followed much later by *Phorenula*. These data emphasize that there is no simple pattern of high numbers of insects during the rains and low numbers during the dry months; the annual cycles of different species differ from each other, so that the composition of the community changes during the course of a year.

The same sorts of seasonal change in community structure can be seen in ponds and lakes. Fig. 6. 14 shows the relative abundance at different months of the year of three species of chironomid midge larvae (Diptera) in a small reservoir. Each species is most abundant at a different time of year. *Cladotanytarsus* is most common during the hot dry months, *Polypedilum* occurs only during the rainy periods, while *Cryptochironomus* is abundant for the greater part of the year, but relatively scarce during the rainy season. The precise conditions which produce these changes are still being studied. One factor is probably silt: the rains bring much silt into the reservoir as a result of surface run-off from surrounding land, and this may prevent certain species from feeding successfully. Another factor may be the extent of decay of the detritus which is the primary food resource of these larvae. Detritus is carried into the reservoir mainly during the rains. There are indications that while some species can exploit this detritus when it is fresh, others may require that it should have undergone some decay before it can serve as a source of food.

Seasonal migrations

A further factor which may influence the seasonal structure of a community in an area is the migration of animals from one place to another. There are, for example, annual seasonal migrations of many of the larger mammals in East Africa; these correlate with the annual cycle of the rains, so that the animals move from areas where the feeding has become poor to better feeding grounds. Such migrations can be illustrated by the annual cycle of movement of ungulates in the Serengeti National Park, which lies close to the south-east corner of Lake Victoria in Tanzania. With the onset of the rains, there is young growth of grass in the southern plains and there the animals tend to congregate (Fig. 6.15). As the dry season progresses and their food supply becomes exhausted, the zebra move away to the west, to be followed by the wildebeest (Fig. 6.16) and somewhat later by Thomson's gazelle (Book 1 Fig. 16.5a). As the grazing in the west becomes used up, the zebra move into the more northern part of the Park, followed again by the wildebeest, while the tommies later scatter rather more widely. With the return of the rains, all three species move once more to the plains in the south-east. Fig. 6.15 shows the localities of the main aggregations of wildebeest at different seasons of the year.

In this cycle of movement there is a clear feeding relation between the three species. The zebra graze down the upper

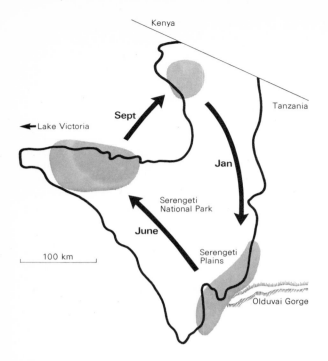

6.15 Sketch map of Serengeti National Park showing the annual cycle of migration of wildebeest from one major feeding ground to another. (After Kruuk from Watson).

6.16 The Blue Wildebeest, *Connochaetes taurinus*. The adult stands between 1·0 and 1·3 m at the shoulder.

parts of the grass shoots to expose the softer leaf-bases which form a significant part of the food of the wildebeest following them (Table 6.5). The grazing of the wildebeest in turn exposes the herb layer beneath the grass and this forms an important fraction of the food taken by the tommies. Thus, not only do the migrations result in the exploitation of resources in different areas, but the feeding activity of one species makes a resource available to another.

Table 6.5 Percentage composition of food assessed from stomach analyses of ungulates in Serengeti National Park (*Data from Gwynne and Bell*)

Species	grass stem	grass sheath	grass leaf	Total grass	di-cotyledons
Zebra (*Equus burchelli*)	51·0	48·7	0·2	99·9	0·1
Wildebeest (*Connochaetes taurinus*)	30·1	52·7	17·2	100·0	0·0
Thomson's gazelle (*Gazella thomsoni*)	20·9	37·5	2·9	61·2	38·8

A second example of such seasonal migration is that of many insectivorous birds which spend the months from September to April in Africa and then fly to Europe where they breed, returning to Africa again the following September. It is estimated that more than 3 000 million birds may be involved in this annual migration which also is connected with the resources available. During the months the birds are in Africa, insects are relatively scarce in the winter conditions of the higher latitudes. When the migrants arrive in Africa, most of them go to the savanna areas south of the Sahara where insects are fairly abundant. During the months which follow, the intertropical convergence zone (I.T.C.Z.) moves southwards, so that rainfall is low to the north of the Equator (p. 42) and it is assumed that insects become less abundant. Whether the migrants also tend to move southwards is not known; they certainly occur further south in forest clearings and in such places insects are plentiful. More research is, however, needed to determine the fate of the majority of the migrants. Our immediate interest lies in the fact that the arrival and departure of these vast numbers of insectivorous birds radically alter the structure of certain animal communities.

Another example of seasonal migration is that of the flying swarms of the Desert Locust, *Schistocerca* (Orthoptera). Fig. 6.17 summarizes the typical annual cycle in West Africa. In early June swarms start to leave the dry lands of North Africa and move south across the Sahara to Niger and Mali where the northward movement of the I.T.C.Z. has brought rains, providing good feeding and

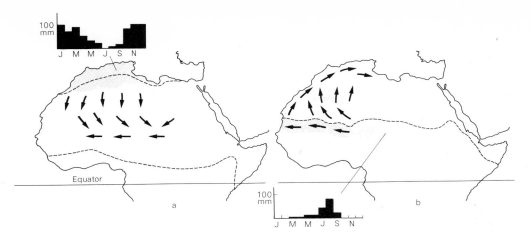

6.17 Pattern of seasonal migrations of the Desert Locust, *Schistocerca*, in West Africa. In both maps broken lines indicate the approximate positions of the 50 mm isohyets (lines of equal mean monthly rainfall) at the times (a) of most southerly movement of the I.T.C.Z. (December–January) and (b) most northerly movement (August). The two small histograms show the typical local annual rainfall patterns in the two breeding areas which are indicated by stippling. From about March onwards swarms start to develop in North Africa and are presently carried southwards by winds blowing towards the I.T.C.Z. which is moving northwards. Breeding occurs in July and August in the northern sudan savanna and new swarms start to develop in September and October; these are carried by a complex pattern of winds back to North Africa where breeding occurs early in the following year. More complex seasonal movements which occur in Arabia and East Africa are not shown. (From various sources).

suitable conditions for reproduction. Later in the year, in October and November, with the onset of the dry season as the I.T.C.Z. moves south, new swarms migrate north again to the better feeding and breeding conditions in North Africa and there they remain until the rains end. In East Africa the annual cycle is more complicated, but the same principle of seasonal migration from one feeding ground to another applies. As with migratory birds, the incursion of large populations of herbivorous insects into an area will affect community structure.

Local migrations

Much more modest migrations into suitable areas can also occur. For example, a weaver bird, the Black-faced Dioch *Quelea* (Fig. 6.18), normally feeds upon fallen grass seeds in East and Central Africa and the sudan savanna belt of West Africa. When the rains start the seeds germinate and are no longer of value as food. The birds may remain in the area for a short time further, feeding on termites, but after that they move across the rain front to new feeding grounds. There is, for example, a favoured feeding area for *Quelea* near Lake Chad. As the I.T.C.Z. moves southwards bringing with it the rains, the birds migrate north to where the grass has grown and set fresh seed; at the same time insects on which the birds can feed have become abundant. The feeding potential of the area, and especially the protein supply, is now at its maximum and the birds breed, moving slowly southwards once more to follow the optimal feeding conditions. Presently the

6.18 The Black-faced Dioch, *Quelea*, one of the many weaver-birds.

grasses shed their seeds and when they die down the birds resume their habit of feeding upon dry seed until the following rains (Fig. 6.19).

Migrations of primary consumers, such as the ungulates in Serengeti National Park and *Quelea* in Chad, reflect movements from one satisfactory feeding locality to another. Local migration of some members of a com-

107

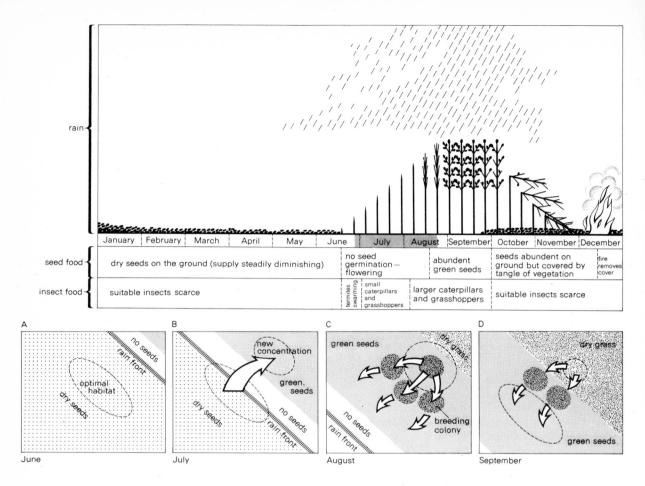

6.19 The migrations of *Quelea*. The upper drawing shows in diagrammatic form the seasonal cycle in an area in the sudan savanna in Chad. During the period indicated by the stippled area immediately below the drawing, local conditions are unsuitable for feeding and the *Quelea* migrate northwards across the rain front. The four lower diagrams show the migration pattern. In June dry seed is still available, but in July as the rains arrive, conditions become unsuitable and the birds migrate northwards across the rain front. In August feeding conditions are optimal, breeding takes place and breeding colonies separate off, following the I.T.C.Z. southwards. By September the birds may have returned to their original locality. They will then continue southwards until fire clears the dry grass and exposes the seeds below: this may lead to a second and subsidiary northward migration. (After Ward).

munity may similarly result in movement of associated higher-order consumers. Fig. 6.20 shows a map of a small region on the shore of Lake Malawi where there was an isolated pocket of the tsetse fly, *Glossina morsitans* (Diptera). During the dry season the fly was limited to certain damp areas near rivers or swamps, but during and after the rainy season it spread out over the grassland. This local migration of the fly probably reflected the local movements of its prey and is not to be interpreted as due to an inability of *G. morsitans* to survive in the exposed grassland during the dry season.

Succession of communities

The food webs in an area may be modified by the activity

of their constituent organisms in such a way as to modify the primary resource and thus make it available to a different community of animals. This we have already seen (p. 105f) in the way in which the grazing activity of zebra changes the environment, making it suitable for wildebeest, while they in turn modify the environment and make it suitable for Thomson's gazelle.

Such changes are especially obvious in some very limited resource such as a fallen log in a forest. When a fresh branch or tree trunk falls to the ground, it is first attacked by the adults of a number of different species of woodboring beetle (Coleoptera). These penetrate the bark and feed upon the phloem. Here they oviposit and their larvae also feed upon phloem. As this attack develops, the holes bored in the bark by the beetles provide an entry for various species of fungus as well as small arthropods such as mites and springtails (Collembola) (Fig. 4.15). These also live upon the phloem. There is thus established a first community whose activity loosens the bark, making the phloem accessible to still more organisms such as larval diptera, many of which feed upon the fungi, as well as various predatory beetles which feed upon the larvae of other beetles. Ants (Hymenoptera) and centipedes (Arthropoda: Chilopoda), although not limited to decaying wood, may also invade the microhabitat.

In time the phloem resource becomes exhausted, but meanwhile the sapwood is being attacked. Early disintegration of the sapwood depends partly upon the fact that certain beetle larvae excavate chambers in the sapwood and

in these they pupate. But other beetles, as well as wood wasps (Hymenoptera), directly attack the sapwood, making it accessible to fungi. With the loosening of the bark, termites (Isoptera) may also be able to establish themselves and exploit the sapwood for food. Analysis of the species of animals present at this stage shows that most of them are different from those found during the earlier stage when phloem was the main resource: there is a new and distinct community associated with the exploitation of the sapwood.

Finally the sapwood is reduced to a pulpy mass, while the bark breaks away. Much of the wood falls to the ground to be attacked further and incorporated into humus, while the heartwood starts to disintegrate as a result of attack by still other species of fungi, making it available to termites and various insect larvae.

The precise course of events in any particular log will be influenced by various factors such as the extent of exposure to sunlight, the rainfall, the species of tree and so forth. But the general pattern of events is always the same. Each community creates conditions which allow the next to establish itself, while the earlier communities die away as the primary resource they were exploiting is exhausted. The whole process must not, however, be thought of as a series of distinct steps, but rather as a continuous event. This changing pattern of communities is a succession but there is no climax, since the resource being exploited is not renewable.

Another example of such a succession is provided by animal dung, which, unlike a fallen branch, is initially uniform in composition. Clearly the precise details of events will vary from one type of dung to another and depend also upon environmental conditions. With cow droppings, females of various species of Diptera are immediately attracted and oviposit on the dung. As the surface dries the species visiting the dung change, so that during the first day or two eggs are deposited by flies of various species. The larvae feed upon the dung and some four or five days later they pupate either in the dung itself or in the neighbouring soil. The burrowing activity of the fly larvae makes openings and galleries within the dung and these provide entry for small, dung-feeding beetles as well as for beetles which feed upon fly maggots. They are joined by small wasps (Hymenoptera) which parasitize the maggots by laying their eggs inside the maggot's body. A community of decomposers, predators and parasitoids is thus established. This community is short-lived. The tunnelling activity of the larvae allows the dung to dry out and within about a week the first community is replaced by a second, composed of other species which have similar trophic relations to the first but are adapted to drier conditions. Finally, as the dung breaks into smaller, drier fragments, still other species of beetle complete the process of decomposition. Here too the action of a community upon the resource it is exploiting modifies the environment and leads to a succession of species.

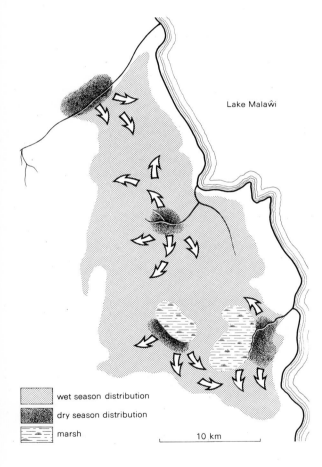

Lake Malaŵi

wet season distribution

dry season distribution

marsh

10 km

6.20 Distribution of the tsetse fly, *Glossina morsitans*, in an isolated pocket on the west shore of Lake Malaŵi. During the wet season the fly is widely distributed (light stipple) but at the height of the dry season is restricted to limited, typically humid areas (dark stipple). The dry-season distribution of the fly may be a reflection of concentration of its prey in moist areas and not of a requirement of the fly for humid conditions. (After Shircore).

Destruction of communities

We have so far considered changes in community structure which involve normal biological processes, even if these, like the destruction caused by a locust swarm, may be catastrophic in their effects. There are, however, other agencies, some natural, some due to human intervention, which may have marked effects upon community structure. One question which has to be considered is how far such events may produce permanent change.

Fire

A common type of major disturbance to the savanna community is grass fires. The passage of a grass fire produces local but transient high temperatures. Using thermocouples placed at different levels in the vegetation it has been found that at the surface of the vegetation temperatures may rise to 600°C but will fall back to normal levels within 6 min. Within tussocks of grass the maximum temperature recorded in one set of experiments was only 65°C, while at 5 mm below the soil surface there was normally only a slight rise in temperature although this might last for as long as 30 min (Fig. 6.21). The picture is different where there is an accumulation of woody litter as prolonged burning of wood will produce a far greater heat flow into the soil, so that even at depths of 3 cm temperatures may rise slowly to about 75°C and then gradually return to normal.

The savanna grasses show adaptations related to the common occurrence of natural grass fires during the dry season (p. 88). What is the effect of such fires upon the fauna? There are two different questions we may ask: firstly, what is the immediate effect of the passage of a fire? and, secondly, what are the effects of annual grass fires upon the numbers and types of animal in the community? The numbers of animals can be expressed as numbers of individuals per unit area and this is usually spoken of as the 'population density'.

The immediate effect of fire on population density depends, of course, upon the type of animal being considered. Birds and many adult insects will fly away, but very many of these insects may be immediately eaten by birds; the sight of glossy starlings catching insects just in front of an advancing line of fire will be familiar to many of you. Small mammals may run before the fire or, if they have burrows, may retreat into shelter until the fire has passed. Within the burrows the temperature will not rise significantly, but the animals do face the hazard of suffocation by smoke. With grass fires there is no evidence that many small mammals are normally killed. Thus, for example, in one plot of about 17 ha in North America, only three dead mammals could be found when the area was carefully surveyed after the passage of a fire. If for some reason the animals are encircled by fire then many may be killed, and there is also good evidence for many deaths when fire moves through woody trash left behind from some types of tree-felling operations.

The effect upon arthropods which cannot fly is very different: there is considerable destruction. For example, in grassland plots studied in Ivory Coast the total weight of arthropods per 100 m² before a fire was 60 g, while after the fire the weight was slightly less than 20 g; that is, the biomass had fallen to one-third. If the total number of animals is considered, we get a rather different answer; the number fell by less than 40 percent (Table 6.6). The two

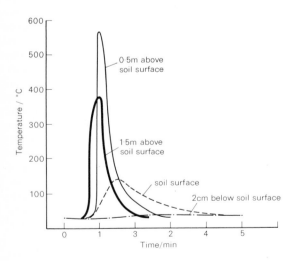

6.21 Temperatures above the soil, at the soil surface and 2 cm below the soil surface during a period of 5 min while a front of fire passed through a stand of dry grass. Temperature at 2 cm below the soil surface increased from an initial value of 33·5°C to a maximum of 37·1°C: in this type of burn even a thin layer of soil is very effective as insulation. (After Pitot and Masson).

Table 6.6 Effect of grass fire upon biomass and numbers of arthropods (100 m⁻²) *(Modified from Gillon)*

	Eve of fire	One day after fire	% reduction	One month after fire
Biomass (g)	60·1	19·5	67·6	19·8
Numbers				
Grasshoppers	135	9	93·3	200
Caterpillars	83	23	72·3	30
Mantids	84	39	53·6	36
Aphids etc	331	11	96·7	17
Large Hemiptera	201	53	73·6	64
Cockroaches	104	86	17·3	29
Arachnids; mostly spiders	1 341	1 273	5·1	533
Total	2 688	1 710	36·4	1 044

Note: These values were obtained by removing all vegetation from sample quadrats of 25 m². The data thus relate to three separate quadrats as the sampling method, while providing very complete data, temporarily destroys the habitat.

results differ because the fire tends especially to kill the larger insects such as the late instars of grasshopper nymphs and caterpillars as well as the bigger Hemiptera. Small, sedentary Hemiptera, like aphids and scales, will also be destroyed. Small active insects such as cockroaches are far less affected and the very small spiders drop to the shelter of grass tussocks or retreat into their burrows as the fire approaches; their loss is also relatively small.

Recovery from the effects of fire will depend on the characteristics of the area burnt. In grassland, natural fires are frequent and recovery may be fairly rapid. Large numbers of insects which had previously depended upon the litter for food will be re-established only when fresh litter becomes available during the following dry season. On the other hand actively moving herbivores, like grasshoppers, will rapidly repopulate the area to exploit the new growth of grass. Nevertheless, field trials in Ivory Coast showed that even after a year the grassland arthropod fauna had not fully recovered its numbers compared with that in an unburnt control area (Fig. 6.22). If, however, the area does not burn every year, the population will recover completely.

Regular annual burning of grassland previously exposed to less regular fires will change the habitat and affect the fauna. Repeated destruction of litter leads to a fall in the water-retaining capacity of the soil and, as a result, such areas become very dry in the period before the rains. This has been shown to affect the population of small mammals. In such areas in Ivory Coast there was a sharp fall in rodent numbers towards the end of the dry season before the grass was burnt. Numbers in protected grassland did not show such a decrease; in some places there was an actual increase in population density as a result of immigration. There are, moreover, indications that insects tolerant of drier conditions are more common in grassland subjected to regular annual burning than in areas where fires are less frequent.

Where fires are a relatively rare event, recovery may be much slower. There is evidence from such an area in America that many of the small mammals driven out by the fire soon returned to the burnt area. In the experimental plots a large number were trapped alive before the fire was started. Each rodent had a small piece of tissue punched out of the pinna of one ear so that it could be recognized again; it was then released. Trapping in the burnt area four months after the fire resulted in the recapture of many of these marked animals. The rate of recovery of the population depended upon the type of habitat. In grassland, the population had nearly returned to its previous density in less than a year; in macchia, where the covering of bushes had been destroyed, recovery was much slower and the population density was still below that of control plots even after two and a half years.

A similar slow recovery has been observed for an isolated population of *Glossina* on the shore of Lake Victoria. An accidental fire destroyed large numbers of trees and shrubs, thus reducing the shade available for the flies. During the 10 months before the fire the population of the area was very similar in numbers to that in a comparable control area. In the following 10 months the population in the control area doubled, but that of the area exposed to fire fell by 50 percent. Even 17 months after the fire there was no indication of a complete recovery of the population.

The effects of fire upon animal communities thus depend upon local circumstances. Where there is already a fire climax, the passage of a fire can be regarded as a normal event which, like the changes between wet and dry seasons, produces effects from which the fauna regularly and rapidly recovers; indeed, the life cycles of some members of the fauna relate to this annual cycle (p. 77). On the other hand, where fire is a rare 'accident', recovery may be far more protracted.

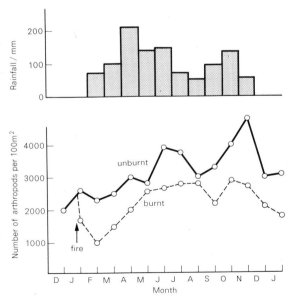

6.22 Values for the total number of arthropods collected from burnt and unburnt sample plots in Ivory Coast. Note that the total population of the unburnt plot remains consistently greater; the burnt plots do not show the same increase in population after the October rains as do the unburnt plots: the relative scarcity of litter offers less protection from desiccation to the surface-living and soil arthropods. (After Gillon).

Drought

The community in any area may also be affected by irregular, unpredictable changes in rainfall and we may ask whether this type of event produces any permanent change in the fauna. One closely studied example was the total drying out of Lake Chilwa in Malaŵi during the dry season of 1968. The lake is normally filled from a limited

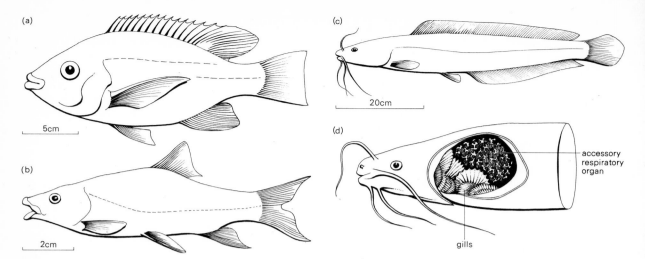

6.23 Outline sketches of (a) *Tilapia* (b) *Barbus* and (c) *Clarias*. *Clarias* has an accessory respiratory organ within the opercular cavity. This is shown in (d) where the operculum has been cut away to show the gills and accessory organ. This structure allows the catfish to respire in air and may be one reason why it was able to survive the drought in Lake Chilwa longer than the other two species of fish.

catchment area of about 30 000 km² and has no outflowing river. As a result the water is slightly saline, equivalent to about 0·05 percent sodium chloride solution, that is about 10 times the salt concentration normally found in freshwater. Chilwa is a shallow lake, the depth being usually no more than 3 m, but it produces a considerable quantity of fish, nearly 10 000 tonnes being landed in a good year. This catch is of three species only (Fig. 6.23): a *Tilapia* species found only in this and an adjoining lake, the common catfish, *Clarias*, and a small minnow, *Barbus*. As the water receded there was heavy fish mortality in the lake until only some catfishes survived, and even these were killed when the lake finally dried out completely.

What were the effects of this disaster upon the fauna and flora of the lake? To comprehend the events which followed refilling of the lake, it is necessary first to look at the water composition. The first filling came directly from the rains which fell into the lake basin. Subsequently more water was added by the rivers as well as by run-off from the land. The water falling directly into the lake became saline since salt had remained when the lake dried out. The water entering as run-off or from the rivers had a far lower salt content. The two water masses, being of different density, did not mix. Thus shortly after the lake filled there was a central region of saline water surrounded by a ring of freshwater (Fig. 6.24). Subsequently, when the rains ceased, mixing occurred and the original uniform, slightly hypersaline condition was re-established.

After filling, planktonic organisms rapidly reappeared in both the central and peripheral zones. Among the phytoplankton the first to appear was the blue-green alga *Oscillatoria* (Book 1 Fig. 17.7c), which is able to resist desiccation. This was followed by the establishment of a

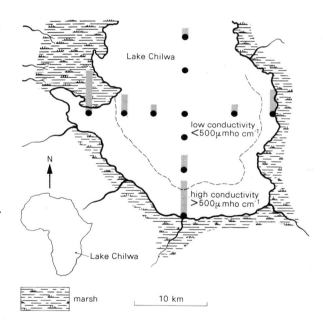

6.24 The southern section of Lake Chilwa, Malaŵi. The lake is surrounded by swamp and the inflowing rivers are shown. There is no drainage. When the lake refilled after drying completely in 1968, a central saline area and a peripheral ring of freshwater formed. The broken line indicates the approximate boundary between the two water masses. As the lake was recolonized, there was a great increase in bottom fauna in the peripheral zone. The black circles indicate positions of sampling stations for bottom fauna. The vertical bars are proportional to the biomass of animals per m². Where there is no bar, no animals were found in the bottom deposit. (After McLachlan).

diverse flora, mainly in the peripheral areas. Most of the new phytoplankton entered the lake from the rivers and in run-off waters; it differed markedly from the original phytoplankton which had been dominated by blue-green algae. Zooplankton reappeared within ten weeks and, like the phytoplankton, was less abundant in the central region.

The bottom fauna showed a very similar pattern of change. About ten weeks after the start of the rains, the fauna began to reappear and within a fortnight the weight of bottom-living animals increased from 1 mg m^{-2} to 4 000 mg m^{-2}. This rapid increase in the population was limited to the periphery (Fig. 16.23) and here the fauna was composed almost entirely of one species of midge larva. When, however, the two water masses mixed, this midge larva disappeared from the bottom fauna.

As far as the fish were concerned, *Clarias* was being caught within one month of the rains and the 1969 commercial landings were equal to those of 1966 and 1967. *Barbus* took longer to re-establish itself and *Tilapia* was slower still. As the lake had dried out some of these fish had retreated into swampy lagoons and also into the rivers where they remained in pools when the flow of water ceased. They were thus able to re-invade the lake area once the water returned. During the initial months after refilling certain species of fish normally restricted to the swamps and rivers appeared in the peripheral, low-salinity areas and then, once water mixing had taken place, disappeared again.

It is clear that, following the catastrophe, the previously existing community very rapidly re-established itself from the surrounding swamps and rivers, but there was a transient invasion of other species which were able to exploit the exceptional situation of an extensive, low-salinity, peripheral water mass.

The potential of organisms to re-invade an area following a natural disaster is shown graphically by the events which followed the destruction of all life on the island of Krakatau (p. 8). After the major volcanic eruption of 1883 the island communities were slowly re-established by invasion from Java and Sumatra. After 25 years there were more than 200 different species of animal present. After 50 years there were more than 700 species of insect, 6 reptiles, 4 mammals and about 30 species of resident birds, and much of the island was covered by a young forest. Despite its isolation from the nearest land by a strait about 40 km across, a fauna as well as a flora was gradually re-established (Fig. 6.25).

After a major disaster re-establishment of a community normally takes place by invasion from surrounding areas. But the speed and extent of this depends upon the nature of the primary producers. In a lake the phytoplankton will recover very rapidly, and the marginal vegetation slightly less rapidly. But if an area of forest is totally destroyed by fire, the damage may take many, many years to be made good. Thus the extent to which a community will suffer as a consequence of an irregular disaster

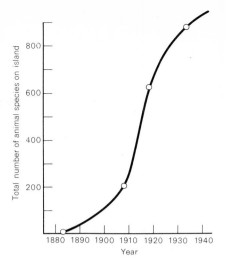

6.25 Graph showing the rate of recolonization of the island of Krakatau with animals. (Data from various sources).

is dependent upon the nature of that community, and no valuable quantitative generalizations can be made.

Modifications of communities by invasion

The changes in community structure which we have so far considered all relate to species of plants and animals which have existed in the area for a very long time, even though their local distribution may have changed. A further change can occur in which a community is modified by the invasion of a species from outside. The weed *Tridax* was introduced to West Africa only half a century ago (p. 1); it is now so abundant that it must have considerably reduced the proportion of earlier-established species in weed communities. Similarly the arrival of the Argentine Ant in the Cape of Good Hope peninsula at about the beginning of the century has resulted in the extermination locally of most species of indigenous ants (p. 273). It is, however, possible that the Indian Myna bird which was introduced into Natal has had little or no effect upon the local fauna as it has remained strictly limited in its distribution to the larger towns, its populations increasing as the towns themselves have grown. The niche which it now fills in cities such as Durban may have originally been occupied by an indigenous species, but we have no records of the situation before the myna was introduced. It has also been suggested that introduction of trout into the cold mountain streams of Natal resulted in a drastic reduction in numbers of one species of *Barbus* and the total extermination of a small minnow. This was attributed to the carnivorous habits of the trout which were considered to have destroyed the fry

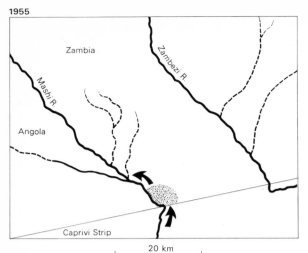

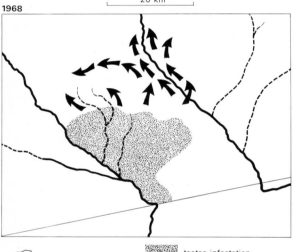

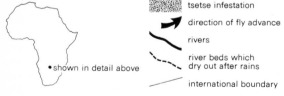

tsetse infestation

direction of fly advance

rivers

river beds which dry out after rains

international boundary

• shown in detail above

6.26 Sketch maps showing the invasion of Zambia by tsetse fly from the Caprivi Strip in 1955 and its subsequent spread across to the Zambesi River. Note that there are no data on events to the west of the Mashi River as this area is in Angola. (After Park *et al.*).

of the endemic species. Recent studies suggest however that the disappearance of both the native species of fish was due to other causes which modified the quality of the rivers in which the animals had lived.

It sometimes happens that the population density of an animal in one locality increases and, as a result, the species spreads into neighbouring areas which it has not previously colonized. Such an event is illustrated in Fig. 6.26,

which records an invasion of *Glossina morsitans* from the Caprivi Strip into Zambia. There are no data on events in the Caprivi Strip or in Angola, but detailed studies were made in Zambia, since the invasion of the fly was a potential threat to the cattle-raising industry to the east of the Zambesi. The initial invasion followed the course of the Mashi River and then spread north-eastwards into suitable savanna country to reach and cross the Zambesi. While the incursion of a high-order predator such as *Glossina* may not greatly modify the patterns of food chains in the newly occupied territory, it is an event of considerable practical importance for man.

Invasion by new species may also follow changes in the environment which are due to human activity. Fig. 6.27 shows the spread of breeding colonies of the Cattle Egret in the south-west of the Cape Province of South Africa since the beginning of the century. Originally confined to four isolated localities, the bird has become widely distributed during the past 65 years. There is reason to believe that this is partly a consequence of more land being opened up for cattle ranching: the common association between these birds and cattle will be familiar (p. 209). It has probably also been aided by the construction of large numbers of small dams which provide the bird with the water it requires. We are in fact observing a consequence of a major change in environmental quality as a result of agricultural activity: the primary resource within the locality has been artificially altered. The invasion of the Cattle Egret is one well-documented example of the many changes in community structure which can follow from man's ability to alter the environment.

Modifications of communities by disease and extermination

Spread of one organism is frequently accompanied by reductions in the populations of others. If the organism causes a fatal disease in a common animal which has little or no immunity, an epidemic may well develop, resulting in a drastic fall in numbers of the host. If the species concerned is a dominant member of the community, a long-lasting fall in its numbers may have considerable effects on the whole ecosystem.

Fig. 6.28 records events associated with such an epidemic in the northern part of the Orange Free State during the years 1940 to 1942. The victim was a gerbil, *Tatera brantsi* (Fig. 6.29), a small rat-like rodent which lives in groups in burrows and feeds mainly on bulbs, grasses and seeds. When its numbers are high, it can do serious damage to grain crops, but it is also important because it is susceptible to plague and can act as a source of infection for man. This plague epidemic among the gerbils spread rapidly through the local population so that by early 1941 none was recorded. Fig. 6.28 shows that subsequent recovery failed to re-establish the population to its former density. *Tatera* is not only a significant primary consumer,

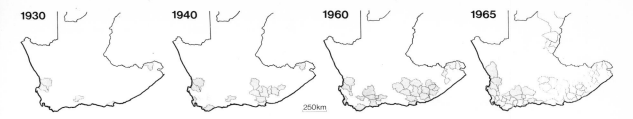

1930 **1940** **1960** **1965**

250km

6.27 The spread of Cattle Egret in the Cape Province of South Africa. The map shows outlines of administrative districts in which cattle egret were reported to have been established (a) up to 1930, (b) up to 1940, (c) up to 1960 and (d) in 1965. Note the steady increase in the bird's range over the 35 years. (After Siegfried).

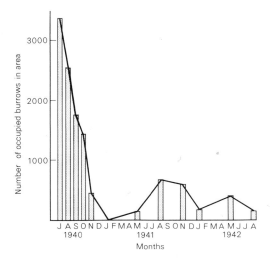

6.28 Data on the relative abundance of gerbils in an area of about 300 km² in the northern Orange Free State during and after a plague epidemic in the population. Population density was assessed by determining the number of burrows occupied at any time. When the population recovered, it occupied only about one-fifth of the total area. (After Davis).

6.29 A female and young of the gerbil, *Tatera brantsi*. Note the reduced front legs. Length of adult, excluding tail, is about 12 cm.

but also prey for carnivores. Such a reduction in its numbers is likely to have had secondary effects, but these were not studied.

We do, however, know a great deal about events in England which followed a comparable massive destruction by disease of a primary consumer, namely the European rabbit, *Oryctolagus cuniculus*. This animal had always been abundant and was both prey for many wild carnivorous birds and mammals and a source of relatively cheap meat as well as of fur. In 1953 a highly destructive virus disease of rabbits called myxomatosis became established in England, so that within a few years the population of rabbits was reduced to a small fraction of its former size. This affected many areas where intensive grazing by rabbits had previously kept grass short and prevented shrubs from establishing themselves. Some wild flowers which had formerly been rare now became common, while tree seedlings were able to survive so that open grassland started to turn to scrub woodland. In some places the nesting sites of ground-nesting birds were rendered unsuitable by the vigorous growth of coarse grasses. The carnivores were also affected: among the mammals, the numbers of the small carnivorous stoats fell while foxes and weasels, also small carnivores, took as prey far larger numbers of a small rodent, the vole. The buzzard, a bird, also killed more voles than before. The ecological consequences of the destruction of a dominant primary consumer can thus be very far-reaching.

The spread of agriculture with the growth of human populations results in the destruction of many former communities and their replacement by new and very different forms of life. But another aspect of human activity also affects community structure.

Two events in the history of Europe have had profound effects upon the rest of the world. One was the invention of firearms, giving man far greater powers of killing animals than before; the second, advances in navigational science which allowed white men to sail all over the world. As a result of these, man has completely exterminated a very considerable number of species of animal over the last few hundred years. The limited faunas of islands have been especially affected. The harmless, flightless dodo (Fig. 6.30) which lived only on the island of Mauritius was wiped

115

6.30 A drawing of the dodo as reconstructed on the basis of fragmentary remains and travellers' reports. No complete specimen exists. The bird stood about 1 m high.

out, partly by European sailors, partly because pigs, brought to the island by the sailors, destroyed the dodos' eggs. The last specimen was killed nearly 300 years ago. Similarly, Dutch settlers in the Cape exterminated two species of antelope as well as the quagga, a close relative of the zebra. Today there are more than 20 species of African mammal whose numbers have been so reduced as a result of hunting and of agriculture that they too may well become extinct. Some indeed now remain only in national reserves.

The ecological results of past events of this type cannot be fully known, since those responsible for the extermination of these species were little interested in the wider consequences of their actions. The total destruction of animal or plant species by human activity does however have possible implications for the future and these we will consider later (p. 371).

Communities of plants and animals

If you go to a village and ask the people who live there what they do, you will probably find that many are farmers but that some may be specialists in making beads, mending motor cars, working in leather, teaching the young children and so on. In another village some 50 or 100 km away, the pattern will be repeated. Sociologists would describe each of these villages as a community and within each village community the things which people do are very similar. Nevertheless the people may be different; they may belong to different tribes, wear different clothes, have different customs, speak different languages.

What is true of village communities is true also of communities of plants and animals. As you move from one area of shrub savanna to another the general appearance of the one closely resembles that of the next. Plants with the same life-forms occur; primary consumers such as grasshoppers and caterpillars are both present; secondary consumers like small mammals, lizards and insectivorous birds are always to be found. But the actual species of plants, insects and vertebrates may be different.

The same situation is to be found upon rocky shores. Whichever rocky shore you visit, there you will find encrusting algae, limpets and barnacles. Once again, as with the shrub savanna, the species may be different but the types of organism which make up the community are the same. This pattern repeats itself on a far wider scale. The types of organism which form the rocky shore communities of subtropical America and Australia are broadly similar to those of Africa but again different in detail. So, like the villages, communities within any biome are the same and yet also may be different.

Within the village different individuals may do different sorts of work, with the farmers being the dominant members of the community. We can see a rough parallel to this in, say, the rain forest. Trees are the dominant members of the community, but the vegetation of the different synusiae, the epiphytes upon the trees, the shrubs, herbs and mosses may be regarded as having different types of employment within the forest. To suit their 'employment' they will have different life-forms.

The concept of niche

We can make this idea more objective by replacing the word 'employment', which relates only to human societies, by the word 'niche'. The forest, from its dominant structural component of tall trees, provides a variety of 'niches' which can be occupied by other types of plant, each making use of the environmental resources provided by or beneath the trees. Almost all higher plants require some type of surface as a resource so that they may be anchored; they need some space as a resource so that they may spread their leaves to photosynthesize. Within the forest there is a large number of different types of 'space', characterized more especially by differences in light intensity, water supply and humidity. As a result there is a large number of distinct niches available within the forest, and exploiting the resources of these niches are different species of plants whose life-forms are adapted for survival and growth in the circumstances characteristic of each particular niche.

This idea allows us to understand why there is a broad similarity between the life-forms of the plants to be found in the rain forest, whether it be in New Guinea, the Congo basin or the basin of the Amazon in South America. In each case the high trees provide a set of closely similar niches occupied by plants with similar life-forms.

We can extend this idea to other biomes, although as conditions, especially of water supply, become less favourable, the number of available niches becomes fewer since the plants themselves are more stunted and the ground layer more exposed.

The niches of consumers

The concept of 'niche' as being some set of environmental resources open to exploitation is applicable to consumers as well. Clearly one essential resource for any consumer is food, but others such as shelter and suitable conditions for reproduction are equally important. The diversity of plant forms provides a diversity of food sources, as well as a diversity of places, microhabitats for the smaller invertebrates, which different animal species may exploit. In different places similar plant communities will offer a set of similar niches to the consumers, and animals of broadly similar structure and habit will occupy the same sort of niche wherever it may occur.

Thus, for example, the surfaces of rocky shores provide a suitable niche for the growth of encrusting algae; encrusting algae are a food resource which provides one aspect of a niche characteristically filled by limpets. Whether the shore is on the Atlantic or the Indian Ocean, the basic environmental features are the same, offering similar niches and thus the pattern of plant and animal life-forms repeats.

At the other extreme the same is true of deserts. In the warm deserts of both North America and South-west Africa the vegetation is dominated by succulents of very similar life-form, while the desert animals of both continents have many functional characteristics in common: thus in both there are species of snake, taxonomically very distinct, which nevertheless show 'side-winding', a specialized pattern of locomotion suitable for movement across sand, while the long-legged jerboas (Fig. 4.20) of Africa are paralleled by the kangaroo rats of America (Fig. 6.31).

Perhaps most striking is the way in which the marsupial fauna of Australia includes species which are broadly similar to those of eutherian mammals of other continents. The most familiar marsupials, the kangaroos (Book 1 Fig. 18.74), are very distinct, but there are many others whose appearance and ways of life have led to their being called marsupial mice and rats, shrews and moles, squirrels, cats and wolves. In other words, most marsupials in Australia occupy closely similar niches to some of the eutherian mammals elsewhere and, correlated with this, they have similar life-forms.

The origins of the differences

We can in this way comprehend the structure of different communities and the reasons for the similarities between communities in comparable biomes in different parts of the world. We must now consider the differences, corresponding to the fact that the people of one village have one set of agricultural practices and those of another village some distance away a different set.

Let us imagine that we are standing at the southern end of Lake Mweru. If we move in a southerly direction across Zambia nearly to Lake Kariba, we will travel through about 600 km of almost unbroken savanna woodland. If we sample the plant communities at the northern end of this line and compare them with those at the southern end, we find that while some species occur in both localities, others are found in one and not in another. As we go southward, conditions become more arid and mean temperatures during the dry season lower. Thus at the two ends of the line across a single biome, environmental conditions are somewhat different; correspondingly, some species can survive only towards one end of the line and some only nearer the other, though some, of broader tolerance, occur at both ends.

The same type of gradation of species composition may be recognized in the limpets around the southern coast of the continent (Fig. 6.32). At Port Nolloth on the west coast there are seven species; at East London on the east coast there are eight. Three species occur in both localities but the others are different and one of the three widely distributed species is absent further east near Durban. These changes partly correlate with changing temperature of the seawater; as we travel east species which thrive in cooler water are replaced by those requiring higher temperatures for growth and survival. We shall presently see

6.31 The Kangaroo Rat, *Dipodomys*, which occurs in deserts in the United States, looks very similar to the jerboa (Fig. 4.20) found in the arid areas of Africa. Nevertheless they are very different in detailed anatomy and belong to different families of the **order Rodentia**. Length of the adult, excluding the tail, is about 15 cm.

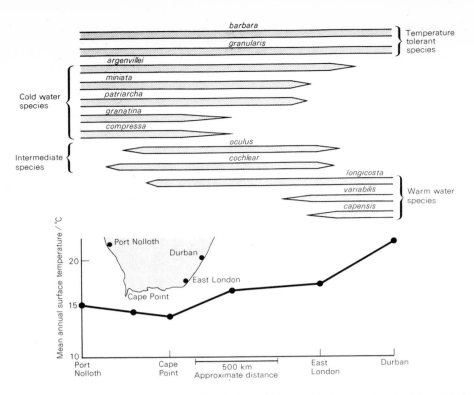

6.32 Distribution of various species of the limpet, *Patella* (Book 1 Fig. 20.9b), on rocky shores along the southern coast of Africa. The distribution is discontinuous as rocky shores are separated by long stretches of sandy beach. Note that the limpets include species limited to colder waters, others limited to warm waters, some which have a wide range of temperature tolerance and others which are unable to survive at either end of the coast line studied. (After Stephenson).

(p. 272) how some of these different species of limpet have in fact distinct niches where they occur together on the rocky shore.

In both these instances there is a relatively gradual change in environmental conditions, so that the changes in species composition are gradual. If the changes in environmental conditions are more abrupt – for example, if the nature of the rock formation from which the soil is derived changes—then we shall have correspondingly sharp changes in the flora and, with these, of the fauna. We may perhaps pass from one biome to another. This is what we would find if we travelled north-west from Lake Mweru until we came to the Congo forest.

Within Africa as a whole we find another phenomenon. The northern sudan savanna is a similar biome to that of parts of Botswana and Namibia, but the species which form the communities are very different. The two areas are separated by a barrier of the moist savannas. On a larger scale this is true also of the Congo and Amazonian forests separated by the barrier of the Atlantic Ocean: they are similar biomes and have very similar structure in terms of life-forms, but the species which build up their communities are different. To comprehend this situation, we have to understand the past history of the organisms, a matter which we shall discuss much later (p. 485).

We may thus recognize a community as being a set of organisms exploiting locally available resources: some of these are provided by the soil or water; some by the members of the community itself. The generally prevailing environmental conditions will determine the life-forms of the dominant producers and these provide the further niches exploited by smaller or less abundant forms of plants. The resulting set of producers provides in turn niches for primary consumers and these for higher-order consumers.

Three factors modify this picture. Firstly, in an extensive community there will be environmental gradients from one part of the community to another; this will lead to changing species composition along the gradient. Even where communities are discontinuous, like those on rocky shores separated by long stretches of sandy beach, the same effect can be seen. Secondly, the organisms within the community interact, adding greater complexity to the whole. Finally, the interactions between the community and the inorganic world around it as well as between members of the community may change the community itself so that there will be a 'succession' until an equilibrium, the 'climax community', is reached.

The understanding of the processes of natural change within communities, whether these variations be diurnal, seasonal, or on a longer time span, is of practical importance. Unless these are known erroneous conclusions may easily be drawn as to the effects of human interference upon communities. If man is to 'manage' the world to meet his immediate needs for food and his equally important need, once adequately fed, for relaxation, then he must comprehend communities and their dynamics: ignorance can lead, as it has in the past, to grand schemes turning to total failures.

Problems

1 Certain species of plant or animal are regarded as useful indicators of particular communities within a biome. What would you expect to be the characteristics of those species which are especially useful for this purpose?
2 Experiments on the effects of fire on rodent populations in the United States are described on p. 111. It is suggested that one effect of fire is that small rodents are more exposed to predation when their cover is destroyed. Is the slower recovery of the population in macchia than in grassland in keeping with this suggestion? Explain your reasoning.
3 The succession of animals in a rotting log and in cow dung is described (p. 108f). To which trophic category would you assign these animals? Describe how you would attempt to study the succession of insects in cow dung.
4 It is suggested (p. 117) that there is a relation between sea temperature and the particular species of *Patella* found on rocky shores at different places around the south coast of Africa. Do the results shown in Fig. 6.31 constitute evidence in favour of this suggestion? If temperature is indeed a major factor determining the distribution of a species of *Patella*, does it follow that temperature is directly affecting the species? What alternative hypothesis can you suggest which might lead to the same observed result? How would you attempt to distinguish between these hypotheses? Can they both be valid?
5 Fig. 6.24 records an invasion of Zambia by *Glossina morsitans* from the Caprivi Strip. It is suggested that this may have been due to an increase in the population density of fly to the south-west of Zambia. Suggest an alternative hypothesis which might account for the movement of the fly.
6 A zoologist compared the faunas of two similar biomes, one in tropical Africa and one in tropical America. He found that in many cases he could 'pair' two species, one from each area, as having closely similar adapta-

tions. With other species, such 'pairing' was not possible. When he examined the data he found that the proportion of 'pairs' was greater with first-order consumers than with second-order consumers, and that for second-order consumers greater than that for third-order consumers. Suggest an hypothesis which might account for this observation.

Bibliography

Further Reading

Buchsbaum, R., Buchsbaum, M.   *Basic Ecology*, Boxwood Press, 1964, Chaps. 4, 5 and 6

Elton, C. S.   *The Ecology of Invasions by Animals and Plants*, Methuen, 1958

Kormondy, E. J.   *Concepts of Ecology*, Prentice-Hall, 1969, Chap. 5

MacArthur, R., Connell, J.   *The Biology of Populations*, Wiley, 1966, Chap. 7

Odum, E. P.   *Ecology*, Holt, Rinehart and Winston, 1963, Chaps. 5 and 6

Whittaker, R. H.   *Communities and Ecosystems*, Collier-Macmillan, 1970, Chap. 3

Ziswiler, V.   *Extinct and Vanishing Animals*, Longman, 1967, Chaps. 3 and 4

Bell, R. H. V.   'A Grazing Ecosystem in the Serengeti', *Scientific American*, 1971, Offprint no. 1228

Cooper, C. F.   'The Ecology of Fire', *Scientific American*, 1961, Offprint no. 1099

Dietz, R. S.   'The Sea's Deep Scattering Layers', *Scientific American*, 1962, Offprint no. 866

Gans, C.   'How Snakes Move', *Scientific American*, 1970, Offprint no. 1180

Johnson, C. G.   'The Aerial Migration of Insects', *Scientific American*, 1963, Offprint no. 173

Marples, M.   'Life on the Human Skin', *Scientific American*, 1969, Offprint no. 1132

7 Communities—decomposers and the soil

In our discussions of both biomes and communities we have emphasized especially those organisms which on land live on or above the surface of the soil, and in the seas or freshwaters live either in the water or on the surface of the rocks or muds. We now turn to consider the soil organisms. The bottom deposits of the seas and lakes, like the soil on land, are of prime importance in the processes of decomposition, but we will not elaborate upon their biology here, partly because they are less easily observed than terrestrial soils, partly because they have been less intensively studied.

Onto the surface of the soil fall dead vegetation, the bodies of dead animals and the excreta of living ones. Here the process of decomposition starts. Soluble materials may get washed into the soil by light rains, while vegetable litter is also carried mechanically down into the soil by the activities of some of the large soil animals such as ants, termites and earthworms, there to be decomposed by bacteria, fungi and smaller animals. The soil also contains living roots of surface-growing plants which remove mineral salts liberated during decomposition.

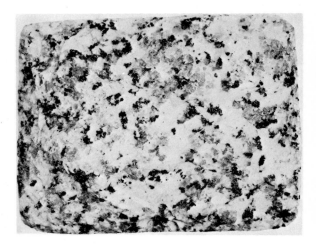

7.1 Polished slab of granite rock. The white crystals are felspar, the glassy crystals are quartz and the dark crystals are hornblende and biotite.

The origin and composition of soil

We must first consider whence comes the soil in which these processes of decomposition occur, and how these processes in turn affect the soil.

Inorganic substances in soil

By far the greatest part of most soils consists of inorganic particles derived from the weathering of rocks. In some places, such as mountains and deserts, rock is exposed at the surface and is thus subject to the slow processes of physical weathering. Rocks warmed in the sun may cool rapidly after sunset and as a result they may crack. Such weakened rock then becomes susceptible to the weathering effect of water which, penetrating into the cracks, will tend to enlarge them, carrying away the smaller particles. But in most places rocks are already covered by a layer of soil, and have been so covered for many millions of years. Consequently present-day weathering, which is of most interest to us, must take place below this soil mantle. In these conditions weathering is brought about by chemical action, and is more rapid. The most important weathering agents are downward-percolating water and, in shallow soil, plant roots. The soil atmosphere is rich in carbon dioxide, which dissolves in water to give a weak solution of carbonic acid; other weak acids enter the soil solution as products of decomposition, and as solutions of nitrogen and sulphur oxides removed from the atmosphere by rain. Soil water causes the slow disintegration of rocks with which it comes in contact.

Any rock consists of a characteristic mixture of chemical compounds known as minerals, and these may differ in their resistance to chemical weathering. For example granite (Fig. 7.1) consists of crystals of a great variety of minerals (Table 7.1), the most abundant being quartz and varieties of felspar and mica. Felspars and micas are both aluminium silicates, but crystals of the former are hard whereas those of the latter are readily split into thin flakes. In addition to aluminium, silicon and oxygen, felspars contain various proportions of sodium and potassium, or of calcium and sodium; micas contain potassium and sometimes iron and magnesium also. Quartz is simply silicon dioxide, SiO_2; it is very resistant to weathering, and in soil derived from weathered granite it persists as grains

Table 7.1 Composition and properties of the principal minerals occurring in granite. Elements separated in a formula by a comma can replace each other in any proportion in the crystal structure. Percentages given are for average proportions; individual granites may depart widely from these (*Data from Holmes, and Ahn*)

Mineral	Chemical formula	Appearance	Resistance to weathering	Average percentage in granite
Quartz	SiO_2	glassy crystals, fracture irregular	very resistant	31
Muscovite (white mica)	$KAl_2(AlSi_3O_{10})(OH,F)_2$	thin transparent flakes	fairly resistant	
Biotite (black mica)	$K(Mg,Fe)_3(AlSi_3O_{10})(OH,F)_2$	thin blackish flakes	fairly resistant	12
Potassium felspar	$K(AlSi_3)O_8$	pinkish rhomboidal crystals	fairly resistant	
Sodium felspar	$Na(AlSi_3)O_8$	whitish rhomboidal crystals	not very resistant	52
Calcium felspar	$Ca(Al_2Si_2)O_8$	whitish rhomboidal crystals	easily weathered	
Hornblende	$NaAlCa_2(Mg,Fe)_4(Al_2Si_6)O_{22}(OH)_2$	dark rhomboidal crystals	not very resistant	2
Iron oxides	Fe_2O_3 or Fe_3O_4	black crystals	easily weathered	2
Other minerals	—	—	—	1

of sand and quartz pebbles. Felspars and micas are much less resistant, and the products of their weathering undergo complex changes eventually to form clay minerals; some free cations are liberated in the process.

Clay minerals form flat crystals (Fig. 7.2), rather resembling those of mica, but very much smaller. As they seldom exceed 1 μm in diameter, they can be seen adequately only under the electron microscope. The most abundant is kaolinite, in which negative charges which can attract cations are restricted to the edges of the crystals. Montmorillonite, which is formed in relatively dry climatic conditions from rocks which are rich in divalent metallic elements, can attract cations to positions within its crystals as well as to crystal edges; largely for this reason, it has a much higher cation-exchange capacity than kaolinite (Book 1 p. 78). In tropical conditions, much of the clay becomes cemented into silt-sized particles.

The end-result of weathering of granite is thus a loamy soil with sand grains scattered in a silt and clay matrix. Many metallic elements may be abundant, because they are liberated from the rock minerals by weathering; these include sodium, potassium, calcium, magnesium, iron and aluminium. Weathering of a sandstone will involve simply the weathering of the cement which bound the grains in the rock; the resulting soil will be mainly sand and relatively poor in inorganic nutrients. In general, the nature of the soil depends largely on the nature of the underlying rocks. Alluvial soils are an obvious exception, as they are

7.2 Crystals of the clay mineral kaolinite as seen under the electron microscope. The crystals are flat, thin and usually six-sided.

derived from material which has been transported and are not directly related to the rocks underlying them.

Humus

While the sand and clay particles form, as it were, the bare bones of the soil, the organic part of the soil brings it to life. By far the most important primary source of soil organic matter is the litter, that is, the dead leaves and branches which fall onto it and the roots which die within it. It is possible to estimate the rate of leaf and twig litter fall by collecting samples in trays of known area (Fig. 15.13); an annual value of about five tonnes per hectare has been obtained in forest. Fall of branches and complete trees is more difficult to estimate but may be about equal to leaf-litter fall. Litter is rapidly attacked by the decomposers, which will be considered later in this chapter, and in consequence the quantity of litter which can be scraped from the soil surface is normally less than the annual fall. A rate of decomposition of about 3 percent per week has been recorded in a West African forest where litter thickness had reached equilibrium.

Just as rock minerals differ in their resistance to weathering, so too do the various constituents of litter. Proteins, starches and sugars are readily utilized by most decomposers, cellulose is digested by many bacteria and fungi though not by metazoan animals, while lignin is more resistant. Consequently humus, which is the colloidal organic substance remaining after the more labile constituents of litter have disappeared, consists largely of lignin and compounds derived from it, and, tightly combined with it, various nitrogen-containing compounds such as amino-acids. Humus decomposes at an annual rate of only 1 to 5 percent, as compared to about 170 percent for fresh litter. If all the litter were to end up as humus the soil would contain enormous quantities of humus. The fact that the humus content even of a forest topsoil is seldom more than 5 percent shows, however, that most of the carbon originally present in the litter is lost as carbon dioxide through the respiration of decomposing organisms before it can be incorporated into humus. In fact only about 10 percent of litter eventually becomes humus.

Humus is a difficult substance to describe. It is colloidal and amorphous, not crystalline, and, as it consists of a complex mixture of substances, it has no definite chemical composition or structure. It is predominantly negatively charged and therefore has a high affinity for cations (Book 1 p. 78). It also tends to become attached to clay particles which it binds together. It has a dark colour and, as a result, topsoil is usually browner than subsoil, but the colours of different soils may be a poor guide to their humus content: a black montmorillonite clay may contain no more humus than a red forest-zone topsoil. The elements in humus are commonly present in the following proportions—carbon : nitrogen : sulphur : phosphorus = 100:10:1:1. As the humus is gradually decomposed by

fungal activity, simple compounds of nitrogen, sulphur and phosphorus are liberated from it together with adsorbed cations; this process is called 'mineralization' of humus and is an important source of soil nutrients.

Soil structure and pore space

Between and even within the soil particles are the pores that contain the soil water and air. In a dry, homogeneous clay the combined volume of the pores may reach 50 percent of the total soil volume, but because clay particles are small the pores will be very narrow. In a homogeneous sand the pore space may also only be 50 percent, but all the pores will be relatively wide and interconnecting. If rain falls on such soils, the large pores of the sand will allow water to penetrate readily and to percolate down through the soil; at field capacity (Book 1 p. 272) the sand will have quite a low water content and be well aerated. Water will penetrate the clay more slowly, but because the pores are narrow they will hold water by capillary attraction; at field capacity the water content will be high but there will be very little air in the soil. Thus homogeneous clays are readily waterlogged. A good soil should contain both narrow, capillary pores for holding water, and wider, non-capillary pores for drainage and aeration; this will be the case if the particles are not spaced uniformly but aggregated into small lumps or crumbs.

One of the most desirable features of humus is its ability to stick the particles of the soil together, giving it a good crumb structure (Fig. 7.3). There will be capillary pores within the crumbs and non-capillary pores between them. As we shall see, the faecal pellets of some soil-feeding invertebrates are also coherent and thus form crumbs.

Soil profiles

We have seen that materials are added to the soil from above and from below (Fig. 7.4). Litter is accumulating and decomposing, and humus is being formed, at the soil surface; weathering is taking place where the soil reaches

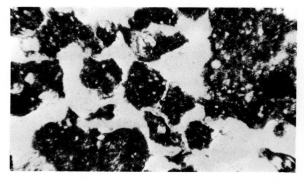

7.3 Thin section of forest soil as seen through a microscope, showing small dark-coloured crumbs cemented by humus (×40).

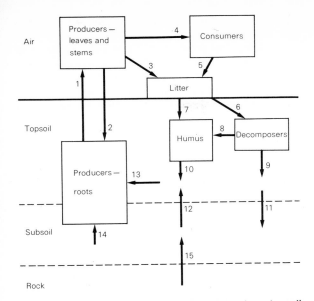

7.4 Diagram summarizing the relationships (numbered) between soil, organisms and rock. For numbers, see Problem 1.

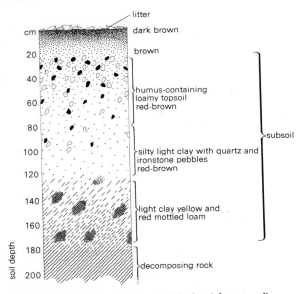

7.5 Diagram of a profile in well-drained forest soil. Note the layer of stones (black) near the top of the subsoil.

the underlying rock. Water movement tends to redistribute the products of decomposition and weathering along concentration gradients. Soil is consequently stratified. A vertical section of the soil is called a profile; the layers of the profile are called horizons. Fig. 7.5 shows a profile of a typical forest soil. Uppermost is the litter layer where decomposition is proceeding most rapidly, and where much of the soil fauna is concentrated. Immediately below this is

the topsoil which contains partly decomposed fragments of litter which have been pulled into it by soil animals, and also the greater part of the humus. The litter layer is very liable to desiccation during drought and contains less available nutrients than the topsoil; hence the bulk of the feeding roots of plants are concentrated in the topsoil. The subsoil comprises that part of the soil below the zone where incorporation of humus is taking place. Usually it contains very little organic matter; it may also lack unaltered rock minerals. It is consequently poorer than the topsoil in plant nutrients and the quantity of feeding roots in the subsoil is very much less than in the topsoil. Finally there is the layer of decomposing rock. Fig. 7.6 shows the

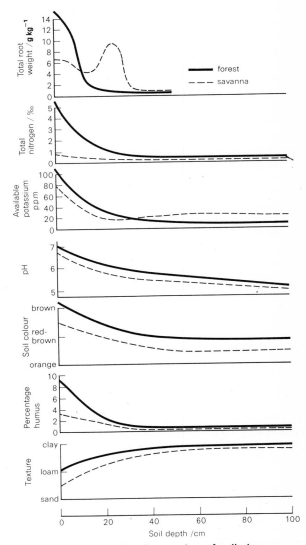

7.6 Changes with depth of a number of soil characteristics, in typical well-drained soils of forest and savanna.

changes with depth of a number of soil properties and of root mass in typical forest and savanna soils. Topsoil, because it is stained by humus, generally has a darker colour than the subsoil; it also tends to have a higher pH because the cation-exchange complex is abundantly supplied with metallic cations derived from weathering, and there is consequently less room for hydrogen ions. The topsoil is less well-defined in savanna soils partly because they contain less humus and partly because what humus there is comes largely from root decomposition within the profile; most dead leaves and twigs are burnt during the annual fires.

Soil depth

The depth of the profile depends on the relation between the rate of weathering of rock (w) and rate of removal of soil by surface erosion (e). If $w = e$, soil depth will remain constant. If $w > e$, soil depth will increase and if $w < e$, soil will become shallower. Under wet tropical conditions of abundant moisture and high temperatures, weathering is rapid. Forest cover protects the topsoil against erosion, both because its canopy breaks the full force of rainstorms and because the litter and roots hold the soil in place. Consequently it is under tropical forests that the greatest depths of soil are found, sometimes of more than 30 m. Weathering is slower in the drier conditions of savanna, and savanna vegetation gives much less protection against erosion; for both these reasons savanna soils therefore tend to be shallower. Soils may be shallower on steep hillsides because erosion is faster in such places.

The deeper the soil, the greater the volume in which plants can root. Although most of the nutrients are concentrated in the topsoil, the subsoil provides a reservoir of moisture during drought, and even though nutrients are less concentrated there, the greater volume of soil may provide significant total quantities. But if a soil is to be fertile it should not be so deep that the nutrient-rich weathering horizon is beyond the reach of plant roots, as is the case in many forest soils.

Redistribution of materials within the soil profile

Fig. 7.6 shows that the highest proportion of clay in the profile is found in the upper subsoil and the lowest in the topsoil. The reason is that clay particles may be washed for some distance down the profile by rainwater. The upper horizon which is subject to such loss is sometimes called the A-horizon, while the horizon in which leached material is deposited is called the B-horizon. In very acid soils, which are more common in cold temperate regions than in the tropics, part of the humus goes into solution and is readily washed through the profile to accumulate in a dark-stained B-horizon as an impermeable (pan) layer, called an organic pan. In most slightly acid or neutral tropical soils

the humus is not mobile and the B-horizon is therefore not distinguishable by its colour.

In addition to being washed down the profile, clay minerals in old tropical soils are themselves slowly weathered and decomposed, enriching the soil with the sesquioxides of aluminium (Al_2O_3) and iron (Fe_2O_3); this is the leading characteristic of red tropical latosols. In fact bauxite, the ore from which aluminium is obtained, is merely soil which has been exposed to weathering for so long that practically nothing is left in it but Al_2O_3.

Origin of iron pan

In well-aerated soil, iron is present in the oxidized trivalent (ferric) form and is then very insoluble; in waterlogged soils, on the other hand, iron exists in its more soluble divalent (ferrous) form. This iron can diffuse in solution through a deoxygenated, but not through an oxygenated, soil. If soil from below a swamp is examined, it will be found to have a generally blue, greenish or grey colour, but may show red streaks of ferric iron compounds along the root-channels through which oxygen can enter. In general, if aeration conditions are variable within a soil it will be mottled grey and red. Because ferric compounds are precipitated in the red, aerated patches, the concentration of dissolved iron in their vicinity is low; as a result iron will diffuse from the grey to the red parts of the soil along concentration gradients.

Such mottled soils are not restricted to swamps; they also occur very widely in the subsoil under forest, particularly where the rainfall is fairly high, and are often exposed in road cuttings. When the cutting is first made this mottled horizon is soft and easy to cut, but after a few months of exposure to drying it may begin to harden irreversibly (Fig. 7.7).

| 0 | 10 | 20 | 30 |

mm

7.7 Block of iron pan. Notice that the softer channels in the block have eroded leaving the harder parts as protruding ridges.

It is generally supposed that the iron-pan sheets (p. 79), now found mainly in savanna, were formed from mottled subsoil which was originally soft and under forest, but which was subsequently exposed at the surface. There is evidence that forest extended more widely at certain times in the past than it does now (p. 62) and according to this theory, hardpans are the fossil remnant of forest soils. Whatever their origin may have been, it is clearly very important in farming practice to avoid exposing a soft mottled subsoil by allowing topsoil to be eroded away.

Soils and topography

We have so far presented evidence that soils may be influenced by a variety of factors, including parent rock, climate, and by the litter and activities of plants and animals. A further factor of great importance is topography. In Chap. 5 we looked at the way in which savanna vegetation changes along the slope, according to the nature of the soil. Table 7.2 summarizes the major differences between soils from various positions on the slope in West African forest. The upper-slope soils are the best aerated and consequently have a bright red lower topsoil. Middle-slope soils are moderately aerated and tend to be orange-brown while soils in the valleys are often swampy, at least seasonally, and have pale colours, with mottling quite close to the surface.

Table 7.2 Variation with position on slope of soil properties in West African semi-deciduous forest

Position on slope	Aeration	Texture	Colour of lower topsoil	pH of topsoil
Top	good	loamy	red to red-brown	about 7
Middle	moderate	silty clay	dark brown to yellow-brown	5·5–6·5
Bottom	poor	sandy to silty clay	grey- mottled with orange	about 5

Soil as an environment

Soil organisms depend mainly on organic matter for food. As we have seen, the decomposing litter and humus and also the bulk of plant roots are concentrated in the topsoil; consequently it is here that almost all the soil biota are to be found. They live on the surfaces of soil particles, whence they obtain adsorbed water, and in the pore spaces of the soil whence they obtain air. Humus, too, is associated with particle surfaces and plant rootlets grow through pores.

Many soil organisms are aerobic and the majority, such as the fungi, nematodes, small arthropods, worms and snails lose water readily. The availability of air and the water content of the soil are both therefore of considerable biological significance. Both are influenced by the texture of the soil, as the available volume between the soil particles will be determined by the size and shape of the particles, and by the degree of crumb structure which the soil possesses. Capillary pores, which retain water, maintain the humidity of the soil environment and non-capillary pores aerate it. There is little difference in composition between air within the soil and the atmosphere; oxygen concentration is very slightly less but carbon dioxide concentration may be markedly greater, reaching values as high as 0·5 percent by volume.

Waterlogging of a soil results in the expulsion of air from the pore space, and is thus damaging to aerobic organisms. The anaerobic organisms which are encouraged by waterlogging include denitrifying and sulphur bacteria. The former use nitrate ions as a source of oxygen, liberating nitrogen gas, and thus reducing the fertility of the soil for plants. The sulphur bacteria reduce sulphate ions to toxic sulphides that are injurious to most other soil organisms.

Soil pH is an important environmental parameter for many organisms. Bacteria are less tolerant of low pH than are fungi, and this is one reason why very acid soils may be deficient in nitrate. At pH values below 5·5 phosphate ion combines with aluminium and iron hydroxides to give insoluble phosphates which are not available to plants. Above pH 7, phosphate availability is reduced by combination with calcium and magnesium. Aluminium is more soluble at low pH, and plants growing in acid latosols must have a high tolerance of the normally toxic aluminium ion. In a neutral or slightly acid soil, the clay particles tend to be clustered into small aggregates, to which the humus is firmly attached. Such a soil has a better structure and is better aerated than an alkaline soil, which usually contains free sodium ions which cause the particles to disperse. Alkaline soils are unfavourable to most plants. Soils tend to be acid when they are exposed to leaching by heavy rainfall, because the metallic cations ('bases') which are washed out are replaced in the cation-exchange complex by hydrogen ions. Soils developed in sands which are poor in bases may similarly tend to be acid if rainfall is high. On the other hand low rainfall and base-rich parent material may allow sufficient bases to remain in the soil solution to give a neutral or alkaline reaction. Fig. 7.8 summarizes the causes and effects of variation in soil pH.

The food web in the soil: sampling soil organisms

Before we can examine the interrelationships between organisms in the food web we must first discover what organisms are present, and in what quantity. This is by no means easy. In the first place, we cannot see into the soil directly, as we can look into the canopy of a tree. More-

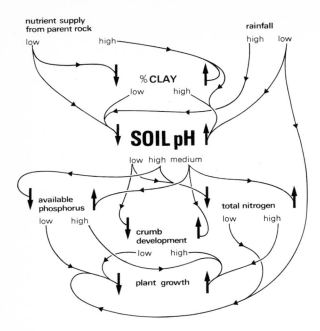

7.8 Diagram showing the interrelationships between soil pH and the factors which affect it and are affected by it. The level of a factor may be increased (shown by thick upward-pointing arrow) or decreased (shown by thick downward-pointing arrow) by the operation on it of another factor. The effect of this other factor may vary according to whether it is at a high, low or sometimes medium level. For example, a high rainfall tends to reduce soil pH. The actual pH found does not, however depend only on rainfall but also on other factors, including clay content and rate at which the parent rock supplies nutrients. The diagram thus distinguishes between *reduction* in pH and *low* pH.

over, while we are removing soil for examination, the larger animals may be alarmed by the disturbance and escape from our sample through their tunnels. The smaller organisms, especially the fungi and bacteria, may be so firmly attached to the soil particles and humus that we can remove only a proportion of them. In general, different methods will give us different results and we must build up a piecemeal picture of the populations. We shall now consider the methods available for sampling the more important groups of organisms.

Sampling fungi and bacteria

It is possible to estimate soil bacteria directly by shaking a known weight of soil with a given volume of water, and examining a known volume of the suspension through a microscope; but bacteria embedded in humus will not be visible and therefore not counted. Other objections to this method are that it may not be easy to distinguish dead from living bacteria, nor one species of living bacterium from

another. To identify bacteria we must prepare a pure culture whose staining reactions and response to various growth media can be studied. This is achieved by spreading a known volume of the soil extract over nutrient agar in a petri dish and observing the colonies which develop on the agar. Colonies can then be subcultured: that is, a few cells from the colony are allowed to multiply in a second culture vessel, so that the species can be identified. For example, only the chemosynthetic bacteria such as nitrifiers can flourish on an inorganic medium. Table 7.3 shows the numbers of bacteria recorded from various soils.

Table 7.3 Numbers of bacteria in different kinds of soil. Estimates are based on direct counting under the microscope; the method of spreading a suspension over an agar plate and counting colonies as they develop would give much lower estimates (*Data from Russell, and Meiklejohn*)

Locality	Soil type	Number of bacteria ($\times 10^9$ per gramme of soil)
Rothamsted, England	arable field	1·01
	grass field	3·04
Muguga, Kenya	arable field	3·3
	grass field	2·0

Fungi are even more difficult to deal with than bacteria, largely because we cannot define an individual fungus; fungi consist of indefinite lengths of hyphae lying within and between the soil particles. It is possible to obtain some idea of fungal biomass by direct observation under the microscope. Culturing diluted soil extracts will show many of the species present and give some idea as to which are the most abundant. Unfortunately many 'toadstools' (Book 1 Fig. 19.13) fail to form sporophores in culture and therefore cannot be identified.

The roots of flowering plants form by far the greater part of the biomass in most soils. To estimate their abundance and distribution we can dig a pit about 1 m deep, remove samples of equal volume from different depths down one side of the pit, and separate the roots by washing the soil in a sieve. Fig. 7.6 shows results obtained in this way in the forest and savanna zones of West Africa. Such figures are only approximate as many of the finest roots will adhere to soil particles and be lost during the washing process; moreover, dead roots cannot be separated readily from live, and species cannot usually be distinguished.

Sampling the soil fauna

In attempting to obtain a quantitative picture of the soil fauna, we are faced with the difficulty that the organisms concerned may vary in size from small amoebae to giant rainworms (Oligochaeta) of a length of 50 cm or more. Clearly no one method can be used.

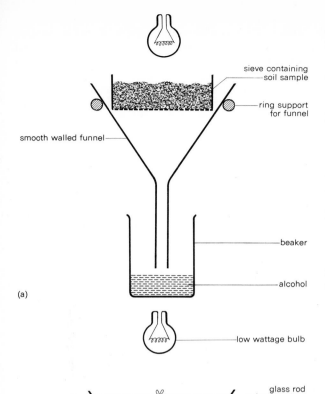

sieve containing soil sample

ring support for funnel

smooth walled funnel

beaker

alcohol

(a)

low wattage bulb

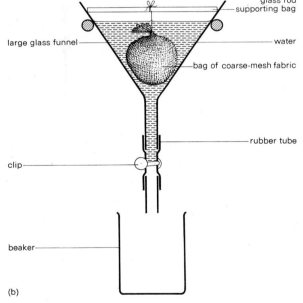

glass rod supporting bag

large glass funnel

water

bag of coarse-mesh fabric

rubber tube

clip

beaker

(b)

The larger members of the soil fauna, such as earthworms, woodlice, centipedes, millipedes, beetles and beetle larvae, can be extracted from a known volume of soil directly by hand sorting. Sieving the soil into a series of different grades may assist in finding the organisms quickly.

A very large number of tiny soil arthropods cannot, however, be collected in this way. With a fresh soil sample, it is possible to drive a fraction of these animals out of the soil by allowing it gradually to dry out. The method employed is shown diagrammatically in Fig. 7.9a. The soil sample is spread upon a wire mesh surface. Above the sample is a source of heat, commonly an incandescent light bulb, while the sieve stands within a funnel at the lower end of which is a dish containing some fixative such as 70 percent ethanol. The heat from the lamp slowly warms and dries out the soil sample from above. The soil fauna responds by migrating downwards, so that it will ultimately fall through the wire mesh and be collected in the dish below.

This method will provide a reasonably complete sample of the smaller, more mobile arthropods, but it has the disadvantage that it requires the use of fresh soil samples, since it depends upon the behaviours of the soil animals. Moreover it does not readily separate the nematodes which are an important fraction of the total fauna. These can be sampled by a comparable procedure carried out in water (Fig. 7.9b). The soil sample is suspended in a bag of coarse-mesh cloth and the water slowly warmed from above. This has the effect of driving live nematodes downwards into the cooler water below and finally out of the bag where they fall into the stem of the funnel.

(c)

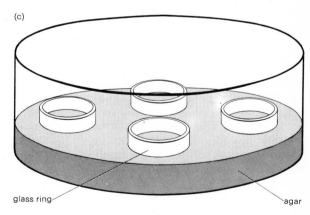

glass ring

agar

7.9 (a) A funnel for the extraction of small arthropods from a sample of soil. As the sample warms up and dries out, any living arthropods tend to move downwards and will finally fall through the meshes of the sieve into the receiver below. (b) A comparable method for the extraction of soil nematodes. The soil sample is suspended in a fabric bag in water which is slowly warmed from above by the lamp. The nematodes will swim downwards and out through the meshing of the bag to collect at the bottom of the funnel. By opening the clip, they may be transferred to the beaker and then examined. (c) Method used for estimating the population density of heterotrophic Protozoa. Small, sterile glass rings are pushed into the agar to form wells into each of which is run a dense suspension of soil bacteria. Soil extracts of different dilutions are then added to the wells. For further explanation see text.

The smallest arthropods and the cysts of nematodes cannot be successfully sampled in these ways. A third method, which has the further advantage of not requiring fresh soil samples, depends upon the fact that the cuticle of arthropods is not wetted by water. If the soil is broken up and agitated, arthropods will tend to collect in the surface layer. This action is enhanced by the use of salt solutions of a density of about 1·2; in such solutions both small arthropods and the cysts of nematodes will float up to the surface. In practice, the soil sample is broken up by being passed through a fine sieve. It is then suspended in a salt solution and violently aerated. This frees the fauna from the soil particles and the air bubbles assist in carrying the material to the surface. After aeration, the soil is allowed to settle; the surface layer is then decanted off and the material collected is sorted under a dissecting microscope.

Finally there is the problem of sampling the Protozoa. To determine the numbers of heterotrophic bacteria-feeding forms, one method uses dense suspensions of an aerobic soil bacterium. Small volumes of suspension are poured into wells formed by small glass rings embedded in agar (Fig. 7.9c). A soil sample of 10 g is shaken with 5 cm^3 of dilute sodium chloride solution for five minutes and from the supernatant liquid a series of dilutions are prepared. 0·05 cm^3 samples of each dilution are then introduced into different wells and the plate incubated for a fortnight. The presence of one or more bacteria-feeding Protozoa in a sample will be shown by the fact that they will have eaten the bacteria, leaving a clear area. Where there are no Protozoa, the bacteria will remain. With sufficient replications, it is then possible to determine the lowest dilution in which such Protozoa occur and hence their abundance in the soil sample.

The food web in the soil: decomposers and consumers

Animals are usually said to be decomposers if they live in the soil and feed on dead organic matter. They may be described as saprobes, but they do not differ from sub-aerial consumers in any fundamental way. Both groups of organism obtain proteins and carbohydrates from their food, metabolize some of it liberating carbon dioxide, deaminate amino-acids liberating simple nitrogen compounds, excrete inorganic ions, and assimilate much of the rest into their own tissues. In the soil are also secondary consumers which are predatory on the saprobes, higher-order consumers and so on. At each stage in the web some dissipation of organic material and some liberation of simple inorganic compounds will occur.

There are seven broad categories of material which decomposers can exploit as sources of energy, namely leaves, twigs, stems, dead bodies of animals, faecal material and the roots and underground storage organs of plants. Thus the energy input into the soil ecosystem is derived both from producers and from all levels of consumers. Typically the material which enters the system is dead or dying, but living root systems may be attacked and exploited as food in the same ways as are the aerial parts of plants.

When either plant or animal tissues die, energy-consuming processes cease; during life, these had protected the cells from uncontrolled activity of their own hydrolytic enzymes. On the death of a cell, hydrolysis of the cell contents commences: this process is spoken of as 'autolysis' and will make sugars, amino-acids and lipids available to bacteria, saprophytic fungi and saprozoic Protozoa. The exploitation of these materials is frequently enhanced by the secretion by the saprophytes of hydrolytic enzymes. A number of small Metazoa are saprozoic, including some species of nematode worm which have a muscular pharynx which allows them to suck up the fluid materials formed during autolysis (Fig. 7.10a). In feeding in this manner, such nematodes will also ingest bacteria and they are thus partly consumers of decomposing organisms.

It should be noted that animal feeding does not decompose more than a minor part of the litter which falls onto the soil surface, because most of the litter consists of plant cell walls, that is, of cellulose and lignin. Most metazoan animals do not produce the enzyme cellulase by which cellulose may be digested. This enzyme is found, however, in certain fungi and bacteria. Cellulase can be detected in a fungus by culturing it on a medium containing macerated filter paper as the sole carbohydrate; if the fungus thrives, it must produce cellulase. Cellulose is absent from humus, because it is completely broken down to simple sugars during attack on the litter by fungi and bacteria.

The lignin molecule is more complex than that of cellulose, and is much more resistant to enzymes. It is altered by fungi and bacteria but is broken down only very slowly and hence is an important constituent of humus (p. 122). It follows that animal feeding does not contribute directly to either formation or mineralization of humus, but indirectly its importance is very great.

Larger invertebrate decomposers

Together with saprophytic and saprozoic organisms are others which eat the dead plant or animal tissues. We have already described the changing communities associated with the decomposition of a mass of dung (p. 109); similar changes occur during the decomposition of the carcass of a small vertebrate, unless it is rapidly 'cleaned' by ants. Plant litter is directly ingested by a wide variety of organisms including earthworms, millipedes (Arthropoda: Diplopoda), woodlice (Crustacea: Isopoda), slugs and snails. These large animals break up the litter mechanically, either with sclerotized mouth parts as do the arthropods, or with a radula as do the slugs and snails (Book 1 Fig. 18.44). Many earthworms have a highly muscular gizzard in which ingested material is fragmented before being

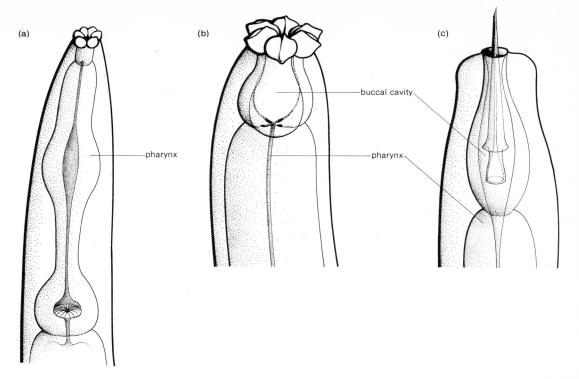

(a)   (b)   (c)

buccal cavity

pharynx

pharynx

7.10 The pharyngeal structure of various nematodes. (a) A species which feeds upon decaying matter and bacteria. The pharynx is a simple, muscular suction-pump which draws fluid into the alimentary canal. (b) A carnivorous species with powerful teeth around the mouth; the lining of the buccal cavity also carries teeth arising from the plate-like structures which lead into the pharynx. (c) A nematode which feeds upon the contents of plant cells; the buccal cavity carries a hollow stylet-like structure which can be extruded and driven through plant cell walls making the cell contents available as food.

passed on to the intestine where digestion occurs (Fig. 7.11). As the broken litter passes through the alimentary canal of these different types of animal it is subject to the action of digestive enzymes and probably also to attack by bacteria within the alimentary tract. The faecal pellets which are voided commonly contain mucus and bacterial polysaccharides which hold together the fine particles, so as to produce faecal 'crumbs'. These are not readily dispersed by water and enhance the granular texture of many soils. The faecal pellets of millipedes and isopods are generally formed only of indigestible plant material, but earthworms also ingest soil particles and as a result their activity tends to mix the plant material intimately with the soil. Small particles of litter may be ingested by some species of mite (Arachnida: Acari) and also by certain Collembola (Fig. 4.17).

The mechanical breakdown of litter brought about by the larger invertebrates increases the surface area of material available for attack by bacteria and fungi, and within the faecal particles the processes of decomposition continue. The importance of these animals to the general

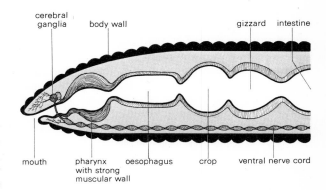

cerebral ganglia   body wall   gizzard   intestine

mouth   pharynx   oesophagus   crop   ventral nerve cord
         with strong
         muscular wall

7.11 Diagrammatic sagittal section through the anterior end of an earthworm. All structures except the alimentary canal and nerve cord have been omitted for clarity. The strongly muscular pharynx leads into an oesophagus and crop behind which lies a muscular gizzard in which the food is broken up before being passed to the intestine.

129

process of decomposition has been studied by placing leaf discs in nylon bags of different mesh size. Fig. 7.12a shows the results of one such experiment in a temperate climate; 50 discs were placed in each bag and the bags then buried to a depth of 2·5 cm. The coarse mesh permitted all types of soil organisms to have access to the discs; one of the fine-mesh bags excluded the larger invertebrates but allowed bacteria, fungi and small arthropods to enter. At intervals the bags were dug up and the area of leaf destroyed was measured. Fig. 7.12a shows that after about three months, 70 percent of the leaf surface had been destroyed in the coarse-mesh bags, but only about 15 percent in the bags of a fine-mesh material. Fig. 7.12b shows the results of similar experiments in Nigeria during the rainy season. Events are much faster and decomposition by micro-organisms and small arthropods is relatively more important. There was a 70 percent loss of material from the coarse mesh bags within six weeks, by which time only about 40 percent of the material in the fine mesh bags had decomposed.

Earthworms and termites

In temperate soils the large detritus-eating invertebrates constitute the bulk of the biomass of soil organisms; in woodland, values for earthworm biomass may sometimes exceed 100 g m^{-2}. In tropical conditions earthworms are commonly far less abundant. Thus in a forest in Nigeria a biomass of only about 10 g m^{-2} was found; nevertheless, at the higher temperatures, the quantity of litter and soil eaten annually per hectare is far greater than in temperate lands. Termites, which do not occur as soil organisms in most temperate regions, can reach a biomass of 50 g m^{-2} and it has often been suggested that they play a similar role to the earthworms of temperate soils. As we have already seen, earthworm faecal pellets, formed of a mixture of soil and broken litter, are important in establishing a crumb structure in the soil. Furthermore, the burrowing activity of earthworms is probably of considerable significance in enhancing the aeration of soils, thus increasing the general metabolic activity of decomposing organisms. It also increases drainage, so that there is less run-off of rainwater, and it thus tends to reduce erosion. There is, moreover, good evidence that earthworms, possibly indirectly by enhancing bacterial action, increase the quantities of ammonia and nitrate in the soil. Indeed in pasture land in New Zealand, the introduction of earthworms from the northern hemisphere nearly doubled the annual yield of grass.

The action of termites is very different. While earthworms are scattered throughout the topsoil and upper part of the subsoil, the activity of termites is centred on their nests. In foraging they commonly build galleries below the soil surface, but the walls of these are usually cemented, so that tney contribute less to the aeration and drainage of the soil than do earthworm burrows. The activity of earth-

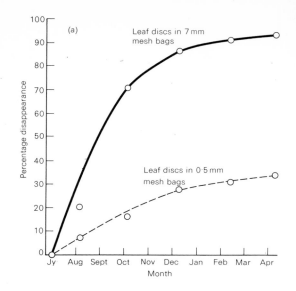

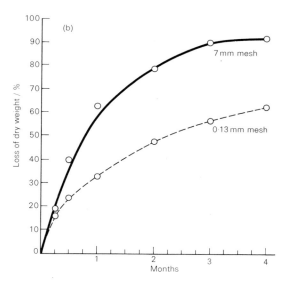

7.12 (a) Rate of decomposition of discs of oak leaves in nylon bags. The bags were buried below 2·5 cm of soil and dug up at intervals. The area of damage to each leaf was determined graphically. The larger mesh size allowed earthworms and other large soil invertebrates to feed upon the discs. The smaller mesh allowed access of only very small invertebrates such as mites and Collembola. A further set of bags, of 0·003 mm mesh, excluded all invertebrates but not soil micro-organisms. In these bags there were no visible signs of breakdown, even after nine months. (b) The results of similar experiments during the rainy season in Nigeria. Note the more rapid rate of decomposition and the greater importance of the smaller invertebrates. (Data from Russell-Smith).

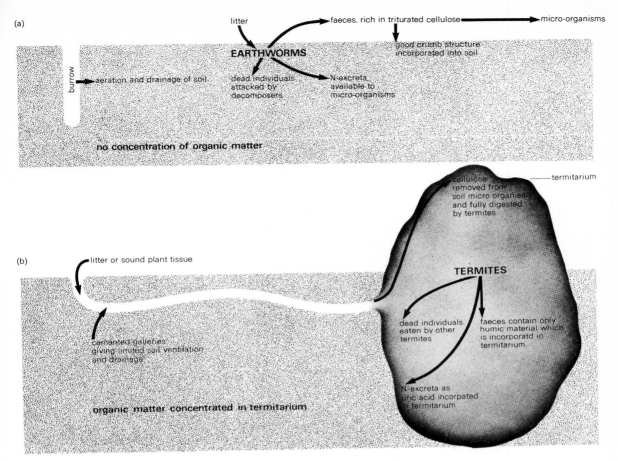

(a)

litter

faeces, rich in triturated cellulose ➙ micro-organisms

EARTHWORMS

good crumb structure
incorporated into soil

burrow ➙ aeration and drainage of soil

dead individuals
attacked by
decomposers

N-excreta
available to
micro-organisms

no concentration of organic matter

cellulose
removed from
soil micro-organisms
and fully digested
by termites

termitarium

(b) litter or sound plant tissue

TERMITES

cemented galleries
giving limited soil ventilation
and drainage

dead individuals
eaten by other
termites

faeces contain only
humic material which
is incorporatd in
termitarium

N-excreta as
uric acid incorpated
in termitarium

organic matter concentrated in termitarium

7.13 Diagrammatic summary of the relationship of (a) earthworms and (b) termites to the process of decomposition in the soil.

worms makes cellulose more readily available to micro-organisms and the activity of these may enhance the productivity of the soil. Termites, however, with the help of bacteria or Protozoa which inhabit their gut, digest completely the cellulose which they take to their nests and thus tend to reduce the microbial population. They also remove to their nests material which would provide the basis for a useful nutrient-holding humus. In short, there is little resemblance between the activities of the two types of organism beyond the fact that both attack litter. Fig. 7.13 summarizes these differences in diagrammatic form.

Consumers

What organisms feed upon the decomposers? We have already mentioned that certain nematodes ingest bacteria; some rhizopods and flagellates also prey on bacteria. The fungi are a source of food for a great diversity of forms; yeast cells may be ingested by Protozoa and nematodes as well as by slugs and woodlice. The larger detritus feeders are preyed upon by centipedes (Arthropoda: Chilopoda)

which also feed upon the many types of insect larva found in soil. Some of these, such as the larvae of the ground beetles, the Carabidae, and the rove beetles, the Staphylinidae, (Fig. 7.14) are themselves predatory on mites and Collembola; the former also feed on young earthworms and other insect larvae. Carnivorous nematodes, with powerful 'teeth' around the mouth (Fig. 7.10b), also occur and feed on other nematodes, small earthworms and mites; there are also carnivorous mites feeding upon nematodes and Collembola and even carnivorous species of fungi which trap and feed upon nematodes (Fig. 7.15).

Exploitation of roots

The second source of food comes from the root systems of plants. Living root tissues and root storage organs are attacked by a variety of consumers, some of which can cause serious economic damage to agricultural crops. For example, the fungus *Fusarium oxysporum* invades the underground parts of some varieties of banana, causing severe disease (p. 295). Some species of soil-living nematodes have fine stylets which allow them to penetrate the

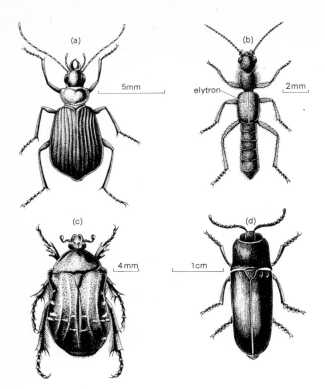

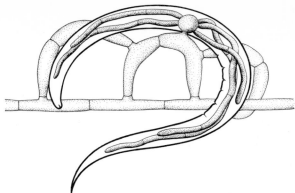

7.15 A nematode which has been trapped by a fungus. The fungal hyphae in this species develop adhesive knobs which catch soil-living nematodes; the fungal hyphae then grow into the body of the nematode.

7.14 Adult representatives of various families of beetle whose larvae are found in the soil. (a) A ground beetle or carabid. (b) A rove beetle or staphylinid; this family is characterized by the fact that the forewings or elytra do not cover the abdomen. (c) A chafer beetle or scarabaeid; the huge Goliath Beetle which has a body length of about 10 cm and occurs in West Africa is a member of this family, as are also the dung beetles and the rhinoceros beetles. (d) A click beetle or elaterid, so-called because the adults have a special righting mechanism, should they fall on their backs. If the beetle is turned upside down, it flexes the joint between the prothorax and the mesothorax which carries the elytra. The joint is then abruptly extended with a loud 'click'; as a result the abdomen strikes the ground sharply and the beetle is thrown into the air. Large species of click beetle may reach a length of more than 5 cm.

cell walls of root tissues (Fig. 7.10c) while others penetrate completely into the roots and might be regarded as plant parasites rather than consumers. Among these is *Meloidogyne* which attacks tomatoes (p. 297). Yam tubers are also subject to attack by nematodes; while these may cause relatively little damage to freshly harvested yams, they are responsible for the 'dry rot' which can develop in stored yams since the worms continue to feed and reproduce within the tissues of the tubers. Slugs and snails can both damage rooting systems and destroy tubers, but the most serious attacks upon living roots are made by insect larvae. Some of these are the larvae of moths, but far more common are the larvae of beetles, including those of the

chafers and dung beetles, the Scarabaeidae, and the Elateridae or click beetles (Fig. 7.14). The larvae which attack yam tubers develop into rhinoceros beetles as adults. Predatory upon these consumers are the same types of organism which we have already considered in relation to those responsible for litter breakdown.

Vertebrates in the soil

Finally, there are a few vertebrates which may be regarded as members of the soil ecosystem. Many vertebrates burrow into the soil for refuge, but these contribute only incidentally to the food available to smaller soil organisms or they may destroy soil organisms incidentally by their activities. They cannot be considered true members of the soil fauna. Other vertebrates, such as some of the small carnivores, feed at least in part upon the larger soil invertebrates, while the aardvark (Book 1 Fig. 18.82) feeds upon soil-living termites; such animals thus have a closer link with the soil community. There are, however, a few truly soil-living vertebrates. These include a group of blind, limbless amphibia, the Gymnophiona, which superficially resemble earthworms both in shape and skin texture. They are carnivorous, like their relatives the toads, and feed upon insects. The 'blind snakes' are subterranean and likewise feed on insects. Finally there are the mole-rats which are burrowing rodents feeding largely on tubers and roots; their activity can be recognized by the mounds of earth which they throw up on the surface of the soil while excavating their tunnels.

Nutrient cycles

The chemical elements are distributed between the various components of an ecosystem: living producers, consumers and decomposers; non-living organic matter in the soil,

soil exchange complex, and undecomposed minerals in the soil and underlying rocks. Table 7.4 shows the quantities of important nutrient elements in a forest and in a savanna. The biogeochemical cycles (Book 1 p. 7) by which these elements pass from one component to another of the ecosystem, are not quite closed, even in the absence of disturbance. Solutes are leached from plants and soils by rain, and the losses incurred in this way can be estimated by the analysis of river water (Table 7.5). In an equilibrium situation, these losses will be made good by the weathering of rock minerals and from the dust and nitrogen compounds which are washed into the soil from the atmosphere. Table 7.4 shows that much of the ecosystem's nutrient store is in the vegetation; much of this will be lost when the vegetation is cleared to make way for farms. Nutrients will subsequently be taken from the ecosystem in exported crops as well.

Table 7.4 Quantities of important nutrient elements (kg ha^{-1}) in forest and savanna. The figures give total nutrient content for the plants, and available nutrients for the soils. Note the high proportion of nutrients stored in the vegetation (*Data from Nye and Greenland*)

Element	Forest at Kade, Ghana				Savanna at Ejura, Ghana			
	Living plants	Dead branches and leaves	Soil (rooting depth)	Approx. % of total in soil	Living plants	Dead branches and leaves	Soil (rooting depth)	Approx. % of total in soil
Nitrogen	1 590	260	4 600	70	140	4	1 800	90
Phosphorus	120	20	10	10	30	1	20	40
Potassium	860	50	650	40	200	4	190	50
Calcium	2 100	570	2 600	50	270	2	2 900	90
Magnesium	330	60	370	50	90	3	380	80

Table 7.5 Removal of inorganic ions by various rivers from their catchment areas (*Data from various sources*)

	R. Volta, West Africa	R. Pra, Ghana	R. Mississippi, North America	R. Thames, England
Mean annual flow near river mouth (m$^3 \times 10^{10}$)	4·0	0·9	55·8	0·3
Catchment area (km$^2 \times 10^3$)	394	22	3 280	16
Mean annual water removed (m^3 per m^2 of catchment area)	0·10	0·40	0·17	0·22
Average nutrient contents of water (parts per million)				
Calcium	4·5	7·8	34·0	76·0
Sodium	3·1	13·2	11·4	8·7
Magnesium	2·8	3·8	8·9	4·8
Potassium	1·9	?	2·6	4·1
Sulphate	1·1	4·8	25·5	39·1
Chloride	3·0	9·1	10·3	12·2
Nitrite	0·3	1·1	2·7	?
Mean annual nutrients removed (g per m^2 of catchment area)				
Calcium	0·5	3·1	5·8	16·7
Sodium	0·3	5·3	1·9	1·9
Magnesium	0·3	1·5	1·5	1·1
Potassium	0·2	?	0·4	0·9
Sulphate	0·1	1·9	4·3	8·6
Chloride	0·3	3·6	1·8	2·7
Nitrite	0·03	0·4	0·5	?

Each element undergoes cycling. The cycles of greatest practical interest are those of elements which are in short supply either because they are absent from or rare in rocks, because their compounds are very soluble and easily leached (for example nitrogen) or sparingly soluble and relatively unavailable (for example phosphorus). Potassium, magnesium and calcium are generally abundant in the rocks (p. 120) and we have also seen (Book 1 p. 78) that cations are readily adsorbed on soil particles. Anions are adsorbed to a lesser extent; of these nitrate, phosphate and sulphate are all rare in rocks and soil, and commonly limit plant growth. Soil phosphorus is discussed on p. 290; we shall now consider the special problems of nitrogen.

Nitrogen cycle

The main reservoir of nitrogen is the atmosphere, and the nitrogen-fixing organisms which convert gaseous nitrogen to compounds which are eventually used by the other organisms in the ecosystem, are thus of great importance.

The ability to fix nitrogen is restricted to prokaryotic organisms (Book 1 p. 161), that is, bacteria and blue-green algae. Nitrogen is reduced to ammonia by an endergonic process which requires six electrons supplied by a reducing agent such as ferredoxin for the reduction of one molecule of nitrogen gas. Nitrogen-fixing bacteria are saprophytic, obtaining the necessary energy from respiration of sugars. The blue-green algae obtain the sugar they need from photosynthesis; in these organisms the problem of isolating the oxygen-liberating process of photosynthesis from the strongly reducing process of nitrogen fixation is solved by the segregation of the latter in specialized colourless cells called heterocysts which are shown, but not labelled in Book 1 Fig. 17.7d.

Blue-green algae are abundant in rice-fields and fix considerable quantities of nitrogen there. They may also be important for nitrogen fixation in non-waterlogged soils, though not so important as bacteria. It is not surprising that nitrogen fixation should proceed more rapidly in the moist, humus-rich forest soils than in dry savanna soils with less organic matter. Symbiotic nitrogen-fixers (p. 224) may be important in agricultural practice, but little is known of their contribution in natural soils.

Forest soils also derive adequate nitrate from oxidation by nitrifying bacteria of the ammonia compounds resulting from mineralization. In savanna, on the other hand, there is evidence (Fig. 7.16) that nitrifying bacteria are much rarer than in forest. The fact that nitrite-oxidizing bacteria in particular are usually absent from the soil under such common savanna grasses as *Hyparrhenia* and *Andropogon* suggests that these bacteria may be inhibited by exudations from the grass roots. It has been suggested that the resulting nitrate deficiency, while disadvantageous to the farmer, may help the grasses to compete favourably with plants with higher nitrogen requirements.

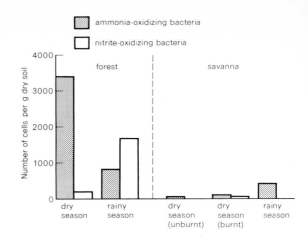

7.16 Numbers of nitrifying bacteria in a soil under mature forest and a soil under *Hyparrhenia* savanna. Notice that the populations of both types of nitrifying bacteria are much lower in the savanna, and that nitrite-oxidizers are only found when the savanna has been burned. (After Meiklejohn).

The roles of fauna and microflora in the soil

A good soil for primary producers must have three characteristics: it must hold an adequate supply of water, be well aerated and provide ample nutrients. The first two of these requirements depend largely on the proportions and properties of the non-living components of the soil: inorganic particles and humus. The last depends mainly upon the activity of the soil organisms responsible for mineralization of litter and humus. It is important to realize that mineralization is not some extraordinary process, peculiar to soil organisms, but is simply a consequence of excretion. The only special feature of soil organisms is that their food is litter or derivatives from it, and thus the minerals in their excreta are the products of decomposition.

Fig. 7.17 shows, in very simplified form, the food web of the soil. You will recognize the fundamental similarity between this diagram and the terrestrial food web shown in Book 1 Fig. 1.3. In both cases there are primary resources, formed by the activities of primary producers. Primary consumers feed on these and are in turn the resource for higher-order consumers. The microflora—fungi and bacteria—are equivalent to primary consumers; fungi which trap nematodes (Fig. 7.15) are exceptional in being higher-order consumers. The most significant way in which fungi and bacteria differ from the fauna is in their ability to break down the cellulose and lignin of which plant litter very largely consists. For this reason, and also because of their high rates of reproduction and metabolism, the microflora may be responsible for up to 90 percent of total soil metabolism.

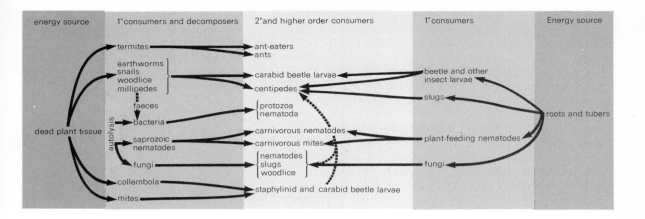

7.17 Simplified diagrammatic summary of the food web within the soil. Several types of organism as well as very many of the links have been omitted for clarity. The broken line leading to 'centipedes' shows part of the food web leading to a third-order consumer.

The soil fauna has two main functions in decomposition. Firstly, as shown by the data in Fig. 7.12, initial breaking-up of litter by animals such as earthworms can be an important preliminary to microbial attack. Secondly, animals are much more mobile than bacteria and fungi, and the dispersal of the microflora through the soil may be greatly speeded by their ingestion and subsequent release in the faeces of animals. The intestinal contents of many soil animals provide a very favourable environment for the multiplication of microbes; the number of bacteria in the faeces of some soil invertebrates may be as much as five times greater than that of an equal weight of the soil in which they live.

We can sum up by saying that micro-organisms are the true decomposers. They are nevertheless dependent for their activities upon the soil fauna, and together with them form an ecosystem which is basically similar to other ecosystems.

Problems

1 Attempt to identify and briefly describe each of the processes numbered in Fig. 7.4.
2 Suggest explanations for the following features of Fig. 7.6:
   (a) The difference between forest and savanna soils is greater in the case of nitrogen than in the case of potassium.
   (b) Clay is less abundant in the topsoil than in the subsoil, while the reverse is true for humus.
   (c) Maximum concentration of roots occurs at a greater depth in savanna than in forest soils.

3 What would be the approximate weights per ha of nitrogen in the forest and savanna soils shown in Fig. 7.6 (a) in the uppermost 10 cm of soil (b) between 10 and 20 cm depth of soil (c) between 20 and 30 cm depth of soil?
4 It is suggested in the text that Fig. 7.16 supports the hypothesis that *Hyparrhenia* roots may inhibit nitrifying bacteria. What other explanations of the data are possible? What further investigations would you perform to decide between the various hypotheses? It has been suggested that poor growth of crops in land cleared from *Andropogon* savanna may also be due to inhibition of nitrification. What assumption concerning the availability to crops of different nitrogen compounds is implied by this hypothesis? How could this assumption be tested?
5 Towards the top of the profile in Fig. 7.5 may be seen a layer in which stones are concentrated. Such 'stone-lines' are a common feature of tropical African soils. Two explanations have been suggested to account for stone-lines: (a) they date from a past dry period at which time they formed the stony surface of desert; (b) they result from the activities of termites which bring fine soil to the surface and leave the stones behind. What kinds of evidence would be useful in deciding between these theories?
6 When land is cleared for mechanical cultivation there is a risk that removal of topsoil may result in serious loss of fertility. What precautions might be taken to minimize this risk? Is the problem likely to be more serious in forest or in savanna? Explain.
7 The watershed of the River Pra lies entirely in forest,

whereas that of the River Volta lies mainly in savanna. In the light of these facts, comment on the differences between the rivers in water composition (Table 7.5).

8 Judging from the data in Tables 7.5 and 16.2, would you say that cropping or leaching is usually the more important cause of nutrient depletion of soils? What will be the effect of subsistence as compared to export cropping?

9 Which of the important plant nutrients do not occur in the common minerals of granite listed in Table 7.1? How does the plant obtain such nutrients?

10 How could you estimate for a soil (a) the level of termite activity (b) the effects of termites on soil fertility?

11 A study of two woodland millipedes showed that one species normally reproduces only once in its lifetime while the other has several annual broods. The former feeds upon widely dispersed leaf litter, the latter upon dead wood in which it also lays its eggs. Pieces of dead wood of a size suitable for colonization by the latter species are relatively rare. Show how the patterns of life history of these two decomposers may be related to survival on their different types of food resource.

Bibliography

Further reading

Ahn, P. M.　　　*West African Soils*, Oxford University Press, 1970

Baker, K. F.,　　*Ecology of Soil-borne Plant*
Snyder, W. C.　　*Pathogens*, Parts 2, 3 and 4, John Murray, 1965

Hudson, H. J.　　*Fungal saprophytism*, Edward Arnold, 1972, Chaps. 1, 2 and 3

Jackson, R. M.,　*Life in the Soil*, Arnold, 1966
Raw, F.

Nye, P. H.,　　　*The Soil under Shifting Cultivation*,
Greenland, D. J.　Commonwealth Agricultural Bureaux, 1960, Chaps. 1, 2, 3 and 4

Russell, E. W.　　*Soil Conditions and Plant Growth*, Longman, 1973

Wills, J. B. (ed.)　*Agriculture and Land Use in Ghana*, Oxford University Press, 1962, Chaps. 6, 7 and 8

Bormann, F. H.,　'The Nutrient Cycles of an
Likens, G. E.　　Ecosystem', *Scientific American*, 1970, Offprint no. 1202

Delwiche, C. C.　'The Nitrogen Cycle', *Scientific American*, 1970, Offprint no. 1194

Edwards, C. A.　'Soil Pollutants and Soil Animals', *Scientific American*, 1969, Offprint no. 1138

McNeil, M.　　　'Lateritic Soils', *Scientific American*, 1964, Offprint no. 870

Maio, J. J.　　　'Predatory fungi', *Scientific American*, 1958, Offprint no. 1094

Savory, T. H.　　'Hidden Lives', *Scientific American*, 1968, Offprint no. 1112

Part 3
The natural history of the food web

8 Relations between producers and consumers

In previous chapters we have seen that plants and animals are not scattered haphazardly over the surface of the earth, but occur in characteristic assemblages or communities. The number of such communities is very large, and it has been impossible in this book to deal with more than a few of them. Indeed a complete catalogue would, by itself, be not only massive but also uninformative. It is however possible to make interesting generalizations about communities. We have already pointed out that each community occurs within a certain range of environmental conditions, and that communities of a particular habitat, such as the seashore, may have many features in common even though they occur in different parts of the world. Some of the adaptations shown by communities to the main environments of sea, freshwater and land were considered in Book 1 Chaps. 20, 21 and 22.

In Chap. 6 we made the point that the members of a community are members of a common food web, and that the position of any organism within the web has profound influences on its structure and mode of life. In this and succeeding chapters we shall examine in greater detail the kinds of interrelations commonly found between the members of a food web. If the number of different communities is very large, the number of food webs is equally large. Each web includes very many organisms, and the possible number of interrelations is vastly greater again. To make sense of this abundance of relationships we shall look for a small number of unifying themes and patterns, illustrating them by representative examples.

To survive in a community, a species must be successful in securing food from a lower trophic level, and in avoiding being eaten by organisms of a higher trophic level. Losses of individual organisms are inevitably heavy (p. 252); a species will persist only if a sufficient number survive. We have already considered the ways in which plants in general obtain food (Book 1 Chaps. 7, 8 and 9), and the special adaptations of plants of the principal communities (Book 1 Chaps. 20, 21 and 22). We must next consider the ways in which they attempt to avoid being eaten.

Defences of producers against consumers

You may have wondered why it is that producers survive at all. What prevents them from being eaten up completely by consumers? One answer lies in the existence of predators: any large increase in the numbers of primary consumers is sooner or later controlled by a corresponding increase in the numbers of predators (see Chap. 15). A second answer lies in the abilities of the plants to defend themselves.

What are these defences? The ways in which consumers may avoid predation (Chap. 9) are easy to understand. They may run away or hide, either in a hole or by finding a background against which they are camouflaged. They may stand and fight using spines, teeth or claws, or produce noxious substances. Plants cannot of course run away. Sensitive plants such as *Mimosa pudica* will fold their leaves when touched, but whether this is a defence reaction is not known. A very few, such as *Lithops* (Fig. 8.1), are camouflaged. The great majority of plants depend on chemical defences; some also have mechanical defences, such as thorns.

Mechanical defences

Thorns are especially characteristic of the plants of dry savanna and semidesert. Most *Acacia* species, often the

8.1 *Lithops* growing in subdesert karroo in South Africa. The subspherical succulent leaves are difficult to distinguish from surrounding pebbles.

dominant trees in Sahel-type savanna (p. 59), are thorny (Fig. 8.2); hence the name 'thorn-scrub' sometimes given to this type of vegetation. Over-grazing of such savanna may weaken the grass and allow its replacement by *Acacia* thicket which is rejected by cattle.

Many of the succulent plants of semidesert are also thorny; this is particularly true of the cacti (Book 1 p. 279). Several thorny species of prickly pear (*Opuntia*) have become established in the drier parts of South Africa. The stem is flattened and fleshy; because of its high water content it is useful as cattle and sheep fodder during drought provided it is not the sole source of food. Before it can be eaten, however, the farmer must first remove the plant's defences. These are of two kinds (Fig. 8.3): long, sharply-pointed thorns which in the intact plant prevent the mouth of a large animal from reaching the stem, and around the spine bases, tiny barbed hairs which break off in the animal's skin and cause great irritation.

Sharp-pointed hairs which break off in the skin form a dense felt on the fruit of the itching bean, *Mucuna pruriens*, (Fig. 8.4); these hairs contain chemical substances which cause intense itching and inflammation, by stimulation of histamine production in the skin. (Histamine is the substance liberated by injured tissue which is responsible for the localized swelling around a wound.) Any one who has once attempted to collect the pods of this plant with bare hands is unlikely willingly to repeat the experience.

In some plants irritating barbed structures are found not on the surface but within the tissues. These are raphides, javelin-shaped crystals largely of calcium oxalate about 50 μm long which occur in special cells within the leaves, stems, tubers and pericarp of such plants as *Xanthosoma* (Fig. 8.5), the cocoyam. If a piece of fresh cocoyam leaf is cut while being examined under the low-power objective of the microscope, raphides can be seen to be flung out when the cells which contained them are damaged and turgor is released. If you attempt to eat raw cocoyam leaf or tuber, the ejected raphides will penetrate the lining of your mouth, causing great discomfort. Boiling makes cocoyam safe to eat because it kills the cells, so that they lose their turgor and thus the ability to shoot out raphides. If leaves of the grape-vine *Vitis* are

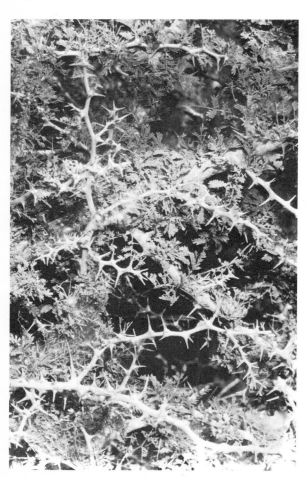

8.2 *Acacia* sp.; branches protected by sharp thorns.

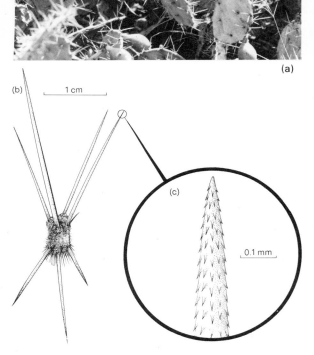

8.3 (a) *Opuntia* sp. showing clusters of thorns growing from the flattened, succulent branches. Note the egg-shaped fruits which are edible when ripe. (b) Group of thorns showing also the shorter bristles around the thorn bases. (c) Tip of thorn as seen under the microscope; note the barbs.

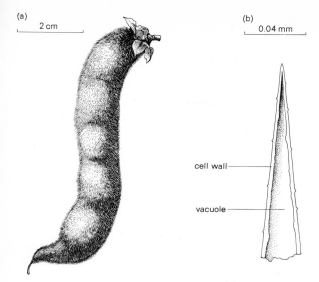

(a) 2 cm

(b) 0.04 mm

cell wall

vacuole

8.4 *Mucuna pruriens*, the itching bean. (a) Fruit which is covered by unicellular hairs 1·5 mm long which are easily detached from the base. (b) Tip of hair, highly magnified. There are minute lumps on the thick wall which help to hold the hair in the skin of an animal which touches it. The extreme point of the hair readily breaks off releasing an irritant solution from the vacuole.

treated with hydrochloric acid the raphides are dissolved. Larvae of the hawkmoth *Pterogon* (Lepidoptera) will not eat untreated *Vitis* leaves, but will accept those in which the raphides have been destroyed in this way.

Hairs which remain attached to the plant may also afford it protection. We have seen how hooked hairs on fruits may aid their dispersal (Fig. 1.10e). Tiny hooked hairs are sometimes found also on leaves and twigs. Their function was quite unknown until the recent discovery that in the passion-flower vine *Passiflora adenopoda* such hairs trap the abdominal appendages used by butterfly larvae (*Heliconius*) in walking, puncturing the cuticle and thus allowing the body fluids of the larvae to escape. The larvae are immobilized and soon die as a result of desiccation. The leaves of other species of *Passiflora* which lack hooked hairs are eaten by the caterpillars of *Heliconius*.

The action of *Passiflora* hairs is a purely mechanical one, but several plants (for example, *Mucuna*) carry hairs which not only puncture the skin but also liberate irritating substances. The best-studied example is the temperate nettle *Urtica*, in which the tip of the sharply-pointed hair is fragile; when it breaks off, the contents of the hair are released into the skin. Irritation is caused mainly by a mixture of acetylcholine and histamine. 'Stinging' hairs, working presumably on the same principle, are found on the common tropical African weeds *Tragia* (Fig. 8.6), *Urera* and *Laportea*.

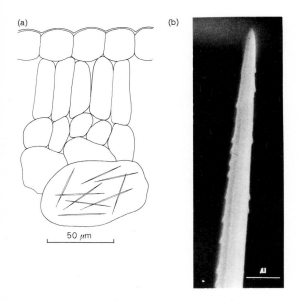

(a)

(b)

50 μm

8.5 Raphides of the cocoyam *Xanthosoma*. (a) Section through a leaf showing a raphide cell and a few remaining raphides from the hundreds which it originally contained; each raphide is a single calcium oxalate crystal about 50 μm long. (b) Tip of a raphide as seen under the electron microscope; note the barbs and the grooves through which the irritating contents of the cell can flow into the tissues of the mouth.

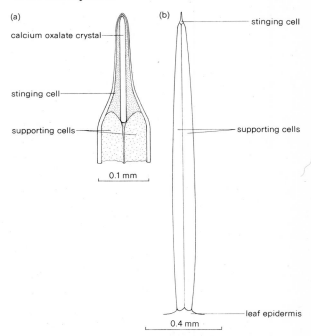

(a)

calcium oxalate crystal

stinging cell

supporting cells

0.1 mm

(b)

stinging cell

supporting cells

leaf epidermis

0.4 mm

8.6 Stinging hair from the leaf of the twining herb *Tragia*. (a) The terminal cell includes a single sharp crystal of calcium oxalate which breaks in the skin, allowing the stinging substance which is also contained in this cell to flow into the wound. (b) The rest of the hair serves to support the stinging cell.

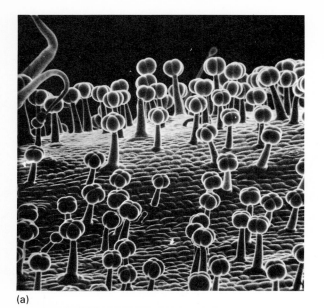

(a)

(b)

8.7 Trapping of aphids by sticky hairs of the wild hybrid potato *Solanum tuberosum × berthaulti*. (a) Glandular hairs. (b) The tarsus, or foot, of the leg of an aphid stuck down by the secretion of a hair, as seen under the electron microscope. The bulbs on the tops of the hairs are about $\frac{1}{20}$ mm in diameter.

Another principle is employed as a defence against aphids by three species of *Solanum* related to the potato (*S. tuberosum*). The leaves and stems of these species possess glandular hairs (Fig. 8.7) tipped by cells that secrete a liquid which, clear at first, becomes black and sticky when exposed to the air. An aphid which attempts to walk over the plant may rupture some of the cells and become firmly stuck down, like a fly on sticky fly-paper.

In tests on one of these species, *S. polyadenium*, 30 percent of the aphids released onto it were immobilized within an hour; subsequently they died of starvation.

Chemical defences

The essential substances which are common to all higher plants were considered in Book 1 (Chaps. 4, 5 and 9); they include carbohydrates, lipids, proteins, co-enzymes, nucleic acids and nucleotides, chlorophylls and lignin. Although these jointly contribute the bulk of the organic matter of any higher plant, they include only a minority of the substances found in the plant kingdom. Plants contain an enormous variety of so-called 'secondary' substances such as gums, terpenes, glucosides, alkaloids, tannins and phenolic compounds. Many of these are of considerable commercial importance. Many alkaloids are useful as drugs, for example the tranquillizing compound reserpine in *Rauvolfia*, or in beverages, as caffeine in tea and coffee, theobromine in cocoa and so on. Some glyco-

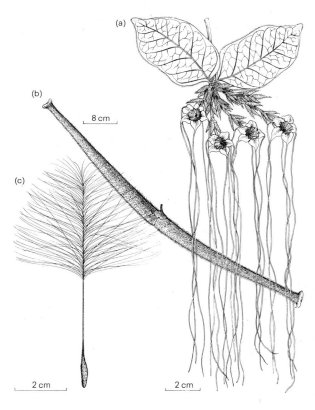

8.8 The arrow-poison plant *Strophanthus hispidus*. (a) Flowering shoot, showing the long 'tails' at the tips of the petals. (b) Fruit just before dehiscence. (c) Seed, which is wind-dispersed with the help of a parachute of hairs. The glucoside strophanthine is obtained from the seeds.

sides, such as those extracted from species of *Strophanthus* (Fig. 8.8), were used in the past as arrow poisons and are now employed medicinally to control the heart rate. Many phenolics and terpenes are useful as flavourings, some phenolics are dyes and some terpenes are rubbers, while tannins are used for tanning leather. Because of their economic value there has been much research into the chemical structure of these secondary substances and their pathways of synthesis within plants, as well as into their distribution within the plant kingdom. Their biological significance, however, has scarcely been considered. Botanists of the early nineteenth century believed, as do many herbalists even today, that these substances were put into plants by a beneficent Providence solely for the use of His favourite creature, Man. A later generation of botanists regarded them as waste products of metabolism, and of no biological significance. It is only in recent years that evidence has begun to accumulate which suggests that their most important role may be that of chemical defence against consumers. Much of this evidence is indirect and as yet unsupported by critical experiment but, taken as a whole, the theory provides a far more plausible explanation than any other so far suggested for the great diversity of secondary substances; it gives also a rational basis for further experimentation.

It is a striking fact that the majority of plants are, at least to some extent, toxic. Caution is necessary in the consumption even of many crop plants. Cocoyam is not only disagreeable to eat when raw because of the piercing action of raphides, but is also slightly toxic when cooked because the calcium oxalate of which the raphides consist is poisonous. Cassava tubers always contain poisonous cyanogenic glycosides in the peel; bitter varieties contain them in the flesh also. Glycosides consist of sugar combined with other substances; in cyanogenic glycosides, these include hydrogen cyanide which is fatal to man even at very low concentrations; cyanide is released when such glycosides are digested in the alimentary canal. Bitter cassava can be made fit to eat only by lengthy boiling followed by thorough washing. Wild forms of the yam *Dioscorea dumetorum* contain a poisonous alkaloid, dioscorine, and poisoning may result if they are eaten in mistake for cultivated, less toxic, forms of the same species.

The only plant organs which can be eaten with benefit to the plant itself are ripe fruits: these may be fleshy and pleasant-tasting to attract the animals which disperse the seeds. Fruits plucked before ripening will not yield viable seeds, and it is probably not a coincidence that these are often sour, as are unripe oranges, or poisonous as in akee apple (*Blighia sapida*).

Latex

Within the tissues of many species of plant lies a ramifying system of fine tubes, laticifers, containing a viscous liquid,

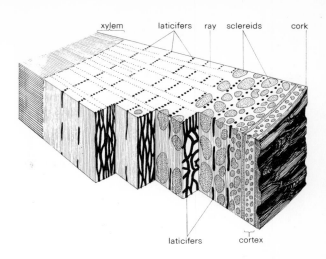

8.9 Diagram to show the distribution of laticifers (latex-containing tubes) in the phloem of the Pará rubber tree *Hevea brasiliensis*. When the tree is tapped for rubber, the phloem is cut across with a sharp knife thus allowing latex to flow from the severed laticifers. (After Esau).

latex (Fig. 8.9). Because the latex is under turgor pressure it will flow out if the plant is wounded; it may then clot in a manner reminiscent of blood. Commercial rubber is obtained by coagulating the latex of the Pará rubber tree (*Hevea brasiliensis*) and chewing gum from latex of the sapodilla tree (*Achras sapota*). Although a great deal is known about the properties of those kinds of latex which are useful to man, the possible value of latex to the plant itself has received only scant attention. It is probable, however, that latex will serve to wash away or trap insects which wound the plant, and also to seal the wound against invasion by fungi. Latex is frequently toxic, and the poisons which it contains may augment its value as a defence mechanism. *Opuntia*, a succulent cactus introduced to Africa from America, is protected only by its spines and barbed hairs (p. 138); if these are removed it is readily eaten by stock. The succulent plants indigenous to Africa, such as species of *Euphorbia* and *Aloe* (Book 1 p. 281), are often somewhat spiny, but their defence lies mainly in the possession of poisonous latex. *Aloe* yields a very bitter phenolic substance, aloin, which is used in medicine as a strong purgative. The latex of many succulent *Euphorbia* species has been used as arrow poison. The merest trace of latex of *E. poissoni* (Fig. 8.10) wiped on the lips will cause an unpleasant burning sensation lasting several hours. *Calotropis procera* (Fig. 8.11), a small shrub which grows as a weed in subdesert and dry savanna areas, has latex which contains a heart poison, calotropin.

8.10 The succulent shrub *Euphorbia poissoni* growing in rocky savanna in West Africa. It contains extremely pungent white latex.

8.12 Most of the grass in this picture has been grazed low by cattle. The ungrazed patch in which the man is standing consists of the grass *Bothriochloa bladhii* whose leaves are strongly aromatic and unpalatable to cows.

8.11 *Calotropis procera*, a shrub of semi-desert regions which also grows as a weed of roadsides in dry savanna. The abundant white latex is poisonous.

Defence against domestic stock

Many savanna plants are toxic to domestic stock such as cattle and sheep. If allowed to range freely, animals soon learn to avoid plants of disagreeable taste (Fig. 8.12), but if they are penned on pasture where toxic species happen to be common, deaths may result. The shrub *Leucaena leucocephala* is rich in protein, and may be a useful fodder in small quantity, but taken in larger amounts it is toxic, causing loss of hair. The main toxic agent is not a compound synthesized by the plant itself, but the element selenium which accumulates in the plant to reach a concentration much higher than that in the soil. Some species which are valuable fodder grasses when raised under conditions favourable to rapid growth may become toxic after drought, thus perhaps protecting themselves against grazing at a time unfavourable to rapid recovery. For example, the foliage of sorghum (*Sorghum bicolor*) and guinea grass (*Panicum maximum*) may produce cyanogenic glycosides in response to drought.

Defence against insects

For most plants the important consumers are not man or large herbivores, but insects; it is therefore to be expected that many plants will contain substances which are poisonous to insects. The best known are those compounds which are extracted from plants for use as insecticides. In East and South Africa the insecticide pyrethrum is produced on a large scale from the young flower heads of *Chrysanthemum cinerariaefolium* (Fig. 8.13). Rotenone, another insecticide, is obtained from the roots of the woody leguminous climber *Derris elliptica*; this substance is also effective as a fish poison. Also leguminous is the shrub *Tephrosia vogelii* (Fig. 8.14),

8.13 Field of pyrethrum (*Chrysanthemum cinerariaefolium*) in East Africa. The flowers are dried and powdered to obtain a powerful insecticide.

which is grown all over Africa for use as a fish poison as well as for killing fleas and lice.

The most powerful natural insecticide is perhaps the familiar alkaloid nicotine, obtained from tobacco, *Nicotiana tabacum;* 0·06 g of pure nicotine, the quantity which could be extracted from about five cigarettes, is sufficient to kill a man. Nicotine is synthesized in the roots of the plant and thence translocated to the shoot, poisoning non-resistant insects which eat the leaves. Tobacco belongs to the same plant family as potato, *Solanum tuberosum*, and the shoot of one can be grafted to the root of the other. This technique has been used to demonstrate experimentally the effectiveness of nicotine in defence against consumers. When larvae of the Colorado potato beetle, *Leptinotarsa decemlineata*, were put to feed on the leaves of a *Nicotiana* shoot grafted to a *Nicotiana* rootstock, all shortly died. When placed on *Nicotiana* leaves of a shoot which was grafted to a potato stock and therefore nicotine-free, 61 out of 80 survived.

The effects of compounds such as alkaloids and glycosides on the organs of the animals which they poison have been well known for a long time. Recently suggestions have been made as to the mode of operation of other plant substances. Tannins are abundant in many plants, and especially so in the bark of trees such as *Acacia*

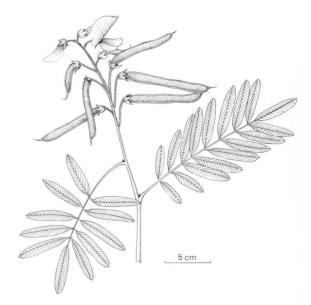

8.14 *Tephrosia vogelii*, a shrub which is grown throughout tropical Africa as a fish poison. Fish are intoxicated and easily caught when the crushed pulp of the plant is mixed with the water in river pools.

143

and *Rhizophora* which are used for tanning leather, but their function was not apparent until experiments were made with the larvae of the winter moth, *Operophtera brumata*, which feeds on the young leaves of the temperate oak tree, *Quercus*. It was found that the leaves are palatable to the larvae shortly after flushing when they contain only 0·2 percent of tannin, but that mature leaves with a 2 percent tannin content cannot support larval growth. Tannin reacts with protein to form a complex which is not broken down by animal proteases; addition of tannin to the artificial casein diet on which larvae were successfully reared reduced their average weight increment from 25·2 to 11·7 mg after 13 days.

A very different type of action is shown by plant substances which resemble certain insect hormones. There are in insects two hormones which affect development; one, ecdysone, is principally concerned with the process of moulting while the other, juvenile hormone, is involved with the changes which occur at metamorphosis (p. 309). Chemicals which have an action similar to the first of these have been found in about 50 of over 1 000 different plants which have been tested. When ingested some of these prevent normal development of certain insects and can be active at minute concentrations. Thus, for example, the inclusion of one such compound in the diet resulted in less than 10 per cent of the larvae tested becoming adults. The other type of compound is found in certain coniferous trees and, apart from killing certain insects which ingest it, it has a sterilizing action on their eggs.

Resistance to fungi

Usually the reasons for differences between crop varieties in resistance to fungi are not known, but in the case of black rot disease of sweet potato roots, caused by the fungus *Ceratocystis fimbriata*, resistant varieties are found to produce more ipomeamarone, a terpene-like substance which is toxic to the fungus, than do non-resistant varieties (Table 8.1). Ipomeamarone is not a normal

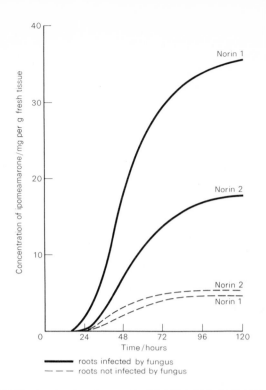

8.15 Production by the roots of two varieties of sweet potato (*Ipomoea batatas*) of the substance ipomeamarone which is toxic to the parasitic fungus *Ceratocystis fimbriata*. Both varieties respond to fungal infection by increasing their production of ipomeamarone but Norin 1 which is much more resistant to the fungus than Norin 2, produces this substance in greater quantity. (After Akazawa and Wada).

constituent of sweet potato roots, but is produced in response to injury. Fig. 8.15 shows that the quantity produced is increased by the presence of the fungus, especially in the case of the resistant variety.

Resistance to nematodes

The substances mentioned above are produced by plant cells and remain within them, or at least do not diffuse far. Plants which liberate toxic substances into the soil are of particular interest because of the possibility that they could be used for the control of soil-living pathogens. Such a plant is *Tagetes patula*, a marigold, which reduces populations of the plant-parasitic nematode *Paratylenchus* by as much as 90 percent; the active substance has been isolated and identified. The Mary Washington variety of asparagus is resistant to nematode attack, and it also apparently secretes a nematocide into the soil. The nematode *Globodera rostochiensis* causes considerable

Table 8.1 Quantity of ipomeamarone synthesized during 24 h by roots of different varieties of sweet potato following infection with black rot fungus, *Ceratocystis fimbriata* (*Data from Akazawa and Wada*)

Variety	Resistance status	Ipomeamarone synthesized (mg g^{-1} fresh tissue 24 h^{-1})
Norin 10	very high resistance	45·5
Norin 1	high resistance	16·4
Norin 2	low resistance	8·9
Norin 3	very low resistance	1·6

losses in potato, and much effort has been devoted to searching for resistant varieties, particularly among the potato varieties of the Andes of South America where the crop was first domesticated. Some forms of one of these, *Solanum tuberosum* subspecies *andigena*, are not only resistant, but reduce by as much as 70 percent the population of nematode eggs in the soil (Fig. 8.16). The roots of this potato liberate into the soil a substance which causes the eggs to hatch. The larvae penetrate the roots but are unable to complete their development; consequently the egg population is not replenished.

Appreciation of the importance of protective devices in plants has been slow, partly because of the difficulty in finding a criterion by which to judge success. We may find that one particular species of plant is less palatable than another to some particular insect consumer. How can we tell whether this is of importance for the survival of the resistant species? This is not a difficult question to answer for an animal; the removal of a considerable part of its body will kill it either immediately or within quite a short time. On the other hand a plant may apparently be scarcely affected by the loss of a few leaves or roots. We may suspect that its vigour will be reduced, but it is difficult to test the significance of this in a natural community. Leaves and rootlets are in any case short-lived organs.

Although it is difficult in this instance to obtain direct experimental proof for the survival value of what appear to be adaptations, work in other areas of biology is providing increased support for the working hypothesis

that 'organisms make sense'. In other words, it is generally true that organisms can survive only if they are efficient, and do not produce structures and substances that are of no value to them. Making a thorn and making alkaloids are both activities which require the expenditure of energy, which could otherwise be used for producing obviously useful structures such as leaves and roots. Herein perhaps lies the answer to the question as to why *Opuntia* does not have poisonous sap as well as long thorns. Just as the money spent on defence is a burden on the budget of a country, so too defence expenditure must be a burden on the energy budget of a plant. The 'arms race' is also a concept which can be applied to plants in their relation to insects. A plant which acquires a new 'weapon', such as nicotine, will eventually be attacked by an insect, such as the tobacco hornworm, which is resistant to it.

Food finding by primary consumers

So far we have examined the natural history of the food web with regard to the factors which tend to disrupt the first link in the chain. Clearly we can also ask about phenomena which may assist primary consumers in finding suitable sources of food. Sight, smell, taste and perhaps texture are the sensory stimuli of importance here and we are concerned with how the characteristics of different types of food may relate to the sensory equipment of different herbivores. Analytical studies of the factors that determine which plant materials will be eaten by herbivores and which rejected have so far been made almost exclusively upon insects.

Food location by smell

Food finding in insects may depend upon smell. For example, if locust nymphs or hoppers are placed in a large, sealed vessel through which air is blown, they tend to walk downwind. If, however, the air is first passed across freshly cut grass, the hoppers will move upwind. The results of such experiments are summarized in Table 8.2. The intensity of the response of the hoppers to the smell of grass was affected by the time since they last fed.

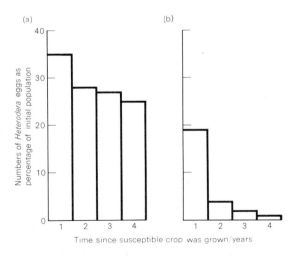

8.16 Concentration in the topsoil of eggs of the nematode *Globodera rostochiensis* which attacks the roots of potato. (a) Shows the gradual decline in numbers when land is fallowed or when non-susceptible crops such as wheat, barley and sugarbeet are grown. (b) Shows the much faster decline in egg population when resistant potato variety *Solanum tuberosum* sub.sp. *andigena* is grown. (After Cole and Howard).

Table 8.2 Direction of response of starved hoppers of the desert locust, *Schistocerca*, in air currents with and without the smell of grass (*After Haskell et al.*)

Air current content	Percentage of hoppers orienting		Total number tested
	Upwind	Downwind	
No smell	34	66	262
Smell of grass	93	7	120

Hoppers which had just fed showed almost no response; 68 percent oriented downwind. When, however, they had been starved for eight hours, 70 percent oriented upwind towards the source of the smell. The fact that this response is shown by starved but not by recently fed hoppers suggests that it can have significance in food finding.

Food location by sight

The potential importance of vision for insects which feed from coloured flowers is suggested by the fact that many insects have colour vision. This has been studied, for example, in the honey bee. If a small dish of sugar solution is set out near a hive, the bees will soon find the food. If such bees are marked with a small dot of paint so that individuals can be recognized, the same bees can be seen to visit the food source repeatedly. In other words, the bees can be trained to come to a source of food. This sort of experiment may now be carried out with a series of different coloured cards spread out upon a table. Each card has on it a small dish containing water, except for one, say blue; on this blue card the dish contains sugar solution. The bees learn to come to the table for food and will soon fly directly to the dish over the blue card. The cards are then moved about, so that the blue card is in some different place among the rest. The bees will still fly directly to the dish on top of the blue card. Clearly they are distinguishing the blue card from the rest and one might attribute this result to the ability to distinguish the colour blue from the other colours.

By itself, this experiment is not critical. If we took a black-and-white photograph of the cards, different colours would appear as different shades of grey, since some reflect more light than others. It is possible therefore that the bees are not responding to blue as a distinct colour: they may have no colour vision but have learnt to associate the food source with some particular shade of grey. This point was tested by putting out a coloured card among cards of a number of different shades of grey: the bees indeed selected the coloured card from among the grey ones, indicating that they are, at least to some extent, capable of distinguishing different colours.

Food location by sight and smell

Flower selection in bees is also influenced by scent, so that smell as well as sight is involved in locating a source of nectar. Just as it is possible to test the ability of bees to distinguish between different colours by training them to select one particular feeding dish out of many, so too bees can be trained to come to a food source, such as sugar solution, which has associated with it some particular scent. The bees were offered a choice of small, identically coloured boxes each with an entrance hole cut in one side. Most of the boxes were empty; one contained sugar solution and either a flower or a chemically purified flower scent. After a period of training, all the boxes were replaced by empty ones, except for one which contained the source of scent but no sugar solution. The bees entered only this box. The boxes were moved about to eliminate any effect due to their relative positions, but this did not affect the behaviour of the bees.

Attractiveness of flowers to bees can thus depend both on colour and on scent. Similar experiments have shown this to be true for other pollinating insects. The relative importance of these clues has been studied in bees by training foragers initially to a blue box containing both food and flower scent. They were then offered the choice of a blue box containing no scent and a yellow box with scent. In conditions where the bees were forced to make a choice some distance from the boxes (Fig. 8.17), they mostly went to the blue box. But where they were able to approach both boxes closely, they chose the one with the scent. Thus it seems that, at least in bees, their distance response is to colour, but their short-range response is to scent. In further experiments, scented and unscented coloured discs were placed in the field, and the numbers of foraging bees attracted to the two types of disc were noted; about 60 percent selected the scented discs. This effect is not very great, but the importance of the scent is shown by the fact that while more than 60 percent of the foragers actually settled on the scented discs, less than 2 percent settled on the unscented ones.

Food recognition by taste

Responses to the sight or smell of food may take an insect into the general area where acceptable plants occur, but

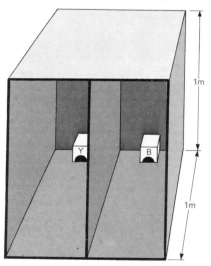

8.17 Training boxes Y (yellow) and B (blue) used to test the relative importance of colour and scent in flower selection by bees. Each box was enclosed within a large box open on one side so that the bee was made to select at a distance of at least 1 m from the training boxes. (After von Frisch).

Table 8.3 Response of silkworm larvae when various extracts from mulberry leaves are added to a minimal diet (*Data from Hamamura*)

Extract added	Extract believed to contain	Mean number of faecal pellets dropped overnight
Methanol extract (M)	attractant and biting factor	52
Ether extract of M (E)	biting factor only	4
Hot-water extract (W)	swallowing factor only	5
E + W	biting and swallowing factors	52
M + W	all three factors	144

taste seems to be mainly involved in the final choice of which plants any insect will attack. There can be three distinct phases in this process. The first is that of finding a suitable food plant, the second is that of biting it and the third that of actually eating it. In some instances these three responses have been shown to depend upon three distinct chemical substances. This is true of silkworm larvae. In a study of their feeding responses, the larvae were allowed to feed overnight upon a medium which contained 3 percent agar, 1 percent sucrose and 5 percent paper fibre. The paper served simply to give bulk to the faecal pellets which were collected and counted, thus providing a measure of the intensity of feeding. To this medium were added different fractions extracted from mulberry leaves, the normal food of the larvae. Table 8.3 summarizes briefly the types of result obtained.

Some insects are limited to a single food plant (monophagous), some will eat only a few (oligophagous) while others feed on a wide variety (polyphagous). Experimentally it is easier to determine what factors are of significance in the feeding of monophagous and oligophagous insects since, as in the silkworm, these are likely to be specific attractive or stimulatory chemical substances. The action of such a substance may be illustrated by experiments on two varieties of water melon. One was a normal edible variety; the other was a bitter variety, the taste being due to the presence of a steroidal chemical. Specimens of both types of fruit were cut in half and equal numbers of the halves left in the open for 24 h. At the end of that time the insects on the two types of fruit were collected. The results obtained are shown in Table 8.4: the bitter melon was rejected by both bees and wasps, but was very attractive to a small beetle. That the response of the beetle was due to this specific chemical was demonstrated in a further series of experiments. This bitter principle is thus acting as a repellent to some species and as an attractant to others.

The larvae of a moth, *Plutella* (Lepidoptera) are similarly attracted by substances which are repellent to other animals. The larvae will feed upon a number of plants such as cabbage (*Brassica*) belonging to the family Cruciferae. All of these contain mustard oils which are chemically combined with sugars to form glycosides.

Table 8.4 Insects found on bitter and non-bitter water melon after 24 h exposure of samples (*Data from Chambliss and Jones*)

Insect	Average number of insects per sample	
	Bitter	Non-bitter
Honey bee	0·6	3·5
Wasp	0·0	6·0
Cucumber beetle	78·4	7·5

These substances repel most insects; however, as illustrated by the data in Table 8.5, they stimulate the feeding of *Plutella* larvae. In this experiment the leaves of various plants were painted with a mustard oil glycoside and it was noted how vigorously the leaves were attacked. Lettuce leaves presumably contain some substance which is repellent to the larvae and this protects them from attack even in the presence of the added chemical.

This response to mustard oil glycosides is not peculiar to *Plutella*. It is also shown by the larvae of a butterfly, *Pieris*, which feeds on cabbage, and by the Cabbage Aphid (Hemiptera). There is furthermore a small wasp (Hymenoptera) which parasitizes the aphid and this also is attracted by the smell of mustard oils. Finally there is a fungus *Plasmodiophora*, which attacks cabbage; its spores are stimulated to germinate by mustard oils. Here we have an example of a number of organisms, primary and secondary consumers as well as a decomposer, which form

Table 8.5 Feeding response of *Plutella* larvae to leaves of different plants treated with mustard oil glycosides. Intensity of feeding response was in proportion to the number of + signs; − indicates no feeding response (*Data from Thorsteinson*)

Source of material	Untreated	Treated
Onion	−	+ + + + +
Cucumber	−	+ + + + +
Pea	−	+ +
Lettuce	−	−

a tiny community bound together by their responses to a secondary plant substance which serves to protect the plant from attack by a far wider range of consumers.

The food preferences of a considerable number of monophagous or oligophagous insects are determined by the presence of secondary plant substances. Although these substances are repellent to most insects, in these species they act as positive stimulants to feeding behaviour. Since such chemicals will be found in only a few species of plant in any one habitat, such insects will attack only one or a few plant species within that habitat. We can thus understand the basis of at least some cases of restricted food preference. How can we explain the fact that some insects attack a wide variety of plants? One possible explanation is as follows: assuming that such insects will feed on any plant material unless it is positively repellent or distasteful, the extent to which a secondary plant substance is repellent to a particular species will depend upon the sensitivity of the insect's chemoreceptors. This pattern of sensitivity is likely to differ from one species to another. No single species will be sensitive to all repellent substances; each is thus able to feed upon a diversity of the available plants.

Fig. 8.18 expresses these ideas diagrammatically. A to G represent different secondary plant substances synthesized by different species of plant. The + signs indicate the presence in an insect of a chemoreceptor responsive to this substance. Stimulation of the receptor may result in the insect being either attracted or repelled. A zero indicates the absence of a responding sense organ. Species 1 and 2 which are monophagous and oligophagous respectively show positive attraction to certain substances; species 3 and 4 are both polyphagous but will attack different ranges of plant material as a result of the difference in their sense organs. Note that species 2, 3 and 4 all have sense organs which respond to substance C, but that the behavioural responses of the insects to this stimulus differ. To test whether such differences in fact occur would require an extensive study of the specificity of responses of the chemoreceptors of a number of polyphagous insects and this has not, as yet, been undertaken.

Attraction of pollinating insects

So far we have considered the ways in which primary consumers recognize their food and emphasized the ways in which the producers attempt to protect themselves from attack. Nevertheless, many flowering plants depend upon insects, birds or bats as agents to effect cross-pollination (Book 1 p. 300 ff). Such flowers may be expected to display characteristics which will stimulate the sensory equipment of their pollinators.

We have already seen one aspect of this in the fact that bees have colour vision (p. 146). Experiments using both behavioural responses and recordings of nerve impulses from the eyes have shown that many other insects have colour vision as well. This differs from our own in one important respect: the range of wavelengths to which an insect eye is sensitive extends further into the ultra-violet and less far into the red (Fig. 8.19). As a result, two flowers

Chemicals produced by different plants	A	B	C	D	E	F	G
1 Monophagous insect:							
sensory response	+	+	+	+	+	+	+
behavioural response	repelled	repelled	repelled	repelled	repelled	attracted attacks	repelled
2 Oligophagous insect:							
sensory response	+	+	+	+	+	0	+
behavioural response	repelled	repelled	attracted attacks	repelled	repelled	can attack	attracted attacks
3 Polyphagous insect:							
sensory response	+	0	+	0	+	0	0
behavioural response	repelled	can attack	repelled	can attack	repelled	can attack	can attack
4 Polyphagous insect:							
sensory response	0	+	+	0	0	+	0
behavioural response	can attack	repelled	repelled	can attack	can attack	repelled	can attack

8.18 Diagram showing a possible hypothesis to explain how different insects may have differing ranges of food plant. The responsiveness of each insect's chemoreceptors to the different chemicals is indicated by +, meaning that the sense organs are responsive, or by 0, meaning that the sense organs do not respond. The behavioural response likely to be shown by each insect towards each species of plant is also indicated.

Wave length	300	400	500	600	700	nm
Colour	ultra-violet	violet indigo blue	green	yellow orange	red	

8.19 Range of spectral sensitivity of the eye of a man and a honey bee.

both of which appear uniformly coloured to us may have distinct patterns for the eye of an insect. This can happen if each petal has two chemically different pigments, one of which reflects ultra-violet light while the other does not (Fig. 8.20). Such ultra-violet reflecting pigments are not found in flowers pollinated by bats or birds. Moreover purely red flowers are rare; most red flowers have some blue pigment in them and, where this is absent, the flower is usually pollinated by birds or bats. Thus there is a clear-cut relation between certain aspects of flower colour and the characteristics of the eyes of pollinators.

Observations on bees collecting nectar, and thus incidentally cross-pollinating flowers, show that individual bees, recognized by small paint marks, will regularly visit the flowers of only one plant species, even though several different species are available. This, spoken of as 'flower constancy', persists from day to day. Different individual bees from the same hive will show constancy for different species of flower. When a bee first flies out to forage and alights upon a flower, she does not immediately find the nectar, but probes about with her extended proboscis until she finds the food. After a few visits, however, she goes immediately to the source of nectar. She has clearly learnt something about the structure of the flower. From this one can appreciate the value of 'flower constancy', as the time a foraging bee will need to spend on a flower while collecting nectar will be considerably reduced.

Honey guides

We can also ask whether flowers have any features which are used as clues by bees to find the source of nectar. It was suggested long ago that the colour patterns to be seen on different flowers might serve as such clues (Fig. 8.21). These markings were spoken of as 'honey guides' but the

8.20 Photographs of the flower of the Evening Primrose *Cenothera*. (a) Taken with a normal camera. The lenses filter out ultra-violet light, so that the photograph shows what is seen by the human eye. (b) Taken with a special camera with lenses allowing the passage of ultra-violet light. The flower is illuminated with ultra-violet light and the camera fitted with a filter to absorb visible light. The apical part of each petal reflects the ultra-violet light, the basal part absorbs it. Since the eye of a bee is sensitive to ultra-violet light, it will 'see' a pattern.

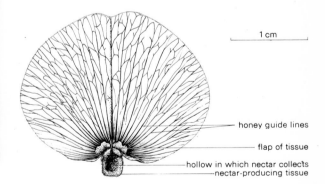

8.21 Uppermost petal of *Crotalaria* flower. The broad part of the petal is yellow, bearing a pattern of purplish lines which converge and become more obvious towards the base where the nectary is located. This pattern may serve to guide a bee towards the nectar. The flaps of tissue keep from the nectary insects which are too small to push them aside and therefore also too small to work the pollination mechanism (see Book 1 Fig. 24.7).

149

evidence that this is indeed their function was circumstantial. Thus, for example, it was found that while only 24 out of 177 regularly shaped flowers visited by bumble bees had honey guides, 60 out of 179 irregularly shaped flowers carried such markings. It was argued that there would be greater difficulty in finding the nectaries of an irregularly shaped than of a regularly shaped flower and that correspondingly 'honey guides' were much more common on the former.

The problem has been studied experimentally with both honey bees and bumble bees; the animals were trained to come to flat, coloured shapes using honey as a bait. Subsequently their behaviour towards similar models in the absence of any bait was observed. In experiments with bumble bees various shapes were used (Fig. 8.22). The first experiment asked the question whether a pattern made a flower model more attractive. Bumble bees were trained simultaneously to two models *a* and *b*. Subsequently, when their responses at a distance of about 60 cm from the models was observed, it was found that they made no selection between them. The patterned model was not in itself more attractive from a distance: thus the function of the 'honey guides' was not just to make the flowers more attractive.

When the bumble bees approached any model closely, they would dip down towards it, but not alight. Commonly they made such movements several times before flying away. We may regard this movement as a preliminary to settling and the place where the bumble bees would have settled was noted. In these experiments two slightly different models, *c* and *d*, were used. The position of first and then of subsequent responses with the two models are summarized in Table 8.6. It is clear that in both cases the initial response was to alight upon the edge of the flower model and further that the tendency to alight subsequently on the centre of the model was greatly enhanced by the presence of the guiding lines. This is interpreted as implying that in foraging a bumble bee will first alight upon the edge of a flower, where the colour contrast with the background is greatest, and that it will subsequently tend to follow any pattern of lines or dots which, usually, lead it to the nectaries.

We have seen that honey bees learn the way to the nectaries of the flowers they visit: the role of guide lines in this learning process has been shown by further experiments with models. Bees were first tested with a model

Table 8.6 Responses of bumble bees to models *c* and *d* in Fig. 8.21 (*Data from Manning*)

Position of	Model c		Model d	
	Edge	Centre	Edge	Centre
first response	119	3	128	8
subsequent responses	124	58	45	232

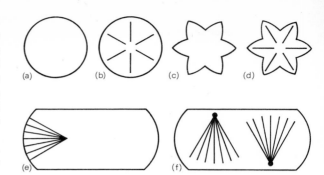

8.22 Drawings of models used in experiments on honey guides. In (a), (b), (c) and (d), the models consist of yellow lines on a blue background: in (e) and (f), of blue lines on a yellow background. (After Manning and Free).

such as *e* and their alighting points noted. They were then trained with a different model *f* in which honey rewards were placed at the two points of intersection of the fans of radiating lines. They were then tested once more with model *e*. The results obtained are summarized in Table 8.7. They show clearly that many of the bees had learnt to use the pattern as a guide to the point of intersection where the reward had been found.

Table 8.7 Responses of honey bees to model *e* before and after training with model *f* (*Data from Free*)

Position of landing	On intersection	On guide lines	Elsewhere	N
Before training	8·3%	69·4%	22·2%	36
After training	34·6%	57·3%	8·1%	136

*N is the number of observations made.

From such experiments there seems good reason to accept the original hypothesis that lines and rows of dots leading towards the nectaries of flowers do indeed act as 'honey guides'.

Pseudocopulation in orchid flowers

While in these examples the bait ensuring pollination is food, some orchids of the genus *Ophrys* have exploited a totally different response of insect pollinators. Their flowers, which secrete no nectar, resemble in shape and coloration the females of certain hymenopterous insects and the males, in attempting to copulate with the flowers, collect pollen and in this way ensure cross-fertilization of the plants (Fig. 8.23). Different species of *Ophrys* resemble the females of different species of solitary bees and wasps. Furthermore in many species of Hymenoptera the females produce odours, characteristic for each species; these are attractive to the males. Odours closely similar to those of

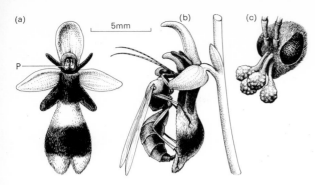

(a) (b) (c)

5mm

P

8.23 (a) The flower of the orchid *Ophrys insectifera*. The position of the pollen sacs or pollinia is indicated by P. (b) Male bee attempting to copulate with the flower. Note that the insect's 'face' is at the level of the pollinia. (c) Head of the male after attempted copulation showing the pollinia attached to the 'face'. (After Wickler).

the relevant species of insect are produced by the flowers of different species of *Ophrys*. It seems likely that in searching for a mate, the male bee or wasp is first activated by this smell; as a result he will be stimulated to seek for a female near the orchid flowers.

The success of this method of cross-pollination depends upon the male insects being attracted to the flowers as readily as to females of their own species. In some species of *Ophrys* the odour produced by the flower is more attractive to the males than that produced by the female insects. Further, in some species of Hymenoptera the males emerge from the pupal stage each year about a fortnight before the females, so that the orchid flowers receive their full attention.

Our analysis of the feeding responses of phytophagous insects shows that, like habitat selection, food selection is not a matter of chance but is determined by behaviour; this is true also of the pollination of flowers. It shows further that there can be within a community sensory interactions between members of different trophic levels and that certain characteristics of the producers relate to those of the sensory equipment of the first-order consumers. Their interrelations are thus closer than would appear from a purely formal description of the food web of a particular community. As we shall see, the relations between first- and higher-order consumers similarly result in a variety of phenomena which are comprehensible in terms of their trophic interrelations.

Problems

1 Why may the proportion of trees which bear thorns be higher in arid and semi-arid areas than in moister regions?

2 How do plant cells protect themselves against the cyanide and tannin which they produce?

3 What answer would you make to the suggestion that substances which are effective as drugs were put into plants by God to help man cure his ailments?

4 On p. 139 it is stated that *Pterogon* will not eat vine leaves unless they have first been treated with hydrochloric acid. Does this prove that intact leaves are protected against the moth by the raphides which they contain?

5 It is stated on p. 7 that fruits contain far more tannins and phenolic compounds when unripe than when ripe. How may this situation be of advantage to plants?

6 The following structures are found more commonly on young than on mature leafy shoots: functional extra-floral nectaries, stalked glands, stipules, gummy exudate, tiny hooks. What explanations can you suggest?

7 The rare gymnosperm *Gingko* still occurs semi-wild in China, and is known from fossils to have existed as a genus for at least 200 million years. Recent investigations have shown that it produces several chemical substances which are toxic to bacteria, fungi and insects, and that it is remarkably free from pests and diseases. It has been suggested that its good chemical defences may have contributed to its extraordinary longevity. Do you find this suggestion convincing? What further data would help you to make a decision?

8 On p. 146 an experiment is described in which it is shown that bees can learn to associate a particular coloured card with the presence of sugar solution. It is implied that the bees therefore distinguish this card by its colour, or some other visual quality of the card. Is there any other sensory stimulus to which the bees might be reacting? What further experiment is required to make the demonstration of colour vision fully critical?

9 Using the data provided in Table 8.3, set out fully the arguments that mulberry leaves contain three distinct chemical substances involved in the feeding responses of silkworm larvae.

10 *Plutella* larvae and the beetles attacking bitter melon both show responses to secondary plant substances. On the basis of the data provided in Tables 8.4 and 8.5 can it be concluded that these substances have similar actions?

11 Design an experiment to test whether the feeding response of cucumber beetles is increased by the bitter chemical found in one variety of water melon.

12 On p. 147 it is suggested that the reason why *Plutella* larvae do not attack lettuce leaves (Table 8.5) is that the latter contain a repellant. Suggest an alternative hypothesis.

13 It is desired to see whether the shape, as opposed to the colour pattern, of a flower is of significance to a bee. How would you attempt to investigate this problem?

Bibliography

Further reading

Darwin, C. R. *The Fertilization of Orchids*, John Murray, 1862

Faegri, K., *The Principles of Pollination Ecology*,
van der Pijl, L. Pergamon Press, 1966, Chap. 10

Frisch, K. von *The Dancing Bees*, Methuen, 1966, Chaps. 8 and 9

Procter, M., *The Pollination of Flowers*, Collins,
Yeo, P. 1973

Watt, J. M., *The Medicinal and Poisonous Plants*
Breyer-Brandwijk, *of Southern Africa,* 2nd edn,
M. G. Livingstone, 1962

Ehrlich, P. R., 'Butterflies and Plants', *Scientific*
Raven, P. H. *American*, 1967, Offprint no. 1076

Estes, J. W., 'William Withering and the Purple
White, P. D. Foxglove', *Scientific American*, 1965, vol. 212, Part 6, p. 110

Grant, V. 'The Fertilization of Flowers', *Scientific American*, 1951, Offprint no. 12

Hodgson, E. S. 'Taste Receptors', *Scientific American*, 1961, Offprint no. 1048

9 Relations between predators and prey

We may ask the same questions about the higher links in the food web as we have asked about the first link. What mechanisms are used by prey for protection against the attacks of predators? What specializations have predators to allow them to find their prey?

The answer to the first of these questions shows parallels to what we have already seen in plants. Like plants, animals may attempt to deter predators by being difficult or dangerous to feed upon, by the use of repellent chemicals or by not being easy to recognize as potential prey.

Mechanical protection against predation

A hard outer covering like the shell of a snail, a bivalve mollusc or a crab will clearly give protection against a considerable number of predators, as will also the heavy armouring of the tortoise. In the same way a battery of spines like those of sea urchins (Echinodermata), hedgehogs (Book 1 Fig. 18.80) and porcupines (Fig. 9.1) will provide great protection. Spines may also provide effective protection for insects; if you have handled a large, live grasshopper, you will probably have experienced

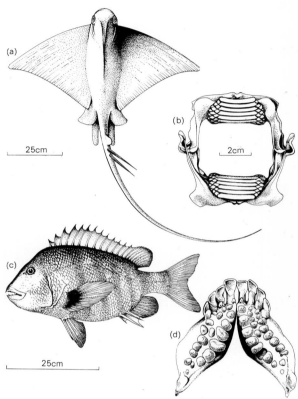

9.2 Adaptation of the teeth of fish to feeding on molluscs and sea urchins. (a) The Eagle Ray, *Myliobatis*, (Elasmobranchii), which feeds upon clams and oysters, crushing their shells with its flattened teeth, illustrated in (b). (c) A teleost, *Archosargus*, which can feed on sea urchins and has crushing teeth (d).

the effectiveness of the spines on its hind legs. There are nevertheless predators which are capable of meeting the challenge of most of these devices. Some fish have flattened teeth which enable them to feed upon freshwater snails, and similar adaptations for feeding upon bivalve molluscs are found in some marine fishes; some other species have heavy teeth with which they can crush the shells of sea urchins (Fig. 9.2). One mammal, the Sea Otter, which lives off California and which feeds partly on bivalves, partly on sea urchins, dives down to collect its prey which

9.1 The porcupine, *Hystrix*, with its quills erected in an attitude of defence. (After Bourlière).

153

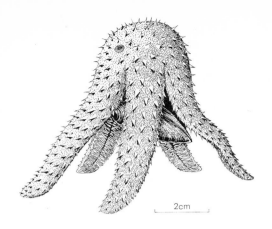

9.3 A starfish holding a mussel between its arms before pulling the shell valves apart. (After MacBride).

9.4 The Blue-bottle, *Physalia*. This animal is pelagic and supported in the water by a large, gas-filled float. Beneath the float is a cluster of polyps, some of which have long trailing tentacles armed with nematocysts. These serve as 'fishing lines' to catch prey. *Physalia* belongs to the Class Hydrozoa of the Phylum Coelenterata. Jellyfish are medusae, not polyps; most of the large common species belong to the Class Scyphozoa.

it brings back to the surface together with a flat stone; then, lying floating on its back, it places the stone on its chest and breaks the shell of the bivalve or the sea urchin by hammering it on the stone. Bivalves have other predators: a starfish can hold two shell valves by the tube feet (Book 1 Fig. 18.49) of different arms and slowly pull the valves apart (Fig. 9.3). Once the shell is partially opened, the starfish pushes its stomach out through its mouth and starts to digest the tissues of the bivalve. There are also snails which can bore holes through the shells of bivalves; this allows the snail to insert its proboscis and feed upon the tissues of the bivalve. This boring action depends upon mechanical rasping with the toothed radula (Book 1 Fig. 18.44); in some species it is aided by the secretion of sulphuric acid in the saliva which will soften the shell. The heavily shelled giant snail, *Achatina*, is not commonly eaten by large predators except man, but the mouth of its shell is a 'weakness' in its armour and it is attacked by a carnivorous snail, *Natalina*, by the larvae of certain diptera and also by the larvae and adults of some beetles.

Porcupines are sometimes killed by lions, but more commonly by leopards and by the Hunting Dog, *Lycaon*. Tortoises are also eaten both by lions and hyaenas as well as by the Cape Raven. This bird will fly with a tortoise in its bill to a height of about 15 m and then allow it to fall upon a rocky surface. This process may be repeated three or four times until the shell is sufficiently broken for the raven to be able to prise it open. In a rather similar way seagulls will pick mussels off the rocks and then drop them from a height to smash open the shell.

Chemical protection against predators

Aquatic animals

A second pattern of defence against predators is found in some soft-bodied animals or in arthropods whose exoskeleton does not give protection against larger predators. Many of these animals produce some distasteful or toxic material. Thus, for example, jellyfish (Coelenterata), which look very vulnerable, are protected by their nematocysts (Book 1 Fig. 18.15): these will be discharged into any predator. In some coelenterates, like the common Bluebottle, *Physalia* (Fig. 9.4), the poison in the nematocysts is sufficiently potent to be dangerous to man. Certain softbodied sea slugs (Mollusca: Gastropoda) secrete a strong acid from cells in the skin: as a result, if they are taken into the mouth by a fish they are spat out again. The flesh of several species of slow-swimming fish, such as the Porcupine-fish *Diodon* (Fig. 9.5), is poisonous. In some animals toxins are associated with the mechanical protection afforded by spines. This is true of the sea urchin *Diadema* (Echinodermata), which has hollow, slender, finely pointed spines. Poisonous spines are carried by some fishes, such as the Stone-fish, *Synanceia*, found among reefs off East

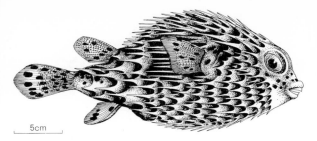

9.5 A Porcupine-fish, *Diodon*. As well as being protected by spines, this slow-swimming fish has poisonous flesh. (After Grassé).

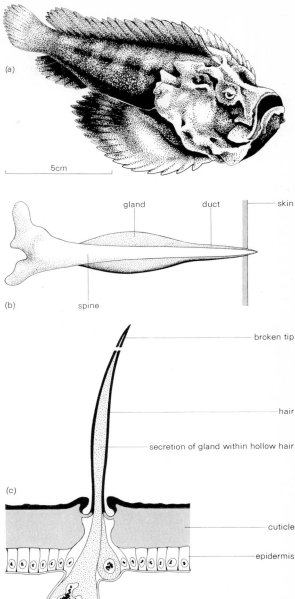

9.6 (a) The Stone-fish, *Synanceia*, which occurs among reefs off the coast of East Africa. The dorsal spines have associated with them poison glands. (b) Detail of the structure of a dorsal spine and its glands. If the skin covering the spine is forced downwards onto the gland, the pressure forces the poison out along the ducts so that it is released deep in the wound made by the spine. (c) Diagram showing the structure of an urticating hair of a caterpillar.

Africa (Fig. 9.6a). In this fish there' is a row of dorsal spines buried in the skin. Each spine carries two poison glands whose ducts run towards the tip of the spine, each lying in a groove (Fig. 9.6b). If one should tread upon the fish the skin around the spine is forced downwards as the spine enters the foot, compressing the poison glands. The tip of each duct is plugged with connective tissue and, if the pressure on the glands is sufficient, the two plugs are ruptured and the poison ejected violently, deep into the wound caused by the spine.

Terrestrial animals

Among terrestrial animals the sticky, mucous secretions of slugs and snails, although probably not toxic, protect them against attack by ants. The sluggish toad is protected by the poisonous secretions of its skin glands, especially of the parotid glands, which lie just behind the head in a position at which a mammalian predator is likely to bite. The toxins from these glands are extremely potent and may cause a dog to foam at the mouth, sometimes to run a fever, and even to have convulsions. After one such experience a dog is unlikely to attack another toad. Soft-bodied insect larvae, especially those of Lepidoptera, many of which feed in exposed places, would appear to be very vulnerable. Some caterpillars, however, carry long, hollow hairs; each is finely pointed and connected to a small, toxin-producing gland (Fig. 9.6c). Such hairs readily penetrate human skin, the tip breaking off to liberate the toxin which causes intense irritation. These 'urticating hairs' make the caterpillars unpalatable to birds, and they may perhaps serve also to protect the larvae against attack by ants.

Poisonous secretions are produced by a wide variety of terrestrial arthropods. Sometimes, as in scorpions, these are primarily concerned with prey-killing rather than defence. Others are purely defensive: the stings of bees and wasps will be familiar. Many millipedes have glands along the sides of their bodies, and if one is attacked, the glands in that region of the body will discharge a repellent secretion. A very different device is found in caterpillars of the Swallowtail Butterfly, *Papilio*. Just behind the head

155

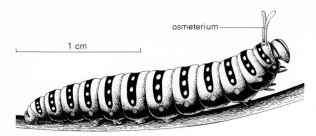

9.7 The caterpillar of the Swallowtail Butterfly with the bladder-like osmeterium extruded. (After Cuvier-Griffith).

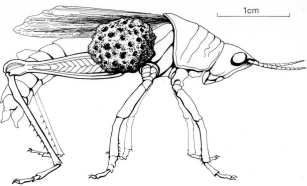

9.8 Drawing of the grasshopper *Poikilocerus* extruding its repellent secretion. (After Fishelson).

is a bladder-like structure shaped like two horns (Fig. 9.7). This is normally withdrawn and cannot be seen, but if the animal is attacked, it will push out this structure which is covered with a repellent secretion. The caterpillar will then swing its head round towards the predator and wipe the secretion over it. If one of these caterpillars is tethered close to the entrance of an ants' nest, the secretion will effectively protect the larva from attack by ants so long as the supply lasts. In less artificial conditions, where the caterpillar is free to move away, the protection provided will be much greater. A more general defence against large predators such as birds and mammals is seen in the repellent glands of the big lubber grasshoppers, which rarely if ever fly. These include *Phymateus* which is found all over sub-Saharan Africa and *Poikilocerus* which occurs in North Africa and the Sudan. The repellent glands are situated on the dorsal surface of the animal; if it is attacked, their secretion is poured out over the cuticle and flows down the sides of the body, sometimes being blown up into a frothy mass over the spiracles by air pumped out from the tracheal system (Fig. 9.8).

Some insects can actually direct their secretion against the predator. For example, the big, brightly coloured bug, *Platymeris*, produces a toxic saliva which it normally uses for killing its prey. If attacked, however, the insect will release a jet of saliva in the direction of the predator. So powerful is the spray that it may carry as far as 2 m. A similar type of defence is found in the bombadier beetles (Fig. 9.9a), but these animals eject the secretion from the tip of the abdomen which contains a complex glandular structure. A digitate gland pours a solution of quinol and hydrogen peroxide into a reservoir (Fig. 9.9b). When the animal is irritated the valve normally closing the outlet of this reservoir is opened and the contents are forced into a second chamber, which contains a mixture of the enzymes catalase and peroxidase. The catalase causes the breakdown of the hydrogen peroxide to oxygen and water, while the peroxidase causes the oxidation of quinol to *p*-benzoquinone. These reactions are strongly exothermic so that there is an intense local liberation of heat. The resulting expansion of the oxygen forces out the contents of the second chamber in an explosive jet which, apart from being repellent owing to the presence of the quinone, is also extremely hot.

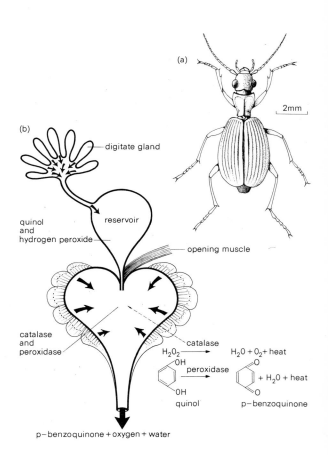

9.9 (a) A bombardier beetle. (b) Diagram of the structure of the abdominal glands responsible for producing the offensive secretion.

Protection of insect eggs

Many arthropods can, by such methods, repel potential predators and thus obtain an opportunity to escape; the repellent material may remain upon the animal for a considerable time so that it continues to be protected. There are, however, certain stages in the life histories of animals during which escape is impossible. The eggs of insects are one such example and some of these also are protected by repellent chemicals. Thus, for instance, the eggs of certain lacewing flies (Neuroptera) are supported upon narrow stalks which carry drops of repellent secretion, protecting the eggs from attack by ants. Another example is provided by the eggs of some species of the mosquito *Culex* (Diptera). The eggs are laid in groups or 'rafts' which float on the surface of water; on the top of each egg is a droplet of an ant-repellent chemical. During the rainy season, the water level of the pools in which these mosquitoes lay their eggs will fall between storms and the egg rafts may be stranded at the edges of the pools. Although the eggs will survive, they are liable to predation by certain species of ant and in this situation the repellent chemical has survival value. That the chemical is indeed repellent has been shown by watching the responses of ants to the material, and especially by noting what percentage of time the ants spent in inspecting or carrying the specimens and what percentage in cleaning themselves. Trials were made, not only with *Culex* eggs, but also with the eggs of a blowfly and with small pieces of paper soaked in sugar solution. The results obtained are summarized in Table 9.1: the material from the eggs clearly causes the ants to spend far more time in cleaning themselves than in attempting to handle the material to carry it back to the nest.

Such an experiment provides a quantitative assessment of the action of the repellent. Another method which has been used to obtain quantitative data upon the activity of irritant materials depends upon the reflex cleaning response of cockroaches. If a small drop of irritating fluid is placed upon a ventral abdominal plate of a cockroach, the animal will attempt to clean off the material by scratching movements of its hind leg. Using decapitated cockroaches, repeatable values were obtained for the time interval be-

Table 9.1 Response of the ant *Lasius* to repellent material from the eggs of *Culex pipiens* (*Data from Hinton*)

Material offered	Ratio of time in contact with material to time spent in cleaning
Culex egg raft	1:5
Sugar paper	1:0·002
Sugar paper with repellent	1:9
Blowfly eggs	1:0·0
Blowfly eggs with repellent	1:3

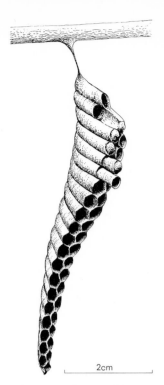

9.10 The nest of the social wasp *Rhopalidia*.

tween the application of the drop and the start of the cleaning response. The briefer the response time, the more irritant the material. This sort of technique has been used to study the action of various defensive secretions, many of which are mixtures of different chemicals. Certain of the chemicals have been found to serve not primarily as irritants but to enhance the action of the irritant by causing it to spread rapidly over the surface of the cuticle.

Not only eggs are liable to attack by ants; so too are the brood in the nests of some wasps. The nests of various social wasps such as *Rhopalidia* are attached to branches of trees and bushes by long stalks (Fig. 9.10). The female of *Rhopalidia* smears an abdominal secretion onto the stalk and this material is repellent to ants. In field observations of a nest, 81 ants approached the stalk by which the nest was attached, but only five attempted to walk down it. That this was indeed due to a secretion from the abdomen was shown by attaching small pellets of cotton wool soaked in sugar solution to the ends of fine wires hung from twigs of a tree which ants were actively foraging. Some of the wires were smeared with material from the wasps' abdominal glands; an equal number of untreated wires served as controls. In five such trials 647 ants collected sugar solution from the control wires but only 181 from the treated wires. Similar behaviour is shown by females of the wasp *Belonogaster* (Fig. 11.24).

The origin of arthropod poisons and repellents

We have already seen that many plants produce substances which are toxic or repellent to certain insects, and also how certain of these have been used as clues for food recognition by some insect species. The question arises as to whether the toxins or repellents of phytophagous insects are derived from their food plant or are synthesized by the insects themselves. The former proves to be the case in a limited number of species.

Grasshoppers may produce a brown fluid from the mouth if they are irritated. The substance produced by one species of flightless grasshopper can be repellent to ants: whether it is or not depends upon the plants on which the grasshopper has fed. If the animals are kept upon a diet of the weed *Eupatorium*, then the material they regurgitate is repellent, but if they are fed on lettuce it is not. It thus seems reasonable to suppose that the repellent chemical is derived directly from the food.

Many plants of the family Asclepiadaceae, which includes *Calotropis procera* (Fig. 8.11), contain toxic materials which have a characteristic action on the mammalian heart; these poisons are called 'cardiac glycosides'. Their presence serves to protect the plants from large mammalian herbivores which normally avoid eating them. Associated with these plants is a number of insects which concentrate these toxic materials in their bodies; they include grasshoppers, butterflies and bugs. Among these grasshoppers is *Poikilocerus* (Fig. 9.8). Experiments using birds and small mammals which had not previously seen the grasshoppers showed that the froth-producing display alone was sufficient to repel some of the birds. Others, such as jays, did eat the grasshoppers. The toxin, however, made them vomit and subsequently they would not eat any more. The same was found to be true of mice. Hedgehogs, surprisingly, will eat these grasshoppers without distress; one specimen was fed two or three every day for a week with no ill effects; hedgehogs are, however, very resistant to the action of cardiac glycosides. These results are of interest firstly in showing us that a display, such as frothing, may alone protect an insect effectively against some predators, and secondly that a toxic material, as a second line of defence, may give protection against other predators but not necessarily against all. Not all insects feeding on asclepiads can concentrate these toxic materials. Some contain toxic compounds which they synthesize themselves.

Learning by predators

There are thus two rather different ways in which arthropods can make themselves unpleasing to predators. A repellent substance secreted over the cuticle may give effective protection against other arthropods and some protection against vertebrate predators such as toads, geckos, birds and mammals. In many animals, however,

Table 9.2 Response of three jays to repeated presentations with a distasteful Monarch Butterfly (*Data from Brower*)

Bird No.	Response	Trials				
		1–10	11–20	21–30	31–40	41–50
1	Not touched	5	9	9	9	9
	Pecked	4	1	1	0	1
	Killed	1	0	0	1	0
2	Not touched	3	3	9	9	8
	Pecked	7	5	1	1	2
	Killed	0	2	0	0	0
2	Not touched	0	2	2	1	3
	Pecked	3	7	6	7	5
	Killed	7	1	2	2	2

Note: Specimens which were 'pecked' were touched by the bird but any damage was so slight as to make survival in natural conditions highly probable. Specimens which were 'killed' were so badly damaged by the birds as to make recovery unlikely.

the chemical believed to provide protection is in the blood. Such a chemical could only be effective if the animal were actually eaten; we might therefore conclude that the material is of no protective value. But, as in the case of the grasshopper *Poikilocerus* and the jay, birds can learn to recognize distasteful insects and subsequently avoid them. The progress of such learning is illustrated in Table 9.2 which summarizes some results of an experiment with three jays. The birds were presented with specimens of the distasteful Monarch Butterfly *Danaus* (Fig. 9.17a) and their reactions noted. None of the birds ate a specimen, but all three at first examined the specimens by pecking at them. Bird 1 quickly learnt not to touch most specimens, Bird 2 was rather slower and Bird 3 failed to learn to leave the specimens alone. Even with Bird 3, most specimens would probably have survived the examination, and the number it killed fell very markedly after the first ten trials. With the Monarch Butterfly learning was less rapid and less complete than with the grasshopper; all the birds continued to peck at some specimens.

Many caged birds will display considerable alarm at the sight of an insect which they have learnt is distasteful. Such behaviour is shown, for example, by hoopoes and by at least one species of hornbill. This may serve to teach other birds to recognize and avoid particular distasteful insects without the necessity of sampling them. Learning to recognize distasteful insects is not, of course, peculiar to birds; it occurs in other vertebrates as well.

Many of the chemicals which give insects protection against vertebrate predators are not simply ill-smelling or evil-tasting, but have physiological actions on the animals as well. If a bird does eat the larva or adult of the Monarch Butterfly, the bird is invariably sick about ten minutes later (Fig. 9.11). It might appear that this long-delayed 'punishment' would be less effective than some

9.11 (a) A jay eating a Monarch Butterfly and (b) subsequently vomiting.

more immediate experience. Experiments with birds show, however, that if they are constantly offered food containing a substance like quinine or mustard, which although distasteful has no other action, the birds will grow accustomed to the taste and finally do not reject the food. If, however, a substance with a distinct physiological action is used, such as the emetic potassium antimony tartrate, then the birds reject the material for a far longer time. In other words, a physiologically distressful reaction is a more effective stimulus to learning than a purely distasteful chemical.

'Warning coloration'

If the success of unpalatability as a defence mechanism against vertebrate predators depends upon the predator learning quickly to recognize the particular species, then clearly any features of the prey which might assist in its recognition would be of survival value. The prey should stand out clearly against its background and advertise its unpleasantness, so that it can be easily observed and avoided. Taking the insects as an example, we find that most distasteful insects are brightly coloured, generally with a contrasting pattern of different coloured bands or

patches. Black and yellow or black and red are two common colour combinations. They will be familiar in many wasps and may be regarded as a 'warning' of their sting; the venomous bug *Platymeris* is black with a bright red patch in the middle of each fore-wing and a red band on the femur of each leg.

Not only are such insects conspicuous but, unlike palatable species, they are commonly sluggish and show little tendency to escape. Moreover their advertisement is commonly reinforced by crowding; the crowded black and yellow nymphs of the Elegant Grasshopper *Zonocerus* (Back cover, 1) may well be familiar. The presence of several different species of warningly coloured insects on the same plant may perhaps serve to enhance the advertisement and hence their protection. One final point is that many warningly coloured butterflies and grasshoppers are exceptionally 'tough' and able to withstand rough handling by possible predators. Thus, for example, one warningly coloured butterfly was observed to be attacked nearly 30 times by a bulbul before the bird was able to kill and swallow it.

These colour combinations are not peculiar to insects. Certain tree frogs which are active during the day 'advertise' themselves and the secretions of their skin glands similarly; thus, for example, *Phrynomerus* (Fig. 9.12) has a striking pattern of red and black. Brightly coloured birds like hoopoes and ground hornbills as well as the white egrets and the black drongos are often distasteful and unacceptable to many carnivores. Similarly many mam-

9.12 The Red-banded Frog, *Phrynomerus*. The general body coloration is black with two longitudinal red stripes, showing white in the photograph. The specimen is an adult male which is croaking. The globular structure below the mouth is the croaking sac which acts as a resonator. The male is about 6 cm long.

9.13 The African weasel, *Poecilogale albinucha*. Note the striking black and white pattern of the coat.

mals which can emit an evil smell are banded black and white; an example is the African weasel, *Poecilogale* (Fig. 9.13). Black and white banding is also to be seen as a 'warning' in the spines of the Great Crested Porcupine (Fig. 9.1).

Warning coloration is not invariably of this form; the most suitable advertisement will depend upon the background colour of the environment. Thus, for example, there are in the desert several species of completely black beetles which are active in the daytime and can easily be seen against the sandy background: it has been suggested that their uniform black colour may give the most effective warning possible in such an environment.

Is there any evidence that, say, brightly coloured insects are indeed avoided by vertebrate predators? One way in which this can be investigated is to examine the food taken by various insect-feeding vertebrates and determine what percentage of the insects eaten are brightly coloured, that is, have 'warning coloration'. This has been done by putting insects out on feeding tables for wild birds. By scoring how commonly the different insect species were accepted as food, three broad categories could be recognized: highly acceptable, acceptable and only slightly if at all acceptable. Ninety different species fell into the first category and none was brightly coloured. Thirty-one species belonged to the third category; of these, 19 were strongly marked in red, orange or yellow and 5 further species had well-defined colour patterns. It would thus appear that those insects which are brightly coloured tend to be avoided by birds. Very similar results have been obtained from an examination of the stomach contents of nearly 1 000 tree frogs belonging to eight different species. 11 585 insects were recovered and only 20 of these were considered to display any form of warning coloration.

Observations of this type are supported by laboratory trials. The data in Table 9.2 relate to the responses of jays to the distasteful Monarch Butterfly. In each of these experiments, a distasteful butterfly was offered together with one which was palatable and lacked warning coloration. Although no specimen of *Danaus* was eaten by any of the three jays, the palatable butterflies were almost invariably eaten. The difference in behaviour of the birds towards the two sorts of butterfly can be expressed by the time between presentation of the specimen and its being taken by the bird, called for simplicity the 'acceptance time'. With the palatable butterfly, all 310 specimens offered were accepted; the average acceptance time was less than 2 s. With the butterfly showing warning coloration, out of 256 specimens offered, only 109 were taken and these mostly by Bird 3. The mean acceptance time was about 15 s. Even when the distasteful butterflies were not totally rejected, the birds were hesitant about taking them.

Mimicry

If being distasteful offers protection, and if survival depends upon the predator learning to associate a particular pattern of coloration with distastefulness, then clearly two species having closely similar patterning are likely to give each other mutual protection. To express the matter in simple numerical terms, let us assume that a predator has to kill six warningly coloured individuals before it learns to avoid the members of that species as food. If two species are so similar in appearance that they are confused by the predator, then the loss of individuals to each species will be halved. Such close resemblances are not in fact uncommon. Fig. 9.14 shows two butterflies which, although they belong to different families, have closely similar wing patterns: both are distasteful and both occur in the same localities.

The question arises as to whether this sort of resemblance does in fact convey any protection. In England there are three moths which belong to three separate genera and

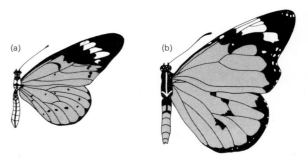

9.14 Two butterflies of different families showing very similar patterns of wing coloration. (a) *Acraea encedon*; (b) *Danaus chrysippus*. The shaded areas are orange, the remaining areas are black or white, as shown. The wingspan of *A. encedon* is about 5 cm; that of *D. chrysippus* about 7 cm. (After Owen).

two separate families. In all three species the hind wing is largely red, while the fore-wing is black with bold spots in red, white or yellow (Fig. 9.15). A House Sparrow, caged since a fledgling, was allowed to taste the adults of one of the three species; these were rejected. When, subsequently, the sparrow was given other specimens of the same species it displayed marked alarm and escape responses. These behaviours were shown also when the sparrow was offered either of the other two moths. Although the resemblance between the three species is by no means detailed, it was sufficient, at least in this experiment, to ensure that experience with one species gave protection to the other two.

Common warning colours or Müllerian mimicry

The biological significance of such resemblances or 'common warning colours' was first appreciated by a German biologist, Fritz Müller, while working in South America. Close resemblance in appearance between different animals is commonly spoken of as mimicry. This is a somewhat misleading term as a mimic requires a model to imitate and in the case of 'common warning colours' one cannot say that any particular species is acting as a model for others. Nevertheless the expression 'Müllerian mimicry' has long been in common use to describe similarity of warning colours found among two or more distasteful animals.

While two distasteful species can acquire mutual protection by resemblances between their patterns of warning coloration, it is also clear that a palatable species could obtain protection if it resembled a distasteful species. This would be true mimicry with one species, the mimic, looking like another, the model. This phenomenon is also found, and is known as 'Batesian mimicry'.

Batesian mimicry

Fig. 9.16 shows two robber flies (Diptera) which mimic big wood-boring bees (Hymenoptera). The bee models are on the top row and their fly mimics below. The fly in the centre shows the typical appearance of a robber fly. Fig. 9.17 shows another example; the animal on the left is the model, that in the middle the mimic and that on the right another butterfly of the same genus as the mimic, but showing a totally different pattern of wing coloration from that of the model. This deception by coloration applies only at the level of the visible effect. Thus, for example, there is red coloration on the wing of a distasteful Swallowtail Butterfly and also on the wing of a palatable species which mimics it. Chemically the pigments are different: the one has indicator-like properties, turning yellow when exposed to hydrochloric acid gas, while the other shows no such change. Thus model and mimic may achieve the same appearance using different pathways of pigment

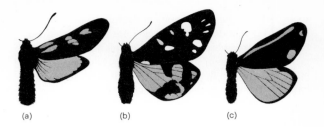

9.15 Wing patterns of (a) the 5-spot Burnet, (b) the Scarlet Tiger and (c) the Cinnabar moths. The light stipple is a yellow colour; the darker stipple represents red; the remaining areas are darkly coloured or white as shown. Note that in each insect the hind wing is dominantly red, the front wing a broken pattern on a dark background. The wingspans of the adult moths are about 3 to 5 cm.

9.16 Two different species of wood-boring bees (1 and 2) and their robber fly mimics (3 and 4). 5 shows a typical robber fly.

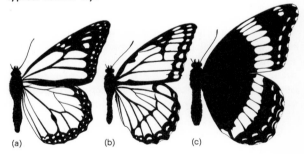

9.17 Wing patterns of (a) the Monarch Butterfly, *Danaus plexippus*, (b) its mimic, the Viceroy, *Limenitis archippus*, and (c) another species the same genus, *Limenitis arthemis*. The wing span of the Monarch is about 9 cm; its mimic is smaller with a span of about 5 cm.

synthesis. Moreover, apart from the visible effect, such as wing colour and patterning in butterflies, the rest of the anatomical structure of model and mimic may be quite different. It is this which permits us to determine the genus to which the mimic truly belongs. (See also Back cover, 3)

Once again we may ask whether there is any evidence to support this idea; do predators in fact confuse the two species so that the mimic gains protection from its resemblance to the model? This question has been approached both by simple observation and by quantitative experiment. An example of the former relates to three different birds: a drongo, a flycatcher and a shrike. All three birds have black plumage and are not easily distinguishable in the wild. While the drongo is ill-smelling and inedible, being rejected by smaller carnivores, the other two birds are palatable. Tests were made with a cat which had had experience with drongos and had developed a strong dislike for them. When a drongo, a flycatcher and a shrike were all offered to the cat, it refused all three birds.

Quantitative studies can be illustrated by further details of experiments using jays. Two sets of birds were used. One set served as controls: these birds were presented with two butterflies at a time. One was a palatable, non-mimetic butterfly (that is, one whose wing pattern does not resemble that of some other, unpalatable species) and the second a palatable mimic, the Viceroy (Fig. 9.17b). The behaviour of the birds was recorded both in terms of the way each specimen was treated and by its 'acceptance time' (p. 160). The second set of birds, the experimental animals, was presented at first with pairs consisting of a non-mimetic butterfly and of a Monarch (Fig. 9.17a), the unpalatable model mimicked by the Viceroy. This was continued until each bird showed a consistent pattern of rejection of the Monarchs; the birds were then considered to have been trained to recognize that Monarchs were unpalatable. After this period of training, the pairs of butterflies presented to the birds included a palatable, non-mimetic specimen and either a Monarch or a Viceroy. As Table 9.3 shows, previous experience of Monarchs resulted in a high percentage of Viceroys being totally rejected by the trained birds and none was eaten. Measurements of the acceptance times in the control series gave an average value of 4 s for the non-mimetic butterflies and of 8 s for the Viceroys. On the other hand, the acceptance time of Viceroys by the birds which had previously experienced Monarchs averaged

26 s, reflecting the 'uncertainty' of the birds about the specimens offered to them.

Such results show clearly that the resemblance of a palatable mimic to a distasteful model can provide the mimic with considerable protection. Such mimicry was originally recognized by the English naturalist Henry Bates and is therefore referred to as Batesian mimicry. It may find expression in ways very different from the similarity of wing pattern in butterflies or of plumage among certain birds. There is, for example, a long-horned grasshopper in Africa whose first-instar nymph mimics an ant. Much of the body is darkly pigmented but the abdomen has lateral and ventral areas of a green colour which, seen against the vegetation on which the grasshopper moves, provide the impression of the narrow waist and swollen abdomen of an ant (Fig. 9.18).

To be successful in such mimicry the mimic must not simply resemble its model, but must also behave in the

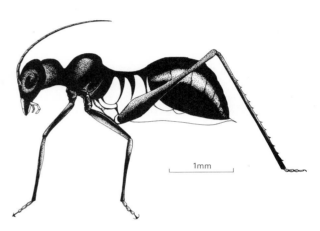

9.18 Early nymph of the long-horned grasshopper *Eurycorypha*. The body colour is black with ventral and lateral green areas (shown as white) so that, seen against grass, the animal resembles an ant. The adult has large green forewings which resemble the leaves of a plant.

Table 9.3 Responses of jays, trained to pairs of butterflies including either palatable or non-palatable specimens, to subsequent pairs containing models or mimics (*Data modified from Brower*)

Experiment	Choice offered to birds during training period	Choice offered to birds during experimental period	Experimental period: percentage of Viceroys		Number of specimens
			not touched	eaten	
1	Palatable non-mimetic Palatable mimic (Viceroy)	Palatable non-mimetic Palatable mimic (Viceroy)	10	60	100
2	Palatable non-mimetic Unpalatable model (Monarch)	Palatable non-mimetic Either Viceroy or Monarch	70	0	60

same sort of way. Thus, while the majority of moths are nocturnal, moths which mimic distasteful butterflies are active by day when their models are on the wing. This daytime activity is also shown by a moth which mimics a big wasp-like hymenopteran, a hornet; the moth has not only a yellow and black banded abdomen, but its wings are devoid of scales, so that they are translucent like those of the model. Sometimes the similarity of behaviour is expressed in the way the mimic walks. There are, for example, certain two-winged flies which mimic wasps. The models have long antennae which are constantly in motion as they move. The antennae of two-winged flies are very small, but the mimetic flies hold their front legs forwards beneath the head and wave them actively, thus increasing the resemblance to the model. Another example is a moth which mimics a digging wasp. Although moths normally fly with their legs flexed close to the body, this mimic allows its legs to hang downwards in a manner typical of many wasps, including the model. Some wasp-mimics even display stinging movements if they are captured although they have no sting. One entomologist described such an insect as follows: 'the hymenopteroid appearance of the beetle with its false sting was so striking that, although reason told me it was a beetle, instinct . . . almost prevented me from handling it'.[1]

Protection from predators by concealment

Coloration

Batesian mimics achieve protection by looking like something else. They hide their real nature and in doing this they represent a special case of avoidance of predation by concealment. More commonly concealment is achieved by a close matching in appearance of the animal to its background. Sometimes this may depend upon little other than a general coloration of the integument. Thus, for example, many species of grasshopper have a green pigment in the integument; this makes it less easy for predators with colour vision, such as lizards, birds and primates, to detect them. Similarly, of 50 different species of mammal which occur in the Sahara, 39 are distinctly sandy in colour; the remaining 11 species are more typically animals of the desert border and not true desert species. The coloration of one of the bats, *Pipistrellus kechlii*, is correlated with its environment in this way. The animal is found in southern Europe and there is dark brown; specimens of the same species from the Sahara are, however, yellowish in keeping with the general coloration of their environment. The same type of phenomenon has been found in an area around Lake Magadi, to the south-west of Nairobi. Here in the Rift Valley is an area of rather barren flats of a sandy colour and extending over an area

of about 30 km². In this very isolated locality the bigger mammals which are active in the day, such as wildebeest, zebra and wart-hog, are all of a pale sandy colour, compared with their more usual grey or brown coloration or striping. The coat colours of the nocturnal predatory mammals like jackal, hyaena and wild cat do not however differ from those of specimens from other places.

Experiments have demonstrated that such colour matching with the background has real protective value. Anaesthetized specimens of a number of different species of grasshopper were set out on small plots of various types of natural background. Different species matched different backgrounds in colour but specimens of each species were exposed on each type of background. The grasshoppers were preyed upon by various wild birds and the number of those which were eaten on different types of background noted. Of 114 grasshoppers which did not match the colour of their background, 84 percent were eaten; of an equal number on backgrounds which matched their coloration, only 34 percent were found by the birds. In another, rather similar experiment three domestic hens were used as predators. When the birds were released into a plot containing 40 grasshoppers whose colours contrasted with that of the background, they found and ate all the grasshoppers within one minute. With a similar number of grasshoppers whose colour matched the background the hens found only 6 in one minute and after four minutes had found only 12. Even after 80 minutes, two grasshoppers had still not been found, although a turkey had been admitted to help the hens in their search!

Countershading

The concealing effect of such coloration can be enhanced in various ways. One is to reduce the effect of directional illumination which, despite any general similarity in coloration to the background, may nevertheless make the prey apparent because its shape stands out in varying tones of light and shade. Consider Fig. 9.19a, which represents a uniformly coloured, fish-like object against a grey background. The light is coming, as it normally does, from above. The upper part of the object reflects the light and stands out clearly as does the lower part which is shaded. In such a situation uniform coloration affords little protection. The quantity of light reflected from the lower surface can be increased if the pigment on the under-surface contains relatively more white than that above, while the reflection from the dorsal surface would be less if it were darker. Illuminated from the side (Fig. 9.19b) the object would stand out against the background. When, however, the object is illuminated from above (Fig. 9.19c) this pigmentation pattern compensates for both reflection and shading and the object is effectively concealed. This principle, known as 'countershading', is found in many animals such as toads whose whiter belly skin is in marked contrast to the brown skin of the back, in many buck such

[1] Quoted in H. B. Cott. *Adaptive Coloration in Animals*. Methuen. 1957

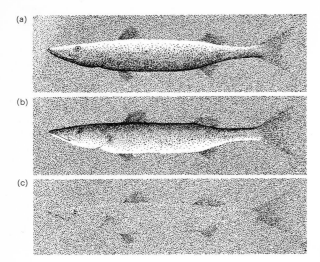

(a)

(b)

(c)

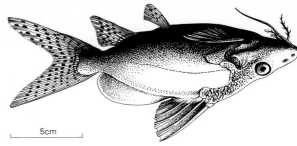

5cm

9.20 *Synodontis*, a freshwater catfish which normally swims upside down, as shown. Note that the pattern of countershading is the reverse of that normally found in fishes. The ventral but upper surface is dark, while the dorsal but lower surface is light coloured.

9.19 Drawings illustrating the principle of countershading. (a) A uniformly coloured fish illuminated from above stands out, partly because the ventral shadow contrasts with the brighter upper surface. (b) A 'countershaded' fish seen by lateral illumination. The dark upper surface now contrasts with the lighter ventral surface. (c) A countershaded fish illuminated from above. The light ventral surface reduces the effect of the shadow and the dark dorsal surface reduces the bright reflections seen in (a). (After Cott).

(a)

as Grant's gazelle (Book 1 Fig. 16.5b) and also in birds like francolins which have light-coloured breast feathers. It is also well marked in actively swimming fish whose silvery ventral scales contrast with the darker dorsal ones. The pattern of countershading must of course relate to the normal attitude of the animal. This is well illustrated by the coloration of *Synodontis*, a freshwater catfish which normally swims upside down; in this animal (Fig. 9.20) the dorsal surface is light coloured, while the ventral surface is deeply pigmented. Fig. 9.21 shows another example. (b) shows the caterpillar of a Hawk Moth in its normal position, dorsal surface downwards. In (c) the caterpillar has been placed on the top of the twig and the light colour of its dorsal surface now makes it stand out strikingly from the background.

Fishes require protection, not only from a possible observer on the flank, but also from predators above or beneath the fish. For this reason the dorsal coloration of fish tends to blend with the colour of the bottom beneath them or, in oceanic fishes, with the dark blue-green of the sea. On the ventral surface, however, the scales are not just white but silvery, reflecting back the maximum quantity of light so that the fish contrasts as little as possible with the light from the sky overhead.

Is there any evidence that countershading does in fact

(b)　　　　　(c)

9.21 (a) Larva of the Eyed Hawk Moth walking on a horizontal surface. This larva normally rests dorsal side downwards, (b), and is correspondingly countershaded. If placed in the 'normal' position with the dorsal surface uppermost, (c), the larva stands out clearly against the background. The length of the larva is about 4 cm. (After Cott).

9.22 Drawings to show the principle of disruptive coloration. If you look at the book from about 2 m away, the 'zebra' on the right will no longer be recognizable, although the rump pattern will remain. The drawing on the left will remain distinct. (After Cott).

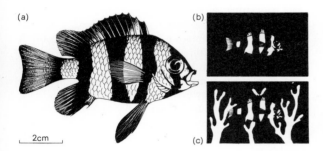

9.23 (a) *Pomacentrus*, a reef-living marine teleost: the black banding stands out against a background coloration of white with yellow fins. In (b) the fish is shown against a black background. The result is that it no longer has a 'fish-like' outline. In (c) the fish is even more effectively concealed against a broken environmental pattern.

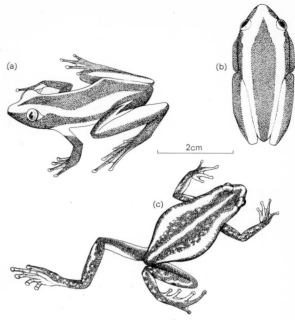

9.24 (a) The Reed Frog, *Afrilaxus*. When moving, the dark brown and white pattern may break up the animal's outline, but its movement is likely to attract attention. When at rest, as in (b), the patterns on the body and legs are so. arranged as to form a single arch of colour which has no relation to the shape of a frog. (c) The Sedge Frog, *Hyperolius*. The general body colour is brown; the lighter streaks a brilliant green.

protect prey from predators? Experiments have been made using recently killed caterpillars of Hawk Moths. These were placed upon a tree in a cage. Some were in the normal position, hanging downwards; others were fixed so that the dorsal surface was uppermost. Birds were admitted into the cage and the numbers of each type of caterpillar they found were noted. The birds found significantly fewer of the caterpillars placed in their 'normal' position.

Disruptive coloration

Concealment of the outline of an animal can also be achieved by streaks or blotches of pigment whose arrangement contrasts with that of the shape of the animal. This is the principle of 'disruptive coloration', illustrated diagrammatically in Fig. 9.22. If you lean the book open against a wall and move away, you will see that at quite a short distance the drawing of the zebra on the right is no longer recognizable, although the pattern of stripes on the rump remains clear. The drawing on the left, in which the

pattern of lines follows the outline of the body, does, however, remain obvious.

Such disruptive patterns are found in many small fishes, especially those living in coral reefs (Fig. 9.23), in tree frogs (Fig. 9.24) and in the young of ground-nesting birds. Seen in their natural environment, the pattern of pigmentation breaks up their outline and renders the animals far less conspicuous. This is perhaps also the significance, in a slightly different way, of the brilliant yellow- or green-striped patterns of certain frogs. In the field, while the general brown coloration of the body blends with the background, the predator's eye is drawn to the obvious streaks of colour, which have no particular relation in shape to a frog (Fig. 9.24c). Fine broken patterns, like the spots of leopard, may conceal the animal's shape against a dappled background of broken light and shadow made by leafy shrubs in sunlight.

Colour change

Any animal which relies for concealment upon the general

coloration of the integument will be forced to remain in a very limited environment. Indeed, many green-coloured savanna insects may become obvious during the dry season when the grass turns brown, although they are well concealed during and after the rains when the grass is green. An ability to change colour with the seasons is obviously advantageous. This habit is very strikingly shown in many mammals, such as the small carnivorous stoat and the Arctic Fox; these live in high latitudes where snow lies on the ground for several months of the year. In the autumn the animals moult, replacing a mottled brown summer coat by a white one. The following spring they moult again to resume their appropriate summer pelage. This change is not limited to mammals; similar seasonal colour changes are shown by certain arctic birds as well.

Changes of this sort are not found in Africa, but we do find striking changes in coloration both of mantids (Dictyoptera) and grasshoppers (Orthoptera) to blend with the changing coloration of the grass, from green during the rains to brown during the dry season, or even to black after a passage of fire (Table 9.4). The protection given by these changes has been demonstrated by exposing to predation brown and green individuals of the Praying Mantis, *Mantis religiosa*, on both brown and green plants. Ten days after 70 specimens had been placed in situations where their colour contrasted with the background, only 14 remained; of 40 specimens whose colour matched the background, none had been destroyed.

In some species of grasshopper a wide range of colour forms is found, varying from bright green through various shades of orange and brown to black. The relative proportions of individuals of different colours changes during the course of a year and any one individual hopper may change its colour from one instar to the next. Thus a hopper which is brown when it emerges from the egg may remain brown throughout its life, or it may turn green or black.

The mechanisms controlling this type of adaptive colour change have been studied in a common African grasshopper, *Gastrimargus* (Fig. 9.25). Two factors are involved. Newly hatched nymphs are brown. If they are kept on a white or light grey background, the percentage of nymphs which are light grey in body colour increases with succeeding moults; these grey nymphs have little black pigment in the epidermis. On a black background, however, the percentage of hoppers black in body colour increases (Fig. 9.26a). In such an experiment a bright green background produces light-coloured but not green-coloured individuals. There is thus a response to background brightness such that the quantity of dark pigment increases on a dark background and becomes less on a light-coloured one.

The factor which mainly determines whether nymphs have a green pigmentation is humidity (Fig. 9.26b). A group of nymphs cultured on a light-coloured background in conditions of high humidity will contain a higher percentage of green individuals than a group cultured in a low humidity. If, however, they are cultured on a black background, this results in such heavy deposition of black pigment that any green coloration is obscured (Fig. 9.26c).

These observations lead to an explanation of the events underlying the seasonal colour change. During the rains the colour of the vegetation is green, and this type of background results in deposition of relatively little black pigment; at the same time the high humidity leads to the formation of green pigment which shows up clearly. In the dry season, the lower humidity decreases the tendency to produce green pigment while the darker background stimulates the formation of more black pigment: the resulting hopper is brown. Finally on burnt, blackened grass there will be a heavy deposition of black pigment, regardless of the prevailing humidity, although adults may show limited patches of green on head and thorax. Not until new grass appears will the black coloration be lost, even if the humidity has risen earlier.

Such a colour change is a relatively slow process. An animal which can change colour fairly rapidly would

Table 9.4 Types of coloration of grasshopper species collected from burnt and unburnt areas of savanna in the Sudan (*Data from Hocking*)

Condition of grass	Habit of grasshoppers	Number of species		Total
		Pale-coloured	Dark-coloured	
Unburnt	plant-resting species	31	1	32
	ground-resting species	3	3	6
	total	34	4	
Burnt	plant-resting species	7	15	22
	ground-resting species	0	27	27
	total	7	42	

Note: Ground-resting species are either more abundant or perhaps more easily collected in areas where the grass has been burnt.

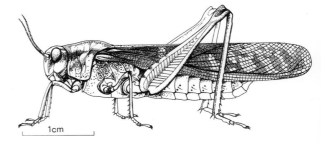

9.25 The common grasshopper, *Gastrimargus*, (Dirsch, 1965).

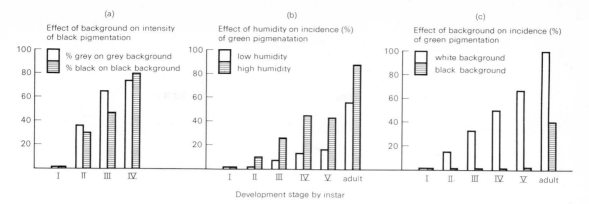

9.26 Effect of background and humidity upon the development of green and black pigmentation by the hoppers of *Gastrimargus*.

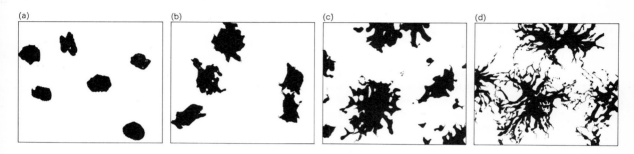

9.27 Drawings based upon photomicrographs of the web of the foot of the Clawed Toad, *Xenopus* (Book 1 Fig. 21.16), showing four different conditions of pigment dispersal of the melanocytes. Each pigment-granule mass in (a) is about 20 μm in diameter. (After Hogben and Slome).

clearly have the advantage of being able to move freely between different types of background while retaining protective resemblance to the background. Such an ability is found among a variety of animals including many prawns and shrimps (Arthropoda: Crustacea), octopuses and squids (Mollusca: Cephalopoda), bottom-living fishes and frogs and lizards.

The survival value of such colour change has been examined experimentally using the Mosquito-fish, *Gambusia*, which can adjust its colour to correspond in tone with the background. Numbers of these small fish were adapted in black- or white-walled tanks; equal numbers of the two sorts were then released into a tank either with black or with pale grey walls. Three different predators were used: a penguin, a heron and a sunfish. Table 9.5 shows that in each experiment, lasting less than 15 min, more of the specimens whose colour contrasted with the background were eaten.

These changes in colour are brought about by pigment-containing cells in the skin or, in crustaceans, beneath the cuticle. In frogs and toads, for example, there are cells in the skin which contain granules of the black pigment melanin. These cells, melanocytes, have an irregular branching outline (Fig. 9.27). The pigment granules with-

Table 9.5 Percentages of Mosquito-fishes adapted to different coloured backgrounds eaten by three different predators in two different coloured tanks (*Modified from Sumner*)

Predator	Colour of tank	Percentage of fish eaten	
		Adapted to black background	Adapted to white background
Penguin	Pale grey	61	39
Heron		62	38
Sunfish		66	34
Penguin	Black	27	73
Heron		39	61
Sunfish		22	78

in the cells may be distributed throughout the whole cytoplasm of each melanocyte, thus forming a screen which covers any underlying pigment. The granules may also concentrate into a tiny speck within each cell, so that any underlying pigment can be seen. In this way the animal may change colour from a dark brown, when the pigment

167

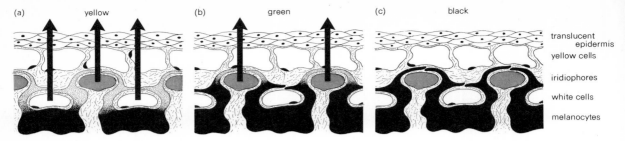

(a) yellow   (b) green   (c) black

translucent
epidermis
yellow cells

iridiophores

white cells

melanocytes

9.28 Diagrams showing the arrangement of pigment-cell layers in the skin of a chameleon. For further explanation, see text.

is dispersed, to a lighter colour when the pigment is concentrated (Back cover, 4).

Particularly striking is the range of colour change shown by some lizards. Thus, for example, in a small chameleon, *Lophosaura*, the colour of the skin on the dorsal surface can change from a yellow shade, through green to black. The flanks also display colour changes, but they are less extreme in range. The skin of the dorsal surface of the chameleon contains four different types of pigment cell. Immediately below the translucent horny scales are scattered cells containing a clear yellow pigment. Beneath these is a layer of cells, the iridiophores, which are packed with tiny crystals; these reflect light of shorter wavelengths, so that when seen by reflected light they have a green-bluish tinge. Beneath these lie cells which appear white by reflected light, and finally there is a layer of melanocytes (Fig. 9.28).

When the pigment in the melanocytes is fully concentrated, most of the light entering the skin is reflected from the white cells, and having been filtered twice by the yellow pigment, produces a yellow colour (Fig. 9.28a). The branches of the melanocytes run between the outer cell layers and when the pigment is partly dispersed, it first forms a screen covering the white cells (Fig. 9.28b). Light entering the skin is now reflected by the iridiophores. In first passing through the yellow cells, the longer and shorter wavelengths will be partly filtered out. Only the light of short wavelength will be reflected by the crystals of the iridiophores and this light is relatively more intense in the green than in the blue wavelengths. On passing through the yellow pigment layer a second time, the shorter blue waves are further absorbed and the resulting colour appears as a bright green (Fig. 9.29). Finally, when fully dispersed the pigment of the melanocytes will screen the iridiophores; all light entering the skin is absorbed, so that it appears to be black (Fig. 9.28c).

In different areas on the flanks, certain of these cell layers are missing, but melanocytes are always present. As a result although colour changes will still occur, the range is more limited than on the dorsal surface.

In a similar fashion bottom-living flatfish can change colour; moreover, they can adopt patterns of pigmentation which correspond broadly to that of the substrate on which they lie. If, for example, they are placed on a back-

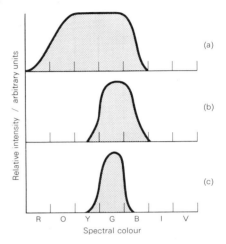

9.29 The physical mechanism by which a green coloration is produced by the skin of a chameleon which contains no green pigment. (a) The layer of yellow cells filters out both longer and shorter wavelengths of light. (b) Of the light reaching the iridiophores, only that of the shorter wavelengths is reflected. There is relatively more green than blue in this reflected light. (c) On passing through the layer of yellow cells for a second time, the shorter wavelengths are further reduced in intensity compared with the green.

ground of large black and white squares, the melanocytes in large areas of the skin will have the pigment dispersed to produce a pattern which approximates to the background. If the background is of smaller black and white squares, the pattern adopted by the fish has correspondingly smaller areas of dark pigment.

Resemblance to specific objects

A general colour resemblance to the background will provide some measure of protection against predators, but there are also many animals which resemble quite specific objects found in their habitats. Many grasshoppers (Orthoptera) look like grass stalks, others like stones, while some resemble the bark of trees. Some mantids (Dictyoptera) also resemble the bark of trees (Back cover, 2), or may have broad flat, green wings so that

9.30 Photograph of an East African hawk moth, *Xanthopan*, resting on the bark of a tree. Note the way in which the patterning of the moth's wings helps to conceal it.

(a)

(b)

5cm

9.31 (a) A 'pipe-fish' with outgrowths from the body resembling fronds of a seaweed. (b) A related pipe-fish, or 'sea-horse' showing the body form more typical of this group.

they look like leaves; others have narrow wings and narrow abdomens and, with their front legs held out together in front, resemble fine twigs. Fig. 9.30 shows a moth whose wing pattern very closely resembles the bark on which it rests. There are Hemiptera which resemble the thorns of acacias and both spiders and mantids which resemble flowers. Perhaps the most surprising protective resemblance is that of certain insects and spiders to the droppings of birds. The experiences of naturalists underline, in different ways, the closeness of the resemblance. One describes an adult moth which occurs in Tanzania as follows:

On one occasion I observed what I thought to be one of these moths on a leaf, but after a close examination from a distance of only a few inches I discovered (to my own satisfaction) that it was after all only a bird dropping. Just as I turned away the said bird dropping flew off.[1]

A different experience is reported by an entomologist who had collected several butterfly larvae which resembled bird droppings and had just brought them back to the laboratory for examination.

A few minutes later I saw what I supposed to be one of these caterpillars accidentally dropped, lying on the doorstep and picked it up. However it turned out that I was quite deceived . . . the object was really excrement dropped by a captive bird.[2]

Such resemblances are not limited to insects. Frogs and geckos may also be patterned to resemble bark. Nor are they limited to land animals; they are found also in the sea. The common sea slug, *Aplysia* (Mollusca: Gastropoda), not only resembles in colour the seaweed on which it is found, but may hold its body in such a fashion as to resemble the fronds of the weed. Other sea slugs resemble the sponges and sea anemones among which they move. One of the most striking examples is a fish which has on its body numerous outgrowths resembling seaweed (Fig. 9.31a). Since these fish are anyway curious in appearance, we also show a related species which lacks such structural concealment (Fig. 9.31b).

Once again we may ask whether such resemblances have any real value. This matter has been tested using looper caterpillars which very closely resemble small twigs (Fig. 9.32). The experiments involved using jays as predators and the particular birds used had never seen such caterpillars previously. They were first introduced to lengths of twig of about the same size as the caterpillars, and soon learnt that twigs were not edible. Jays which had not been fed for at least 12 h were then released singly into a cage in which there were both natural twigs and caterpillars. If the caterpillars were alive and moved, they were quickly found by the birds; freshly killed caterpillars were,

[1] Quoted in H. B. Cott, *Adaptive Coloration in Animals*, Methuen, 1957
[2] M. Haviland, *Forest, Steppe and Tundra*, Cambridge University Press, 1926

9.32 A caterpillar which resembles a twig. Note the way in which it stands straight and at an angle from the branch. This specimen is about 6 cm long.

however, never recognized as food within a period of 10 min and even when the birds were assisted after this time by placing other food close to the caterpillars, the mean time for discovery in a series of five trials was almost 30 min. In natural conditions the caterpillars do remain completely motionless during the day and these experiments suggest that their resemblance to twigs has real protective value. Different species of the same genus of looper caterpillars live on different species of tree; what is striking is that the caterpillars of each species resemble the shape of twig characteristic of the tree on which they normally occur.

A far simpler method of disguise is used by some animals, namely that of covering the body with small fragments of material collected from the habitat in which they live. In some instances the covering may be relatively simple, like that of a South African beetle which covers its back with small pellets of mud. This habit is shown also by a predatory bug *Acanthaspis*, which lives in crevices of termite mounds. The nymphs cover the back with sand particles, with the remains of corpses of insects they have eaten and with fragments of plant debris. All this is held together by a silken secretion produced from hairs on the abdomen. When caged with predatory ants, the nymphs will turn round to present the covering to any ant which threatens to bite them; moreover, if one attempts to pick up a nymph, the covering comes away easily and the nymph escapes. Thus when animals cover their surfaces with foreign objects, this is not necessarily a matter of concealment alone. The covering may serve principally as a mechanical protection, especially against ants.

Moth caterpillars may enclose themselves in a case of small twigs or grass fragments (Fig. 16.34). Others have hooked bristles over the surface of the body. By spinning a thin layer of silk on one surface of some fragment of plant material, they are able to attach it to a bristle; in this way they cover themselves with material already common in the environment in which they live. One of the most remarkable examples of this type of disguise is that of a small marine crab, *Hyas*, which covers its dorsal surface with pieces of material from its habitat. If it is put into a different environment, it will discard its previous disguise and take on a new and more appropriate one.

Either by being unacceptable to predators or by concealing themselves, very many animals achieve protection. Those which are unpalatable are commonly sluggish, relying on their unpleasantness to make escape unnecessary. Those which conceal themselves, that is, are 'cryptic', often move slowly or, like the looper caterpillars discussed above, depend upon being completely motionless. But there are large numbers of animals which depend upon their speed or upon their ability to fly for their safety. Such animals, if they are to escape successfully, must be able to detect a predator while it is still approaching. This may depend on vision; for example, the eyes of herbivorous mammals are situated on the sides of the head, thus providing as wide a field of view as possible (Book 1 p. 218). Detection also often depends on smell: human scent alone may well alarm wild mammals, and a human hunter will, as far as possible, approach his prey from upwind, so that his smell is not carried towards the animal he is trying to kill. Noise too will alert animals to potential danger.

Protection by group formation

Animals living in groups may be especially conspicuous and we may ask whether this habit itself has any protective value. One common example is that brightly marked and usually ill-tasting caterpillars or grasshoppers may be found together, their numbers advertising their 'warning' coloration. But there are also herds of game animals, flocks of birds and shoals of fish. That such aggregations can provide protection from predation is shown by the data summarized in Table 9.6, which lists the percentage of successful kills by lions on herds of different sizes. It is clear, especially with wildebeest and zebra, that lone

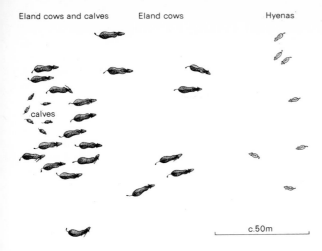

Eland cows and calves　　Eland cows　　Hyenas

calves

c.50m

9.33 Sketch showing the positions adopted by a herd of eland cows and young when threatened by a group of hyaenas. Note that although hyaena mainly hunt by night, they may do so also in the daytime. (After Kruuk).

animals are far more likely to be killed than are individuals moving in small groups. Large herds are, however, more vulnerable; this is partly because it takes several seconds before the whole of a large herd is made aware of danger and in this time a lion may have successfully attacked, and partly because at water holes large herds may be so densely packed that escape is difficult.

Protection by herding is thus partly due to the greater potential of a group to detect danger. But in some species the group may act as a unit to protect its members and especially the young. Fig. 9.33 shows the positions adopted by a herd of eland cows to protect calves which had been attacked by a group of hyaenas. Similarly, buffalo are reported to defend the group by turning towards a lion which comes near the herd; the predator is thus faced with a line of horns and will normally move on.

Furthermore, predators may be confused by the presence of large numbers of prey and fail to make a kill; a predator

Table 9.6 Success of hunts by lions of different game species in herds of different sizes (*Data from Schaller*)

| | *Prey* | | | | | |
| | *Thomson's gazelle* | | *Wildebeest* | | *Zebra* | |
Herd size	*% success*	*N*	*% success*	*N*	*% success*	*N*
1	33	64	47	19	60	5
2–10	21	164	13	8	21	19
11–75	25	165	9	11	23	26
>75	33	24	50	20	33	6

N is the number of hunts observed

will therefore commonly attempt to concentrate upon a single individual. The cheetah, for example, may run a considerable distance in pursuit of a single buck, passing others which are closer and could have been more readily brought down. Similar behaviour is shown by hawks which in attacking a flock of pigeons will follow a single bird, while falcons will circle round an individual to isolate it from the flock prior to a kill.

The shoaling of fish may have a further value. A predator, once it has discovered a shoal, will probably eat all the fish it can. It is, however, likely to be a considerable time before the predator can find another shoal, since the total number of shoals in an area is limited. Mathematical studies suggest that if the fish were scattered at random in the same area, not only would the chances of encounter between predator and prey be greater, but the predator, never being able to gorge itself upon the prey and thus usually being ready to accept any fish it encounters, would actually kill more. In a rather similar fashion, the aggregation of locust hoppers, which occurs when population density is high, may serve to reduce total mortality from predatory birds.

Alarm pheromones

In such conspicuous groups of animals there are commonly alarm signals which, coming perhaps from only a single member of the group, will alert the others to take whatever is the normal protective behaviour of the species concerned. Among insects these warning signals are often chemical. Substances which are released by one member of a species and which cause changes in the behaviour of other members of the same species are called 'pheromones'. For example, many species of ant release alarm pheromones if they are attacked or damaged. Different species may have chemically different alarm pheromones. The type of behaviour produced by release of an alarm pheromone will depend upon the species concerned: in species with small colonies it may be a scattering for shelter; in other species living in large colonies and armed with powerful mandibles, the ants may move aggressively towards the source of the pheromone. Alarm pheromones are also liberated by bees and wasps. This fact has been exploited by one species of stingless bee which collects food by raiding the nests of other species of stingless bees and feeding on their stores. If scouting robber bees find a nest and attempt to rob it, they are killed by the home bees. This results in the release of the robber's alarm pheromone which has a dual action: firstly, it attracts more robbers to the hive and, secondly, it alarms the species being attacked, with the result that their workers scatter in disorder and offer no effective resistance to the robbers.

Such alarm pheromones are common among the social insects, including the termites. Most insects are, however, solitary; nevertheless some may aggregate, reinforcing the effect of their pattern of warning colours. One such is the

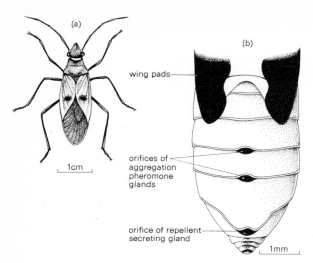

9.34 (a) The adult of the Cotton Stainer, *Dysdercus*. (b) Diagram of the dorsal surface of the abdomen of a nymph of *Dysdercus*. The repellent secretion, which also acts as an alarm pheromone, is released from an opening near the end of the abdomen. There are two more anterior dorsal glands. These secrete a different pheromone which is attractive to other nymphs of the same species, causing them to aggregate.

Cotton Stainer, *Dysdercus* (Hemiptera) (Fig. 9.34a), the nymphs of which have dorsal glands (Fig. 9.34b) near the tip of the abdomen. If a nymph is attacked, the contents of these glands are released and at the same time a drop of fluid is exuded from the anus. The insect kicks this material onto its dorsal surface with the terminal joints, the tarsi, of its hind legs. The material from the anus mixes with the dorsal gland secretion and spreads over the animal's back. The smell of this mixture will not only deter a predator but will cause the individuals in the aggregation to scatter: thus it has a dual role, as a repellent and an alarm phero-mone. Whether such alarm pheromones occur in other insect species which aggregate is still unknown.

A comparable phenomenon is found in some fish which form shoals. The behaviour of these fish is markedly influenced by chemical compounds in the skin. These compounds are released into the water if the skin should be damaged, as will occur if a predator should attack successfully. This was originally recognized in a small freshwater fish, the minnow. To study the effect, minnows were trained to come to a feeding tray for chopped earthworms. Five minutes after the food had been set out and the fish had collected to feed, the material to be tested would be released into the water. Skin extract of minnow caused the fish rapidly to scatter and then aggregate again before swimming away from the 'danger'. Extracts of other tissues had no such effect. Different species of fish respond to their alarm pheromones in different ways; while minnows swim away, a bottom-living species became completely motionless, while goldfish swam down to the bottom and there stirred up the mud so that they were concealed.

Such alarm pheromones are found in the two catfish, *Clarias* and *Synodontis* (Figs. 6.23 and 9.20). An alarm pheromone is found also in the skin of tadpoles of the European toad, *Bufo bufo*; this is a species in which the tadpoles swim in a group. The tadpoles of the frog, *Rana*, do not form aggregations like the toad tadpoles and there is no alarm pheromone in their skin. No studies have as yet been made upon the tadpoles of African frogs and toads.

Alarm signals and noises

Many of the plains game live in herds, and among these conspicuous patterns upon the rump are common (Fig. 9.35); these may serve as warning signals. If one individual

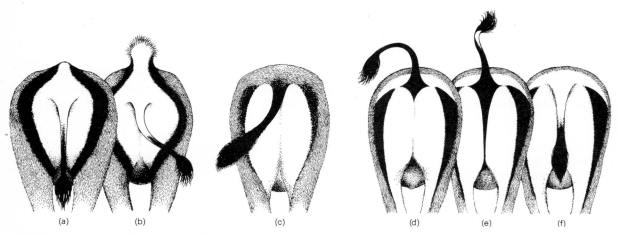

9.35 Rump patterns of different buck. (a) and (b) Springbok, *Antidorcas marsupialis*. Over the rump there is a patch of hairs which can be erected, as in (b). (c) Thomson's gazelle (*Gazella thomsoni*) (d), (e) and (f) Grant's gazelle (*G. granti*); (d) is a male and (e) a female, both with the tail erected; (f) shows the appearance of both sexes when the tail is lowered. (After Guthrie).

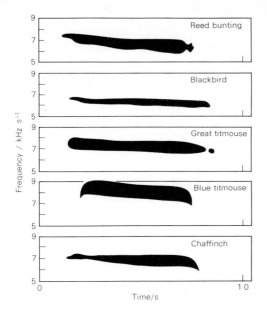

9.36 Warning calls of a number of different British song birds. The calls were recorded on magnetic tape and then played into an instrument called a sound spectrograph. This analyses the frequency content of the noise at very frequent intervals and marks out on a moving chart the frequency bands included in the noise.

Study of these recorded calls shows them each to consist of a long note lasting more than 0·5 s, and at a frequency of about 7 kHz, that is at least one octave above the top note of a piano. (After Marler).

should be alarmed and start to run, it will display its rump pattern as it goes and in this way perhaps warn the other members of the herd of possible danger. Proof that this is indeed a function of these markings is, however, lacking.

Flocks of small birds represent another conspicuous aggregation of animals in which we find alarm signals. These are vocal, not chemical or visual, and are commonly given at the sight of a predatory bird. To make a noise is possibly to draw attention to oneself and the bird which sees the predator might perhaps endanger itself in this way. The warning calls of a number of different species of bird have two features in common (Fig. 9.36). Firstly, each is a single long-drawn-out note and, secondly, it is high-pitched. Both of these features make it difficult for a predator easily to locate the source of the sound. One way of judging from what direction a sound comes is to note the difference in time of arrival of the noise first at one ear and then at the other. This can be done most easily with a noise which consists of a series of short notes, since the comparison of arrival time can be made at the start of each note. With a long note, however, this is more difficult, since while it continues no such comparison can be made. This then is one advantage of the form of the birds' warning call. It is also possible to locate a sound by comparing

its intensity at both ears: clearly, the fewer reflections or echoes, the easier it is to make such a comparison. High-pitched sounds will give echoes from many more surfaces than will low-pitched sounds; a high-pitched warning call will produce many reflections from objects such as leaves and thus tend to confuse the orientation of the predator towards the sound. This difficulty does not, of course, affect the other members of the flock. They have no need to know where exactly is the bird giving the warning call; it is sufficient that it alerts them to possible danger.

There is one other important type of aggregation of animals: namely females with their young. For example, the fry of mouth-breeding fishes like *Tilapia* will return to the parent's mouth when danger threatens (Book 1 Fig. 21.34). The parent recognizes the danger, and signals the young to return by swimming backwards slowly: the young swim towards any dark object and thus are normally led to her mouth. Similarly some female birds will call their young to them if danger threatens; this is familiar behaviour in the domestic hen. In some small mammals even after the young are weaned, the family group remains together when they are actively seeking food for themselves. This is true, for example, of meerkats, social mongooses which are subject to predation by hawks. Any adult meerkat, if in the open, will pause from time to time and look upwards to the sky to see if a hawk is approaching. If a female with young should observe a hawk, she will give a characteristic call which immediately brings the young running to her (Fig. 9.37); she will then move off to cover with the young around her. Meerkats are readily tamed and their owners often find that they can call the young back to the home by making a particular

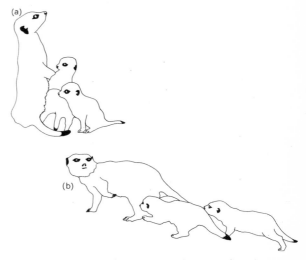

9.37 Drawings from a ciné film of a tame female meerkat and her two young. In (a) the young have run to their mother who is sitting upright watching a hawk. In (b) she moves to greater safety with the young following closely. The female meerkat is about 20 cm long. (After Ewer).

173

sort of whooping noise; the noise is similar to the female's 'hawk warning' call and the young are reacting towards their human guardian in the same fashion as they would towards their mother.

Strategies of protection

The strategies adopted by prey for protection from predators can very broadly be regarded as attempting to offer either minimal or else maximal stimulation to the predator. In the first case the animals are cryptically coloured to give minimal visual contrast with their environment, they are silent to give minimal auditory stimulation, and they probably give off as few odours as possible to give minimal olfactory stimulation. One extreme expression of this strategy of minimal stimulation is the habit of death-feigning in which the animal becomes completely inactive and unresponsive, as a result of which

it may be rejected by a predator as already dead. In the second case the prey will be brightly coloured to give maximal visual contrast and commonly malodorous to give maximal olfactory stimulation. Both may be reinforced by warning noises to give auditory stimulation as well. Thus, for example, the porcupine, unlike most mammals, moves noisily, advertising its presence. If in danger, it will not only erect its spines as a visual threat but also stamp on the ground and shake its tail, which carries quills, making a rattling sound. Similarly the release of distasteful material from the dorsal glands of some lubber grasshoppers may be accompanied by a warning hiss which adds to the deterrent effect. The warning hiss of snakes will be familiar, as also the vicious spitting noise of a young kitten which is cornered by some potential enemy. This latter is little other than bluff; it is unlikely to deter a truly determined predator. The same is true of the hissing of a chameleon which is defenceless.

Table 9.7 Summary of protective mechanism

Protective mechanism	Examples
Mechanical protection	
Shells	Giant snail (*Achatina*)
Spines	Porcupine (*Hystrix*)
Chemical protection	
Toxic secretions	
Coelenterate nematocysts	Blue-bottle (*Physalia*)
Dermal toxins	Toad (*Bufo*); some caterpillars
Specialized toxic glands	*Platymeris* (Hemiptera); wasps; Stone-fish
Toxic substances in tissues	
Synthesized by organism	Five-spot Burnet and certain other moths
Concentrated by organism but synthesized by food plant	Monarch Butterfly (*Danaus*)
Visual protection	
Palatable animals	
Concealing coloration	Chameleon (*Lophosaura*)
Disruptive patterning	Coral fish (*Pomacentrus*)
Concealing coverage	*Acanthaspis* (Hemiptera)
Mimicry of objects such as leaves or twigs	Some mantids
Mimicry of other, distasteful animals (Batesian mimicry)	Viceroy and Monarch Butterflies
Distasteful animals	
Warning coloration	*Platymeris* (Hemiptera); *Zonocerus* adult (Orthoptera)
Common warning colours (Müllerian mimicry)	Five-spot Burnet and related moths
Protection of aggregations	
Distasteful animals	
Warning coloration	Nymphs of Elegant Grasshopper (*Zonocerus*)
Palatable animals	
Alarm pheromones	Various fish; *Dysdercus* (Hemiptera); ants
Alarm calls	Small birds and mammals

Nevertheless these sounds may be sufficient to drive away some predators and they thus provide a measure of protection. Both kitten and chameleon are cryptically coloured and their hissing represents defence once their disguise has been penetrated. It is noteworthy, and in keeping with our generalization, that in both animals the hissing is accompanied by an opening of the mouth to display a bright colour, red in the kitten, orange in the chameleon; that is, the noise is accompanied by a visual display which involves those colours which we consider to be characteristically 'warning'.

We have seen that protection from predators involves a remarkable diversity of mechanisms. Table 9.7 gives a brief summary of the major methods of protection. With the possible exception of the large adult carnivores and bulky herbivores such as elephant and rhinoceros, few animals are completely protected. Some predator, either large or small, will be able to pierce their defence; but even partial protection is of value with regard to the survival of the species. It is not correct to argue, as has been done in the past, that because a protective adaptation fails to give complete protection, it therefore has no protective function.

We have so far considered the adaptations of prey in relation to predation; there is however the other aspect of this link in the food web, namely the methods by which predators find and kill their prey. Most of these are familiar; there is no need to elaborate on how a lion kills a buck, a toad catches a termite or a centipede an insect larva. Some predators do, however, have methods of prey finding or of prey killing which are of particular interest, partly because they are found among the commonest large predatory animals which live in close association with man. It is these which we will consider in the next chapter.

Problems

1 It is suggested on p. 160 that the reason for the small numbers of brightly coloured insects in the stomachs of tree frogs is that these animals avoid catching such insects. If these data related to *Bufo regularis*, would you consider that they constituted valid evidence in favour of this view?

2 One characteristic of the colour change of grasshoppers is that it is not shown equally strongly by all members of a population. Can you suggest an advantage for survival of the species, which might arise from this variability?

3 Colour change is more common in bottom-living than in pelagic fishes. Suggest a possible reason for this difference.

4 Cicadas sing loudly and yet they are very difficult to see even if you stand completely still beneath a tree. To what is this difficulty due?

5 Would you expect fireflies to be palatable or distasteful? Give reasons for your view.

6 The nymphs of the grasshopper *Poikilocerus* can be fed on dandelions; they then contain only minute quantities of cardiac glycosides. Normal specimens of the grasshopper, fed on an asclepiad, were offered to a jay and a mouse. Neither animal had seen the grasshoppers before. The jay ate the grasshopper and was sick later. Subsequently it refused all specimens of the grasshopper, regardless of whether they had been raised on dandelions or asclepiads. The mouse also ate the first grasshopper and was sick. Subsequently it refused grasshoppers which had been reared on asclepiads but ate those which had been raised on dandelions. What explanation would you offer to account for the difference in behaviour of the two animals? How would you test your hypothesis?

7 Warningly coloured insects commonly form aggregations. There is evidence that in some species at least this is due to a pheromone. What experiments would you conduct to attempt to discover whether the aggregation of the nymphs of the Elegant Grasshopper (p. 159) is due to a pheromone?

8 In the chameleon *Lophosaura* there is a well-marked, brownish, lateral pigment band whose margin is, however, blue. Histological examination of these two areas showed the presence of the following types of cell in the skin:

(a) *Band* Orange pigment cells, white reflecting cells, melanocytes.

(b) *Margin* Blue reflecting layer, white reflecting layer, melanocytes.

What other colours would you expect could be shown by these two areas? Explain your reasoning.

9 Fig. 9.16 shows two predatory two-winged 'robber flies' which mimic bumble bees. Field observations show that the mimic robber flies may attack and feed on the bumble bees they resemble.

While there is good evidence that the mimetic resemblance of the fly to the bee confers protection on the fly against attacks by vertebrate predators, it has been suggested that the close resemblance of the predatory fly to its prey assists the fly in making its attack. This has been described as 'aggressive mimicry'. Does the fact that the fly can be a successful predator of the bee constitute evidence in favour of this concept? What other evidence would you seek in studying this idea?

10 Fig. 9.35 shows some examples of rump patterns of plains game. One possible function of these patterns is that they serve as warning signals to other members of a herd. Suggest other possible functions which they might serve.

11 It has been found, by a comparison of 39 matched species pairs, that the songs of savanna birds typically differ in pitch from those of forest birds. Which would you expect to have the higher-pitched song? Explain your reasoning. The song of one group is characterized by having more harmonics than the other. Comment on

this observation. What measurements would you make to assess the validity of your hypothesis?

12 Certain hawk-moth caterpillars are so counter-shaded that they must hang downwards from a twig to obtain protection. What environmental stimuli might be used by these caterpillars to maintain this inverted position? What experiments would you propose to undertake to determine which stimulus is actually used by the caterpillars?

13 Many insects protect themselves from predators by being ill-tasting. Winged termites suffer heavy predation; especially those species which swarm in the daytime. It would seem to be more 'economical' to produce fewer adults which were protected by being unpalatable. Discuss this problem in the light of what you know about the strategies of seed dispersal in plants.

14 It is commonly said that a Batesian mimic must be less abundant than its model. What argument would you put forward in favour of this idea? The experiments described on p. 162 showed that initial experience of Monarch Butterflies resulted in a high percentage of the palatable Viceroy Butterflies subsequently offered being totally rejected by the jays. From this observation, do you consider that the first statement is invariably true? In what circumstances is it likely not to be necessarily valid?

15 There is a subfamily of leaf-feeding beetles popularly called 'flea-beetles' because of their ability to jump. Jumping is a behaviour which is likely to reduce the chance of successful predation by birds. The pupae of flea beetles are parasitized by the larvae of a genus of beetle of a completely different family. The adults of the parasite live in the same habitat as their hosts, but are sluggish. Nevertheless they closely resemble their hosts in appearance. Neither type of beetle is distasteful to bird predators.

What do you consider might be the value to the adult parasite of its resemblance to its host? Outline the design of a model experiment to test the major assumption made in your hypothesis.

Bibliography

Further Reading

Burkhardt, D., Schleidt, W., Altner, H.	*Signals in the Animal World,* Allen and Unwin, 1967
Collias, N. E.	*Animal Language*, BSCS Pamphlet no. 20, Heath, 1964
Brower, L. P.	'Ecological Chemistry', *Scientific American*, 1969, Offprint no. 1133
Denton, E.	'Reflectors in Fish', *Scientific American*, 1971, Offprint no. 1209
Edwards, J. S.	'Insect Assassins', *Scientific American*, 1960, Vol. 202, Pt. 6, p. 72
Ehrlich, P. R., Raven, P. H.	'Butterflies and Plants', *Scientific American*, 1967, Offprint no. 1076
Feder, H. M.	'Escape Responses in Marine Invertebrates', *Scientific American*, 1972, Offprint no. 1254
Fuhrman, F. A.	'Tetrodotoxin', *Scientific American*, 1967, Offprint no. 157
Shaw, E.	'The Shoaling of Fishes', *Scientific American*, 1962, Offprint no. 124
Todd, J. H.	'The Chemical Language of Fishes', *Scientific American*, 1971, Offprint no. 1222
Wilson, E. O.	'Pheromones', *Scientific American*, 1963, Offprint no. 157

10 Adaptations of predators

In considering the protective devices which are found among both producers and consumers to decrease the chances of predation, we have seen how there is an attempt either to reduce as far as possible stimulation of the senses of the predator or alternatively to stimulate them in such a way as to convey a 'warning' or a 'threat'. In a food web, sensory information passes not only from prey to predator but also from predator to prey. It is thus often advantageous to a predator, especially those of active prey such as flying birds, insects or fast-running game, to reduce to a minimum the sensory stimulation offered to its prey and so avoid disturbing it.

Coloration of predators

A chameleon not only obtains protection from other predators by its concealing or cryptic coloration, but may be able to approach within striking distance of some insect which, if alerted, would fly away (Book 1 Fig. 1.4). Similarly the broken pattern of coloration of the coat of a cat provides it with some concealment as it stalks a bird. There are some mantids and also certain spiders which specialize in catching insects which visit flowers. These animals sit in a flower awaiting their prey: they are usually coloured so as to be inconspicuous upon the flowers they normally select as hunting grounds. One may reasonably ask whether this cryptic coloration is of any advantage to the mantid or the spider. Would not insects visit the flowers as readily even if the predators were visible? This matter has been tested using the big yellow flowers of the common temperate weed, the dandelion. Sixteen very small pebbles, each about the size of a spider, were collected: eight of these were black and eight yellow. One pebble was placed on each of sixteen flowers, which were well spaced apart. The numbers of insects visiting the different flowers during a period of 30 min was noted. 63 insects visited the flowers during this time; 57 went to the flowers with the yellow, 'cryptic' stones and only 7 to the flowers with black stones. The potential advantage to a predator of matching its background may thus be considerable. Concealment or 'crypsis' can in this way play two different roles; the protective function is sometimes spoken of as 'procrypsis' and the function in predation as 'anticrypsis'.

Sensory mechanisms in prey finding

The sensory mechanisms employed by most predators are fairly easy to recognize. The hawk and the dragonfly find their prey by sight, as do the frog, the chameleon and the mantid; most of the larger carnivores—the lion, cheetah, leopard, hyaena and Hunting Dog—also find their prey largely by sight. With smaller mammals, smell becomes increasingly important. Thus, for example, the meerkat, a mongoose, will not only kill other, smaller mammals such as mice, but will also feed on insects and millipedes which it locates by smell, digging them out of the ground when once detected. There are, however, a number of animals in which less obvious senses are involved in prey location and some whose structure requires a specialized method of prey catching. We cannot here review all such cases but will, rather, discuss certain common types of animal which exemplify such specializations.

Nocturnal flying predators

It is obvious that a predator may have difficulty in finding its prey if it hunts at night. For terrestrial predators smell may be a clue which leads the predator to its prey, while vision may be adequate if the predator is not very active and information of prey at a distance of little value. This is probably the normal situation with a toad which uses its tongue to catch its prey. There are however two common, typically nocturnal, flying predators which do not seem to rely greatly either on sight or smell; these are the owls and the insect-eating bats.

Owls

Many owls feed upon small rodents and are faced with the problem of finding these animals not simply in the dark, but also when they are moving beneath the litter layer. Vision alone would be of little value in such a situation. Laboratory experiments have been made using one of these rodent-feeding owls, the Barn Owl (Fig. 10.1). The birds were tame and normally lived on a perch in a room which could be made so dark that photographic paper exposed there for an hour showed no difference from an unexposed control. On the floor was leaf litter to a depth

10.1 The Barn Owl, *Tyto alba*. The bird stands about 30 cm high.

This arrangement allows the owl to turn its head directly towards a source of sound and, having checked its location, to fly or glide directly towards it. In this way the owl can find prey which it cannot see. This should not, however, be taken to mean that owls never use their sight in hunting; other experiments suggest that they have very sensitive dark vision and both senses are probably normally used. Many other species of owl have an asymmetrical arrangement of the ears. What is striking is that individuals of two species, while able to find mice in a lighted room, could not be trained to catch mice in total darkness. Neither of these species has asymmetrical ears and their normal feeding habits are very different from those of the barn owl.

Bats

In Africa we have two types of bat. Some eat fruit and probably find their food by sight and smell, and some feed on insects, catching their food while flying, just as do many insect-eating birds.

These insectivorous bats have a remarkable ability to detect and avoid obstructions in their path in the total absence of any light. This was shown clearly by an Italian called Spallanzani in 1793. In one of his experiments Spallanzani hung a number of fine wires from the ceiling of a room. At the bottom of each wire was a tiny bell; if the wire was touched, the bell would ring. Spallanzani released a bat into this room at night and found that it was able to fly around without touching any of the wires. He also showed that blinding bats in no way interfered either with their ability to avoid obstacles while in flight or with their ability to catch insects, but that if he plugged their ears, then they could no longer avoid obstacles. Clearly an animal carrying ear plugs might be distressed for a variety of reasons. To meet this criticism, Spallanzani used two types of metal ear plug; one type was solid and the other was hollow. Any discomfort to the animals would be the same regardless of which type of plug was used, but with the hollow plugs they would still be able to hear.

Table 10.1 shows the results of similar experiments made

of about 5 cm and beneath this a mouse would be released. By the use of special equipment, the activity of the owl could be observed by infra-red light to which the owl's eyes are not sensitive. In sixteen trials, the owl failed to pounce directly on the prey on only four occasions and on no occasion did it land at a distance of more than 5 cm from the mouse. The behaviour of the owl strongly suggested that the noises made by the mice in moving or feeding were the sensory clue used by the bird; the owl would turn its head to face the source of sound and then, having waited until the mouse made some further noise, it would launch itself from its perch. If one or other ear was blocked, the accuracy of location by the owl was greatly impaired and the owl would now land as much as 50 cm away from the prey.

We have already discussed some aspects of the localization of sound (p. 173). Consider a source of sound some distance away from the head of an animal; the animal will have little difficulty in turning to face the sound since its intensity will be greater in one ear than the other. But if the source of sound is not in the same horizontal plane as the ears, then it would have to move its head up and down to find the position in which the loudness is at a maximum. It would make nodding movements and be unable to face towards the sound source without such movements.

The Barn Owl, however, does not make such movements. This is because the position of the external opening of the ear is not at the same level on the two sides of the body; that is, the arrangement of the ears is asymmetrical. The left ear is more sensitive to noises which arise from below the horizontal, the right ear to noises above the horizontal.

Table 10.1 Experiments on avoidance of fine wires by bats treated in various ways (*Data from Griffin and Galambos*)

Experimental treatment	% misses	N	Control treatment	% misses	N
Eyes covered	76	2016	Eyes not covered	70	3201
Ears plugged with solid tubes	36	580	Ears plugged with hollow tubes	66	636
Mouth covered	35	549	Mouth not covered	62	442

N is the total number of trials with each treatment

178

in 1940. Bats with a wing span of about 25 cm were required to fly through a barrier of fine wires of about 1 mm diameter. The wires were spaced about 30 cm apart and the number of times a bat flew through the barrier without touching any wire was recorded. It was calculated that this would happen by chance in about 35 percent of trials. The table makes it clear that the bats were able to avoid the wires regardless of whether their eyes were covered, but they were not able to do so if they could not hear or if their mouths were blocked.

The reasonable conclusion is that obstacle avoidance, and by extension food finding, depend in some way upon sound. The fact that the bats lost their ability to avoid obstacles when their mouths were blocked suggests that this must depend upon sounds made by the bats themselves; moreover, fine wires are not a source of sound even if flying insects may be. The sound produced by bats is effectively inaudible to the human ear, but suitably sensitive microphones and electronic recording apparatus can be used to show that the sounds made by bats are brief pulses, commonly less than 3 ms in duration and at frequencies of 30 to 60 kHz. The highest frequency detectable to the human ear is about 20 kHz, but the ears of bats are sensitive not only to much higher frequencies than these, but also to very weak sounds. Flying insects, such as moths and beetles, will produce well-marked echoes in response to the sound pulses emitted by the bats, and insect-feeding bats can thus detect some of their prey by orienting on these echoes. Smaller insects such as mosquitoes may possibly be detected directly by the noise made by their wings.

Such a method of catching flying prey has not gone unanswered in the 'war' between predator and prey. Many moths have auditory organs, although only few are known to make any noise. These auditory organs can detect the cries of bats, and moths have been observed, when chased by a bat or even when exposed to artificial bat-like noises, to make complex avoiding movements or simply to fall directly to the ground (Figs. 10.2 and 10.3); these actions are often successful in allowing the moth to elude the bat.

There is one further parallel to a situation we have already seen. Certain distasteful moths make a noise, a clicking sound which contains the high frequencies to which a bat's ear is sensitive. There is reason to believe

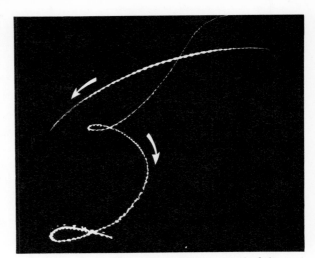

10.2 Traces based on a photographic record of the flight paths of a bat (upper smooth curve) and of a moth (broken curve), the moth successfully avoided the bat.

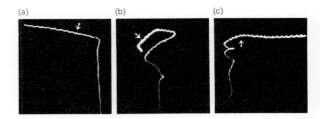

10.3 Traces of photographic records of moth flight paths. In each case, at the arrow, bat-like ultrasonic pulses were played from a loudspeaker. Three different patterns of avoiding dive are shown.

that this is the equivalent in sound of a warning coloration: that it is a warning noise. This possibility has been studied by feeding bats with palatable mealworm larvae, thrown in the air so that the bats can take the food while flying. As a larva was thrown up, the bats heard a tape recording, either of the noise made by a moth or of the noise made by another bat. The number of times the bats caught the larvae or turned away from them was recorded. Table 10.2 summarizes the results of one such experiment: clearly the noise made by the moths usually caused the bats to turn away from the larvae.

Muddy water: electric fish

The muddy waters of many rivers provide a very different sort of habitat in which a predator may have to hunt without being able to see its prey. Here we find the electric

Table 10.2 Experiments on the responses of bats to tape recordings of noises made by moths and bats (*Data from Dunning and Roeder*)

Experimental situation	Number of trials	Percentage of larvae attacked	avoided
No sound	681	99	1
Bat noise	309	85	15
Moth noise	465	14	86

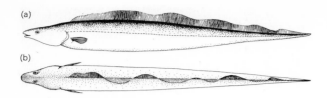

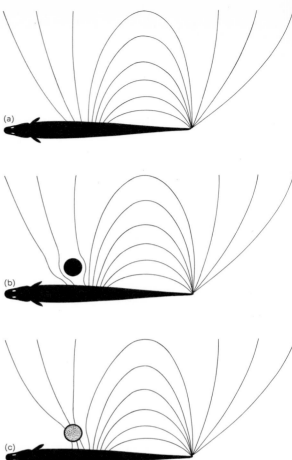

10.4 The electric fish, *Gymnarchus*.

fish *Gymnarchus* (Fig. 10.4). Muscular contraction is associated with a flow of electric current. On each flank of this fish there runs forward from the tail a thin strip of highly specialized muscle cells. These generate brief pulses of electrical energy with a repetition frequency of about 250 Hz. At each pulse the tail becomes electrically negative with respect to the fish's head and there will thus be an electric field around the fish (Fig. 10.5a). Along the sides of the fish are special sense cells which respond to this electric field and which will 'inform' the fish if the pattern of the field is changed in any way. Any object whose electric conductance is different from that of the water will, if placed within the field, alter its pattern (Figs. 10.5b and 10.5c); its presence can thus be detected by the fish.

What sort of evidence have we for such statements? One simple experiment uses a moving magnet to upset the pattern of an electric field. Specimens of *Gymnarchus* isolated in aquarium tanks are usually relatively inactive. If the walls of a tank are covered with black paper and a magnet is moved up and down close to one wall but outside the tank, the fish responds by making the characteristic movements of attack. It seems reasonable to suppose that the fish's response is due to the disturbance of the pattern of the electric field which it both generates and detects.

More critical experiments involve training the fish. If the fish makes the 'correct' response, it is rewarded with a little food. If it makes the wrong response it is punished by touching it gently with a metal rod. Using this system of rewards and punishments it was possible to test whether a specimen of *Gymnarchus* could learn to distinguish between two porous containers which were completely identical except that one was filled with wax and the other with water. They looked exactly the same but had different electrical conductivities; as a result the two containers would distort the fish's electric field in different ways. The two containers were lowered into the water at the same time; the water-filled container was sometimes on the right, sometimes on the left. Behind each container was a small fragment of food; the task set the fish was to identify the 'correct' container and be allowed to obtain the food. It proved possible to train the fish almost invariably to take food from behind the water-filled container and to neglect the other; that is to say, the fish could distinguish one container from the other. The remarkable ability of the fish to discriminate between objects of different conductivity is illustrated in Table 10.3 which summarizes results

10.5 (a) Diagram showing the pattern of the electric field around *Gymnarchus*. (b) If an object of low conductivity is placed near the fish, it modifies the pattern of potential difference along the side of the body. (c) If the object has a high conductivity, a different pattern will result.

Table 10.3 Discrimination by *Gymnarchus* between aquarium water and various mixtures of distilled water and aquarium water (*Data from Lissmann and Machin*)

Test solution (% distilled water)	Number of trials	Percentage correct responses
75	97	82
50	15	80
25	108	79
12·5	22	63*

*This value is not significantly different from that expected by chance.
Note: '75% distilled water' will be a mixture of 75 parts of distilled water and 25 parts of aquarium water.

10.6 The electric catfish, *Malapterurus*.

of experiments in which it was attempted to train the fish to distinguish between a container filled with normal aquarium water and one in which the aquarium water was diluted with distilled water. It shows that the fish could distinguish a mixture of three parts of normal water and one part distilled water from normal aquarium water. These results are thus in keeping with our hypothesis that what the fish is normally sensing is any change produced by some foreign object in the pattern of the electric field; in this way it finds its food.

Gymnarchus uses its ability to produce electric pulses to detect its prey. The electric potential it generates is less than 0·1 V; you will not get an electric shock if you handle a live specimen. The Electric Catfish *Malapterurus* (Fig. 10.6), however, has electric organs which can produce a discharge of up to 350 V; so if you handle one, you may well get a shock. It is possible that the catfish uses this electric organ to stun its prey; this is certainly the case with some marine electric fishes, such as the electric rays.

Finally, it is noteworthy that some other fishes—for example, the catfish *Clarias* (Fig. 6.23)—have no electric organs, but nevertheless have sense organs which would allow them to detect the electric pulses of fish such as *Gymnarchus*. These sense organs may be of value in avoiding predators. This is, however, only a possibility; whether it is indeed the case has yet to be examined.

Flying prey

Certain types of prey may be difficult to catch, not because they are difficult to see but because they are very active and are not limited to moving over a surface. This is true, for example, of flying insects. Most of their predators, such as birds and dragonflies, are also able to fly, but a number of slowly moving terrestrial animals also feed upon such insects. These include mantids, toads and chameleons, which all depend upon the use of a fast-moving structure which allows them to snatch up a resting insect before it can fly off. The mantids use their specialized fore-legs, toads and chameleons the tongue. All three animals may take some time 'adjusting their aim' before they strike, but the movement involved in catching the prey takes only about 0·05 s.

Spiders' webs

A completely different solution to the problem of catching

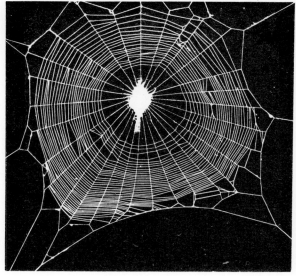

10.7 The orb web of the spider *Argiope*. The adult will build webs 20 cm or more in diameter.

flying insects lies in the use of a trap; this is the solution found among some of the web-spinning spiders. Not all spiders spin webs; some hunt in the open and leap onto their prey, while others may tie their prey down by squirting over it sticky, silken threads. Many spiders spin webs over the surface of the ground and, in this way, trap insects running on the surface or among the litter (Book 1 Fig. 18.59). But other species build webs which are stretched out between twigs and branches and with these they are able to catch flying insects. A web with an evenly spaced spiral of silk is called an orb web (Fig. 10.7).

The silk is a fibrous protein built of molecules which are long straight chains. It is synthesized by glands in the abdomen of the spider. Many spiders produce several different sorts of silk, each serving a different purpose, and there are different glands secreting the various types of silk. Table 10.4 summarizes the variety of glands found in the common European Garden Spider, *Araneus*, and also shows the functions of their secretions.

At the end of the spider's abdomen are small, finger-like projections, known as spinnerets. The silk is extruded as a fluid from small apertures or spigots on these spinnerets. The various glands have distinct openings; Fig. 10.8 shows a plan of these in *Araneus*. As the fluid is extruded, the tiny jet comes under tension, thus causing the molecules to align with one another; this results in the formation of a thread of silk.

Two obvious questions arise. Firstly, how does the spider manage to build so complex a structure away from any support other than the bushes to which the edges of the web are attached? Secondly, how is so flimsy a structure effective in catching prey?

Table 10.4 Number, position and function of the different silk glands of the European Garden Spider, *Araneus* (*Data from Pewakall*)

| Name of gland | Number of glands opening on spinnerets | | | Function of secretion |
	Anterior	*Median*	*Posterior*	
Ampullate	2	2	—	drag lines, scaffolding of web
Aggregate	—	—	6	viscid thread of spiral
Cylindrical	—	—	4	enveloping eggs
Piriform	200	—	—	attachment discs
Aciniform	—	200	200	swathing silk wrapped round prey

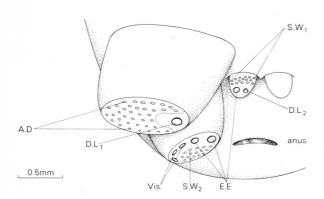

10.8 Diagrammatic representation of the spinnerets of *Araneus*, showing the arrangement of the spigots opening from the different glands. A.D. attachment disc glands; D.L. drag line glands; E.E. egg envelope silk gland; S.W. swathing silk glands; Vis. viscid thread glands. Note that the numbers of spigots of the attachment disc and swathing silk glands are far greater than shown in the diagram.

Construction of an orb web

The precise details of the way in which an orb web is constructed vary somewhat from species to species, but the principles remain the same. The first action of the spider is to establish a 'bridge line' of silk. This she does by extruding a silken thread from her spinnerets. This is pulled out by the wind and may, by chance, attach to some object. The spider now moves along this thread, eating it as she goes and replacing it by another thread at the same time. Thus, as she moves, the spider forms a link between the original line and the newer, stronger line which replaces it. Once the bridge line is completed, the spider anchors a second thread at one end and then moves along the bridge line spinning out this second thread so that it is slack. This we will call the 'hub line'. On reaching the end of the bridge the hub line is secured (Fig. 10.9a). The spider now moves back once more, but this time along the hub line. When she reaches about the middle of the line, she attaches

a third line to the hub line, using special 'attachment-disc silk'. Then she lets herself fall, spinning out thread as she goes until she reaches some firm object below. To this she attaches the line down which she has dropped. The web now consists of the bridge line and three radial lines from a central point, the hub (Fig. 10.9b).

The spider climbs back to the hub and then moves out along one of the radii, spinning out a loose line as she goes. About half-way along the radius she stops and attaches the thread (Fig. 10.9c.1). She then moves back along the newly spun thread and when about half-way along its length, she attaches yet another thread (Fig. 10.9c.2). She then moves back to the hub and out along another radius, carrying the new thread with her; about half-way along this radius, she stops, pulls taut the thread she has been carrying and then attaches it to the radial line (Fig. 10.9d.3 and e). This will produce a figure of several triangles. The outer threads are called 'frame threads'.

This operation is now repeated between the two remaining radial pairs and, if it is done perfectly, it will produce a hexagonal arrangement of frame threads joined to the hub by six radial lines (Fig. 10.9f). Note that the frame threads are not attached to any surrounding objects. The spider now proceeds to add further radii. This she does by attaching a thread or 'drag line' to the hub. She next moves out along a radius to the frame, carrying the drag line with her. Then she walks some distance along the frame, stops and pulls the drag line taut. Moving along the drag line, she returns once more to the hub, strengthening this new radial thread by the addition of further silk as she goes.

With the completion of the radii, the spider next strengthens the hub region of the web by putting down a close spiral of silk. This is done by standing with her 'head' at the centre of the hub and slowly rotating; meanwhile she spins out thread which is laid down in a spiral.

Finally the spider lays down the major spiral structure of the web. Moving out from the hub, she walks around in a circle, spinning as she goes and pausing at each radius to attach the thread with an attachment disc. As she moves,

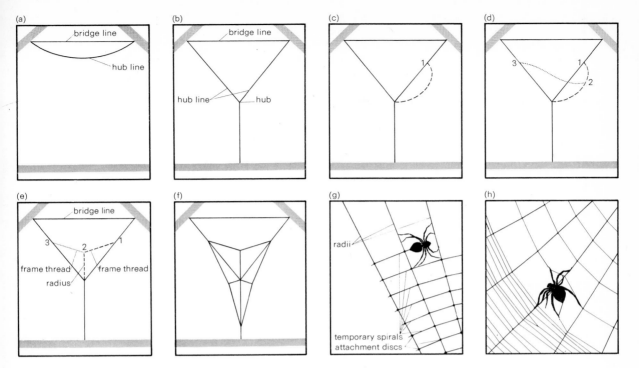

10.9 Stages in the construction of an orb web. For further explanation, see text.

she keeps her inner legs on the thread she has previously spun; in this way an evenly spaced spiral is produced (Fig. 10.9g). When she has nearly arrived at the frame threads, the spider reverses her direction. She now walks back along the spiral she has laid out, eating the thread as she goes; for this reason it is described as a temporary spiral. As she moves back she lays down more spirals than were used in the temporary spiral (Fig. 10.9h). They are of a different sort of silk which is coated with a sticky material. As the thread is stretched, the sticky compound breaks up into small droplets giving this 'viscid' thread a bead-like appearance; the sticky material on the threads of the 'viscid spirals' makes the web an effective trap.

Catching prey in the web

Even if sticky, the web is frail and unless the spider takes action quickly any insect which is caught may well escape. An insect landing on the web will set up vibrations in the web and these are detected by the spider which commonly sits at the hub with her legs spread outwards. From this position, presumably by identifying which radial threads are in vibration, the spider can run rapidly to her prey. If, however, she is in some other part of the web, she will return immediately to the hub and from there move outwards to the prey.

Many prey organisms escape only with difficulty, but moths and butterflies (Lepidoptera) can often escape from a spider's web at the expense of losing some scales. Table

Table 10.5 Details of captures and escapes from the webs of ten specimens of *Argiope* observed over a period of six months (*Data from Robinson*)

Moths and butterflies caught	46
Moths and butterflies escaped	55
Other insects escaped	12
Other insects caught	not recorded: probably considerably more than 500

10.5 summarizes observations upon escapes from the web of an *Argiope*; the data are incomplete since none are given for the number of trapped insects other than Lepidoptera. At a most conservative estimate this must have been 500 and was in fact probably vastly greater. Thus, for example, one of the specimens on which these observations are based caught as many as 70 small bees during the course of a single hour.

What then is the normal pattern of prey catching in *Argiope* and how is it modified if a moth or butterfly is caught? Usually, as soon as the spider has caught her prey, she throws bands of silk over it with her hind legs, thus binding it to the web. The spider then turns the prey round and round, wrapping it in further bands of silk. Once wrapped, the prey is given several brief bites which probably serve to inject poison. The prey in its wrapping is then cut out from the web and carried back to the hub in the fangs or chelicerae (Book 1 p. 210) or, if it is bulky, suspended from a thread. At the hub the female rests for a while before she starts to feed. She drives her chelicerae into the prey and then regurgitates a drop of fluid from her stomach. This fluid, which contains digestive enzymes, flows into the wound in the prey and there starts digestion of the tissues. In a short while the fluid is sucked back and then more is regurgitated. This process is repeated until external digestion is completed; the remains of the prey are then crushed with the chelicerae and the spider sucks up any fluid which remains.

With a lepidopteran a different tactic is usually followed. The prey is attacked immediately and the spider holds its bite for several minutes. Then, once the prey has been killed, it is wrapped and carried back to the hub to be eaten. In this latter pattern, the 'long bite' results in rapid death so that the prey has little chance of escape; in the more usual pattern the prey may remain active for a considerable time but, not being scale-covered, it is unable to escape once it is imprisoned in silk.

Such then is one way in which a web is used to catch flying insects. But not all web-building spiders conform to this pattern. There is, for example, a spider *Agelena*, which is found in Gabon; each individual is less than 1 cm in length, but as many as 700 share a common web, consisting essentially of a horizontal sheet of silk which may be 3 to 4 m² in area. From the surrounding vegetation silken trap lines hang down onto this platform; these may reach a length of more than a metre. An insect flying through the trap lines will commonly fall onto the platform; the vibrations which it sets up cause large numbers of these small spiders to rush out and kill it by biting. Subsequently they feed upon it. In this way the spiders of the colony can trap insects which individually they would be unable to capture.

Ant-lions

A trap of a completely different principle is used by the ant-lion. Ant-lions are the larvae of certain members of the order Neuroptera, insects whose adults are commonly referred to as 'lacewings'. The larva digs a shallow conical pit in sandy soil, throwing the sand out by a jerky movement of the head. It sits buried at the bottom of this pit with only the front of its head and its long curved mandibles projecting above the surface. Any small surface-running insect which walks over the edge of the pit will dislodge some grains of sand which, falling to the bottom of the pit, alert the ant-lion. The ant-lion, with a head movement like that used in pit-excavation, then throws sand towards the potential prey. This is likely to dislodge the prey which falls to the bottom of the pit and is immediately seized in the mandibles of the ant-lion (Fig. 10.10).

Lures

Flying insects are free to move in all three dimensions and

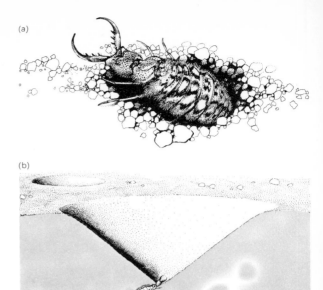

10.10 (a) An ant-lion larva. The size of the larva will depend upon its age. It may be 2 cm or more in length shortly before pupation. (b) Diagram showing how the larva sits in a pit. (c.f. *Ceratias*, Book 1, Fig. 20.18).

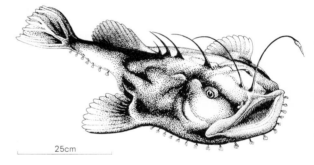

25cm

10.11 An angler fish, *Lophius*. Note the lure; the small projections from the edge of the body are said to resemble fragments of alga and serve to break up the outline of the body.

catching them thus presents a difficulty to predators. The same is true of fishes, and a spider's web might be regarded as equivalent to a fisherman's net. Men also catch fish using bait on the ends of lines, but in this they are not unique; certain marine fishes, angler fish, utilize the same principle (Fig. 10.11). From the head projects a mobile spine from the tip of which hangs a strand of tissue which ends in a structure which serves as bait. In some species this crudely resembles a worm and a twitching movement of the spine serves to keep the bait in motion. The bait hangs down just in front of the open mouth of the angler fish and any small fish which comes to inspect the bait is likely to be snapped up by the angler.

Snakes: limbless predators

Almost all terrestrial predators have legs and these are used sometimes for chasing the prey, sometimes, as in mantids, for catching it, and sometimes, as in spiders, for manipulating it once it is caught. But one important group of terrestrial predators lack all legs; these are the snakes which must rely purely upon movements of the trunk and jaws to catch and overpower their prey. Some of the smaller snakes, such as the Garden Snake *Duberria*, feed upon slow-moving invertebrates like slugs and snails; others prey on insects, myriapods and earthworms. Since the snakes are relatively faster moving, they can easily catch and hold their prey with their mouths. An alternative source of food is provided by completely inactive objects such as birds' eggs; a few snakes, including the common *Dasypeltis*, have certain special features which allow them to deal with this type of food (p. 186).

Large, active prey must first be immobilized, since the teeth of snakes are fine-pointed structures, unsuited for any cutting or chewing action. The prey has to be swallowed whole and the teeth serve principally to move food backwards into the oesophagus. One way in which some snakes immobilize the prey is to seize it with the jaws and then to wrap the body round the prey, squeezing it to death, probably by asphyxiation. This is the habit, for example, of the common House Snake *Boaedon*, which feeds upon rats and mice, lizards, geckos and frogs. (Fig. 10.12) Pythons use the same method of food capture; they can coil their bodies extremely rapidly around any animal they catch. Death can occur in a few seconds; once dead the prey can be swallowed gradually. These snakes have remarkable ability to swallow very large prey. For example, an African Python, *Python sebae*, of about 4·5 m length was found to have swallowed a reedbuck of about 27 kg; another of about 5·3 m length had swallowed an impala weighing 60 kg.

A different method of prey immobilization, and the one which has given snakes their reputation for being dangerous, is the use of poison. The major role of the venom is to allow the snake to overpower large and active prey. This is seen clearly in the behaviour of a puff adder offered a rat as food. If hungry, the snake will strike at the rat, injecting

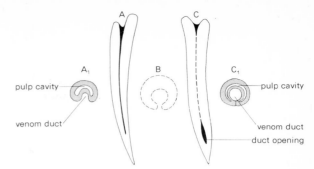

10.13 Diagram of snake fangs. In A there is an open groove, as shown in the section A_1; in C there is a closed duct which opens near the tip of the fang. C_1 shows C in section, while B shows how the structure of A and C are related.

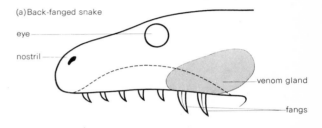

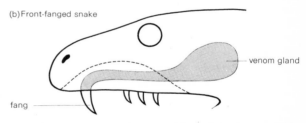

10.14 Diagram showing the position of the fangs of (a) a back-fanged (opisthoglyph) snake and (b) a front-fanged (proteroglyph) snake. The broken line indicates the margin of the maxillary bone. Snakes which can erect their fangs are described as 'solenoglyph'.

its venom, but it will then retire or remain inactive for a considerable time while the venom acts upon the prey. After five minutes the snake will start to seek its prey and then slowly swallow the corpse head first.

The poison or venom of snakes is secreted by glands which open into the mouth cavity close to the roots of specialized teeth called fangs. These teeth may either have a deep groove down which the poison will flow, or be hollow as a result of the closure of this groove; the fang then acts rather like a hypodermic needle (Fig. 10.13).

In some snakes, such as the boomslang, *Dispholidus*, the fangs lie towards the back of the upper jaw, the maxilla, and the venom can only be injected provided the snake is able to bite deeply. In others, such as the cobra, *Naja*, the mamba, *Dendroaspis*, and the ringhals, *Hemachatus*, the fangs are at the anterior end of the maxilla (Fig. 10.14); as

10.12 A house snake swallowing a rat.

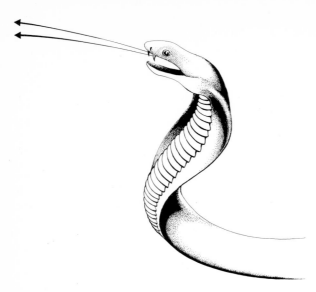

10.15 The cobra, *Naja*, spitting out two jets of venom. The venom is forced out of the orifice near the tip of each fang. Not all species of *Naja* can spit.

Let us return to the egg-eating snake *Dasypeltis*. This snake often eats quite big eggs; if it were to crush such an egg in its mouth, much of the contents would flow out. In fact it swallows the egg whole. Certain of the vertebrae behind the head are specialized, each having a mid-ventral spur, a hypapophysis (Book 1 p. 136) (Fig. 10.17B) which actually projects through the dorsal surface of the oeso-phagus. These spurs are bent anteriorly and as the egg is moved backwards, its shell is cut open by the spurs. The immediately anterior vertebrae also have hypapophyses, but these are blunt projections which crush the shell. The contents of the egg are forced out and flow back to the stomach. Finally the empty eggshell, crushed and split along its length but held together by the shell membrane. is passed back to the mouth and discarded by the snake. In this way, not only is none of the contents of the egg lost, but the shell fragments which might well cut through the thin wall of the gut, are cleanly discarded.

Snakes have a sinister reputation as deadly killers of

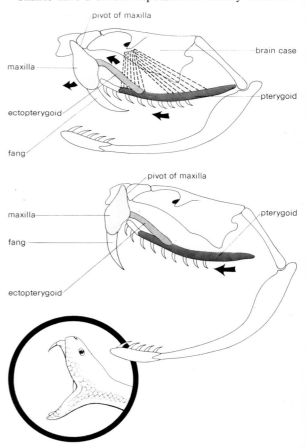

10.16 The mechanism of fang erection in a solenog-lyph snake. Compare the shape of the maxilla with those shown in Fig. 10.14. The mouth is not fully opened in the lower figure. The small sketch shows the way the fangs point forwards when the snake opens its mouth fully.

a result the venom can be injected in a single shallow bite. The cobra and the ringhals have the habit of squirting out their venom from the base of the fangs as two fine jets (Fig. 10.15); the venom can in this way be thrown as far as 2 m. This makes these snakes especially dangerous to man for if the venom strikes the cornea of the eye, it can lead to blindness unless given immediate attention. This be-haviour is, however, defensive and almost certainly not concerned with prey catching.

The fangs of the cobras and mambas are relatively short since they must be accommodated within the mouth when the jaws are closed. In the vipers the fangs are folded back beneath the roof of the mouth when it is shut. When a viper strikes, it erects the fangs so that they point almost directly forwards. This allows the fangs to be long. While the fangs of a 4 m mamba are only 0·7 cm long, a Gaboon Viper, *Bitis gabonica*, one-third of this size, may have fangs more than 2·5 cm in length.

The mechanical principle used in erecting a viper's fangs is explained in Fig. 10.16. The bones of the upper jaw are not rigidly attached to the braincase as they are in a mammal; they can be moved. As the mouth is opened, muscles originating on the braincase and inserted on a bone called the pterygoid, pull this bone forwards. This movement is transmitted to a second bone, the ectoptery-goid, which in turn thrusts upon the posterior face of the rather square maxilla, causing it to rotate around its dorsal margin, so that the fang is swung forwards. The movements of the fangs on either side are independent: a viper or a puff adder can open its mouth and erect one fang but not the other. It may even open its mouth in a yawn and erect neither.

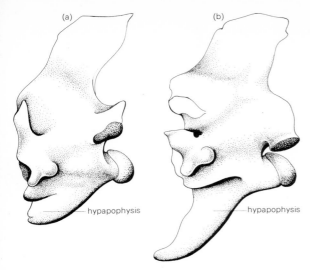

<small>(a)</small>   <small>(b)</small>

hypapophysis   hypapophysis

10.17 Egg crushing and slicing vertebrae of *Dasypeltis*. The egg is cut open by the pointed hypapophyses of the more posterior 'neck' vertebrae (b) and then crushed by the blunt hypapophyses of the immediately anterior vertebrae (a).

man. Probably not more than 1 000 deaths from snake bite occur annually in the whole of Africa: far more people die each year as a result of motor-car accidents.

The web of sensory information

The last few chapters have been largely concerned with problems of the sensory information which passes between producer and consumer or between consumers of different orders. What a consumer accepts as food is in general determined by sensory information. Even in bivalve molluscs which in filtering water appear to take any suspended particles which they can trap (Book 1 Fig. 18.46), there is evidence that in many species a sorting process occurs; not everything which is collected is accepted as food. Certainly some consumers, like the marine burrowing lugworm, *Arenicola* (Book 1 Fig. 20.27b), may exercise little or no selection. The lugworm's choice of habitat is, however, in itself a choice of food.

Not only is the choice of food determined by sensory information but, as we have seen, the structure and the habits of all potential food organisms are strongly influenced by the sensory equipment of the consumers which prey upon them, while these predators, in their turn, will be affected also in structure and habit by the sensory potentials of their prey.

In Chapter 1 of Book 1 we saw how a food web might be regarded as an expression of the pathways by which matter and energy flow through an ecosystem. We can now recognize that the links which determine the detailed pattern of the food web within any community are sensory links and further that the 'quality' of this sensory informa-

tion may to some extent determine how much matter and energy will pass by one route rather than another. If, in an ecosystem, there are two equally abundant potential sources of food for a consumer, the organism which is more readily discovered or more palatable is likely to be eaten more often than the one which is more cryptic or more distasteful.

We can thus look at a food web in two ways. We may regard it as a series of tubes or pipes along which flow matter and energy and also as a series of sensory links which involve the passage of some type of information, either as chemical compounds or as light waves or sound waves, between the members of the web. A link may be built of a single type of sensory stimulation, that is a single sensory modality, but commonly several different types of sensory information are involved.

In quantitative terms this picture is to some degree over-simplified, as the behaviour of consumers will be affected by factors other than those of sensory information. We have already seen that consumers may display preferences for certain types of food; such preferences, however, may not be constant. Thus many birds, once they have found a particular food item, will continue to seek and accept this preferentially. In some mammals there are indications that if offered the possibility, they will feed upon a varied diet. Except in its broadest outline, the food web should not be regarded as a static set of interrelations in any one eco-system, but as a changeable series of relations between different organisms.

While many inherently interesting facts may emerge when we investigate the details of the sensory exchanges which occur within a community, their study is not simply one of idle curiosity. A knowledge of these details may, in particular cases, be of considerable economic importance. Thus, for example, the recognition that some particular secondary plant substance is attractive to an insect pest may lead plant breeders to produce varieties which lack this substance and will therefore be free of the pest, while other varieties may be produced containing a substance repellent to the pest. Such knowledge may also be turned to account in attempting to control pests with poison baits. One remarkable example has arisen in keeping certain lake-side farms free from destruction by hippopotamus. The hippos were driven away by spraying around the farms a chemical whose smell resembled the scent of lion.

Problems

1 The stomach contents of a number of different tree frogs have been analysed. In a sample of 360 specimens of *Afrilaxus*, 337 specimens of flying insect were found; in a sample of 438 other tree frogs only 79 specimens were obtained. This has led to the suggestion that the pattern of skin coloration of *Afrilaxus* (Fig. 9.24) is anticryptic rather than procryptic. Explain the reasoning.

2 On p. 180 the description of an experiment which in-

volved the training of *Gymnarchus*, it was stated that a reward, in the form of food, was placed behind both containers in the fish tank. Why was the food not placed only behind the container at which the fish was being trained to take food?

3 When a puff adder bites a rat, it retires and waits until the rat is dead. Why may it be advantageous for the snake to retreat from its prey in this fashion? How do you think it finds its prey again? How would you test your hypothesis?

4 On p. 185 we described the 'catching threads' of a spider's web as being covered with beads of a sticky material. In some spiders, however, each of these threads is formed from a mass of very fine threads which entangle the prey. Spiders of one group remake their webs daily; those of the other group may not. Which group would you expect to have to spin a fresh web each day? Give reasons for your opinion.

5 *Gymnarchus* will feed on other fish. Some 'electric fishes' which, like *Gymnarchus*, produce only weak electric signals, feed upon midge larvae from the bottom of rivers. What do you consider may be the function of the electric discharges in such fish?

6 Would you describe the coloration of a chameleon as being procryptic or anticryptic or both?

Bibliography

Further reading

Gamow, R. I., Harris, J. F.　'The Infrared Receptors of Snakes', *Scientific American*, 1973, **Offprint no. 1272**

Gilbert, P. W.　'The Behaviour of Sharks', *Scientific American*, 1962, Offprint no. 127

Griffin, D. R.　'More about Bat Radar', *Scientific American*, 1958, Offprint no. 1121

Lissmann, H. W.　'Electric Location by Fishes', *Scientific American*, 1963, Offprint no. 152

Pennycuick, C. J.　'The Soaring Flight of Vultures', *Scientific American*, 1973, Vol. 229, Pt. 6, p. 102

Roeder, K. D.　'Moths and Ultrasound', *Scientific American*, 1965, Offprint no. 1009

11 Social life

In the previous chapter we described the habits of a small spider *Agelena* which, by living with fellow members of its species, its 'conspecifics', in a large communal nest, is able to prey upon insects far larger than it could attack alone: the quantity of food available to these spiders is thus much greater than would otherwise be the case. Spiders, like most predators, are aggressive animals and usually quite willing to accept other spiders for food. To be able to live together, this aggressive behaviour towards conspecifics must in some way be prevented. Usually individual *Agelena* do not display aggression towards each other. If, however, prey falls upon the platform one spider may rush at another as if to bite it. As it moves it holds its front pair of legs outwards, rather like antennae. When these touch the second spider, the aggressor does not press home the attack. Apart from this essential change in behaviour, there is one other specialization within this social community. Note that we are here using the term 'community' in a more limited sense than in Chap. 6. We speak of a 'social community' to make the difference clear. Young spiders which have just emerged from the cocoon do not go out to attack prey. They commonly remain close to the mouth of one of the several nests or refuges which are built into the platform. Some adults will bring fragments of food to the young. Within this social community we may thus recognize three elements which characterize most social relations between animals: a common absence of aggression, a behavioural check upon aggression should it occur and some type of bond between adults and young.

Parental care of the young

The vast majority of animals are solitary, living independent lives, and the individuals of any one species affect their conspecifics only in so far as they exploit the same resources of their environment. If these are abundant, the individuals have little effect upon one another. There is one major exception: all animals which mate must, if only for a brief time, form some relationship with a conspecific of the opposite sex. Such an event may last only a few minutes. If, however, it is prolonged, if the mating pair remain together after they have mated, a distinct type of relationship is established, as it becomes possible for the parents to feed and defend the young. This will be familiar among the birds. In some species, such as the Hamerkop and *Quelea*, the two parents co-operate in the building of the nest and then take turns in sitting on the eggs, that is, in incubating them. In other species such as the sunbirds and bishopbirds only the female sits upon the eggs and while incubating she is fed by the male; in a few cases, for example the Button Quails, the males incubate the eggs.

Once the eggs have hatched, the parents will feed the young. This may be done by both parents as in bulbuls and Glossy Starlings, by the female alone as in bishopbirds or by the male only as in the Button Quails. Presently the young fly away and the two parents then commonly separate, although in some cases the same two individual birds may come together to breed in the following season. This is true, for example, of the Crowned Eagle in Kenya in which one particular female was observed to mate with the same male each breeding season over a period of five years. The male then died and the female mated twice subsequently with another male before she in turn died or was killed. Such behaviour is moreover not limited to large birds; for example, the same marked pair of Orange-breasted Sunbirds was observed breeding in the same territory for three consecutive years, although the pair separated outside the breeding season.

Rather similar relations exist among mammals. In many instances, once mating has occurred, the pair separate. The male has no prolonged relation with the female, although they may both remain within the same herd or flock. This is the case with our various domestic animals such as cattle, sheep and horses as well as their wild relatives such as buck and zebra, and also many others, such as cats, hares and elephants. But in other species a more enduring bond may exist between the parents, and sometimes also between parents and young, so that a family group is formed. Such a group may maintain its coherence only until the young are mature and then break up; this is true of the Golden Jackal, *Canis aureus*. With lions, the group may be permanent, united around a single male; when they mature the young males are driven off, but the young females remain with the family grouping. In the most extreme case the individuals of all ages remain together to form a cohesive and co-operating society. This we see, for example, in pack-hunting animals like Cape Hunting Dog in which the pack as a whole is concerned with prey killing. From the viewpoint of trophic relations, the pack,

189

or society, may be regarded as a single unit in the food web. Such group cohesion is seen also among the herbivores in which members of a single herd contribute by their alertness to their mutual defence. Both these relations found expression also in primitive human hunting communities **where the group was more effective both in hunting** and in defence than a single individual would have been.

This type of social interrelationship between conspecifics depends not only on the existence of a bond lasting at least until the young are capable of finding their own food, but also upon life span: the parents must survive until the young can fend for themselves. While this is the case with birds and mammals, among invertebrates adult life may be very brief and, as in mayflies (Ephemeroptera) and some butterflies, the female may die long before her eggs hatch. Nevertheless some female insects will protect and tend the eggs until they hatch. For example, in some earwigs (Dermaptera) the female lays her eggs in a hole in the ground. She remains with the eggs, turning them over and licking them from time to time; if she is removed, the eggs die. A few days after the young nymphs have hatched, the female leaves and the insects scatter. Similarly in some species of Hemiptera, the female will stand guard over her egg mass until the young emerge. In one genus the male guards the eggs; if he is driven off, he will return to his post as soon as the disturbance has passed. In these cases, there is some evidence that the behaviour of the parent protects the eggs from attack by parasitic insects.

Social insects

In almost all the examples we have just described the young nymphs or larvae disperse shortly after hatching. But the young of some insects may remain together with the parent and a small society can thus be formed. The stability of this society depends upon the fact that the founding female is long-lived and continues to reproduce, so the population of the society grows rapidly. This situation is strikingly elaborated among the familiar social insects, the ants, the bees and the wasps (Hymenoptera). Among the termites (Isoptera), the society is slightly more complex in that a bond is initially formed between male and female and that the male also is long-lived, unlike males of the social Hymenoptera; as a result both parents remain as part of the society.

Termites (Isoptera)

It is convenient to begin a study of insect societies with the termites and we will take as examples two common forms. The one, *Trinervitermes*, common in savanna, builds low mounds or termitaria standing perhaps 50 cm high and about 25 cm in diameter (Fig. 4.18). The colonies may reach a density of about 500 mounds per hectare. The other example is *Macrotermes* which builds vast mounds, reaching a height of 2 m or more (Fig. 4.19 and Book 1 Fig.

23.10). These nests are formed from soil particles cemented together by the faeces of the workers.

Castes

If you break open a mound of *Trinervitermes* and collect a large sample of the termites, you will find a number of different forms. Some are almost completely white with no brown, sclerotized cuticle: these are nymphal stages. Some of the individuals have brown cuticle, especially clearly marked on the head capsule: these are adults. Examination of the adults shows that they fall into two types or castes. Some have roughly circular heads seen in dorsal view; these are members of the worker caste and are all females. The others, which are smaller, have a long snout-like projection at the front of the head. These are the soldiers; they are all males and their sole function is to protect the workers while they are gathering food, and the nest should its entrances be broken open (Fig. 11.1).

Examination of the head of a soldier under a microscope shows that the snout contains the duct of a large gland which fills much of the head capsule and secretes a white viscid fluid. At night workers and soldiers leave the nest and foraging parties go out in search of grass and small seeds. The foragers spread out over an area of 2 to 3 m² and may climb grass stems to a height of about 2 m in their search for food. The sides of the route followed by the foragers are lined by soldiers, spaced apart at intervals of about 1 cm and facing outwards to meet any attack. If ants should attack, the soldiers eject the fluid from their head glands; if this should strike an ant, the animal will retreat. Applied directly to an ant, the secretion is highly toxic.

Neither workers nor soldiers have well-developed gonads, although they are fully adult. At certain times of year a third type of adult will be found which, unlike the

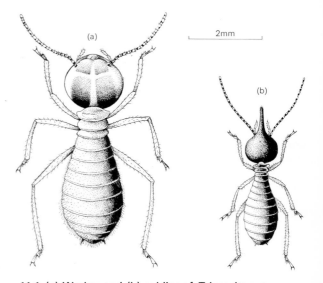

11.1 (a) Worker and (b) soldier of *Trinervitermes*.

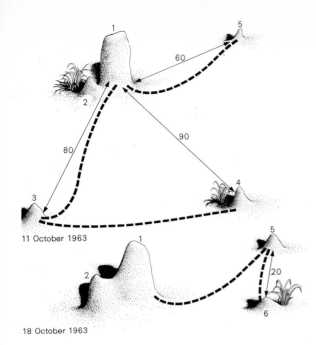

11 October 1963

18 October 1963

11.2 Plan of nest sites of *Trinervitermes*. On 11th October 1963 the main nest mound, 1, had associated with it four smaller mounds, 2–5. A week later mound 2 had become more closely incorporated with 1; 3 and 4 had been abandoned and a new mound, 6, started. Distances are in cm; the broken lines show the arrangement of subterranean passages connecting the mounds. (After Bodot).

workers and soldiers, is winged and will become sexually mature. These familiar flying termites are spoken of as 'reproductives', and include both males and females.

Finally, a thorough search may bring to light an adult with a swollen abdomen, in company with a smaller adult which resembles a winged reproductive that has lost its wings. These are the queen and the king, the only two fully sexually mature individuals within the colony.

The nest

The nest is constructed of curving surfaces, floors and roofs, with curving pillars supporting the roofs. Movement from one part of the nest to another is easy in this sponge-like complex of chambers and the royal pair are not restricted to a single chamber as they are in the nests of *Macrotermes*. The nest extends into the soil below the mound for a distance of as much as 50 cm, the whole nest being roughly spherical in shape. It is estimated that a colony may contain 20 000 to 50 000 individuals. These are often not restricted to a single mound; the colony may occupy several mounds joined together by tunnels which lie 2 to 3 cm below the surface of the soil. Fig. 11.2 shows the plan of one such mound system. At various points,

side passages from the tunnels come close to the surface of the soil and then break up into a series of fine corridors which open at the soil surface but are plugged with earth during the daytime; it is from these corridors that the foraging bands of workers and soldiers emerge at night. The many mounds allow the colony to forage over a wide area, while providing shelter into which workers and soldiers can retire. The mounds also provide temporary storage for the materials gathered by the workers. A study of the contents of the nest mound shows that freshly collected grass, cut into lengths of about 5 mm, is stored just below the dome of the nest mound. Here temperatures will be high during the day and the grass will dry out most rapidly.

Annual cycle of a colony

By regular sampling of the nests of one species of *Trinervitermes*, it has been possible to build up a picture of the annual cycle of events as it occurs in northern Nigeria where there is a single rainy season each year (Fig. 11.3). The rains end in August, and during September and October foraging activity by the workers is very great; the colony is building up reserves as, in the dry months that follow, air humidity falls sharply, making conditions unsuitable for foraging. About January nymphs of the reproductives start to appear; they can be recognized because, unlike the nymphs of workers and soldiers, they have short wing pads on the thorax. During the following months these reproductives become increasingly abundant; they are being fed upon the reserves laid in by the workers the previous year and these reserves are supplemented by sporadic foraging when conditions outside the nest at night are suitable. The rains start about the beginning of April and for a while foraging activity increases, but increasing rainfall appears to hinder the workers, which become inactive about the middle of May. At the beginning of June there is a major flight of reproductives away from the nest; smaller flights may occur later. The colony remains inactive until the rains cease and then a fresh period of very active foraging starts the annual cycle once again.

When the reproductives leave the nest, they fly for a short distance and then land and shed their wings. The female gives off a scent, a pheromone, which attracts a male and the pair move off, the female leading and the male following close behind her. The female finds a suitable crack or crevice as a refuge and the animals then burrow into the soil where they excavate a small chamber. Here they mate and the female starts to lay eggs. These take about a month to develop and the young nymphs need a further month to become adult. As a result adult workers and soldiers are mature by early September and can start foraging at a time when conditions are most suitable. The growth of the colony is rapid and by the end of the first year the mound may be 10 cm or more in diameter. How soon a colony starts to produce reproductives is not known.

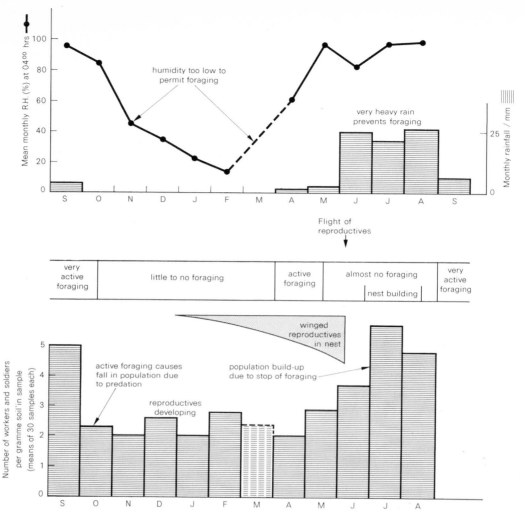

11.3 Diagram showing the annual cycle of population in the nest of a species of *Trinervitermes* in northern Nigeria. The humidity data relate to the locality in which the observations were made. Local rainfall data were not recorded; the data shown relate to a neighbouring locality and are indicative only of the normal annual cycle. No observations were made in March; the value for population size is an interpolation. Note the way in which weather conditions affect foraging activity and the level of this activity affects the size of the nest population. (After Sands).

In this termite society we can see that the same essential biological functions of care of the young are performed as by a pair of birds or mammals. The difference lies in the fact that particular members of the society are specialized in their behaviours and structure to perform certain limited roles. The king and queen are concerned exclusively with reproduction; the workers collect food, build the nest and tend both the young and the royal pair, while the soldiers are involved with defence. There is a certain crude parallel here with human societies where different individuals undertake different types of work, but the analogy must not be pressed as there is no permanent specialization in human societies: people who build houses or grow crops may well in time of war become soldiers instead, and at any time may become parents.

Macrotermes

The big, mound-building *Macrotermes* provides us with many parallels to and some striking differences from *Trinervitermes*. If we examine the inhabitants of a mound, of which there may be as many as two million, we find once again that there are two common types, namely workers and soldiers. The soldiers differ from the workers in having very powerful and prominent mandibles; they do not have an elongated snout as in *Trinervitermes* and the mandibles are their sole offensive weapon (Fig. 11.4). A further point of difference is that the soldiers are all sterile females, while the workers are of both sexes. Large workers are sterile males, smaller ones sterile females. A third difference is that the king and queen are to be found

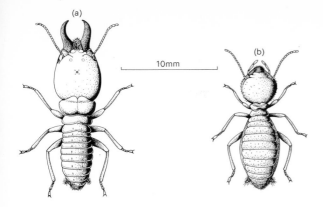

(a)

(b)

10mm

11.4 (a) Soldier and (b) worker of *Macrotermes*.

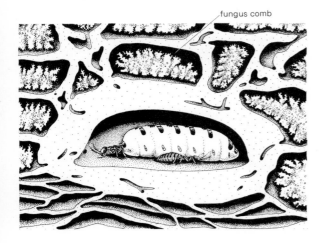

fungus comb

11.5 The Queen, with swollen abdomen, and by her the King in the royal chamber of a *Macrotermes* nest. Note that neither can escape. In the surrounding chambers are masses of fungus comb. A fully developed Queen may reach a length of 9 cm.

inside a special chamber which can be entered only by narrow tunnels; while these allow the workers access to the royal pair, they are too narrow to allow either the king or queen to leave the chamber (Fig. 11.5). The abdomen of the queen is vastly more swollen than that of a queen of *Trinervitermes* and it is estimated that she can lay more than 30 000 eggs a day. Lastly, if the other chambers of the nest are examined, they will be found to contain vegetable matter upon which there is usually a dense growth of fungus. In a few chambers will be found deposits of grass fragments and sawdust.

Fungus 'gardens' of Macrotermes

The workers in foraging bring back to the nest fragments both of wood and grass. These are first stored and then eaten by the workers. During passage through the gut, most of the cellulose of this food is digested by the activity of intestinal bacteria, but the lignin is not affected. The fungus combs are built up from the faeces of the workers and the lignin is digested by the fungus mycelium. The products of this digestive activity, in the form of fungus, are then eaten by the workers so that indirectly they utilize the lignin in the wood brought into the nest. This sequence of events has been followed by staining newly gathered food with a dye called fluorescein. This glows brightly in ultraviolet light and is thus useful in tracing the pathway of the food. Within 48 h the stain was to be found in the guts of the workers, but it did not appear on the fungus combs for at least 60 h.

Not only are the workers dependent upon the fungus: the fungus, *Termitomyces*, is found nowhere but in the nests of termites. We have here an example of an association between two very different types of organism and one which parallels the presence of cellulose-digesting bacteria and Protozoa in the rumen of cattle (Book 1 p. 105). The difference is that, while in cattle digestion by the associated decomposers occurs exclusively in the alimentary canal, in *Macrotermes* this digestion partly takes place outside the body. The parallel can be pressed further: in some species of termite there are cellulose-digesting flagellates in the gut (Book 1 Fig. 18.7d). These are essential for the life of the workers; if the flagellates are killed, the workers slowly starve to death (p. 219).

The adult workers feed both on the material they harvest and on the fungus growing upon the combs, but the royal pair, the soldiers and the nymphs are fed by the workers which regurgitate droplets of partly digested food which are taken up by members of the other castes. The nymphs produce a secretion which is attractive to the workers, so there is an actual exchange of material between them. This process of exchange, called trophallaxis, is found in some other social insects.

To maintain so vast a population, far more intensive foraging is required than by a colony of *Trinervitermes*. Foraging intensity has been estimated by determining the ratio of the weight of freshly collected material to the weight of the fungus combs: this measure corrects, at least in part, for differences in size of the nests sampled. By completely destroying two or three nests each month, some indication of the annual cycle of foraging activity can be obtained. Foraging continues throughout the year, although there is greatest activity after the rains; as with *Trinervitermes*, very heavy rain diminishes foraging. The ability of these termites to maintain foraging activity at all seasons depends upon three things. Firstly, the quantity of metabolic water produced by the workers is estimated to be sufficient to make good the normal loss of water from the mound, so that even during the dry months there is no need to protect the nest from the loss of water which will occur as a result of foraging. Secondly, the nests go very deep and may perhaps reach the watertable. Lastly, the workers construct covered ways of earth up the trunks of trees and within this cover foraging can continue during the day. At night, in favourable conditions, workers and soldiers may forage on the surface.

The foundation of a new colony follows the pattern we have already described for *Trinervitermes*. Foraging activity starts about three months after the mating or nuptial flight.

Ants

Ants resemble termites in many ways: not only are they social, but the workers are wingless foragers. There are also many points of difference. Firstly, the stages of development are different. From the egg there emerges a limbless maggot-like larva which will presently pupate. In some species, such as the Sugar Ant *Camponotus*, the larva spins a cocoon within which it moults to a pupa; in others such as the Red Ant *Oecophylla*, no cocoon is formed. Secondly, unlike the termites, the only reproductive individuals in the colonies are queens. After mating, the male dies, but the queens of some species may live for several years; one queen of an English species of ant lived in an observation nest for 14 years. Thirdly, there is no distinct soldier caste. The workers, which are all sterile females, may as in *Oecophylla* (Fig. 11.6) and the Brown House Ant *Pheidole* (Fig. 11.7) be of two distinct sizes: these are best described as 'major' and 'minor' workers, although the major workers are often called 'soldiers'. In the Driver Ant *Dorylus* there are no such distinct forms but a continuous range of sizes from small to large workers. Certainly in some species the major workers do play the role of soldiers; for example, when *Dorylus* is moving out to forage, the largest workers line the edges of the column. In *Oecophylla* the major workers are more active as foragers than the minors; the opposite is true of *Pheidole* and the major workers hide if a nest is disturbed. The major workers of one species of *Camponotus*, *C. maculatus*, when isolated will not tend the brood; those of a different species, *C. werthi*, will do so. The full significance of the occurrence of major and minor workers is still not understood.

In some genera such as *Crematogaster* the workers have a sting which they can use as an offensive weapon, but most commonly the mandibles are used in fighting and defence as will be familiar to anyone who has been attacked by *Dorylus*. In species which lack a sting, such as *Oecophylla*, there are special glands near the tip of the abdomen from which the ants can eject chemical substances which repel their enemies. One such substance is formic acid; its name reflects the fact that it was first isolated in 1749 by dry distillation of ants. Different species produce different mixtures of these chemicals, some of which probably enable the toxic compounds to spread over the surface of any insect which is being attacked. Finally,

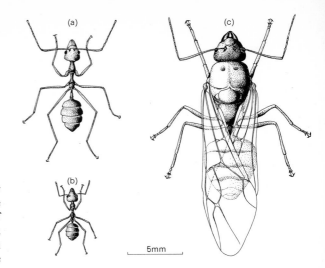

11.6 (a) Major and (b) minor workers of *Oecophylla* as well as (c) a winged virgin female. The female will shed her wings and, as she matures, her abdomen will swell to more than twice its former length.

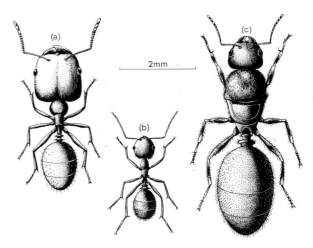

11.7 (a) Major and (b) minor workers, and (c) queen of the Brown House Ant *Pheidole*.

unlike termites, all ants will accept animal material as food. Some like *Dorylus* are almost exclusively carnivorous, some tend to specialize in collecting one particular type of prey such as termites; other species supplement insect prey with plant material and especially with sugars derived from aphids and scale insects, as well as from the extra-floral nectaries of flowers (p. 227).

Food finding by ants

You will frequently have observed that if a source of potential food is left unprotected, it very rapidly attracts large numbers of ants which carry it away in small fragments to their nest; the corpses of large insects may be dragged along by many workers. How do foraging workers appear so rapidly around a source of food? In some species, such as *Pheidole*, if a scouting forager finds prey which it cannot drag back to the nest unaided, it will return to the nest laying a trail of scent, a pheromone, produced by a gland near the tip of the abdomen. Once in the nest the scout stimulates other workers to leave the nest and these, roughly following the trail laid by the scout, find their way to the prey. The alerting of these workers is probably due partly to the release inside the nest by the scout of the trail pheromone, partly to the excited movements made by the scout.

Ants' nests

In natural conditions any area may support a large number of independent colonies of ants (Fig. 2.8) and each colony will have a clear-cut foraging area within which subsidiary nests may be established. Thus a colony of the Sugar Ant *Camponotus* may spread over an area of about 15 m² and occupy about 20 discrete chambers within this area. Its maximum foraging range from the centre of the colony is about 10 m but, owing to the presence of adjacent colonies of other ants, it may be able to forage over only about 10 percent of the potentially available area (Fig. 11.8).

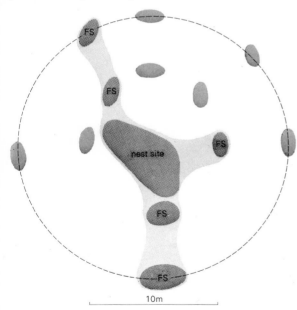

11.8 Foraging area of a nest of *Camponotus*. To identify the workers belonging to the nest being studied, they were fed sugar containing a small quantity of a salt of radioactive gold. F.S. represent the location of the main foraging sites of the colony. Note that although these lay as far as 10 m from the nest, the colony occupied only a limited area within this radius. The circle is of radius 10 m and centred on the nest. There may be as many as 250 nests of this species per ha. (After Lévieux).

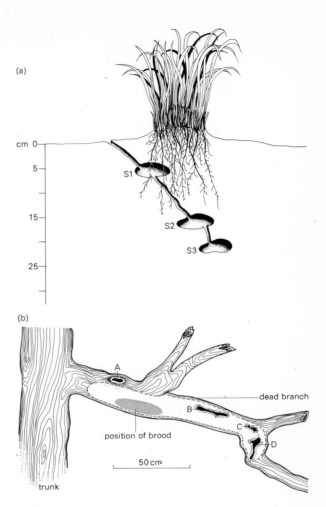

11.9 (a) Nest of a young colony of the ground-nesting ant *Camponotus*: note that several chambers have been excavated. A mature colony may contain 1500 workers. (b) Nest of a colony of *Platythyrea* inside a dead branch: A, B, C and D are entrances to the nest. (After Lévieux).

Termites build their nests in a wide variety of places; the nests may be completely below ground level, partly above ground as in *Trinervitermes* and *Macrotermes*, in wood or even in trees. The same is true of ants. In many, like *Pheidole* and *Camponotus*, the nest is below the ground (Fig. 11.9a); the entrances to the nests of some species can be recognized by the small heaps of 'spoil' built up by the ants as they excavate below ground to enlarge their nests; mound building by tropical ants is very rare. Many species establish nests in dead branches or in fallen, rotting wood (Fig. 11.9b), while others, like some of the Cocktail ants, *Crematogaster* (Fig. 11.10a), build their nests in trees (Fig. 11.10b). The nests of different species of *Cremato-gaster* are found at different heights above ground level in

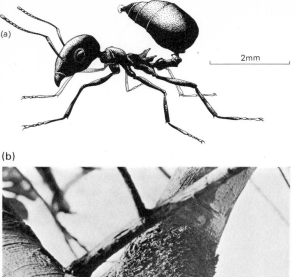

(a)

2mm

(b)

11.10 (a) Worker of the 'cocktail' ant *Crematogaster* showing its characteristic stance when it has cocked its tail and (b) its carton nest in a tree. The nest is about 0·5 m long.

Oecophylla. It is formed by drawing leaves together and securing them with silk which is produced not by the workers but by the larvae. A worker (Fig. 11.11a) will carry a larva to a spot where a line of workers is holding two leaves together, gripping one leaf with their mandibles while standing on the other (Fig. 11.11b). The worker carrying the larva touches it with its antennae; this causes the larva to thrust out its head and where it touches a leaf, there it will attach the end of a silken thread. The worker then moves the larva to the other leaf where it is again made to touch the surface, thus spanning the two leaves with a thread of silk. By moving the larva backwards and forwards between the two leaves, a fine webbing of silk is laid down, binding the leaves together. In the course of time the leaves will wither, but the workers continue to use these nests until they become torn or are finally broken away from the tree by storms.

Driver ants

There is one type of ant which does not build a permanent nest. This is the Driver Ant, *Dorylus*. You will probably be familiar with the winged males; they are the 'sausage flies' with long brown abdomens, commonly attracted to lights in the evening. *Dorylus* makes foraging raids from a temporary underground nest generally excavated amid the roots of a tree; the nest is a large cavity or chamber up

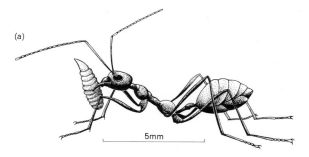

(a)

5mm

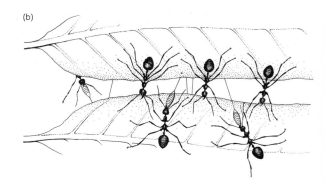

(b)

11.11 (a) Worker of *Oecophylla* holding a larva. (b) Workers holding together the edges of two leaves while others use the larvae to produce silk to bind the leaves together. (After Doflein).

the forests. These nests are built of a material called 'carton' prepared from chewed plant fibres. It is commonly said that these fibres are cemented together with the ants' saliva, but in the carton nest of one species the fragments of fibre are initially bound together, not by saliva, but by 'honey dew', a sticky, sugar-rich secretion produced by some scale insects (p. 211). Fungus mycelium then grows, exploiting the sugars, and the remains of the hyphae serve to bind the fragments together permanently. The matter requires critical re-examination in other species.

Possibly the most remarkable type of nest is that built by

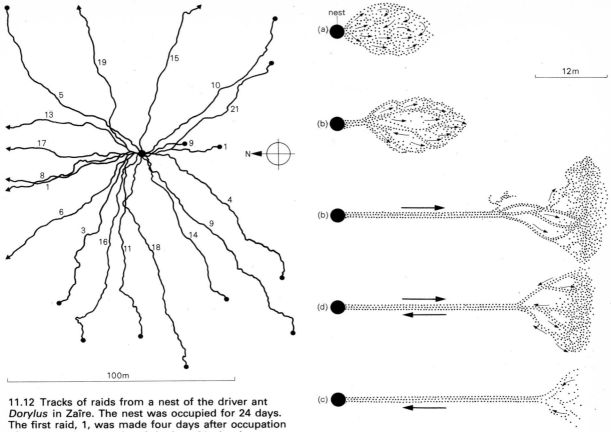

11.12 Tracks of raids from a nest of the driver ant *Dorylus* in Zaïre. The nest was occupied for 24 days. The first raid, 1, was made four days after occupation of the nest site started and the last, 21, the day a move to a new site was commenced. Lines ending in arrows indicate raids which went further than is shown on this map. The numbers beside each track indicate the day the raid was made. On two days, 1 and 9, two raids started, but in each case only one developed. On two other days, 7 and 12, no raid occurred. The varying distances over which the raids extended were due to local topographical conditions. (After Raignier and van Boven).

11.13 Pattern of development and ending of a raid of *Dorylus* from a nest. For further explanation see text. (After Raignier and van Boven).

to 1·5 m in diameter and about 1 m high. Here the colony may stay for only a week or remain for two months or more. Normally workers pour forth from the nest at least once a day to start a raid. Raids develop in different directions on different days, so that the whole area surrounding a nest is effectively exploited (Fig. 11.12). When a raid starts the workers initially fan out over a broad area, collecting food as they go (Fig. 11.13a). As the leading ants move forwards trails are formed immediately behind the advancing front. As the front moves further from the nest a single column of ants is formed along which new recruits move towards the head of the raiding party (Fig. 11.13b). The column may move over the surface or in some stretches travel in tunnels excavated by the workers. Each raid sweeps out a path 10 m or more broad (Fig. 11.13c). The head of the raiding party moves at about 20 m

per hour and the maximum distance reached from the nest is about 200 m. Presently workers start to return, following the path of the main column back to the nest (Fig. 11.13d and 11.13e). Such raids commonly last for about six hours, but raids lasting twice as long have been observed; well over a million workers may be included in a raiding party.

Once a nest is established, the queen lays abundant eggs and while these are developing the colony will remain attached to that particular nesting site. Once the larvae pupate, the whole colony, comprising perhaps 20 million workers, moves off in column to seek a new temporary nest in some other area. This migration may take as long as four days. When a new nest is established, the cycle of egg laying, brood development and raiding starts again (Fig. 11.14). This migratory habit can be related to the effectiveness of the raiding parties: were the ants not

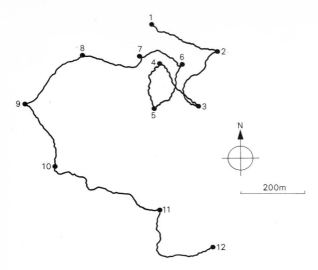

11.14 Successive locations of nests of a colony of *Dorylus* during a period of seven months. The paths followed by the colony between successive nest sites are indicated. The distance travelled between successive sites ranged from 130 to 335 m. The data shown in Fig. 11.12 were obtained while the colony was at nest site 3. (After Raignier and van Boven).

migratory, they would have to search at ever-increasing distances from the nest for prey, whereas periodical migration takes them to new hunting grounds.

Colony foundation

The winged stages of ants, attracted to lights at night especially after rain, will be familiar. In many species such as *Pheidole* both sexes are winged and fly away from the nest to mate. The female will then excavate a small cell in the soil. Here she sheds her wings, starts to lay eggs and later tends her brood until workers have developed. But this is not the invariable pattern. In *Dorylus* the queens never have wings and a new colony is founded by the division of an existing one. In the Argentine Ant, *Iridomyrmex*, which in Africa is limited to the southern tip of the continent, the males leave the nest, but the females, although winged, do not. The males will enter other nests and there mate with the virgin queens which presently shed their wings. As a result very large numbers of queens may be found within a colony, and some will eventually leave the nest together with a number of workers to establish a new colony. Different again is the behaviour of the Pugnacious Ant, *Anoplolepis*: there is a mating flight during the rains, but some of the females return to their original nests, so that colonies containing two or three queens are not uncommon at the end of the rainy season. During the year some or all of these may die, but a queen-less colony can maintain itself by the adoption of a new queen.

Bees and wasps

Very distinct from the termites and the ants are the bees and the wasps. They differ in three significant characteristics. Firstly, the workers are winged, so that the pattern of foraging for food is different. Secondly, most bees and wasps construct nests which are partitioned into small cells; within the protection of these cells the larvae develop, only one larva being found within a single cell. Finally, while all termites and all ants are social, some wasps and some bees are solitary: indeed the social habit is found in only a relatively small percentage of the species in both groups.

The honey bee

The nests of honey bees have long been exploited by man as a source of sugar. A rock painting in Spain made more than 10000 years ago shows a nest of wild bees being robbed, while in Egypt domesticated bees were kept in pottery hives shaped rather like drain-pipes as early as 2600 B.C. The same type of hive is still in use today. Partly because of their economic importance, honey bees have been far more extensively studied than any other social insect; but the fact that they are domesticated and will live in the artificial conditions of observation hives enhances their suitability for experiment.

In the bees' nest we find a queen, males (or drones) and sterile female workers. The queen is about 1·7 cm in length and markedly larger than the workers, which can be distinguished from the slightly larger drones by their smaller eyes, the presence of a sting and by the specialized structures for pollen gathering on their hind legs.

Within the nest are two major types of cell: one is used for storage of honey and pollen and the other for the developing larvae. These cells are made of wax which is secreted in small plates by glands on the ventral surface of the abdomen of the workers. Each wax plate is removed by the spines on the lower edge of the pollen comb (Fig. 11.19); the hind leg is then extended forward beneath the body. In this way the plate is carried to the mandibles which grasp it and mould it to the required shape. Cells in which worker larvae develop are about 5 mm across from wall to wall, while cells containing drone larvae are slightly larger; these cells are normally arranged so that the developing insect lies horizontally within the cell (Fig. 11.15). Cells from which queens will emerge are much larger and are attached to the surface of the brood comb with the opening downwards; as a result they are very conspicuous (Fig. 11.16).

The queen normally remains within the hive, attended to by the workers. She is fed upon a protein-rich secretion from glands which lie within the worker's head-capsule.

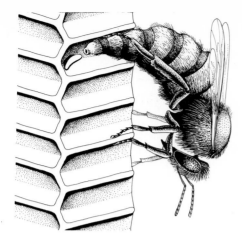

11.15 Queen bee depositing an egg in a worker cell. Note that the cells are almost horizontal. The queen is about 1·7 cm in length.

11.16 Queen cells placed on the surface of the brood comb. Each cell opens at the bottom.

This secretion is sometimes spoken of as 'royal jelly' but 'brood food' is perhaps a better term.

The activities of worker bees

Responsibility for the running of the hive falls upon the workers. By following the behaviour of individual bees marked with small dots of paint for recognition, it has been found that the life of a worker—about five weeks during a time of active foraging—is generally divided into two phases. When young the worker is a 'household bee', remaining within the hive; here she will clean out cells from which other workers have emerged, feed the developing larvae, assist in the construction of new comb and accept both nectar and pollen brought back to the hive by the foragers. After about the first three weeks of life, she becomes a forager or 'field bee', collecting nectar, pollen, water or a material called 'propolis' which is a resinous substance obtained from certain plants and used to fill small holes or cracks within the hive.

This sequence of events in the life of a bee is set out in an idealized form in Table 11.1. But this is not to be regarded as a rigid programme. Young household bees may both feed brood and secrete wax, while if a group of young bees is isolated, some will take over the role of foragers. The behaviour of the household bees is closely related to the immediate needs of the hive; if there is an unsatisfied need for more pollen, for example, this will be experienced directly by the young workers and may be a stimulus which modifies their behaviour, so that they become field bees collecting pollen.

Table 11.1 The succession of events in the life of a worker bee.
Note that this is an idealized description: any individual worker may deviate from this pattern, depending upon special requirements which may arise within the colony

Age (days)	Major source of food	State of brood-food glands	State of wax glands	State of scent glands	Tasks
1–3	pollen	developing	inactive	inactive	brood-cell cleaning
4–5	pollen and honey	developing	inactive	inactive	feeding older larvae with honey and pollen
6–12	pollen and honey	active	developing	inactive	feeding young larvae with brood food
12–21	pollen and honey	regressing	active	developing	comb repair; processing of materials collected by field bees; guard duty; nest cleaning; first flights
>22	pollen and honey	inactive	inactive	active	foraging

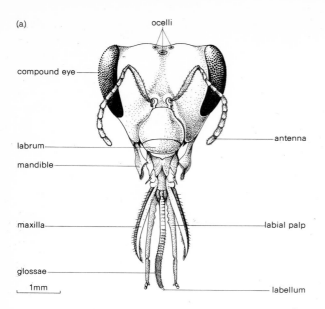

(a)

ocelli

compound eye

labrum

mandible

maxilla

glossae

1mm

antenna

labial palp

labellum

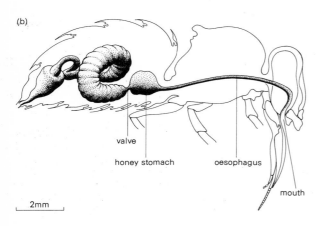

(b)

valve

honey stomach

oesophagus

mouth

2mm

Nectar and honey

In visiting a flower a bee will extend its mouth parts (Fig. 11.17a) and suck up the nectar into a 'crop' or honey stomach near the front end of the alimentary canal (Fig. 11.17b). Nectar contains about 60 percent water and a mixture of sugars, especially glucose, fructose and sucrose. While in the crop, the sucrose is hydrolysed by the action of a sucrase. The preparation of honey from nectar involves a very considerable reduction in its water content, a typical honey containing only about 20 percent water. When a forager bee returns to the hive it will give most of the nectar it has collected to one or more household bees (Fig. 11.18a). These then repeatedly regurgitate and swallow the fluid in small drops (Fig. 11.18b). As this process goes on, water is evaporated from the nectar until it is finally converted to honey. It is then placed in a honey-storage cell which, when filled, is sealed off with a cap of wax.

Pollen collection

In visiting flowers, a bee may also gather pollen. Much of this will collect on the hairs of her body, but some is deliberately wetted with regurgitated nectar and tends to

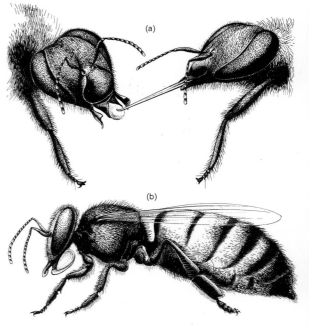

(a)

(b)

11.18 (a) A household bee, on the right, taking nectar from a forager which holds a drop of the fluid between her mandibles. (b) A household bee preparing honey by concentrating the nectar by evaporation. The regurgitated drop of nectar is held by the partially extended proboscis. (After Park).

11.17 (a) The head and mouth parts of a worker bee. The median lobes of the labium, the glossae, are fused to form a long proboscis which terminates in a labellum. When a bee feeds on nectar, the proboscis is extended, the labial palps are held out sideways, but the two maxillae lie close to the proboscis. The proboscis is inserted until the tips of the maxillae touch the food source. The labellum then makes rapid lapping movements which drive the fluid up a groove in the proboscis, carrying it to the mouth cavity. The mandibles are used for the manipulation of wax and pollen. (b) Diagram showing the arrangement of the alimentary canal of a worker bee. The long oesophagus leads into a crop or 'honey stomach', where nectar is stored by the worker until she returns to the hive. The nectar is prevented from flowing onwards by a valve or 'honey stopper'.

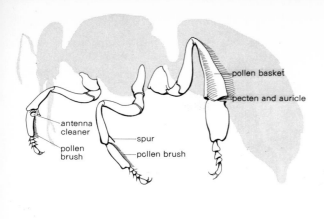

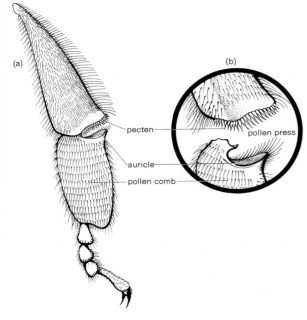

11.19 Diagram to show the main structural features on the legs of a worker honey bee. The wings and all hairs except those of the pollen brushes have been omitted for clarity. (a) shows the inner surface of the hind leg and (b) the structure of the two components of the pollen press separated and in greater detail.

stick to the hairs of the head and thorax. The anterior part of the body is then cleaned by the action of 'pollen brushes' on the fore legs (Fig. 11.19). Brushes on the middle legs also clean the body and collect pollen from the front pair of legs. The pollen collected on the pollen brush of one middle leg is removed by the action of the pollen comb of the opposite hind leg. This pollen is removed from the pollen comb of one leg by rubbing the inner surfaces of the two hind legs together, so that the pollen comb of the one leg is cleaned by another small comb with stout hairs, the pecten (Fig. 11.19a), on the opposite leg. The pollen falls onto a small platform, the auricle which is just beneath the

pecten. The bee then flexes its leg, thus pushing the sticky pollen mass upwards into the pollen basket on the outer surface of the leg. The pollen thus comes to be consolidated into two small lumps on the outer surface of each hind leg; this gives a successful pollen-gathering bee its characteristic appearance with a yellow pellet on each hind leg.

On returning to the hive the pollen-gathering bee will find a cell in which to deposit its load. It hangs into the cell and prises the pollen out of each basket with the middle legs; in this action the long spine on each middle leg possibly plays a part. Later a household bee will tamp down the pollen load onto other pollen in the cell, possibly adding more nectar or honey; when finally filled the cell will, like a honey cell, be capped. The pollen and honey mixture which is stored in this way is sometimes spoken of as 'bee bread'.

Recruitment of foragers

A successful colony depends upon the success of its foragers. We have already seen how an ant scout which finds a rich source of food may alert its nest mates which will follow a pheromone trail laid by the scout to the source of food. Clearly, since it may fly distances of more than 1 000 m to collect food, this sort of behaviour is not possible for a bee. Nevertheless if you put out a small dish of honey mixed with water, you will find that shortly after the first bee has found the food source, others may come rapidly to the spot. It seems reasonable to suppose that, in some fashion, the first bee has been able to 'inform' other workers as to the position of the food source.

How this is done was discovered by the German zoologist Karl von Frisch. He used an observation hive in which the surface of the combs on which the workers walk could be seen through sheets of glass. He put out a source of food and arranged for the first bee which found the food source to be marked with paint so that it could be recognized when it returned to the hive. Von Frisch found that this worker performed a 'dance' upon the vertical face of the comb. The bee danced in a figure-of-eight pattern and as it ran up the central axis of the figure, it moved its abdomen sharply from side to side: this was therefore called the 'tail-wagging dance'. As this bee danced, other workers nearby became excited and followed the dancing bee (Fig. 11.20).

The question now arises as to how a dance of this sort can convey information as to the location of a source of food. There are two things which a new recruit could usefully know: one is the direction in which she should fly, the other is how far or perhaps for how long she should fly. Von Frisch studied this problem by putting feeding dishes at different distances and bearings from the hive. He found that the further the food from the hive, the longer was the central axis of the dance figure and the larger the loops of the figure-of-eight. As a result the number of dance figures made per unit time was less the further away

11.20 The tail-wagging dance. The pathway of the dance is shown by arrows; the bee will turn to right and left alternately. The lateral movements of the abdomen are suggested by the hatched lines. Potential foragers follow the dancing bee. In this sketch the dance indicates that the food source lies in the direction of the sun.

the source of food. Thus, for example, if the food was only about 300 m from the hive, the dancer would complete about 30 dance figures in a minute, but if the food was 3 000 m from the hive, she would complete only about 10. This was sufficient to guide a new recruit to within about 150 m of the food source.

Von Frisch also found that the orientation of the long axis of the dance figure correlated with the bearing of the food source. The information about bearing was not, however, related to true north, as we use in our human navigational systems, but in relation to the direction of the sun. If the food lay directly towards the sun, the bee oriented on the vertical face of the comb so that the axis of the dance was directly upwards; if the food was directly away from the sun, then the axis was downwards. If the food lay, say, 30° to the left of the sun, then the axis of the dance was inclined at 30° to the left of the vertical and so on (Fig. 11.21). New recruits can in fact fly, on the basis of this information, in a direction within 15° from the correct bearing.

In this way the new foragers are provided with approximate information upon the position of a new food source. They are in fact probably assisted by the fact that the dancing bee will carry with it perfume from the flowers at which it has been collecting nectar and this may well allow

the new recruits to make a more critical search in the general area to which they have been guided.

Von Frisch was, however, surprised to discover that new bees could be recruited to a source of food even when the sun was hidden behind cloud. He observed that this was possible so long as some parts of the sky were free of cloud, but not when the sky was completely overcast.

Light waves coming from, say, an electric lamp bulb can be shown experimentally to vibrate in all possible planes equally; but certain sources emit light in which waves vibrating in one plane are relatively more abundant than the rest. This light is described as being partially polarized. Light from the blue sky is partially polarized; but the major plane of polarization is not the same all over the sky. There is a pattern, and this pattern changes as the sun moves across the sky. Von Frisch suggested that it was possible that, unlike ourselves, bees might be able to see this pattern and could thus continue to orient their flight even if the sun were not visible.

If bees perform the tail-wagging dance on a horizontal

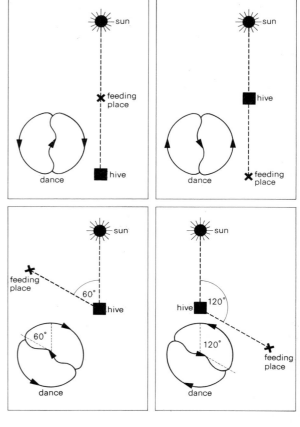

11.21 The 'convention' of the tail-wagging dance. The axial run indicates the direction of the food source relative to the sun, using the convention that the direction of the sun is vertically upwards on the comb face.

surface, they can no longer orient in relation to gravity; the axis of the dance is then on the bearing of the food source. This can take place upon the surface of combs laid horizontally in an observation hive and exposed to the sky by a glass cover. Von Frisch found that the forager bees would dance correctly even if the sun itself was obscured by cloud. He then replaced the glass cover of the observation hive by a sheet of 'polaroid', a material which partly polarizes the light which passes through it. He found that if he rotated the sheet of polaroid, and thus changed the apparent pattern of polarization of light from the sky, the dancer changed the direction of the axis of her dance. Detailed examination of the patterns showed that the behaviour of the dancer agreed with von Frisch's expectations; if the pattern of polarization presented to the bee was one which did not occur naturally, the dance pattern was disorganized.

Caste determination

The queen moves about the hive laying eggs in empty cells. Once the eggs hatch, the larvae are given food by the workers. The worker places food beside the larva within the cell, but does not feed the larva directly. For the first three days after hatching, the larvae are provided liberally with brood food; subsequently they are fed largely on a mixture of honey and bee bread and in far less generous amounts than during the first few days. When the larvae pupate the top of the cell is sealed off by the workers and the adult will later bite through the cap and emerge. The feeding of larvae in queen cells is different: these larvae are provided throughout larval life with a constant excess of food and much of this is brood food. When a queen emerges, the dry remains of uneaten food are commonly to be found within the cell, a condition never found in drone or worker cells.

These facts suggest that the type of food the larva receives determines whether an egg destined to become a female develops into a queen or a worker. Certainly if a larva less than three days old is removed from a worker cell and placed in a queen cell, it will develop into a queen. What is not yet clear is the nature of the difference in the diet which determines the caste of the adult which emerges. Two, not necessarily conflicting, views have been put forward. One emphasizes that the potential queen larva has constant access to food throughout development; the other that the food provided for the queen contains far more brood food than that given to worker larvae, and it has therefore been suggested that there is some specific material in brood food which determines the pathway of development. So far, however, it has not proved possible to produce queens from worker larvae by experimental manipulation of the diet and the nature of the process involved in caste determination is still not known.

The worker bees are structurally different from the queen, which lacks, for example, complex pollen-gathering apparatus on her hind legs. Nevertheless the workers have rudimentary ovaries. If the queen is removed from the hive, the ovaries of many of the workers start to develop and some will lay eggs; moreover, the workers start to construct queen cells. Thus the presence of the queen exerts an inhibitory influence on both the physiology and behaviour of the workers. The queen can be made a prisoner inside a small wire mesh cage and left in the hive, and, if this is carried out with several colonies, a few will start constructing queen cells. If, however, each queen is placed inside a double mesh cage (Fig. 11.22), so that the workers cannot make contact with her, then queen-cell construction starts in all the colonies. Such results suggest that the queen is producing a pheromone, taken up by the workers when they groom her, and that this inhibits both ovarian development and queen-cell construction.

Further experiments have shown that this pheromone, referred to as 'queen substance', is produced by the mandibular glands of the queen and is spread among the workers when they feed each other.

Foundation of new colonies

The life of a worker is only a few weeks, at least during those times of year when the colony is actively collecting food, but the queen may live for two to three years. Nevertheless new colonies must be founded. At times when the food supply is abundant, the workers construct many queen cells and in these larvae develop. Soon after the first of these has been sealed into its cell to pupate, the old queen together with many of the workers leave the colony as a 'swarm'. The swarm will fly off and then settle while scout bees search for a new and suitable place in which to establish a hive. Presently the swarm will fly away from its temporary resting site and start building a new nest.

Meanwhile, within the old nest, the first queen to emerge will move about the nest and if she meets any sealed queen cells, she tears them open with her mandibles; the destruction of the cells which might contain rival queens is completed by the workers which kill the larvae or pupae. If, however, a second queen successfully emerges, the two will usually fight when they meet, until one or other is stung and killed.

11.22 Queen bee enclosed in a double wire cage. For further explanation see text.

The new queen is still a virgin, but about five days after she emerges, she will fly out from the hive on a nuptial flight. As she goes she attracts to her a crowd of drones and during this flight, which may last for about half an hour, mating occurs. The queen then returns to the hive and will subsequently make one or more further nuptial flights; as many as three in a day have been observed and the most recorded for a single queen is twelve. On each flight the queen mates with a different drone. Shortly afterwards she starts to lay eggs.

Other social bees

Honey bees have been very intensively studied, but there are many other types of social bee. These include the common small stingless or 'sweat' bees; in some species the adults are less than 2 mm in length. Unlike honey bees which do not cover the comb with any protective material but prefer to nest in holes, some species of stingless bees build nests in the open. Such nests are covered on the outside with a protective sheath built up from wax platelets and resin; inside, the bees construct cells supported upon sheets of wax. Commonly these combs are horizontal, but those of at least one species are, like the combs of honey bees, arranged vertically (Fig. 11.23). This nest is divided into an upper and lower chamber with brood comb in both chambers; royal cells are found in the lower chamber while large cells containing reserves of honey and bee bread are situated beneath the wall of the nest but outside the brood chambers. These bees differ from honey bees in that each

brood cell is first almost filled with food and the queen then lays an egg in the cell. Subsequently the cell is closed by the workers so that the latter never feed the larvae directly.

It may seem surprising that stingless bees should be able to survive predation from insects such as ants as well as from birds and mammals in search of honey. In these bees the mandibles are effective weapons and if a nest is disturbed by a large predator, vast numbers of bees will emerge to defend the colony. In swarming over the aggressor they characteristically enter any available openings such as the nostrils and the ears; their attack is thus directed against especially sensitive places. Anyone who has experienced an attack by sweat bees will realize how effective this can be. Smaller predators will be attacked with the mandibles and may be repelled by an unpleasant odour produced by the bees. More surprisingly the bees may attempt to immobilize the attackers by covering them with wax or even with honey.

In these bees the structural difference between queens and workers remains strongly marked. In others, such as the heavy 'bumble bees' found north of the Sahara, the workers cannot be distinguished structurally from the queen but are rather smaller in size. These bees usually build their nests in the earth and each colony is relatively small, containing about 150 to 300 individuals. No neat combs are found within the nest and brood cells are subsequently used to store honey and bee bread. Yet other species of bee are solitary; the female excavates cells in soil or in the tissue of plants. Then, like the stingless bees, she fills these with food and, having laid her eggs, closes each cell.

Wasps

Just as some bees are solitary, so too are many wasps. Wasps differ from bees in being predators, especially of other arthropods, and their mouth parts are of a biting type. Nevertheless the adults appear to take only fluid food; the arthropods they catch and kill are fed to the larvae. Many solitary wasps excavate cells in the soil or rotten wood. They fill the cells with suitable food for the developing larvae: this may be some species of spider, caterpillar or beetle larva, depending upon the species of wasp. The wasp stings the prey, paralysing it so that it is still 'fresh' when the larva first emerges from the egg.

Among some colonial wasp species there is no clear differentiation between queens and workers. This is true of the common *Belonogaster* which makes small nests of up to 300 cells supported upon a stalk (Fig. 11.24). The nests are constructed, not of wax, but of a paper-like material made from chewed fragments of wood. The young larvae are fed upon insects which are first chewed up into a paste by the females. Nests may be started by single females, but in certain circumstances several females may join together to found a nest. All of these are fertile and none can be regarded as the queen. When new females emerge, they will first act as workers for the colony, nursing the brood

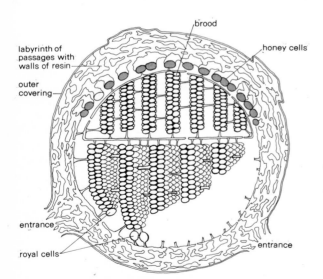

11.23 Diagram showing the structure of the nest of one species of the stingless bee *Trigona* from Gabon. In this species the brood comb is vertical; in most it is horizontal. The nest of this species is built among the branches of trees and is about 20 cm in diameter. Some species build their nests in the sides of abandoned termite mounds. (After Durchan and Pain).

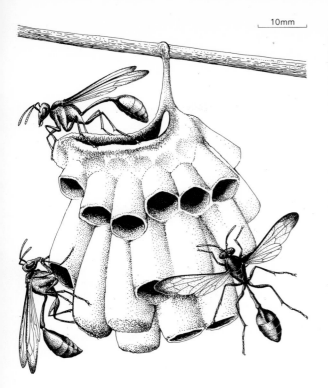

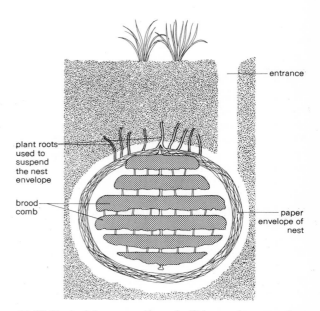

11.24 Nest of the wasp *Belonogaster*.

young females mate and then hide away until the following spring when they will start new colonies. This behaviour, which differs markedly from that of honey bees, is possibly related to the fact that the nests of *Vespula* contain no food reserves. It is the food-storing habit which allows bee colonies to last throughout the winter in the higher latitudes.

The characteristics of social insects

There are four features common to almost all insect colonies. The first is that the queen is long-lived so that she and her offspring can form a social community. Secondly, reproductive activity is limited to one or a few females. We have seen that in honey bees the queen produces 'queen substance' which is taken up by the workers and has the effect of preventing the development of their ovaries. There is evidence of a similar type of chemical sterilization in termites. If the king and queen are removed, some of the nymphs become fertile and can maintain the colony; normally, however, sexual maturation of such 'supplementary reproductives' is inhibited. A different situation exists among the wasps. In *Vespula* the ageing queen probably produces a pheromone which stimulates the workers to build both queen and drone cells. Such a substance has been isolated from old queens of the related *Vespa*, the hornet, and if it is fed to the workers of a young colony, they will start to build queen cells. Nothing is yet known about control in ants: indeed in some species of

and subsequently foraging. When fully mature they mate and become egg-laying females. From successful colonies, females may fly away to start new nests. The males are markedly inactive, remaining upon the nest and being fed by the females.

Another common wasp is *Polistes*: its characteristic nest is broader than that of *Belonogaster* and is suspended from a short stalk. In this genus slight structural differences distinguish fertile females from workers. The colony may be started by a single female or by several females. Unlike females of *Belonogaster*, only one of these continues to lay eggs; the others become foragers. The first brood will contain workers and when these emerge, the founding females other than the queen disperse or are perhaps killed. When the colony grows, small swarms, each of a young queen with several workers, fly away to start new colonies.

Caste differentiation between queen and worker is far more marked in the genus *Vespula*. In tropical conditions new colonies are started by a queen flying away with a swarm of workers. The nest, unlike that of either *Belonogaster* or *Polistes*, is enclosed in an outer covering of paper and may be found either hanging from the branch of a tree or buried in the ground. Brood cells are arranged within the nest in horizontal sheets, each hanging from the one above but unlike the nests of bees, there are no cells in which reserves of food are stored (Fig. 11.25). In temperate climates the colony lasts only for a year. In the autumn the

11.25 Nest of the wasp *Vespula*. This species may also construct its nests in trees. These nests may be 15 cm or more in diameter and contain as many as 3000 workers.

ant the workers do lay eggs and these serve as food for both the brood and the queen.

This limitation of reproductive activity to a single female can be associated with a third feature, namely that of the development of distinct castes: a single worker caste in honey bees and *Vespula*, but several different types of worker in many ants as well as specialized soldiers in termites. In honey bees and *Vespula* differences in larval feeding determine whether an individual becomes a worker or a queen. The mechanisms of caste determination in ants and termites are not yet fully understood. There is some evidence that in ants the production of sexual individuals depends upon the larvae being fed exclusively on a protein-rich secretion from glands in the heads of the workers. Those which become workers are fed on this material when young but subsequently they receive food rich in sugars rather than protein. The control in termite colonies is even less well understood; not only is there control over the production of reproductives but a balance in numbers between workers and soldiers is maintained. If soldiers are removed, others will develop to replace them. If there are too many soldiers, some will be killed by the workers until the normal ratio between workers and soldiers is restored.

These specializations of function within the colony enhance its efficiency. The changing patterns of behaviour of a worker bee with age ensure that the various tasks needed to maintain the colony are undertaken, so that a balance between different activities is achieved. This succession of tasks with age is found also in the workers of at least some species of ant and termite, while specialization is enhanced by their more complex caste system. Within each colony there is thus a division of labour, so that each individual is dependent upon the others.

Trophallaxis

The fourth characteristic of these insect societies is that there is commonly an interchange of food or of glandular secretions between different members of the colony. Fig. 11.26 shows the way in which food labelled with radio-active phosphorus is rapidly spread among the workers of an ant colony. This exchange is called trophallaxis. It has been suggested that it is the mechanism which serves to bind the colony together and more especially that food or secretions received by workers from larvae are a 'reward' which ensures that the workers will tend the brood; but trophallaxis probably has different functions in different types of colony.

In *Vespa* there is an exchange between larva and worker; the larvae produce a secretion which contains amino-acids and this is ingested by the adults. Adult *Vespa* have no protein-digesting enzymes; protein collected by the workers is fed directly to the larvae which can digest it. The requirements of the workers for amino-acids are thus met as a result of their trophallactic relation with the

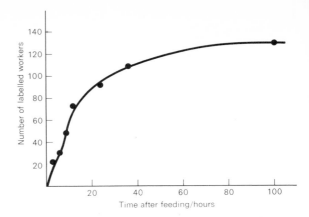

11.26 Distribution of food among worker ants. Laboratory colonies each of 200 workers of the Argentine Ant, *Iridomyrmex*, were fed for a short time with sugar solution containing a compound labelled with radioactive phosphorous. The food source was removed and the number of workers containing the isotope determined at intervals thereafter. (After Markin).

larvae. This curious arrangement has the advantage that the growing larvae have 'first choice' of any supply of protein and the continuation of a supply of workers is thus ensured, even if that of protein is temporarily limited.

In bees no exchange of food occurs between workers and larvae; in this instance the workers cannot be regarded as being 'bribed' to tend the brood. Food exchange does occur between foragers returning with nectar and the household bees which will convert the nectar to honey; but exchange is not limited to this. One important consequence of the habit is that it serves to distribute the 'queen substance' pheromone among the workers. There is moreover considerable hostility between bee colonies and much evidence that this is due to the fact that the inhabitants of each hive have a characteristic and individual odour. There is thus a possibility that the food exchange between the workers serves to distribute the hive odour. In other social insects the distribution of pheromones within the colony may also be a major functional role of trophallaxis.

Trophallaxis can thus serve different functions in different species of social insect. Behaviours such as brood-tending are most probably inherited patterns which do not require a material 'reward' for their expression. Nevertheless there is evidence that when ants groom either the brood or another ant, this behaviour depends upon a secretion from epidermal glands of the individual being groomed. It appears more reasonable to regard such secretions as 'triggers' releasing grooming behaviour rather than as 'rewards': this view is not in conflict with the fact that these epidermal secretions are 'attractive' to worker ants. To be successful as a link in a chain of events resulting in a larva or another worker being groomed, it is necessary both to bring the grooming worker to the individual to be groomed and then to trigger the appropriate behaviour.

Neither need involve anything which we, as human beings, would describe as a material 'reward'.

There is much evidence that social bonds among other species of animal have an essentially similar basis, namely that each individual provides stimuli which evoke social responses from one or more conspecifics. These stimuli may be given for only a short time as when two individuals of a species come together only to mate. If, however, both stimuli and responses are given for a longer period, then there will be a more enduring bond which, depending on the species, may last until the young disperse or even longer.

In this chapter we have examined relations between members of a single species, relations which may be essential for the survival of the young and which may be of very great complexity, resulting in the aggregation of vast numbers of individuals in a single place. Specific associations between organisms of *different* species also occur and we will examine these in the next chapter.

Problems

1 A scientist wished to discover whether the scent trails laid by a certain species of ant provided information about direction: that is, whether an ant placed somewhere in the middle of the trail could tell in which direction lay the nest and in which lay the food. To investigate this he used the experimental arrangement shown in Fig. 11.27. The nest was at N, the food at F

11.27

and to get from one to the other the ants had to move across a T-shaped bridge which was arranged as shown. What change in the experimental arrangement did the scientist subsequently make in order to answer his question and what observations were necessary?

2 Consumers which occur in very dense populations rapidly exhaust the food resources of an area. This is probably the reason for the migratory habit of driver ants. Name two economically important primary consumers in Africa which show a similar pattern of migratory behaviour.

3 If the queen is removed from a colony of honey bees, the ovaries of many of the workers start to develop. It has been suggested that the queen produces a secretion which is removed from her by attendant workers while they groom her and then distributed through the hive as a result of the exchange of food between the workers. This substance is believed to inhibit the development

of the ovaries of the workers. Suggest how you might test this hypothesis.

4 How has it been shown that the same parents in the Orange-breasted Sunbird may come together in successive years to breed?

5 Given that the accuracy of distance information transmitted by a tail-wagging dance is ± 75 m in range and $\pm 15°$ in bearing, how large an area will a new recruit have to inspect if the food source is 500 m, 1 000 m and 2 000 m from the hive? Bees which find a food source 5 000 m from the hive do not attempt to recruit new workers. What area would a recruit have to search at that distance?

6 It is suggested that one type of information transmitted during the tail-wagging dance is the scent of the food source. Why do you consider that this may be of importance in food-finding for a new recruit? How would you attempt to verify your hypothesis experimentally?

7 Why is it better 'economics' for the young queen to remain in the old nest and the old queen to go off to establish a new nest?

8 In a study of the composition of the brood of ants' nests, large numbers of nests of one species were excavated at regular intervals over a period of a year. On examination of the results it was found that on the average there were twice as many larvae as eggs and twice as many pupae as larvae. What variable in the life history of this species might produce such a result?

9 Using the index, prepare a summary, with examples, of the different roles which are played by pheromones.

10 The trail pheromone of an ant has recently been identified chemically. It has a molecular weight of 139 daltons. The ants are so sensitive to this substance that it has been calculated that 0·33 mg would be sufficient to make a trail completely around the earth. Assuming the distance around the equator is 40 000 km and that Avogadro's number is 6×10^{23}, how many molecules per cm would there be in such a trail?

11 The finding of a mate can often depend upon visual signals. What are the circumstances in which pheromonal sex attractants are likely to be important?

12 Pheromones are volatile. Ants produce both alarm pheromones and trail pheromones. Which class would you expect to be the more volatile? Give reasons for your opinion.

13 Some stingless bees lay odour trails which lead other foragers to a food source. This method of 'guidance' is considered to be of greater value for a forest-dwelling species than would be communication of distance and direction by the use of a tail-wagging dance. Suggest why this may be the case.

Bibliography

Revision reading

Hall, J. R.   *Senior Tropical Biology*, Longman, 1970, pp. 308–10

Mackean, D. G.   *Introduction to Biology*, tropical edition, Murray, 1969, pp. 180–84

Stone, R. H., Cozens, A. B.   *New Biology for Tropical Schools*, Longman, 1969, pp. 40–48

Further reading

Butler, C. G.   *The Honeybee*, Oxford University Press, 1949

Butler, C. G.   *The World of the Honey Bee*, Collins, 1954

Carthy, J. D.   *The Study of Behaviour*, Arnold, 1966, Chap. 7

Davis, D. E.   *Integral Animal Behaviour*, Collier-Macmillan, 1966, Chap. 5

Evans, S. M.   *Studies in Invertebrate Behaviour*, Heinemann, 1968, Chap. 7

Kirkpatrick, T. W.   *Insect Life in the Tropics*, Longman, 1957, Chap. 10

Miller, E. M.   *Biology of Termites*, BSCS Pamphlet no. 17, Heath, 1964

Richards, O. W.   *The Social Insects*, Macdonald, 1953

Skaife, S. H.   *African Insect Life*, Longman, 1954, Chaps. 5, 20, 21 and 22

Skaife, S. H.   *Dwellers in Darkness: an Introduction to the Study of Termites*, Longman, 1955

Skaife, S. H.   *The Study of Ants*, Longman, 1961

von Frisch, K.   *The Dancing Bees*, Methuen, 1966

Esch, H.   'The Evolution of Bee Language', *Scientific American*, 1967, Offprint no. 1071

Krogh, A.   'The Language of Bees', *Scientific American*, 1948, Offprint no. 21

Luscher, M.   'Air-conditioned Termite Nests', *Scientific American*, 1961, Vol. 205, Pt. 1, p. 138

Morse, R. A.   'Environmental Control in the Beehive', *Scientific American*, 1972, Offprint no. 1247

Topoff, H. R.   'The Social Behaviour of Army Ants', *Scientific American*, 1972, Offprint no. 550

von Frisch, K.   'Dialects in the Language of Bees', *Scientific American*, 1962, Offprint no. 130

12 Associations between organisms of different species

Birds and mammals

Some time during the year there will probably be white Cattle Egrets, *Ardeola*, on your school compound. If you watch them feeding, you will see they are picking things out of the grass: they feed on insects (Table 12.1). These birds are called cattle egrets as they are often to be seen in company with herds of cows; they may also be seen with larger game animals in the savanna. Although neither is dependent upon the other, the birds and the large herbivores form an association which we might regard as a fragment of a community. The origin of the association is simple; the cattle or game, as they move, disturb grasshoppers and other insects, thus making these easier for the egrets to find.

There is another common association between a bird and game animals: the tick bird or Red-billed Ox-pecker, *Buphagus*, often perches upon the backs of animals like buffalo, rhinoceros or large buck. Here there is a more immediate feeding relation as the birds search for and eat the ticks on the game. Examination of the stomach contents of 58 of these birds showed that 55 of them had been feeding on ticks (Arachnida); the average number of ticks per stomach was 41. The stomachs of birds contained the remains of biting flies which had presumably been attempting to feed upon the game, while only 4 stomachs

Table 12.1 Major food items of the cattle egret in the Western Cape Province of South Africa during the dry season (Dec.–Jan.) and the rainy season (June–July) (*Data simplified from Siegfried*)

| | Frequency of occurrence (%) | |
	Dec.–Jan.	June–July
Grasshoppers	70·6	36·2
Crickets	44·1	37·5
Caterpillars	91·2	75·0
Beetles	52·9	40·0
Spiders	23·5	71·2
Earthworms	0·0	72·5

Note: Frequency of occurrence (%) is the percentage of all stomachs examined which contained remains which could be assigned to the relevant category. The high frequency of occurrence of earthworms during the rainy season is striking. At this time of year they constitute nearly 60 percent of the total food intake by weight.

contained the remains of insects such as Orthoptera or Coleoptera which might have been collected from the ground. Thus the birds find their food almost exclusively on the animals with which they associate; the animals in turn are given some protection from the attacks of ticks and biting flies.

Associations of this type are not limited to tick birds. The Spur-winged Plover, *Hoplopterus*, is commonly found associated with basking crocodiles. There is evidence that this bird finds some of its food by eating tsetse fly which attack the crocodiles; it also feeds on leeches (Annelida: Hirudinea) attached to the crocodiles. The crocodiles often open their mouths as they lie basking in the sun and the birds may be seen picking at objects on the gums and tongue of the crocodiles. Once again both partners gain something from the association.

Fish cleaners

A remarkable parallel to this sort of association is to be found in many tropical coral reefs as well as in the cooler waters off New Zealand where certain species of shrimp (Arthropoda: Crustacea) and fish feed on material they obtain by cleaning the surfaces of other fishes (Fig. 12.1). These fish-cleaners do not move about at random seeking fish they may clean, but remain at definite places, to which fishes come to be cleaned. Underwater divers have observed fishes 'queuing up' for the attentions of one of these cleaners; the fish will even tolerate the cleaners entering their mouths and gill cavities to clean their gills. The cleaners not only remove organisms like leeches, as well as food particles, from the mouth and gill cavities, but they will also clean away any diseased or damaged tissues around a skin wound. None of the fishes which

12.1 *Labroides*, a cleaner fish which occurs in coral reefs off East Africa and southwards as far as East London.

clean in this way is exclusively dependent for food upon its cleaning activities; some of the shrimps, however, rely entirely on the fishes which they attend to provide their food.

Ants, aphids and scales

A rather different type of feeding association connects aphids and some scale insects (Hemiptera: Homoptera) (Fig. 12.2) with ants. Aphids feed by inserting their piercing mouth parts into a sieve tube of a plant (Book 1

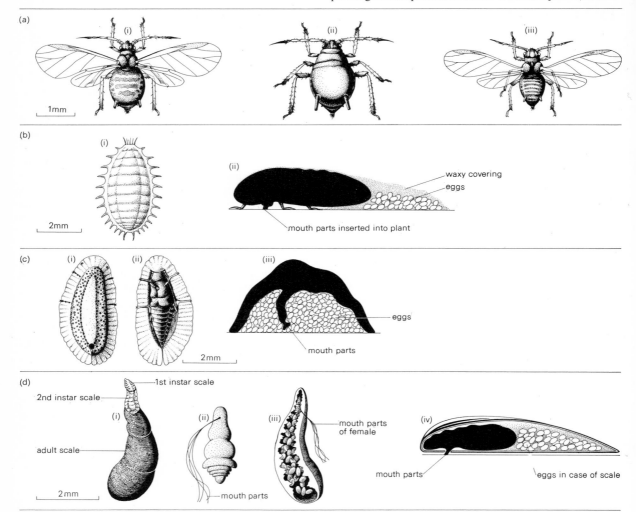

12.2 Various common types of Hemiptera Homoptera: (a) Aphids: (i) a winged female, (ii) a wingless, adult female, (iii) a winged male. Honey dew is excreted from the rectum. From the back of the abdomen project two tubes, the cornicles; these produce a waxy secretion which may temporarily paralyse the larvae of ladybird beetles which prey upon aphids and other Homoptera.
(b) A mealy bug: (i) the wingless female of *Planococcoides citri*; the female remains active and may have long threads of wax projecting from the body. (ii) Diagram showing the female and her eggs which are deposited beneath a wax secretion behind the abdomen. The male is winged or 'alate'. Many mealy bugs can act as vectors of virus diseases.
(c) A soft scale: (i) dorsal view, and (ii) ventral view of *Coccus hesperidum*. Although the female has legs, only the first instar nymphs move actively. The female may have a thin waxy or resin covering (iii) Diagram showing the female and her eggs which are held beneath her.
(d) A hard scale: (i) dorsal view of female Mussel Scale, *Lepidosaphes pinnaeformis*; the two anterior oval structures are the cast skins of the first two instar nymphs. The posterior part is a resinous case enclosing the female's eggs. (ii) Ventral view of the adult female: she totally lacks legs, but the first instar nymph can move. (iii) Ventral view of a scale whose lower surface has been broken to show the eggs. (iv) Diagrammatic view of the female within the scale covering. 'Red Scale', *Aonidiella*, is also a 'hard scale'. The males of both soft and hard scales are minute and winged.

12.3 (a) An aphid feeding on plant tissue and exuding a drop of honey dew from the anus. The insect, which is about 1 mm in length, feeds by inserting its stylets into the phloem cells of the plant. (b) The Clove-tree Soft Scale, *Saissetia zanzibarensis* secreting a drop of honey dew and (c) adult scales covered with a growth of mould. (After Way).

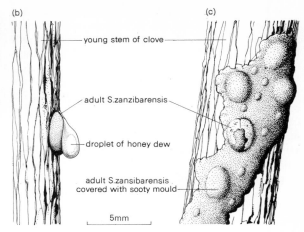

young stem of clove

adult S.zanzibarensis

droplet of honey dew

adult S.zansibarensis covered with sooty mould

5mm

p. 93). Phloem is rich in sugars and to obtain an adequate supply of amino-acids, an aphid must ingest more sugar than it requires. In some species the excess is voided from the anus as a sweet fluid known as 'honey dew' (Fig. 12.3). If an aphid is left undisturbed, it will kick the drops of honey dew clear with its hind legs. In many scale insects, the honey dew may collect around the scale and will then be utilized by various fungi. Ants can stimulate an aphid to void accumulated honey dew by stroking the abdomen of the aphid with their antennae. The honey dew is exuded from the tip of the abdomen and eaten by the ant.

This association is not, however, beneficial only to the ants. Fig. 12.4 shows data on three experimental populations of a scale insect grown on seedlings of the clove tree, *Eugenia caryophyllata*. On one set (a) nests of the ant, *Oecophylla*, were established, but on the other two there were no ants. It is clear that the population of scales grew much more rapidly in the presence of ants. This is because, in the absence of ants, the honey dew produced by the scales is attacked by moulds and the scales which lie beneath die, possibly from lack of oxygen, partly from a failure to moult. The excess honey dew can easily be washed away and one set of seedlings (b) was watered with a fine spray twice daily. Nevertheless the growth of the population of scale was not as rapid as in the presence of the ants. This is partly because the ants are more effective than water in removing small growths of fungus and will also remove dead scales.

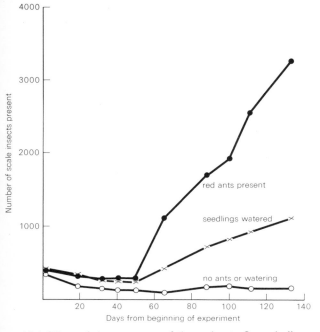

12.4 Effect of the presence of the red ant, *Oecophylla*, and of daily watering in the absence of the ant to remove honey dew, upon the growth of Clove-tree Soft Scale. The lowest line shows the effect of honey-dew accumulation in the absence of ants upon the growth of the population. (After Way).

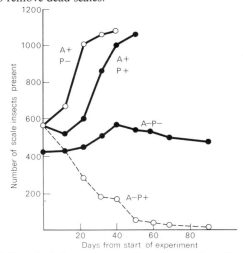

12.5 Result of the presence of ants upon the effect of a parasitoid on populations of Clove-tree Soft Scale. A+ indicates red ants present; A− red ants absent; P+ parasitoid present; P− parasitoid absent. Note that in the absence of the red ant, the parasitoid effectively controls the population of scale insects. (After Way).

Aphids and scales, being very slow-moving or completely sedentary, are easy prey for many small carnivorous insects such as the beetles commonly called 'ladybirds'; they are also attacked by many small wasp-like Hymenoptera which lay their eggs inside the bodies of the scales. When in association with ants, the latter may eat or drive off many aphid predators and parasitoids. Fig. 12.5 compares the growth or decline of populations of the Clove-tree Scale in the presence or absence of both its major parasite and of the red ant. In this experiment, as seen by the broken line, the population was destroyed within three months, but if ants were present, the rate of growth of the population was only slightly affected by the parasite. Thus the scales and aphids obtain protection as a consequence of their common association with ants.

In some cases this association is very highly developed. This can be seen from data relating to field collections of the scale *Planococcoides njalensis*, one of the vectors of swollen-shoot virus of cocoa. Of 189 267 specimens collected, only 840 were taken from trees without attendant ants. One feature of this association is that there is marked specificity between the ants and the scales: this is illustrated in Table 12.2 which shows that while *P. njalensis* occurs on trees occupied by the ant *Crematogaster*, it is replaced by a different scale, one which does not transmit swollen-shoot virus, on trees occupied by the red ant, *Oecophylla*.

Some species of ant build shelters over scale insects. Thus of 23 082 aggregations of scales found on 1 180 cocoa trees tended by *Crematogaster*, only 4 352 were not covered with 'tents' by the attendant ants. It has been suggested that these shelters protect the scales from attack by predators and parasites. This is certainly not always true. *Oecophylla* builds silken shelters over the Clove-tree Scales; nevertheless many scales within these shelters were found to be parasitized. An alternative hypothesis is that these shelters serve to protect the ants from rain. Some ants move scale insects from one part of a tree to another, carrying them between their mandibles. Thus studies of Clove-tree Scales have shown that, although aggregations of young tend to build up, aggregations of more than 400 individuals were never found in the field, nor did these aggregations remain in one place indefinitely. The ants move the scales from one part of a tree to another depending upon the season of the year. On one occasion a whole colony of red ants was observed abandoning a dying tree and moving to a new one; many of the workers were carrying scale insects with them as they went. The ants moreover adjust the number of scales to their own population, killing off any excess. This appears to be related in some fashion to the supply of honey dew. When an experimental colony was provided with honey, there was an extensive destruction of scale insects which stopped immediately the source of honey was removed. Such close attention by the ants both to the protection and the abundance of the scales has led to the expression that the ants 'farm' the scale insects.

'Symbiosis'

Table 12.3 summarizes the relations between the organisms in the various associations we have described. These are clearly different from the relations between producers and consumers or between predators and prey. Their common characteristic is a close physical relationship between members of different species. To describe such relationships, the German botanist de Bary invented in 1879 the term 'symbiosis'. He included within this category the 'symbiotic relationship' between algae and fungi in the lichens, and the close physical association

Table 12.3 Relations between different pairs of organisms. The thin, broken arrows point to some characteristic of one member of the pair; the heavy, unbroken arrows point to the member of the pair which benefits from this. Note that in (a) only one member of the pair benefits from the association, while in (b) and (c) both benefit. The relations shown by spur-winged plovers and by cleaner fish are basically similar to that found in the tick bird

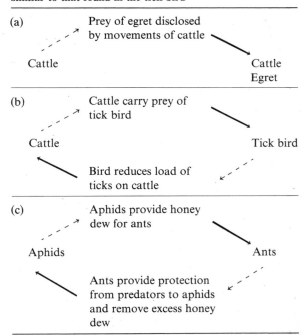

Table 12.2 Relation between occurrence of dominant ants and scale insects. The data are expressed as the mean number of scales per tree (*Data from Strickland*)

Dominant ant	Scale insect	
	Planococcoides njalensis	*Stictococcus sjostedti*
Crematogaster	49·5	0·03
Oecophylla	0·28	56·1

between parasites and their hosts, as well as the types of relationship we have just described. This broad usage of the term 'symbiosis' has persisted in the United States. In Europe, however, the term has come to be used in a narrower sense, carrying the implication that there is some type of mutual advantage in the association; thus the relations between ants and scale insects would be regarded as symbiotic, while parasitism would not. In this chapter we will discuss the characteristics of many further types of relationship involving close physical contact between organisms but, because of the present ambiguity of its meaning, we prefer not to use the term 'symbiosis'.

It may be useful to summarize briefly the types of association we are going to discuss. Parasitism is the most familiar example and is essentially a trophic relation, usually between one consumer and another. Although many organisms living in the guts of animals are parasitic, there are others whose activities are of advantage to the host. These are normally decomposers which assist in the digestion of food. But not all such trophic relations between consumers and decomposers involve the decomposer's actually living in the alimentary canal. We have already seen one such example in the relation between *Macrotermes* and the fungi which live in its nests (p. 193). Close trophic associations can also exist between primary producers and consumers as well as between producers and decomposers such as the algae and fungi in lichens (Book 1 p. 229).

There is a second type of association whose major characteristic is the provision of protection for at least one partner, as when one species of animal lives in the nest or burrow made by some different species. Protective associations and trophic associations are not two clearly distinct categories: a parasite which has a trophic relation with its host may also obtain protection.

Trophic relations and parasitism

In the terms we have already developed to describe the trophic relations within an ecosystem, an ant feeding on honey dew may be regarded as a decomposer, since it is not predatory on the insects producing the food. To what trophic level are we to assign shrimps which clean fishes? In removing unwanted food particles they may, like ants feeding on honey dew, be regarded as decomposers; in feeding upon leeches they are, like tick birds, high-order consumers; in feeding upon the tissues of the animals they clean, they are also consumers even if they are possibly benefiting these fish by cleaning their wounds and sores.

This latter type of relationship is clearly not very far removed from that of animals like mosquitoes and tsetse flies, leeches and ticks which differ from the majority of predators in not normally killing the prey upon which they feed. The association between a mosquito or a tsetse fly and its host is transient; having once fed, it leaves the host. The association between a blood-sucking leech and a fish

or between a Blue Tick and a cow may be permanent in so far as these animals may spend their whole life upon a single host. These latter we commonly include among the parasites, and since they live upon the outer surfaces of their hosts, call them ectoparasites. Parasitism is not, however, to be regarded simply as a special case of predation: in very many cases it is, but not invariably. An adult tapeworm (Book 1 p. 198) such as *Taenia*, (Platyhelminthes: Cestoda) living in the gut of a man, is feeding upon the products of digestion of the man's food, not upon the tissues of the man. If the man is feeding upon cassava, so too is the tapeworm.

A definition of parasitism

We may define parasitism as a particular type of *permanent* feeding association in which one organism, the parasite, depends for its food supply in some fashion upon the metabolic activities of another organism, the host. By this definition neither mosquitoes nor tsetse flies are parasites since their association with a host is only transitory, while a tapeworm is a parasite since it depends for its food upon the ability of the host to synthesize digestive enzymes.

Some characteristics of parasites

We commonly regard parasites as organisms which harm their hosts in some fashion. Certainly the parasites of which we are especially aware fall into this category; they are the ones of economic importance to man. But not all parasites are obviously harmful. For example, a disease found widespread over Africa is amoebic dysentery; the patient passes faeces which are mostly a mixture of blood

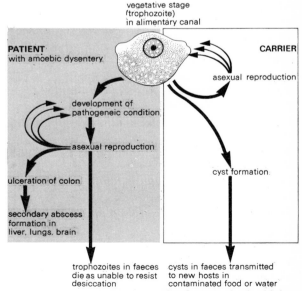

12.6 Diagram showing the major features in the biology of *Entamoeba histolytica*. The amoeba is about 20 μm in diameter.

and mucus, in which will be found the causative agent of the disease, *Entamoeba histolytica* (Protozoa: Rhizopoda) (Fig. 12.6). What is relevant to us at the moment is that this organism, which can attack and destroy the lining of the colon causing severe ulceration, is often found in individuals who have no symptoms whatsoever of amoebic dysentery. The parasite is living in the colon of these people without causing any disease: indeed it is possible that in this condition the amoebae are partly feeding upon bacteria and food particles in the hind gut. Here then is an animal which is unquestionably a parasite but which is only sometimes harmful to those who carry it. A second parasitic amoeba of man, *Entamoeba gingivalis*, occurs on the gums and between the teeth in many people. It feeds upon fragments of tissue and leucocytes, so that it is unquestionably a parasite. There is no evidence, however, that it does any significant harm to its host. For most parasites, the less damage they do to their hosts the greater is their chance of survival. An ectoparasite which is a constant source of irritation is more likely to be destroyed by the cleaning or grooming activities of the host than is one which does not cause irritation. A species of internal parasite, or endoparasite, commonly but not invariably is at an advantage if the host is not damaged, as it is then more likely to be able to propagate successfully. This is precisely the case with *Entamoeba histolytica*. The amoebae in the faeces of a patient with dysentery will die since, any sanitary measures apart, they cannot survive once they leave the host. It is the amoebae in the symptom-free individuals that are successful in propagating the species. In this non-pathogenic state the amoebae produce resistant cysts which are passed out with the faeces and become a source of potential infection of other individuals. This is one reason why this particular parasite is so difficult to eradicate: the people responsible for the spread of the disease are those who harbour the parasite while showing no symptoms, that is, who act as 'carriers'. A campaign for the eradication of amoebic dysentery which depended upon a direct elimination of the parasite by drug treatment would require an examination of the faeces of all members of the community who do *not* show the disease, as these are the people who might require medical attention. The magnitude of the problem may be recognized from the estimate that 400 million people harbour the parasite and of these 80 percent show no symptoms.

Transmission of parasites by insect vectors

Endoparasites, like all other animals, have to find their habitats. We have already examined one example of this in considering the way in which the ciliated miracidium larva of *Schistosoma* finds the snail intermediate host (p. 26). There are two common locations of parasites in vertebrate hosts: the alimentary canal and the blood stream. Very many of the blood-living parasites are distributed by biting insects, so that the problem of finding their habitat is closely related to the problem of food finding by the vector insects. Thus, for example, tsetse are attracted to large moving objects: this is why they tend to follow and settle upon motor cars and lorries and why fly control commonly involves the spraying of cars with insecticide at control points. Clearly this type of response will take tsetse fly, and thus indirectly *Trypanosoma* (Protozoa: Flagellata), to the game on which they feed.

Female mosquitoes are attracted to warm objects and high humidity, while a slight increase in the carbon dioxide concentration of the air stimulates them both to greater searching activity and to fly upwind, a response likely to lead them to their host. Humans wearing a device to absorb almost all carbon dioxide expired attracted only about half as many *Anopheles* as did control subjects. Mosquitoes are also attracted by chemicals associated with secretions from the skin, including, at least in the case of the yellow fever mosquito *Aedes aegypti*, both the amino-acid lysine, which is a constituent of sweat, and also L-lactic acid. The D-isomer of lactic acid is not however attractive. Fig. 12.7 summarizes the significant stimulus sequence for long-range host finding by one species of *Anopheles* which responds directly to the odour of the host. *Culex* responds to carbon dioxide concentration and hence orients to its hosts over a shorter range. Here again mosquito-distributed parasites depend for their transmission on the host-finding behaviour of the vector.

The parasites must also be able to re-enter their vectors. In this they are not totally passive. There is, for example, a nematode parasite of man called *Wuchereria*; the adults, which reach a length of up to 100 mm, are to be found in the lymph glands. In some patients this leads in old age to a condition known as elephantiasis in which there is gross swelling of some organ, such as a leg or a mammary gland or the scrotum. The female worms liberate larvae about 250 μm long; these, known as microfilariae, make their way into the blood stream and are distributed from host to host by various mosquitoes including *Anopheles gambiae*. These vector mosquitoes are active only after dusk and the microfilariae are to be found in the blood vessels close to the skin only at that time: during the day they accumulate in the tissues of the lungs, whence they distribute themselves throughout the circulation in the evening. Thus the behaviour of the microfilariae ensures that at the time the vector is active they are in the correct place to be ingested.

Plasmodium

A rather different cycle in relation to the biting habits of the insect vector has been found in malaria parasites. The life cycle of *Plasmodium* (Protozoa: Sporozoa) has been described in outline earlier (Book 1 Fig. 18.6). Fig. 12.8 adds certain details. The stage of the parasite within the blood cell is called a trophozoite. These trophozoites

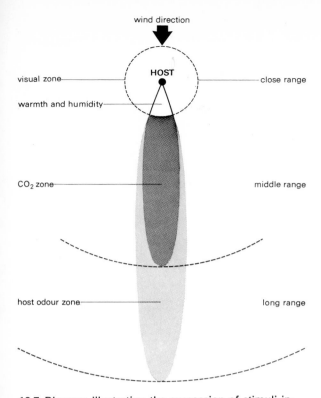

wind direction

HOST

visual zone — — close range

warmth and humidity —

CO_2 zone — — middle range

host odour zone — — long range

12.7 Diagram illustrating the succession of stimuli involved in host finding by mosquitoes. Wind passing across the host carries a plume of carbon dioxide and host odour; the latter carries further downwind. If a mosquito flies into the plume, it turns to fly upwind. Not all species can orient in the odour zone, but all will in the carbon dioxide zone. Immediately adjacent to the host warmth and high humidity as well as visual stimuli lead the insect to the host. (After Gillies and Wilkes).

periodically divide to form from 8 to 32 new cells, the actual number depending upon the species. These cells, known as merozoites, are released into the blood plasma when the corpuscle in which they developed breaks up; they will then invade new blood corpuscles. Not all trophozoites, however, form merozoites. Some grow within the blood corpuscles to form male and female gamete-producing cells, or gametocytes. When a blood meal is taken by a mosquito, any trophozoites or merozoites are digested. The blood corpuscles in which lie the gametocytes are also digested, but the gametocytes themselves are not affected. The male gametocyte undergoes a series of nuclear divisions and then forms elongated whip-like structures each containing a nucleus. These are the male gametes, and the process of their formation is called exflagellation. A male gamete fuses with a female gamete to form a zygote, which passes through the gut wall of the mosquito to its outer surface and there, within a cyst, undergoes repeated divisions to form infective cells, the sporozoites.

These various events do not occur at random. The division of the trophozoites to form merozoites takes place in all red cells almost at the same time. In *Plasmodium vivax*, this happens once every 48 h. The characteristic fever coincides with the break-up of the infected red blood corpuscles, possibly as a result of the release of some toxic metabolite. A new generation of gametocytes is also formed every 48 h. The question arises as to whether these can successfully infect a mosquito at any time during this period.

This has been studied by infecting monkeys with a species of *Plasmodium* closely related to human plasmodia but with a 24 h cycle. There are two ways in which the infectivity of the gametocytes may be judged: one is to determine the number of gametocytes which will display exflagellation. Since this event is triggered simply by a fall in temperature, all that is required is to draw a sample of blood, allow it to cool for about 20 min in a moist atmosphere and then to make a smear. It is convenient to express the number of exflagellations as so many per 10^5 or 10^6 red blood corpuscles. If this examination is made at regular intervals, a marked peak of exflagellation is found shortly

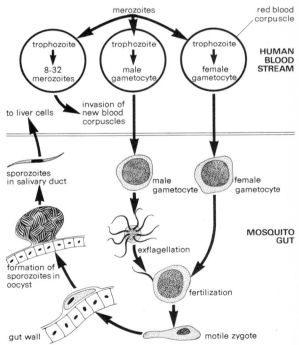

merozoites — red blood corpuscle

trophozoite — trophozoite — trophozoite — HUMAN BLOOD STREAM

8-32 merozoites — male gametocyte — female gametocyte

to liver cells — invasion of new blood corpuscles

sporozoites in salivary duct — male gametocyte — female gametocyte

formation of sporozoites in oocyst — exflagellation — MOSQUITO GUT

gut wall — fertilization

motile zygote

12.8 Diagram illustrating certain points in the life history of the malaria parasite, *Plasmodium* (see also Book 1 Fig. 18.6). The number of merozoites formed from a trophozoite depends upon the species of *Plasmodium*. A merozoite is about 1·2 μm in diameter and a mature trophozoite or a gametocyte is about 10 μm; the male gametocyte is about 5 μm in diameter after exflagellation and the zygote about 13 μm in length. The oocyst on the outer wall of the gut may be 50 μm in diameter and each sporozoite about 10 μm in length.

215

before midnight (Fig. 12.9a). Although the number of gametocytes in the blood may remain fairly constant over 24 h, they are most infective in the evening.

This finding may be checked, and is confirmed, by feeding mosquitoes on the host at different times during a 24 h period. After about a week, the mosquitoes are dissected and the number of sporozoite cysts on the outer surface of the gut is counted. Again, while mosquitoes fed upon the host during the day have very few cysts, they are numerous in mosquitoes allowed to feed at about midnight (Fig. 12.9b).

A plant-parasitic nematode

It is clear from these findings that the characteristics of the infective stages of parasites may correlate with the behaviour of the vectors which distribute them. In both the examples described above, the cyclic behaviour of the parasite may be regarded as an adaptation to the periodic behaviour of the vector.

A very different situation arises in some parasites of plants. For example, certain nematode parasites attack various crops the females encysting on the roots (Fig. 12.10a): one of these which attacks potatoes and tomatoes. The larvae feed within the roots of plants, and larvae must be available to attack new plants at the appropriate season of the year. When fully mature the adult males leave the roots of the plant and move through

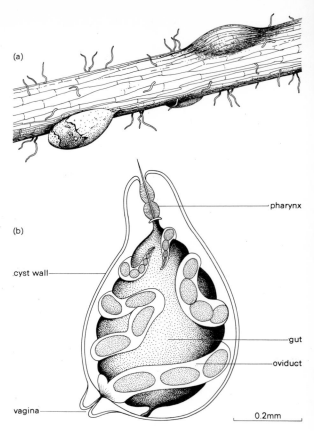

12.10 (a) Females of a cyst-forming nematode within the tissue and projecting from the tissue of a plant root. The female when she emerges from the root is white; she will be fertilized by a wandering male. The eggs are retained in the oviduct. When the female dies, her cuticle hardens to form a cyst within which the eggs develop to the infective larval stage but do not emerge until suitably stimulated. (b) Diagram showing the structure of a female shortly after fertilization. A female may produce up to 400 eggs.

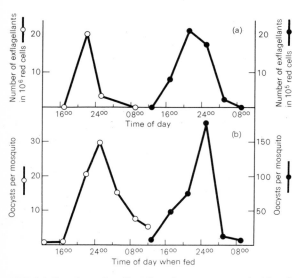

12.9 (a) Number of exflagellated gametocytes in blood samples drawn at different times of day or night. (b) Number of oocysts developed in mosquitoes fed at different times. In both (a) and (b) the data refer to observations made over a period of nearly 48 h. Note that the scales for the left- and right-hand curves are different. The data for (a) and (b) were obtained in two different experiments. (After Hawking).

the soil in search of females which usually remain attached to the surface of the roots. The female does not release her fertilized eggs but retains them. When she dies her swollen body forms a resistant cyst within which the eggs develop; the larvae then remain dormant within the cyst until the ground is planted with a new crop. As the new plants develop, they release various organic substances into the soil. One of these, if it diffuses through the cyst wall, stimulates the dormant larvae to emerge from the cyst and attack the young roots. Encysted larvae can survive for up to seven years.

Transmission of gut parasites of carnivores

Parasites which become sexually mature in the alimentary canal of carnivores often depend for transmission upon these hosts feeding upon some other animal which serves as an intermediate host. In this circumstance it may be of value to the parasite if it can modify the behaviour of the intermediate host so as to make it more liable to be eaten by the definitive host, in which the parasite will become sexually mature. We may illustrate this phenomenon by two examples. There is a tapeworm *Ligula* (Platyhelminthes: Cestoda), the adult of which is found in fish-eating birds. The life history is shown in outline in Fig. 12.11. One of the fish infected by *Ligula* is called a rudd. Rudd normally move about in shoals, but if a rudd is infected by *Ligula* its behaviour changes; it leaves the shoal to swim alone and often tends to swim on its side near the surface. These changes, resulting from infection with the parasite, make the infected rudd more likely to be eaten by the definitive host, a bird.

A second example relates to a tapeworm *Multiceps*, which is adult in dogs and jackals and has sheep as an intermediate host. The life cycle is outlined in Fig. 12.12. The bladderworm or cysticercus commonly lodges on the surface of the sheep's brain and as it grows, perhaps simply by pressing on the brain, it affects the movements of the sheep, leading to a condition known as 'blind staggers'. In this state the sheep is likely to fall prey to a dog or jackal and thus the parasite will complete its life cycle. It has also been suggested that the fevers associated with both malaria and sleeping sickness change the behaviour of the host so as to make him more liable to successful attack by the arthropod vector.

It must not however be assumed that such changes in the behaviour of intermediate hosts are common. The known instances are relatively few, although further study may well show that they are more common than has been realized.

If you look again at the outline of the life history of *Ligula*, you will see that it has a familiar appearance; it is a food chain, but in place of some minute producer at the start of the chain there is the ciliated larva of a parasite. Many parasites which live in the alimentary tract of their definitive hosts have complex life histories which on analysis are found to represent part of the food web leading to the definitive host.

Transmission of gut parasites of herbivores

Parasites of carnivores may return to their definitive host by infecting some lower-order consumer. Gut parasites of herbivores have a different problem. They may depend, as does *Entamoeba*, upon one host eating food contaminated by the faeces of another, infected host. But when the parasite has an intermediate host, it must have some way in

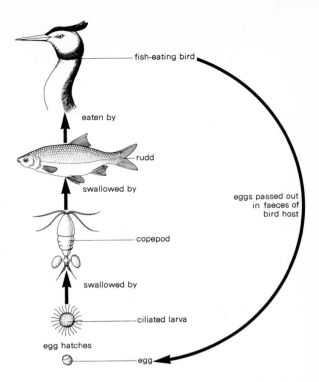

12.11 The life history of the tapeworm *Ligula* (Platyhelminthes: Cestoda). Note the similarity between its route back to the definitive host and that of a typical aquatic food chain.

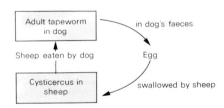

12.12 Diagrammatic summary of the life history of the tapeworm *Multiceps*. Compare with that of *Taenia* (Book 1 Fig. 18.31).

which it can associate itself directly with the food of the definitive host. We can understand the life history of the liver fluke *Fasciola* (Platyhelminthes: Trematoda) (Fig. 12.13) in this light. To make the point clearer this is contrasted with that of another fluke, *Heterophyes*, whose definitive host is commonly a carnivore—a dog or cat. In the liver fluke the cercarial stage, leaving the snail intermediate host, encysts upon a blade of grass. A cyst in this position has a reasonable possibility of being eaten by a sheep; this cyst is comparable with the metacercarial stage in the second intermediate host of *Heterophyes*. Yet another parasitic fluke found in sheep, *Dicrocoelium*,

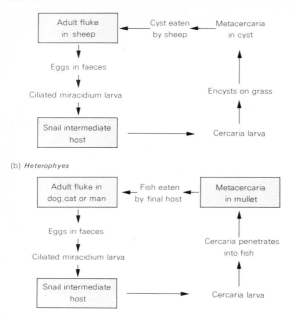

(a) *Fasciola*

Adult fluke in sheep → Eggs in faeces → Ciliated miracidium larva → Snail intermediate host → Cercaria larva → Encysts on grass → Cercaria in cyst → Cyst eaten by sheep → Adult fluke in sheep

(b) *Heterophyes*

Adult fluke in dog, cat or man → Eggs in faeces → Ciliated miracidium larva → Snail intermediate host → Cercaria larva → Cercaria penetrates into fish → Metacercaria in mullet → Fish eaten by final host → Adult fluke in dog, cat or man

12.13 Diagrammatic summaries of the life histories of two flukes (Platyhelminthes: Trematoda): (a) *Fasciola* and (b) *Heterophyes*. Compare with that of *Schistosoma* (Book 1 Fig. 18.29). The snail intermediate host of *Fasciola* is frequently *Lymnaea;* that of *Heterophyes* is *Pirenella*.

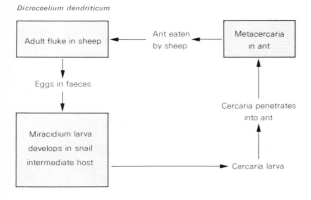

Dicrocoelium dendriticum

Adult fluke in sheep → Eggs in faeces → Miracidium larva develops in snail intermediate host → Cercaria larva → Cercaria penetrates into ant → Metacercaria in ant → Ant eaten by sheep → Adult fluke in sheep

12.14 Diagrammatic summary of the life history of the fluke *Dicrocoelium*. Note that in both this species and *Fasciola* a sheep is the definitive host, and that the metacercarial stage of *Dicrocoelium* in an ant is trophically equivalent to the encysted metacercaria of *Fasciola*. There is no free miracidium larva in *Dicrocoelium;* the eggs are ingested by a snail and the miracidial stage occurs in its tissues.

shows a variant of this type of behaviour (Fig. 12.14): it has a true metacercarial stage in an ant. You may well consider that the probability of a sheep eating an ant is extremely low. The metacercariae of *Dicrocoelium*, however, affect the ants they infect in such a way that the ants become immobile, grasping onto any vegetation. The immobile ant is thus playing a role comparable to the cyst formed around the cercaria of *Fasciola. Mesocoelium*, a fluke which is adult in the Rainbow Lizard, *Agama*, uses both pathways. The metacercariae may occur in certain ants, but, more commonly, they are enclosed on cysts in the vegetation.

Reproduction of parasites

It is often said that the probability of a parasite successfully completing a life cycle is very small and that as a result it is characteristic of parasites to produce very large numbers of eggs; thus, for example, a pork tapeworm may in a lifetime produce about 7×10^9 eggs. The liver fluke produces less than 40000 eggs but these numbers are multiplied by secondary reproduction in the snail host, so that potentially about 7×10^6 infective cysts are formed. Most parasites require such very high reproductive potentials to be able to maintain their species. This, however, is in no way peculiar to parasites; it applies also to large numbers of marine organisms including polychaete annelids, bivalve molluscs, echinoderms such as sea urchins and also many fishes, all of which have to face the very considerable hazards of larval life.

The fauna and flora of the alimentary tract

As well as *Entamoeba histolytica*, there are other amoebae which can occur in the alimentary tract of man, causing no disease and exploiting a ready food source in a protected habitat; nevertheless, since their food supply depends upon the metabolic activity of the host, they fall within our definition of parasitism. Such gut-living organisms 'damage' their hosts only in so far as the host is deprived of some small fraction of its total food intake. Should the amoebae become vastly abundant, they might compete seriously with the host for the available food. Competition for available food is, however, not uncommon when consumers anywhere reach high population densities; indeed the only really remarkable feature of these gut-living amoebae is that their normal habitat is within the body of another organism.

There are, moreover, some gut-living organisms which positively contribute to the well-being of their 'hosts'. We have seen how the synthetic activity of some bacteria can serve as a source of vitamins for their 'hosts' (Book 1 p. 154), while bacteria in the rumen of cattle and sheep, by their ability to digest cellulose, indirectly make this material available to their hosts (Book 1 p. 105); a similar relation exists between certain flagellates and some species of termite (Book 1 p. 190). The dependence of these termites upon their intestinal flagellates is shown by their inability to survive upon a diet of cellulose once the flagellates have been killed either by a fairly brief exposure of the termites to high temperature or to a high oxygen pressure. Thus, for example, while workers of one termite species lived for only a month on a diet of wood and filter paper after a brief exposure to oxygen at high pressure, untreated controls survived for more than ten months. The flagellates break down the cellulose to glucose and, in the anaerobic conditions prevailing in the termite's gut, the glucose is further degraded to acetic acid, a process which provides the flagellates with energy. The acetic acid is excreted by the flagellates into the lumen of the gut: there it is absorbed into the blood of the termites and taken up by cells which, having an adequate oxygen supply, can metabolize it fully.

Associations between consumers and decomposers: insects and fungi

Certain associations between consumers and producers or decomposers differ from the typical parasitic pattern in that the behavioural or the metabolic activities of the consumer are in some measure concerned with ensuring a continuing supply of nutrients for the producer or decomposer. This type of relationship exists between certain termites and the fungus they 'cultivate' in their fungus beds (p. 193). It differs from simple food hoarding, as the food supply is actively growing.

Another example is to be found in the Ambrosia Beetles (Coleoptera), which are gregarious but not social. The larvae of these beetles live in wood, excavating tunnels beneath the bark where they both feed and pupate. Their main source of food is not, however, the wood they eat but a fungus which is parasitic on the wood and grows upon the walls of the tunnels. Some species of these beetles will attack a very wide variety of host plants; two which are common in Africa are recorded from 93 and 150 different kinds of tree, many of them, such as coffee, of commercial value. Other species, such as one which attacks *Triplochiton*, are very much more restricted in their range of possible hosts.

As long as the beetles are active within the tunnels, they maintain, in a manner not yet understood, a pure culture of fungus. The fungus is found associated only with the beetles; whether different species of ambrosia beetle have characteristic species of fungus is still uncertain. The question thus arises as to how fresh fungal infections are started. The answer to this is that fungal spores are carried by the adults from one tunnel system to another. In the females of one of the common African species a pair of pockets, formed by intuckings of the cuticle, lies between the first and second thoracic segments (Fig. 12.15). These

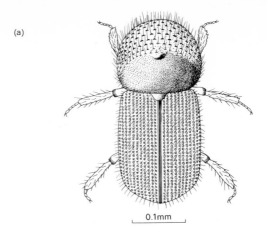

(a)

0.1mm

(b)

elytron

mycetangium with gland

first thoracic segment

head

abdomen

12.15 (a) Female of the Ambrosia Beetle *Xyleborus dispar*. (b) Diagrammatic section through a female of *Xyleborus dispar* showing the arrangement of the mycetangium.

contain the spores of the ambrosia fungus and have in their walls glands whose oily secretion probably serves to protect the spores from desiccation and may also supply nutrient material. In another species the pockets are found at the bases of the mandibles of the females. These pockets or mycetangia ensure the distribution of the fungus by females attacking new host plants. Exactly how the spores are collected into the mycetangia and how they are subsequently released is far from clear.

Here then we have a regular and widespread association between a boring beetle and a fungus: its similarity to the association between fungi and certain termites is obvious. In both cases the insect cultivates a fungus as a source of food; in both the fungus receives protection and is freed from competition with other fungi by the activities of the insects.

Associations between producers and consumers: corals

A very different type of association, but one in which there is again a highly specific link between organisms of different trophic levels, is found in reef-building corals (Coelen-

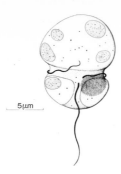

12.16 The free-living stage of the dinoflagellate, *Symbiodinium*, which is found within the endodermal tissues of corals.

terata: Anthozoa) all round the world. In these corals are found unicellular algae which lie within the cytoplasm of a special type of endodermal cell. The algal cells are spherical and about 10 μm in diameter; when cultivated away from the tissues of a coral, they prove to be dinoflagellates (Fig. 12.16; see also Book 1 Fig. 20.3). The numbers of these algal cells or zooxanthellae can be very considerable; values as high as 30000 mm^{-3} of tissue have been found.

Neither partner of this association is fully dependent upon the other: the dinoflagellates can occur as normal members of the phytoplankton, and corals which grow in the dark of overhanging rocky shelves are devoid of zooxanthellae. Nevertheless there is good evidence that both partners gain from the association.

The zooxanthellae have been graphically described as 'imprisoned phytoplankton', but the number of algal cells within the tissues of the coral is far greater than would be found in an equal volume of seawater. This high density is possible because the algae can utilize phosphate and nitrogenous waste produced as a result of the metabolism of the coral polyps. The close association of the algal cells with those of the polyps ensures a constant supply of these nutrients: neither is likely to become a limiting factor in growth.

This activity of the algae is illustrated indirectly by the results shown in Table 12.4. Coral polyp colonies can be freed of their zooxanthellae by keeping the specimens in

the dark. Such zooxanthella-free specimens and also normal corals of approximately the same size were placed in a standard volume of seawater and the change in phosphate concentration in 24 h determined. All the specimens were exposed to normal daylight, but not directly to the sun. While the phosphate concentration in the seawater around the specimens which lacked zooxanthellae rose markedly, there was only a slight increase with a normal specimen of *Psammocora*, and the specimen of *Favia* totally depleted the water of phosphate. Similar results were obtained when the concentration of ammonium ion was studied.

Thus, so long as the coral polyps are in places where they receive good illumination, the polyp tissues offer exceptionally favourable conditions for algal growth. As a result the productivity of the algae within the corals is very high. It has been estimated that coral will 'fix' between 1500 and 3000 g carbon per m^2 of colony surface in a year. This is about 100 times greater than the productivity, measured as carbon fixation, of the most productive waters in the temperate seas.

Since corals can live without zooxanthellae, the question arises as to whether the presence of the algal cells alters in any way the metabolism of the corals. It has been found that the rate of skeleton formation, measured by the rate of incorporation of radioactive calcium into the skeletal material, is much greater in light than in the dark and very low even in light for specimens which lack zooxanthellae (Table 12.5).

It is suggested that this increase in rate of skeletal deposition depends upon the fact that the zooxanthellae, by removing carbon dioxide, accelerate the process of deposition of calcium carbonate. The sequence of events may be as follows (Fig. 12.17). Calcium ion diffuses through the tissues of the polyp to the layer of ectoderm immediately in contact with the skeleton. The metabolism of these cells produces bicarbonate ions which react with the calcium ions to yield calcium carbonate in the form of aragonite according to the equation

$$Ca^{2+} + 2HCO_3^- \rightleftharpoons CaCO_3 + H_2CO_3 \qquad 12.1$$

If the carbonic acid is rapidly removed, the rate of deposition of aragonite will be increased. In the tissues of the

Table 12.4 Effect of corals upon the phosphate content of seawater, expressed as mg P m^{-3} (*Data from Yonge and Nicholls*)

Coral	Specimens lacking zooxanthellae		Specimens with zooxanthellae	
	Initial value	After 24 h	Initial value	After 24 h
Psammocora	4·20	33·12	3·41	3·85
Favia	4·20	15·82	3·41	0·00

Table 12.5 Uptake of radiocalcium by specimens of *Manicina*, naturally with or without zooxanthellae and maintained in light or dark. Values are expressed in relation to the nitrogen content of the skeletal material as μg Ca mg N^{-1} h^{-1} (*Data from Goreau and Goreau*)

	In light	In dark
With zooxanthellae	13·4	1·8
Without zooxanthellae	0·7	—

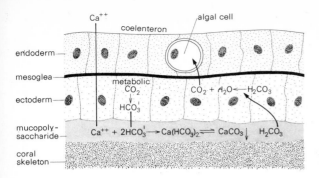

Ca++

coelenteron

algal cell

endoderm

mesoglea

ectoderm

mucopoly-
saccharide

coral
skeleton

metabolic
CO_2

HCO_3^1

$CO_2 + H_2O \leftarrow H_2CO_3$

$Ca^{++} + 2HCO_3^1 \longrightarrow Ca(HCO_3)_2 \rightleftharpoons CaCO_3 \downarrow \quad H_2CO_3$

12.17 Diagram showing a hypothetical scheme to explain the role of algal cells in the process of skeleton secretion of a coral. Calcium ions diffuse into a thin layer of mucopolysaccharide and there react with bicarbonate ion produced by the metabolic activity of the endodermal cells. The calcium bicarbonate is reversibly converted to calcium carbonate and carbonic acid. The carbonic acid diffuses through the tissues and there, under the influence of carbonic anhydrase, forms carbon dioxide which is absorbed by the algal cells. The result is that the reaction leading to the formation of calcium carbonate goes towards the right. (After Goreau).

Table 12.6 Incorporation of radiocarbon, expressed as total counts per minute, into different fractions of the coral *Pocillopora* 24 h after exposure to radioactive bicarbonate (*Data from Muscatine and Cernichiari*)

	In light	In dark
In algal cells	4 268 000	203 000
In polyp tissue	4 350 000	201 000
In skeleton as carbonate	927 000	336 000

If algal cells are extracted from the coral and cultured, they liberate glycerol into the culture medium. This activity is enhanced by a substance, as yet unidentified, which can be extracted from the tissues of the polyp. Thus the polyp cells may affect the metabolism of the algal cells, but whether this occurs in living coral has yet to be determined.

Associations between producers and decomposers: lichens

Lichens are dual organisms consisting of a layer of algal cells embedded in a matrix of fungal hyphae (Book 1 p. 228). The association between the two organisms is so close that the dual nature of the lichen was not discovered until 1866. We have seen that coral organisms may sometimes lack zooxanthellae; in this condition they may grow more slowly, but their morphology is unaltered. Lichen fungi, on the other hand, are not known in nature without their algae. When reared artificially in alga-free culture not only do they grow extremely slowly, but they fail to produce the compact thallus of characteristic shape which is seen in the intact lichen. The fungi are thus completely dependent upon the algae, a condition we describe by saying that, for the fungus, the association is 'obligate'.

This association is, in part at least, a trophic one. Movement of photosynthate from the algae to the fungal partner has been shown by experiments using radiocarbon. Thus, for example, the lichen *Peltigera polydactyla* was exposed for a 4 h period to carbon dioxide containing ^{14}C; subsequently 40 percent of the radiocarbon was found in the purely fungal medulla (Fig. 12.18). The alga *Trebouxia*, when freshly isolated from a lichen, releases substantial quantities of the polyhydric alcohol ribitol into the culture medium, but after some time in culture the rate of exudation declines. It seems probable that in intact lichens the fungus, in some manner as yet unknown, stimulates exudation of photosynthetic products from the algae. Vitamins may also be produced by the algal partner; biotin is released by *Coccomyxa*, the alga in *Peltigera aphthosa*.

An understanding of these trophic relations explains how lichens can commonly grow on the surface of bare rocks where there is no organic material available to the

polyps is the enzyme carbonic anhydrase which is also found in mammalian red blood corpuscles (Book 1 p. 118). This catalyses the reaction

$$H_2CO_3 \rightleftharpoons CO_2 + H_2O$$

The removal by the zooxanthellae of carbon dioxide formed in this reaction will produce conditions in which the reaction of equation 12.1 will go towards the right and thus, indirectly, the zooxanthellae accelerate the rate of deposition of skeleton. This hypothesis receives some support from the fact that treating corals with a specific inhibitor of carbonic anhydrase decreases the rate of deposition of skeletal material.

The interrelation has another facet. The very high productivity of the algal cells suggests that photosynthetic products might pass from the algae to the corals. This transfer has been demonstrated by placing small specimens of corals in seawater containing radiocarbon (^{14}C) as sodium bicarbonate and then, after 24 h, separating the coral tissue from the underlying skeleton. The tissue is broken up so as to smash the cells of the polyps and free the algae. The algal cells can be separated from the remains of the polyp cells by centrifugation and the radioactivity of the two samples determined. All radioactive material must have been derived initially from the photosynthetic activity of the algal cells. The data are summarized in Table 12.6 which shows that nearly half the radioactivity has been transferred from the algae to the tissues of the polyps; other experiments show that the material liberated from the algal cells is incorporated into both lipid and protein in the cells of the polyps. Note also that some of the radiocarbon has been incorporated into the skeleton.

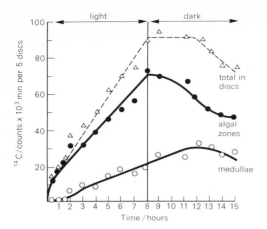

12.18 Total uptake of radiocarbon by discs of the lichen *Peltigera* in light and dark, as well as the distribution of the photosynthetic product between the algal layer and the fungal medulla. Note that photosynthetic product not only accumulates in the medulla during the time of exposure to light but continues to accumulate in the dark, although its concentration in the algal layer is falling. (After Smith).

fungus for decomposition. It also explains why when growing on tree trunks, lichens do not generally attack the bark. From the viewpoint of the algae, the contribution of the fungus to the association appears to be mainly mechanical. The alga may benefit from protection against excessive illumination; for example, in pure cultures of the alga *Trebouxia* photosynthesis is inhibited at high light intensities. Moreover fungal hyphae quickly absorb liquid water or water vapour, and thus may be important in providing the alga with an environment sufficiently moist for photosynthesis.

Mycorrhizas

The soil in close contact with roots usually contains more fungi and bacteria than soil further away from roots. These organisms are presumably attracted to root surfaces by local enrichment with organic substances that emanate from living roots as well as from decomposing cortex that is shed during secondary thickening.

Some of the fungi associated with root surfaces may produce hyphae which penetrate the root, behaving either as parasites of living cells, or as saprophytes of dying tissues. Very commonly, however, the roots remain apparently healthy despite habitual invasions by fungal hyphae. The term 'mycorrhiza' is used for such root–fungus structures which are of characteristic shape, and which are normally produced in place of rootlets.

Ectotrophic mycorrhizas

A mycorrhiza of *Eucalyptus* is illustrated in Book 1 Fig. 19.16. In this association the hyphae form a tight mantle around the rootlet and branch hyphae penetrate between the cells of epidermis and cortex. This type of mycorrhiza, termed ectotrophic, is found in most species of *Eucalyptus* and of pine, *Pinus*. Among indigenous tropical African trees it is rather uncommon, though occurring in some woody members of the Leguminosae, such as *Afzelia*. Ectotrophic mycorrhizas (Fig. 12.19) lack root hairs, and in fact the rootlet tissue has no direct contact at all with the soil. Fungus and tree can be reared separately, but they generally grow less well. Table 12.7 shows that in nutrient-deficient soils, non-mycorrhizal pine seedlings produced only about half as much dry weight as mycorrhizal seedlings and were notably deficient in phosphorus. Other experiments have shown, however, that in heavily manured

Table 12.7 Mean weights and mineral contents of mycorrhizal and non-mycorrhizal seedlings of *Pinus virginiana*. Weights in mg per seedling (*After McComb*)

	Mycorrhizal seedlings	*Non-mycorrhizal seedlings*
Fresh weight	1 230	592
Dry weight	323	152
Nitrogen	5·8	2·9
Phosphorus	0·6	0·15
Potassium	2·2	1·0

12.19 Part of the root system of *Pinus* showing long roots bearing short forked mycorrhizas (×1·5).

soils mycorrhiza may fail to develop, but that seedlings nevertheless grow vigorously. It appears that ectotrophic mycorrhizas are better able than roots to obtain nutrients from poor soils, probably because the hyphae which ramify from the mycorrhiza into the soil are able to penetrate humus and decomposing litter. In addition, because they are narrow, hyphae have a very large surface area available for absorption in relation to their weight; they also extend much further than do root hairs. It has been estimated that for hyphae with diameter of 5 μm, the surface area may be 4·2 m^2 per gramme dry weight. Translocation of absorbed nutrients readily occurs within the hyphae.

Fungi isolated from ectotrophic mycorrhizas can be grown in culture. Although they are basidiomycetes (Book 1 p. 226 ff) they lack enzymes which attack cellulose and lignin, and are therefore unable to compete successfully with the more vigorous saprophytic fungi. Radiotracer studies have shown that they depend for carbohydrates almost exclusively on sugars translocated to the roots from the leaves of the trees with which they are associated. An ectotrophic mycorrhiza is thus a trophic association in which the higher plant obtains inorganic nutrients in exchange for carbohydrates.

Endotrophic mycorrhizas

In other types of mycorrhiza, said to be endotrophic, the hyphae do not form a definite mantle around the root but penetrate the living cells of the root, where they are digested. Such mycorrhizas have been most extensively studied in orchids (Fig. 3.31). Orchids produce tiny dust-like seeds which may weigh as little as 1 μg; they therefore lack a food-store sufficient to allow the embryo to develop unaided. For successful growth, the seedling must be invaded by suitable fungal hyphae immediately after germination. The seedling then goes through an essentially heterotrophic stage in which all its food requirements are met by the digestion of fungal hyphae. The majority of mature orchids have green leaves and can survive without mycorrhizas, but others are devoid of chlorophyll and remain heterotrophic throughout life (Fig. 12.20).

The fungi associated with orchids are basidiomycetes, but differ from those forming ectotrophic mycorrhizas in being able to decompose cellulose. They are highly competitive saprophytes in the soil and some, such as *Armillaria mellea* and *Rhizoctonia solani*, can be parasitic on the roots of other plants. In these orchid mycorrhizas, the higher plant obtains both carbohydrate and inorganic nutrients from the fungus; the benefit to the fungus is not apparent.

The most widespread mycorrhizas, occurring in a majority of plants including most crops, are endotrophic mycorrhizas in which the fungus is a phycomycete (Book 1 p. 223 ff), *Endogone* (Fig. 12.21). Unfortunately these mycorrhizas are the least well-known, largely because it has

12.20 A completely saprophytic orchid which lacks green leaves. The fleshy mycorrhizal roots of the orchid can be seen clustered at the base of the stem.

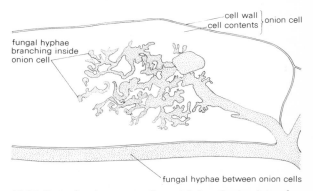

12.21 Part of onion root cell containing the hyphae of *Endogone*, an endotrophic mycorrhiza-forming fungus. The hyphae are eventually digested by the higher plant.

not been found possible to culture *Endogone* on artificial media, and partly because the morphological changes caused in the roots are less dramatic than in the mycorrhizas described above. Nevertheless experimental evidence of their importance is beginning to accumulate. Table 12.8 shows that increased dry weight is often shown by higher plants as a result of formation of this kind of mycorrhiza.

Table 12.8 Total dry weights of seedlings of various species of plant infected and non-infected by the mycorrhizal phycomycete *Endogone*. Weights in g (*from various authors*)

Species	Mycorrhizal	Non-mycorrhizal
Maize	3·00	2·37
Tobacco	2·72	1·65
Tomato (low-phosphorus medium)	0·39	0·09
Tomato (high-phosphorus medium)	0·74	0·70

Nitrogen-fixing root nodules

The ancient Greeks and Romans knew that crops belonging to the family Leguminosae, for example beans and peas, may improve the fertility of soil, but it was not until the late nineteenth century that the explanation was found to lie in the ability of the bacterial nodules on the roots of these plants to fix nitrogen, that is, to convert nitrogen gas into compounds which can be utilized by plants. The importance of nodules is exemplified by an experiment in which it was found that nodulation resulted in an increase of the nitrogen content of a soybean crop from 70 to 100 kg ha^{-1}.

The nodule-forming bacteria, members of the genus *Rhizobium*, can exist indefinitely in the soil, living as saprophytes. Each species of *Rhizobium* is able to grow only in a restricted number of species of Leguminosae. If the bacteria encounter suitable roots they invade a root hair, thence passing to the cortex where they multiply and stimulate the production by the plant of a parenchymatous capsule. In Fig. 12.22, showing a transverse section

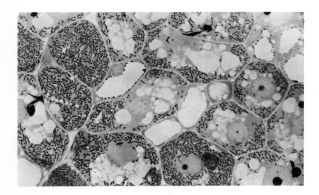

12.22 Transverse section of a nodule on the root of a leguminous plant showing the bacteria (stained dark) in the root cells.

through a nodule, it can be seen that the bacteria are present in large numbers inside the cells in the centre of the nodule. A freshly-cut, active nodule is pink in colour due to the presence of a pigment, leghaemoglobin, which is closely similar to the haemoglobin in the blood of vertebrates. The absence of this colour indicates that the nodules are moribund or ineffective in fixation.

The enzyme responsible for nitrogen fixation, nitrogenase, is a reductase which requires molybdenum as a co-enzyme, ATP as an energy source and a reducing agent, probably reduced ferredoxin, as a source of reducing electrons. Ferredoxin is itself reduced by electrons from the reactions of aerobic respiration which are also the source of ATP (Book 1 p. 44). Nodules are thus the site of intense respiration as well as of nitrogen fixation. It has been estimated that nodules metabolise 15 to 20 g of carbohydrate for each gramme of nitrogen fixed. The function of the leghaemoglobin is not yet known with certainty, but it may provide a reservoir of oxygen for respiration while maintaining a low oxygen concentration in the cells where reduction of nitrogen is proceeding. The product of nitrogen reduction is ammonia, which can then be utilized by the plant for the synthesis of amino-acids.

This process of nitrogen fixation is dependent upon the association of the root-nodule bacterium and the higher plant. Unlike free-living nitrogen-fixing bacteria in soil, *Rhizobium* is unable to reduce nitrogen in pure culture. This trophic relation parallels that of mycorrhizas: the decomposer depends upon the higher plant, presumably for the supply of carbohydrate necessary for nitrogen fixation, while the plant can utilize the product of the metabolic activity of the bacterium. The closeness of the interdependence is emphasized by the fact that neither *Rhizobium* nor the leguminous plant can alone synthesize either the nitrogenase or leghaemoglobin: the haem prosthetic group (Book 1 p. 37) of the latter is synthesized by the bacterium while the globin is synthesized by the plant.

Animals sharing a common shelter: shore dwellers

If we return to a consideration of parasitic associations, we can recognize not only that parasitism represents a particular type of trophic relation between two organisms, but also that the parasites commonly occupy relatively stable habitats which provide protection from potential predators. Somewhat parallel cases of associations between free-living organisms also exist. We will describe two of these.

The first relates to many of the animals living upon muddy or sandy shores. Both are unstable and exposed habitats and are characteristically occupied by consumers with an ability to burrow into the substratum. This situation has been exploited by certain other animals which regularly use these burrows for shelter. Thus, for example, in one estuary near the southern tip of Africa, there are

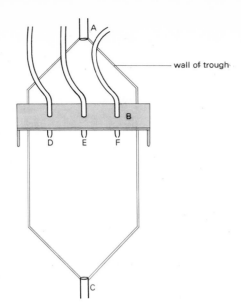

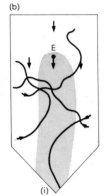

four common burrowing animals: three are large shrimp-like crustacea and the fourth is a worm. In the burrows of these animals are commonly found small crabs, another but smaller shrimp, a bivalve mollusc and a small fish. Different animals are characteristically associated with different burrowers: the bivalve is found only in the worm burrow, the fish in the burrow of only one of the three species of shrimp. On the other hand, the small shrimp may occur together with any of the four primary burrowers. Similar associations between shrimps and fish, worms and bivalves are found in the mud flats off Lourenço Marques, nearly 900 km to the north, but the species involved are different. The small animals obtain not only shelter, but probably also a continuous supply of fresh, food-laden seawater brought into the burrow by the pumping activities of the burrow makers. They are not known to harm the larger animals in any way.

The constancy of species involved in these associations suggests that some behavioural elements are concerned in their establishment. This has been examined in the case of a small crab found in the tubes of two species of polychaete worm. The crab shows a marked preference for seawater in which one or other of these worms has been kept (Fig. 12.23). It shows no response however to water in which have been kept other species of worm with which it does not normally.occur.

Animals sharing a common home: termites, ants and their 'guests'

A second, very different type of shelter is provided for some animals by the nests of ants and termites. In such nests we find a wide range of different types of small arthropod including spiders, mites, lepidopterous and dipterous larvae as well as beetles. Such animals are spoken of as 'inquilines' or in common language as 'ant guests'. This latter term carries the implication that all these animals are positively encouraged by the ants; this is true of some, but not of all. More than 2000 species of inquiline insects are known of which more than half are beetles. For example, 76 different species of rove beetle (Fig. 7.14b) occur in association with one species of the driver ant *Dorylus* (p. 196).

Study of the habits of inquilines of ants shows that they may be divided into three categories. In the first are those which are scavengers or predators upon the brood and are attacked by ants. They may depend for their safety upon their agility, but at least one rove beetle belonging to this category produces a secretion which is attractive to its 'hosts'; it can distract an attacker by this for sufficiently long to make good its escape. The members of the second category are mostly predatory and are said to be ignored by their hosts. The third and most interesting group, found also in termite nests, are insects which are actively en-

12.23 (a) Plan of apparatus to study the responses of marine animals to chemicals produced by other species with which they are associated. Seawater enters the trough at A. The platform B supports three jets D, E and F which can be used to introduce solutions into the water flowing through the trough. (b) Responses of a crab which commonly occurs inside the tubes of marine worms. (i) Normal seawater enters the trough and a dilute solution of a dye is released at E; the outline of the plume formed by the dye is indicated by stippling. The tracks of four crabs are shown. (ii) Water in which a worm has been kept is released at E; the outline of its plume is shown as well as the track of a single crab. Note the way the crab's track turns repeatedly so that it tends to remain within the plume of water. (iii) As (ii) but now the whole trough is flooded from A with water in which the worm had been kept. The crab's track is again characterized by frequent turns and is markedly different from those in (i). (After Davenport).

225

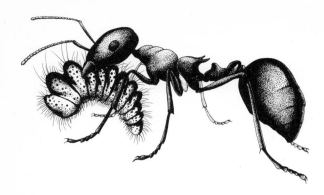

12.24 Worker ant carrying the humped-up caterpillar of a 'large blue' butterfly.

couraged by the ants or termites although these inquilines prey upon the young instars of their hosts. One of the most remarkable of such relations is with the larvae of certain butterflies (Lepidoptera), belonging to a family commonly called 'the blues' because of their most usual wing colour. In one 'blue' from South Africa, *Lepidochrysops*, the female lays her eggs on a plant and there the first two larval instars live, feeding upon the plant tissues. There too the larvae moult to the third instar, but they then wander off the plant and have next been found inside the nests of the ant *Camponotus* (Fig. 11.9). What happens between has never been observed with the South African caterpillars. In a European species with a very similar life history it is known that if the wandering caterpillar is met by an ant, the larva exposes a gland near the hind end of the abdomen and the ant starts to feed upon the secretion of the gland. Quite abruptly, after the ant has been feeding for some time, the larva blows out its thoracic segments; the ant then picks up the larva in its jaws (Fig. 12.24) and carries it back to the nest. The third and fourth instars are passed in the ant's nest and there the caterpillar pupates. When the adult emerges it makes its way out of the nest, largely ignored by the workers, and then, having gained the open air, expands its wings and flies off. Not all 'blues' are treated in this way; some have no association with ants at all, but the larvae of one genus, *Poecilmitis*, are cared for on their food plant by the ant *Crematogaster* (Fig. 11.10), being sheltered by large carton 'tents' built around them.

Glandular secretions are probably also the reason why certain rove beetles are common in the nests of termites. Comparison of the structures in the epidermis of these inquilines and related but free-living beetles shows the former to have certain glands not present in the latter. Some of these beetles achieve a marked resemblance in shape to termite workers. Fig. 12.25 shows an extreme case in which the abdomen of the beetle is bent round so as to conceal its thorax and further carries three pairs of leg-like appendages. The significance of this mimicry is not understood. It occurs also in rove beetles which live with ants. In this case, since the adult beetles may accompany

foraging ants, it is suggested that the similarity protects the beetles from attack by birds; certainly experimental studies have failed to provide any evidence that the ant-like shape is of significance in the relations between the beetles and the ants. The larvae of these beetles, although they may feed upon the brood of their hosts, are tended by the ants and treated in the same way as the brood, being carried from one part of the nest to another as conditions of temperature and humidity change. This response also depends upon glandular secretions produced by the beetle larvae, which further exploit their position by getting the worker ants to feed them (Fig. 12.26). In doing this, the begging movements made by the beetle larvae are closely similar to those made by ant larvae.

One advantage indirectly gained by these arthropods which live in the nests of ants is that, because the ants will defend their nests against potential predators, the inquilines are protected by the ants from predation.

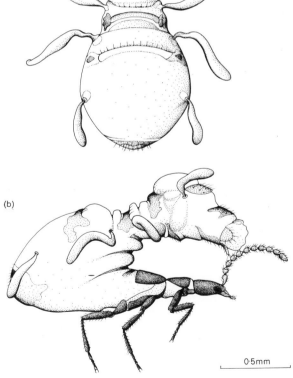

12.25 (a) Dorsal and (b) lateral view of a rove beetle which occurs in termite nests in south-west Africa. Note the way in which the abdomen is flexed over the head and thorax, and the various 'appendages' it carries which recall the antennae and legs of a termite. (After Kistner).

226

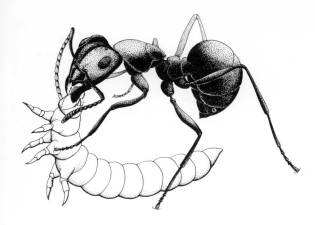

12.26 Beetle larva soliciting food from a worker ant which is feeding it. (After Hölldobler).

Plant protection by predatory ants

We have described (p. 210f) how ants utilize honey dew produced by aphids and scales as a source of food and how the bugs obtain protection from both predators and parasites. Many ants attack not only higher-order consumers but also herbivorous insects. In this way ants can protect

Table 12.9 Effect of the presence of the Brown House Ant, *Pheidole* (Fig. 11.7) on the abundance of Citrus Red Scale, *Aonidiella*. These data come from a trial in which 801 trees were kept free of ants; 800 trees occupied by *Pheidole* served as a control. Note that heavy scale infestation is far more common on the ant-infested trees (*Adapted from Steyn*)

Level of infestation (scales per fruit)	Ant-infested trees	Ant-free trees	% ant-infested trees
0–1	280	589	32
2–10	222	133	63
11–100	166	78	68
101–1 000	76	1	99
>1 001	56	0	100

trees from the attacks of herbivores, although with some species of ant, this protection may be 'bought' at the expense of increased populations of aphids and scale insects. This effect may be seen in the data given in Table 12.9.

This characteristic of certain ants has been used to control various pests of economically important tree crops in place of extensive use of insecticides. Thus the damage caused to coconuts by the phytophagous bug *Pseudotheraptus* is far less on trees which harbour the aggressive Red Ant *Oecophylla* (Fig. 11.6) than on those which support colonies of the smaller *Pheidole* (Fig. 11.7) which does not prey upon the bug (Table 12.10). Clearly if it were possible to ensure that *Oecophylla* occurred on all trees, then a very considerable measure of protection would be achieved.

It should not be supposed, however, that ants are always useful in protecting trees. The reverse may also be true. Two pests of citrus trees are Red Scale, *Aonidiella* and Soft Brown Scale, *Coccus* (Fig. 12.2). The latter produces honey dew, but the former does not. The presence of ants such as *Pheidole* on citrus trees will protect both scales from attack by parasitoids and predators even though the Red Scale is not exploited by the ants for honey dew. If the ants are prevented from having access to the trees, then, Table 12.9 shows, the population of Red Scale is reduced.

Encouraging association

If ants can confer protection on plants or trees, it would clearly be of advantage to a plant if it were in some way attractive to such ants: if, for example, there were an ant-attractant comparable to the honey dew of aphids. In many plants such as *Morinda* there are small clusters of sugar-secreting cells on the leaves, sometimes near the petiole, sometimes near the tip of the leaf (Fig. 12.27). These are called extra-floral nectaries and unquestionably serve to attract ants. In this way the plants probably gain protection from attack by herbivorous insects and, what is perhaps also important, the ants are less inclined to exploit the floral nectaries as a source of food and thus are less likely to drive off pollinating insects visiting the flowers.

The swollen-thorn acacias

In certain species of thorny acacia trees not only are ants encouraged by the presence of extra-floral nectaries, but

Table 12.10 Effect of dominant ant species upon the damage to coconuts in Zanzibar by the phytophagous bug *Pseudotheraptus* (*Data from Way*)

Dominant ant	Number of trees	Nuts per palm	% of nuts with more than ten lesions	Total insects from ten trees collected in knockdown samples
Oecophylla	43	72·3	3·2	84
Pheidole	115	13·4	62·2	837

12.27 Ant (*Crematogaster* sp.) visiting a cup-shaped extra-floral nectary on a shoot of the tree *Morinda lucida*. An unoccupied nectary may be seen on the node below.

12.28 *Acacia drepanolobium* showing swellings at the base of the paired thorns. At the end of each swelling is a small hole through which the ants, which live there, can pass. The thorns are about 6–8 cm long.

Table 12.11 Effect of ants upon the abundance of injurious insects on swollen-thorn acacias (*Data from Janzen*)

	Trees occupied by ants	Trees unoccupied by ants
Number of shoots examined	847	793
Percentage of shoots with insects	13	59
Injurious insects per shoot	0·22	2·67

Table 12.12 Comparison of growth and mortality of swollen-thorn acacias with and without attendant ants (*Data from Janzen*)

	Ant-infested trees	Ant-free trees
Number of trees dying in 9 months	11	30
Number of trees examined	39	39
Mean length increment of suckers in 7 weeks (cm)	72·9 ± 37·4	10·2 ± 9·8
Number of suckers	29	42
Quantity of material grown from cut stumps (g wet wt)	41 750	2900
Number of stumps	72	66

the bases of some of the thorns are enlarged to form hollow chambers; these provide shelter in which the ants keep their brood (Fig. 12.28). The association of ants with these swollen-thorn acacias is very common; thus, for example, of 2 532 such trees examined in East Africa, only 89 had no attendant ants. The effect of the presence of ants on the abundance of other insects has been studied by counting the number of injurious insects on a large number of shoots of trees, only some of which had attendant ants. The results show that the presence of the ants decreases the population of injurious insects by more than an order of magnitude (Table 12.11).

The activities of the ants are not limited to predation on other insects. They may also keep the soil below the trees free from other plants. In certain places this activity prevents the growth of vines which otherwise rapidly shade out the acacias, and it may possibly increase the supply of water and nutrients directly available to the trees. As a result of all these effects, trees with attendant ants grow more rapidly and survive better than those without (Table 12.12).

On many trees there may occur swellings or galls; these are due to a direct irritant action of insects which attack the tissues of the trees. The insects feed upon the gall tissues and are provided with protection as a result of the growth response of the plant, but there is no evidence that these galls are of any value to the tree. Such galls might be regarded as a consequence of insect parasitism on a plant. The evidence suggests that the swollen thorns on acacias are, at least to some extent, part of the natural growth habit of the plant and not galls produced in response to the presence of ants. This has been most clearly shown by a study of 40 acacias grown, as far as possible in insect-free conditions, in a greenhouse in Canada from seed collected in East Africa. After two years of growth, 38 of the young trees had swollen thorns, with an average number of 27 per tree. The two trees which failed to produce any were stunted and their growth presumably abnormal.

Hermit crabs and sea anemones

An association in which one organism gains protection by the presence of another and in some fashion 'encourages' the association is not peculiar to the swollen-thorn acacias. A very different example is provided by some hermit crabs. Hermit crabs have elongated abdomens so that, despite their name, they more closely resemble shrimps than common crabs (Fig. 12.29). The abdomen of a hermit crab, unlike that of a shrimp, is not protected by well-developed, chitinous plates; the crab tucks its abdomen into an empty snail shell which it carries around with it everywhere, usually leaving it only to move to a new and larger shell as it grows.

Sea anemones may frequently be found growing on the snail shells in which some species of the hermit crabs live (Fig. 12.30). This is not a casual relationship. If an anemone is removed from a shell, allowed to settle upon the floor of an aquarium tank and then offered another suitable but empty shell, the anemone may grip the shell in its tentacles, release its foot or 'pedal disk' from the surface and, bending its body, transfer the pedal disk to the shell. The anemone has a preference for certain types of shell; its behaviour of transferring in this way is a response to some chemical, probably a protein, on the surface of the snail shell. The anemone will show this behaviour whether the shell is occupied by a crab or not, but the crab may also be active in transferring the anemone to the shell (Fig. 12.31). In doing this it makes prodding movements at the anemone; these stimulate the anemone to release its pedal disk from the substratum and to transfer to the shell occupied by the crab. Depending upon the species of anemone and the species of crab, the transfer may be due to the activity of the anemone alone, or to the activity of

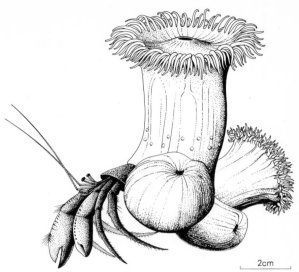

12.30 A hermit crab carrying four anemones on its shell.

12.31 (a) A crab lifting a sea anemone in its claw and (b) depositing it on its dorsal surface. Note that this is not a hermit crab. The relation between crabs and anemones involves other crabs as well as the hermit crabs.

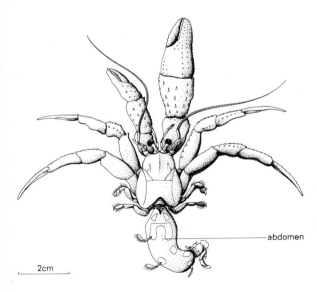

12.29 A hermit crab removed from its shell. Note the soft abdomen which is slightly coiled.

abdomen

the crab alone, or both partners may be active in the transfer.

What may be the significance of this association? In one species in which the crab takes an active role in transferring anemones to its shell, the presence of an anemone gives the crab protection from attack by octopuses. When a crab was introduced into an aquarium tank containing an octopus, it was almost immediately attacked. Six crabs in their shells but lacking anemones were all extracted and eaten by the octopus. Six other specimens, each with an anemone, were left untouched by the octopus after several attacks. In these cases, when the octopus attempted to take the crab with an arm, the arm was rapidly withdrawn as soon as it touched the anemone and was stung. Within 24 h the octopus had learnt to leave these crabs alone.

The association is of protective value to the crab. Whether it is of any benefit to the anemone is not clear: it has been suggested that the mobility which the anemone indirectly acquires by being carried around by the crab enhances its chances of finding food. Such a hypothesis is, however, not easily tested.

The characteristics of associations

If you survey the various associations that have been described, you will be able to see certain features which are of general importance. All the associations appear to provide a benefit of some sort to at least one of the partners, whether this be simply a place in which to live, protection from predators, or a supply of food. In some cases the association, while of value, is not essential for survival: cattle can survive without tick birds and ants without aphids. In others the association is essential for one or other partner: parasites must find a suitable host in which to live, while harvester termites must have intestinal flagellates to digest the cellulose in their diet. Clearly there is variation in the extent to which an association is necessary for survival and it is not possible to draw any sharp boundaries between different degrees of benefit. In certain associations both partners benefit; for example, the sugars of the extra-floral nectaries of the swollen-thorn acacias provide about half the energy requirements of the ants which live upon these trees, while, as we have seen, the survival of the trees may be dependent upon the activities of the ants.

Classification of associations

Attempts have been made to build up a system of classification of these associations based upon the degree of dependence of the partners within an association as well as the extent to which there is actual exchange of material between them. Such schemes have the disadvantage that the categories proposed are imprecise; they may also assign to different categories associations which are clearly closely related in other ways. This is perhaps most easily made clear by reference to the associations between hermit crabs and sea anemones. We have described a case in which the crab is active in effecting the transfer of an anemone to its shell and have given evidence that the association is beneficial to the crab; we have assumed that it may also be of value to the anemone. This same anemone is found upon the shells inhabited by a different species of hermit crab, which, however, appears to take no part whatsoever in bringing about the association; it is dependent for its establishment on the responses of the anemone alone. Nor is there any evidence that the crab benefits as a result of the association. Nevertheless there seems little reason to doubt that these two associations are closely related and differ only quantitatively. Existing systems of classification would, however, assign these two associations to different categories.

The regularity of patterns of association

A more profitable question is to ask how far the various associations we have described have any general ecological relevance: how far are they isolated phenomena which, by their curious character, have attracted attention? Certainly there are associations which are in some fashion unique. Thus, for example, there is one species of *Paramecium* which has algae in its cytoplasm; there is one species of fish which lives in the cloaca of sea cucumbers (Echinodermata: Holothuroidea). Nevertheless many of the patterns of association we have described are representative of very common phenomena.

Examination of the contents of the alimentary canal of any vertebrate will almost certainly reveal the presence of parasitic worms: examination of the blood will probably detect blood parasites. The particular species involved will differ, but we can recognize the gut and the blood as being two types of habitat which provide resources of both food and shelter and which are almost invariably occupied by parasites. Similarly a study of the fauna of the sandy mud of estuaries in almost any part of the world will show the presence of animals whose burrows provide shelter for other species. What is even more striking is that there are close similarities between the structure of these communities whether they are found on the coast of Africa or that of California. In both places we find burrowing worms with associated crabs, burrowing shrimps associated with both crabs and small fishes. Wherever it may be geographically, the nature of the habitat is such as to make a burrowing habit almost essential and once burrows have been established they offer a protective resource which is exploited by other animals. Again, the association between ants and aphids occurs in both temperate and tropical lands, while in all five continents the nests of ants are exploited by other small arthropods as potential shelter and possibly as a source of food. The details of the associations vary; what is important is that the resource provided by ants' nests is one which is universally exploited. Perhaps a more striking example is that of the swollen-thorn acacias; these are to be found in both Africa and Central America. Different trees and different ants are involved, but the pattern of relationship is closely similar. Even the habits of ambrosia beetles are not limited to some single species: more than 30 different beetles belonging to at least 12 different genera cultivate ambrosia fungus and they are to be found attacking timber in Asia and tropical America as well as in Africa. There are moreover other timber-boring beetles which depend upon other types of fungus and many of them share with the ambrosia beetles the habit of distributing fungal spores contained in myce-tangia.

Association and habitat resources

In broad terms these associations stem from the fact that one organism can provide some type of resource which can be exploited by another. In the majority of cases this resource, whether it be an ant's nest, the blood stream of a vertebrate or the tissues of a coral polyp, is sufficiently widely distributed to ensure that, however varied may be the details, the same types of association are likely to be consistent features in the structure of broadly similar communities.

Problems

1 On p. 209 it was said that crocodiles often open their mouths as they bask in the sun. What do you consider may be the significance of this pattern of behaviour?

2 If a polyp ceased to feed upon zooplankton and became totally dependent upon materials liberated by the zooxanthellae in its tissues, how would you describe the relationship between the polyp and the algae?

3 Fig. 12.9b shows data relating to the periodicity of formation of cysts of sporozoites of *Plasmodium* in mosquitoes. Why are these data alone insufficient to show that there is a cycle of infectivity of the gametocyte of *Plasmodium*?

4 The definitive host of a parasite is the one in which the parasite becomes sexually mature. Other hosts are called intermediate hosts. Which is the definitive host of (a) *Schistosoma*, (b) the tapeworm *Taenia* and (c) the malaria parasite *Plasmodium*? Does *Trypanosoma* have a definitive host? Explain how you arrive at your conclusion.

5 Cleaner fish usually have an obvious pattern of coloration. There are also some predatory fishes which have a very similar pattern and behave in a manner resembling cleaner fish. Instead of cleaning 'customers', they attempt to feed upon them. How would you describe this phenomenon?

6 From your knowledge of the physiology of the mammalian alimentary canal, what do you consider may be the major difficulties of a metazoan gut parasite in establishing itself and surviving in the small intestine? Which of these difficulties will be met by biochemical and which by anatomical adaptations?

7 Hydra (Fig. 6.5) is a small, solitary polyp found in freshwater. There are some 30 different species of hydra of which two, assigned to the genus *Chlorohydra*, contain green algae in their tissues. It is possible to produce specimens which lack these algal cells. The polyps produce buds and the rate of bud formation is a convenient index of their growth rate. The data in the table below compare the rate of bud formation of normal and alga-free specimens of *Chlorohydra* in different conditions of feeding. What conclusions may be drawn from these results? What might be their implication in terms of the distribution of different species of hydra in natural waters?

Rate of growth of cultures of *Chlorohydra* expressed as the total number of polyps present each day. The cultures were fed on the larvae of brine shrimps (*Data after Muscatine*)

Day	Fed daily		Fed every other day		Fed every third day	
	Normal	Albino	Normal	Albino	Normal	Albino
1	16	17	16	15	16	15
2	26	26	24	20	24	19
3	33	34	34	26	36	28
4	55	54	42	28	37	29
5	90	83	60	32	46	31
6	—	—	85	45	70	31

Note: All cultures were fed on Day 1. No observations were made upon the daily-fed cultures on Day 6.

8 Intracellular algae occur in a few species of Protozoa, including one species of *Paramecium*. Do your answers to Problem 7 suggest that *Chlorohydra* and this particular species of *Paramecium* could represent specific cases of a more general ecological phenomenon? Explain the reasons for your conclusion. Given access to all possible relevant information, what points would you examine to test the validity of your suggestion?

9 Do you consider that a mammalian foetus should be regarded as a parasite?

10 On p. 212 it is stated that ants will move scale insects from one part of a tree to another. Many scale insects have motile first-instar nymphs, so that the activity of the nymphs themselves may be responsible for their distribution. While ants have been seen carrying scale insects, it is necessary to demonstrate that these can survive being moved. Suggest the design of an experiment to show that the ants are in fact able successfully to move scale insects about.

11 On p. 219 an experiment is described which shows that if the intestinal protozoal fauna of termite workers is destroyed by exposing the termites to oxygen at high pressure they cannot survive. This is interpreted as meaning that the intestinal fauna is necessary for the survival of the termites. What further experiment is required to show the validity of this hypothesis? Explain why it is necessary.

12 Toxins produced by the malaria parasite cause a fever at the time the gametocytes are maximally infective. We have suggested (p. 216) that the occurrence of maximum gametocyte infectivity during the evening is an adaptation of the parasite to the activity cycle of the mosquitoes. The production of toxins might also be regarded as an adaptation in so far as it will increase the probability of the vector successfully attacking the host. The same argument might be put forward in relation to the debility associated with nagana caused by *Trypanosoma* in cattle. Discuss this view, indicating what further types of information it might be of value to obtain.

13 A trial was set up using mosquito traps laid out in a line at measured distances from a baiting point. The traps were so constructed as to collect only mosquitoes flying upwind towards the baiting point. The traps were operated daily from dusk to dawn and the catch at each trap was recorded. As bait, two calves were used in one series of experiments; in a second a cylinder of carbon dioxide was arranged to release gas at a rate equal to that being normally exhaled by the two calves. Unbaited control catches were also made. The following table, based on data from Gillies and Wilkes, shows the mean number of unfed females of two mosquitoes, *Anopheles melas* and *Culex tritaeniorhynchus*, caught in each trap each night.

| Species | Bait | Distance of trap from bait (m) | | | | | |
		5	10	20	40	60	80
A. melas	Calves	290·4	79·5	41·4	23·5	9·6	5·3
	CO_2	84·9	25·3	11·7	10·9	12·1	9·6
	Control	13·1	10·4	14·3	12·1	11·3	8·7
C. tritaenio-rhynchus	Calves	86·0	17·8	8·7	2·8	1·9	1·4
	CO_2	37·6	9·4	4·6	1·7	1·3	1·9
	Control	1·6	1·4	1·1	1·6	2·3	1·2

(a) Present the data in suitable graphical form.

(b) Assuming that the bait produces a plume of stimulus downwind, as shown in Fig. 12.7, describe the differences in response of the two species of mosquito.

(c) To which species does Fig. 12.7 more closely relate?

14 Review the various types of mechanism used for the establishment of intra-specific associations between organisms. Select one case in which the mechanism, if it exists, is not known and suggest a series of experiments which might be undertaken to investigate its characteristics.

15 A very large number of different species of inquilines are found in the nests of ants and termites; very few occur in those of bees and wasps. It has been suggested that this difference arises partly from the fact that the nest architecture of the two groups is very different and partly from the fact that while the nests of ants and termites are commonly in the soil, those of bees and wasps are usually arboreal. Elaborate these ideas.

Bibliography

Further reading

Cheng, T. C.	*Symbiosis*, Pegasus, New York, 1970
Croll, N. A.	*Ecology of Parasites*, Heinemann, 1966, Chaps. 3 and 4
Evans, S. M.	*Studies in Invertebrate Behaviour*, Heinemann, 1968, Chap. 4
Smith, D. C.	*The Lichen Symbiosis*, Oxford Biology Readers, Oxford University Press, 1973
Smith, D. C.	*Symbiosis of Algae with Invertebrates*, Oxford Biology Readers, Oxford University Press, 1973
Arditti, J.	'Orchids', *Scientific American*, 1966, Offprint no. 1031
Batra, S. W. T., Batra, L. R.	'The Fungus Gardens of Insects', *Scientific American*, 1967, Offprint no. 1086
Denison, W. C.	'Life in Tall Trees', *Scientific American*, 1973, Offprint no. 1274
Hawking, F.	'The Clock of the Malaria Parasite', *Scientific American*, 1970, Offprint no. 1181
Hölldobler, B.	'Communication between Ants and Their Guests', *Scientific American*, 1971, Offprint no. 1218
Limbaugh, C.	'Cleaning Symbiosis', *Scientific American*, 1961, Offprint no. 135

Part 4
Population ecology—the study of the numbers of organisms

13 Counting populations

So far we have considered in qualitative terms the inter-relations between the organisms which form communities. We have, however, recognized (Book 1 chap. 1) that within any food web there will be a loss of energy as material is transferred from one trophic level to another, resulting in a 'pyramid' of energy. This energy is contained as chemical potential energy within the organisms which constitute the food web. As a result the pyramid of energy finds concrete expression as a pyramid of biomass; the total quantity of living matter at any one trophic level is usually less than that at the trophic level below. In turn this pyramid of biomass may, in certain conditions, be expressed as a pyramid of numbers; the numbers of organisms in any one trophic level are frequently greater than those in the trophic level above. It is, however, important to realize that, unlike the pyramid of energy, pyramids of numbers and biomass are not inevitable. Within a forest there may be far fewer primary producers, in the form of trees, than of herbivorous animals feeding upon them. Similarly a large carnivore may support a considerable number of ectoparasites and endoparasites. Such general statements about the pyramid of numbers are obvious, but if we are to comprehend in detail the relations existing within any particular food web, then it is necessary to make accurate, quantitative statements rather than broad generalizations.

Consider the food webs shown in Fig. 13.1. Fig. 13.1a shows a general statement which could apply both to the quantitative relations shown in Fig. 13.1b and to those in Fig. 13.1c. Clearly these are very different; while the situation depicted in Fig. 13.1c is advantageous to a fisherman, that shown in Fig. 13.1b is not. Figs. 13.1d and 13.1e show two terrestrial food webs reflecting the same sort of difference in emphasis.

If we are to obtain such quantitative information, we must be able to assess the numbers of organisms per unit area of land or unit volume of water: that is, we must have methods of sampling the populations quantitatively. Such methods will obviously be determined by the nature of the organisms concerned. A vast number of different techniques have been developed and we can here review only those which have most general application.

It is important to distinguish from the outset methods which can give absolute values of population density from those which sample the population in some standard and comparable manner but which, by their nature, can give only relative not absolute values. Thus, for example, there are many types of insect trap which will provide a series of comparable samples, and by using these we can follow annual changes in population density and the way in which it is affected by various environmental disturbances. This type of information is of the greatest practical value in the study of change; it has no value if numbers of organisms or the biomass per unit of space are required.

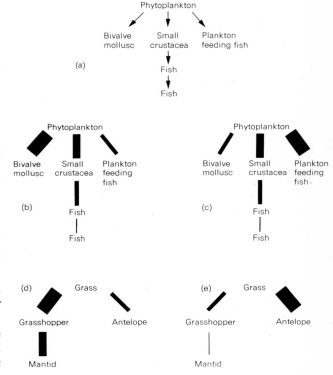

13.1 Quantitative differences between hypothetical food chains. (a) A diagram of a food chain with no quantitative information on the relative importance of the different links. (b) and (c) The same food chain with the movement of biomass within the chain indicated by the relative thickness of the bars. Note that while in (b) most of the phytoplankton is consumed by bivalves, in (c) it is mostly consumed by fish. (d) and (e) A comparable situation in an abbreviated terrestrial food chain.

Plankton

It is convenient to start by considering methods of sampling plankton. Both marine and freshwater plankton can be sampled by the use either of bottles or of nets. If the plankton is abundant, a bottle is satisfactory. The type of bottle normally used is cylindrical, closing at its upper and lower surfaces by flat plates. When the bottle is closed, it will contain a known volume of water. The open bottle is lowered into the water on a line and when it has reached the required depth a heavy weight or 'messenger' is allowed to run down the line. When the messenger arrives at the bottle, it strikes a catch which puts into operation a mechanism like that shown in Fig. 13.2, which causes the plates at both ends of the bottle to close. The sample is then brought to the surface and decanted into some other container. A suitable fixing solution is added, the bottle labelled and put aside for later examination.

If it is the phytoplankton which is of interest, the fixatives commonly used are either formaldehyde or iodine solution, the latter acting as a stain. In the laboratory, the original sample is shaken up and some small volume removed and placed in a flat-bottomed vessel. The plankton is allowed to settle and then examined under a microscope. The number of organisms is counted and then, by simple proportion, the number in the original water sample can be calculated. While counting may be carried out using an ordinary microscope, it is more convenient to use one in which the sample is studied from below, so that the organisms can be examined not through the depth of water from which they have been allowed to settle, but only through the thin glass on which they have come to rest.

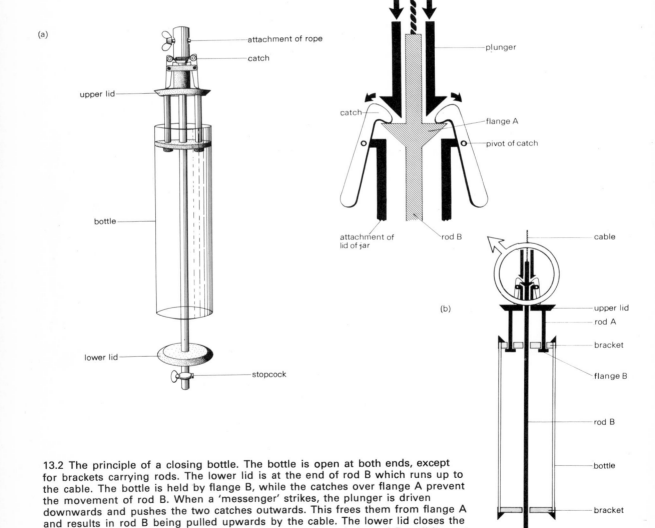

13.2 The principle of a closing bottle. The bottle is open at both ends, except for brackets carrying rods. The lower lid is at the end of rod B which runs up to the cable. The bottle is held by flange B, while the catches over flange A prevent the movement of rod B. When a 'messenger' strikes, the plunger is driven downwards and pushes the two catches outwards. This frees them from flange A and results in rod B being pulled upwards by the cable. The lower lid closes the bottom of the bottle, and the bottle is then drawn upwards by rod B until it meets the upper lid and is thus completely closed.

Special 'inverted' microscopes are manufactured for this purpose (Fig. 13.3). Essentially the same technique can be used to count zooplankton, but special attention to fixation is required if it is desired to count small soft-bodied planktonic animals like Protozoa.

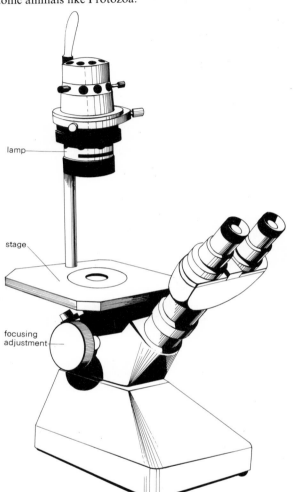

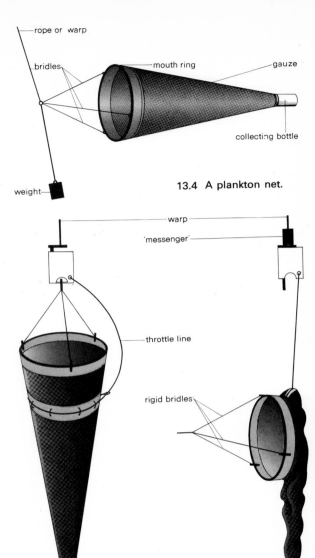

13.4 A plankton net.

13.3 An inverted microscope. The objective is below the stage and faces upwards; the object being studied is illuminated from above. The advantage of this system is as follows. Imagine that you have a suspension of plankton containing, say, about 100 organisms per 10 cm³ water. To count these you might take a sample of 25 cm³. If the sample is put into a shallow vessel, the area which has to be examined will be very considerable. It is possible to reduce the 'search area' by using a glass cylinder of fairly small diameter and allowing the organisms to settle on the bottom. They will now, however, lie below a considerable depth of water and thus probably cannot be brought into focus using an ordinary type of objective. It is also unsatisfactory to try to insert the objective of a microscope into a tall, narrow vessel. By having the objective beneath the vessel and viewing the organisms through its glass bottom, both these difficulties are avoided.

13.5 Closing mechanism for a plankton net. The throttle line runs around the net shortly behind the ring. A 'messenger' is dropped down the 'warp' and activates a mechanism which releases the bridles and allows the throttle line to close around the net.

Alternatively, plankton may be sampled by pulling through the water a cone-shaped net which has a bottle at the narrow end of the cone to collect the sample (Fig. 13.4). Depending upon the mesh of the net, organisms of different size groups will be caught. This method is not satisfactory for sampling phytoplankton owing to the very small size of the organisms: they either pass through a coarse-meshed net or rapidly clog up the holes of a fine net.

Whereas the volume of a closing bottle is known, it is

necessary to calculate what volume of water has been 'fished' by a plankton net. The area of the opening is known; if we know also the distance through which the net has travelled, we can obtain a close estimate of the volume of water filtered through the net. It may, for example, be necessary to determine the variation in numbers of planktonic organisms at different depths. The easiest way to do this is to lower a net to some predetermined depth and then slowly pull it up again. When the net has reached a second predetermined depth, perhaps 10 m less than the first, a messenger is dropped down the line to activate a mechanism which closes the mouth of the net (Fig. 13.5). The net may then be pulled to the surface without catching more planktonic organisms. It is in this sort of way that the data shown in Fig. 6.8 were obtained.

In all population sampling it is necessary to attempt to recognize the limitations of the method. What sorts of difficulties arise in sampling plankton by these methods? The closing bottle has the disadvantage, at least with zooplankton, that as it is lowered through the water the animals swim away from the disturbance which it creates. It tends therefore to give values which are less than the 'true' value. Similarly, direct underwater observation of plankton nets in action shows that the towing rate affects the size of the catch. If the net is towed too fast, the water is not able to flow through the meshes fast enough and as a result much will be forced around the sides of the opening: if the net is towed too slowly larger animals can swim away or even out of the mouth of the net. We have already noted that the size of organisms caught depends upon the mesh of the net; any one mesh size will be selective, catching organisms of one size-range preferentially, while others falling outside that range will appear less frequently in the catches than they actually occur in the population. We shall encounter this same problem in connection with fish nets shortly. Of course, for relative values, which are adequate for the study of change in population numbers with depth or with season, these difficulties may not be serious.

There is a second consideration. We have implied that if we take a water sample with a closing bottle and remove a small quantity, a subsample, counting this is sufficient. We have, however, no reason to believe that if we took a second subsample, using exactly the same technique, we would obtain an identical numerical value. Almost certainly we would not: our first and second subsamples will differ. If we repeat this subsampling process many times we can obtain a 'mean' value which will be closer to the 'true' value of the number of organisms than most of the subsample values. Such a procedure will allow us to determine, by a suitable statistical method, the 'error' of our observations.

There is one further difficulty, arising from the fact that the plankton may not be uniformly scattered through the water mass: there may be areas rich in phytoplankton and adjacent areas in which it is relatively scarce. It is thus essential to have in mind the possibility of non-uniform

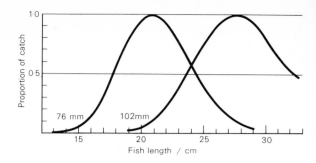

13.6 'Catch curves' of two gill nets for *Tilapia galilaea*; the smaller net had a mesh size of 76 mm and the larger one of 102 mm. Each curve shows the relative proportions of fishes of different lengths which the net would catch. (Ater Lelek and Wuddah).

distribution when planning an investigation of the plankton of any water body.

Errors of these types, arising from the selectivity of the sampling equipment, from the fact that any one sample will provide only an 'estimate' of the true value and finally from the fact that the organisms of interest may not be uniformly distributed, enter into every procedure concerned with the determination of the sizes of populations. They are not peculiar to the sampling of plankton and should be borne in mind in considering other methods of sampling as well.

Fish

Planktonic organisms can be sampled by the use of suitable nets. Determination of the absolute size of fish populations is, however, very difficult. Although fish can be caught in nets, these provide no absolute quantitative data since the volume of water 'fished' by a net is completely unknown. Relative data, such as changes in population size, may however be determined using gill nets. Just as a plankton net is selective, depending upon the mesh of the net used, so too is a gill net. Fig. 13.6 shows 'catch curves' for gill nets of two mesh sizes. From a population containing equal numbers of individuals of all sizes, each net catches one size preferentially and fishes larger or smaller than this are caught relatively less often. A picture of the size composition of a population is sometimes required: it is then necessary to use a number of nets of different mesh size and the data thus obtained must be corrected using the characteristic 'catch curve' of each net.

Where the interest lies, as it commonly does in practice, in following changes in the sizes of fish stocks, valuable information can be obtained by recording commercial landings of fishes. Provided both fishing techniques and the number of hours worked by fishermen remain the same from year to year, records of fish landed will provide data upon changes in the size of the exploited population.

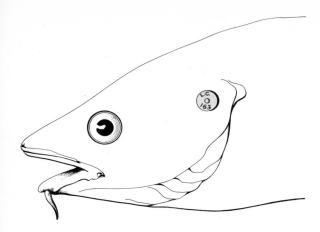

13.7 Sketch of the head of a fish with a marking tag inserted into the operculum.

Such circumstances are uncommon, but it is possible by suitable sampling to estimate the total number of man hours spent fishing in any one month or year and, if the total fish landings can be estimated, we can obtain a value for the weight of fish landed per man hour. If fishing techniques change, clearly the interpretation of the data becomes more difficult.

Lincoln Index

In limited volumes of water, such as fish ponds or small lakes, the size of the population of different species of fishes may be determined by catching a number of fish, marking them suitably (Fig. 13.7) so that they may be recognized again, and then releasing them. After an interval another catch is made and the number both of marked fish and of the total catch of that species noted. It is then easy to estimate the size of the population. If we assume that the total population of the species in the pond is N and we initially capture and mark M, then, provided the population mixes freely, the proportion of marked fishes in the second sample should be M/N. So we may write

$$\frac{\text{marked fish recaptured } (m)}{\text{total fish recaptured } (n)} = \frac{M}{N}$$

or
$$N = nM/m$$

Since M, m and n are all known, we can calculate N.

This procedure for calculating population size is often referred to as the 'capture–recapture' method and the expression derived above is spoken of as the 'Lincoln Index'. It is clearly applicable in a wide variety of circumstances, not only to fishes in a small water body. There are, however, certain limitations and underlying assumptions. One obvious limitation is that it can be used only for a population of which the range of movement is relatively restricted and defined; the latter qualification is essential if we are to express the resulting data in the form of numbers per unit area or volume. Numbers alone, although useful in fish or game management, allow no comparisons to be made between populations in different localities. Secondly, as mentioned above, it is assumed that the marked animals will mix freely and randomly with all other members of the same species of the population being studied. This assumption may be unjustified for a number of reasons. Animals frequently move in groups; thus many fish swim in shoals while baboons go in troops whose members recognize one another and do not mix with members of other troops. Thirdly, it is assumed that the marked animals spread over the whole area occupied by the population, and this assumption may also be unjustified. Many animals have a particular locality or 'home range' out of which they commonly do not move. This is true of many mammals and birds, of certain amphibia and even the limpets of the rocky shores. While the tide is in, limpets move about freely, browsing on algae; but as the tide goes out each limpet returns to its proper 'home' and will remain there until the tide returns. Fourthly, sufficient time must elapse between the first and second samplings to allow the population to mix; clearly the less active the animal the longer the period of time required. During this time, however, the population must remain effectively constant in numbers. There should be no tendency for individuals to leave the population, either to emigrate or to die. If there are losses by either of these means, even if they are balanced by an equal immigration and an equal number of births, some of the marked individuals may have emigrated or died and as a result the number recaptured will be too low.

Despite these limitations, the technique is useful, and in checking to see how far any of the above difficulties limit its application, much of interest may be learnt about the biology of the species being studied.

Two more sophisticated techniques for ascertaining fish stocks deserve brief mention. One, especially applicable in shallow water, depends upon the fact that if a direct electric current is passed through the water, the fishes are attracted to one electrode and on touching this are temporarily stunned. They may then be collected and counted. Such a technique has been used in determining fish populations of rivers; several men with stunning gear move together along a stretch of river so as to allow all fish within a given area to be collected and counted. In lakes stunning gear may be towed behind a boat and the number of fish caught on a standard run counted, but this latter procedure will, of course, provide only relative data. The second technique depends upon the use of echo-sounding (p.103). With modern echo-sounding equipment it is possible not only to locate shoals of fishes, but also to estimate the sizes of the shoals. Standard echo-sounding cruises regularly repeated within some area can provide

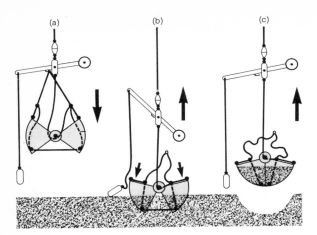

13.8 A grab, showing one pattern of closing mechanism. As the weight strikes the bottom, the arm moves upwards and the two lines holding open the jaws of the grab slip off the hook which holds them. As the grab is pulled up, the jaws will close.

relative data upon changes in the populations of shoaling fishes.

Bottom fauna

Quite different methods have to be used to sample the bottom fauna. The commonest depends upon the use of a grab which is dropped overboard with its jaws apart (Fig. 13.8). On striking the bottom the jaws close and gather up a sample of bottom material. The area enclosed within the jaws of the grab when it reaches the bottom is easily measured and the resulting counts of captured animals can be expressed in terms of some standard unit such as number per m². Clearly the effectiveness of this type of gear will depend upon the physical characteristics of the bottom being sampled. The grab will work excellently upon any soft bottom, but samples taken from stony bottoms may not be satisfactory as the grab may fail to close completely.

Rocky shores

Counting sedentary organisms upon a rocky shore is relatively straightforward. A square of known dimensions is marked out and all the organisms within that area counted. The principle is simple, although difficulties certainly arise, as in dealing with a surface which has deep cracks in which animals may find shelter. If active animals, like crabs, are to be counted, then special techniques may be necessary—for example, the erection of barriers.

Sampling in the sublittoral zone is now commonly done by using diving equipment, while in recent years permanent underwater laboratories have been erected in some places so that continuous observations are possible.

Freshwaters

Sampling within the littoral zone of a lake or pond again requires special methods depending upon the nature of the bottom and the abundance of vegetation. On a stony shore free from plants, it is convenient to enclose some relatively limited area within a frame and then, removing the stones by hand, collect all the attached organisms. At the end of this process the remaining animals which may be active swimmers have to be collected using a small net. Where there are hydrophytes, two distinct problems arise: that of estimating the population of hydrophytes, and that of estimating the numbers of the associated fauna.

Plants such as *Nymphaea* which grow as isolated indi-

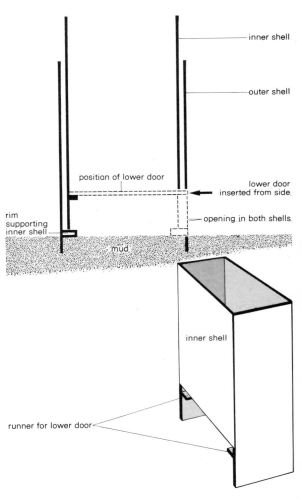

13.9 Gerking sampler for collecting fauna on hydrophytes. The rectangular outer shell is put in position, and the inner frame is inserted. A pair of scissors, pushed through the side opening, is used to cut the stems of the hydrophytes. The lower door is then placed in position and the inner shell withdrawn. A grab is then lowered into the outer shell to obtain a sample of the bottom fauna.

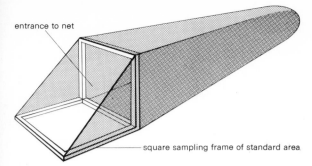

entrance to net

square sampling frame of standard area

13.10 A Surber sampler. The sampler is placed on a stream bed with its opening facing upstream. All material lying within the sampling frame is collected or washed into the net.

viduals present no particular problem: numbers can be counted in random quadrats to obtain the mean density. Many hydrophytes, however, reproduce vegetatively by rhizomes and stolons, and in such cases counts may be made of vertical shoots rather than of individual plants. For many purposes, it is more meaningful to estimate the weight of plants removed from known areas; fresh weight, determined after allowing plants to drain for a fixed length of time, is sometimes satisfactory, but dry weight is less subject to error.

The hydrophytes themselves will support a fauna, while there will be yet more organisms living on and in the bottom beneath the plants. The former may most easily be sampled by placing plant specimens in some large container and then searching the material for animals. Here difficulties arise in the choice of specimens of the plant so as to ensure that a representative and random collection is made, in determining how best to express the resulting data and also in collecting actively swimming organisms like aquatic bugs which may simply be resting upon submerged leaves or roots. Various sampling devices are available to solve these problems; one is illustrated in Fig. 13.9. The bottom itself is best studied by the use of a grab.

In streams collection of data on the abundance of hydrophytes can be undertaken using the same methods as in the littoral zone of a lake. Collection of animals has,

however, to take into account the water movement. One method of sampling the bottom is to use a Surber sampler (Fig. 13.10). This consists of a frame fitted with a bag, which is placed on the downstream side of the frame. Material within the area of the frame is then sampled, any animals dislodged being swept into the bag. Fish populations may be sampled by any of the techniques applicable to still water.

There is one specialized technique which is worth mention; it is used for the estimation of the density in a water body of the infective cercaria larvae of *Schistosoma* (Platyhelminthes: Trematoda). This may be done by lowering into the water a cage containing mice. The cage is fitted with cork or polystyrene floats so that it dips only a few centimetres into the water: in this way the bellies of the mice are submerged and left exposed to possible infection for about three hours. The mice are kept in the laboratory for about two months and then killed. The mesentery between the gut and liver is removed and the hepatic portal vessels inspected for the presence of schistosomes. The intensity of the infestation of the mice or the number of mice showing infection can provide an index of the relative abundance of cercaria larvae.

Terrestrial plants

Population estimation on land will clearly be very different for plants, for small animals like insects and for larger ones like birds or mammals. All methods of estimating the

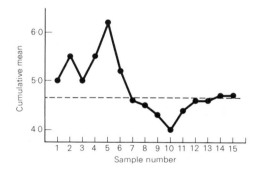

Table 13.1 Illustration of the procedure for determining population density by consecutive sampling of randomly chosen blocks within a larger area. In this example an area 50 × 50 m was subdivided into 5 × 5 m blocks, each given a serial number. The blocks to be sampled were then selected at random and the number of specimens of a particular species of plant present recorded. After each sampling, the cumulative mean (the total number of plants counted divided by the number of plots sampled) was determined. As shown in the graph above the variation in value of the cumulative mean decreases with sample number. Once the cumulative mean is acceptably constant, sampling can cease; in this way the sampling of all 100 blocks can be avoided.

Block number	34	41	17	89	87	4	28	32	13	45	59	3	91	8	69
Number of plants	5	6	4	7	9	0	1	4	3	2	8	7	5	6	4
Cumulative mean	5·0	5·5	5·0	5·5	6·2	5·2	4·6	4·5	4·3	4·0	4·4	4·6	4·6	4·7	4·7

population density of plants depend upon direct counting, but the area over which the count is made will depend upon the size of the plant and its abundance. A very large sample area will have to be used to obtain a meaningful value of the population density for some particular species of tree in a rain forest; a relatively small sample area will suffice where small herbs or grasses are of interest. The principles used to obtain a good estimate are the same in each case, however. Samples should be taken at random within the population which is to be assessed. This may be done by delimiting, either on the ground or on a map, an area of more or less homogeneous vegetation, and dividing this into blocks each of the size of the sample to be used. For large herbs in grassland, an area of 50×50 m might be suitable; this is then divided in one hundred 5×5 m blocks, each of which is assigned a serial number. The blocks to be sampled are then chosen by drawing lots, that is, by writing the numbers 1 to 100 on separate pieces of paper, folding the papers and shaking them in a large tin. Pieces of paper are then picked out at random. A count is made of the plants in the block indicated and the process is then repeated. Clearly it would be wasteful of effort to continue this process until all hundred blocks had been examined. The procedure adopted is to determine, after each sampling, the cumulative mean count and plot this value for successive samples (Table 13.1). As more samples are taken, the values of cumulative means will approach a constant value. Once several successive means of almost equal value have been obtained, sampling can stop.

If it is required to follow changes in population density of a species along an environmental gradient, the procedure described above must be repeated in adjacent areas.

Insects

There is a considerable variety of methods for sampling terrestrial insects. In grassland, they may be collected by sweeping with a heavy net. To collect from trees, a white sheet is spread beneath the tree and the branches beaten with a heavy stick; the insects which are dislodged are then collected and counted. Beating in this way will knock down insects like caterpillars; nevertheless many, like scale insects, may be very firmly attached on leaves or twigs, while others may be sheltering in axillary buds or flowers or in tunnels excavated within the tissues of the leaves. None of these, of course, can be sampled by beating. Depending upon the normal microhabitat of the animal concerned, some special sampling method has to be devised. It may, for example, be relevant to collect a standard number of leaves or of shoot tips from a predetermined number of trees. Not only should the trees be selected in some random fashion, but every effort should be made to collect plant material from different heights and sides of each tree. For certain tree-living insects very indirect methods of assessment of numbers have been used. In woodland, for instance, cloth trays of standard area have

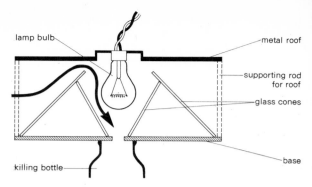

13.11 Diagram showing the principle of a light trap. The roof protects the bulb and killing bottle from rain. The curved arrow shows the path taken by an insect to enter the killing bottle. There are very many designs of light trap, some of which are more selective than others; the pattern illustrated has relatively low selectivity.

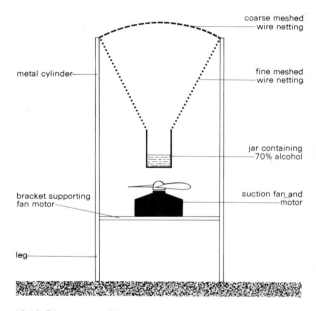

13.12 Diagram to illustrate the principle of one pattern of suction trap. Air is drawn downwards by the suction fan and small insects are caught on the fine-meshed wire and collect in the jar of alcohol.

been set out beneath the trees to catch the falling faecal pellets of caterpillars. These pellets often have characteristic shapes so that changes in the relative abundance of different species may also be assessed. Such a technique has the advantage that the population being studied is not in any way disturbed by the sampling process.

The fact that insects are attracted to light is exploited in the design of various light traps (Fig. 13.11), while small insects such as midges and mosquitoes may be sampled by a trap which sucks in large volumes of air, filtering out any insects which are drawn in with the air stream (Fig. 13.12).

Vessels buried in the ground with their openings just at ground level may be used to collect insects which run on the surface, as they will fall into such a 'pitfall' trap. Another device is a water trap: this is a rectangular trough painted yellow on the inside and filled to a depth of about 5 cm with water containing a little detergent. Such troughs are set out in places where sampling is required and are especially effective in catching small insects such as aphids.

Biting flies

Certain rather special methods deserve mention. One is concerned with estimating the abundance of mosquitoes which bite man. The technique is simple: during the appropriate time of day one or more men sit with bared legs and, using small glass tubes, catch each mosquito which attempts to bite them. A similar method is used to assess the abundance of tsetse fly: a cow is tethered in a locality where it is desired to estimate the density of fly and as flies alight upon the cow, they are caught with small nets and preserved for subsequent inspection. Clearly this technique is limited in so far as each cow has to be attended. An alternative method is to use a trap in place of a cow, and a number of such traps have been developed. Each consists essentially of brown hessian cloth spread over a wooden frame to form a prism-shaped structure (Fig. 13.13). The upper surface is flat and the lower edge open, while on the top is a glass box connecting with the inside. Tsetse flies fly downwards and enter through the bottom slit and then, attracted by the light, they fly into the box. Periodically the boxes are emptied and the catch counted. In a third method, what is called a strip census is taken: that is, the number of individuals of some species observed while walking along a standard path is noted. In tsetse-fly studies this method is commonly called a 'fly round'. A party of three men walk along a path of about 8 km in length cleared through the bush where it is desired to study the population. The path is selected so as to lead through stretches of the various types of vegetation found in the locality. To attract flies two of the party will carry with them a white sheet rather like a placard or a banner in a political demonstration. In one procedure posts are marked every 100 m along the path and at each post the party stops and collects all flies visible in the immediate area. Each sample is preserved separately so that values for the population densities in different vegetational types can be calculated. The results are usually expressed in a somewhat arbitrary unit of the number of male flies which would have been caught along a path of 10 000 m, excluding those flies which are newly emerged and have not yet fed.

The problem of developing satisfactory sampling techniques can be illustrated by the difference in age composition of the female tsetse flies caught by these three methods. By examination of the gonads of females, it is possible to determine how many times each female has ovulated, thus providing a scale of age. Data obtained from a study

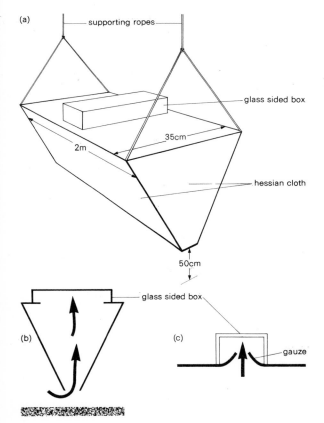

13.13 Diagram showing the construction of a Harris tsetse fly trap. (a) Brown hessian cloth is stretched over a wooden frame to form a prism-shaped structure open at the bottom and carrying a glass-sided box on its upper surface. Ropes suspend the trap from adjacent trees, or a special carrying frame may be used. (b) The trap in section showing the flight path of a fly. (c) Detail of the entry to the box to show the 'valve' arrangement to prevent escape of the flies.

Table 13.2 Percentage of females of the tsetse fly *Glossina pallidipes* **of different age classes caught by three different methods** (*Data from Saunders*)

Method	Age class (Number of ovulations)				
	0	*1*	*2*	*3*	*4+*
Fly round	53	11	14	5	16
Cattle as bait	22	16	9	10	43
Hessian trap	6	16	17	12	49

of the ages of females of *Glossina pallidipes* collected in the same area by the three methods are summarized in Table 13.2, which shows that the modal age of the flies caught by hand on a fly round was in class 0, while those of both the live-bait and trap-caught individuals were in class 4+. This does not necessarily mean that one method is better than another; hand catching may collect a greater proportion of young females than occurs in the population as a whole, while the traps may collect a disproportionate number of older flies. While all three methods can, in principle, provide data on changes in the abundance of flies there is reason to believe that fly rounds, on which have been based many studies of methods of tsetse control, are in fact unsatisfactory as a sampling technique (p. 332).

Locusts and ticks

In assessing the density of locust populations an essentially similar method of strip census is adopted. Counting is limited to adults as these can be forced to fly upwards and are thus easily seen. In one technique several men, spaced evenly 3 m apart, move forwards along the line and each man counts the number of locusts which fly up within 1·5 m on either side. Even spacing is achieved by the use of a marked rope which is carried forwards and kept taut so as to ensure that each man keeps the correct distance from his neighbours. As an alternative, allowing surveys of far greater areas, a motor vehicle, driven slowly along a predetermined path, is used to 'flush' the adults whose numbers are noted by an observer sitting upon the roof. A helicopter flown at a height of about 3 m above ground can be used in place of a vehicle.

Finally, the size of tick populations in grassland can be assessed by a strip census in which the ticks are collected by dragging across the grass a bar to which are attached

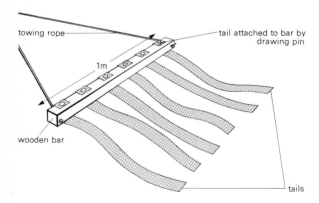

13.14 Diagram showing an arrangement of cloth 'tails' for collecting ticks. Each tail is about 10 × 45 cm and held on the bar by a drawing-pin, so that it may be easily replaced. Single sheets of cloth may also be used, but in rough ground the tails ride the vegetation more closely.

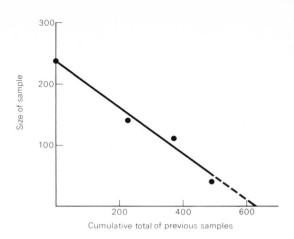

13.15 Graph of results obtained by repeated standard sweeping of the same area. The number of animals collected in any sweep is plotted against the total number of animals collected in previous sweepings. Thus, for example, the number collected in the first sweep is plotted against zero as no previous animals had been collected; the number collected in the second sweep against that collected in the first, the number in the third sweep against the sum of the first and second and so on. By extrapolation the total population can be assessed.

several long strips of flannel cloth (Fig. 13.14). Ticks which are ready to attach to hosts will grip the cloth. The bar is dragged a standard distance and then each tail of cloth is removed from the bar, rolled up and placed in a labelled tube for subsequent examination. Fresh 'tails' are fitted and the process repeated.

Estimates of absolute population size

All these methods are selective in what they catch and none provides data on the absolute size of the population. Where circumstances permit, absolute numbers for some species may be obtained using 'knockdown sampling', for example, by drenching a tree with some insecticide (Book 1 Fig. 1.5). Similarly attempts have been made to determine the true size of locust populations by collecting all locusts within a large number of quadrats following aerial spraying with insecticide. In grassland an estimate of the absolute numbers of certain species may be obtained by an extension of the technique of sweeping. A selected area of known size is swept for a standard time, say five minutes. The animals collected we will call 'sample 1'; their numbers will subsequently be determined. The process is then repeated in the same area to obtain a second sample, sample 2; this will of course have fewer animals in it than sample 1. Third and fourth samples are taken in the same way. After each sample has been counted, either as a whole or by particular species, the numbers taken in each sample are plotted against the total number previously collected

(Fig. 13.15). The points commonly fall on a straight line and by extrapolation it is possible to assess the total population. This method can be used with groups or even species which are very abundant in the sampling area. It will not be of use with relatively rare animals nor, of course, with those which are not effectively sampled with a sweep net, either because they fly or because they are very small. A more direct method, and one especially valuable in studying small insects, is to enclose a standard area of grass and then using a small suction trap arranged rather like a hand-operated vacuum cleaner, draw off all the insects within the selected area.

With many commercial field crops it is possible to estimate the absolute population of relatively inactive insects such as caterpillars or burrowing larvae by collecting and examining whole plants. Knowing the density of planting and the total area under the crop, the total population may be calculated.

When an insect pupates in the ground during a particular season of the year, absolute values of population density may be obtained by using 'emergence traps'. Net-covered frames of standard size are placed at randomly selected points in the area under study and the numbers of adults counted as they emerge (Fig. 13.16). While such a technique can be used to obtain absolute numbers, it is providing data upon only one instar of the life cycle as also does the use of a strip census for estimating locust populations. This may be adequate for many practical purposes, but it is important to bear this limitation in mind.

Tagging for capture—recapture

The Lincoln Index may be used with many insects to determine local population density. In its simplest form, individuals are caught or trapped and then marked with a small spot of paint. It may, however, be necessary to follow short-term changes in some relatively small population, and in this circumstance far more information can be obtained if individual marked specimens can be recognized on recapture. For this purpose dots of paint are placed on different positions on the body, each representing a different numeral. By combining different marks a large number of different individuals can be distinguished (Fig. 13.17).

Terrestrial vertebrates

With large terrestrial vertebrates, methods of determination of population density again vary with the species being considered. With large birds in a restricted habitat, direct counts may be possible. This has been used particularly with sea birds which nest in large colonies on cliff ledges; in other habitats, such as woodland, counting may be assisted by trapping and ringing the birds so that individuals can be recognized. The method of strip census is also used, recording either all sightings or only those of

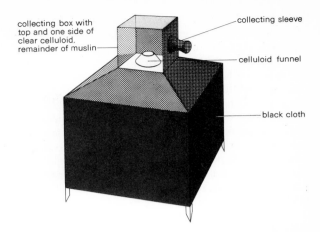

13.16 An 'emergence' trap. The pointed feet are driven into the ground so that any adult insects emerging are trapped; they fly upwards towards the collecting box which is made partly of clear plastic to admit light.

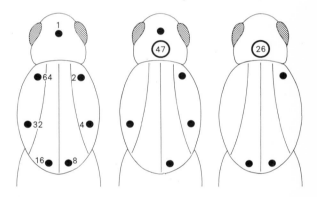

13.17 Scheme for number coding an insect with small dots of paint. The convention is shown on the left and two examples of its use on the right. The maximal possible number of individuals which could be coded in this way is 127. More complex codes using different colours have been used where very large numbers are involved.

singing males, as these are likely to be more easily seen and therefore provide more consistent numerical data. Changes in population density may be studied by using annual nest counts which give data upon the number of breeding pairs.

With small mammals in the wild or in reserves, the Lincoln Index is often applicable. Various methods of tagging are used, such as branding, cutting off one toe or making a small clip in one ear. With larger species metal tags and coloured collars can be employed; collars, when they can be used, have the advantage that individual animals can be recognized without disturbance. In open savanna it is sometimes possible to determine population density by surveying a large area from a light aircraft. With large and relatively rare animals like elephant, it may be possible to count the individuals. Where herds of game are concerned, an experienced observer can judge the numbers in a herd fairly well, but more accurate values can be obtained using aerial photography and counting the numbers of animals to be seen on the photographs. In exceptional circumstances it may be possible to enclose an area and then drive out all game through one narrow gap, counting the number and type of each species leaving the area. Such a 'drive' may also be organized using a large number of people deployed initially in a rectangle. All those on one side now start to move across the area; animals which run out must pass between two people and, as they do so, they are noted and a total count is eventually obtained. Relative numbers are often obtained by strip census, counting the number of individuals seen when moving along some predetermined and standard path, either on foot or in a vehicle. If estimates of absolute numbers are made on several occasions, it may be possible to 'calibrate' this census technique. It should, however, be remembered that some game may be attracted by the clearings of roads and that other species tend to avoid them. Changes in population may also be followed by noting changes in the abundance of fresh droppings observed along a census strip, or in the quantity of food eaten; liberal quantities of food are put out daily at certain points and the quantity consumed noted. This latter method has, of course, many limitations. If it were applied for a long period to a rapidly breeding and very mobile animal such as the black rat, there would be a local build-up of population around the abundant food supply. An indirect method, exploiting the habits of the animal being counted, was used to obtain the data on gerbil abundance shown in Fig. 6.28. Gerbils are nocturnal and live in burrows; if these are lightly blocked during the day, the animals will reopen them at night. Thus a count of the number of reopened burrows gives a measure of the number of animals living within a warren system.

Populations of parasites

Finally, it may be required to measure the population density of parasites. This may involve two different types of question: one concerns the number of individuals parasitized and the other the number of parasites per individual. Where the hosts can be destroyed, direct counting of larger metazoan parasites is possible, more especially as the individuals of any one species are usually limited to a single organ within the host. With blood parasites, the numbers may be determined by examination of blood samples, using a technique essentially similar to that for making a white blood cell count. When the host cannot be destroyed, indirect methods have to be used. The degree of infestation with a gut parasite may be judged by counting the number of eggs found in a sample of faeces. Eggs of some parasites may be separated from other faecal matter by mixing the faeces with a dense salt solution, the eggs being readily collected because they float.

Where rapid estimates of infection rate are required it may be necessary to use some clinical symptom. For example, the incidence of malaria in a human population may be estimated by determining the percentage of children between the ages of 2 and 10 whose spleens are enlarged. The edge of the spleen can be felt by gently pressing on the abdominal wall, and by noting the position of the edge, any abnormal enlargement of the spleen can be detected. The value of such a technique lies in its simplicity compared with the more laborious routine examination of blood smears. The presence of certain metazoan parasites can be detected by injecting just beneath the skin a small volume of saline extract of the parasite being studied; this solution will contain parasitic antigens. If the individual being examined has produced antibodies in response to the presence of the particular parasite, he will display a small local weal or swelling at the site of injection of the antigen. This technique has been developed successfully for certain parasites; it would be particularly valuable for the diagnosis of schistosomiasis, but fully satisfactory methods of preparing specific antigenic extracts have not yet been found.

Clearly there is no simple way of obtaining either absolute or relative estimates of the population density of any organism. Unless the total population can be directly counted, it is essential to use samples and to extrapolate from these if required to the total population. For any sampling method to be satisfactory the samples collected must be taken at random within the area being studied. In relatively uniform conditions, this may appear easy but even in a totally artificial situation, like a large field sown with maize, the population density of some insect pest, if studied in detail, will probably prove to have a different value in the centre from that towards the edges of the plot (Table 13.3). In any natural environment, conditions are likely to be far more heterogeneous than in this example, and the selection of sampling stations is then of great im-

Table 13.3 Population density of animals 5 m from the edge of a field of alfalfa expressed as a percentage of the population density 30 m from the edge. Figures refer to animals found in the plant layer (*After Boness*)

Spiders	165
Mites	165
Hemiptera Heteroptera	480
Aphids	93
Other Hemiptera Homoptera	76
Beetle larvae	280
Adult Diptera	100
Adult Hymenoptera	190

portance in determining the validity of the answer obtained. Almost all sampling methods are to some extent selective, as we have illustrated by the differences in catch composition found in using three different techniques to sample populations of tsetse fly. The final choice of technique will be determined both by the type of question which it is desired to answer and by the particular circumstances in which the sampling is to be done.

Problems

1 You are responsible for the supervision of the fisheries of a large inland lake. Fishing is carried out from canoes by the use of gill nets. It is required to determine changes in 'fishing effort' (weight of fish landed per man day) over a period of several years. What data would you require to estimate the effort? How do you think they might be obtained? Suggest why such data may be of interest.

2 To estimate the size of the population of edible crabs in a lagoon, 400 crabs were trapped, marked and released. After four days 374 crabs were trapped and of these 87 had been previously marked. What was the estimated size of the population?

3 Can you use a gill net to determine fish populations by the Lincoln Index method?

4 Live traps can be used to determine the populations of small mammals in an area, using the Lincoln Index. Suggest one or more patterns of behaviour which might invalidate the use of the method for certain species.

5 An entomologist claimed to be able to assess the population density of tsetse fly by using the Lincoln Index procedure, the flies being collected from a tethered ox and then marked and released; after several days the ox was tethered again and all flies feeding were collected. Among other objections to this proposal, it was claimed that the resulting values would be too high. What was the reasoning behind this contention? What bias would you expect if the 'fly-round' technique were used instead?

6 The following data were obtained in a series of repeated sweeping of a 25 m^2 quadrat. The numbers relate to a single species of grasshopper. What was the population density?

Sweep	1	2	3
Number	103	46	20

7 Explain the assumption underlying the procedure used in graphical determination of total population in the previous problem.

8 Why is the technique of repeated sweeping of no value in determining the population density of species which are rare in the area under study?

9 A zooplankton net of 20 cm diameter at its mouth was hauled vertically through 10 m and then closed. The catch was fixed in formalin and then suspended in 5 l water. A 100 cm^3 sample was removed and the copepods present were counted under a microscope. 143 copepods were found. What is the estimated number of copepods m^{-3} of seawater?

10 A 2 l sample of water was collected from a lake using a closing bottle. Fixative was added and the plankton allowed to settle. The final volume of water after removal of the supernatant liquid was 70 cm^3. A subsample of 0·1 cm^3 was taken and the number of cells of one species of alga counted using an inverted microscope: 246 cells were counted. What was the density of the original sample, expressed as cells cm^{-3}?

11 Water traps described on p. 241 are very effective in catching aphids. Experience has shown that they are most effective if painted yellow, but why this should be so is not known. Explain why a little detergent is added to the water in the trap.

Bibliography

Further reading

Dowdeswell, W. H.	*Practical Animal Ecology*, Methuen, 1963, Chaps. 3, 4, 7, 8, 9 and 10
Sankey, J.	*A Guide to Field Biology*, Longman, 1966, Sections C, D and E
Wickstead, J. H.	*An Introduction to the Study of Tropical Plankton*, Hutchinson, 1965

14 The growth of populations

Population density changes with time

Whether our assessment of population density is relative or absolute, we are able to follow the changes in the numbers of individuals in a population over a period of time. When we do this we find, in keeping with common experience, that the numbers of any one species are fairly constant from year to year. This can be illustrated by data on the mean annual relative density of tsetse fly in a particular locality at Shinyanga in Tanzania extending over a period of 23 years (Fig. 14.1a): numbers change from year to year but never exceed 200 and rarely fall below 20. Shorter-term changes are illustrated in Fig. 14.1b: here too the maximum change is about one order of magnitude. Such relatively stable populations are typical of many species. Although there may be some annual change in abundance, especially if there is a restricted breeding season, nevertheless the numbers of such species do not alter very greatly with time. Other species, especially many insects, may be abundant only for a limited season; during the rest of the year they may be either in a resting stage or else occurring in only very small numbers. When suitable conditions arise, the numbers of such species may build up very rapidly and then fall again quite abruptly. Such a sequence of events can be particularly marked when annual agricultural crops provide suitable food for certain insects for a short period. It is illustrated in Fig. 14.2a for the Cotton Leaf-hopper, *Empoasca* (Hemiptera) (Fig. 14.3). The crop is sown in the Sudan in late August; by October the numbers of the insect increase rapidly to reach a peak in November. If the peak numbers of successive years are plotted we find, as with the tsetse fly, that the value varies from year to year (Fig. 14.2b), but that again the maximum recorded variation is about one order of magnitude.

Observations such as these allow us to formulate various questions. We may ask, for example, what is the maximum rate at which a population might, in some specified conditions, be expected to grow. If we find that field observations show a population to be growing far less quickly than we might expect, the question arises as to what is holding back its growth. We can also ask what factors prevent a population from growing indefinitely, and why the peak population varies from year to year.

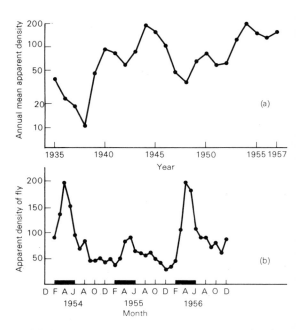

14.1 (a) Change in annual mean 'apparent density' (obtained from fly round data) of the tsetse fly *Glossina swynnertoni* over 23 years. Note that apart from 1937 and 1938 when the population crashed, its numbers remained relatively constant from year to year. The vertical scale is logarithmic. (b) Monthly 'apparent density' of *Glossina palpalis*. Note that each year as indicated by the black bars there is a peak population around April, although the peak was less marked in 1955 than in the other two years.

The rate of growth of a population

Let us start with a simple numerical example. Consider an animal, say an insect, in which each female lays 100 eggs. We will assume that the ratio of males to females in the progeny, the sex ratio, is $1 \cdot 0$. If we start with a single pair, the parental (P) generation, then the next generation, the first filial (F_1) generation, will consist of 100 individuals,

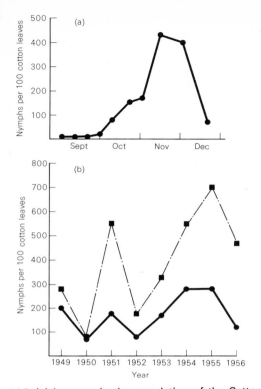

14.2 (a) Increase in the population of the Cotton Leaf-hopper *Empoasca* during one season in the Sudan Gezira. (b) Annual peak density of *Empoasca* on cotton in the southern (full line) and northern (broken line) Gezira; the two districts are separated by about 175 km. Note that while the annual peak populations in the two areas differ in absolute value, the pattern of change from year to year was the same in both localities.

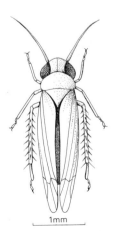

14.3 The Cotton Leaf-hopper, *Empoasca lybica* (Hemiptera).

50 males and 50 females. The 50 females will produce 50×100 eggs, so that the second filial (F_2) generation will be 5 000 individuals, the third filial (F_3) generation $2\,500 \times 100$ individuals and so on. The ratio of the number of individuals in one generation to that in the one before is always 50; that is, it is a constant. It is also true, because of the assumption we made about the sex ratio, that the number of females in one generation will be 50 times that in the previous generation. This ratio of the numbers of females in successive generations we call the 'net reproductive rate' (R_0).

Let us now generalize this idea. If there are N_0 females in the P generation, then there will be $R_0 N_0$ females in the F_1 generation, $(R_0 N_0)R_0$ or $R_0^2 N_0$ in the F_2 generation, $(R_0^2 N_0)R_0$ or $R_0^3 N_0$ in the F_3 generation and so on. In the qth filial generation, the number of females will be $R_0^q . N_0$; so we can write

$$N_q = R_0^q . N_0$$

Note that if the sex ratio is unity, this formula will tell us what is the total number of the qth population, provided we use the total parental population as the value of N_0.

The value of R_0 will, of course be very different in different species of organism. For many marine animals with planktonic larvae, the theoretical value of R_0 may be a million or more; for some mammals the value may be 20 or less.

Such a treatment is satisfactory if we are dealing with an organism in which the duration of the reproductive period of the females is short in relation to the total duration of each successive generation; the population would indeed increase in a series of abrupt steps. Many populations consist, however, of individuals of all ages, so that reproduction may be taking place at any time or, if there is a limited reproductive season, only a fraction of the population will reproduce. Such variations can be treated mathematically and we could build up a series of special equations. There is one very general case which is worth further study.

For simplicity we will assume that all individuals can reproduce; this would be true for example of some aphids (Fig. 12.2) whose populations can at times consist of parthenogenetic females only. We will further assume that each individual has the same reproductive potential. At any time the number of new individuals being added to the population will be some fraction, b, of the total population N, that is $b \times N$ (or $b.N$). We will also assume that all individuals have the same life span so that loss from the population due to death can be expressed as $d \times N$ (or $d.N$) since at any one time a constant fraction, d, of the population will be dying.

With these simplifying assumptions, we can write

rate of change of population numbers (dN/dt)
$$= b.N - d.N \quad \mathbf{14.1}$$
$$= (b-d)N$$

It is obvious that the size of the population will increase if $b > d$, be constant if $b = d$ and decrease if $b < d$.

The 'intrinsic rate of increase'

For constant conditions we can replace $(b-d)$ by a constant, r, which is spoken of as the 'intrinsic rate of increase' of the population. So that

rate of change of population numbers $(dN/dt) = r \cdot N$

Provided r is positive, the population will increase and will increase more rapidly as time goes on. We can calculate the size of this population at any time by 'solving' this differential equation. This tells us that

$$N_t = N_0 e^{rt}$$

where N_0 is the initial population, e the exponential function, $2 \cdot 718$, and N_t the population after a time t.

Thus, for example, if we know that the population of weevils in a maize store is 1 000 today and that the value of r is 0·01 per day, we can compute that the population will be

$1\,000 \times e^{0 \cdot 01 \times 30}$ after one month,
$1\,000 \times e^{0 \cdot 01 \times 60}$ after two months,
and $\quad 1\,000 \times e^{0 \cdot 01 \times 180}$ after six months.

The same method of computation can be used for bacteria, unicellular algae, Protozoa and man.

The quantity r has been here defined with a number of simplifying assumptions. We may ask two questions: do any populations actually grow in this manner? and secondly, is there any practical value in being able to determine r or R_0 for particular species?

We might reasonably expect a population to grow in the exponential manner implied by this relation in conditions where there is an abundant food supply for a primary consumer. Such conditions are likely to prevail during the time of the establishment of a pest infestation upon a young crop and also where there is bulk storage of material like maize. It is easy to test whether the observed growth is in keeping with the equation since we can write

$$\log N_t = \log N_0 + rt \log e$$

which is a straight-line relation. Thus if we plot $\log N$ against time, we shall obtain a straight line if the growth of the population is in keeping with the law; the slope of the line will be proportional to r.

Characteristics of the intrinsic rate of increase

Fig. 14.4a and b shows two such examples. The first relates to the initial growth of a population of *Empoasca* upon cotton in the Sudan: clearly, during this period of about eight weeks the population was growing exponentially. The second presents data for the increase in numbers of a small beetle, *Lasioderma*, in bagged cocoa in Ghana: while between November and March the exponential rate of increase of the population was constant, it subsequently increased. How are we to interpret such an observation? It shows that the value of r is not always constant for any

particular species; rather it will vary with environmental conditions. Temperature is one factor likely to influence its value. For example, the value of r for the Cotton Stainer, *Dysdercus* (Hemiptera) (Fig. 9.34), was found to be 0·26 per week at 20°C and 0·92 per week at 30°C. An increase of r with temperature is to be expected, since the duration of the juvenile stages will be shorter and the insects will therefore reach sexual maturity sooner. In this case there were additional effects: far more adult females laid eggs at the higher temperature and the number of eggs each female laid was greater. Both of these are equivalent to an increase in the value of b in equation 14.1

The action of a different type of environmental factor on r can be illustrated by determinations of its value for one of the snail vectors of *Schistosoma* when it is grown at

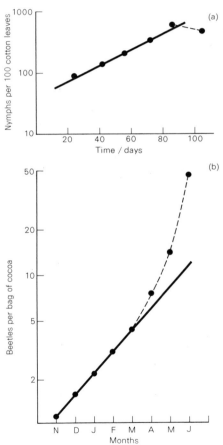

14.4 (a) Increase in infestation of *Empoasca* on cotton plants at a station in the Sudan Gezira, showing an exponential growth of the population up to the peak. (b) Increase in infestation of the beetle *Lasioderma* in bagged cocoa in central Ghana. Note that although the population increases initially with a constant value of r, in the later months of the infestation the value of r increases.

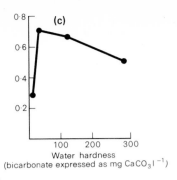

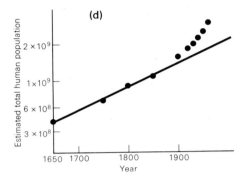

14.4 (continued) (c) Effect of water hardness on the value of r at 25°C for the snail *Biomphalaria* (Fig. 18.3), a vector of *Schistosoma*. (d) Increase in estimated total human population since 1650. The older the values before 1900 the more uncertain they are; estimated values for 1650 differ by nearly 100×10^6. Whether high or low values for this date are used, they make little change in the general trend of population growth.

constant temperature but in waters of different 'hardness'. The value of r was found to be low in soft water and greater in hard water but to be maximum in water of medium hardness (Fig. 14.4c). These differences arise because in soft water, although the rate of egg laying is high, the adults survive for only a short time so that the total contribution of any individual to population increase is small. In hard water, on the other hand, the snails live well but their rate of egg laying is approximately halved, so that r is less than in water of medium hardness. In the example shown in Fig. 14.4b, it seems reasonable to suppose that during the later months of the year some environmental changes occurred which resulted in an increase in the value of r and thus the growth of the population did not continue to follow a simple exponential law.

Fig. 14.4d shows similar data for the estimated total human population. The estimates suggest that while r was probably approximately constant until about 1850, it has started to increase in the last hundred years and, furthermore, its rate of increase is rising. The most recent data are, of course, the most reliable; the trend they show has led many to worry about a 'population explosion'. We shall return to consider this matter later (p. 354ff).

One advantage of the parameter r is that it summarizes in a single value the resultant effect of a wide range of different factors. But of what practical use are determinations of its values? An obvious application arises in dealing with problems of storage of food materials. It is possible to assess approximately how much damage to stored food will be done by insects and thus by different population densities of insects. From knowledge of the values of r in different environmental conditions and of the conditions in the place of storage, it is possible to make some estimate of the maximum time for which material can be stored without suffering unacceptably high levels of damage. Again we may find from our study of r that the population growth of some stored-products pests is very markedly affected by relatively small changes in temperature or humidity or maybe the water content of the food material. It may then be possible to make recommendations about the manner in which the material should be stored so as to reduce the rate of population growth as much as possible. Moreover, it can happen that material is stored for some relatively short period, after which the store is emptied and fresh material introduced. During the first storage period the pest population grows and when the store is emptied, some individuals will be left behind. This will be the population N_0 for the next development of infestation. If we know sufficient about the rate of population growth, as well as the extent and therefore the economic cost of the likely damage, we can assess whether or not it will be economically profitable to clean out the store with chemical fumigants before the second supply of food is introduced. For similar reasons much work has been done to determine what environmental factors affect the intrinsic rate of increase of the vector snails of *Schistosoma*; this can be of value in determining whether, at any particular time of year, intensive snail-destruction measures may be required.

In other circumstances, it may be useful to know how breeding can be increased rather than reduced. One of the newer methods of insect control requires the artificial breeding of large populations of a pest; these are then sterilized chemically and released (p. 311). To determine the economic practicality of such a procedure, it is essential to know the likely yield of individuals from a breeding colony. Comparisons of the value of r in different breeding conditions are then of great importance in assessing what would be the minimum cost of breeding the required numbers of insects for sterilization. With such information one can compare the cost of this method with other possible methods of pest control.

The characteristics of mortality

If equation 14.1 represents the condition in a natural population, the population will continue to grow indefinitely provided b is greater than d. But we know from experience that, with the exception of man, populations do not go on growing indefinitely. Eventually the value of d increases, so that the population is held in check. To understand the factors which affect the sizes of populations, we must therefore examine the causes of death in a population, that is, mortality.

Survivorship curves

As a first step in the study of the causes of death, we can examine how the chances of dying vary with age. To do this we consider a typical population of 1000 individuals at the time of their birth and plot the number which have survived at different times thereafter. This is spoken of as a 'survivorship curve'. The data may be plotted in two ways: commonly the logarithm of the number of survivors is plotted against time, but actual numbers can be plotted against time instead. To make comparisons easier, the values of time on the horizontal scale are given in terms of percentages of the maximum life span. In this way we eliminate the difficulty that the life span of some animals may perhaps be only 30 days, of others 30 years.

Construction of survivorship curves

How can we construct such curves? With laboratory populations this is not difficult as a sample of individuals all of the same age can be readily obtained and their mortality pattern followed. For example, using an insect which lives on grain or maize it is relatively simple to collect 1000 eggs and then to follow how many of these hatch, how many die at different larval instars and so on. Many data of this type are available but they tell us little of what may occur in natural populations in the field.

The construction of survivorship curves for birds and mammals requires the marking of the young in such a way that we can identify the members of the sample being studied; we have already discussed various techniques by which individual animals may be recognized' (p. 243). A census of the population is then taken at intervals. Relatively few such studies have been made owing to the practical difficulties of the procedure.

If, however, there is reason to believe that the rate of birth per annum is nearly constant and there is no significant immigration into or emigration from the population, then a graph showing the age composition of the population will be equivalent to a survivorship curve. Such conditions are approximately fulfilled by wildebeest (Fig. 6.16) in Kenya. Fig. 14.5 shows the distribution by age of the population shortly after the young have been born: clearly there is heavy infantile mortality and subsequently a steady loss of adults, a few animals surviving for as long as sixteen years. The same technique can be used to determine the survivorship of some forest tree. If it is assumed that trunk diameter is approximately proportion-

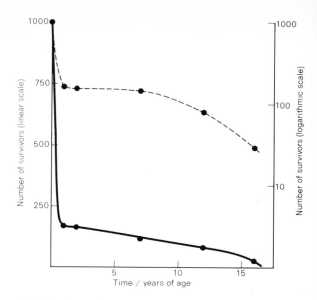

14.5 Survivorship curve of male wildebeest. Note that both a linear and a logarithmic scale have been used. Logarithmic scale – broken line; linear scale – full line.

al to age, then by measuring a large sample of the population, including the young saplings, a survivorship curve can be obtained.

Methods of determining age of animals

Such an approach to the study of the pattern of mortality requires a knowledge of the ages of the animals sampled from the total population; if possible, sampling should not involve the killing of the animals. In the investigation of age distribution in the wildebeest population, some animals were shot for other studies in connection with reproductive physiology, but many were temporarily anaesthetized by shooting at them a dart rather than a bullet. The dart is constructed so as to act as a hypodermic syringe which injects an anaesthetic as it strikes the animal (Fig. 14.6). This allows inspection as well as marking of individual animals which are then brought round by a further injection which antagonizes the anaesthetic; the individuals can then return to the herd.

There is a wide variety of methods by which the age of animals may be determined. With insects, where one instar can frequently be distinguished structurally from another, information is needed about the duration of the different instars in the prevailing environmental conditions, of which temperature is particularly important. With mammals a knowledge of the weight or height of a juvenile may be of value, provided data on how these change with age is available, but once the animals are full grown, this method has no value. The sequence of loss of milk dentition and

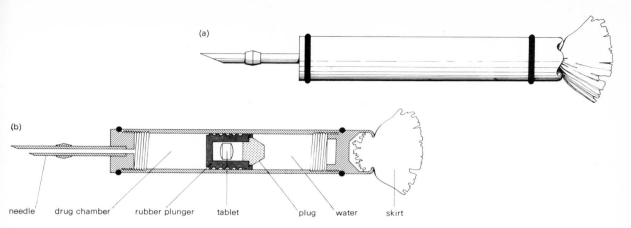

needle   drug chamber   rubber plunger   tablet   plug   water   skirt

14.6 Detail showing the principle of action of a hypodermic dart used to immobilize wild game for inspection. The dart is discharged by gas pressure from a special rifle. The initial movement dislodges the plug. As the dart strikes its target, water in the rear compartment is carried forward by inertia and reacts with the tablet to cause an evolution of gas. This drives the rubber plunger forwards so that the contents of the drug chamber are driven out through the needle. The gun can be used up to a range of about 50 m.

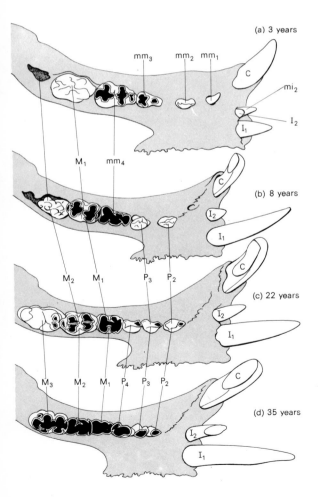

14.7 (left) Changes in the cheek teeth patterns of the lower jaw of *Hippopotamus* with age. Only the left side of the jaw is shown. (a) 3 years old. The second 'milk' incisor (mi_2) has not yet been shed and all four milk molars (mm_{1-4}) are still present. Cheek tooth 5 (M_1), a true molar, has erupted, but not 6 (M_2) although its cavity or alveolus has opened in the bone. (b) 8 years old. The canine is worn; milk molars 1 to 3 have been lost and the last two replaced by permanent cheek teeth, the premolars (P_2 and P_3). Note that the surface of mm_4 and M_1 are now worn down. (c) 22 years old. The second incisor is more fully erupted; mm_4 has been replaced by P_4; all three premolars are showing wear; the wear on M_1 is much greater, M_2 is showing signs of wear, as is M_3 which has started to erupt. (d) 35 years old. I_2 is worn; P_{2-4} are now heavily worn down as are M_{1-3}.
Note that the scales of these drawings are not the same: M_1 is typically about 4–5 cm long.

the effects of wear upon the crown pattern of the cheek teeth (Fig. 14.7) may also assist. Here again, data from individuals of known age must first be obtained.

Determining the age of fishes is a matter of very considerable practical importance and, in favourable conditions, this can be done by an examination of scales. Since, unlike birds and mammals, fishes grow continuously throughout their lives, their scales increase in size as the fishes grow older. Moreover they are not uniform in composition; two distinct types of material are laid down in a regular sequence, and as a result scales have a banded appearance when seen under the microscope. This process of deposition of alternating layers of material continues almost independently of environmental conditions, but the rate of growth of fishes and of their scales depends upon the quantity of food they eat. If the fish are growing rapidly, the bands are well separated; if for any reason the

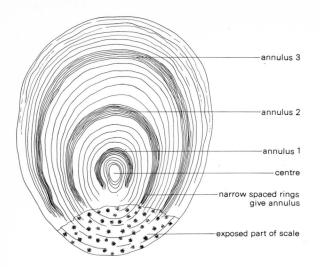

annulus 3

annulus 2

annulus 1

centre

narrow spaced rings
give annulus

exposed part of scale

14.8 Drawing of a fish scale to show the spacings of
rings which crowd together during periods of relatively
poor growth to form annuli.

fish are growing slowly the bands are close together, forming a distinct 'annulus' (Fig. 14.8).

In temperate conditions fish normally have a fairly
restricted spawning season and during this period there is
a slowing down of growth so that an annulus is laid down.
The age of an individual fish may then be assessed by
counting the number of annuli to be seen on a scale. In
tropical waters this method is not readily applicable,
partly because in many species there is no marked seasonal
pattern of spawning; nevertheless trout which were introduced from Great Britain into the cool mountain streams of
Kenya and South Africa do show scale annuli which are
believed to correlate with spawning. In other species the
formation of distinct annuli has been attributed to changes
in environmental temperature which may also be expected
to affect growth rate. If annuli are present in a tropical
fish, they are usually ill defined and there is a possibility
that two or more may be formed in a year. Until the
reasons for the formation of annuli are known for any
particular fish species, they cannot be used as a method of
absolute ageing; they may however give information upon
the relative ages of different specimens. The lenses of the
eyes of fishes can also be used in this way; so too can con-
cretions found within the ears, called 'otoliths'. Both lenses
and otoliths when examined in section can show annuli
and in certain cases these are more easily interpreted than
those on scales. In some species growth rings in the spines
of the pectoral fins have been found to provide the best
material for analysis.

Patterns of survivorship

We may now consider survivorship curves themselves in
greater detail, starting by examining the shapes of curves

which can arise if we make different assumptions about the
pattern of mortality. We might, for example, assume that
there is no mortality for the greater part of the life span,
but that when the population reaches a critical age, individuals start to die from old age. This clearly is an unnatural assumption: in all populations some individuals
will die before reaching old age, owing to accidents of one
sort or another. Fig. 14.9a represents a second possible
pattern in which there is a constant accident rate throughout life until the changes associated with old age or
senescence become important. In this example the accident
rate is low, so that the rate of fall in numbers is relatively

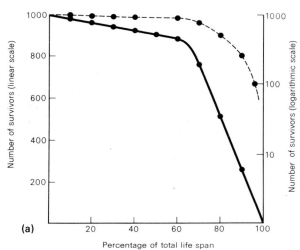

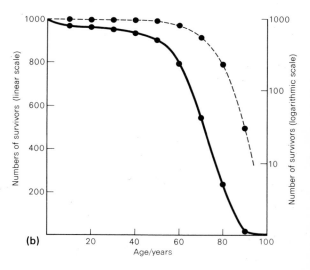

14.9 (a) Hypothetical survivorship curve constructed on
the assumption that the population decreases initially
at the rate of 2 percent for every 10 percent of the
total life span until 60 percent of the span has been
completed. (b) Survivorship curve of males in England
and Wales in 1961. Logarithmic scale – broken line;
linear scale – full line.

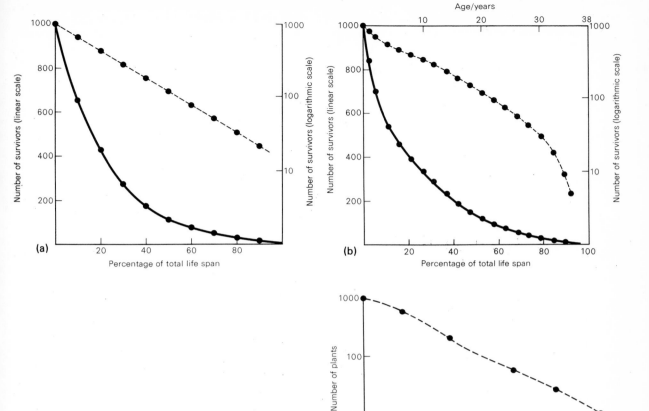

14.10 (a) Hypothetical survivorship curve constructed on the assumption that the population decreases regularly at the rate of 35 percent for every 10 percent of the total life span. (b) Survivorship curve of the black rhinoceros in East Africa. (c) Survivorship curve for the annual plant *Erigeron*. Logarithmic scale – broken line; linear scale – full line.

slight until the onset of senescence. The upper curve, which is a logarithmic plot, is linear until about 60 percent of the life span has been passed. This sort of relation is found in human populations in those developed countries which have efficient health services; Fig. 14.9b is an example based on data from Great Britain for 1961. It reflects an artificial situation and is unlikely to be met in the wild.

Fig. 14.10a has been drawn assuming the same basic pattern, but in this case a far higher accident rate. As a result the population is already quite small before changes due to senescence become significant. Survivorship curves such as these occur in natural conditions among animals which are almost immune to predation. Fig. 14.10b shows the survivorship curve for the Black Rhinoceros, *Diceros bicornis*; a similar curve for the temperate herb *Erigeron canadensis* is shown in Fig. 14.10c. Here too there is evidence of an almost constant rate of loss from the population.

The value of plotting survivorship curves upon a logarithmic scale is shown by a comparison of Figs. 14.10a and 14.10b. If you examine the lower curve of each graph in which the data are plotted on a linear scale, you will see no marked difference between them. The logarithmic plots are, however, very different: that in Fig. 14.10a, in which the rate of decrease of the population is constant, is a straight line; that in Fig. 14.10b shows that there are marked changes in the rate of decrease of the population at different ages. Plotting data in this manner may thus serve to emphasize changes in the pattern of mortality with age which may not be clearly shown by plotting the data on a linear scale.

Finally, there is a pattern of survivorship curve which relates to species in which there is very extensive destruction of individuals in the first period of life. This is true of many marine animals with planktonic larvae. Thus, for example, it has been estimated that each female of one species of barnacle produces 130 000 early planktonic larvae, but that only 26, that is 0·02 percent, survive to settle on a rocky surface. Such a pattern of survivorship will produce a curve like that in Fig. 14.11a. This type of curve is by no means unique to animals with planktonic larvae. Fig. 14.11b shows the survivorship curve for a trout, and this is broadly similar to that for the wildebeest (Fig. 14.5). Fig. 14.11b shows a further advantage which can arise from plotting survival data on a logarithmic

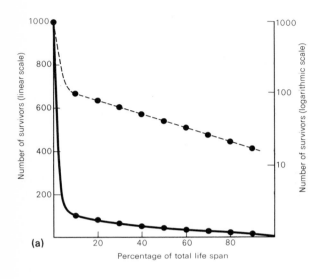

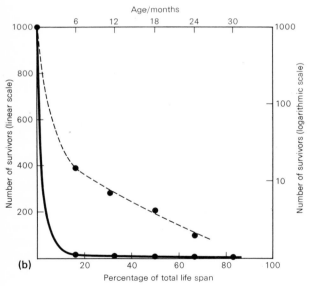

(a)

Age/months

(b)

14.11 (a) Hypothetical survivorship curve computed on the assumption that only 10 percent of the initial population survive after the first 10 percent of the life span and that the remaining population is reduced thereafter at a rate of 20 percent for each 10 percent of life span. (b) Survivorship curve for trout in a stream. Logarithmic scale – broken line; linear scale – full line.

scale. The relatively few survivors after the first six months of life render the graph plotted on a linear scale quite useless; the data when plotted on a logarithmic scale suggest that after this critical period there is an almost constant rate of mortality in this species.

Causes of mortality

Examination of survivorship curves tells us the general pattern of mortality within a population. It may be possible to recognize further that mortality rates are different at different periods of life and we may wish to enquire why this should be so. Just as the intrinsic rate of increase, r, summarizes in a single quantity the total effect on population growth of a wide variety of different phenomena, so too a survivorship curve tells us only about the resultant effect of many different events. We must turn to a detailed analysis of particular cases if we are to carry our enquiry into mortality further.

We will take as an example the factors which lead to mortality among wildebeest, as these have been fairly closely studied. There is a heavy loss of newborn calves especially during the first fortnight of life, due partly to predation by hyaenas, partly to starvation if the calf should lose its mother in the herd: the greater the size of the herd, the more likely is this latter event. As a result some 40 percent of the calves die in the first few months of life. Later in the year there is a second major loss of young due to an epidemic disease, possibly a mild form of rinderpest. This further reduces numbers, so that at the end of their first year less than 40 percent of the calves remain and these form about 15 to 20 percent of the whole herd. Thereafter loss is chiefly due to predation, lion being responsible for about 90 percent of the kill. Such loss will, of course, be largely determined by the number of lion. But losses are also influenced by weather conditions. When there have been good rains, the herds scatter and there is better survival of young since herd size is smaller. If there is drought, the herds aggregate; this tends to increase the losses of young calves and can also lead to the death of adults by more frequent accidents, especially near possible sources of water.

Density-dependent and density-independent mortality

You will see that in wildebeest there are two very different types of event which can lead to mortality. One is essentially haphazard in operation, stemming from the weather in the form of drought or late arrival of rains. The effect of the other is closely related to the size of the herd at any one time; the extent of the mortality increases as the population density increases. Mortality factors with such a relation to population size are spoken of as being 'density-dependent factors'; those which act at random, resulting in the death of some animals in a fashion unrelated to population density are called 'density-independent'. These two categories are not, however, as clear-cut as this description might suggest. While loss of wildebeest calves is dependent upon herd size, herd size is itself influenced by the rains and the rains vary independently of population density. Thus, from year to year, calf mortality will be related to rainfall, so that at one level of analysis it is density-independent, while at the same time the more immediate cause of mortality, herd size, is exercising a density-dependent effect. Nevertheless the distinction has value since the action of density-dependent factors is open to further analysis.

The action of density-dependent mortality factors

We can reassess the possible pattern of population growth introducing the idea of a density-dependent mortality. Increase in the population will, as in equation 14.1, still be a function of the density of the population but mortality rate, previously treated as a constant d, will now increase in some fashion as the population grows. For simplicity's sake, let us assume that it increases linearly with increasing population; thus, the mortality rate will be $d \times N$ (or $d.N$). As in equation 14.1, the actual number of deaths is also proportional to the size of the population and will thus be equal to $d.N \times N$ or $d.N^2$.

We can then write:

rate of change of population numbers $(dN/dt) =$
$$b.N - d.N^2 = (b - d.N)N$$

The effect of this upon the growth of the population is shown in Fig. 14.12. One curve is constructed using our original exponential expression (14.1)

rate of change of population numbers $(dN/dt) =$
$$(b - d)N$$

and the other using the new assumption, namely

rate of change of population numbers $(dN/dt) =$
$$(b - d.N)N$$

The grey area emphasizes the increasing difference in size of the two types of population as they grow. You will notice that the new curve is S-shaped; it is often spoken of as a 'sigmoid curve' and sometimes as a 'logistic curve'.

This new equation describes what might occur when, say, a new crop is invaded by an insect. As the population starts to grow, predators become increasingly effective, since the chance of a predator encountering its prey becomes greater; the predators will therefore remove an increasing percentage of the population. If the numbers of predators remain effectively constant, the numbers of the prey will become stable at some particular level. Such a situation will arise when the mean time from birth to reproduction, the mean generation time, of the predator is very long compared with that of the prey. Vertebrate predators of

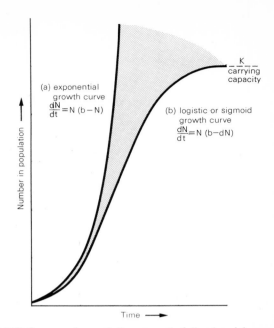

14.12 Curves of population growth following (a) exponential and (b) logistic rules of growth. The logistic curve reaches an asymptotic value referred to as the 'carrying capacity', K.

insects, such as some birds and lizards, fall into this category. If, however, the predator has a short mean generation time, then the abundance of food for the predator may result in an increase in its population: the pressure exerted on the prey increases and the situation is no longer stable. In the next chapter we will examine the possible consequences of such an event.

Types of density-dependent factors

We have so far discussed the action of predation as a density-dependent factor, but there may be other density-dependent causes of mortality. One of the most obvious is food supply. If this is constant then, should the population increase above a certain level, there will be insufficient food and numbers may fall either directly as a result of starvation (Fig. 14.13a) or indirectly as a result of a decrease in reproductive rate or, in the case of birds and mammals, of an inability to feed the young (Fig. 14.13b).

The asymptote of a logistic curve, that is the value to which it eventually tends, can be considered in this context of food supply. Its value is the maximum population size which can be supported by the available food resource. For this reason the value of the asymptote is often spoken of as the 'carrying capacity' (K) of some habitat for a particular species of consumer. This will apply equally to primary and higher-order consumers, since the concept is independent of the nature of the food supply.

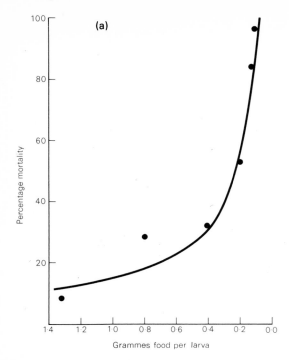

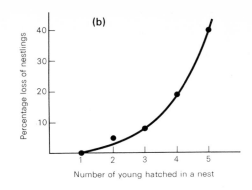

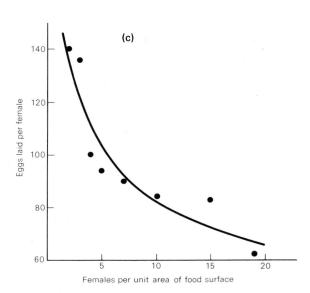

14.13 (a) Mortality in cultures of the Meal Moth, *Plodia*, which can be a pest of stored maize. Note the way in which percentage mortality rises sharply as the available food per larva decreases. (b) Mortality of nestlings of *Quelea*. Note that the losses increase as the number of young in the nest increases. Such losses are due directly to starvation. (c) Number of eggs laid per female of the Meal Moth at different densities. Note that each female lays about half as many eggs in crowded conditions. A further effect on oviposition potential is that crowding of larvae leads to the production of stunted females which lay fewer eggs.

Further, this limit may not be set by food supply. Some other limited resource of the habitat, such as shelter, may determine the value of *K*, as may the action of predators.

If population numbers increase above *K*, then mortality will increase and numbers will fall; if it falls below *K*, mortality will decrease and numbers will rise. Note that we are dealing with an equilibrium condition and we would not expect the population numbers constantly to equal *K*, but rather that they will vary or oscillate around *K* as a mean value. The frequency and magnitude of these oscillations will depend in a complex fashion upon the interaction between the reproductive potential of the species and the mode of action of the density-dependent factor. The fact that the action of density-dependent factors leads not to a stable population, but to one whose density varies around a mean, is expressed by describing their effects as 'regulating' population density.

As we have already indicated natality can also be affected by population density; if the reproductive rate falls as population density rises, we shall have the same effect as when the mortality rises with increasing numbers. We might rewrite equation 14.1 in a form such as

rate of increase in population numbers $(\mathrm{d}N/\mathrm{d}t) =$
$$(b/N - d)N$$

This will result in the rate decreasing as *N* increases; it becomes zero when $b = d.N$.

Population density can affect reproductive success by mechanisms which vary with different species (Fig. 14.13c). In the fruit fly *Drosophila*, oviposition rate falls at high population densities partly because the females are disturbed while ovipositing. In the flour beetle *Tribolium* (Fig. 14.14), the adults will eat eggs so that the number which survive depends upon population density. The consequence of this is shown in Fig. 14.15; the irregular oscillations of population numbers around a mean reflect the regulatory action of this behaviour. Very different effects are to be found in mammals. Fig. 14.16a shows results obtained from a laboratory colony of mice given

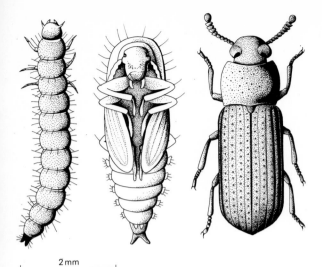

2 mm

14.14 Larva, pupa and adult of the flour beetle, *Tribolium.*

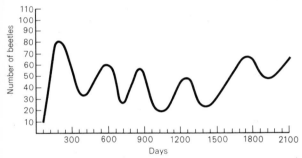

14.15 Population density of a culture of the beetle *Tribolium* followed over a period of six years. The oscillations are due to the habit of the adults of eating any eggs they may encounter.

14.16 (right) (a) Changes in the numbers of a penned population of mice. After 74 weeks the population was allowed access to a second pen and reproductive activity recommenced. (After Crowcroft). (b) The effect of population density on mean litter size per female, based on data obtained from four growing colonies of wild mice maintained with abundant food and shelter in indoor pens. Note that the mean litter size fell with increasing population density: this effect could be due either to a reduction in the number of breeding females or to a reduction in the number of young born to each female. Other data indicate that the former was the more important factor in reducing mean litter size. (c) Effect of population density of elephant on the age of puberty of females (After Hanks and McIntosh).

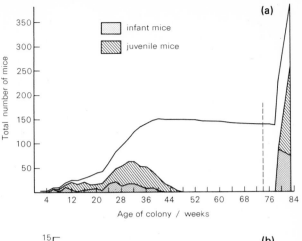

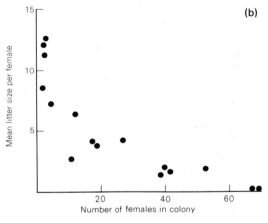

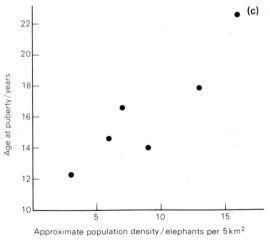

adequate shelter and abundant food: after about 42 weeks all reproduction ceased, but resumed again when the colony was allowed to expand into a second pen. Low reproductive success in this instance stemmed partly from a decrease both in the proportion of females which produced litters and in the number of young in a litter (Fig. 14.16b). In crowded conditions, the number of young successfully weaned may also fall, or all may die before they are weaned. In the wild, small rodent populations may show marked oscillations in density; it remains uncertain, however, how far this is attributable to direct effects upon reproductive success. Such effects of popula-

257

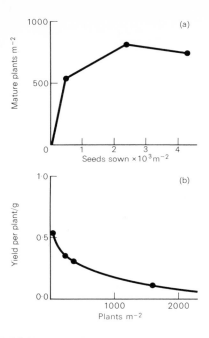

14.17 (a) Number of poppy plants, *Papaver rhoeas*, maturing in plots sown with different densities of seed. (After Harper). (b) Yield, in g dry weight per plant, of clover sown at different densities and harvested after 19 weeks.

tion density on reproduction are not limited to small mammals; they are observed also in the elephant. The length of the reproductive life of females is shorter when the population density is high, while the age at which the females become sexually mature is greater (Fig. 14.16c) and the mean time interval between births grows longer. All these effects will reduce the rate of growth of herds.

Other types of density-dependent regulation can be readily appreciated. An excessively high population of a small herbivore may destroy the shelters within its habitat and thus make it more liable to predation; frequent contact between individuals may result in the rapid spread of some disease, and, at least in some mammals, high numbers can result in abnormally violent fighting, leading to death. Less obvious effects of population density have also been found. For example, crowding of tadpoles results in retarded growth and commonly failure to metamorphose despite the presence of abundant food: there is some evidence that this is due to a material released into the water by the tadpoles.

Density-dependent factors will also control the size of plant populations. Fig. 14.17a shows the number of poppy plants successfully reaching maturity in pure stands sown at different seed densities; it appears probable that the size of the population was being regulated by a fungal infection, which will spread more easily among seeds or

seedlings at high density. In other species the regulating factor may be competition between the individuals for light; faster-growing individuals will shade out others. Alternatively growth may be checked so that the quantity of new tissue formed by each plant falls as population density increases (Fig. 14.17b).

In certain special circumstances a high density of seeds may result in an increase in the proportion which form seedlings, for example, when a hard layer forms on the soil surface which must be broken for the seedlings to emerge. This may sometimes be achieved by the collective action of many germinating seeds while an isolated individual is unable to break the soil cover and will die.

A final example of the consequences of the operation of a density-dependent factor is the migratory behaviour shown by some species when population densities become high. As a result of the migration, the density falls locally. For instance, the Red Locust, *Nomadacris*, occurs as a solitary grasshopper in parts of Tanzania, and intensive study has failed to detect any density-dependent factors which significantly check the growth of its population in these areas. Since it is from these places that swarms arise, they are spoken of as 'outbreak areas'. When the population density of the solitary forms becomes great, their behaviour and also their appearance change. The nymphs or hoppers aggregate into bands and when they become adult vast numbers will fly away in swarms, so that the population density within the outbreak area is sharply reduced.

It should not, however, be assumed that all migrations are direct responses to high population densities. Clearly short-distance migrations of colonies of *Dorylus* are connected with ensuring an adequate food supply (p. 197). If the colony did not move, supply of food would certainly become a density-dependent regulating factor. The migration is not itself a direct response to population density as it is with *Nomadacris*, nor, probably, are those of the weaver bird *Quelea* and the army worm *Spodoptera*, which is in reality a moth (Fig. 14.18). The migrations of both of these animals appear to be immediately controlled

1cm

14.18 The adult of the Army worm, *Spodoptera*. There are several species of which only one is migratory.

by factors other than population density. This applies also to the annual movements of migrant birds, both between Eurasia and Africa and within Africa. Such movements are certainly related to the food supply, but the migrations themselves depend for their timing upon changes in hormonal balance in the birds and there is no evidence, at least at present, that these endocrine changes are affected by population density.

A very different method of population regulation is particularly well marked in many species of bird: this is the establishment of a breeding territory (Fig. 2.29). Frequently at the onset of the breeding season, each male bird will select some area which is within the bounds of a locality suitable for nesting. Here he will sing and attempt to attract a female, and he will defend this area by fighting with other males of his own species. Such 'fighting' is commonly limited to threat displays and stereotyped forms of combat. The nearer a bird is to the centre of its selected territory, the more violent its threat while further away the threat becomes less intense. In this way the locality becomes divided up into distinct territories. If the population of breeding birds is low, the size of each individual territory may be considerable; if the population is high, then the territories are smaller, but there is a lower limit to the size of the territories for any species. If there are more potential breeding males than possible territories available within the locality, some of the males fail to breed as they cannot establish nesting sites. As a result of this behaviour the density of breeding pairs in any locality has an upper limit which regulates the population density. This is not to say that the numbers in the population remain constant; differences in weather conditions from year to year will affect such things as the supply of food and as a result fewer young will survive in some years than in others. Nevertheless, as a consequence of this behaviour, the numbers of individuals of a particular bird species within an area are kept within a fairly narrow range.

Density-independent factors

What is the effect upon population numbers of density-independent factors? It is these which normally determine the peak density of a population which has a well-marked annual cycle of abundance. One can visualize density-independent factors as acting in a variety of ways. The simplest perhaps relates to an insect which has a high r and establishes itself each year upon some annual weed. We will assume that the weed starts to grow actively during the rainy season but once the rains cease environmental conditions become unsuitable for the insect and most of the adults die: the time during which conditions are suitable for the growth of the insect population will therefore depend upon the duration of the rains. If the rains stop early, the insects will fail to reach a high population density, but some will survive during the dry season. Clearly the numbers of such individuals may depend upon

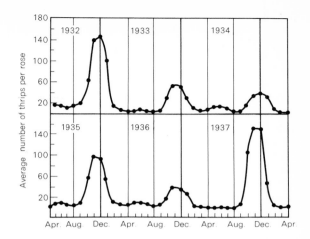

14.19 Annual cycles of abundance of thrips, a small phytophagous insect: this species feeds upon rose flowers. In October each year the population builds up. Its peak is partly determined by prevailing weather conditions, but partly by the number of survivors during the preceding dry season. (After Andrewartha and Birch.)

the peak numbers of the previous year. A good year can result in a high density of survivors, a 'poor' year in a low density. As a result the initial level of infestation in any year will be determined by the peak of the previous year. That is to say, in the equation

$$N_t = N_0 e^{rt}$$

the value of N_0 varies from year to year. In a 'good' year N_t will be high. This will result in a high value of N_0 the following year. If the weather conditions in the second year are again satisfactory, the peak population will be greater as a result of this high initial value of N_0. The peak population of any one year will thus be the resultant of events in the previous year as well as in the immediate year in which the population is growing. The value of N_t in both years will be determined by weather conditions, that is, by density-independent factors (Fig. 14.19).

Predicting peak populations

The practical consequences of the peak populations of some species being determined by the action of density-independent factors are that it is possible, given sufficient data, to construct empirical equations which can be used to predict the magnitude of the peak population of a pest insect in any one year. Clearly such predictions may be of great value, as they can determine the effort which has to be employed to control the pest and ensure that money is not wasted upon control measures at a time when they are not in fact required.

To illustrate the types of relations which emerge, we will

consider two cases. One refers to the Red Locust, *Noma-dacris*, the other to the Cotton Leaf-hopper, *Empoasca* (Fig. 14.3).

In the outbreak areas of *Nomadacris*, egg laying occurs during November when there are rains. Adults die towards the end of the rainy season and the new generation of locust hoppers emerges at the end of December. These hoppers become adult in early March and will normally oviposit the following November. Observations show that the size of the population in any one year is markedly affected by the heaviness of the rains when the parents of these hoppers were developing. Consider Fig. 14.20; the population density of F_2 is affected (*a*) by the rains which occurred during the time of oviposition and early development of F_1 (Rain 1), and also (*b*) by the density of F_1, as well as (*c*) by the magnitude of the rains at the time when the eggs of F_2 are being laid (Rain 2). The values of these three factors can be inserted into the following empirical equation to forecast the density, *y*, of the F_2 population of adults about July or August

$$y = 6 \cdot 518 - 0 \cdot 160 x_1 + 0 \cdot 425 x_2 + 0 \cdot 092 x_3$$

where *y* is expressed in arbitrary units on a scale of 1 to 5, x_1 is the rainfall (in inches) during the time the P generation is ovipositing, x_2 the density of the F_1 population (on the 1–5 scale) and x_3 the rainfall (in inches) during the time the F_1 generation is ovipositing. Such a relation may be used to predict several months ahead whether the F_2 generation is likely to be so dense that action must be taken to prevent swarm formation.

Note that the greater the value of x_1, the less will be the value of *y*. Two suggestions have been advanced to explain this relation. One is that if Rain 1 is heavy, there is dense grass cover left the following year when F_1 is ovipositing; dense cover is unsuitable for egg laying and thus oviposition is poor. Alternatively, it has been suggested that if Rain 1 is heavy, the watertable remains high and rises again rapidly during Rain 2. Damp soil is also unsuitable for successful egg development. These two explanations are not, of course, mutually exclusive; both effects may be involved.

In the case of *Empoasca* it was first recognized that there was a marked inverse correlation between rainfall early in the cotton-growing season and peak abundance of the leaf-hopper (Fig. 14.21a). Moreover, peak populations were markedly greater on stands of cotton to which nitrogen fertilizer had been added. This suggested that the inverse relation between high rainfall and peak population was probably indirect, that heavy rains reduced the nitrogen content of the leaves of the cotton and that this, in turn, lowered the rate of population build-up. Peak population is reached immediately before natural regulating agencies start to reduce the population. These agencies normally come into action at about the same time in each annual population cycle, so that the slower the build-up of the population, the lower its peak. With this informa-

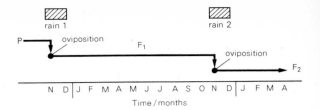

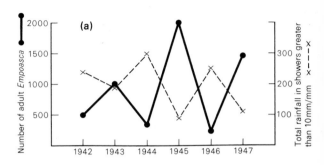

14.20 The relation between successive generations of *Nomodacris* and the rainfall in an outbreak area. For further explanation see text.

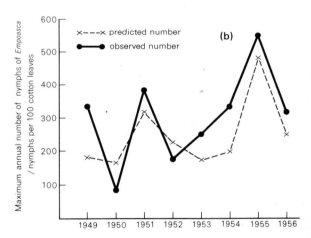

14.21 (a) Numbers of *Empoasca* adults collected in a standard number of sweeps at the peak of infestation in different years and the total rainfall in showers greater than 10 mm precipitation. (After Hanna.) (b) Observed and predicted maximum infestation of cotton with *Empoasca* in the Sudan Gezira. For further explanation see text. (After Joyce.)

tion and a series of observations collected over several years, it is possible to predict the approximate size of the peak population of *Empoasca*, *y*, using the empirical formula

$$y = 2144 - 0 \cdot 0017 x_1 + 0 \cdot 0133 x_2$$

where *y* is population density expressed as nymphs per 100 cotton leaves, x_1 is the rainfall (in mm) between July and mid-August and x_2 the quantity of nitrogen (in local units of weight) added as fertilizer per feddan ($= 0.42$ ha). Fig. 14.21b shows the predicted and observed peak values for one region in the Sudan over a period of eight years. Such an empirical relationship has, of course, validity over only a restricted area and cannot be applied to cotton grown everywhere; it does, however, give a useful prediction over the whole length of the Gezira which extends from north to south over more than 150 km.

Populations of fish and men

So far, in considering the action of density-independent mortality factors, we have limited our discussion to insects whose life span is only a year or less. If we consider the case of an animal which survives for several years, the effect of 'good' years and 'bad' years on the total size of the popula-

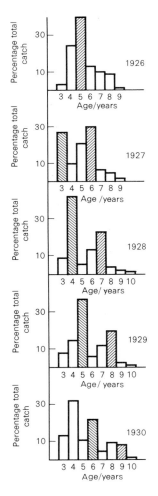

14.22 Histograms showing the percentage distribution by age or 'year class' in catches of a marine fish in successive years. Fish younger than three years were not taken in the nets. For further explanation, see text.

tion will be cumulative. This can most readily be understood by reference to Fig. 14.22 which shows an analysis of fish catches over a series of years. Each catch has been divided into a series of age classes, determined from scale counts (p. 251) and the composition of the catch then expressed as the percentage of each class in the total sample of the catch.

If you examine the data for 1926, you will see that year-class 5 is much the most abundant. From 1927 to 1929 the same class remains markedly larger than the catch from adjacent younger or older age classes. Clearly 1921 was a relatively 'good' year: so too was 1924 which first appears in the catch in 1927 as three-year-old fishes. The importance of these two 'good' years for the total catch can be expressed by saying that together they constituted 57 percent of the whole in 1927, 65 percent in 1928 and 56 percent in 1929. Clearly such information is of practical use in predicting the economic value of landings from a fishery in any one year. In this example the irregular effect of density-independent factors on the total population is damped out, so that the very marked changes such as can occur with short-lived insects are not so obvious.

The same technique of analysis is applicable to human populations. The data are commonly expressed as a series of horizontal bars with the youngest age class at the bottom, the data for males to the left, for females to the right. Fig. 14.23a shows such data for Sweden in 1950. For convenience of reference, the dates of births of some of the age groups have been inserted. You will see that the three age classes corresponding to the period from 1926 to 1940 contain fewer people than might be expected from the data for earlier years. They may be described as 'bad' years with regard to recruitment to the population. That they do indeed reflect a fall in the birth rate can be seen in Fig. 14.23b which shows the mean annual number of live births for each decade from 1871. While the number of live births per annum was reasonably constant during the years 1871 to 1920, it fell sharply below 120 000 during the two decades 1921–30 and 1931–40, to rise again during the final decade; this is in keeping with the fact that the two bottom bars of the base of the pyramid in Fig. 14.23a are broader than those of the immediately older age groups. Such data are of considerable social value as they permit us to predict the likely future age composition of any human population. The importance of this we will discuss later (p. 357).

In this chapter we have examined some of the factors affecting population growth. Unchecked growth never occurs in nature, but from a knowledge of the parameter r, the intrinsic rate of increase, we can obtain information upon the extent of mortality actually occurring at any one time. Mortality may be the result of environmental causes, the magnitude of whose effect is unrelated to the density of the population. It may also be caused by density-dependent factors whose intensity of action increases with increasing population density. These will, in certain cir-

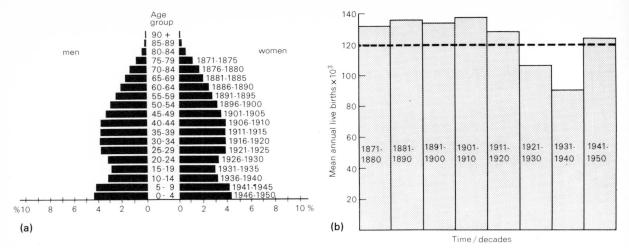

14.23 (a) Age pyramid for the population of Sweden in 1950. The values show the numbers of men on the left, women on the right and are expressed as percentage of the total population. (b) Changes in the value of the mean annual number of live births in Sweden between 1871 and 1950.

cumstances, serve to regulate the size of the population, so that it varies only within relatively narrow limits. Density-independent factors may control the peak size of a population and, at least in tropical savanna, usually are of far greater significance than density-dependent factors.

Of major importance in influencing population density are food supply and predation; it is therefore essential to have an understanding of the nature of the interactions determined by the number of individuals at different trophic levels and how these may affect population density: such interactions we will consider in the next chapter.

Problems

1 A sample of 100 specimens of a stored-products beetle was placed in a large jar containing food. Each female laid 20 eggs in a lifetime; the sex ratio was unity. Calculate the size of the population after 4, 6, 8 and 10 generations. Attempt to plot the size of the population against generation number using both a linear and a logarithmic scale. Explain why, when using a logarithmic scale, you obtain a straight line.

2 Direct observations of marked individuals can provide information for constructing a survivorship curve for a species of bird. Individuals may be marked and recognized by using small coloured rings slipped around the leg. If you have rings of four different colours and put three rings on each bird, how many individual birds could be differently marked? If the maximum number of rings which a bird can tolerate is four, what is the maximum number of birds which can be distinctively ringed?

3 One proposed method of controlling a certain fly is by the release of abnormal individuals into the population. Large numbers have to be released and the flies have to be derived from a single initial pair. For one species of tsetse fly, the highest obtainable value of r was found to be 0·0173 per day. Starting with a single pair, it is desired to produce a final population of 40 000. How long would this be expected to take?

4 The mean annual live birth rates in Sweden for recent quinquennia (five-year periods) have been as follows:
1941–45   121·9 × 10³
1946–50   124·9 × 10³
1951–55   108·6 × 10³
1956–60   105·5 × 10³

Sketch the probable shape of the age pyramid for the population for 1960.

5 Standard monthly samples were collected from the littoral zone of a small lake. All specimens of the nymphs of one species of mayfly (Exopterygota: Ephemeroptera) were separated and their body length measured to the nearest mm. The data were tabulated by size class and the following results were found:

Size class (mm)	Dec.	Jan.	Feb.	Mar.	Apr.	May
			Month			
2·0–3·9	2	2	1	0	0	0
4·0–5·9	5	6	4	0	0	0
6·0–7·9	9	15	12	3	0	0
8·0–9·9	7	26	20	8	0	0
10·0–11·9	3	28	26	17	2	0
12·0–13·9	1	12	29	23	8	0
14·0–15·9	4	2	28	27	18	2
16·0–17·9	10	0	10	30	25	8
18·0–19·9	21	3	0	29	28	18
20·0–21·9	29	8	0	12	32	23
22·0–23·9	31	15	1	0	27	28
24·0–25·9	27	27	11	0	9	31
26·0–27·9	24	27	18	0	1	29
28·0–29·9	6	4	2	0	0	8

(a) What is the expected duration of the aquatic stages of the life of this species?

(b) When does oviposition occur?

(c) What would you expect to be the size composition of the collection made in June? Explain how you arrived at your conclusion.

(d) What is the rate of growth of the nymphs?

6 Suggest a number of density-independent factors likely to affect population numbers of annual plants in the savanna. Will attack by harvester termites be density-dependent or density-independent?

7 Recent studies have shown that the maximum r value for elephant is probably 0·04 per annum; that is to say the herd will increase by 4 per cent each year. Assuming that the population can expand indefinitely, calculate the size of a herd of elephants after 100, 500 and 1 000 years, if it initially consisted of 20 adults.

8 Laboratory cultures of two different species of insect both held at $T°C$ were found to have the same value of r. On increasing the temperature by 10°C the value of r for both cultures increased by the same amount. Detailed study showed, however, that the natality rate of one species had increased far more than that of the other. Explain how this type of result might occur.

9 Two insects, one with an r value of 0·1 per day and the other of 0·4 per day, start with initial populations of 400 and 100 insects per plant respectively. Using a graphical method, determine after how many days the numbers of the insect with the higher r value will equal those of the other insect.

10 The fish fauna of a large lake was sampled by using a number of nets of different mesh size. The lake was sampled each month for a period of seven months. Each month all specimens of one particular species were collected, counted and measured to the nearest cm. The following results were obtained.

Size group* (cm)	June	July	Aug.	Sept.	Oct.	Nov.	Dec.
4·0	9	0	0	0	0	0	0
6·0	43	15	7	0	0	0	0
8·0	308	198	32	31	0	0	0
10·0	54	75	241	122	5	17	0
12·0	21	11	39	95	208	97	9
14·0	0	2	7	13	14	105	187
16·0	9	5	2	5	5	13	23
18·0	57	36	46	3	9	13	9
20·0	462	346	158	29	25	25	8
22·0	71	131	346	461	239	169	35
24·0	56	39	27	59	201	261	411
26·0	81	56	37	12	35	17	39
28·0	204	193	154	83	7	11	15
30·0	65	45	47	72	143	75	46
32·0	0	13	0	7	6	36	33

*The size group 4·0 cm includes all fish within the size range 3·0 to 4·9 cm, that for 6·0 cm those within the range 5·0 to 6·9 cm, and so on.

(a) Read the other questions below and then display these data by a series of suitable histograms. A scale of 1 mm = 20 fish is satisfactory.

(b) In any one month the number of fish collected in the different size classes is different. What do you consider this implies about the biology of the fish? Explain how you come to your conclusion.

(c) The number of fish in size class 20 cm in June was much greater than that in the size class 8·0 cm. Assuming that the nets collect a representative sample of the entire population, what explanation would you offer for this observation?

(d) Attempt to determine the growth rate of the fish.

(e) Does the growth rate change with age? If so, in what way?

11 Use the following data to plot a survivorship curve for

Day	0	3	8	20	35	40	45	50	55	60	65	70
Number of bees	1 000	970	820	800	770	740	600	320	100	60	5	0

worker honey bees. The brood cells are sealed on the eighth day and adult workers emerge on the twentieth. From the information available to you about the biology and behaviours of worker bees, suggest an interpretation of the form of the curve.

12 A study was made of the population of a species of grasshopper in an area of 400 m². Each day a sample of the population was collected within the study area and 50 specimens, chosen at random, were marked on the thorax with a small spot of coloured paint. On the first day red paint was used and on the three subsequent days blue, green and yellow respectively. At the end of the period a single specimen might carry two or more spots of paint. The numbers of individuals carrying different coloured marks were noted each day, as well as the total size of the sample. The results obtained are set out in the table below. Suggest an interpretation of these findings.

Day	1	2	3	4	5	6	7
Total number of specimens recaptured	—	212	220	206	234	223	218
Red marks recaptured	*50 specimens marked*	21	15	12	10	8	6
Blue marks recaptured	—	*50 specimens marked*	20	17	13	9	7
Green marks recaptured	—	—	*50 specimens marked*	22	16	13	11
Yellow marks recaptured	—	—	—	*50 specimens marked*	21	14	13

Bibliography

Further reading

Boughey, A. S.   *Ecology of Populations*, Collier-Macmillan, 2nd ed. 1973, Chap. 2

Kormondy, E. J.   *Concepts of Ecology*, Prentice Hall, 1969, Chap. 4

MacArthur, R., Connell, J.   *The Biology of Populations*, Wiley, 1966, Chap. 5

Odum, E. P.   *Ecology*, Holt, Rinehart and Winston, 1963, pp. 89–109

Solomon, M. E.   *Population Dynamics*, Arnold, 1969, Chaps. 1, 2, 3 and 4

Wilson, E. O., Bossert, W. H.   *A Primer of Population Biology*, Sinauer Associates, 1971, pp. 92–127

Andrewartha, H. G.   'Population Growth and Control: Animal Populations', in *Population Control*, ed. A. Allison, Penguin, 1970

Brown, L.   'Population Control among Large Mammals', in *Population Control*, ed. A. Allison, Penguin, 1970

Harper, J. L.   'The Population Biology of Plants', in *Population Control*, ed. A. Allison, Penguin, 1970

Perrins, C.   'Bird Populations', in *Population Control*, ed. A. Allison, Penguin, 1970

Reid, R.   'Protozoan Populations', in *Population Control*, ed. A. Allison, Penguin, 1970

15 Interactions between populations

In the previous chapter we developed an equation (p. 255) to describe the growth of a population in which a density-dependent factor came into action and showed that if this factor were a predator, provided its numbers remained effectively constant, the population of the prey would stabilize close to a value K, the carrying capacity. We will now try to relate this idea to the patterns of life cycle of different organisms to see if it proves possible in this manner to provide satisfactory explanations of the relative stability of populations.

Population regulation

We must, at the outset, distinguish between factors which can 'control' the numbers of a population and those which 'regulate' them. Regulatory factors are those which are effective in keeping the population density of a particular species within certain broad limits, factors which prevent numbers from rising excessively or sinking to extinction. Controlling factors include those like weather, which may act irregularly and serve temporarily to reduce the numbers of a population. Thus, for example, we apply insecticides to control insect populations, but not to regulate them. Our immediate concern is to understand the ways in which the population densities of different types of organisms are regulated, as it is this process which results in some species being abundant within a community while others are scarce. Population regulation is thus the process which determines the quantitative relations of the organisms within a community.

Patterns of life cycle
Tsetse and wildebeest

We can recognize three principal types of life cycle. The first is characteristic of animals with a long life span, like the wildebeest, or of those which breed continuously through the year, like the tsetse fly. The population density of tsetse fly remains relatively constant from month to month (Fig. 14.1b); the population is living at or close to the carrying capacity of its environment and any increase in population will therefore be resisted by several density-dependent factors such as predators of the adults including flycatchers, dragonflies and spiders, as well as parasitoids

of the pupae (Fig. 15.1a). The wildebeest exemplifies a different pattern in which the population shows a sharp annual increase due to the limited breeding season, but most of this increase is fairly quickly offset by heavy infantile and juvenile mortality, due in part to various density-dependent factors (Fig. 15.1b). The population is thus brought back to a value close to the carrying capacity and until the following breeding season will fall at a steady rate, largely due to the activity of predators. The rate of this fall will itself be partly density-dependent so that the size of the population at the onset of each breeding season will tend to be constant; for example, the population of wildebeest before the breeding season in a private reserve in the Northern Transvaal in South Africa, was estimated in three successive years to be 2 077, 2 087 and 2 549. Although annual differences in weather may shift the size of the post-breeding population up or down, the density-dependent action of predation tends to bring the population back again to a basal value. Regulation of the size of the wildebeest population is thus effected mainly by density-dependent factors which produce extensive mortality before the individuals reach an age at which they can start to reproduce: R_0 therefore remains relatively constant.

The millet-grain midge

A second type of life cycle is that of animals whose adults are strictly seasonal in occurrence, so that there is only a brief time of active reproduction; the rest of the year is passed in some dormant stage. Thus, for example, in Senegal the Millet-grain Midge, *Geromyia* (Diptera) (*gero* is the Hausa word for millet), spends the greater part of the year as a pupa within fallen, dried millet flowers in a state of dormancy called diapause. Shortly after the onset of the rains, when the millet is in flower, the flies emerge. The females oviposit in the flower heads and the total development time from egg to adult is about 12 days. Some four or five overlapping generations are completed before further flowers cease to be available. In each generation about 5 percent of the pupae enter diapause and these will be the founders of the infestation of the following year.

This type of cycle is shown schematically in Fig. 15.1c. During the dormant period there will be loss to the population as a result of predation of pupae and such loss will

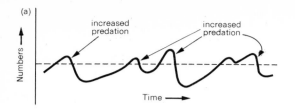

(a)

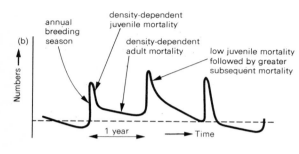

(b)

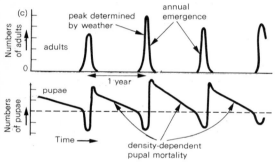

(c)

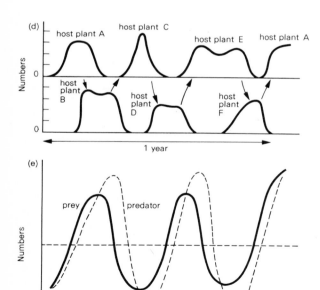

(d)

(e)

15.1 (left) Possible patterns of variation in population densities of animals with time. (a) A population which is held near its carrying capacity by the action of density-dependent forces. (b) A population with a restricted annual breeding period. Density-dependent factors acting primarily upon the juveniles keep the density of the population shortly before reproduction within narrow limits. (c) The population of an insect with annual adult emergence. Peak adult population will be determined by prevailing weather conditions; density-dependent predation of the resting stage will regulate population density. (d) Annual cycle of a rapidly reproducing insect which migrates from one host plant to another. Density upon any host plant will be dependent upon r but may be regulated by parasites and predators. After each migration the population must rebuild. (e) Cyclic variation in numbers of prey and predators which can arise when their generation times are of similar duration.

probably be density-dependent. With the return of favourable conditions, the population will start to build up rapidly owing to the short generation time. The peak reached will be strongly determined by climatic factors which will affect the value of r, the intrinsic rate of population increase. Thus the value of K, the carrying capacity, has little significance. In this respect the situation differs from that of the wildebeest in which the increase in numbers of the population is determined by the number of pregnant females, a number closely related to K.

As the population of the insect increases, changing environmental conditions or lack of food will check the growth of the adult population and may lead to its final extinction. If, however, the population should continue to increase, predation pressure will build up and this may lead to a crash of the population. In the case of the Millet-grain Midge, lack of food normally prevents a further increase in the population, but if new flowers continue to be available for infestation, the growth of the population is maintained until it is checked by parasites. This is shown in Fig. 15.2 which illustrates the results of an experiment in which a series of four sowings of early and late bulrush millet was made so that fresh flower heads were available for a period of two months. The population of flies increased until the flowers of the third sowing were very heavily infested; then the numbers of adults fell sharply, so that the fourth sowing was almost free from attack. The crash in numbers was due to the very high density of parasites.

Thus, in this type of life cycle, either density-dependent or density-independent factors may bring the population increase to an end. In either case, the size of the peak population will be a function of r. Then the dormant phase follows, with a return to some value of N_0 which is likely to vary little from year to year. In events of this sort the concept of carrying capacity is normally irrelevant, although clearly a series of favourable years might result in the actively reproducing population starting from so high a

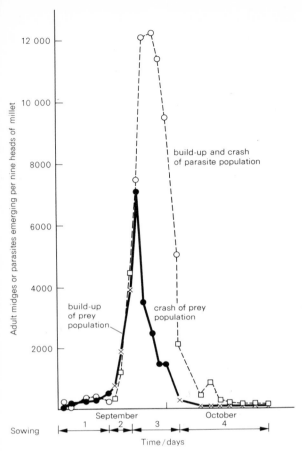

15.2 Variation in the population density of adults of the Millet-Grain Midge and its parasites in Senegal. Four successive plantings of millet were made to provide food for succeeding generations of midges. Note the way in which the abundance of midge and parasite rise together and how, at the third sowing, the parasite population increases while that of the midge crashes. The parasite population subsequently falls, but remains greater than that of the midge during the last crop in October, thus preventing any new increase in the midge population. (After Coutin and Harris.)

level as to bring about an early crash owing to the animals' destroying their own food supply.

The African Bollworm

Regulation of the Millet-grain Midge population occurs during the resting stage when the population is not actively reproducing. A somewhat comparable situation, from the viewpoint of the farmer concerned with pests attacking his crops, is that of insects which attack some annual plant and then, rather than becoming dormant, migrate to spend the rest of the year upon other plants. Density-dependent factors will again probably regulate their numbers while

on their alternative hosts (Fig. 15.1d). One such pest is the African Bollworm, *Heliothis armigera* (Lepidoptera) (Fig. 15.3), which attacks cotton in Uganda. The moth infests a variety of other crops as well as cotton, being commonly found on maize or sunflowers between April and July before the cotton plants flower (Fig. 15.4). Cotton is attacked from mid-August to January; for the rest of the year, when no crops are available, the larvae live on wild plants. The moth is subject to attack by seventeen different species of parasite as well as by a virus disease. Because larvae are always present, the population density of larval parasites remains high and, as a consequence of their density-dependent regulatory action, the larval population rarely exceeds 25 000 ha^{-1}; at this density it is not a serious pest.

A striking contrast is to be seen in the life cycle of the same species of insect in South Africa, where the cycle

15.3 The adult of the African Bollworm, *Heliothis armigera*.

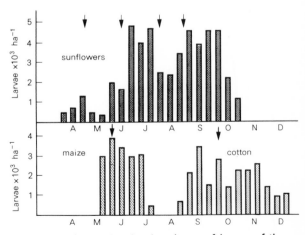

15.4 Weekly variation in abundance of larvae of the African Bollworm, *Heliothis*, on three crops in Uganda in 1954. The arrows indicate the time of flowering of each crop. There were four sowings of sunflowers. Note that the larvae occurred on all three crops, attacking whatever plants might be available at any time. (After Coaker.)

resembles that of the Millet-grain Midge in Senegal. Most of the pupae of the moth enter a diapause during the cool, dry months, although a small population of moth larvae, which serves as a reservoir for parasites, is probably present on wild plants at this time. When favourable conditions return, the moths emerge and they may give rise to a dense population of larvae since the parasite population will have fallen to a low level while the moth pupae are in diapause. As a result, although the moth is not a serious pest in Uganda, it can have serious economic consequences in South Africa. Thus in different environmental conditions, the population cycles of the same species of insect may show different patterns. In Uganda the size of the population of bollworm is closely determined by K; in South Africa the peak population may be largely determined by r.

The population numbers of the Millet-grain Midge are normally regulated during the dormant stage, so that the value of N_0 varies little from year to year. A comparable type of regulation is found in some annual plants in which the quantity of seed set per unit area is almost independent of the density of mature plants (Fig. 15.5). In this way, after each flowering season, the population is brought back to an almost constant level. N_0 will vary very little but, in this case, the population density of mature flowers will be affected by the weather conditions experienced during germination and seedling growth, that is, by density-independent factors.

Cyclic changes in population size

The third situation relates to populations in which rapidly reproducing prey persists in the environment through the year and in which there are predators which can also

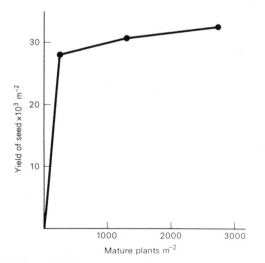

15.5 Seed yield from plants of *Agrostemma*, the 'corncockle', a common weed in temperate wheat fields. Note that the total yield of seed per unit area is almost independent of the number of mature plants. (Data from Harper.)

reproduce rapidly. In such a circumstance, as the population of the prey grows, more food will be available to the predator and its own population will increase. An increase in the numbers of predators will lead to a fall in the number of the prey. This will be followed by a decrease in the numbers of the predator, a consequent increase in the numbers of the prey and so on. As a result the numbers of the prey may be expected to oscillate in a rhythmic manner (Fig. 15.1e).

This differs from the regulation of numbers of the tsetse fly (p. 265) in that many of the tsetse's predators are long-lived and their numbers will therefore exert a constant pressure on the fly. Although the numbers of tsetse fly may rise and fall, their change due to changing predator pressure will be relatively slight. In the type of situation we are now considering the population structures of both predator and prey are unstable and their numbers may undergo large fluctuations. It is important to realize that this kind of regulation can occur wherever the generation times of predator and prey are of about the same order of magnitude. The relation may exist between phytoplanktonic algae and copepods, between phytophagous insects and their parasitoids, and between small predatory mammals and their prey (Fig. 15.6). The time scale of the oscillations will, of course, vary with the generation time.

Many attempts have been made to produce this type of effect in laboratory populations of predator and prey. Fig. 15.7a shows results of experiments using two species of mite (Arachnida). One fed on oranges, the second was predatory on the first. In a simple environment, such as that provided by a number of oranges in a suitable container, the population of the prey built up rapidly, followed by that of the predator which then totally destroyed the prey and finally died out itself as no further food was available. In a more complex environment, in which the mite which fed upon oranges could temporarily escape the predator, the sort of oscillation we have postulated was found (Fig. 15.7b).

A simple predator–prey relationship in which both organisms have life spans of the same order of magnitude is thus likely to be unstable and will probably lead to the total elimination first of the prey and then of the predator. In more natural conditions various situations arise which, as in the second experiment, preserve the prey from total destruction and thus the predator from final starvation. An example of this is provided by the control of the weed St John's wort, *Hypericum perforatum*, in Australia. This is a pest of grazing land, displacing good forage and being poisonous to stock if eaten in quantity. It has been partly held in check by the introduction of a beetle, *Chrysomela gamellata* (Coleoptera), which attacks and kills the weed. In any locality in which this occurs, the beetle will sooner or later also die off for lack of food. But the beetle is unable totally to eradicate the weed which can 'escape' into woodland where the beetle does not penetrate. As a result fresh local infestations of weed build up until by

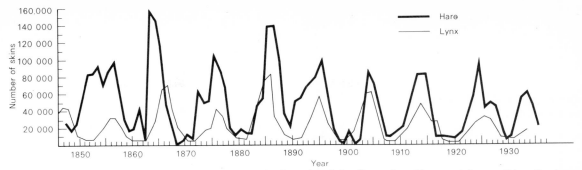

15.6 Variations in the probable population densities in Canada of the Snowshoe Hare and its predator, the lynx, over a period of 90 years. The data are based upon the number of skins of the two animals brought by hunters to market. Note that each build-up of the lynx population is usually followed by a fall in the numbers of hares and that low numbers of lynx correspond with low numbers of their prey. Compare with Fig. 15.1e. (After MacLulich.)

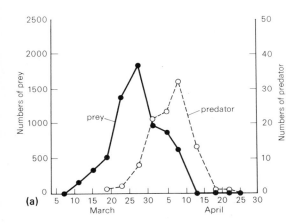

15.7 Model experiments on predator–prey interactions. (a) Variation in the numbers of a mite which feeds on oranges and of another mite which preys upon it. Note that the predator exterminates the prey and then dies out. (b) As 15.7a, but in a more complex environment where the prey could escape the predators by spreading more rapidly to new sources of food. In this situation there is a cyclic oscillation in population density. (After Huffaker.)

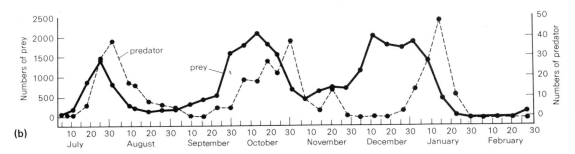

chance beetles are carried to the area; then the cycle of weed destruction followed by starvation is repeated. The weed is thus able to persist by having a wider ecological tolerance than the consumer which feeds upon it.

The Millet-grain Midge provides us with a second example. In the admittedly artificial conditions of the experimental trial shown in Fig. 15.2 the parasites almost completely eliminated the adult midge population. There is a marked similarity between these results and those shown in Fig. 15.7a. In the case of the Millet-grain Midge, however, the pupal diapause serves to protect a fraction of the population from destruction and, on a different time

scale, we again have a situation which parallels that shown in Fig. 15.7b.

There are other circumstances which can prevent prey from being hunted to extinction by its predators. Thus there may be a difference between the minimum temperature at which the predator and its prey can reproduce; if the prey can reproduce at a lower temperature than the predator, then it may seasonally escape intensive predation and be able to build up its numbers once again. With some predators there is evidence that when a particular type of prey becomes scarce, the predator will cease searching for this species and switch to another which is more abundant.

Similarly territorial behaviour of predators may restrict their density, and so limit the intensity of pressure on their prey. In these and several other ways prey can escape the threat of extinction by unchecked predation and cycles of limited oscillation are established.

The effect of diversity on regulation

One factor of considerable importance in this matter is the complexity of the ecosystem itself. Where the numbers of some primary consumer are being regulated by only one or a few species of predator, large oscillations are likely to occur. Where there are many predatory species attacking, for example, insects at different stages in the life cycle or at different times of year, the system is likely to show far greater stability in numbers of the prey. This is probably the mechanism which regulates the bollworm population in Uganda; its large number of parasitoids collectively prevent the moth population from building up at any time of year to a level serious enough to demand special control measures like the use of insecticides. Such a conclusion has considerable practical importance. It implies that simplification of an ecosystem, such as occurs when land is cleared to allow effective mechanized agriculture, may result in phytophagous insects, previously regulated in numbers and held at a population density where they had no economic significance, becoming serious pests since the simplified environment can no longer support the previous wide range of predatory species.

From these examples we may see how, in general, the numbers of different organisms within a community tend to be held within characteristic limits, although in a highly diverse ecosystem the total pattern of interactions will be very complex. The action of density-dependent factors at certain points in the life history of a species will be such as to correct any imbalance which may arise owing to changes of climatic conditions from year to year. Nevertheless in any one year, peak populations may be affected by climatic conditions which can therefore be of prime importance in practical problems of pest control.

Competition

Suppose that a community contains a species A and we introduce from some other region with similar environmental characteristics another species B with the same food requirements and the same habits as A. What will happen? When Species A alone is present, the habitat has a carrying capacity for species A of K_A. But species B exploits the same food resources, so that its presence will have the effect of reducing the food available to A. Clearly the population of A must decrease and the greater the population of B, the less will be the value of K_A. In a similar manner the presence of A will lower the value of K_B. This

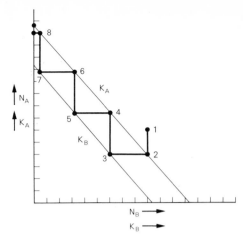

15.8 Diagram to illustrate the principle of competitive exclusion. For further explanation, see text.

we describe by saying that the two species are in competition.

We can represent this situation graphically as in Fig. 15.8. When the population density of species B, N_B, is zero, K_A has its maximum value and then decreases as N_B increases. The same relation exists between N_A and K_B. Further, if the population density of A increases so that its value lies to the right of the line representing K_A, it will tend to fall again, as it has exceeded K_A; if it falls to a value to the left of the line, it will subsequently increase. The same relations apply to the population density of B and the line representing K_B.

Consider what happens if the two population densities have values represented by the point 1: the population density of A is greater than the carrying capacity, so N_A will fall to point 2. Here, however, the population density of B exceeds K_B, so it will fall to point 3. The value of N_A is now less than K_A, so the population of A will increase until it reaches point 4 and so on. At all points the position is unstable and stability will only be attained when B has been completely eliminated.

Competitive exclusion

This conclusion can be generalized as follows: If two species are both competing for the same resources, only one species will normally survive. This is referred to as Gause's Principle of Competitive Exclusion. Of course, the values of K_A and K_B both depend on the environmental situation, and since it is usually the species with the lower K value which will be excluded, results may be different in different environmental conditions. This can be illustrated by reference to laboratory experiments on two species of flour beetle, *Tribolium castaneum* and *T. confusum* (Coleoptera) (Fig. 14.14). A series of cultures was set up, some at 24°C and 30 percent R.H., others at 34°C and 70 percent R.H. Each species would grow in either of these conditions if cultured alone. In mixed cultures at the lower temperature and humidity only *T. confusum* ultimately survived; at the higher temperature and humidity the opposite was true: *T. castaneum* excluded *T. confusum*.

Comparable situations can sometimes be studied in the field. The larvae of the barnacle *Balanus* (Arthropoda: Crustacea) will settle on plastic plates over the whole intertidal zone between mean high water spring tides (MHWS) and mean low water spring tides (MLWS) (p. 27). On a rocky shore, adults are found over a more limited zone between mean high water neap tides (MHWN) and MLWS (Fig. 15.9a). Higher up the shore is another barnacle, *Chthamalus*. If, over an area of shore, the specimens of *Balanus* are removed and any new specimens settling are destroyed, then adult *Chthamalus* are found from MHWS to mean tide level (MTL) (Fig. 15.9b). When, however, both species occur together, *Chthamalus* is found only between MHWS and MHWN; below that there is only *Balanus*. *Balanus* is thus able to exclude *Chthamalus* from the zone between MHWN and MTL (Fig. 15.9c). This is because the number of *Balanus* larvae

which settle in this zone is far greater than that of *Chthamalus* larvae; moreover, *Balanus* grows faster, so that individuals of *Chthamalus* are crushed or smothered. The zone successfully occupied by *Chthamalus* lies at the top of the shore, where *Balanus* is unable to survive long periods of exposure.

This species of *Balanus* is typically found in cold waters; the species of *Chthamalus* extends into warmer water. The distribution we described is found in fairly cold waters: in lower latitudes, *Balanus* is unable to compete so effectively with *Chthamalus* and both species may occur together in the zone above MTL.

A similar relation exists between two species of small voles (Mammalia: Rodentia): one of these, of the genus *Clethrionomys*, is normally found in woodland and the other, of the genus *Microtus*, in grassland (compare the earlier discussion of deermice, p. 28). On islands where both genera occur, they keep to their typical habitats. But on islands where there is only one or the other species, it will spread all over the available area. Here too we have evidence of competition between fairly closely related forms which leads to a limitation of the distribution of each when they occur in the same locality: that is to say, they mutually exclude each other.

A rather different type of relation is that between two varieties of the common temperate weed, the dandelion. These varieties have different characteristics. In freshly disturbed ground, variety A establishes itself more rapidly than the other variety, D. This is because A sets about three times as much seed as D does, and A has therefore a greater chance of initially colonizing a new habitat. Nevertheless, D will also become established in time and the two varieties will be then in competition. D then gradually ousts A, because it grows more rapidly and shades out the plants of A, until finally only D remains.

Co-existence

If we accept this concept of competitive exclusion, how then are we to explain the occurrence together of two closely related plants or animals? The reasonable assumption is that they differ from each other in some fashion which reduces or avoids competition for potentially limiting resources such as light or space or food. Examination of particular cases will allow us to test this hypothesis.

A common observation is that different species of poppy can grow together forming stable communities. The size of a population of poppies is very markedly influenced by density-dependent factors, with the result that the numbers of each species within a given area is strongly regulated (Fig. 14.17a). This regulation appears to act on each species independently even when they are growing in the same area. The population thus remains stable, since the density of no single species becomes sufficiently great for competition to develop with the rest.

The mobility of animals can lead to a very different

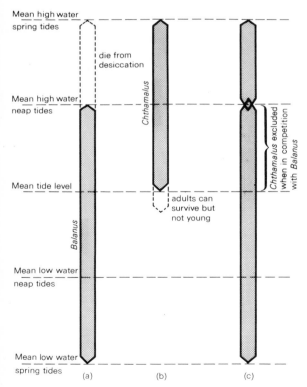

15.9 Diagram showing the range of barnacles on a rocky shore. (a) *Balanus* alone; (b) *Chthamalus* in the absence of *Balanus;* (c) Both species together. (Simplified from Connell).

result. Frequently within one locality closely related species are active in slightly different habitats so that, being spatially separated, they do not come into significant competition. This can be seen in the case of the forest monkeys (Table 4.6). The three species of *Colobus*, although they all have a common source of food, tend to distribute themselves for feeding and sleeping into the upper, middle and lower layers of the forest trees: the same is true of *Cercopithecus* (p. 67). A similar stratification of feeding and roosting sites is found in the three common, forest-dwelling, fruit-eating bats of West Africa. Table 6.4 illustrates a rather different relation between three grazing mammals which live together; each tends to select its characteristic food from the available grass. Indeed, the feeding preferences of one of these species tend to make food available for another (p. 64).

This separation into different habitats within a locality is not peculiar to the mammals. Table 2.4 shows a similar tendency for the aquatic larvae of three midge species, each having a characteristic preference for a particular type of substratum. Fig. 15.10 shows details of the distribution on a rocky shore of seven different species of the limpet *Patella* (Mollusca: Gastropoda; Book 1 Fig. 20.9). It will be seen that where species have a common source of food, there is only a slight overlap between their distributions.

A final example of this type of relation can be taken from the terrestrial insects. There are two species of the solitary wasp *Dasyproctus* (Hymenoptera) (Fig. 15.11) in Uganda. Both excavate nests, which may be about 20 cm long,

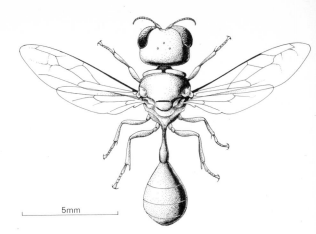

5mm

15.11 *Dasyproctus* female: a small wasp which provisions its larvae with two-winged flies.

inside the stems of plants. The female will fly off to catch a fly, stings it so that it is paralysed, and then carries it back to the nest. Here she lays an egg upon the body of the fly and then goes off to catch and sting more flies to provide food for the larva which will shortly emerge. When she has added some 12 to 20 further flies, she builds a partition wall of chewed pith across the stem and then seeks a further fly on which to oviposit. When complete the entire nest may contain some six to ten cells, each containing a young larva provisioned in this way.

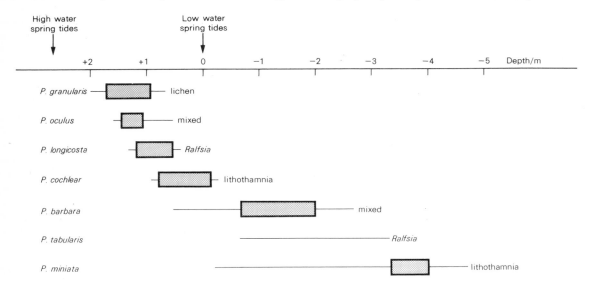

15.10 Diagram showing the distribution of seven species of grazing limpets on a shore transect in warm coastal water near Cape Town. Depth is shown relative to MLWS. The black rectangle indicates the region of abundance of each species; the thin line indicates the maximum range. The dominant type of food taken by each species is indicated on the right. *Ralfsia* is an encrusting brown alga; lithothamnia have a similar habit, but are red algae. Note that there is almost no overlap in distribution of species which have the same major item of diet. (Simplified from Branch.)

Both species of *Dasyproctus* occur in the same area, but there is no competition between them. Not only do they hunt for flies in different types of vegetation, but they generally collect different species of flies with which to provision their nests, while the nests are built in different sorts of plant; one species excavates its nest almost exclusively in *Rubus* stems, while the other uses a variety of monocotyledons.

There are other ways in which competition between closely related forms is avoided. Fig. 15.12 illustrates one; it shows the growth pattern of two species of sand lizard which occur together in Central Africa. It is clear that they reproduce at different times of the year, so that the mature adults are not in competition; that is, the separation of related forms is temporal, rather than spatial.

Empty niches

If two species do occupy the same niche, then one will in the course of time almost certainly oust the other. It should not, however, be assumed that in any particular habitat all niches are already filled. Invaders may find an empty niche and be able to establish themselves without driving out any of the previous inhabitants, although there may follow a readjustment of the average population densities of the original species. Invaders may also find their niche already occupied and yet be able successfully to establish themselves at the expense of the native species. Such invaders have been rare in the recent history of Africa and there appears to be no record of the total

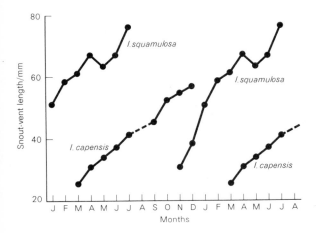

15.12 Mean body lengths recorded for monthly collections of two species of sand lizard of the Central African genus *Ichnotropis*. Note that when *I. squamulosa* is adult, *I. capensis* is juvenile. By having different reproductive seasons, competition for food between the two species is reduced or avoided. Part of the data has been plotted twice to make the pattern of temporal relations between the species clear. (Data from Broadly.)

elimination of a native species by an invader. One example of limited local elimination is provided by the Argentine Ant, *Iridomyrmex humilis*, which first became established in Cape Town by 1908; there it has exterminated all the native ants except for the Driver Ant, *Dorylus*. Since that time it has spread out over the low-lying parts of the Cape Province, but so far has failed to establish itself permanently on the high inland plateau. The danger of destruction or restriction of the range of native species by exotic plants or animals is always present and the good intentions of people introducing exotic organisms can lead to disastrous results. One well-documented example has been the introduction of the American Grey Squirrel into Britain. In most areas it has proved to be more successful than the native Red Squirrel whose range is now very restricted, while the grey squirrel has become a serious pest as it destroys young trees.

Competition between species with high intrinsic rates of increase

In discussing competition between two species already established within the environment, we have examined only the effect of one species upon the value of the carrying capacity, K, for another species. We may, however, ask what would be the outcome if two rapidly reproducing, phytophagous insects attacked a crop at the same time in conditions where there were no obvious limits to population growth. In this case the species with the greater intrinsic rate of increase, that is, with the greater value of r, will be expected to become the more abundant, but both populations will grow until they finally come into competition. At this point they will start to affect each other and, with the check on population growth, there will be a period of instability until usually the species with the higher K value alone survives.

This is not, however, always so, as forms of interaction between species may occur which have not been allowed for in our theoretical discussion. In Nigeria stored groundnuts are liable to infestation by the beetle *Tribolium* and also by a moth, *Plodia*. Both feed upon the nuts which are not normally limiting in quantity. Laboratory determinations showed that the values of r applicable to the local conditions were higher for the moth than for the beetle. One might therefore expect that in infested nuts, moth caterpillars would be more abundant than the larvae and adults of the beetle, that is, that the moth would be the more serious pest. This expectation was not fulfilled. The beetle was a serious pest, but the moth of little importance. Insecticidal applications were therefore made to the ground-nuts to control the beetle. These were highly successful for this purpose, but the moth now became a serious problem. This result arose because the relation between the two species is not simply one of competition for food. The beetle acts partly as a predator, eating the moths' eggs; at densities of 250 moth eggs and 320 beetles per 10 g shelled nuts, about two-thirds of the eggs were eaten. The beetles may also reduce oviposition by the moth, since they will bite the legs of any ovipositing moths they encounter (Table 15.1). The moth population was thus being regulated in a density-dependent fashion by the beetle. What might appear at first to be a simple competitive relationship between two organisms at the same trophic level proves to be more complex since the beetle acts as both a first- and a second-order consumer. The importance of this example is that it shows clearly how theoretical conclusions can be misleading unless the assumptions upon which they are based are valid.

Table 15.1 Effect of *Tribolium* upon oviposition of the moth *Plodia*. A single pair of moths was introduced while mating into each *Tribolium* culture. Standard-sized dishes with lids were used in both experimental series. While 10 g of ground-nuts gave the adult moths space into which to 'escape', 20 g of nuts almost filled the dishes, so that there was effectively no 'escape' (*Data from Adeyemi*)

| Cultures of 10 g of nuts | | Cultures of 20 g of nuts | |
Number of Tribolium	Number of moth eggs laid	Number of Tribolium	Number of moth eggs laid
0	287	0	270
40	200	40	105
160	173	160	13
320	120	—	—

Numbers within a food web

We must now attempt to take a step further our analysis of the numbers of organisms within a food web, for the practical reason that it may lead us to some understanding of how many food animals we may remove from the sea or from a pasture without damaging a population's ability to maintain itself. We want, in other words, to find out how we can maximize our efficiency as predators; that is, how to obtain the maximum yield of food from a resource without destroying it.

To understand certain basic quantitative relations which arise in trying to answer this question, we will begin by making a calculation, using many simplifying assumptions as well as arithmetically convenient numerical values. Consider the food chain:

phytoplankton → copepods →

fish of species A → fish of species B

We can ask the question: How many phytoplankton cells must be present in a pond so as to produce sufficient food to maintain the population of fish B at a given constant level? We will use the following values for our calculation:

	Weight of an individual	Time taken to reproduce
Phytoplankton	0·1 mg	2 days
Copepod	1·0 mg	20 days
Fish A	1·0 kg	360 days
Fish B	5·0 kg	—

We will also assume that a copepod eats 1 mg of food daily.

For simplicity, we will ask the question in the form: If a pond contains a single 5 kg specimen of fish B, how much phytoplankton must be present to maintain a steady state? In answering the question posed in this way, we shall speak of fractions of a fish, since we are dealing with relative quantities. Should you find this difficult, it may make it easier if you multiply all values by 1 000: this will not affect the final conclusions.

To find the answer to our problem we must know how much food or energy is taken by each of the three consumers each day. Most of the food eaten goes to supply the needs of energy metabolism, so we shall not be greatly in error if we make the further assumption that the necessary food intake is directly proportional to metabolic rate. Metabolic rate is not directly proportional to body weight, but, as experiment has shown, to some power function of weight. That is

$$\text{metabolic rate} = kW^a$$

where k and a are constants. The value of a is normally less than 1·0 and we will take a value of 0·66, which is close to the modal value found for a large number of different species.

We know that a copepod of 1 mg eats 1 mg of food a day. It follows that a fish of 1 kg must eat $(10^6)^{0·66}$ mg or 10^4 mg or 10 g daily. Similarly a fish of 5 kg will require $(5 \times 10^6)^{0·66}$ or $29·3 \times 10^3$ mg or 29·3 g daily. For simplicity we will call this 30 g.

Fish B must thus be able, on the average, to eat 30 g of fish A daily. We have assumed that it takes 360 days to produce a full-grown specimen of fish A and since the population is assumed to be stable, the new fish produced will be available for fish B as food. If it takes 360 days to produce 1 kg of fish A, then $\frac{1000}{360}$ g of fish A will be produced daily, that is, 2·78 g. To produce 30 g daily we shall therefore need $\frac{30 \times 360}{1000}$ fish, that is, approximately 11 fish.

Following the same line of argument we can conclude that 11 specimens of fish A require 110 g of copepods daily, that is, 110×10^3 copepods. To meet this demand, it is necessary to have a stock of $20 \times 110 \times 10^3$ or $2·2 \times 10^6$ copepods, since each copepod takes 20 days to reproduce its own weight. The necessary food for this number of copepods will be $20 \times 2·2 \times 10^6$ algal cells, since each weighs 0·1 mg and reproduces in 2 days.

We can now summarize these results as two pyramids, one of numbers and the other of biomass, as follows:

	Algae	Copepods	Fish A	Fish B
Numbers	4.4×10^7	2.2×10^6	11	1
Biomass	4.4 kg	2.2 kg	11 kg	5 kg

Note that, as we had previously expected (Book 1 p. 6), the numbers of organisms decrease as we move upwards from one trophic level to another but this is not true of biomass. Clearly, if we alter the times needed for reproduction, we will get different sets of values. If, for example, we assume that each algal cell reproduces every day, then the necessary biomass or 'standing crop' of algal cells will be only 2.2×10^7 or 2.2 kg, while if the copepods took 60 days in which to reproduce themselves, their necessary stock would be trebled to 6.6 kg, as their 'productivity' would have been reduced to one-third.

This example serves to emphasize that the productivity of any organism is not a simple function of the biomass present; it is also affected by the growth rate of the organism. It is indeed obvious that if you regularly remove the same quantity of meat from two flocks of farm animal, one of which grows half as quickly as the other, the result on their numbers will be very different. The numbers of the slow-growing species may decrease with time while the faster-growing species may actually increase in number.

One way in which this effect of growth rate upon the productive yield of an ecosystem finds expression is in the differences in the standing crop (or biomass) of plankton in temperate and tropical waters. The standing crop is, in general, much less in the tropics, but, as a result of higher temperatures, the growth rate of the plankters is higher. Consequently if other conditions—such as the supply of nutrients—are not limiting, the same final yield of plankton-feeding fish may be obtained in tropical waters with a smaller standing crop of plankton.

We can look at our calculation in a different way. Let us replace fish B by a fisherman. Our calculation shows that, from this particular pond, a fisherman could remove 11 kg of fish A every 360 days for an indefinite period. This is called the maximum sustainable yield. If the fisherman removes more, then the population of fish A will decrease since not sufficient individuals will remain to reproduce themselves. This is the situation described as over-fishing. Clearly the value of the maximum sustainable yield is a matter of considerable practical importance.

About 10 percent of the energy content of the material passed from one trophic level to another is used in the production of new material (Book 1 chap. 1); this proportion is only about 5 percent or less for homeothermic vertebrates which use a considerable quantity of their energy intake in thermoregulation. If we knew the productivity of the producers, we could calculate the expected yield at each subsequent stage in a food chain. In this way we might be able to estimate the maximum sustainable yield at any trophic level for any ecosystem. Such a calculation is not restricted to seas or lakes; it can be made for

terrestrial ecosystems as well. The productivity of producers within any ecosystem is spoken of as 'net primary productivity'. We may first consider the ways in which we might measure its value.

Methods of measuring primary productivity

Phytoplankton

The easiest way to measure primary productivity of phytoplankton is in terms of oxygen production during photosynthesis. Two bottles are used, one transparent and the other painted black to exclude light. Both are filled with water from the pond or lake whose productivity is to be assessed, and suspended for a measured period of time by strings in the lake at the depth from which the water samples were taken. Then the oxygen contents of the bottles are measured using the Winkler method. The phytoplankton in the dark bottle will have reduced the original oxygen content of the water by respiration (R), whereas in the light bottle the oxygen content of the water will have increased by the amount of the excess of photosynthesis (P) over R, i.e. $P - R$. It is clear that the final difference between the oxygen concentrations of the bottles will be $P - R + R$, which is P.

This method involves a number of assumptions, one of which is that respiration rate is the same in the dark as in the light. If radioisotope facilities are available, a more satisfactory method is to measure the rate of incorporation of added radiocarbon into phytoplankton in the water sample. The radiocarbon is normally added as a bicarbonate.

Aquatic macrophytes and land plants

The productivity of aquatic macrophytes can also be measured by radioisotope techniques, but the basis of the most commonly used method, both for these and large land plants, is the repeated measurement of biomass. As a simple case we may consider the measurement of maize productivity. At the time (t_0) when the crop is planted the maize biomass (B_0 g m^{-2}) consists only of the sown seeds. When it has been growing for a fortnight or so (t_1) there will be a cover of green shoots whose biomass (B_1 g m^{-2}) can be found from the dry weights of random samples. Productivity will then be

$$\frac{B_1 - B_0}{t_1 - t_0} \text{ g m}^{-2} \text{ week}^{-1}$$

After about two months (t_2) the crop can be sampled again to determine biomass (B_2), but by this time some of the leaves may have died and fallen. Because we want to know the productivity throughout the growing season we have to estimate the weight of leaves which have died (D_2) and also the weight of leaves eaten by predators (E_2), and add these values to our final biomass.

The productivity between first and second occasions of sampling will thus be

$$\frac{B_2 - B_1 + D_2 + E_2}{t_2 - t_1} \ \text{g m}^{-2} \ \text{week}^{-1}$$

In general terms, if we use ΔB for increase in biomass and t for change in time, then productivity (P) will be

$$P = \frac{\Delta B + D + E}{t}$$

Productivity determined in this way excludes losses due to respiration by the plant, and is therefore termed net productivity.

It is easy to use the same method to find shoot productivity of savanna grasses. At the end of the dry season there are no shoots so all the biomass subsequently found must have been formed during the period of observation. Growth of the roots of savanna grasses is much more difficult to determine, as without further investigation we are not able to estimate what proportion of them has survived from the previous growing season.

Measurement of the primary productivity of forest vegetation is the most difficult, because plant tissues of all ages are inextricably mixed together. The outer layer of wood on a stem may have formed this year, but the deeper layers will be older. The leaves on one plant may all have been produced during the past month while those on another may have survived more than a year. In temperate deciduous forests this difficulty does not arise because leaf production and fall occur more or less simultaneously in all the trees, while in transverse sections of stems it is possible to distinguish annual rings of wood increment. Although calculations to disentangle the production of one year from that of the next are tedious, they are not impossible. Even in tropical forest, rough estimates have been made by measuring the girths and heights of trees at intervals, and calculating their annual increase in biomass. To this value must be added the annual production of leaves and twigs. This is most readily measured by collecting falling dead leaves and twigs (litter) in nets raised on sticks a little distance above the forest floor (Fig. 15.13) and weighing the 'catch' each month (Fig. 15.14). We can then determine annual production by making the reasonable assumption that the quantity of leaves in the forest canopy remains constant from year to year. The difficulties are such, however, that any estimate of tropical forest productivity is subject to considerable error. Even the estimation of rates of timber production in natural forest is by no means easy, as similarly-sized individual trees of the same species may increase in girth at very different rates.

Productivity of different biomes

From measurements of this sort we can obtain information

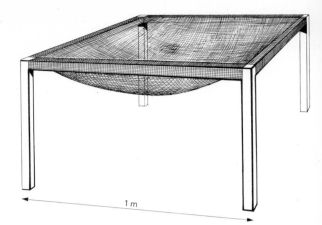

15.13 Litter trap consisting of a framework of sticks supporting a shallow bag of 1 mm mesh nylon mosquito netting.

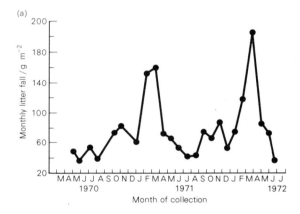

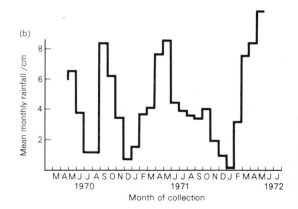

15.14 (a) Results of litter sampling in a Ghana forest. Litter fall reaches a maximum each year towards the end of the dry season. (b) Mean monthly rainfall in the same locality. (After John.)

Table 15.2 Primary productivity of some regions of the world (*Data from Whittaker*)

Biome	Mean productivity (dry g m^{-2} y^{-1})	Mean biomass (dry kg m^{-2})	% of total world productivity
Desert	70 or less	0·7	0·8
Open sea	125	0·003	25·3
Inshore waters	350	0·01	5·8
Temperate grassland	500	1·5	2·7
Agricultural land	650	1·0	6·4
Savanna	700	4·0	5·5
Temperate forest	1 300	30·0	14·3
Tropical forest	2 000	45·0	24·4
All oceans	155	0·009	33·5
All land	730	12·5	66·5

upon the expected relative productivity of different regions. Some average values of these data are listed in Table 15.2. This shows that there is no constant relation between productivity and biomass, and also that on a global scale, the open oceans are a major source of total primary production, largely because the oceans constitute the greater part of the earth's surface. The biomass per unit area in the oceans is small and hence this high total productivity is not easy to exploit. The second most productive biome is tropical forest. Here too exploitation presents difficulties as the ecosystem can very easily be destroyed.

Maximum yield to man

Knowing the primary productivity of an ecosystem we may attempt to compute its expected yield of material, regarding man as the top predator. Thus in a savanna ecosystem, we can imagine the food web as running

$$\text{vegetation} \rightarrow \text{cattle} \rightarrow \text{man}$$

As Table 15.2 shows, the primary productivity of savanna is of the order of 700 g dry wt m^{-2} year^{-1} Assuming that 5 percent of this is available for new growth of cattle, such productivity should result in a meat yield of 35 g m^{-2} year^{-1}. In fact the yield is lower than this for two reasons. Firstly, not all the productivity is exploited by the cattle; some fraction will be used by other herbivores including insects, birds and small mammals, while part of it is in a form unacceptable to cattle as food. Secondly, not all the primary productivity is exploited by consumers of any sort; some of it returns directly to the decomposers in the soil.

Similar considerations apply to an aquatic ecosystem. On p. 274 we considered a highly simplified situation in which all production flowed along a single food chain. In reality, material is lost from each trophic level, so that we may rewrite the food chain as follows:

phytoplankton → copepods → fish A → fish B

filter feeders and decomposers

Further there will be secondary loops in the food web such as

phytoplankton → bacteria → copepods → fish

so that there may be very many trophic steps between initial production and material becoming available to fish as food.

Obtaining maximum yield

The practical problem facing the herdsman or the fisherman is to exploit the primary productivity with the maximum of efficiency. While range management may ensure that game or cattle in a savanna area will give maximum yield, comparable management of an aquatic ecosystem is far more difficult. It does not even follow that high primary productivity results in the greatest economic yield. Thus, for example, in some European and American lakes the inflow of nutrients, especially phosphate, is very high. As a result there is both high productivity and biomass of algae. Such algae may develop very rapidly, forming a 'bloom'. This is followed by the death of large numbers of algal cells and, as they decompose, the water is partly or completely deoxygenated leading to the death of some consumers. This is a condition of extreme 'eutrophication' and, despite the high primary productivity, secondary production may be reduced. Even if secondary production remains high, other consequences can be serious since in such waters the species of fish which survive may be of lesser economic value than those originally present: high levels of production of fish with little or no commercial value can thus be one result of human activity upon lake ecosystems. On land, the problem is more usually one of excessive exploitation, leading to falling productivity, and the ecosystem may develop into one where the action of natural forces results in erosion so that the productivity decreases even further.

The study of populations of organisms, how they grow and what regulates their size, is of great practical importance in both fisheries and agriculture. We have seen how it relates to problems arising from the attack of insect pests on crops and how it may assist in directing policy to obtain greater yields of meat and fish. It is one aspect of the biological problems of feeding mankind. In the following chapters we shall consider these problems, which will show more fully the practical implications and applications of much we have discussed already.

Problems

1 After the rains the grass grows in the savanna and then withers. Is this type of annual cycle equivalent to any of the patterns of population regulation illustrated in Fig. 15.1? What pattern might describe the regulation of tree population in a deciduous forest?

2 In various years the total number of first-instar larvae of an insect on plants in 25 m^2 plots was counted when different population densities of adults were in the area. The following observations were made:

Numbers of adults 25 m^{-2}	6	12	18	21	24	29	35	38	43
Numbers of larvae 25 m^{-2}	40	120	230	310	430	520	525	460	320

Suggest various effects which might account for such results.

3 Laboratory studies were made upon four different species of parasitic wasp which oviposited in the eggs of a moth. Different numbers of moth eggs were offered to 10 females of each parasitoid for 30 minutes. The parasitoids were then removed and the number of eggs parasitized was determined. The following results were obtained:

Number of eggs	40	80	120	160
Numbers of eggs parasitized by				
Species A	11	19	31	40
Species B	4	11	23	45
Species C	6	10	17	23
Species D	17	29	32	37

Compare the possible importance of the four parasitoids in regulating the population density of the moth.

4 The number of breeding pairs of a territorial bird was observed annually in an isolated woodland. Data were

also collected of the mean number of young birds surviving to fly from the nest each year. The following results were obtained:

Number of pairs	19	44	59	82	99	136
Fledglings per pair	6·5	6·1	4·3	3·6	2·3	1·3

The mean clutch size was 7·6 eggs per nest and was the same in all years.

Do these figures support the view that territoriality in birds can serve as a mechanism of population regulation? Comment on the two extreme values.

5 Imagine an experiment in which a species of house fly is cultured so that the larvae have an unlimited supply of food. The food supply for the short-lived adults is, however, limited. The oviposition rate of the adults is proportional to their food intake, and if the latter falls below a minimal level, no eggs will be laid. Sketch the probable changes in adult numbers with time over several generations.

6 The data presented in Table 2.5 show that *Peromyscus maniculatus gracilis*, which is normally restricted to a woodland habitat, spent almost as much time in one half of the experimental room as the other. Comment on this observation in the light of the information on p. 271 on the distribution of voles on small islands. What experimental investigation with the two subspecies of *Peromyscus* do you consider might be of interest? What technical problems would arise in carrying out such an investigation? Suggest possible methods of solving them.

7 One characteristic of the feeding habits of many insectivorous birds is that they will concentrate their attack upon one particular type of food until its numbers are so reduced as to make it a rarity. The birds will then turn to feeding almost exclusively on some other more abundant food item. When the population of the original prey builds up again, the birds may return to it once more as a source of food.

Make sketches to show how such behaviour might affect the population density of (a) two species of rapidly breeding phytophagous hemiptera and (b) two species of butterfly which both oviposit at the start of the rains and have only one generation a year.

8 Seeds of a weed called shepherd's purse were planted in pots at different densities. The number of seeds set by each plant was recorded and the following data obtained:

Number of plants per pot	Mean seed production per plant
1	23 741
5	6 102
50	990
100	451
200	210

Note that 200 plants produced about 200 seeds each, and that the seed production per plant was approximately double when there were half that number of plants in a pot. Is the seed yield from a single plant as great as might be expected by extrapolation from these two values? At what plant density is the seed yield per pot maximum? Suggest an interpretation of the changes in seed yield per pot with plant density. Can the reduction in seed yield per plant with increasing population density act as a factor regulating population density?

9 On p. 271 we stated that if the flour beetles *Tribolium confusum* and *T. castaneum* are grown in a mixed culture at 24°C and 30 percent R.H., only *T. confusum* survived, while at 34°C and 70 percent R.H. only *T. castaneum* survived. What results would you expect to find from a large number of mixed cultures at, say, 29°C and 30 percent R.H.?

10 Many of the savanna herbivores give birth to their young in a very short breeding season, commonly just before the rains. What advantages do you consider such animals may gain from this?

11 In Fig. 15.6 data are presented of the variations in the probable population densities of the Snowshoe hare and the lynx. What assumption is made in using these data to assess the populations?

12 On p. 265 we defined two types of 'factor'; those which regulate the numbers of a population and those which control them. Insecticides are used to control the numbers of insects. To which of these two categories does the biological control of a pest by the introduction of an exotic predator or parasite belong?

Bibliography

Further reading

Boughey, A. S.   *Ecology of Populations*, Collier-Macmillan, 2nd ed. 1973, Chap. 3

Kormondy, E. J.   *Concepts of Ecology*, Prentice-Hall, 1969, pp. 91–111

MacArthur, R., Connell, J.   *The Biology of Populations*, Wiley, 1966, Chap. 6

Odum, E. P.   *Ecology*, Holt, Rinehart and Winston, 1963, pp. 89–110

Phillipson, J.   *Ecological Energetics*, Arnold, 1966, Chap. 5

Solomon, M. E.   *Population Dynamics*, Arnold, 1969, Chaps. 5–7

Whittaker, R. H.   *Communities and Ecosystems*, Collier-Macmillan, 1970, Chap. 4

Wilson, E. O., Bossert, W. H.   *A Primer of Population Biology*, Sinauer Associates, 1971, pp. 127–64

Evans, H. E.   'Predatory Wasps', *Scientific American*, 1963, Vol. 208, pt. 4, p. 145

Myers, J. H., Krebs, C. J.   'Population Cycles in Rodents', *Scientific American*, 1974, Vol. 230, pt. 6, p. 38

Part 5
The ecology of man

16 Man's food—plant crops

Almost all human beings depend principally on plant crops and domestic animals for their food. Of the crops, the most extensively grown are those staples which provide the carbohydrate that constitutes the bulk of our diet. Within this category the cereals—large-seeded grasses such as maize, rice, wheat, sorghum and millet—are pre-eminent, having the advantages over root crops of easy harvesting, of low water and thus high energy content, and of greater tolerance of storage. Table 16.1 gives figures for the production of the most important staple crops, showing that the world's principal food crop is wheat, closely followed by maize.

In addition to cereals and roots, other plant crops such as starchy fruits, sweet fruits, oily fruits and protein-rich seeds are also cultivated on a wide scale.

Compared with those dependent on agriculture, very few communities in the modern world live by gathering wild plants and hunting, as do the bushmen of the Kalahari and the pygmies of the Ituri Forest of Zaïre. These people show wonderful skill in their knowledge of plants and in their ability to locate those suitable for food, while their hunting methods are ingenious. Nevertheless their numbers remain small because the majority of plants are poisonous or at least inedible (p. 141). 1 km^2 of forest zone can support 120 agriculturalists in south-east Nigeria, but less than one pygmy in Zaïre. The great advantage of agriculture is that it permits the production of much greater quantities of food per unit area of ground, and thus the establishment of large settled communities.

The origins of agriculture

On the time scale of human existence, agriculture is a very recent invention. Man has probably existed in East Africa for at least two or three million years (p. 495), but the first evidence of agriculture dates from less than 10 000 years ago. One of the oldest agricultural settlements known to us is the small village of Jarmo in Iraq (Fig. 16.1). By digging below the present village level, archaeologists have found undoubted remains of cultivated barley and wheat as well as tools used for their cultivation which are 8 000 years old. Among household rubbish were also found bones of domesticated goats and pigs. From the Middle East agriculture seems to have spread quickly into North Africa and thence to the Sudan. Archaeologists have discovered, on the shores of Lake Fayum in Egypt, grain-storage bins in village sites dating back to about 4500 B.C. Although the archaeological evidence is still scanty, we know that millet, cowpea and okra were cultivated in the Sudan about 3500 B.C. and there is evidence for agriculture in Kenya at about 3000 B.C. Agriculture may well have been practised before that time; these are, however, the earliest dates for which we have as yet certain evidence.

It is remarkable that the earliest record of agriculture in

Table 16.1 Production of major crops in 1970 (*Data from F.A.O.*)

Crop	World total (t × 10^6)	North America (t × 10^6)	North America (% of world total)	Africa (excluding S. Africa) (t × 10^6)	Africa (excluding S. Africa) (% of world total)
Wheat	288	46	16	5	2
Maize	232	107	46	11	5
Rice	134	2	1	3	2
Barley	120	18	15	4	3
Sugar	71	5	7	2	3
Millets (including sorghum)	56	18	32	15	27
Citrus	38	10	26	2	5
Soybeans	35	31	89	0	0
Bananas	29	0	0	2	7
Groundnuts	16	0	0	4	25

16.1 Asia Minor, showing the sites of various ancient villages, towns and cities. The earliest site shown is that of Shanider which was inhabited shortly after 9000 B.C.; here were found remains of sheep, and the presence of flint sickle blades indicates that crops were cultivated. Jerico was founded just after 8000 B.C., while Jarmo is about a thousand years later. Alikosh is of about the same date as Jarmo and here remains of unquestionably domesticated goats and sheep have been found. Catal Hüyük is one of the earliest sites in which pottery appears, and dates from about 6800 B.C. Ur, the city of Abraham, is later, the earliest settlement being about 5500 B.C., while the city of Babylon was founded about 2700 B.C. although there were earlier settlements in the area.

the New World dates from almost the same period: 3500 B.C. At this time maize was being domesticated in Mexico. Despite this coincidence, it seems most probable that there was no direct connection between the peoples of the two continents, as quite different crops were involved.

Domestication of cereals

The story of domestication is best known for cereals. If grains are accidentally charred while being roasted they may be preserved in the village sediments in an identifiable condition. Other grains have been impressed in soft clay which has subsequently been baked for pottery; the forms of the grains can be identified. Because they are wind-pollinated, pollen is produced in abundance by all grasses; in some cases, such as maize, this can be identified even after many centuries. Grain crops were harvested with special implements, stored in pottery jars and milled with characteristic grinding stones. All these artifacts are readily preserved, and, when excavated, provide evidence of cereal cultivation.

It is striking that the closest relatives of cereals are grasses which occur as weeds, often in the same field as the crop. For example, the worst weed of cultivated oats, *Avena sativa*, is the wild oat, *Avena fatua*. Wild millet, *Pennisetum cinereum*, grows alongside cultivated *P.*

americanum, and so on. It thus seems probable that the ancestors of cereals were weeds growing on rubbish heaps in pre-agricultural villages. To see the effects of domestication we may now examine the differences between the weeds and the crops developed from them.

Weeds have efficient dispersal mechanisms which enable them promptly to colonize open, temporary habitats (p. 2). Among grasses, the grain is often tightly enclosed by the bracts and sometimes part of the axis of the inflorescence; these structures frequently bear bristles or hairs to aid dispersal. At maturity, these propagules separate from the inflorescence stalk and from each other. In wild species of the genus *Pennisetum*, for example, each propagule consists of one to three spikelets surrounded by an involucre of bristles which adapt it for dispersal by wind. Weedy grasses have small grains, as they germinate under conditions of high light intensity, and large food stores are not essential. Dormancy mechanisms are important to ensure that some seeds remain in the soil as a reserve while others germinate. Cultivated cereals have larger grains, which often protrude beyond the bracts or are only loosely enveloped and can therefore be separated from the bracts during threshing. Grains which are dispersed when ripe will be lost to the farmer during harvest, and in cereals the grains tend to adhere to the inflorescence. There may be no period of dormancy; most grains germinate as soon as they are planted. Fig. 16.2 shows the differences between wild and cultivated species of *Pennisetum*.

Maize is exceptional in that wild forms are not now in existence, but American archaeologists have discovered fossil ears of the weedy ancestor of maize during excavations of Mexican caves in which people lived 6000 years ago. This plant produced small grains tightly enclosed by bracts; the inflorescence was exposed and broke up at maturity. Fig. 16.3 shows the changes which have been produced by domestication; these stages can be found in successive layers of the cave deposits. In modern maize the grains are so well covered by the leaves of the cob that natural dispersal is impossible.

Such changes could have been produced by unintentional selection by the cultivators. Suppose, for example, that a field contained cereal plants which varied in the readiness with which their seeds tended to fall from the inflorescence. During harvest most of the seed would fall from the dispersing variety and the farmer would therefore tend to collect a higher proportion of grain from the non-dispersing variety. If some of the collected grains were sown, the proportion of non-dispersing plants in the crop would be higher than in the previous crop, and so on. Selection for ease of removal in threshing could follow a similar course.

In modern times selection of crop varieties has become the conscious aim of farmers and scientists. As a result there are now many thousands of varieties of crops such as maize, differing in height, yield, composition of the grain, colour and so on. Some are cold-tolerant and can be

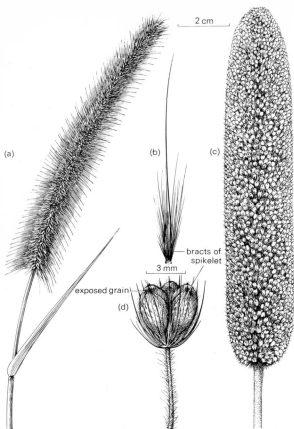

grown in latitudes as high as 50°N; others are cold-sensitive and are restricted to the tropics and subtropics. Wheat is less adaptable than maize and lower-yielding, but subtropical varieties now exist which can be grown successfully in warm parts of Brazil, India and so on. The process of selection of desirable varieties continues today. Since 1966, new varieties of rice and wheat have been made available to farmers after very intensive plant breeding and selection. These have several important new characteristics. The plants themselves are short so that comparatively little energy is diverted into the production of stem as opposed to seed. These varieties are highly responsive to fertilizers and grow very rapidly; for example, the rice matures in 120 rather than 180 days so that three crops may be harvested each year, to yield a total of up to 5 tonnes ha^{-1}. This multiple cropping is possible as the new varieties have only a slight photoperiodic response (Book 1 p. 306) and thus are less sensitive to seasonal effects. These new varieties are of vital importance in attempting to feed the world's constantly increasing

16.2 (above) Wild and cultivated species of the grass genus *Pennisetum*. (a) Flower spike of a wild *Pennisetum;* note the long bristles which surround individual spikelets. (b) Spikelet of the wild species almost hidden by bristles; the grain is completely covered by bracts. (c) Spike of cultivated *Pennisetum americanum* (Bulrush millet) (d) Group of three spikelets of Bulrush millet surrounded by involucre of short bristles. Note that the grain protrudes beyond the bracts.

16.3 (below) Maize cobs from different levels of deposit of a cave formerly occupied by man in Mexico. From left to right the cobs date approximately from 5000, 4000, 3000 and 1000 B.C. The cob on the right is modern.

human population; their development has been spoken of as a 'Green Revolution'.

Domestication of root crops

The tubers of a few wild plants are edible, for example those of some species of *Raphionacme* (Book 1 Fig. 22.17), but the majority are protected from attack by animals because they contain poisonous substances. Some varieties of cassava, for instance, are highly dangerous by reason of their cyanide content and can only be eaten safely after prolonged cooking (p. 141). Wild yams contain various toxic steroids, and from time to time the newspapers report deaths caused by their imprudent consumption. The genus *Solanum*, which includes such edible species as *S. tuberosum*, the potato, *S. lycopersicum*, the tomato, and *S. melongena*, the garden egg plant, contains many poisonous wild species. Domestication of these species must have been a perilous process involving the selection of varieties of low toxicity.

On the other hand the cultivation of root crops requires little sophistication. Each tuber may contain a considerable quantity of food and tuber collection is a straightforward process for which a wooden digging stick can suffice; no threshing and winnowing is required as for cereal crops. Storage is in the ground. For these reasons, it has been suggested that root culture may have preceded cereal culture, but as there may be no characteristic metal or ceramic artifacts associated with root crops, and no preserved tubers, archaeological evidence is scanty or absent.

Domestication of fruits and seeds

Fleshy fruits are the only plant organs which are positively adapted for consumption by animals. Whereas the roots of wild plants and the grains of wild grasses are seldom used as food, wild fruits make a considerable contribution to the diet of almost all peoples. In the savanna zone of Africa the seeds of the shea butter tree, *Butyrospermum paradoxum*, are one of the most important sources of cooking fat; but although the trees may be protected they can scarcely be called cultivated. There are no differences between the seeds of trees growing near villages and those in the savanna far from cultivation. The same is true of the baobab tree, *Adansonia digitata*; Book 1 Fig. 22.27, and of the dawadawa tree, *Parkia clappertoniana*, both of which have important edible seeds. In the forest zone the oil palm, *Elaeis guineensis*, grows semi-wild, and until quite recent times does not seem to have been significantly improved by cultivation.

Notable exceptions are the banana and plantain, *Musa*, whose wild ancestors in south-east Asia have small inedible fruits with large seeds. Domestication of this genus has been accompanied by loss of seeds and consequent sterility. Bananas and plantains must be propagated vege-

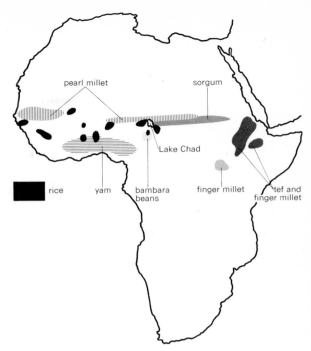

16.4 Map showing the probable areas of origin of different indigenous African domesticated crops. Pearl millet is an alternative common name for bulrush millet. (Simplified from Harlan.)

tatively, and cannot therefore survive for long in the wild.

Spread of crops from centres of origin

Each crop must have originated in a particular restricted area (Fig. 16.4). This centre of origin can be located using a combination of different kinds of evidence: distribution of wild relatives, the number of different varieties, direct archaeological evidence, and even folklore. Some crops remain restricted to a small area around their centre of origin; for example, the cultivated *Ensete*, a relative of the banana, and tef, a small-grained cereal, are restricted to the highlands of Ethiopia. Others have spread widely and the determination of their centres of origin may present some difficulty.

For most tropical African crops there is little doubt as to which are indigenous and which introduced. The indigenous cereals of greatest importance are sorghum (*Sorghum bicolor*, Fig. 16.5), which appears to have been first cultivated in north-east Africa, bulrush millet (*Pennisetum americanum*) which, despite its name, has come from the same region, and African rice (*Oryza glaberrima*), which is cultivated mainly along the great rivers of West Africa, the Niger and the Senegal. Finger millet, *Eleusine coracana*, and fonio, *Digitaria exilis*, are of more local importance.

Yams must have been cultivated in West Africa for a

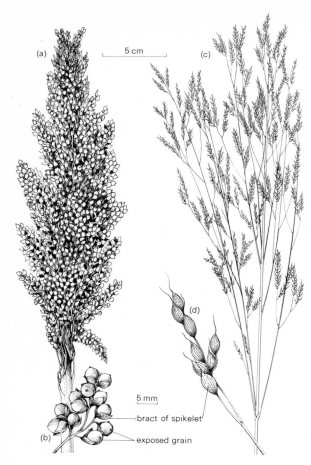

16.5 (a) *Sorghum bicolor*, the cultivated sorghum or 'durra'. (b) A group of durra spikelets; note the exposed grains. (c) *Sorghum arundinaceum*, a wild species which is a common weed. The inflorescence is much less compact than in durra. (d) Spikelets of *Sorghum arundinaceum*; the grains are hidden by the bracts.

very long time, perhaps more than 2000 years. Evidence for the antiquity of their culture includes the facts that the cultivated species, *Dioscorea rotundata* and *D. cayenensis*, are not known in a wild state and also that elaborate rituals attend their cultivation. The taboo among certain peoples on the use of iron implements in yam culture suggests that their cultivation may have antedated the introduction of iron.

Edible protein-rich seeds (Fig. 16.6) which were first cultivated in Africa include the Bambarra ground-nut (*Voandzeia subterranea*), the yam bean (*Sphenostylis stenocarpa*), probably cowpea (*Vigna unguiculata*), various melon seeds such as egushi (*Cucumeropsis mannii*) and the baobab and *Parkia* mentioned above. Including the

vegetable oils from the oil palm and shea butter trees, a full range of vegetable foods was thus available to African farmers before introductions were made from other continents.

Some of these introductions are very old. Bananas and plantains originated in south-east Asia and were probably carried to Madagascar and East Africa by Asiatic travellers about 2000 years ago. Bananas had reached West Africa at the time of the first Portuguese visits in the fifteenth century A.D.; in fact the name 'banana' is probably derived from a West African word.

The Portuguese introduced to West Africa several crops which they carried from South America; the most important of these are cassava (*Manihot esculenta*), red pepper (*Capsicum* spp.) and maize (*Zea mays*). These three crops are so highly productive and adaptable that they have tended to displace their indigenous counterparts, particularly in the forest zone.

Agricultural methods

As crops have changed, so too have the methods for cultivating them. Nevertheless certain basic problems always confront the farmer and certain principles must be observed in facing these problems. Crop plants need help if they are to compete successfully with other plants. Thus before planting the farmer must remove the previously existing vegetation, cutting down trees and cultivating the soil to destroy roots. Weeds which invade the clearing must be controlled. The farmer's procedures must nevertheless preserve soil structure and prevent erosion. The maintenance of soil fertility is a major problem. When man clears an area of ground to use it for cultivation, he is making available to his crops the mineral nutrients formerly used by the natural vegetation. Before the area was cleared the nutrient materials went from soil to plants and back again to the soil. Loss of nutrient material from an area still covered by natural vegetation is small and what is lost is replaced by the processes of rock weathering (p. 120). Once man has established himself in villages, this balance is disturbed. When he harvests a crop and takes it back to the village, he takes away from the land some of the nutrients which formerly cycled between soil and plant cover. Table 16.2 indicates the quantities of inorganic nutrients in various crops. Land can only be cropped continuously if the inherent fertility of the soil is high, as in some soils developed in volcanic ash or recent alluvium, or if a method is devised for returning to the soil sufficient nutrients to replace what has been taken from it.

Early agriculture was sometimes practised in river valleys, such as that of the Nile, in which flood sediments replenish the nutrient store. Household refuse and animal dung may be used to enrich land near villages; continuous cultivation based on this practice is found in the Sudan zone of West Africa at the present day. Under this system land further from the village is not manured and must be

Table 16.2 Nutrients removed from the land when crops are harvested at the indicated yield (*Data from Nye and Greenland*)

Crop	Yield (kg ha^{-1})	Nutrients (kg ha^{-1}) Nitrogen	Phosphorus	Potassium	Calcium
Maize (grains)	1 000	15	3	3	0·2
Rice (grains)	1 000	12	3	4	1
Groundnut (kernels and shells)	700	27	2	4	1
Cassava (fresh tubers)	10 000	22	3	50	4
Yam (fresh tubers)	10 000	34	3	35	1
Banana (fruits)	10 000	22	4	60	1
Cocoa (beans)	500	12	3	10	?

rested under fallow after cropping to allow soil nutrient status to recover.

The system of bush fallow, or shifting cultivation as it is often called, is used by large numbers of peasant farmers in tropical countries at the present time, and in the past has been used widely in temperate countries also. For this reason we must look carefully at shifting cultivation and consider the reasons for its popularity and also its short-comings.

Shifting cultivation

The farmer in the forest zone will clear his chosen patch of forest in the dry season, cutting the smaller trees and bushes, but leaving the trees which are too large to fell. When the cut material has dried sufficiently the farmer will burn it, so that the ground surface is covered by a layer of ashes. After the first heavy rains the farmer will sow the first crop, usually maize, cultivating with his hoe only a few square centimetres around the holes into which the seed is dropped. When the maize is well established he will underplant with a perennial crop, usually cassava or plantain. After the maize has been harvested at the end of the first season the perennial crop continues to grow to be harvested in the following year. A third crop may also be taken before the farm is abandoned to weeds and succession to secondary forest. Fig. 16.7 shows how yields diminish with successive crops after clearing; unless fertilizer is available, it is not worth the farmer's while to continue cropping in the same place, and consequently he clears a farm elsewhere. The length of the fallow period depends largely on the local requirement for land. Where the population is low, twenty or more years will elapse before the secondary forest is once more cleared for farming, but in places of denser population the length of fallow will be correspondingly reduced. As a general rule, fallows shorter than ten years will not allow land to recover adequately, and if such short fallows become the rule soil fertility may show a progressive decline.

By what means does the fallow restore fertility? The roots of trees and shrubs are mainly superficial (p. 47), but some will go deep into the subsoil. Such roots will

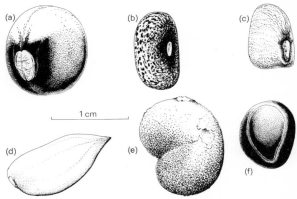

16.6 Protein-rich edible seeds, first cultivated in Africa (all drawn to same scale). (a) Bambarra ground-nut (*Voandzeia subterranea*). (b) Yam bean (*Sphenostylis stenocarpa*). (c) Cowpea (*Vigna unguiculata*). (d) Egushi (*Cucumeropsis mannii*). (e) Baobab (*Adansonia digitata*). (f) Dawadawa (*Parkia clappertoniana*).

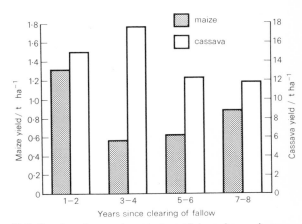

16.7 Results of experiments in which maize and cassava were grown in a continuous rotation for eight years on land cleared from ten-year-old secondary forest in Ghana. The second and third maize crops were reduced by maize rust epidemics. (After Nye and Stephens.)

bring up nutrients from below the depth at which shallow-rooting crops could reach them. The nutrients are translocated to twigs and leaves, and when these die are deposited on the soil surface in the litter. During the processes of decomposition some nutrients will almost immediately be taken up again by plant roots, others will become part of the increasing quantity of humus (Fig. 16.8). Two main processes are thus important in fertility restoration under fallow (Fig. 7.4): firstly, the transfer of nutrients from subsoil (and weathering rock) to topsoil, and secondly, the increase in humus which is both a reservoir of nitrogen and phosphorus and a contributor to the cation-exchange capacity. A third important factor is the increase in soil nitrogen which results from the activity of nitrogen-fixing bacteria during the fallow period.

To summarize: shifting cultivation has many good features from the point of view of a farmer with little capital, who grows crops on forest soils whose fertility is quickly exhausted. Although bush cutting is laborious, the use of fire makes it possible to clear the ground for planting. With the exception of nitrogen and sulphur which are lost as gaseous oxides, the nutrients which were present in the fallow are deposited on the soil surface as ash, giving a good start to the crop. The factors of burning, ash and early rain may stimulate nitrification in the topsoil; nitrate is never found to be limiting in the early stages of cropping. Cultivation is minimal, roots are left in the soil, and a leafy cover is quickly established and maintained through the cropping period; all these features minimize erosion. Finally, the system incorporates an effective method of fertility restoration.

In savanna, on the other hand, the advantages of shifting cultivation are less marked. Because of annual burning a savanna fallow does not build up nutrients nearly as quickly as does a forest fallow, nor does it lead to such a rapid increase in humus. Yields immediately after a savanna fallow are often poor because of the activity of grass roots in slowing nitrification (p. 134). Erosion is not adequately controlled, partly because of annual removal of cover by burning, and partly because the roots of grasses must be dug out to make cropping possible.

Even as a forest system, shifting cultivation is widely condemned, despite the advantages enumerated above. It is obviously wasteful of land. If the cycle consists of two years cropping followed by eight years fallow, it follows that only 20 percent of the land is yielding at any given time. Where land is abundant and the population low this is not serious, but in most African countries the population is increasing at an annual rate of about 2·5 percent (p. 358); forest is thus disappearing rapidly, to the detriment of the timber industry. Increasing pressure on the land leads to shortened fallow, and permanent soil deterioration and erosion. Productivity is low under shifting cultivation; the system first evolved to meet the needs of subsistence agriculture, and it is not capable of generating a surplus sufficient to feed the townspeople of an industrialized economy. For example, in tropical Africa it is estimated that 60 to 75 percent of the people are engaged in agriculture, but considerable quantities of food must nevertheless be imported.

Mechanized agriculture

Advanced, mechanized systems of agriculture can be exceedingly productive. The average value of the annual product of a typical African farmer is only about one-twentieth that of his highly mechanized North American counterpart. Despite the evident potential advantages of mechanized, intensive farming it has not proved easy to substitute it for traditional methods of shifting cultivation, and we should now consider some of the difficulties.

Mechanical cultivation is not easy if the ground is full of large roots and stumps. The need to remove these has several major consequences. The clearing operation requires heavy bulldozers and is thus very expensive. If the farmer is to recover his costs, the land must be cropped efficiently for many more than two years, and this will only be possible if the land has reasonably high inherent fertility, if fertilizers are regularly applied, if weeds are controlled and if the varieties of crops grown are high-yielding. Where rain is insufficient the land may have to be irrigated, thus increasing the capital investment. For efficient mechanical planting and harvesting, monoculture may be necessary, that is, single crops should be grown over much larger areas than is usual in shifting cultivation. Monoculture brings its own problems of greatly increased incidence of crop disease and liability to insect attack. Moreover, the problems of soil conservation are also increased under mechanized systems. Removal of roots reduces soil stability and heavy cultivation may break

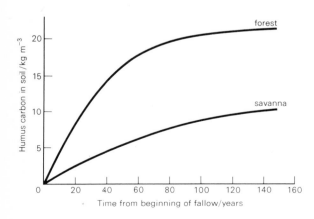

16.8 Increase of humus content of soil during fallow under forest and savanna. (After Nye and Greenland.)

down the soil structure. Addition of inorganic fertilizers will not prevent the humus content of the soil from decreasing under continuous cropping, and this may also cause the soil structure to deteriorate. Clean cultivation may not maintain the leafy cover needed to break the force of the rain. The operation of land clearing itself may result in the scraping off of the upper 10 cm of topsoil in which the bulk of the nutrients may be concentrated.

It is clear that neglect of any of the above considerations may entail the ruin of the whole scheme. Any system of agriculture will be successful only if the returns exceed the input. In traditional systems the input is small, and a comparatively modest return may be satisfactory. A mechanized scheme requires vastly more investment, and yields must be correspondingly much larger; this can be the case only where methods are scientifically sound, and where the levels of organization and management are high.

The history of attempts at large-scale agricultural modernization in tropical Africa is studded with spectacular failures. One of the best-known of these was the Groundnuts Scheme in Tanzania. The intention was to produce annually about 600 000 tonnes of groundnuts from 1·5 million hectares of previously largely uncultivated savanna in three parts of Tanzania. Originally, in 1947, a sum of £25 million was allocated for the project, but the difficulties were such that by 1951, when the scheme was abandoned, the cost had risen to £37 million. Problems were encountered with land clearing (Fig. 16.9) and cultivation, with low rainfall, with disease and so on. The money was largely wasted, and the product of greatest value was the realization that such schemes require much more careful planning, which should include considera-tion of ecological potential. If a mechanized scheme fails, the effects are long-lasting because the complete removal of woody plants will greatly slow down the recovery of the soil and the establishment of a woody fallow.

We shall now consider some of the more important aspects of improved agriculture.

Fertilizers

Two main types of fertilizer are used to maintain soil nutrient levels: organic fertilizers, such as animal manure, and inorganic fertilizers which are mixtures of pure chemicals. Organic manure has the great advantage of adding humus as well as nutrients to the soil, thus improving soil structure and increasing cation-exchange capacity. Another important advantage in countries lacking foreign exchange is that such fertilizers do not have to be imported. On the other hand, animal manure is bulky, and spreading several tonnes of it on each hectare, as may be necessary if its effect is to be noticeable, requires much labour. A major drawback is the difficulty in keeping healthy sufficient farm animals in the large areas which are infested with tsetse fly (p. 16). Northern Nigeria is an example of a country where it has been possible to encourage mixed farming, in which bullocks are used for ploughing and their dung is spread on the fields (Fig. 16.10). The number of northern Nigerian farmers practising this system increased from 2 000 in 1939 to 36 000 in 1964 under governmental encouragement.

Intensification of agriculture in all parts of the world has been made possible by increasing use of inorganic fertilizers. Fig. 16.11 shows that there is a strong correlation

16.9 Giant bulldozer clearing the land during the preparation of the Tanzanian Groundnuts Scheme.

16.10 Bullocks being used for ploughing in the dry savanna zone of West Africa.

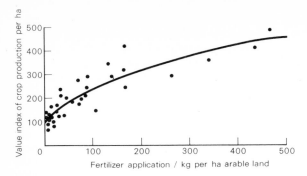

16.11 World-wide relationship between crop yields and fertilizer application. Each point on the graph represents the mean values for one country during the years 1956–58 (FAO).

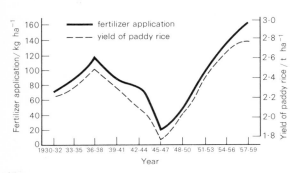

16.12 Effect of level of fertilizer use on the yield of paddy rice in Taiwan in the years 1930 to 1959. Note that the ordinate for yield does not start from zero (FAO).

between quantities of fertilizer used by different countries and the yields which they obtain from their crops. Fertilizers must be used continuously; Fig. 16.12 shows that a decline in fertilizer application to rice fields in Taiwan between 1936 and 1945 was accompanied by falling yields, but that yield increased dramatically after this time when fertilizer again became available.

The application of any fertilizer will not, however, automatically increase the farmer's profits. Much research is needed to find the kinds and quantities of fertilizer required under any set of conditions; in addition, it is necessary to show not merely that yields will be increased, but that the increase will more than cover the extra costs.

Fertilizer response depends not only on the soil, but on the crop; for example, Fig. 16.13 shows that although maize gives a large response to added phosphate on freshly cleared forest soils, cassava does not. The extent of response shown by the maize will depend on its variety. In general, the new high-yielding varieties (p. 281) will require higher levels of fertilizer if their potentialities are to be realized, while traditional low-yielding varieties may be

adapted to poor soils and unable to utilize much fertilizer (Fig. 16.14).

Soils can readily be analysed to find their content of particular elements, but it is not always possible to decide immediately from such results which elements are deficient. For reliable conclusions soil composition must be correlated with the results of experiments, fertilizer trials, in which the yield of a particular crop on unfertilized plots is compared with that on plots given various combinations of fertilizers. Such experiments have shown that although calcium, magnesium, sulphur and boron may occasionally be deficient, the elements which most commonly limit crop yields are nitrogen, phosphorus and potassium.

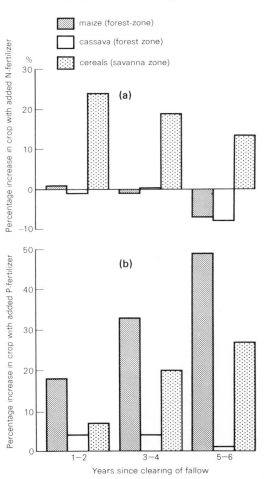

16.13 Increases in yield following application of (a) nitrogen and (b) phosphorus fertilizers; increase is expressed as percentage of yield in unfertilized control plots. Results for maize and cassava are from experiments in which maize and cassava were grown in continuous rotation on land cleared from ten year old secondary forest; Fig. 16.7 gives the control results. The results for cereals come from similar experiments in savanna. (After Nye and Stephens.)

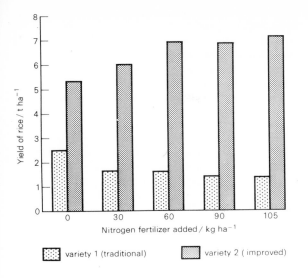

16.14 Response to application of nitrogen fertilizer by two varieties of rice in the Philippines. Variety 1 is a traditional type of rice which responds to increased nitrogen by producing much leaf and long stalks; the yield of grain however is reduced because such plants become top-heavy and are easily blown over in storms. Variety 2 is an improved type which has short stiff stalks even at high levels of nitrogen; fertilizer thus serves its intended function of increasing the yield (After Chandler).

Nitrogen

Fig. 16.13 shows that crops planted immediately after fallow under forest may fail to respond to added nitrogen fertilizer, but that responses are shown after two years cropping, and after savanna fallow. The improvement in nitrogen status under forest fallow is due partly to mineralization of humus and subsequent nitrification and partly to nitrogen fixation by soil bacteria.

Two main methods are available for improving the nitrogen level in the soil during cropping: addition of nitrogenous fertilizers, and encouragement of bacterial nitrogen fixation. One of the most popular nitrogenous fertilizers is ammonium sulphate. It has the advantage over nitrates of being less soluble, and requiring nitrification; for these reasons nitrate becomes available to plants more gradually and over longer periods from ammonium sulphate than directly from a nitrate. The sulphate part of the fertilizer may also serve a useful purpose in many savanna soils, which are frequently sulphur-deficient. Ammonium sulphate is synthesized commercially from sulphuric acid and ammonia; ammonia is manufactured from nitrogen and hydrogen by the Haber process, invented in 1905 by the German Fritz Haber and developed on a large scale in Germany during the 1914–18 war when fertilizers could not be imported to that country.

Encouragement of nitrogen fixation is most readily accomplished by planting a leguminous crop with nitrogen-fixing bacteria in its nodules (Table 16.3). Most of the nitrate fixed is retained within the plants, though some will get into the soil as rootlets and nodules die and decay. Nitrate is rapidly translocated from the roots of leguminous plants into their aerial parts and at maturity the greater part contributes to the stored protein in the large seeds. If the crop is ploughed in as green manure the soil will be greatly enriched with nitrogen. If, on the other hand, the crop is allowed to mature and, as with groundnuts or beans, the fruits are removed, the gain to the soil may be only slight. Leguminous crops do not fix so much nitrogen if the soil is already nitrate-rich; if the fallow period is to be long enough for potassium and phosphate levels to recover, a non-leguminous but vigorously growing fallow plant such as elephant grass (*Pennisetum purpureum*) may be as effective as a legume in promoting an increase in soil nitrate content. On the other hand, where phosphate supply is good and nitrate limits plant growth, the use of a leguminous cover crop (green manure) such as *Mucuna* (Book 1 p. 27) may allow land to be cropped continuously for as long as ten years.

Experiments were started in Nigeria in 1921 to find if leguminous green manures could be substituted for chemical fertilizers. This was found to be possible at Ibadan, on inherently fertile soils in the drier part of the forest zone, but on the poorer, leached soils in the high-

Table 16.3 Change in nitrogen content of soil following different treatments, at Ibadan, Nigeria. Treatments were started and initial nitrogen content of the upper 40 cm of soil was measured immediately after clearing secondary forest in the dry season; much of the topsoil was removed together with the vegetation. Two years later soil nitrogen content was remeasured. No plants were removed from the experimental plots at any time during the two years (*Data from Jaiyebo and Moore*)

Treatment	Increase in soil nitrogen (kg ha^{-1})
Soils left bare	36
Soil kept mulched with spear-grass leaves	56
Planted cover of stargrass (*Cynodon plectostachyus*)	64
Planted cover of the leguminous creeper kudzu (*Pueraria phaseoloides*)	259
Secondary thicket allowed to regenerate	216

rainfall areas of south-east Nigeria even the cover crops would not grow satisfactorily without fertilizers.

Phosphorus

Phosphorus in the soil is ultimately derived from the mineral apatite (calcium phosphate); this substance is rather rare in most rocks and phosphorus is therefore deficient in most soils. While one difficulty with nitrates is their high solubility, as a result of which they are readily leached away (p. 133), phosphate ion forms very sparingly soluble compounds with the iron and aluminium that are so abundant in most tropical soils; the plant can absorb only the small quantities of soluble ion in equilibrium with these insoluble substances. We can express this by saying that phosphorus may have a low potential even where the content is reasonably high.

About one-quarter of the total soil phosphorus is present in the form of organic compounds in humus. Although these compounds are unavailable to roots, they are of great importance because phosphate ion is liberated from them during humus mineralization; experiments using radioactive phosphorus have shown that roots commonly obtain over 90 percent of their phosphorus from the humus-rich topsoil in the upper 30 cm of the profile.

Phosphate fertilizer is derived initially from 'phosphate rock' which contains calcium phosphate: deposits occur, among other places, in North Africa and Togo. Phosphate rock is very insoluble and therefore releases phosphate ion only slowly if added directly to the soil. It is therefore treated commercially with sulphuric acid and the resulting mixture of calcium dihydrogen phosphate and calcium sulphate is marketed as 'superphosphate'.

$$Ca_3(PO_4)_2 + 2H_2SO_4 \rightarrow Ca(H_2PO_4)_2 + 2CaSO_4$$

The calcium sulphate is inert and adds bulk which must be transported with no advantage to the farmer. With excess sulphuric acid phosphate rock will, however, yield phosphoric acid and if further phosphate rock is treated with this material rather than directly with sulphuric acid, a concentrated product containing a very high percentage of calcium dihydrogen phosphate is obtained. This is sold as 'triple superphosphate'.

$$Ca_3(PO_4)_2 + 4H_3PO_4 \rightarrow 3Ca(H_2PO_4)_2$$

Most crops show large responses to phosphate fertilizer even on soil which has just been cleared from fallow (Fig. 16.13).

Potassium

This element is a component of felspars (p. 120) and is less commonly deficient than nitrogen and phosphorus. It is present in the soil as the cation, K^+, and is held in the cation-exchange complex of clay particles and humus. Thus a deficiency may well be a result of a low cation-

Table 16.4 Effects of potassium fertilizer on yield of oil palm in Ivory Coast (*Data from Ochs*)

Annual rate of fertilizer application (kg tree^{-1})	0	0·8	1·2	1·6
Annual yield of palm bunches (kg tree^{-1})	60·1	62·6	90·0	92·2

exchange capacity in the soil. Responses by crops to addition of potash fertilizer are found occasionally, as in oil palm in Ivory Coast (Table 16.4), but by no means invariably.

Irrigation

The nature of vegetation is determined primarily by the quantity and distribution of the rainfall (Book 1 chap. 22). Soils in low-rainfall areas may have ample nutrients, as there is little leaching, but they cannot be used for agriculture unless water supply is increased. One approach to this problem is to reduce the rate at which water evaporates from the soil by covering it with a mulch of dead leaves or, if these are not available, with black polythene sheet. This treatment is particularly effective when a crop is being established in bare soil.

To get good crops in dry areas it is, however, necessary to provide extra water by irrigation. On the Accra Plains of Ghana, with an annual rainfall of 1 000 mm, sugar-cane yields are increased by irrigation from about 20 to 120 tonne ha^{-1}. Natural rainfall can support only one crop of rice each year, but three crops may be obtained if the land is irrigated. Irrigation thus makes it possible to use the tropics' greatest advantage over temperate countries—sunshine and warmth in all seasons.

Continued heavy irrigation can produce new problems. If a high proportion of the irrigation water is allowed to evaporate from the fields, the salts contained in the water will be concentrated by evaporation, and the land will be ruined by increasing salinity. In 1960 West Pakistan was losing arable land at an annual rate of nearly 25 000 ha as a result of this effect. The solution is to increase the flow of water so that salts are washed from the soil.

The annual floodings of the Nile and of the Euphrates and Tigris in Iraq might be regarded as natural irrigation; it is perhaps because of these events that intensive agriculture first arose in south-west Asia and Africa on the banks of these rivers. Egyptian agriculture today is still dependent upon the annual Nile floods, although they are now controlled by various dams. The Gezira scheme in the Sudan (Fig. 16.15) is an example of the successful use of large-scale irrigation. Between 1920 and 1950, a total of about 5 000 km^2 of flat clay land with an annual rainfall of only 350 mm was brought under irrigation with water from the Nile. Cotton from the scheme has brought prosperity to the small farmers who cultivate this land under govern-

16.15 View from the air of part of the Gezira scheme in Sudan, showing experimental plots surrounded by irrigation channels.

ment supervision; they also grow beans and sorghum for food in rotation with cotton.

Soil erosion

Improvement of soil by addition of nutrients and water presupposes the existence of soil to which these things can be added. If the system of agriculture is such that the soil is lost by erosion, the basis for any kind of cropping has gone. We must now turn to consider the factors which tend to increase erosion, and the ways by which it may be slowed down.

The removal of soil by rainwater is a natural and inevitable process. Throughout geological time mountains have been slowly but continuously worn down, and the particles derived from them spread over the adjacent lowlands or deposited in the sea. Natural erosion is, however, a slow process; problems arise because it may be greatly accelerated on agricultural land. In the Ivory Coast, for example, it was found that about 1 tonne ha^{-1} $year^{-1}$ was removed from below forest whereas an adjacent plot of bare fallow lost 100 tonne ha^{-1} $year^{-1}$.

The rate of removal of soil by flowing water is inversely proportional to the size of the soil particles and directly proportional to about the fourth power of the velocity of the water. A forest cover greatly diminishes the force with which rain hits the soil surface, litter and roots reduce the rate at which it flows on the surface, and the crumb structure and porous nature of the topsoil allow rapid percolation into the soil. Water erosion may occur in the beds of small streams, removing soil which is gradually replaced by fresh soil which 'creeps' down the hillsides. This pattern of erosion results in the maintenance under forest of fairly steep, convex slopes.

Savanna affords much less protection than forest to the soil, both because the trees are more sparse and especially because cover is removed from the soil surface each year by fires. Thus the soil may be quite bare when the first storms of the rainy season fall. Rainwater may wash over the surface as sheet flow, and this sheet erosion, continued over thousands of years, produces a landscape of gentle, concave slopes.

Removal of plant cover for farming thus has a more drastic effect in forest than in savanna. The raindrops striking the soil surface directly may shatter the crumbs, blocking the pores with fine particles and thus reducing infiltration. Sheet and gully erosion will then be particularly rapid (Fig. 16.16), as the slopes are steeper than in savanna. Nevertheless although the absolute increase in erosion rate may be less in farmed savanna, the results may be disastrous where, as often happens, a thin layer of soil overlies solid iron pan. The removal of 15 cm of soil may then turn marginal land into land which is quite useless for any form of agriculture (Fig. 16.17).

16.16 An example of gully erosion.

16.17 Exhausted savanna land from which sheet erosion has removed the topsoil, leaving infertile subsoil exposed at the surface. Note the almost complete absence of trees.

16.18 Savanna land which has been ploughed and ridged along the contour. Rainwater is retained in the furrows, instead of rushing over the surface.

16.19 Terraced hillsides in Uganda.

Under shifting cultivation in forest the soil is exposed only once every ten years or so, but under continuous cropping it may be exposed each year, and the structure may be less good because of the lower humus content. Erosion may be slowed by planting on ridges which follow

the contours of the land, but unless land is under very strict management the best form of land use may be to plant permanent tree crops such as oil palm, citrus or rubber. In savanna, contour ploughing and ridging are essential (Fig. 16.18). Terracing has been practised for thousands of years in some parts of the world, such as Java and Peru. Enormous labour is required to construct terraces, and this procedure is likely to be profitable only in areas of very fertile soil, such as the volcanic soils of some parts of Uganda (Fig. 16.19), or where irrigation water is available.

In flat, treeless plains the chief danger to the soil may be the wind. In the great plains of the central United States, imprudent continuous cultivation and soil exhaustion led in the 1930s to the loss of large areas of agricultural land and its conversion to a 'dust bowl'. The topsoil blew away as fine dust, and the erstwhile prairie became semidesert. There is evidence (p. 60) that the blown sand dunes of the Sahara Desert now cover what was once savanna. The answer to wind erosion is to reduce as far as possible the time during which soil is uncovered, and to plant belts of trees at right angles to the direction of the prevailing wind.

Weeds

Productivity of the soil can be raised if we eliminate from the fields other plants which compete with the crops for nutrients and water. These competitors we call weeds. Some weeds are actually parasitic on crop roots; witch-weed, *Striga*, Fig. 16.20, may greatly reduce the yields of sorghum in this way. Table 16.5 gives the results of some experiments on the losses to crops which may result from infestation by weeds.

While diminishing crop yields are a major reason for early abandonment of land under shifting cultivation (p. 285), another reason is the increasing difficulty faced by the farmer in combating weeds; he may in fact abandon his farm when the labour of weeding it becomes little less than the labour of clearing a new farm. In forest these weeds will include some coppice shoots regenerating from stumps, as well as plants establishing from seed. Where do these seeds come from? Some, such as those of *Tridax* (Book 1 Fig. 3.7) are wind-dispersed and blow in from adjacent weedy farms. Others are introduced accidentally by the farmer along with the crop seeds which he plants,

Table 16.5 Comparison of yield and nutrient uptake of maize when grown alone and when grown with weeds. Results expressed as percentages of values for pure maize (*Data from Vengris* et al.)

				Nutrient uptake		
	Yields	*Nitrogen*	*Phosphorus*	*Potassium*	*Calcium*	*Magnesium*
Maize alone	100	100	100	100	100	100
Maize with weeds	57	53	58	44	66	76

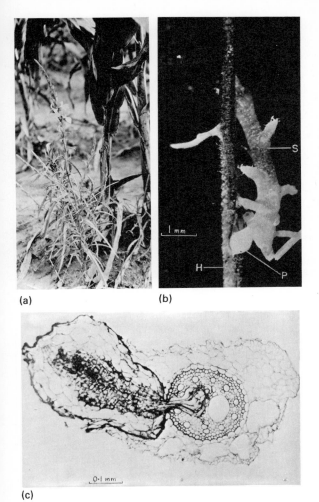

(a)

(b)

20 cm

stolon

(c)

16.20 Witchweed, *Striga hermonthica*, a semi-parasitic herb which is a pest in sorghum fields. (a) Plants of *Striga* growing around sorghum plants in Nigeria. (b) Seedlings of *Striga* (S) attached to sorghum root (H) by a haustorium (P) which has clearly penetrated the host tissues. (c) Transverse section of host root (on right) showing penetration through its cortex and into the stele by the haustorium (on left) of the parasite.

16.21 *Imperata cylindrica*, the spear grass, a serious weed of savanna which spreads by its slender stolons. (a) Drawing to show habit. (b) Savanna heavily infested with *Imperata;* the white inflorescences are produced in response to the first rains following burning.

while yet others may have remained dormant in the soil since the previous cropping cycle. Many weed seeds require light for germination (p. 11) and they receive this when the vegetation cover is removed and when they are brought to the soil surface by cultivation.

The farmer clears weeds mainly by slashing with a cutlass and sometimes by shallow hoeing. Weeds which resist this treatment are clearly at an advantage. One such is the grass *Imperata cylindrica* (Fig. 16.21), which spreads by slender stolons well below the soil surface. In the moister savanna areas, where it is especially abundant, its increase may be sufficient to cause abandonment of farms. During the fallow period it is gradually suppressed by taller tussock grasses such as *Andropogon gayanus*; in fact the completion of this process may be the signal for the farmer to farm the land once more.

Under traditional systems of farming, weeds are a nuisance but they have a certain value in quickly forming a cover which protects the soil surface. Permanent tree crops such as oil palm may require weeding for some years, but leguminous cover crops such as *Pueraria* can be planted to suppress the weeds, and eventually they are shaded out by the crop itself. When arable farming becomes intensive and the amount of capital put into the land has greatly increased, the loss in crop yield resulting from the presence of weeds may be much more serious, and their control more urgent.

In recent years the introduction of chemical herbicides has made it possible to control weeds much more effectively and cheaply than by hoeing and cutting. The discovery of these substances stemmed from research into plant growth hormones (Book 1 p. 60), and the realization that although hormones may stimulate growth at very low concentrations, they may inhibit it or disrupt development if given at higher concentrations. The problem has been to find compounds and methods by which weeds can be killed without the crop being seriously damaged. 2,4-D, for example, one of the best-known herbicides, is more toxic to dicotyledons than to monocotyledons and can therefore be used to control broad-leaved weeds in cereal crops. Simazine, an inhibitor of the photosynthetic mechanism, is much less toxic to maize than to most weeds, dicots as well as monocots, and is therefore a very useful herbicide in this crop. Some herbicides are ineffective against seeds, highly toxic to young seedlings, and again less toxic to older plants (Fig. 16.22). Thus it may be possible to stimulate germination of weeds and to kill them with herbicide before the crop emerges. Alternatively, as when rice is transplanted, spraying may be carried out when the crop has passed the susceptible stage but weed seedlings are still susceptible. Fig. 16.23 shows how the yield of rice may be increased by the use of herbicides.

Monoculture and its problems

By these various methods crop production has been developed to give ever-increasing yields per unit area. For greater efficiency the size of fields has increased, and the same crop of a uniform high-yielding variety may be grown repeatedly on the same land: in other words, monoculture is widely practised. The major disadvantage of crops grown in monoculture is that they make a vast potential source of food readily available to parasites. In mixed cropping the parasite will waste time or resources

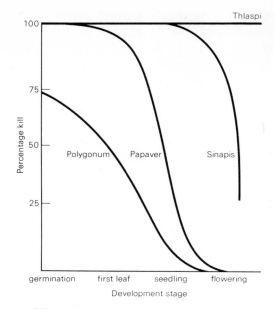

16.22 Effect of spraying four weed species with a 0.2 percent solution of the herbicide MCPA (4-chloro-2-methylphenoxyacetic acid) at different stages in their development. (After Blackman *et al.*)

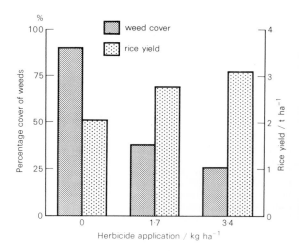

16.23 Effect of the propanil-containing herbicide Stam F-34 on weed growth and rice yield in Ghana. (Data from University of Ghana.)

in getting from one host plant to another of the same kind, and spread will be slow; under monoculture any plant encountered will be susceptible. If crops are rotated from year to year the parasite population will fall between crops, but with continuous monocropping this fall does not occur.

Such crops are thus particularly open to attack by fungal rusts and smuts and by nematode root parasites, as well as to both direct insect attack and insect-distributed virus diseases.

Fungus diseases of plants

Almost all flowering plants are subject to invasion by fungi. In most cases, the fungus may destroy some leaf or root tissue but, provided the damage is of limited extent, the plant may not suffer greatly; indeed, the association may actually be of mutual benefit, as in mycorrhizas (p. 222f). In their natural habitats, plants and fungi have mutual tolerance, but serious disease may arise where crops are brought into contact with fungi for which they have no tolerance.

Panama or wilt disease of bananas, for instance, is caused by the soil fungus *Fusarium oxysporum* forma *cubense* which was presumably leading an unnoticed existence in the soils of central America before banana cultivation began there on a large scale in the nineteenth century. Even then it did not become serious until about 1900 when the scale of banana growing in monoculture had greatly increased. The fungus spores germinate in the soil to give rise to hyphae which penetrate the roots of the host and grow up into the vascular tissues of the corm and thence into the leaf sheaths of the pseudostem (Book 1 Fig. 17.60). As a result the leaves first turn yellow, then hang down, and finally die; the disease may cause the death of the majority of the plants in a plantation.

It is, however, unusual for the whole plant to be killed by a fungal disease; generally the symptoms are restricted to some particular organ. In leaf-spot of ground-nut (caused by *Cercospora*) the spores germinate on the leaves, causing brown spots surrounded by yellow haloes (Fig. 16.24). In severe attacks these may coalesce, resulting in the death of leaves, but more usually the result is a reduction of effective leaf area and therefore also of productivity. Rusts are also leaf diseases. *Puccinia sorghi* is a rust fungus which causes spotting on the leaves of maize, but the leaves are not killed. In 1950 there was a severe epidemic of rust disease caused by the much more virulent rust *Puccinia polysora*, which resulted in widespread killing of West African maize plants.

Smut fungi (Book 1 Fig. 19.17) attack the grains of cereals, causing them to be replaced by a mass of black, soot-like spores. Other fungi parasitize fruits; for example, *Phytophthora palmivora* causes black-pod disease of cocoa (Book 1 Fig. 19.5).

Control of fungus disease

Fungi are in general more sensitive than their hosts to copper, which is therefore a common ingredient of inorganic fungicidal sprays such as Bordeaux mixture (copper sulphate and lime). This mixture is effective against black-pod disease of cocoa; the difficulty is that in order to exercise control it must be used several times

16.24 Leaves of ground-nut showing symptoms of attack by the leaf-spot fungus *Cercospora*.

during the rainy season and this is only economically feasible where losses would otherwise exceed 50 percent or so. Bordeaux mixture is also used to paint the bark near the base of citrus tree trunks to control gummosis disease caused by *Phytophthora parasitica*.

Organic and organometallic fungicides are used against seed-borne diseases. The spores of the fungus, *Sphacelotheca sorghi*, causing grain smut of sorghum adhere to the grain coat of the host, and germinate with it when it is sown. They are killed if the grains are dusted before sowing with an organomercurial compound such as agrosan.

Crop rotation has been a standard method for many years for reducing the build-up of pathogens. Parasite levels will increase during the year that the host crop is grown, but fall again during the years that other non-susceptible crops are in the field (Fig. 16.25). More recently in Europe it has become the practice, for economic reasons, to grow cereals for several consecutive years on the same land, and losses due to 'take-all disease', caused by *Ophiobolus graminis*, have consequently increased. To

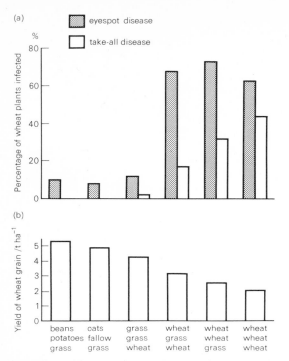

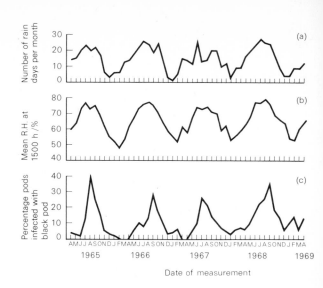

16.25 Effects of various combinations of three previous crops (indicated below each bar of the lower histogram) (a) on the incidence of 'eyespot' and 'take-all' diseases in wheat and (b) on wheat yield. (After Glynne, Salt and Slope.)

16.26 Relationship between humidity and incidence of black pod disease of cocoa at Tafo, Ghana 1965–1969. Graph (a) gives the number of days on which rain fell in each month; (b) gives monthly means of the relative humidity of the atmosphere measured at 15^{00} hours, i.e. when humidity usually reaches its minimum for the day. Note the close correlation with (a). Graph (c) gives the percentage of pods harvested each month which were infected with black pod disease. Note that the peak of infection is usually rather later than the humidity peak, but is clearly related to it. (Data from Dakwa.)

control the disease, and also to allow herbicides effective against weedy grasses to be used, it is now recommended that every few seasons a 'break crop' such as beans should be grown for one or two years. It is of course only possible to use this system of rotation with annual crops; perennial crops will inevitably be on the ground for many years and other means must be found to deal with their parasites.

Correct choice of crop, together with proper cultural methods, will often reduce loss from disease. Take-all disease of wheat is more prevalent on wet, clay soils, and yields will be increased by drainage. With black-pod disease of cocoa there is a high correlation between incidence of disease and humidity (Fig. 16.26); in the wetter parts of West Africa such as Cameroun and Fernando Póo it is accepted that as much as 50 to 70 percent of the crop will be lost to black pod. On the other hand, rice blast disease, caused by *Piricularia oryzae*, is most serious when the soil of the rice field is allowed to dry out.

Crop varieties differ in their resistance to disease, and much work has been put into producing resistant varieties. Panama disease, for example, is very destructive to the Gros Michel type of banana and over the past fifty years this variety has been largely supplanted from its previously dominant position in world commerce by the resistant Lacatan and Dwarf Cavendish types. Attempts are being made to find strains of cocoa which are resistant to black-pod disease, but the fungus itself exists in many strains and it will be very difficult to obtain cocoa which is resistant to all of them. Finally it should be mentioned that new high-yielding crop varieties may be unsuccessful in practice if they are not also resistant to disease. For example, about one-third of the maize crop in the United States was recently destroyed by southern corn leaf blight, caused by *Helminthosporium maydis*, to which the favoured high-yielding variety has proved not to be immune. Of the new rice varieties introduced into Ghana, C463 is desirable because of its long grains but cannot be grown successfully because of its extreme susceptibility to blast disease; the variety IR20 is resistant, but short-grained.

Frequently the best control is obtained by the integration of several methods. Thus in the Gezira scheme in the Sudan the black-arm disease of cotton, caused by the bacterium *Xanthomonas malvacearum*, is controlled by the use of resistant varieties combined with crop rotation and the destruction of crop and weed residues which may harbour the pathogen.

Virus diseases of plants

Symptoms of virus disease are often stunting and distortion of the growth pattern or yellowing of the leaves rather than the rotting which commonly results from fungus infection. A few hardy viruses such as Tobacco Mosaic Virus (Book 1 p. 231) may be transmitted by contact, and it is therefore essential that workers in tobacco fields should be free of contamination. The majority of plant viruses, however, are transmitted from one plant to another by insects, especially Hemiptera. For example, rosette disease of groundnuts, a major cause of failure of the Tanzania Groundnuts Scheme, is carried by the aphid *Aphis laburni*, cassava mosaic (Book 1 Fig. 19.25) by white flies, *Bemisia* spp., and swollen shoot of cocoa by mealy bugs, *Planococcoides*. Vegetative propagation of a crop will often also result in spread of virus diseases; for instance, the very widespread occurrence of cassava mosaic is largely due to the use of infected stem cuttings for establishing new farms.

We can illustrate the problems involved in control of virus disease by reference to swollen shoot of cocoa (Fig. 16.27). Spraying is never effective against viruses themselves, but there is the possibility of attempting to control the vector by treatment with insecticide. In practice this has not proved feasible. Mealy bugs are carried from tree to tree by ants (p. 212) which protect them by carton shelters from predators and also, incidentally, from spraying. Systemic insecticides which are injected directly into the tree will poison mealy bugs feeding on the sap, but there is unfortunately the danger that they will poison men feeding on the cocoa; treatment in any case is uneconomic. Attempts are being made to breed resistant varieties, but so far only partial resistance has been found. The only measure applied on a large scale has been the cutting-out of infected trees and those trees in contact with them. It has been estimated that between 1947 and 1966 a total of 130 million trees was cut down and destroyed in Ghana in an attempt to contain the disease.

Plant-parasitic nematodes

Nematodes (Book 1 p. 200) are one of the most widespread groups of animals, occurring in almost all habitats, including living plants. A few nematodes parasitize the aerial parts of their hosts, but the majority are restricted to the roots, causing damage which is commonly manifested in poor growth or partial failure of the crop.

Among the most serious pests are the temperate *Globodera rostochiensis*, the potato cyst nematode (p. 216), which causes losses of up to £5 million in the British potato crop, and the mainly tropical Root-knot Nematode *Meloidogyne incognita* which attacks tomato, tobacco, cotton, cowpea and soybean. These nematodes are obligate parasites which must grow in host roots in order successfully to complete the life cycle. Larvae hatch in the soil and invade roots, causing local swelling and destruction of root tissue in susceptible species. The female nematode settles in

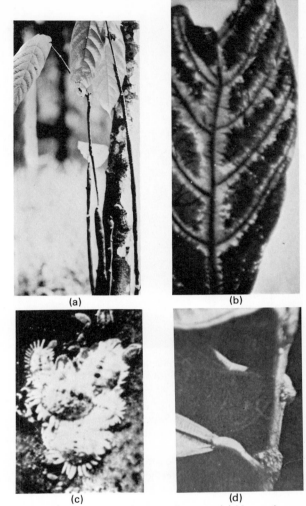

(a) (b)

(c) (d)

16.27 Swollen-shoot disease of cocoa. (a) Young infected cocoa tree; note on the twigs the characteristic swellings to which the name of the disease refers. (b) Infected leaf showing another symptom of the disease, the yellowing of leaf tissue adjacent to veins. (c) Mealy bugs (*Planococcoides njalensis*) on a cocoa twig. The mature insects are 1 to 2 mm long. (d) Carton shelters constructed by ants from chewed wood and covering the mealy bugs which are feeding at the nodes of a cocoa shoot. The ants obtain a sugary solution (honey dew) from the mealy bugs.

this swelling (Fig. 16.28), and after fertilization her body expands to an ovoid or spherical shape to accommodate the ripening eggs. In the case of *Globodera* the female's body wall hardens to form an egg-filled cyst which may lie dormant in the soil for many years; the eggs of *Meloidogyne* cohere in an egg-mass, but are not surrounded by a cyst.

Heavily infested soil may contain as many as 350 eggs per gramme, that is, about one hundred million in the topsoil of one square metre. Damage may be severe where

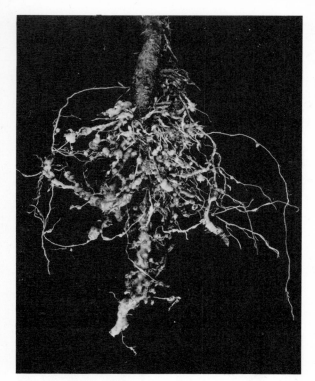

16.28 Root system of tomato plant bearing abundant swellings caused by the Root-knot Nematode *Meloidogyne*.

the egg population exceeds 50 per gramme of soil; methods of control therefore aim at reducing numbers below this level.

If there are no susceptible roots in the vicinity, about 30 percent of the eggs may nevertheless hatch each year; these larvae subsequently die. For this reason, the egg population will be reduced if non-susceptible crops are rotated with host crops. If the initial infestation is very severe, however, it may take as long as ten years for the egg population to be reduced to a safe level. Planting of a resistant variety of a host crop will reduce egg numbers more rapidly because root exudates stimulate hatching even though the larvae cannot successfully invade resistant roots (p. 216). Chemical control of nematodes may be achieved by introducing toxic substances such as nemagon (1,2-dibromo-3-chloropropane) into the soil. Unfortunately the available nematicides are toxic also to man and to crop plants; the soil must therefore be treated some weeks before the crop is planted, and cultivation may be necessary both to introduce the poison, and subsequently to allow its vapours to escape. Treatment is thus extremely expensive and only worthwhile under conditions of intensive agriculture. The best results are likely to be obtained by a combination of crop rotation and use of resistant varieties, with occasional resort to nematicides to deal with especially heavy infestation.

Insect attack on plants

The most familiar and often the most devastating pests of agricultural crops are the insects. Monoculture in particular provides exceptionally favourable conditions for attack by phytophagous insects. When improved, high-yielding varieties of sorghum are grown, losses of nearly 85 percent have been found when no steps are taken to protect the crop; losses of 35 percent of maize from attack by stem borers are also reported. This is partly because many pests spread easily in conditions of monoculture, and with a single crop extending over a large area, new sources of food are readily available. It may not even be necessary for the immature stages to walk from plant to plant. For example, the first-instar larvae of the White Stem Borer of rice, *Maliarpha* (Lepidoptera) (Fig. 16.29), climb to the tips of the rice plants and there spin out a silken thread which may be caught by the wind, enabling the larvae to be distributed over considerable distances; first-instar larvae of many Hemiptera are also readily distributed by air currents. The simplicity of the ecosystem in a monoculture also favours pest attack. The diversity of the organisms within natural ecosystems (p. 270) results in heavy pressure of parasites and predators upon potential pests at all stages of their life cycle. Each simplification of the environment is likely to eliminate some habitats which are necessary for such parasites or predators to complete their life cycles successfully. Even if controlling species are not eliminated, their population densities may be reduced to very low levels. In conditions of total uniformity, populations of phytophagous insects with a short generation time, such as many of the Hemiptera, can build up rapidly and there is likely to be a lag before the parasite population is large enough to check further development of the pest. This sort of situation is illustrated by a dipteran pest of sorghum in East Africa. The crop may be sown in early July and is first harvested in mid-September. Examination of the insects emerging from seed heads showed that relatively few individuals of the pest had been parasitized.

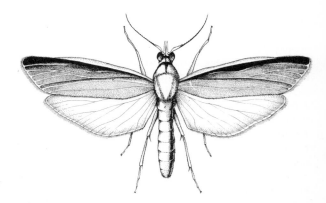

16.29 The adult of the White Stem-borer of rice, *Maliarpha*. The wing span is about 2 cm.

Secondary seed heads develop in late October; by this time the population of parasites has built up and nearly all the insects emerging from the seed heads were parasites of the pest.

Crop protection

Even if monoculture increases the likelihood of insect damage, it frequently offers other advantages, especially in ease of harvesting. If it is adopted, it is commonly necessary to institute programmes of crop protection. Protection from insect attack, whether of food crops or other commercial crops such as cotton and tobacco, wattle (*Acacia*) trees for their tannins or *Eucalyptus* trees for pit props, involves the exploitation of a wide variety of different principles and techniques, some of which are outlined here.

Resistant varieties

Food crops start with an initial disadvantage with regard to crop protection. While many wild plants contain chemicals which protect them from attack by insects (p. 142), these substances are often toxic or at least distasteful to man. As a result there has been selection for varieties which contain little or none of the repellent materials, and crops have thus become more susceptible to insect attack. Nevertheless with non-food crops it has proved possible to select varieties which are resistant to insect attack by virtue of the chemicals they contain. Moreover, some varieties have been produced which have other types of defence against insect pests. Thus cotton varieties grown in East and Central Africa are characterized by the fact that the under-surfaces of the leaves are exceptionally hairy. These hairs, by simple mechanical action, prevent certain Hemiptera from inserting their mouth parts into the leaves and thus give the plant protection from attack. Table 16.6 shows how different varieties of sorghum grown in the Sudan have widely different resistance to attack by the grasshopper *Aiolopus*.

Methods of reducing the intensity of infestation

The size of the peak population of any rapidly reproducing insect will be partly determined by the size of the initial population, N_0 (p. 259). Any measures which will ensure that N_0 is low at the start of a pest's reproductive season will therefore be of potential value. Indeed if N_0 can be kept sufficiently low, the pest may fail to reach a level of infestation which is of economic significance; that is one in which the commercial losses from the pest are greater than the cost of control treatment. Complete elimination of a pest is the objective of crop protection measures only in exceptional circumstances; various control methods have therefore been developed whose primary aim is to keep the level of initial infestation as low as possible.

Table 16.6 Percentage loss of yield of different varieties of sorghum due to attack by the grasshopper *Aiolopus* (*Data from Joyce*)

Variety	Percentage loss of yield
Wad Aker Abiad	45·2
Feterita Maatare	22·2
Feterita Suki	17·0
Mugud Ahmer	3·9

Elimination of alternative host plants

Insects which attack an annual crop may spend part of the year either on alternative host plants or in some inactive state, as does the African Cotton Bollworm (Lepidoptera) (p. 267). If the pest is active all the year round, it may be desirable to reduce the level of N_0 by eliminating the alternative host plant. Thus, for example, in the Sudan the Cotton Leaf-hopper *Empoasca* (Hemiptera) (Fig. 14.3) uses weeds as alternative host plants when there is no cotton growing. In dry years the stand of such weeds is poor and as a result initial infestation of the cotton is low, but in wet years the reverse is true. Clearly, any cultural practice which would reduce the number of available weeds and thus the level of initial infestation might contribute to control. The same idea directed an attempt in Malawi to control *Dysdercus*, the Cotton Stainer (Hemiptera) (Fig. 9.34). This, apart from attacking cotton seed, can survive on the seeds of certain trees. A campaign was therefore mounted to destroy all alternative host trees; this proved, however, to be impractical and the scheme was abandoned. Work in progress on the control of another cotton pest, the Pink Bollworm, *Pectinophora gossypiella*, (Lepidoptera) is endeavouring to exploit the fact that in Central Africa the pest depends upon *Hibiscus dongolensis* as an alternative host; whether it will prove practical to destroy all individuals of this species in the vicinity of cotton fields has yet to be seen.

Phytophagous insects may also pass inactive stages within the dead tissues of their host plants. For example, the larvae of *Maliarpha* (Fig. 16.29) feed on the tissues inside the hollow stems of the rice plants. The last-instar larvae can diapause and may remain dormant in the rice stubble during the dry season for as long as twenty weeks. They then pupate and the adults which emerge are the founders of the new generation. If the stubble is allowed to remain in the fields, the potential size of the new population will be considerable; the burning, flooding or ploughing-in of rice stubble is therefore an important measure of protection against the stem borers. Similar considerations apply to the borers which attack maize and sugar cane.

A very different type of agricultural practice may, however, be of value. Rhinoceros beetles are a serious pest of young palms, both coconut palms and oil palms. The adults bore into the bases of unopened leaves, which may lead to their loss and the death of the tree. It has been found that the damage caused by the beetles is far less if the ground between the growing trees is not cleared of vegetation; Table 16.7 shows quantitative data comparing population densities in cleared and uncleared plots. It is suggested that the effect of ground cover is to make it more difficult for the flying beetles to find the young trees.

Table 16.7 Effect of ground cover on the abundance per ha of rhinoceros beetle, *Oryctes*, in oil palm plantations (*Data from Wood*)

Type of plot	All stages	Adults	Larvae	% of 297 trees damaged by beetles
Bare ground	6061	235	5668	97
Dense cover	709	20	635	37

Trap crops

The fact that insects may have alternative host plants can be directly exploited by the use of 'trap crops', namely

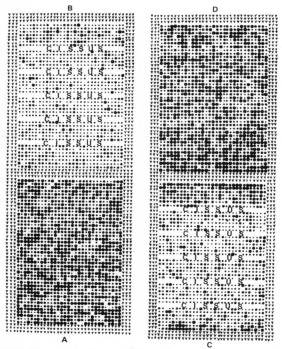

16.30 Plan of the layout of four plots of cotton plants. In the upper left and lower right plots, every seventh row of cotton was replaced by a row of *Cissus*. The rows of *Cissus* were sprayed monthly with DDT. Each dot indicates a cotton plant and the diameter of the dot the level of infestation with *Taylorilygus*. Note that the level of infestation is far lower in the two plots interplanted with *Cissus*. The arrows surrounding each plot represent rows of sorghum. (After Stride.)

plants which, for one reason or another, are preferred by the insect to the plants being grown commercially. The level of infestation of commercial crops may be reduced by planting such trap crops between the rows; the insects may be controlled on the trap crops or the trap crop may be harvested and destroyed. This idea may be illustrated by trials of a procedure designed to protect cotton from attack by an hemipteran, *Taylorilygus*. Although this bug will feed on cotton, it prefers the vine-like herbaceous climber, *Cissus adenocaulis*. In the trial four plots were laid out, each containing 47 rows of 39 cotton plants; in the experimental plots, every seventh row of cotton was replaced by a row of *Cissus* growing upon a suitable screen. Each row of *Cissus* was sprayed once a month with DDT to kill any bugs attracted to the trap crop. To provide a control for the action of the DDT upon the population, the corresponding rows of cotton in the control plots were similarly sprayed. Fig. 16.30 shows the type of result obtained: each circle represents a single plant and its diameter reflects the extent of damage by the bug to the plant. It is clear that there is far less damage in those plots where the cotton has been interplanted with *Cissus*.

Alternative hosts for parasites

A rather similar situation may arise in relation to the parasites of pests. Not only may pests have alternative hosts: so too may parasites. During the time when the pest is unavailable, the parasite may maintain itself upon some other host which lives upon a different type of plant, and the deliberate cultivation of this latter plant in the vicinity of the crop to be protected can then be a valuable measure. For example, there is an hemipteran which attacks grapes in California; a survey showed that while in some vineyards the bug was effectively controlled by a tiny parasitic wasp, in others the wasp was absent. Study of the biology of the wasp showed that, for part of the year, its populations were maintained by parasitization of a different species of hemipteran which is of no economic importance and lives on wild blackberry bushes. It is therefore recommended that small stands of such bushes should be grown in all vineyards, a policy which has resulted in successful control of the pest over a wide area.

Exotic parasites and predators: 'biological control'

In all these examples the control depends upon some aspect of the life history of the pest or of its parasites. The potential of parasites as controlling agents has been exploited in another fashion, which is best illustrated by means of an example. Sugar cane in Trinidad is attacked by an hemipteran for which no fully satisfactory method of control has yet been found. Closely similar to this pest is another hemipteran which occurs in Uganda. It is of no economic importance, living on grass; its numbers are regulated by a parasite. There is a possibility that if this parasite were taken to Trinidad, it might be successful there and build up a population sufficient to control the sugar-cane pest. The first point to be determined is whether the Ugandan parasite will indeed parasitize the bug which lives in Trinidad, and this is now being studied. If this proves to be so, two different lines of enquiry must be followed. One is to develop ways of breeding the parasite and its host in the laboratory, since a considerable number of parasites must usually be released if they are to be successful in establishing themselves in an exotic environment. Further, it may be necessary to release batches of the parasite at regular intervals and this requires the maintenance of laboratory stocks. The other problem is to ensure that the parasite will not attack some other insect in Trinidad whose activities are desirable. If this latter point can be established, the parasites may be released in the hope that they will be able to survive in the new environment. This is a simple example of what is usually spoken of as 'biological control'.

Biological control of phytophagous insects

Biological control of phytophagous insects may be illustrated by the control of Coffee Mealy Bug (Hemiptera) in Kenya. This insect was first noticed in 1923 and spread rapidly not only through coffee but onto farmers' crops. The original home of this pest was not recognized for several years but in 1935 it was realized that it was not an exotic introduced from south-east Asia but had come from Uganda, where it was naturally controlled by a small wasp. Some 500 adults of the parasitoid were released in 1938; it spread quickly and this led to rapid control of the mealy bug. This control was later reinforced by banding the coffee trees with an insecticide to prevent the ant *Pheidole* protecting the mealy bug from attack by the parasite. Farm crops were also effectively protected and yams, which had

been particularly severely attacked, could be grown once more.

A second example is provided by the successful control of the Citrus Blackfly *Aleurocanthus* (Hemiptera) by the introduction of a parasitic wasp originally from Malaya. The blackfly had been a serious pest in the coastal areas of Kenya from 1913 until the release of this parasitoid in 1960, since when there has been completely effective control. Table 16.8 shows that within three years of its release in Natal the parasitoid was well established in an orchard about 5 km distant. In another release, the parasite was observed to have spread in four months about 12 km from its release point and subsequent release elsewhere met with similar success.

A third example is the control of the Eucalyptus Snout Weevil (Coleoptera) which severely damages the trees, and which has been successfully controlled in Kenya, Malawi and Rhodesia by a hymenopterous egg parasite, *Patasson*, from Australia, the original home of the weevil.

Not all introductions are successful. The controlling insect may be unable to survive, either because of unsuitable environmental conditions or because it is destroyed by indigenous predators. Sometimes control is effective only in a limited area. Thus control of the Eucalyptus Snout Weevil by *Patasson* is not successful on the high plateau of South Africa where cold winters check the increase in numbers of the parasites. In certain cases, if it is considered economically valuable, exotic parasites may be bred artificially and adults released each year in the area where their hosts are found.

Biological control has the great advantage that where it is fully successful, no further recurrent expenditure for control is needed. This can be illustrated by the case of Coconut Scale, an hemipteran which was introduced in 1952 onto the island of Príncipe in the Gulf of Guinea. By 1954 it was causing serious damage to the coconut trees and the following year a small beetle known to attack the scale was introduced from the West Indies. The coconut harvest as measured by total production of copra rapidly

Table 16.8 Mortality of pupae of Citrus Blackfly, *Aleurocanthus* **(Hemiptera : Homoptera), due to attack by a parasitic wasp and other causes in Natal citrus orchards. The parasite was released in January 1961. Mortality is expressed as percentage of pupae examined** (*Data from Bedford and Thomas*)

Date	At original release point		At other end of the same orchard		In an orchard 5 km distant	
	Mortality due to wasp	Total mortality	Mortality due to wasp	Total mortality	Mortality due to wasp	Total mortality
15.xi.1961	40·3	79·8	0	22·5	—	—
5.xi.1962	70·8	84·3	—	—	1·4	7·3
24.xi.1963	71·5	96·2	58·3	78·6	58·0	85·6

Note that in the absence of any significant wash population, pupal mortality is relatively low.

recovered. The fall in production had involved an estimated loss of £27 000 per annum, while the cost of eliminating the pest was less than £5 000.

Biological control may be unsuccessful if there has been insufficient preliminary investigation of the consequences of introducing an exotic species. One instance relates to a very beautiful cedar tree, found only on the island of Bermuda in the West Indies. In 1941 the trees were attacked by scale insects and an attempt to save the trees was made by liberating several species of ladybirds, small beetles which feed both as larvae and adults on aphids. This introduction was unsuccessful as the ladybirds were eaten by insectivorous lizards which themselves had been introduced into Bermuda in 1905 in an attempt to control fruit fly. The original introduction of an insectivorous animal which is not very selective in its feeding habits was a serious blunder and ways of eliminating the lizards so as to restore something of the original balance are being studied.

Biological control of weeds

Biological control is not limited to the control of phytophagous insects; it has also been used to control weeds. We have already noted the largely successful control of St John's wort in Australia by the beetle *Chrysomela* which was introduced from the south of France (p. 268). A closely related insect introduced from Australia has been largely successful in controlling this weed in South Africa. Similar very spectacular success was achieved in the control of prickly pear, *Opuntia* (Book 1 Fig. 22.23), in Australia. Cochineal, a dye no longer much used but once in great demand, is extracted from an hemipteran which feeds on prickly pear, and the plant was introduced into the continent in 1787 in order to establish a cochineal industry. The plant had no natural predators among the Australian fauna and spread rapidly, so that by 1925 more than 20 000 km² of land which could have been used for stock raising was covered with a dense stand of prickly pear. Specimens of a small moth, *Cactoblastis*, were liberated in 1928. This moth came from the Argentine which is also a natural home of prickly pear. Like *Opuntia*, *Cactoblastis* had no enemies in Australia and therefore the population grew very rapidly. The success of *Cactoblastis* in controlling prickly pear was striking. Within six years of its first release, the affected area in subtropical Queensland had been reduced to one-tenth of its former extent and the land was made available again for agriculture. The behaviour of *Cactoblastis* on the dense stands of *Opuntia* is precisely similar to that of any rapidly reproducing pest in a monoculture of a crop. But whereas man is interested in preserving his crops, he is interested in destroying *Opuntia* and encouraging the insect which attacks it.

The success of *Cactoblastis* in Australia was undoubtedly due to the fact that the climatic conditions were very suitable and that there were no significant predators of the moth. Attempts to control *Opuntia* in Africa with *Cactoblastis* have been less successful. Although it has been possible to establish *Cactoblastis*, the moth is attacked by various predators: the pupae, for example, are eaten by the ant *Anoplolepis*. But the cochineal insect has been effective in controlling prickly pear in Kenya and Tanzania. In South Africa it has been used to clear the weed from an area of about 500 000 ha, although labour had to be employed for final clearance of the trunks. The cost of this whole operation was less than £200 000: it is estimated that chemical control would have cost £2 000 000. The use of biological control for clearance of *Opuntia* does, however, present a difficulty in that one popular type of cattle fodder in some more arid areas is a spineless variety of prickly pear which is grown deliberately by farmers; this plant is as open to attack by *Cactoblastis* and the cochineal insect as the weed itself. In this situation control of a weed is made difficult because man has produced a variety of the weed which is an economically valuable crop.

Uncontrolled introductions: plant and animal quarantine

Problems can arise as a consequence of deliberate introductions to achieve biological control of some pest. But they can occur in other ways as well. Well-intentioned people have moved both plants and animals to foreign countries where they have come to pose very serious problems. We have already mentioned the introduction of prickly pear into Australia. That continent has also suffered great agricultural loss from the introduction of rabbits by some early colonists. Lacking any of their normal predators, the rabbits became a plague and despite costly measures, nothing effective was achieved until the Australian authorities decided that they could safely release rabbits infected with a virus causing a deadly disease of rabbits called myxomatosis. This virus is spread by mosquitoes and is harmless to the rest of the Australian fauna. Its release has led to almost complete eradication of the rabbit, with resulting greater yield of pasture lands for domestic stock. This is, of course, an example of the biological control of a mammalian pest. Another example relates to the African malaria vector, *Anopheles gambiae*. This is not native to South America, but it appeared in north-east Brazil in 1929, having probably been carried across the Atlantic from Dakar in a French destroyer. Unlike indigenous malaria-carrying mosquitoes, *A. gambiae* will enter houses and breeds in pools in the open. The mosquito spread gradually, and there were severe but minor outbreaks of malaria in 1930 and 1931; in 1938 there was a major epidemic in which 300 000 cases were reported and 20 000 people died. As a result a major campaign employing 3 000 people was mounted to exterminate the invader and within two years this was carried through successfully, at a cost of $2 000 000. A comparable invasion of *A. gambiae* into Egypt from Africa south of the Sahara occurred about 1942, and was followed by a major epidemic; again intensive methods were used, and the mosquito was successfully eradicated by 1945. It is because of events like these that there are stringent regulations controlling the movements of plants and animals from one country to another and that it is routine practice to spray the cabins of aircraft with insecticides when they have landed after long journeys.

It was at one time believed that the water fern, *Salvinia*, (Book 1 Fig. 21.6) which has choked vast stretches of Lake Kariba making these areas unsuitable for fishing, was introduced into Africa from South America. The species of *Salvinia* on Lake Kariba is now known to exist throughout the Old World tropics and to differ from the South American *S. auricularia*.

Toxic chemicals

So far we have examined methods of control which are directly or indirectly related to the biology of the pest. We must now consider the use of toxic chemicals; these are the insecticides. The older insecticides were natural products extracted from plants, like pyrethrins, or else relatively simple toxic materials such as arsenic (III) oxide used to destroy ticks. Inert dusts were also known to have insecticidal properties, their action probably depending upon destruction of the wax layer of the cuticle with resulting increase in water loss and death from desiccation (Book 1 p. 292). In 1939 a major development occurred with the recognition of the insecticidal properties of DDT. This provided for the first time a cheap, synthetic insecticide. In the years which have followed, the range of such insecticides has steadily increased and they have produced both remarkable results and many new problems.

An insecticide such as pyrethrum kills if sufficient is deposited upon the body of the insect; it is therefore called a contact insecticide. Pyrethrum is, however, not very stable and readily breaks down into harmless products. DDT is also a contact insecticide, but it is very resistant to breakdown and is therefore one of a class of persistent insecticides. Clearly insecticides will have varying degrees of persistence, some substances being broken down more readily than others. Thus, for example, if citrus fruit is sprayed with DDT, half the initial dose will still be on the fruit some 40 to 50 days later; dieldrin persists for about as long, while malathion lasts for a shorter period, falling to half the initial concentration in 20 to 30 days. The persistence of DDT is one of the reasons why it has been especially valuable in combating insects like mosquitoes. If a surface, like the wall of a room, is sprayed with DDT, a thin film of the insecticide may remain for a long period; any mosquito which alights upon the surface may, if it remains there, pick up a lethal dose of the insecticide through the tarsi, the terminal segments, of its legs. DDT shares a further characteristic with the pyrethrins and with many other synthetic insecticides, namely that it is lethal to a very wide variety of insects: that is, it is in no way selective in its action. Finally, like the pyrethrins but unlike some other synthetic insecticides, DDT is not lethally toxic to human beings, at least in low doses.

There is a second class of insecticides which are toxic only when ingested; these are spoken of as systemic insecticides. Normally they are applied to seeds as a dressing, to the stems of plants or to the trunks of trees. They are taken up by the plant and transported to the leaves whence they are redistributed in the phloem. Insects eating the leaves will ingest such insecticides while others, like some bugs which insert their mouth parts into sieve tubes, will also take in the insecticide as they feed. Such insecticides have the advantage that their action is far more selective than that of the contact insecticides, as usually only phytophagous insects will be significantly affected by them.

The success of the synthetic insecticides in checking many serious pests in addition to mosquitoes has been spectacular. They have in some places enormously enhanced agricultural productivity; for example, the final crop obtained from a high-yielding variety of sorghum was increased from $1\,200$ kg ha^{-1} to $5\,400$ kg ha^{-1} as a result of insecticidal treatment. Nevertheless in recent years their permanent value has been the subject of much discussion. It is possible to recognize three quite different consequences which have arisen from their widespread use.

DDT

The first specifically relates to DDT. This is a very stable compound and rather than being rapidly metabolized or excreted by animals, it is stored in their bodies in fat. Consider a field crop which has been treated with DDT: there arise from it two food chains. One is short and goes

$$\text{food crop} \rightarrow \text{man}$$

The second is slightly longer and will run

$$\text{fodder crop} \rightarrow \text{cattle} \rightarrow \text{man}$$

Human beings are thus likely to ingest DDT with their food by two different routes; in addition, they may add to their load of DDT if they come into frequent contact with domestic insecticides. Since DDT is only very slowly excreted, it tends to accumulate in the human body. Analysis shows that the concentration of DDT in the tissues of many peoples is surprisingly high (Table 16.9). It must be immediately admitted that no one is known to have died as a result of such accumulation, but this is not to say that the material is not toxic to man; it may be. All we can say for certain is that the lethal dose is very considerably greater than that which is normally ingested with food.

While there is no evidence that DDT has been directly lethal to man, there is much evidence that excessive use has resulted in the destruction of other vertebrates. Furthermore, just as DDT accumulates in human tissues, so too it tends to reach high concentrations in the top carnivores

Table 16.9 Concentration of DDT in human body fat (*Data from Ehrlich and Ehrlich*)

Population	Year	DDT (parts per million)
U.S.A.	1942	0
U.S.A.	1950	5·3
U.S.A.	1955	19·9
U.S.A.	*ca.* 1960	10·7
Canada	1966	3·8
U.K.	1964	3·3
France	1961	5·2
Hungary	1960	12·4
Israel	1963	19·2
India (Delhi)	1964	26·0

of other food chains, including many birds of prey. There is evidence that sublethal levels of DDT have an adverse effect upon the breeding of these birds (p. 380), and there are also significant indications of other undesired consequences following the gradual accumulation of this material in the environment. As a result limitations or complete prohibitions of the use of DDT have been introduced in various developed countries such as Sweden, the United Kingdom and the United States.

There is a second aspect to the use of DDT. Because of its persistence in the environment, it does not remain within the political frontiers of a country in which its use is permitted. Rainwater carries DDT from agricultural land to the rivers and into the sea. There it is incorporated into the food web, so that DDT may accumulate in the tissues of fishes. As a result, DDT is found even in the tissues of the penguins of the Antarctic landmass. Wind erosion will also distribute DDT to other countries, so that many have argued that the possible hazard which it presents can be eliminated only by a global ban upon its use. At this time such a ban is clearly impractical, since many pests which are controlled by DDT cannot be so cheaply controlled by any other measures and indeed in some cases there is no alternative method of control yet known.

Specificity

The second general problem presented by the use of insecticides arises from the lack of specificity in the action of most of them, including the natural as well as the synthetic insecticides. This has become an increasingly serious problem as most synthetic insecticides are comparatively cheap, and they have therefore been much more widely used than the natural products previously available. As we have seen, the upsurge in numbers of a rapidly reproducing phytophagous insect will commonly be checked after some time by an increase in the population of parasites; this may cause a dramatic crash in the numbers of

the pest. (Fig. 15.2). Parasitic insects, however, tend to be very susceptible to the action of synthetic insecticides, so that the application of an insecticide to control some particular pest is likely also to destroy a large number of different species of parasitoid. A few of these may have been parasitic on the particular pest being controlled. Many will be parasitic on other insects, some of which are normally not pests because their numbers are held low by their parasitoids. Such insects may now become pests, because they are not destroyed by the dosage of insecticide being applied to control the original infestation. The application of insecticide to control one pest may, in this way, cause a new pest to arise and this can only be controlled by heavier or perhaps more frequent insecticidal treatments. As a result the overhead costs in producing the crop are increased and the food item may become more expensive.

This sort of phenomenon is illustrated by experience in California where the Cottony-cushion Scale, *Icerya* (Hemiptera), was successfully controlled by a small beetle *Rodolia*, introduced from Australia; the same beetle is used to control Cottony-cushion Scale in Central and Southern Africa. Application of DDT as an alternative control measure in California had the effect of killing the beetle more effectively than the scale, which thus once more became a pest. Fig. 16.31a shows a similar example relating to another citrus scale insect which had become a pest as a result of treatment with DDT; it required a period of three years after cessation of use of the insecticide before commercially adequate natural control could be re-established. Fig. 16.31b shows the results from Malaya of spraying ten rows of oil palms with dieldrin: the result was an increase in abundance of larvae of a lepidopterous pest. A fourth example is provided by the Coffee Mealy Bug whose successful control by a parasitoid we have already described (p. 301). With the introduction of DDT into the coffee plantations, the mealy bug once more became a pest. When DDT was replaced by nonpersistent insecticides, biological control was established once again. There are, moreover, cases where the control of a second pest has resulted in a third species becoming a pest with the resulting further rise in the costs of production. Thus, for example, in cotton fields in Central America the policy of treating successive problems by further applications of insecticide has led to the use of nine different toxins and the need for up to 30 applications to the crop during the six months of the cotton growing season.

It should further be appreciated that the effects of insecticides are not limited simply to the crops to which they are applied. They also affect the soil fauna, especially if the insecticides are persistent like DDT or only slowly destroyed like aldrin and BHC; even 18 months after a single application of BHC, the effect on the microarthropod fauna can still be detected. Insecticides in the soil may destroy the predators which normally regulate the levels of certain insects which attack the roots of crops. Thus, for example, there is a dipteran which attacks the roots of

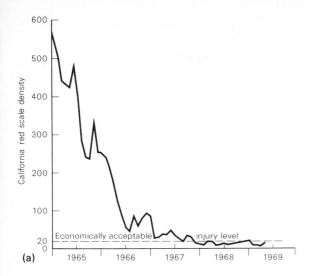

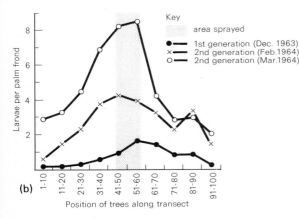

16.31 (a) Density of California Red Scale on a citrus tree over a period of years. Use of DDT had destroyed the natural biological control agents and the scale, unaffected by the DDT application, became a serious pest. A period of about three years was required before effective biological control could be regained. (After Debach *et al.*) (b) Numbers of larvae of a moth on oil palms. The horizontal axis represents distance of trees from the centre of the area which was sprayed with dieldrin. The shading indicates the extent of the sprayed area. The plot was surveyed in December, February and March. Note that by March the level of infestation in the sprayed area was nearly three times that towards the edges of the plot. (After Wood.)

cabbage plants. It has been found that damage to cabbage plants is markedly greater if they are sown in plots which have been treated with insecticide. This is because there is normally heavy predation of the flies' eggs by ground-living beetles and the numbers of these latter are drastically reduced by the insecticide. A similar type of effect can be seen in the microarthropod fauna of the soil around citrus

Table 16.10 Mean number of microarthropods m^{-2} from soil samples of 16 cm depth taken in citrus orchards in the Transvaal, South Africa (*Data from Olivier and Ryke*)

Treatment	Saprophagous mites	Predatory mites	Collembola
Routine application of insecticide	6 400	750	29 750
None	11 000	1 000	14 000

trees. Table 16.10 presents data comparing the numbers of saprophytic and predatory mites (Arachnida) as well as Collembola from an untreated plot and from one in which the trees had been treated routinely with insecticide. Although the insecticide is sprayed on the leaves, much falls directly on the soil and much is washed off by rain. While the numbers of both categories of mite fell, the numbers of Collembola rose very sharply. Predacious mites living in the upper topsoil were completely eliminated and it is probable that this destruction of predators by the insecticide was responsible for the vast increase in the number of Collembola (Fig. 4.17).

Insecticide resistance

The final difficulty with synthetic insecticides is that a very large number of insect pests have now become resistant to the effects of at least some of these insecticides at low doses. This phenomenon was first observed in connection with the use of DDT to control houseflies. DDT was originally used in 1944 to control a typhus epidemic in Italy during the war of 1939–45, but within three years houseflies in certain areas had become resistant to the insecticide. The following year resistance of mosquitoes to DDT was reported for the first time. Fig. 16.32 shows how resistance of a cocoa capsid (Hemiptera) to the effect of BHC has spread in Nigeria in recent years. The problem is underlined by the data shown in Table 16.11.

What might at first appear surprising is that the more effective an insecticide, the more rapidly does resistance usually develop. This can be illustrated by reference to the Blue Tick (Arachnida) which transmits Red Water Fever to cattle. In the eastern part of the Cape Province of South Africa this tick was originally controlled by dipping stock in a solution containing arsenic(III) oxide. This was not very effective as a controlling agent, killing only about 80 percent of the ticks; nevertheless it served for about 35 years. In 1940 it was noticed that in certain areas the ticks had become resistant to the toxin and a new dip based on BHC was used. This was very effective, but within 18 months the ticks started to show resistance. A change was therefore made to DDT, which is rather less effective than

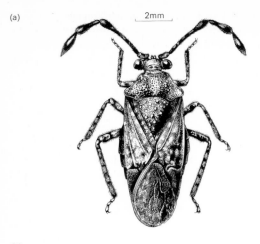

(a)

2mm

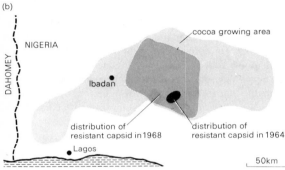

(b)

DAHOMEY

NIGERIA

cocoa growing area

Ibadan

distribution of
resistant capsid in 1968

distribution of
resistant capsid in 1964

Lagos

50km

16.32 (a) *Sahlbergella* (Hemiptera), a cocoa capsid. (b)
Map of the cocoa-growing area in south-western
Nigeria showing the spread between 1964 and 1968 of
γ-BHC-resistant *Sahlbergella*. (After Youdeowei.) There
are two important cocoa capsids in West Africa.
Sahlbergella has developed γ-BHC-resistance in
Nigeria; the other capsid, *Distantiella*, has developed a
similar resistance in Ghana.

BHC; but after six years resistance to this insecticide also
appeared. The reason why resistance develops sooner to
a more effective insecticide will be discussed later (p.447).

There is a further complication. It is frequently observed that if an insect has become resistant to one insecticide, it has also acquired resistance to several others. For
example, Blue Tick which had become resistant to BHC
were found to be resistant also to four other insecticides to
which they had never been exposed. This is because the
particular physiological mechanism of resistance which
had developed against BHC is one which is effective also
against the other insecticides; this phenomenon is spoken
of as cross-resistance.

We have then a situation in which the synthetic insecticides are very powerful agents but have associated with

**Table 16.11 Numbers of species of insects reported as
showing insecticidal resistance** (*Data from Busvine*)

Year	1946	1956	1958	1960	1969
Public health pests	2	20	50	81	102
Agricultural and veterinary pests	8	—	52	—	228

them various disadvantages: they are generally not very
specific in their action, their use may lead to the appearance of new pests and their value can be greatly reduced by
the development of resistance. Moreover, many of the
highly effective synthetic insecticides which have been
developed more recently, although not persistent, are
much more toxic to human beings; it is therefore necessary
to take much greater precautions to protect the people who
are handling them. This can present considerable problems
as warnings of potential danger and of the necessity to observe a variety of safety precautions may go unheeded
with unpleasant or fatal results.

Integrated control

These problems have given rise to the idea that the best
strategy for pest control is one in which the least possible
use is made of insecticides. The idea is not to dispense with
them totally; this is impractical. Rather the ideal is to
apply them only when they are essential and to use, as far
as possible, insecticides which are specific in their action.
This concept is called 'integrated control' and involves the
use of various cultural practices which we have already discussed, the use of exotic biological control organisms and,
where necessary, the use of insecticides. A key principle is
that insecticides should not be applied if there is reason to
believe that the pests concerned are unlikely to do economically serious damage to the crops and, further, that
the application of insecticides be made only at times when
they are likely to be truly effective. Such a policy requires
two things: firstly, close monitoring of the levels of infestation so as to determine when, where and what action
is necessary and, secondly, a willingness of the farmers to
follow instructions precisely and not to make 'unauthor-
ized' applications of insecticide.

The concepts of integrated control can be most easily
understood by reference to three examples. We have
already seen one simple instance: the control of the Coffee
Mealy Bug in Kenya by a parasitoid and the way in which
this biological control is enhanced by treating the stems of
coffee bushes with dieldrin to control ants, while farmers
are discouraged from blanket spraying as this kills the
parasitoid.

A rather more complex example is provided by the

control of citrus pests in South Africa. Up to about 1950 the major pests included four scale insects (Hemiptera) which were controlled partly by spraying with mineral oil and partly by fumigating the trees with hydrogen cyanide, a dangerous and difficult procedure. Around 1950 this type of control was replaced by the use of parathion. Originally a single annual application was sufficient, but with continued use the pests kept reappearing so that several applications had to be made each year; furthermore various other insects such as *Icerya*, the Cottony-cushion Scale and also Citrus Red Mite became serious pests. The cost of insecticidal applications rose steadily until about 1964, when a change from simple chemical control to integrated control was initiated (Fig. 16.33).

Table 16.12 lists the ten major pests of citrus during the time when parathion was being extensively used as a control agent. Three of these were of no significance before the introduction of parathion, and two were significant but not major pests. With the introduction of an integrated programme, only four of the ten remain major pests and only two of these have to be controlled by the use of synthetic insecticides.

How has this change been effected? Indigenous parasites, if allowed free access to the scales, will reduce most to levels at which the loss of fruit is economically acceptable.

Control of Circular Purple Scale has depended upon the successful establishment of a parasitoid imported from California, as has also total control of Mussel Scale which reached pest status in certain areas.

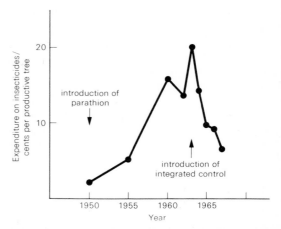

16.33 Annual expenditure on insecticides, expressed as cents per productive tree over a period of 17 years in a citrus-growing area in the Eastern Cape Province of South Africa. (Data from Annecke.)

Table 16.12 Status of major pests of citrus in South Africa under three different types of control programme. The pests are listed in descending order of importance after several years of use of parathion as a control agent (*Based on data from Bedford and Annecke*)

Pest	Fumigation and oil spray	Parathion spray	Integrated control	Control agent or action
Red Scale	Minor	**Major**	Negligible	Indigenous parasitoids
Citrus Red Mite	Not seen	**Major**	Negligible	Indigenous predators
Citrus thrips	**Major**	**Major**	**Major**[1]	Insecticidal spray
Bollworm	**Major**	**Major**	**Major**	Insecticidal spray
Circular Purple Scale	**Major**	**Major**	Negligible	Introduced parasitoid
False Codling Moth	**Major**	**Major**	**Major**	Orchard sanitation[2]
Fruit fly	**Major**	**Major**	**Major**	Poisoned bait
Soft Brown Scale	Minor	**Major**	Negligible	Indigenous parasitoids
Soft Green Scale	Negligible	**Major**	Negligible	Indigenous parasitoids
Karoo thorn Mealy Bug	Negligible	**Major**	Negligible	Indigenous parasitoids

[1] Experience suggests that this pest is also coming under natural control. It has not proved as serious as had been anticipated.
[2] Such actions as twice-weekly removal and destruction of all fallen, infested and out-of-season fruit.

307

As with the control of Coffee Mealy Bug, an essential feature is control of the scale-tending ants, *Anoplolepis* and *Pheidole*. This is achieved in two ways. Firstly, after the crop has been harvested, the trees are pruned so that all low-hanging branches are removed to a height of about 50 cm above ground level, while weeds are cleared, thus preventing the ants from gaining access to the trees by way of overhanging branches. Secondly, the trunk of each tree is banded with 10 cm wide strips of hessian cloth impregnated with a concentrated solution of dieldrin; this stops the ants from climbing the trunks of the trees.

Finally, we will describe the rather different strategy adopted for the protection of the citrus crops in Israel; it provides an illustration of the sorts of problem which arise during a transition from general insecticidal applications to the use of integrated control. Three major pests had to be controlled. The first was Florida Red Scale which is different from the Citrus Red Scale in South Africa and was originally controlled by spraying with mineral oils. It was known that this could be effectively controlled by a parasitic wasp, but biological control was impossible as the second major pest, the Mediterranean Fruit Fly, was controlled by blanket spraying with DDT and this was lethal to the wasp. The third pest was the Citrus Rust Mite, controlled by application of a material toxic to mites in general, that is, a non-selective acaricide. The major problem was to find some replacement for DDT. This was achieved by using a different insecticide, malathion, mixed with protein hydrolysate which is a bait for the female fruit fly; this material is distributed from aircraft but only where and when it is necessary. This is determined by regular recordings from a network of traps containing the synthetic pheromone, trimedlure, which is attractive to the male flies. By this procedure it was possible to stop the use of DDT and to apply the malathion in a form in which it was likely only to kill the fruit fly and, equally important, only when it was necessary. This step then allowed the use of the parasitic wasp to control the Florida Red Scale, with a resulting saving in the quantities of oil spraying which had to be undertaken.

Rust Mite control involved a change in acaricide to one which was selective in action; predatory mites were then able to build up their populations and aid in the control of Rust Mite. Natural regulation has thus been gradually re-established and the Rust Mite is ceasing to be an important pest.

Pheromones in plant protection

So far our discussion has been limited to methods of control which depend upon direct or indirect destruction of a pest. Various other methods of pest control are being investigated and some have been shown to have value in certain circumstances. In almost all species of insect there is sexual reproduction involving coition. Finding a mate is therefore of the utmost importance for survival; in many

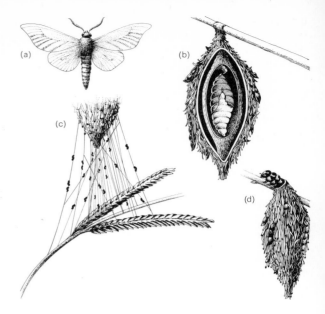

16.34 The Wattle Bag-worm. (a) The male moth; wing span is about 25 mm. (b) The adult female within her bag; her head hangs downwards and the hind end of her abdomen is still enclosed in the pupal casing. (c) Newly hatched caterpillars on silken threads dropped from the bottom of the mother's 'bag'. (d) A fully grown caterpillar with its bag.

species this depends upon the fact that the individuals of one sex, generally the female, emit a pheromone which is highly attractive to individuals of the opposite sex. An example is provided by the Wattle Bag-worm (Lepidoptera) which is found on *Acacia* trees. Each caterpillar builds around itself a protective bag of leaf fragments and within this bag it pupates (Fig. 16.34). Presently a normal moth may emerge; this is the male. The females, which are blind, legless and wingless, never emerge from the bags in which they hang head downwards. A sex-attractant is secreted from glands in the thoracic epidermis and this guides the male to the female. She will lay about 1 500 eggs within the bag. The newly hatched larvae crawl out and, spinning thin lines of silk in a similar manner to the rice stem borer (p. 298), are distributed by wind before they start to build their own bags.

Sex-attractants are produced by the females of many species of moth. Unlike the bag-worms, they usually secrete these pheromones from glands near the tip of the abdomen. When the female is ready to mate, she cocks up her abdomen in a characteristic pose referred to as 'calling'. The males which detect the smell of the pheromone are activated and fly upwind, which will bring them towards the calling female. Many other insect species, such as wood-boring beetles and cocoa capsids (Hemiptera), produce sex-attractant pheromones to ensure that the males successfully find females.

It has been suggested that these substances might be used

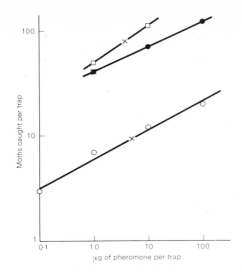

16.35 Relative effectiveness of single female moths (×) and female sex-attractant pheromone at different concentrations in trapping male gypsy moths. The three lines show data from three independent trials in areas of different moth population density. Note that both axes are logarithmic. The position of the points relating to the females have been placed on their respective dose-response lines at values corresponding to the number of moths caught in the female-baited traps. (After Beroza et al.)

as baits for traps to catch males. For such a system to be effective it is essential that the male should be attracted more strongly by the bait than by a female. This requirement can be satisfied, at least in some instances; Fig. 16.35 shows that 10 μg of pheromone is more effective in attracting males than is a single female. Thus only minute quantities of material are required to bait each trap. The pheromone used in these experiments, disparlure, is attractive to the males of the Gypsy Moth whose caterpillars do extensive damage in the United States by defoliating trees. Synthetic disparlure costs about thirty cents per gramme and the traps which might be used for control cost only a dollar for 50. Such small outlay is essential for, if the method is to work, the number of traps laid out in an area must exceed the number of females in the area by a factor of between five and ten. This makes the method of little value where population densities are already high. It does, however, offer the possibility of control in areas of new infestation while population density is still low, as well as maintenance of control in heavily infested areas once the population density has been reduced by other means. One attractive feature of this type of trapping is that it becomes increasingly effective each year it is used, because the determining factor for success is the ratio of traps to adult females. As the population falls, provided control is established, this ratio will increase.

An alternative method of using such sex-attractants is to broadcast the material from aircraft over the infested area, thus confusing the males. Trials have been made using small discs of paper, each of about 1 cm diameter and soaked with the pheromone. These are scattered at a density of about twelve to fifteen thousand fragments per hectare, spreading in this way a dose of about 150 mg of pheromone over the area. Preliminary trials suggest that this method might be very effective.

Other baits

The great advantage of these methods is that many of the sex-attractants are species-specific. Only the pest is trapped and other insects in the environment are not affected. Substances other than sex-attractant pheromones can also be used as baits. Control of locust hopper bands is sometimes achieved by scattering wheat bran or crushed millet mixed with 0·1 percent BHC among the hoppers. The bran is accepted as food and at least sufficient of the hoppers are destroyed to break up the band. The potential effectiveness is considerable: more than 30 kg of hoppers may be destroyed by the spreading of 1 g BHC in this way. The disadvantage lies in having to transport large quantities of bait to possibly remote areas where hopper bands have started to assemble. Another type of bait is protein hydrolysate which is particularly attractive to the Mediterranean Fruit Fly, the citrus fruit pest now found in almost all citrus-growing areas.

Insect hormones in plant protection

A second line of development depends upon the fact that insects, like vertebrates, have hormones, although chemically these are quite different. A complex system of hormones is involved in the process of moulting from one instar to the next (Fig. 16.36) and also in controlling the changes which occur during development. One hormone concerned is called juvenile hormone (JH); its action is to prevent the insect developing adult characteristics. Young caterpillars from which the endocrine organ secreting the hormone has been removed pupate at the next moult and will develop into miniature adults (Fig. 16.37), while insects given an excess of the hormone develop abnormally. It has been found that a variety of plants contain materials which act upon insects in a manner similar to that of JH. One of these occurs in a species of pine tree used in paper manufacture; it is possible that it normally contributes to the defences of the tree against insect attack. This substance has three important characteristics. Firstly, it acts on one particular group only of hemipterous bugs. Secondly, it acts in such a way as to produce abnormal development and finally the death of the nymphs; that is to say, it is toxic and also has a high specificity. Thirdly, it acts even if the substance is placed in minute quantity upon the outside of the insect; it does not have to be injected. It can therefore be applied as a spray. Work is now proceeding to see whether it is possible to produce arti-

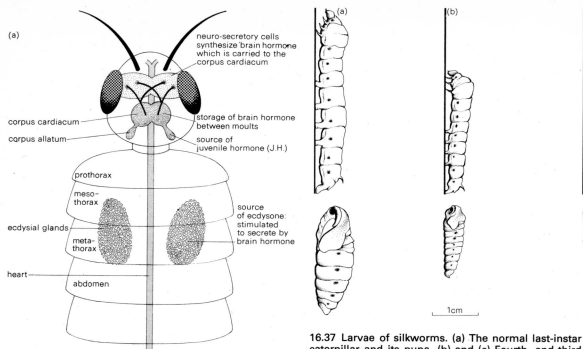

16.37 Larvae of silkworms. (a) The normal last-instar caterpillar and its pupa. (b) and (c) Fourth- and third-instar caterpillars and the pupae they form on moulting if the corpora allata have been removed. (After Bounhiol.)

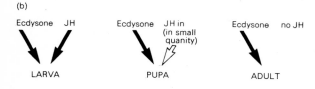

16.36 (a) Diagram showing the relations of part of the endocrine system of insects. Nerve cells in the brain synthesize 'brain hormone' which is carried down their axons to a pair of structures surrounding the heart, the corpora cardiaca. From here the hormone is released into the blood stream and stimulates the ecdysial glands to secrete a second hormone, ecdysone. This causes moulting ('ecdysis'). Behind the corpora cardiaca lie the corpora allata which secrete juvenile hormone (JH) which inhibits the development of adult characteristics at the time of a moult. In adults, JH stimulates the development of the gonads. (b) In the development of a holometabolous insect both ecdysone and JH are secreted during the larval instars. Before pupation, secretion of JH is inhibited and the process of adult development starts. In the final moult to an adult there is also no JH circulating in the blood, although its secretion will be resumed later.

ficial JH-type compounds which might be used to control particular pest species while not affecting others. For example, trials with one of these materials show that 5 μg applied to an individual adult female of the Cotton Stainer, *Dysdercus* (Hemiptera), (Fig. 9.34) causes almost total sterility of eggs laid, while treated nymphs give rise to infertile adults. Similarly such compounds have been shown to lead to the death of the pupae of the biting stable-fly (Diptera), although they have no effect upon parasitoids which feed on the pupae.

More recently it has been discovered that there is in insects another hormone which controls the rate of urine formation. Unlike mammalian anti-diuretic hormone, this hormone produces a diuresis and in excess is lethal as the insect dies of desiccation. Investigations are going ahead to see whether substances of this class are species-specific in action and whether they could be used as chemical control agents.

Methods of reducing fecundity

A final and very different type of control exploits the fact that in many species of insect the females mate only once. If it can be arranged for this mating to be sterile, then there will be no progeny. The method requires males with sperm which are, for some reason, ineffective, that is to say, sterile males. If such males can be produced in large quantities and then released, they would compete with normal males for the females and the value of R_0 for the population would be reduced.

Two ways are known of producing sterile males. One depends upon irradiating the developing insects with gamma-rays, usually from cobalt-60. Such treatment produces abnormalities of the gametes and results in male infertility. The second method depends upon the similar action of various chemicals, which produce sterility if applied in minute quantities upon the cuticle of the insect. They are, however, often non-specific in their action, sterilizing other animals as well as man and so cannot be used as sprays in the field. It is thus necessary to sterilize the insects while kept in cages and also to ensure that the material used is rapidly metabolized. Further it is desirable that there should be a wide margin between the sterilizing dose and the killing dose, as the males must be able to compete effectively with those of a wild, untreated population; any treatment which lowers the vigour of the insects or alters their behaviour is clearly undesirable. In studies of one such material upon males of the Red Bollworm of cotton, *Diparopsis* (Lepidoptera), the toxic dose proved to be 40 times greater than that required to sterilize the males, while the concentration of material applied to the cuticle fell by 50 percent in two days.

Such a procedure has been used as a method of control of the Mediterranean Fruit Fly. This tiny dipteran is particularly suitable as the larvae will feed and develop, rather like *Drosophila*, on artificial culture media to which the chemosterilant is added. It is important to realize the scale of an operation of this type: in one citrus-growing area in Spain, covering only 24 ha, 32 million flies were released over a period of twenty weeks, that is, about 1·5 million flies per week. The trial was successful in so far as the rate of infestation of fruit fell from 95 percent to less than 10 percent, which may well be an economically acceptable loss. Similar success using the same method has been achieved in Nicaragua in Central America, but the scale of the operation here was far larger. In a trial area of 48 km², 44 million flies were released weekly for a period of nine months; the infestation rate of the fruit was reduced by 95 percent.

In both these trials, although the release of sterile males drastically reduced the rate of infestation, it did not eliminate the population. Nevertheless, as in the case of pheromone-baited traps, if the procedure is repeated over a series of years it should lead to final elimination. Clearly an operation of this type is only economically profitable if the pest can in fact be completely eliminated within some reasonable period of time and be highly unlikely to re-establish itself. This effect was partly achieved with a large dipteran, the Screw Worm *Cochliomyia*, which is a pest of cattle in Texas. To achieve initial control 6×10^9 male flies were released annually, at a cost of five million dollars; this may be contrasted with an estimated annual loss of about one hundred million dollars due to the activity of the fly. Table 16.13 illustrates the rapid progress of the control

Table 16.13 Records of screw worms from farmer samplings in Texas (*Data from U.S. Department of Agriculture*)

Year	Screw worms	Other flies of similar habit[1]
1962[2]	49484	2432
1963	4916	6565
1964	223	5257
1965	466	4037
1969	219	—
1970	153	—
1971	473	—
1972	92192	—

[1] The records of 'other flies' serve to control the effectiveness of the reporting network. The low value for 1962 reflects the incomplete recording for that year.
[2] The reporting network of farmers was developed during 1962, which year was therefore under-sampled.

achieved. Screw worm also occurs in Mexico and a barrier zone was therefore established between Mexico and Texas. This has proved ineffective and the screw-worm population of Texas has started to increase again. It does, however, appear that the method has considerable potential for the control of biting flies.

Recently studies have started upon the feasibility of using this method to control tsetse fly. Some idea of the possible scale of such an operation can be obtained from the conclusion that to produce a regular supply of 10000 flies weekly, it would be necessary to maintain a breeding colony of 34000 flies and nearly 700 rabbits for their food. As a further complication of the problem compared with that of the control of *Cochliomyia*, it should be appreciated that in almost any fly area there is more than one species of tsetse which has to be controlled, and each requires the release of the appropriate males.

Stored products

These then are ways in which man has attempted to protect his field crops from the attacks of phytophagous insects and mites. But the matter does not end there. It is necessary to store many agricultural products, so that they are available to the consumer at times other than harvest, or simply while they are waiting to be transported elsewhere. Here insect destruction again becomes important. However, the use of insecticides to protect stored products has fewer attendant difficulties than their use in the field although the use of persistent insecticides and especially DDT is of course to be avoided. Stored products are also attacked by rodents and these can be controlled by various toxic materials. Here too the problem of resistance arises. Rodents in some countries are now showing resistance to a toxic agent which has been used with great success for many years, especially against the Brown Rat, *Rattus norvegicus*.

Table 16.14 Estimated percentage post-harvest wastage of various crops as traditionally handled in Central Africa (*Data from Booth and Coursey*)

Avocado	43
Carrot	44
Garden egg or brindjal	27
Onion	16
Orange	26
Pineapple	70
Sweet potato	95

There are two very distinct types of food item to be stored. One type is what we might call soft foods—tomatoes, onions, bananas, citrus fruit, pawpaw and so forth. These should reach the market in a condition acceptable to the buyer. Food spoilage between harvesting and selling is largely due to mechanical damage to the produce as a result of careless handling. This causes 'bruising' and metabolic changes occur which lead to rotting; bad handling may damage the surface and open the way for rapid fungal attack, while late harvesting results in produce which is 'over-ripe' by the time it reaches the market and is thus rejected by purchasers. Losses of soft foods by spoilage can be very heavy, as indicated by the data in Table 16.14. For longer-term storage during shipment, great care has to be taken, especially against fungal attack and over-ripening. Bananas destined for export must be cut at exactly the correct stage before they have begun to ripen, and quickly transported to the port where they are refrigerated in the ships at about 10°C, the exact temperature depending on the variety. This degree of cooling is sufficient to prevent ripening during the voyage. They are then ripened artificially in the importing country at 20°C, the process being hastened by storage in an atmosphere containing ethylene. Losses from fungal rot are minimized by treating the cut ends of the bunch stems with fungicide, and especially by very careful handling and packing.

The second type of agricultural commodity we may call the hard foods: these include maize, millet, rice and yams as well as the cash crops such as ground-nuts, coffee and cocoa which are mainly grown for export. Most are stored for varying periods during which time they are liable to attack by fungi, insects and mites.

Pests of these sorts generally do better in hot conditions and a low saturation deficit. Many insects depend exclusively upon their food for water. One simple rule therefore is that, wherever possible, the water content of stored foods should be kept as low as possible; grain crops should therefore be dried and then stored in rainproof structures. To keep down the humidity, stores should be built so as to allow ready ventilation of the crop. Effective ventilation also prevents the temperature from rising as a result of metabolism of the crop, of fungi and of insects. These requirements can be met with greater or less efficiency by different types of structure: some traditional, some products of engineering studies.

Even if the crop is well dried and stored, it nevertheless remains liable to attack by insects as well as rodents and sometimes birds and even lizards. Exclusion of vertebrate pests is primarily a matter of good design of storage facilities, but it is far harder to exclude insects. In Ghana, for example, insects are responsible for more than half the damage to village-stored maize, with rodents as the second most important agent: between them, they account for more than 80 percent of all loss. The actual magnitude of the loss increases with time of storage, being about 25 percent of the stored crop after five months and nearly 40 percent after eight months. Some varieties of maize are more subject to insect damage than others; the older, hard varieties are more suitable for storage in villages than newer, softer varieties which may, however, have other desirable characteristics.

When a store is cleared of its contents, insects will remain and can serve as the basis for fresh infestation. If the incoming crop is clean, it is therefore desirable to fumigate the stores before refilling. This is traditionally done by using a fire, but insecticidal application is more efficient. In many instances the crop is already infested with insects such as small beetles and moths. This is particularly so where maize is allowed to dry upon the stalk; it is then attacked by various species which continue to develop and reproduce in the stores. If the crop is likely to be infested when harvested, then fumigation once the crop is stored is also desirable. After fumigation, there may still remain some live insects and, except in highly sophisticated buildings, reinfestation from outside is likely to occur at any time. For this reason potential sources of infestation of the stores should be avoided. Damaged crops, unsuitable for storage, should not be left lying around to serve as a breeding ground for pests; they should be either destroyed or, if used for fodder, kept well away from storage bins.

At major storage depots, bagged material is sometimes stored in the open and covered with tarpaulin or plastic sheets to keep off rain. The bags are stacked in such a fashion as to allow both ventilation and penetration of insecticidal fumigants. Some of the associated problems can be illustrated by reference to ground-nut storage. There are four important pests: the flour beetle, *Tribolium*, the Khapra beetle, *Trogoderma*, another beetle, *Caryedon*, and a moth. Nuts stored in their shells are not liable to attack by either *Tribolium* or *Trogoderma*, but do become infested with *Caryedon*. This beetle only breeds on the surface of stacks and so can be effectively controlled by a surface dusting with BHC. Storage of nuts in their shells is, however, wasteful of storage space and exporters require shelled nuts. Stacks of bagged shelled nuts may be fumigated with bromomethane (methyl bromide) and this will successfully control the Khapra beetle. *Tribolium* is, however, unaffected. Both can be controlled using malathion but destruction of *Tribolium* removes the normal controlling agent for the moth and as a result further insecticidal applications have to be made (p. 273).

In a comparable fashion BHC has been of value in protecting stored maize. When the maize is removed from the cobs the insecticide may be mixed with the grain before bagging. In one trial in East Africa, loss from treated bags after 15 months storage was 6 percent, compared with a 66 percent loss from untreated bags. Insecticidal treatment of the surfaces of grain bags also gives a considerable degree of protection. Maize on the cob can be treated similarly. Such procedures are, however, open to the objection that a persistent insecticide such as BHC if applied carelessly can be a serious health hazard. More frequent treatment with non-persistent insecticides is therefore to be preferred.

Although the use of insecticides may be limited by possible dangers for the human consumer, in the protection of stored products there is no problem of preserving natural predators or parasites such as arises with field crops. Certainly resistance to insecticides occurs but there is a far greater potential for adopting effective control measures with products stored by man in man-made stores. We have quoted distressfully high losses in traditional conditions of storage and there remains an urgent need to devise improved types of store which will use local materials as far as possible, and which will be of a pattern and cost which will be acceptable to the small farmer. Great increases in yield accompanied by heavy investment in power and fertilizers are of little value if storage conditions remain unsatisfactory. Problems of centralized storage are much less difficult, but such facilities are commonly associated only with export. The supply of food to the peoples of the developing countries of Africa requires detailed attention to the special problems of the small farmers and these are likely to be markedly affected by local conditions.

In this chapter we have looked at certain aspects of the production of human food, especially of carbohydrate. Although plant material is a potential source of protein, almost all peoples depend to some extent on animal protein as well and we will next consider some aspects of animal husbandry and fishing.

Problems

1 Fig. 16.8 shows that humus accumulates under fallow much more quickly in forest than in savanna. What may be the reasons for this difference?

2 The points in Fig. 16.11 show considerable scatter. What factors will tend to cause points to lie (a) above or (b) below the mean line? Can we conclude from the graph that crop yields were generally higher in 1958 than in 1956?

3 What could have been the reason for decline in ferti-lizer use in the middle part of the period shown in Fig. 16.12? At the extreme right-hand edge of the graph, the two lines appear to be diverging. What interpretation would you suggest for this?

4 Summarize and comment on the major trends of the results shown in Fig. 16.13.

5 Rice farmers in a certain African country have been advised to grow a mixture of several rice varieties even though one of these varieties is potentially higher-yielding than the others. Suggest possible reasons for this advice.

6 Describe in words the effects of spraying weeds with herbicide, shown graphically in Fig. 16.22.

7 For which of the nutrients in Table 16.5 is competition (a) strongest and (b) lest strong? Explain.

8 The seeds of maize have no dispersal mechanism. What explanation would you offer for this fact and what are its consequences?

9 Explain the principle of orchard sanitation to control False Codling Moth of citrus (described in a footnote to Table 16.12).

10 The four plots shown in Fig. 16.30 were laid out in a long row running ABCD, with the long axis of each plot along the row. The area of plot C adjacent to plot D is fairly heavily infested, while that of plot B adjacent to A is not. Suggest a possible explanation of this difference.

11 Two farmers from the same village were discussing the value of treating their rice crops with insecticide. One was very enthusiastic; the other said it was a waste of money unless all the farmers in the village agreed to do so. Explain the reasoning of the second farmer.

12 In many moths the antennae of the members of one sex are far more elaborately developed than those of members of the other. Suggest a possible reason for this difference. How would you attempt to test your hypothesis?

13 By use of the index, gather as much information as you can on the importance of ants in agriculture. Do ants play more than one possible role? Can this result in a situation where one might want to encourage certain species and to discourage others? Suggest ways in which this might be done. Are ants of most importance in certain types of crop? If so, which?

14 Some methods of controlling insects are more effective at high population densities; others at low. Indicate to which category each of the following methods belongs, giving reasons for your opinion: sterile-male techniques; specific parasites; specific pathogens; sex-pheromone traps; specific predators; wide distribution of sex-pheromone vapours. Do you consider the following methods of control will be affected by population density: insecticides; insect-resistant varieties of plants; destruction of trash after the harvest of an annual crop?

15 Sex-attractant pheromones are produced by many species of moth and by wood-boring beetles, as well as by some species of mimetic butterfly. Why should such substances be of particular value to these three different types of insect?

16 We emphasized in Chap. 10 the importance of the flow of sensory information between organisms of different trophic levels. Which methods of plant protection described in this chapter exploit this concept?

17 It has been found that in the meal worm beetle *Tenebrio*, the male transfers a pheromone onto the female while mating; this pheromone acts as a male repellent. Assuming this type of pheromone to occur in some species of beetles attacking food crops, could this knowledge be possibly put to use in plant protection? If so, then how?

Bibliography

Revision reading

Hall, J. R.   *Senior Tropical Biology*, Longman, 1970, pp. 304–30

Further reading

Cole, S.   *The Neolithic Revolution*, British Museum (Natural History), 1970

Irvine, F. R.   *West African Crops*, Oxford University Press, 1970

Nye, P. H., Greenland, D. J.   *The Soil under Shifting Cultivation*, Commonwealth Agricultural Bureaux, 1960, Chaps. 5, 6 and 7

Oyenuga, V. A.   *Agriculture in Nigeria*, F.A.O., 1967

Tothill, J. D. (ed.)   *Agriculture in the Sudan*, Oxford University Press, 1948, Chaps. 15, 16 and 17

Wallace, H. R.   *The Biology of Plant Parasitic Nematodes*, Arnold, 1963, Chaps. 9 and 10

Wills, J. B. (ed.)   *Agriculture and Land Use in Ghana*, Oxford University Press, 1962

Wigglesworth, V. B.   *Insect Hormones*, Oxford Biology Readers; Oxford University Press, 1974

Braidwood, R. J.   'The Agricultural Revolution', *Scientific American*, 1960, Offprint no. 605

Dovring, F.   'Soybeans', *Scientific American*, 1974, Vol. 230, pt. 2, p. 14

Edwards, C. A.   'Soil Pollutants and Soil Animals', *Scientific American*, 1969, Offprint no. 1138

Jacobson, M., Beroza, M.   'Insect Attractants', *Scientific American*, 1964   Offprint no. 189

MacNeish, R. S.   'The Origins of New World Civilization', *Scientific American*, 1964, Offprint no. 625

Mangelsdorf, P.C.   'Wheat', *Scientific American*, 1953, Offprint no. 25

Mangelsdorf, P. C.   'The Mystery of Corn', *Scientific American*, 1950, Offprint no. 26

Mellaart, J.   'A Neolithic City in Turkey (Catal Hüyük)', *Scientific American*, 1964, Offprint no. 620

Park, C. J.   'Chemical Fertilizers', *Scientific American*, 1965, Offprint no. 328

Schneider, D.   'The Sex-attractant Receptor of Moths', *Scientific American*, 1974, Vol. 231, pt. 1, p. 28

Waterhouse, D. F.   'The Biological Control of Dung', *Scientific American*, 1974, Vol. 231, pt. 4, p. 100

Wigglesworth, V. B.   'Metamorphosis and Differentiation (of Insects)', *Scientific American*, 1959, Offprint no. 63

Williams, C. M.   'The Metamorphosis of Insects', *Scientific American*, 1950, Offprint no. 49

Williams, C. M.   'Third-generation Pesticides', *Scientific American*, 1967, Offprint no. 1075

Wilson, E. O.   'Pheromones', *Scientific American*, 1963, Offprint no. 157

17 Man's food—animals

The second major aspect of agriculture is the growing of animal food for human consumption. During the course of history, man has domesticated for food a wide variety of different animals: cattle, sheep and goats, pigs and hens are all familiar. Possibly less familiar are turkeys, originally domesticated in America long before the arrival of Columbus from Europe, reindeer which live mostly north of the Arctic Circle and are used by the peoples there both as a source of meat and milk and also as draught-animals (that is, for pulling carts and other vehicles as well as ploughs and harrows), yak which live in the central highlands of Asia and the water buffalo which is especially common in south-east Asia and India.

All these animals are first-order consumers; second-order consumers have very rarely been domesticated for food, one exception being a breed of dog eaten by the Chinese. Cats and dogs are the only common domesticated carnivores. Man has found dogs useful in hunting, while cats have helped to keep small rodents such as rats and mice under control. In ancient Egypt, cats were also used in hunting water fowl.

The problem which faces almost all peoples who exploit animals as a source of food is to maximize the yield from the short food chain

primary producer → primary consumer → man

Ecological efficiency and food chain efficiency

Consider a cow feeding in a field of grass. The farmer requires that the cow should make the best use of the grass it eats by turning it into meat. What we wish to ensure is that the value of ratio

$$\frac{\text{energy content of new growth of cow}}{\text{energy content of grass eaten by cow}}$$

should be a maximum. In more general terms, starting with a new-born animal, this will be the

$$\frac{\text{energy content of cow}}{\text{energy content of food consumed}}$$

or, looking on man as a predator and the cow as his prey,

$$\frac{\text{energy content of prey consumed by predator}}{\text{energy content of food consumed by prey}}.$$

This ratio, the 'ecological efficiency' which we have already discussed (Book 1 p. 5), is a measure of the efficiency of transfer of energy from trophic level N to trophic level $N+2$.

Let us go back to the field: if the field is fairly small just sufficient grass may grow to meet the needs of the cow. If the field is much larger, there may be far more grass available than the cow can eat. We can express this situation by another ratio, namely

$$\frac{\text{energy content of food consumed by prey}}{\text{energy content of food available (or supplied) to prey}}.$$

To turn this into a form equivalent to ecological efficiency, we can express it as

$$\frac{\text{energy content of prey consumed by predator}}{\text{energy content of food supplied to prey}}$$

This is a measure of the efficiency of exploitation of the available food resource and is spoken of as the food chain efficiency. Clearly a farmer wants this also to be as great as possible.

Maximizing ecological efficiency

Let us now examine the practical implications of these two types of efficiency, starting with ecological efficiency. Maximizing ecological efficiency involves two rather different things. One is to ensure that the animals consume the maximum quantity of food; the other that the quality of food is the best that can be provided. This latter problem is also related to that of ensuring the maximum food chain efficiency, that is, the maximum efficiency of exploitation of the available resources. We will therefore consider first factors which affect food intake and subsequently the processes of pasture management.

One critical factor affecting successful cattle raising is body temperature. In the tropics and subtropics cattle are normally faced with the problem of reducing their heat load. Tropical breeds of cattle are better able to graze at high environmental temperatures than breeds from temperate zones; the results shown in Table 17.1 reflect the lower heat stress experienced by the zebu. The difference in performance in reducing an imposed heat load is illustrated in Fig. 17.1 which shows data on the rectal tem-

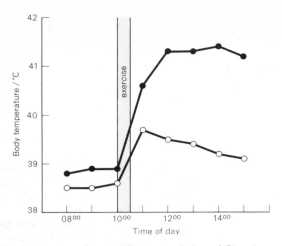

17.1 Responses of two different varieties of Shorthorn cattle to 30 min enforced exercise at an environmental temperature of 32·2°C and 43 percent R.H. Note the way in which the variety better suited for tropical conditions (open circles) shows a smaller and briefer rise in body temperature following the exercise. (After Dowling.)

17.2 A Fulani bull. Note the extensive 'dewlap' beneath the neck, which serves to increase the surface from which heat can be lost, and the hump which allows a localized storage of fat, thus reducing the thickness of the insulating layer of subcutaneous fat elsewhere.

Table 17.1 Mean times (h) spent daily in different types of activity by tropical (zebu) and temperate (Holstein) cattle on free range in Trinidad (*Data from Webster and Wilson*)

	Grazing	*Ruminating*	*Idling*	*Drinking*
Zebu	8·8	9·3	5·8	0·1
Holstein	6·8	8·4	8·7	0·1

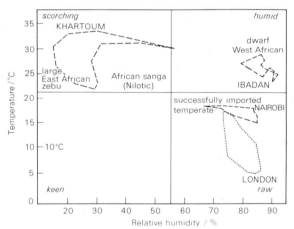

17.3 Climatographs of localities in which particular breeds of cattle are especially successful. Note that while the East African Zebu is especially well suited to a hot dry climate as represented by Khartoum, the West African dwarf cattle thrive in hot, humid conditions as represented by Ibadan. Cattle imported from temperate countries do best in cooler localities, here represented by the climatograph for Nairobi. The fine dotted climatograph is that for London. Each climatograph shows the annual cycle of mean monthly temperature and humidity. (After Hammond.)

perature of cattle before and after 30 min enforced exercise; it is clear that the adapted cattle recovered from the stress far more rapidly than the unadapted cattle. Several factors are of importance in reducing heat stress. Much heat loss from cattle is due to sweating so that a relatively thin hair coat and a large surface area are important. The surface area of tropical cattle, especially those like zebu found in the more arid areas, is increased by such structures as the heavy dewlap below the neck. Concentration of fat in a hump also aids heat loss (Fig. 17.2). Relative surface area increases with decreasing body size and correlated with this we find that large cattle occur characteristically in the more arid areas; in the humid zones the successful cattle are dwarf varieties. European breeds accustomed to temperate conditions are successful in the tropics only in highland areas where the temperature range is lower (Fig. 17.3).

Heat stress is far greater if there is little shade; if the cattle farmer wishes the cattle to graze intensively he should therefore attempt to provide either natural shade, if this is possible, or artificial shade within open-sided shelters with roofs covered with insulating ma-

terial like straw. Abundant water is also necessary to made good the water lost in sweating and panting. Feeding itself increases heat load, as the fermentative processes in the rumen increase heat production within the body by about 50 percent; this is why cattle under heat stress graze less and why, on free range, they graze at night (Book 1 Fig. 10.6).

Intensive feeding

In free-range conditions, much of the food taken by cattle is wasted on metabolic activities associated with movement. If movement can be reduced, ecological efficiency will be increased; this is one consideration which has led to the development of methods of mass-rearing animals in relatively cramped surroundings. Their ecological efficiency is further increased by feeding the animals upon special highly concentrated food preparations. This technique is applied to chickens and pigs as well as to cattle requiring fattening before slaughter. The effectiveness of these procedures is to be judged by a third measure of efficiency, the gross growth efficiency, which is closely related to ecological efficiency and is defined as

$$\frac{\text{energy content of new growth} \times 100}{\text{energy content of food consumed}}$$

With free-range cattle, the value of this ratio is less than 5 percent, while with broiler chicks and intensively fed pigs, it may be over 30 percent. Seen simply from the viewpoint of maximizing the yield of first-class protein, intensive feeding is obviously a most satisfactory idea. It has the added advantage of making it possible to include in the concentrates fed to cattle cellulose from plants which would be unacceptable in natural conditions.

Growth efficiency can be further enhanced in two ways. The first is to add antibiotics to the food concentrate; these reduce the effects of mildly pathogenic or disease-producing organisms and thus increase the growth rate. The second depends upon the use of hormones and especially upon synthetic substances which act like oestrogens (p. 365). During a fattening period, these may be included in the feed or else implanted in the form of a pellet just beneath the skin. The oestrogenic material is then slowly absorbed by the animal from the pellet. Provided this is done at a time when food is plentiful, it can significantly increase the yield of meat. In the United States this procedure has been very widely used and has depended upon a synthetic compound called diethylstilbestrol (DES). This has recently been shown to cause cancer and since the DES cannot be cleared from the tissues of cattle before slaughter, the use of this material has been made illegal. This does not exclude the possibility of using this technique to obtain higher yields: the particular advantage of DES was that it was cheap compared with many other synthetic oestrogens.

Maximizing food chain efficiency

How can we increase food chain efficiency? Clearly in cattle rearing it is desirable that there should be maximum exploitation of the available food without such heavy grazing that the pasture is unable to regenerate: that is to say, we want to obtain the maximum sustainable yield from the pasture. Too many grazers are, of course, more disastrous in the long run than too few, since over-grazing can result not just in destruction of the pasture but also in erosion which is not readily corrected. There is no simple rule which allows us to say that the carrying capacity of African pasture land is one beast to one ha or to ten ha. Carrying capacities vary by a factor of about 200 from closely managed, high-quality pastures to arid grassland; the latter may be able to support as little as one animal on 20 ha.

Over-grazing

If over-grazing is a serious danger, we wish to be able to recognize its characteristics. We can learn something of this from a comparison of range land carrying different stocks of game animals. The data in Table 17.2 relate to conditions in various areas of the Ruwenzori (Queen Elizabeth) National Park in Uganda, where the effects of different intensities of grazing by game have been closely

Table 17.2 Characteristics of pasture under varying grazing intensities in the Ruwenzori National Park, Uganda (*Data from Petrides and Swank*)

	Under-grazed	Quality of pasture Moderate over-grazing	Heavy over-grazing
Number of samples	158	600	710
Surface quality (% of samples)			
with vegetation	24·1	31·7	17·6
bare but protected (by litter or shade)	72·1	15·7	17·0
completely bare	3·8	52·6	65·4
with signs of erosion	0·0	6·1	50·8
Composition of vegetation (% occurrence)			
palatable grasses	71·3	36·3	0·4
unpalatable grasses	5·3	34·5	28·9
shrubs	0·0	4·7	13·3

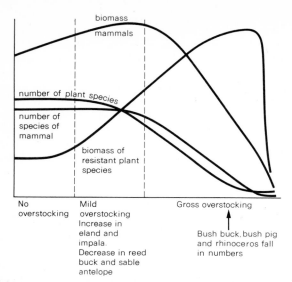

17.4 Diagram illustrating the pattern of change in flora and mammalian fauna with increasing levels of over-stocking in a game reserve. (After Savory.)

studied. The quality of the surface was determined by surveying along transect lines. At every 100 m a wire loop of about 2 cm diameter was dropped on the ground and the presence or absence of vegetation within the loop noted. If vegetation was present within the sample area, its type was recorded and an estimate made of how heavily it was grazed; if there was no vegetation, the presence or absence of litter was noted and also whether there were any indications of sheet erosion. The pattern of change with different levels of over-stocking is illustrated diagrammatically in Fig. 17.4.

From these studies five criteria can be established as reflecting the presence of over-grazing

(a) Reduction in abundance of those palatable grasses which are dominant in lightly grazed areas. As Table 17.2 shows, they were almost completely absent in areas known to be heavily over-grazed.

(b) Increase in abundance of certain other grasses such as *Sporobolus* which are unpalatable.

(c) Increased utilization by the game of unpalatable species of grasses.

(d) Invasion of the pasture by shrubs.

(e) Increase in the percentage of completely bare ground, as well as that of surfaces showing signs of sheet erosion.

Using such data, attempts are being made to determine what percentage of grass removal during an annual cycle can be tolerated without endangering the pasture. The value appears to be of the order of 50 percent. Assuming that a cow requires about 10 kg of dry fodder daily, we can, if we know the annual productivity, make some assess-

ment of the carrying capacity. Such values are useful only in areas where the annual weather conditions are reliable. In other areas they have limited value, for clearly if the rains fail, not only does the growth of new grass fail, but so too does the necessary water supply for the beasts. Thus, in the long run, at least in areas where there is much annual variation in the weather, we are forced back upon the more empirical procedure of constant vigilance for signs of over-grazing and the possibility of having to reduce the size of herds if a gradual fall in yield is to be avoided.

Pasture management

There are other considerations which we must also take into account. To obtain a maximum return from the available growth of grass, the stock breeder must not only avoid over-stocking but preserve the regenerative potential of the pasture. The common pasture grasses are adapted to the seasonal changes from rains to drought (Book 1 p. 277–8). The fresh growth of grass with the arrival of the rains depends initially upon reserves held in the tissues of the dormant plant. Once growth has established young leaves, the products of the plants' photosynthetic activity supply the materials for new growth, while fresh reserves are accumulated. It follows that if stock are allowed to graze very young grass shoots, they may prevent further growth because reserves have been depleted and the young leaves, which are the basis for continued growth, are removed.

In what ways then should stock be managed? Certain guiding principles can be recognized from the ideas we have developed. If stock is to be kept upon a single range throughout the year, the maximum number of animals which can be maintained will be determined by its carrying capacity during the dry season. If more animals are herded than the pasture can support during this time, there will be over-grazing and, with excessive removal of grass cover, sheet erosion when there are rains.

This limitation of carrying capacity can be met in three ways. One is by seasonal movement of herds from one grazing area to another. This has long been traditional practice but becomes increasingly difficult as development and growing populations put more land under cultivation. The second possibility is to have available some type of fodder which can be fed to the cattle when the stand of grass is poor. This presupposes crop cultivation within or adjacent to the herding areas and the utilization by the herds of the remains of crops such as maize or millet once the grains have been harvested.

The third procedure depends upon deliberate management of the available pasture. If effective control of herds is possible and the land can be divided into camps occupied by cattle at different times, permanent damage to the pasture can be avoided by allowing camps recovery periods on a system of rotation. The precise scheme must depend upon local conditions: a simple system is one in which there are four camps and three herds, each camp being grazed continuously at a low stocking rate for three years, while one is kept free of stock. In this camp accumulated grass is burnt off shortly before the rains and then, once the rains have started, allowed to stand ungrazed for about two months so that the grasses can re-establish their reserves. This camp is then opened to one of the herds and another camp allowed to recover from the grazing pressure until the following year.

Pasture does not represent the natural climax and there is therefore a normal tendency for the land to revert to bush. Some shade vegetation must be preserved but the carrying capacity for cattle is higher on grass than in woodland. Thus, for example, in Tanzania, while land cleared of bush could carry about one beast per ha, adjacent bushland pasture had a capacity for only one beast on six ha and, further, showed obvious signs of sheet erosion.

Control of bush can be achieved by burning immediately before the rains when the trees and shrubs have flushed but the grass is still dormant. If fire is to be used to control bush, it must be intense and the land must therefore first be rested from grazing for nearly a year to obtain a good stand of dry grass. This is one reason for allowing a camp almost a full year free of grazing in the pattern of rotational use described above.

Fire can also be used to control pasture composition, especially where coarse, unpalatable grass tends to accumulate. In this case what is required is a light burn which is best made some time before the rains. What is, however, to be avoided is a dry-season burn to obtain fresh grass as feed for cattle. The growth cannot be maintained and, since the burn depletes the reserves of the grasses, it can lead to degeneration of the pasture and subsequent erosion. An alternative method of controlling encroachment of bush is to run a limited number of goats with the cattle. Provided their numbers are kept relatively low, especially if there is little bush encroachment, this can be a valuable management scheme as the productivity of the young trees and shrubs is put to use. Goats running with cattle in over-stocked areas will, however, simply serve to amplify the damage caused by over-stocking as they will hasten the destruction of trees and bushes left as the pasture is destroyed. In such circumstances, goats become agents of increased erosion, making recovery of productive conditions still more difficult.

Condition of the stock: cattle disease

The farmer is not only concerned with the quality of the pasture, but also with the well-being of his stock. We have emphasized the need for shade, and there is also a need for water; but next in importance comes the problem of cattle disease. Much African range land is effectively closed to cattle because of tsetse fly, but within the fly-free areas there are other less spectacular but important disease vectors, the ticks (Arachnida). Four major cattle diseases are distributed by ticks. These take their toll of the calves which, if they survive, acquire an effective immunity against further attack. Especially destructive is East Coast Fever, caused by a sporozoan protozoan and distributed by the Brown Tick, *Rhipicephalus* (Fig. 17.5). While in most areas in East Africa the annual death rate, from all causes, of the calves of free-range cattle lies between 10 and 40 percent, in areas where East Coast Fever occurs, the death rate varies from 30 to 70 percent. Ticks such as *Boophilus* which remain attached to their host throughout their lives can be controlled by regular dipping of the stock, but the Brown Tick drops off its host after it has fed and because of this habit, it is a highly effective vector. Further, since it remains on any one host for but a relatively short time, it can only be controlled by dipping at very frequent intervals, and control is thus difficult. There is no satisfactory drug available against East Coast Fever and any attempt to clear range lands of disease-carrying ticks demands an impractical level of control over the pastures and of movement of cattle. Attempts to produce resistant cattle are going ahead in Australia and this is possibly the most realistic, if long-term, solution to the problem in Africa as well.

Productivity and growth

We may ask a further and rather different question, namely; whether there are any changes during the life of an animal which make it more profitable, from the viewpoint of yield, to slaughter at one age rather than another, that is, whether productivity remains constant throughout the life of an animal or whether it changes in some manner with age.

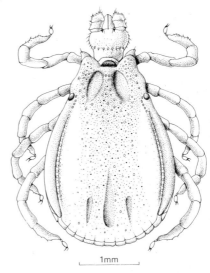

1mm

17.5 The male of the Brown Tick, *Rhipicephalus appendiculatus*.

Let us start by considering a culture of algae. Each algal cell will reproduce to form two cells; these in turn produce four and so on. Provided there is an unlimited supply of nutrients, space, light and carbon dioxide, the growth of the algal culture will follow an exponential pattern so that

$$\mathrm{d}N/\mathrm{d}t = rN$$

Thus the productivity increases continuously with time. In natural conditions this would not occur. The supply of nutrients might become limiting; the culture might become so dense that the photosynthetic rate would fall; the algal cells might produce metabolic products which tended to inhibit their growth. Nevertheless the characteristic growth pattern of unicellular organisms, whether algae, bacteria or Protozoa, is exponential. Growth in the size of the population and growth expressed in terms of biomass are similar because each cell is also an individual organism.

The growth patterns of individual multicellular organisms are different. Whether we express growth in terms of weight or by some measure of change of size, we find that characteristically each organism shows a sigmoid curve of growth. In general terms, the growth rate of a bird or a mammal increases at first and then decreases again until the animal reaches its final size (Fig. 17.6). Similarly, the growth rate of a tree also increases at first and then decreases, becoming less and less as the tree grows older although, unlike a mammal, a tree never stops growing completely. The same is true of fish which continue to grow throughout their lives. In the case of a hemimeta-

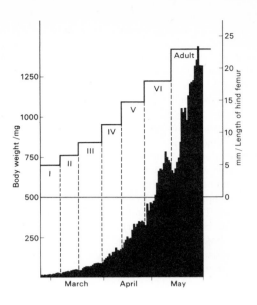

17.7 Daily measurements showing the growth in weight and body size of a female specimen of the West African grasshopper *Orthochtha brachycnemis*. Note that while growth in weight is a continuous process, growth in size, expressed here by the length of the femur of the hind leg, is discontinuous. (After Y. Gillon.)

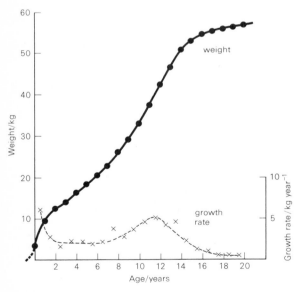

17.6 Human growth and changes in growth rate with age. Note that the curve of growth can be regarded as built of two sigmoid curves: one from conception to about two years of age, and a second from two to late puberty. Growth will cease normally after about 20 years. (Data from Stoudt *et al.*)

bolous insect, the rate of increase in weight may become greater with each instar and in some insects, growth in weight continues for a while after the final moult to an adult (Fig. 17.7). Growth in size may, however, be a discontinuous process with a sharp increase occurring at each ecdysis.

The fact that these patterns of growth broadly resemble that of a population of unicellular organisms in a limited environment suggests that we can regard the individual as a population of cells whose reproductive activity is checked by some factor or factors whose action is proportional to the population size; that is to say, the growth of an organism is increasingly retarded by some negative feedback action which parallels the action of density-dependent influences upon the growth of a population of organisms.

Our problem is to determine at what point the productivity, that is the growth rate, is at a maximum. The growth curve of a cow in Fig. 17.8 shows that the rate of increase is highest when the animal is very young and then falls steadily as it grows old. To obtain a satisfactory yield the animals should be slaughtered at about two years old. If they are allowed to live longer their growth rate is very low and their productivity per unit quantity of food small. Fig. 17.9 shows the growth rates of a hen. The maximum growth rate is at about the time when the bird is half grown, while in the cow the maximum growth rate is relatively much earlier. This difference is a second aspect of the 'broiler' chicken industry; we have already noted the use of food concentrates. The productivity of young hens starts to fall after about three to four months of life and at this age, long before they have become sexually mature, they are killed. This sort of intensive culture is possible because adult hens are able to produce large numbers of eggs which, kept in incubators, serve to provide young chicks for intensive rearing. The same consideration applies to pigs which produce very large litters; only a few

animals need be kept beyond their age of maximum production to maintain the supply of piglets. More particularly, since one boar can 'serve' (that is, mate with) a large number of sows, most of the male animals are not required for breeding purposes. As an extension of this argument, most male cattle should be slaughtered young although clearly, because of their lower reproductive potential, a greater percentage of cows than sows may have to be carried forward to sexual maturity.

Young animals are more productive than older ones, and small animals are more productive than larger ones. If we are concerned with maximizing production per unit time, then rabbits are more valuable than cows. Thus, for example, even though the food chain efficiency of a steer may be greater than that of a rabbit, the latter gains weight about four times as fast (Fig. 17.10). This is one reason why in some countries 'grow rabbits' campaigns have been launched to produce more protein.

We may summarize by saying that it is possible to

a) enhance the ecological efficiency of domestic stock by using breeds which, because of their degree of adaptation to the prevailing climatic conditions, can fully exploit the available food, by attempting to improve the quality of the pasturage available, by slaughtering as many cattle as possible while their growth rate is still fairly high and, in certain conditions, by growing stock on artificial feeds which may be supplemented by antibiotics and hormonal steroids;

b) achieve optimum food chain efficiency by good range management to ensure that the quantity of food available in the dry season is as great as possible and that the number of animals maintained does not exceed the carrying capacity of the pasture, nor fall too low.

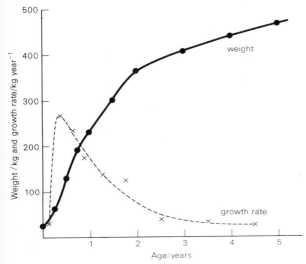

17.8 Growth and growth rate of a cow. Note that the growth rate is a maximum shortly after birth and falls to a very low value after about two years. (After Davis and Hathaway.)

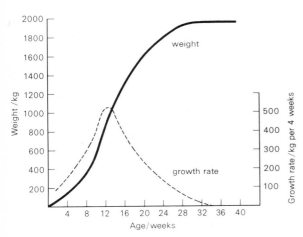

17.9 Growth and growth rate of a hen. Note that growth rate starts to fall after about 12 weeks. (After Marshall and Halnan.)

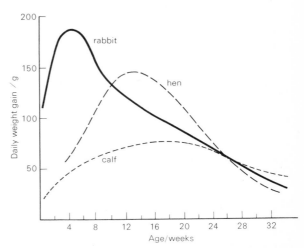

17.10 Comparison of the growth rates of rabbit, hen and calf. Note that the rabbit has a very high initial growth rate. This, coupled with its large litter size, makes it especially suitable for the rapid production of protein in relatively simple conditions.

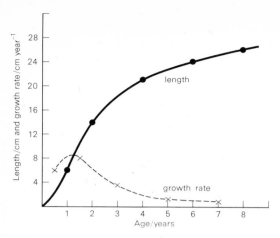

17.11 Growth and growth rate of a herring. Unlike mammals, fish continue to grow throughout their lives, although the rate falls with age. (After Rounsefall.)

Fisheries

We can extend these ideas to a fishery. Like trees, fish do not stop growing as they age, but old fish have a lower productivity than young fish (Fig. 17.11). The situation is more complex than that with domestic animals as fish are subject to extensive predation, and net productivity is therefore also influenced by survival. The study of these interacting factors is usually difficult for purely technical reasons, and they are most easily investigated in a relatively confined habitat. The data in Table 17.3 relate to trout living in a stream in New Zealand. During the first twelve months, the high initial growth rate of a single age group of fishes more than balances the losses by predation, so that total biomass increases, but subsequently loss by predation and other causes becomes greater so that the total biomass starts to fall. If maximum yield is to be obtained, it is desirable to remove most of the fish after about a year. Trout populations which have been introduced into some mountain streams in Kenya and Natal probably show comparable changes.

Fish ponds

Such observations imply that in any fishery it is desirable to remove old fish that have spawned once. This can be readily done in the artificial conditions of fish ponds. We may extend to fish pond culture the ideas we have elaborated in relation to the broiler industry. Fish which are primary consumers are clearly going to be the most efficient. In natural conditions such fish feed either on the phytoplankton or on hydrophytes or on both. One such is *Tilapia* (Fig. 6.23). We can increase productivity by adding fertilizer, either as manure or superphosphate, to fish ponds, since this will result in increased production of algae. *Tilapia* will also eat vegetable matter such as cassava leaves, thrown into the pond. The importance of these steps is shown by the fact that while untreated *Tilapia* ponds in Central Africa had a maximum standing crop of 90 g m^{-2}, fertilization increased this to 213 g m^{-2} and ponds to which both fertilizer and vegetable matter were added reached a maximum standing crop of 616 g m^{-2}.

Intensive culturing of *Tilapia* is, however, difficult as in such conditions the fish come very rapidly to maturity, the fry grow quickly to compete with their parents for food and the result is a dense population of small fish which may be unacceptable for the market. Various techniques of pond management have been developed to avoid this. Introduction of a small number of a predatory species which feeds on fry will keep down the population size and result in the production of large *Tilapia* adults. Artificial crossing of different stocks can result in progeny which are all males; if these are used to stock ponds, then the difficulty arising from early breeding is avoided. It will be appreciated that such ponds require constant management; they cannot be left to 'look after themselves', and high productivity can be obtained only by constant effort.

Lake and sea fisheries

The management of sea fisheries and of some lake fisheries is far more difficult. It is clear that one essential is to preserve an adequate breeding stock. This is no problem for the cattle farmer: he is unlikely to slaughter new-born calves with no thought for tomorrow. But the fisherman cannot 'see' what he is doing and completely unrestricted fishing could lead to destruction of the breeding stock. Ways in which this is controlled include imposing a lower limit upon the mesh of nets that are used, and prohibiting fishing at certain seasons or over spawning grounds or in places where young fish develop.

Like the cattle farmer, the fisherman wants to obtain a maximum yield. In a fishery, we are primarily concerned

Table 17.3 Changes with age in a population of freshwater trout (*Data from Allen*)

Age (months)	0	6	12	18	24	30
Number of fish	1 000	15	7	4	2	1
Mean weight of fish (g)	0·1	57	170	255	340	454
Total biomass (g)	100	855	1 190	1 020	680	452
Change in total biomass per six months (g)		+755	+335	−170	−340	−226

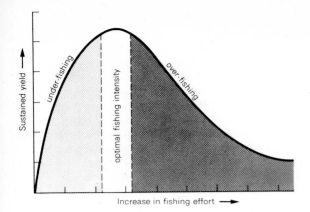

17.12 Relation between yield and fishing intensity. An increase in fishing intensity initially results in an increased yield, but if the intensity of fishing is too high, the stocks are depleted so that the sustained yield of the fisheries decreases. (After Russell-Hunter.)

with yield per unit effort. If, say, ten trawlers are operating in an area and the fish yield starts to fall, clearly more fish will be caught if the size of the trawler fleet is doubled. But the yield per unit effort will be less, so the cost of the fish will be greater and, furthermore, in a short time the actual yield itself may fall. This is the cycle of events known as over-fishing.

We have seen how a cattle farmer wishing to maximize his yield should also try to achieve maximum food chain efficiency. The study of marine fish populations shows a similar type of maximum return (Fig. 17.12). In our example, the ten trawlers were already over-fishing; doubling the trawler fleet will finally result in reduced yield. How can this come about?

Consider a fishery in which 1 000 new young fish join the stock each year. This is being fished at the rate of a 50 percent catch of all members of each age class (p. 261). To obtain more, the trawler fleet is increased so that 80 percent of each class is caught. What will be the effect once a new stable situation has been achieved? The results are shown in Table 17.4: while the total number of fish caught is only slightly less at the lower fishing intensity, more large fish are caught, so that the total weight of fish landed is actually greater at the lower intensity. Depending upon

the characteristics of the fish, and especially upon their age of first breeding and rate of growth, increased fishing intensity may result either in a yield which decreases only slightly with increasing intensity or in one which tends to fall very markedly once over-fishing occurs, even if care is taken to preserve the breeding stock (Fig. 17.13).

Over-fishing, in the sense of lowered sustainable yield as a result of too great fishing intensity, is now very widespread among most of the world's fish stocks. Although there is a need to obtain a maximum yield of protein from the sea, the commercial fisheries policies of different nations are frequently such as to reduce rather than increase the supply of fish food. The reasons for this are principally economic. Much capital has been invested in building large fishing fleets and thus there is unwillingness to agree to a limitation of fishing effort. Since, at the present time, marine fish belong to no one, any country is free to exploit the fish stocks which lie outside territorial waters. Limitation of fishing effort thus requires international agreement and, since each national government is concerned more immediately with its national economy than with global fish production, attempts at achieving rational control of fisheries make little headway. Moreover, certain countries are heavily dependent on sea fisheries for their total protein supply; for example, in both Japan and Sri Lanka (Ceylon) more than two-thirds of the protein in the diet comes from fish, while the total daily protein intake per head in Sri Lanka is at present only about one-tenth of that in the United States. It is thus comprehensible that such nations are very unwilling to agree to any limitation of fishing effort.

Our survey of the biology of agriculture shows that the general principles of food production and of protecting

Table 17.4 Effect of intensity of exploitation on yield of fisheries with an annual recruitment of 1 000 fish into age class II

Age class	II	III	IV	V	VI	Total
Number of each class caught						
50% catch	500	250	126	62	31	969
80% catch	800	160	32	6	2	1 000

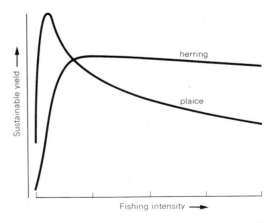

17.13 The sustainable yield of two fisheries at different intensities of fishing effort. Herring are fast-growing, relatively short-lived fish whose net yield, although not increasing with increasing fishing intensity, does not decrease very markedly. Plaice are slow-growing, bottom-living, flat-fish: maximal yield is obtained at low fishing intensity and the yield falls rapidly once this level is exceeded. (After Russell-Hunter.)

the food produced from those organisms which are man's competitors are partly the practical application of the concepts of ecological energetics which we first discussed in Book 1 chap. 1, partly those of population dynamics which we have considered in Chaps. 14 and 15 and partly some of those which we reviewed in considering the natural history of the food web. As our understanding of these has developed, it has been possible to modify agricultural techniques so as steadily to increase agricultural productivity in a world where many still go hungry. We shall revert to other aspects of this problem of food production in the chapters which follow.

Problems

1 Why is the domestication of secondary consumers as a source of food uneconomic?
2 Man has domesticated relatively few herbivorous animals. Studies of the possibility of domesticating other herbivores are now being undertaken. What sort of characteristics do you think might make wild animals suitable for domestication?
3 The world's largest fishery is off the coast of Peru. The fishes caught there are suitable for human consumption, but the bulk of the catch is used to prepare fish-meal; less than 10 percent is used directly for human food, mainly in Japan. The fish-meal is exported to the United States and Western Europe. Comment upon this situation in relation to the world's supply of protein.
4 A cattle farmer living in a hot region of Africa has two enclosures in which he can graze his small herd of cattle. The grazing in one is far better than that in the other. For safety, the cattle must be confined to one or other enclosure at night. To which enclosure would it be better to move the cattle for the night? Explain your reasoning.
5 A lion kills a zebra and feeds upon the carcass; the remains are subsequently eaten by a vulture and a flesh-eating beetle. Distinguish between the ecological efficiency and gross growth efficiency of these events.
6 Suggest the form of a differential equation to describe the sigmoid growth curve of a mammal. Propose a physiological hypothesis which might account for this type of growth curve.
7 Two batches of animals A and B are fed equal quantities of food of equal energy value. The food fed to A contains a higher percentage of undigestible material. Which group will have the greater gross growth efficiency? Explain how you came to your conclusion.
8 Is there any advantage to be gained by adding antibiotics to the fodder of fully grown cattle?
9 An agronomist and an expert in animal husbandry were discussing the measurement of productivity. The latter said that it was a simple matter: all that was required was to measure growth rate. When the growth rate of an animal was a maximum, its productivity was also a maximum. The agronomist could not agree. He said, 'Look at those two fields. The growth rate of the few plants on the field to our right is much greater than that of the large number of plants in the field on the left. Nevertheless the field on the left has the higher productivity.' Explain the source of their disagreement.
10 You wish to measure the growth rates of a tree, a human child, a cockroach and a bacterium. What would be the most convenient measurement to make in each case? If you wanted to compare their rates of growth, would these measurements be satisfactory? If not, what measurements would you try to make?

Bibliography
Further reading

Milne, L. J., Milne, M.	*Growth and Age*, BSCS Pamphlet no. 16, Heath, 1964
Phillipson, J.	*Ecological Energetics*, Arnold, 1966, pp. 17–21 and Chap. 5
Cockrill, W. R.	'The Water Buffalo', *Scientific American*, 1967, Offprint no. 1088
Dyson-Hudson, R., Dyson-Hudson, N.	'Subsistence Herding in Uganda', *Scientific American*, 1969, Offprint no. 641
Hickling, C. F.	'The Cultivation of *Tilapia*', *Scientific American*, 1963, Vol. 208, pt. 5, p. 143
Idyll, C. P.	'The Anchovy Crisis', *Scientific American*, 1973, Offprint no. 1273
Love, R. M.	'The Rangelands of the Western U.S.', *Scientific American*, 1970, Offprint no. 1169
Wilson, W. O.	'Poultry Production', *Scientific American*, 1966, Vol. 215, pt. 1, p. 56

For reference

Hickling, C. F.	*Tropical Inland Fisheries*, Longman, 1961
Russell-Hunter, W. D.	*Aquatic Productivity*, Collier-Macmillan, 1970
Williamson, G., Payne, W. J. A.	*An Introduction to Animal Husbandry in the Tropics*, Longman, 1965

18 Man's health

Hunger, poverty and disease commonly go hand in hand; one reason is that many of those diseases which affect large numbers of human beings are debilitating, making those who suffer unproductive as a result of both physical weakness and inertia.

Types of disease

We can very roughly classify diseases into four major categories. Firstly, there are those which are characteristic of old age, such as coronary thrombosis and many cancers; the former is a condition in which a blood clot forms in the coronary blood vessels which supply the heart muscle, causing the heart to cease functioning properly due to lack of oxygen. Such diseases are the cause of death in more than half the population of developed countries today, but they account for less than 10 percent of deaths in Africa (Table 18.1) and we will not consider them further. Secondly, there are those diseases, usually caused by viruses or bacteria, to which an immunity may be acquired, so that if the patient does not die, he recovers almost completely. Such a disease is influenza; if this should reach epidemic proportions there may be a large number of deaths, but the health of those who survive is

Table 18.1 Causes of mortality in various countries, expressed as percentages of total deaths but excluding infantile mortality[1]
(*Data based upon U.N. Demographic Yearbook*)

| Country | Equatorial Guinea | Sierra Leone (Freetown) | Nigeria (Lagos) | U.A.R. | Republic of South Africa | | Sweden |
					Coloured[2]	White	
Date	1967	1958	1969	1968	1966	1966	1968
Size of sample	1 369	1 816	5 333	465 872	24 004	28 445	81 053
Cause of death							
Respiratory	13·4	4·8	20·7	14·0	18·2	6·2	7·2
Infections and parasitic[3]	26·4	24·4	11·1	2·2	4·0	0·8	0·3
Enteric[4]	4·7	12·9	12·8	39·5	29·0	3·2	2·8
Sub-total	44·5	42·1	44·6	55·7	51·2	10·2	10·3
Neoplasms[5] (including cancer)	1·0	2·1	2·9	1·5	6·3	16·9	19·8
Heart and circulation	6·6	6·8	6·7	10·1	11·1	33·3	37·2
Sub-total	7·6	8·9	9·6	11·6	17·4	50·2	57·0
Approximate expectation of life at birth (years)	41	41	37	52	53	68	74

[1] The completeness of diagnosis will affect the exact value of the results; many deaths due to undiagnosed causes are included in the original data for the first three columns.
[2] 'Coloured' refers to that section of the South African population which is largely of mixed African and European ancestry; no comparable data for the Bantu population are available.
[3] 'Infections and parasitic' include such diseases as measles and malaria.
[4] 'Enteric' includes a variety of diseases of the gastro-intestinal tract.
[5] 'Neoplasms' includes all deaths due to tumours.

usually not significantly affected. Another example is smallpox from which man now protects himself by vaccination, a process of artificial immunization. In some places many years of compulsory vaccination have effectively eliminated the disease. Although smallpox is often far more dangerous than most types of influenza, a patient who recovers from the disease suffers from no lasting effects, apart from marking of the skin. Not all diseases caused by micro-organisms are like this. Tuberculosis, a condition in which lung tissue is gradually destroyed, is one to which immunity is not easily acquired. Exposed to light infections over a long period, individuals may indeed become largely immune. But in many African towns and cities young children are exposed to heavy infection so that the disease may become firmly established and lead to early death. The third category of disease includes those caused by protozoan or metazoan parasites; they too are characterized by eliciting relatively slight immune responses. Such diseases are thus long-lasting and usually become debilitating. There are five such diseases which are especially common in Africa and which we shall consider in detail from the viewpoint of their prevention: these are malaria, human trypanosomiasis or sleeping sickness, onchocerciasis or river blindness, amoebic dysentery and schistosomiasis or bilharzia. River blindness is caused by a nematode worm and schistosomiasis by a trematode; the other three are caused by Protozoa. We have already described something of the life histories of these parasites (Book 1 pp. 189, 190, 198, 201; Book 2 pp. 26, 213ff), and here we will consider how this knowledge may assist in their control. Finally, there are the diseases which are an expression of malnutrition. These are also debilitating and have implications in terms of food production, especially that of protein.

Amoebic dysentery

Diseases in which the causative agent requires an intermediate host offer a large number of different possible methods of control. We may represent the situation schematically, as in Fig. 18.1. Where there is no intermediate host, fewer methods of control will be available and we will first consider such a case, namely that of *Entamoeba histolytica*. Only two types of measure are available: one is to try to prevent the parasite from establishing itself in a potential host and the other is to cure the patient with suitable drugs.

A major problem in the control of this disease is that the infective cysts are passed in the faeces of certain people, carriers, who show little or no sign of having the disease; those in whom the disease is manifest provide no serious danger of infestation to others since the active stage of the parasite, the trophozoite, cannot survive for long outside the body (p. 214). Infection is due to eating food or drinking water contaminated with cysts of the amoebae and therefore, in more general terms, with faecal material; probably the most common source of cysts is polluted drinking water. Infection of this kind can be avoided by the use of piped water linked, in towns, to suitable water-purification plant. In villages where stand-pipes may be the most ready source of water, care should be taken to see that the water reservoir is not likely to be polluted, particularly by run-off water during the rains. Use of human faeces as manure may also lead to infection; cysts may get carried onto the surfaces of vegetables such as salad leaves, and, although the cysts are poorly resistant to desiccation, infection may follow if the vegetables are eaten raw. This danger can be avoided if such vegetables are soaked before use in water containing a mild oxidizing

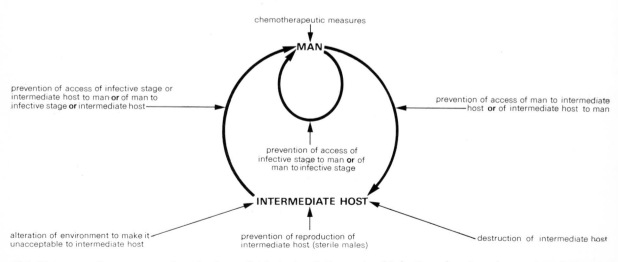

18.1 Diagrammatic summary of methods available to break the cycle of infection of protozoal or metazoal disease-causing parasites of man.

agent such as hypochlorite solution or permanganate; clearly, however, this requires a rather sophisticated approach to the matter of food preparation.

Even if fully satisfactory sanitary measures are adopted, it is still necessary to try to eradicate the parasite from the human population. Parasites in the intestine can be treated with various drugs such as the antibiotic aureomycin. The disease is not, however, limited to a severe diarrhoea; the parasite may sometimes penetrate the gut wall and establish an abscess in some organ such as the liver. This condition can be cured by the use of certain anti-malarial drugs such as chloroquin. Difficulty arises with the treatment of carriers. There is no method of diagnosis available other than the examination of faeces for the presence of cysts: this is a relatively slow process and, since cysts of non-pathogenic amoebae may also be present, requires some skill. Where satisfactory sanitation with water purification and water-borne sewage can be established, then the most economic measure would probably be an eradication campaign based upon the use of drugs, without attempting to distinguish between carriers and non-carriers.

Schistosomiasis

Schistosomiasis, which occurs in many parts of Africa (Fig. 18.2), is probably the most serious human disease today; about 150 million people suffer from the parasite. Like amoebic dysentery, it is a disease related to poor sanitation since the parasite is distributed by man either in urine or in faeces. Unlike *Entamoeba*, *Schistosoma* has an intermediate host, an aquatic snail (Fig. 18.3), which is invaded by a ciliated larva, a miracidium (p. 26). The parasite multiplies within the snail and infective larvae, cercariae, finally emerge to swim in the water. A cercaria larva penetrates through the skin of a man to establish a new infection (Book 1 p. 198). Infection with *Schistosoma* can cause death, but more usually it leads only to chronic ill-health and a reduction in the initiative of the patient to undertake work. In the initial stages there may be significant loss of blood and subsequently damage to the liver and spleen. It is estimated that in the Nile delta the widespread occurrence of schistosomiasis lowers the potential labour output of the farmers by about 35 percent.

Curative drugs such as Ambilhar (niridazole) are available and mass treatment is widely employed in Egypt; the drugs can, however, have unpleasant side-effects and many patients do not report regularly for treatment. These measures therefore do not prevent the re-establishment of the parasite after cure.

One strategy is to attempt to eliminate the snail intermediate host, either by killing it directly or by removing its food supply. The snails can be very abundant in the ditches of irrigation systems: these are defined and limited water bodies and can be kept clear of snails by adding copper salts or various synthetic, organic snail-poisons,

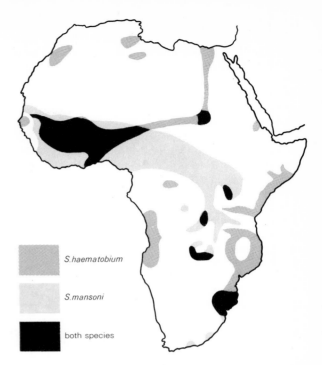

18.2 Map showing the distribution of the two species of *Schistosoma* in Africa. (After Piekassi.)

S.haematobium

S.mansoni

both species

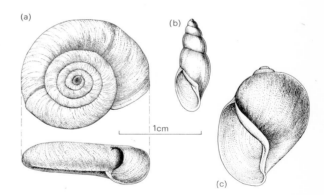

1cm

18.3 Various species of snail can serve as intermediate hosts for the two species of *Schistosoma*. They include species of (a) *Biomphalaria* and *Bulinus*. The latter is a very large genus with two subgenera: (b) is a member of the subgenus *Bulinus* and (c) of the subgenus *Physopsis*.

molluscicides, to the water. Knowledge of the seasonal pattern of reproductive activity of the snails can reduce the quantity of toxic materials which have to be used. Such control measures have been successful in an area of about 300 km² in the Nile delta, but depend upon a strong disciplined organization. Regular application of molluscicides has been successful also in the Sudan Gezira.

In rivers and streams, small reservoirs and lakes this method of control is not satisfactory as the toxic materials are rapidly diluted and, if used at adequately high concentrations, kill fish and other animals. Attempts have been made to keep particular areas much used by man clear of snails by using herbicides to destroy the water weeds on which the animals feed. Such measures also encounter the difficulty that doses of chemicals adequate to destroy the weeds are toxic to other organisms as well. Mechanical clearing has proved more effective. Fig. 18.4 compares the abundance of snails in a cleared and uncleared length of shoreline of the Volta Lake in Ghana. It would obviously be desirable if voluntary labour units were to keep the areas around fishing villages free of weed, thus reducing the chances of infection.

Snails are eaten by various fish (Fig. 18.5) and parasitized by a number of different sorts of animal, including certain fly larvae. There is even one species of snail which will feed upon those species responsible for transmission of schistosomiasis. These carnivorous snails have been used successfully on the island of Puerto Rico as biological control agents, but since they feed also upon young plants, such as growing rice, their use is limited: it is generally agreed that they could not be safely introduced into Africa.

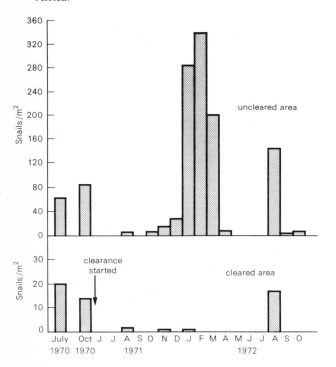

18.4 Abundance of schistosome snail vectors at two localities on the Volta Lake. In one area mechanical weed clearance was started in 1970. During January and February 1972, the dry season, there was no peak of snail population in the cleared area. Note that the vertical scales for the two histograms are different and that the horizontal scale is not continuous until June 1971. (Data from Odei.)

18.5 *Tetrodon*, a freshwater fish which eats snails. It has no commercial value and is often killed by fishermen. (After Daget.)

Strictly enforced sanitary habits would break the life cycle of the parasite and in some areas, especially around Lake Kariba, a special campaign has been mounted to provide better sanitation and to encourage its use. Even relatively simple sanitary rules could assist in keeping down the rate of infection of snails. Similarly it is theoretically possible to prevent infection by avoiding exposure of the body to infected waters. Such measures are, however, obviously difficult to enforce: young children can hardly be expected not to bathe in a stream or lake in hot weather, and the general use of rubber boots, suggested by one authority, does not seem to be very realistic.

There is no single measure which can be taken to control schistosomiasis, except in certain localities where the main source of infection comes from irrigation canals. Nevertheless, considerable contributions towards reducing the infection rate can be made by local weed removal, by protection of fish which feed on snails and by education as to the nature of the disease so as to encourage desirable sanitary habits. With full rural sanitation the disease should eventually cease to exist.

The three remaining diseases which we will consider all have in common the characteristic of being transferred from one individual to another by the bite of some species of dipterous fly. They differ, in practical terms, in so far as there has been very great success in the control of malaria, but full control of sleeping sickness and river blindness has yet to be achieved. We will first consider the methods used for the control of malaria and then see why control of the other two diseases has proved to be less easy.

Malaria

At the beginning of the present century malaria was regarded as responsible, directly or indirectly, for more than half the deaths occurring in the world in any one year. This picture has changed markedly, especially within the last twenty years, as a result of highly organized campaigns to eradicate the disease. About 70 percent of the people who at one time were exposed to risk of malaria now enjoy freedom from the disease. But there remain significant areas of the world, including Africa south of the Sahara, where eradication campaigns have yet to be undertaken.

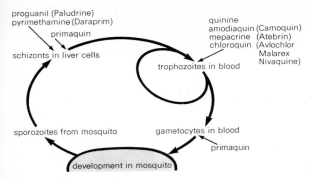

proguanil (Paludrine)
pyrimethamine (Daraprim)
primaquin

schizonts in liver cells

quinine
amodiaquin (Camoquin)
mepacrine (Atebrin)
chloroquin (Avlochlor
Malarex
Nivaquine)

trophozoites in blood

sporozoites from mosquito

gametocytes in blood

primaquin

development in mosquito

18.6 Diagram showing the site of action of the common anti-malarial drugs. Compare with Fig. 12.7. Primaquin is normally used only to clear schizonts and gametocytes from an individual who has been using chloroquin or some similar drug and leaves a malarious area.

In such places the disease, when not fatal, results in heavy loss of working time. It is estimated that between 15 and 20 percent of potential hours of productive labour are lost as a direct result of the fever; care of patients requires further unproductive effort and even when they are free of the fever, there is a marked reduction of individual drive, possibly as a result of the associated anaemia.

The disease is caused by a protozoan, *Plasmodium*, and is spread from man to man by the female *Anopheles* mosquito (Book 1 p. 189). The disease can be cured by a wide variety of drugs, some of which, like proguanil (Paludrine), are of prophylactic value (Fig. 18.6); that is, they give protection against the disease becoming established in the body. In some areas anti-malarial drugs have been used on a large scale. In one isolated district in Tanzania, for example, the incidence of malaria was

dramatically reduced by supplying the people with salt containing an anti-malarial drug: the frequency of infection among the children fell from about 80 percent to 2 percent. Such a method has, however, been used in Africa only in exceptionally favourable circumstances. There is, furthermore, some development of immunity to the disease. As a result, it is commonly urged that while prophylactic drugs, all of which have slight toxic effects on man, should be taken by those who are working in a malarious area for short periods, people who normally inhabit such a region should attempt instead to build up an immunity. Moreover, as a result of very extensive use of anti-malarial drugs in certain areas, particularly in connection with the protection of military personnel during wars, drug-resistant strains of *Plasmodium* have developed. Thus, for example, in both East and West Africa some strains of the most common species of *Plasmodium* are resistant to the drug pyrimethamine.

The disease may also be controlled either by preventing contact between man and the vector or by attempting to eliminate the vector. *Anopheles* is normally active from dusk to dawn (Fig. 18.7) and the individual may protect himself from being bitten in a number of familiar ways. In the open, protective clothing can be worn but is usually unwelcome; it is also possible to apply to the skin various chemicals which are repellent to any mosquito which settles to bite. Where the person is not moving actively, the use of 'mosquito coils' produces a localized smoke containing insecticidal pyrethrins. Within houses, depending upon their structure, more elaborate precautions may be taken such as the use of mosquito-proof screens and mosquito nets as well as the application of domestic insecticides. The walls of houses and huts can be treated with persistent insecticides, but the success of such a

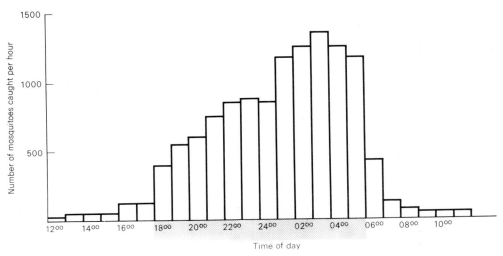

18.7 Changes in activity of *Anopheles gambiae* at ground level in a Uganda forest. Mosquitoes were collected as they landed to bite. The total number of *A. gambiae* collected each hour is shown. Note the way biting activity rises sharply at dusk, increases in intensity throughout the night and falls again at first light. (Data from Haddow.)

329

measure is limited, partly because some materials used for building rapidly absorb the insecticide, so that it soon ceases to be effective. This can be particularly marked with certain types of mud house; of the persistent insecticides, BHC is more effective in such circumstances than DDT. Further, some mosquito species do not settle on walls, but may just enter a dwelling, feed and fly out again, while others are irritated by the insecticide and will not remain in contact with it for long enough to absorb a lethal dose. Clearly, insecticide application to walls may be of limited value.

The second possiblity is to attempt to eradicate the mosquito either as an adult or during its development. Destruction of adult mosquitoes depends primarily upon house spraying and this has proved to be highly successful where buildings are suitable. Nevertheless the difficulties found in the use of synthetic insecticides in agriculture p. 303f) arise also in the control of insect vectors of disease. In West Africa, for example, *Anopheles gambiae* has become resistant to dieldrin and BHC, while there is concern about secondary effects of persistent insecticides upon the fauna as a whole.

Control and destruction of the aquatic stages depend upon a variety of techniques. Different species of mosquito have differing preferences for oviposition sites (p. 19): this knowledge has been used to make necessary water supplies, such as those in irrigation ditches, unattractive to female mosquitoes. The steps taken will depend upon the habits of the particular species occurring in the area and they may therefore be very different in different places. Thus, for example, in some places irrigation ditches are made unsuitable for oviposition by growing shading vegetation along their edges; in others all vegetation is cut down to give as little shade as possible. In certain instances changes in the quality of the water may make it unacceptable as an oviposition site. Thus deliberate organic pollution, produced by the decay of fresh-cut vegetation thrown into the water, has been used to prevent oviposition by *Anopheles gambiae*; elsewhere encouragement of some particular species of water weed, such as *Chara*, has been found to be of value.

Many mosquito species may oviposit in minor and often transient water bodies such as temporary pools and puddles formed after rain, in holes in trees, in leaf axils, in drains and gutters and in discarded cans. Clearly such types of oviposition sites are not amenable to major control measures and this is one reason why in eradication campaigns destruction of adults can be critically important. Nevertheless some advantage is to be gained by encouraging people to destroy such minor breeding sites, or to avoid creating them by thoughtless actions.

Where major breeding sites have been identified, it is possible to destroy larvae and pupae. The larval and pupal stages of mosquitoes are aquatic (Book 1 p. 262); the larva feeds on small particles in suspension in the water and both stages are air-breathing, the individuals coming to the surface from time to time to refill their tracheal vessels with air. Spraying the surface of the water with fine particles of materials toxic to the larvae will lead to their being taken in with the food. In recent years dusts of DDT and various other synthetic insecticides have been used in this way, but earlier the copper–arsenic compound Paris Green was employed. Alternatively the water surface can be covered with a thin layer of oil: when larvae or pupae rise to the surface to breathe, the oil enters the tracheal system and the animals are killed by suffocation. Clearly there must be limitations on the use of this method, as the oil film greatly reduces gas exchange between the water and the air and this may have serious secondary consequences for animals like fishes, as well as their prey. In small ponds which remain filled with water throughout the year, the small predatory fish *Gambusia* (Fig. 18.8) can be used as a control agent.

In a malaria eradication campaign the first objective is to reduce the mosquito population to so low a level that the likelihood of transmission from one individual to another is greatly reduced. But total eradication of the vectors is unlikely to be achieved and large-scale reduction in the mosquito population must therefore be followed by chemotherapeutic measures so as to eliminate residual parasites from the population. This requires full co-operation from the inhabitants to ensure that any case of fever can be treated immediately, but it is also necessary to carry out large surveys using blood smears which are examined for malaria parasites, since individuals with well-developed resistance may carry the parasite without showing any symptoms of the disease.

The success of malaria eradication campaigns over the last twenty years has been very impressive; the further consequences of this success we shall examine later (p. 355). Here it is necessary to emphasize that the disease can only be held in check, even after an eradication campaign, by constant vigilance and full attention to detailed control measures. If anti-malarial controls are allowed to slacken as a result of a lack of visible threat, the situation can rapidly deteriorate. This indeed has happened in Sri Lanka (Ceylon). By 1963 incidence of malaria on the island had been reduced to 100 notified cases during the year. Such success resulted in an easing-off of control measures: the disease soon started to build up again and in 1968 there was a major epidemic with over a million reported cases. This is an example of a general problem, namely that

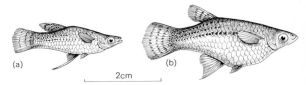

18.8 *Gambusia*, a small predatory fish used to keep small water bodies clear of mosquito larvae (a) male; (b) female.

control of many insect pests can be maintained only by constant effort; the fact that the pest has caused no visible damage for many years can lead to a reduction, either as financial economy or in human effort, of the steps needed to maintain control.

Sleeping sickness

There are two forms of sleeping sickness in Africa: Gambian sleeping sickness caused by *Trypanosoma gambiense* and spread mainly by the tsetse fly *Glossina palpalis*, and Rhodesian sleeping sickness, caused by *Trypanosoma rhodesiense* and spread mainly by *Glossina morsitans* (Book 1 p. 190). The Rhodesian type of the sickness is more rapidly lethal but probably less common, occurring in isolated pockets (Fig. 18.9). The disease is initially characterized by intense headache, insomnia and anaemia and later by wasting of the body and sleepiness. The two parasites differ in one important respect: while *T. gambiense* can live only in man and its tsetse vector, *T. rhodesiense* can also live successfully in cattle and in certain game, especially bushbuck. We can represent this difference diagrammatically as follows:

$$T.\ gambiense$$
$$man \longleftrightarrow G.\ palpalis$$

$$T.\ rhodesiense$$
$$man \longleftrightarrow G.\ morsitans \longleftrightarrow cattle\ and\ bushbuck$$

The implication of this difference is that Gambian sleeping sickness can potentially be permanently eradicated if the link between man and fly is broken for sufficiently long. *T. rhodesiense* can, however, persist in its reservoir hosts.

In such a situation, it might be possible to control and largely eradicate *T. gambiense* by destroying the parasite in man. A prophylactic drug, pentamidine, is available for such a purpose; it will also cure patients during the early stages of the disease before the parasite has penetrated into the central nervous tissues. Mass prophylactic treatment has been attempted, for example, in the former French colonies in West Africa between 1932 and 1953, and proved to be remarkably successful. Thus while in 1941 7 000 new cases were found per million people examined, by 1953 this number had fallen to 1 275 per million. Complete eradication by such a campaign could not be expected since visitors from neighbouring countries continued to reintroduce the disease and, since the fly remained, fresh infestations could be started.

Such a method of control cannot be undertaken with *T. rhodesiense*. Firstly, no prophylactic drug is available, although the disease itself can be cured with a drug known as Mel B (melarsoprol). But more important, elimination of the parasite from man can produce no permanent solution as reinfection will occur from the reservoir hosts.

The alternative is to attempt to control the vector. The

18.9 Occurrence of Gambian and Rhodesian sleeping sickness in Africa.

Gambian sleeping sickness

Rhodesian sleeping sickness

habits of the two vectors are very different, and as a result they present very different problems for their control. *G. morsitans* is found in open savanna woodland; *G. palpalis* is restricted to more humid environments such as mangrove swamps and rain forest, but especially important is its ability to spread along the wooded banks of streams and rivers in savanna country. This habitat preference of *G. palpalis* has been the basis of campaigns against sleeping sickness, especially in savanna regions of Nigeria. The aim is to eliminate the fly by destroying its limited habitat through clearing woody vegetation from along the banks of streams. This procedure was used, for example, in a trial scheme at Anchau to the east of Zaria in the Sudan savanna zone of Nigeria. As a first step the entire human population was evacuated from an area of about 1 800 km². This was followed by selective bush clearing along the lengths of streams, with intense clearing for about 2 km at any boundary of the area so as to act as a barrier against reinvasion. Once this had been effected and the population of tsetse eliminated, some 50 000 people reoccupied the area. For such a scheme to be successful, it is of course essential to prevent a new population of tsetse from becoming established; thus all people and vehicles entering the area must be treated with insecticide to prevent reintroduction of the fly. Further it is desirable that the population should be free from trypanosomes before being resettled: the clearing operation should therefore be complemented by prophylactic and curative treatment of the people concerned.

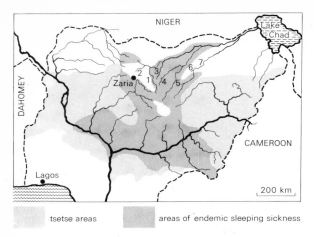

18.10 Sleeping sickness and tsetse fly areas in northern Nigeria. The area in which tsetse occurs is greater than that in which sleeping sickness is endemic. The map shows the main river systems draining the plateau as well as areas in which tsetse eradication by clearance of riverine vegetation has been undertaken. 1 is the area of the Anchau scheme, which was followed by clearance of area 2 north of Zaria. Areas 6 and 7 have been cleared and other areas, 3, 4 and 5, in the same drainage basin partly cleared. The centre of the drainage system is naturally free of fly. (Simplified from Duggan.)

In the Anchau scheme less than 900 km of river bank were cleared of vegetation. Subsequently more than 10 000 km of stream and river have been cleared in northern Nigeria (Fig. 18.10). Clearly this is a major operation. Very striking improvements in the health of the population have been achieved even when clearing has been limited to the immediate vicinity of villages and river crossings. In one such project, the infection rate in the area fell to 1 per thousand, compared with 28 per thousand in a neighbouring but untreated area. In recent years the use of insecticides has replaced vegetation clearing as a method of control of *G. palpalis*. While this is effective, the treatment is not lasting, as there is always some residual population of fly which builds up again, usually within a year.

Control of *G. morsitans* is a far more difficult matter. Unlike *G. palpalis* it is widely dispersed. It was originally believed that the fly was periodically restricted to certain vegetational types. This idea was based upon distributional surveys using the 'fly round' technique, but this method of sampling is unsatisfactory (p.242) and indeed, although many trials using selective clearing have been made, most have been unsuccessful. Even in the one trial in which selective clearing appeared to have been highly successful (Fig. 18.11), there is reason to believe that the disappearance of the fly may have been due to some cause other than the clearing operations.

The control of *G. morsitans* by use of insecticides has also been attempted. Since buried pupae (Book 1 p. 311)

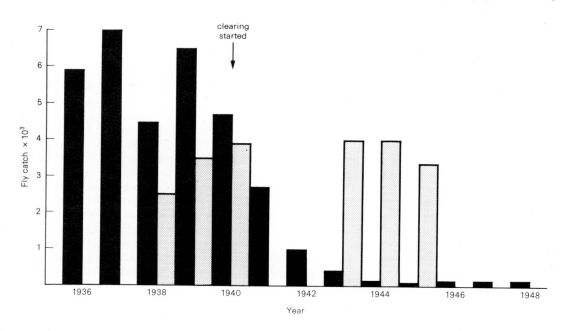

18.11 The alleged effect on the abundance of *Glossina morsitans* of selective clearing of vegetation from a small stream valley in the region of Abercorn, Tanzania. There are some doubts as to whether the clearance was in fact the cause of the fall in the population of fly. The black bars indicate the total number of flies caught annually at seven fly pickets around the area. The light-coloured bars relate to the catch at a fly picket in an adjacent control area. The total area cleared of fly was about 700 km²; the area cleared of vegetation only 15 km².

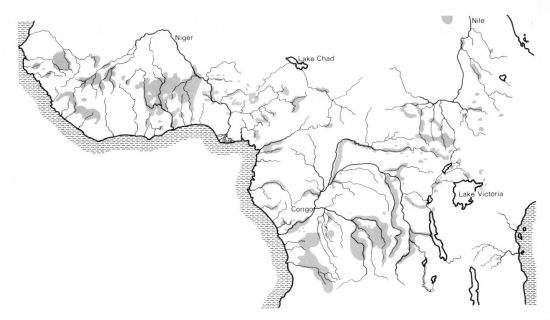

18.12 Map showing the distribution of the main river systems and occurrence of river blindness in tropical Africa. Note the close correlation of the disease with the rivers. The programme of control illustrated in Fig. 18.13 relates to the very large area of central West Africa where the disease is endemic.

will not be affected, it is necessary to make several applications at fairly short time intervals. As the fly is widely distributed the usual technique is to apply the insecticide by spraying from aircraft, that is, in a completely unselective manner. The method was successfully used to clear tsetse from Zululand about 1950; this was a practical proposition as these flies were in a completely isolated pocket. The cost of such an operation is however very great, being more than £50 km^{-2}; to envisage using this measure over the whole range of territory occupied by *G. morsitans* is completely unrealistic and indeed one of the largest of such operations so far attempted in Central Africa covered an area of only 1 600 km^2.

G. morsitans, although it lives in the fairly arid conditions of lightly wooded savanna, cannot tolerate places where there are almost no trees or thickets. Indeed the destructive effect of elephant upon woodland has led to the suggestion that it could serve as a biological control agent of the fly; in fact, in Uganda restriction of elephants to reserves led to a thickening of bush outside the reserves and to a resulting spread of *G. morsitans*. By exploiting man's own destructive habits this same principle has been used for the control of Rhodesian sleeping sickness, which can be checked by encouraging movement of population from scattered villages into small towns of about 3 000 people. In these conditions, provided the resettlement is associated with active farming, the clearing of a wide area

around the town for farm land makes it unsuitable for occupation by the fly and leads to a halt in the spread of the disease. Clearly this method is applicable only to crop-growing peoples; it is of no value for communities of cattle breeders. Nevertheless, the method has been highly successful and Rhodesian sleeping sickness no longer reaches epidemic levels.

River blindness

Onchocerciasis or 'river blindness', which has a wide but discontinuous distribution in tropical Africa (Fig. 18.12), is caused by a nematode worm, *Onchocerca*. Its larvae, microfilariae, invade the cornea of the eye and if they should die there, an opaque scar is formed; heavy invasion can thus result in blindness. The disease is transmitted from man to man by the biting blackfly *Simulium* (Book 1 Fig. 18.34). Although the fly will feed upon other mammals and also birds, the parasite appears to be specific to man; thus, like *Schistosoma*, it could be eradicated if it were possible to organize a mass campaign using drugs which could be taken without medical supervision. There is as yet no chemotherapeutic agent which fulfils this requirement; the disease certainly can be cured by drugs but these may have secondary effects and therefore require trained supervision for their safe administration.

The socially debilitating character of the disease is illus-

333

trated by conditions in places where both fly and parasite are very abundant. In such areas more than one-fifth of all males over the age of 30 may be blind and the community thus not only loses potential workers, but gains dependants. Spread of blackfly results in migration of people away from rivers to higher ground which is burnt to open land for cultivation. This may in turn result in soil erosion and the creation of gullies in which the fly can breed during the rains, leading to still further migration until large areas of badly eroded land are left unpopulated and unproductive.

Like those of mosquitoes, the larvae and pupae of *Simulium* are aquatic (Book 1 Fig. 21.29). Unlike the larvae and pupae of *Anopheles*, both stages of *Simulium* can respire under water and those of most species are to be found only in fast-running water (p. 25). Most of the methods which have been used for the destruction of mosquito larvae are therefore not applicable to the control of *Simulium*. Furthermore the fly bites by day and not, like *Anopheles*, by night: methods of preventing people from being bitten are thus effectively limited to protective clothing and skin repellents, neither of which can be utilized on any large scale.

The larval stages of the fly can be killed by releasing DDT in the waters of streams and rivers. This method of control has been used successfully to eradicate the species of *Simulium*, *S. neavei*, which occurs in Kenya, thus freeing an area of 15 000 km² of the disease. The more widespread species, *S. damnosum*, presents the difficulty that unlike *S. neavei* the adult is capable of flying over considerable distances; for example, marked fly have been recovered 5 km from the release point six hours after release. The Kainji dam site in Nigeria is regularly reinfested from a river in Dahomey which is more than 100 km away. Furthermore the duration of the larval stage is brief, varying from a week to a fortnight depending upon temperature. Thus, if a length of river is to be kept clear of larvae and pupae, it is normally necessary to treat the water with DDT very frequently as there is constant re-establishment of the population. An exception to this is provided by the Nile below Jinja. Here the nearest focus of reinfestation is more than 150 km away, so that the chances of reinvasion are low; applications of DDT are made only when essential and the period between them has varied between three months and more than four years. As a result the rate of new infection of some 300 000 people who live in the area has fallen from nearly 100 percent to less than 1 percent.

The aquatic stages of *Simulium damnosum* must have running water for survival and this fact has been the basis of some campaigns to exterminate the fly. For example, in the north-west corner of Ghana and in Upper Volta, the Black Volta river flows throughout the year (Fig. 18.13). The other two rivers of the Volta basin both cease to flow in the dry season, as do most of the tributaries of the Black Volta. It has therefore been suggested that if the Black Volta and its perennial tributaries were treated regularly

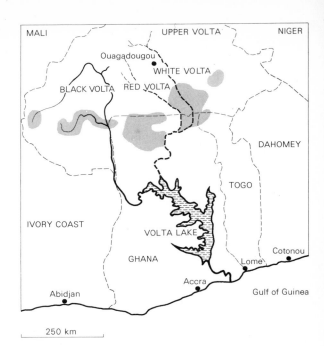

18.13 The Volta basin. The three major rivers and the main tributaries of the Black Volta are shown; other tributaries are omitted. The shaded areas indicate the extent of endemic river blindess. The Black Volta (continuous line) and its two tributaries flow all the year. The Red and White Voitas (broken lines) stop flowing for part of the year. (Simplified from Waddy.)

with DDT throughout several successive dry seasons, it might be possible to eliminate the fly. If this policy should prove successful an area of more than 400 000 km² might be cleared of the fly. Nevertheless a source of reinfestation from fly will remain in the south, so that a barrier zone to prevent invasion will be necessary. The local topography assists in this, although regular insecticidal treatment of rivers in the barrier zone will be essential. The successful clearance of this area would provide a basis for subsequent extension of eradication campaigns into other adjoining areas.

Nutrition and malnutrition

The final category of ill-health which we have to consider is that which arises from living on a diet inadequate in one or more ways. The food taken by man has to satisfy a variety of needs. Firstly, it must supply sufficient energy to meet his daily requirements. This is normally provided by carbohydrate and fat. Although the energy requirements of the body could be met by carbohydrate alone, a certain minimum intake of fat is required since fat molecules are degraded in metabolic processes. There are furthermore certain essential lipids, just as there are essential amino-acids (Book 1 p. 152). Secondly, the diet must contain sufficient protein to replace any normal loss and, with growing children, sufficient actually to increase the quantity of body protein; moreover, this protein must contain adequate quantities of all essential amino-acids. The third requirement is that the diet should provide all necessary vitamins. Finally, it must include various mineral constituents such as sodium, potassium and calcium ions as well as others such as iron and iodine required in far smaller quantities.

Daily energy requirements

In assessing the adequacy of a diet we may ask, firstly, how much energy-giving food is required daily and, secondly, how much is provided by the common constituents of the diet. Clearly the answer to the first question will vary both with age and with the type of work being done. A one-year-old child expends less energy than an adult; a man who spends his days working in the field or in a mine expends

Table 18.2 Daily energy requirements (kJ)

Age (years)	Light work or play	Heavy work	Very heavy work
1–3	4600	—	—
5	6300	—	—
8	7500	—	—
11	8400	—	—
18	11700	14600	—
Adult	9600	11300	16700

more than one who sits in an office. Table 18.2 gives approximate values in kilojoules for the daily requirement of various categories of people. Note that daily energy requirement is often spoken of as the 'daily calorific requirement' since, until recently, the kilocalorie was the normal unit of measurement. Table 18.3 shows the energy

Table 18.3 Energy value, protein and vitamin contents per 100 g of different foodstuffs (*Data from Platt*)

Type of food	Energy content (kJ)	Protein (g)	Thiamine (mg)	Niacin (mg)	Vitamin C (mg)
Cassava, fresh	640	0·7	0·07	0·7	30
Cassava flour	1430	1·5	0·04	0·8	0
Plantain	535	1·0	0·05	0·7	20
Yam, fresh	435	2·0	0·10	0·4	10
Yam flour	1325	3·5	0·15	1·0	0
Maize, whole	1520	10·0	0·35	2·0	0
Maize meal, refined	1480	8·0	0·05	0·6	0
Rice, lightly milled	1480	8·0	0·25	2·0	0
Rice, polished	1470	7·0	0·06	1·0	0
Millet (bulrush)	1520	11·0	0·30	2·0	0
Wheat flour (White)	1470	10·0	0·08	0·8	0
Cowpea	1420	22·0	0·90	2·0	—
Ground-nut, fresh	1400	15·0	0·50	10·0	10
Kidney bean	1420	24·0	0·50	2·0	—
Lentil	1420	24·0	0·50	2·0	—
Pea, dry	1410	25·0	0·80	2·5	—
Fish, fresh	400	18·0	0·03	1·5	—
Fish, dried	1300	63·0	0·10	6·0	0
Sardines, tinned	1300	20·0	—	4·0	—
Beef, lean	840	19·0	0·10	5·0	—
Beef, corned	950	23·0	0	3·5	0
Eggs	660	13·0	0·12	0·1	—
Milk, fresh, cows	270	3·3	0·05	0·1	1
Milk, tinned, unsweetened	585	7·0	0·06	0·2	2
Green pepper	155	2·0	0·06	1·0	150
Tomato, fresh	85	1·0	0·06	0·7	25
Orange	220	0·8	0·08	0·2	45
Pawpaw	160	0·6	0·03	0·2	50

content per 100 g of different types of foods. They have been divided into four classes. The first group comprises those which have a high carbohydrate but very low protein content; these are mostly the common root crops and fruits like plantain. The second also have a high carbohydrate content but contain markedly more protein, while the third category are the protein-rich foods, formed mostly of the muscles of different animals and also hens' eggs. The last class are the fresh fruits.

Protein requirements

From such a table we could invent a variety of diets adequate to meet the energy requirements of an individual. But this is insufficient: we must also know how much protein is required daily. Experiment shows that the minimum daily need of an adult is 1 g per kg of body weight. Thus a man weighing 70 kg will require 70 g of protein daily. So too will a woman of the same weight, unless she is pregnant; in this circumstance she will need more, as she has to provide protein for the baby developing inside her. Thus pregnant mothers require more protein daily than do their husbands.

The daily protein requirements of growing children are far greater in proportion. A one-year-old child needs about 3 g of good-quality protein per kg body weight. Thus, although the absolute weight of protein he needs may be less than that of his father, he needs relatively more if he is to be fully healthy. Similarly a mother nursing a baby is supplying the baby with protein, so, just as when she is pregnant, she needs more protein than her husband.

Table 18.3 shows that a diet of only cassava, yam or plantain is quite insufficient to keep anyone in good health. A man expending 10 000 kJ per day would need to eat about 1 500 g of cassava daily and would obtain only about 10·5 g of protein. His protein requirement might almost be met if the diet were of maize instead; he would need to eat only 660 g of maize each day to meet his energy requirements and, according to the Table, he would then obtain 66 g of protein. Lastly, our man could meet his energy requirements were he to eat about 700 g of beans daily; this would provide him with about 160 g of protein. Clearly such calculations are abstract, since nobody eats one type of food alone. Nevertheless in many places the food is often very largely a protein-poor root crop, supplemented by insufficient quantities of protein-rich food like dried fish.

In the foregoing discussion we assumed that a daily intake of 1 g of any protein per kg body weight will be adequate, but in fact this is only so if the protein can be completely digested and absorbed and if it contains adequate amounts of all the essential amino-acids. Both of these conditions are met by 'first-class protein' as in hens' eggs, milk and meat.

On the other hand, most vegetable proteins are less valuable. Some are poorly digested and their amino-acid composition can be such as to reduce total absorption, for there is evidence that scarcity or lack of one of several amino-acids may result in poor absorption of others. In general, vegetable protein is deficient in three of the essential amino-acids, namely tryptophan, methionine and threonine. We express this by saying that such protein is of poor 'quality'. This deficiency in quality can be made good if more protein is taken daily than our original value of 1·0 g kg^{-1}. A value of about 1·5 g is probably generally sufficient to meet the relative deficiency of essential amino-acids; thus 160 g of bean protein would be just about sufficient to meet an individual's needs when judged in terms of quality. This does not however apply to maize which contains only very small amounts of tryptophan as well as of another essential amino-acid, lysine. An exclusive diet of maize would not supply sufficient of these two amino-acids to keep a man in health.

In recent years new varieties of maize have been developed which have an acceptably high lysine content and also a greater proportion of tryptophan. Such maize, however, differs markedly from the familiar crop and, while it has been used on a limited scale as a constituent of baby foods, it needs special milling and cannot be cooked in traditional ways. Attempts are now being made to produce further varieties which combine the characteristics of ordinary maize with the improved quality of protein. This, if it can be done, will take time and it will be longer still before sufficient of the possible new variety can be harvested to make seed generally available for crops. Such considerations underline the importance both of a mixed diet and, as far as possible, of including in the diet protein of animal origin.

Vitamin and mineral deficiencies

So far we have considered only the protein and energy needs of the body. There are, however, diseases caused by lack of other dietary constituents, and we will discuss four examples; three are due to deficiency of particular vitamins and the fourth to lack of the element iodine.

Pellagra

First we will consider a disease called pellagra. This is characterized by a loss of weight, an abnormal condition of the skin, and diarrhoea, accompanied by mental disturbances in extreme cases. The disease is primarily caused by an inadequacy in the diet of the vitamin niacin, of which about 20 mg a day are normally required by an adult. The vitamin occurs in meat, in liver and in groundnuts. Indeed any diet rich in first-class protein prevents pellagra since tryptophan can be converted in the body to niacin. But there is a curious relation between niacin and maize. Whole maize grain contains about 2 mg of niacin per 100 g, but milling reduces this, so that well-milled maize flour contains far less. Moreover, there are reasons to believe that maize contains some substance which antagonizes the action of niacin. As a result peoples for whom maize constitutes an important part of the diet are prone to pellagra unless they also have an adequate supply of other protein in their food.

Beriberi

The second disease, as yet rare in Africa, is called beriberi; it is due to insufficiency of the vitamin thiamine (B_1). The disease may take various forms, and is not easily diagnosed. The vitamin occurs in green vegetables, meat, fruit and milk and is especially abundant in rice and maize grains and also in beans. The daily requirement is about 1·25 mg. While whole grains of both rice and maize are rich sources of thiamine, much of the vitamin is lost in modern methods of treatment of the grains. Maize contains about 0·35 mg 100 g^{-1}—about one-quarter of the daily requirement— but refined maize flour contains only 0·05 mg 100 g^{-1}. Similarly rice prepared by pounding and winnowing contains about 0·25 mg 100 g^{-1}, but milled and polished rice, the normal product sold in shops, has lost almost all its thiamine, as the germ and testa have been removed. The increasing use of mill-prepared products by growing urban populations thus increases the likelihood that beriberi will become more common. For good health, traditional methods of preparing cereals are better.

Scurvy

Finally, insufficient vitamin C leads to scurvy. The vitamin is abundant in fresh fruits, such as oranges and pawpaw as well as fresh green peppers. There is thus no reason why this deficiency should arise provided such commodities are taken to the peoples of the more open savannas where such fruits do not grow well.

Goitre

One serious mineral deficiency in some areas in Africa is that of iodine, insufficiency leading to goitre. This can be relatively easily corrected by the addition of minute quantities of potassium iodide to the salt, and treatment is thus a problem of public health administration.

'Protein-energy malnutrition'

So far we have looked at the problems of what should constitute a sound diet and at certain diseases which arise from the absence of certain essential constituents. But in many places there are states of ill-health which are described in general terms as the result of 'protein-energy malnutrition'. This especially affects young children; it is estimated that in Ghana alone some 20 000 young children die each year because of this condition.

Adults in some areas may be malnourished during the 'hungry season' if there are not adequate facilities to store foods after the harvest or if the harvest of a year has been very poor. But once food is available in good supply, an adult quickly recovers from the ill-effects of undernourishment and there is no permanent damage provided the subsequent diet contains adequate protein. With children, the effect is quite different. 'Protein-energy malnutrition' can cause permanent damage, since it is in childhood that bodies are built up. Even after cure by an adequate diet, the child which has suffered from this kind of malnutrition will remain stunted and, far more serious, there is evidence which suggests that the inadequate supply of protein during this critical period of growth may result in permanent brain damage.

Two different types of protein-energy malnutrition are recognized. The one, called marasmus, is a consequence of insufficient food as a whole: the child is receiving a completely inadequate diet. The other is more specifically due to protein deficiency and is called kwashiorkor, its name in a Ghanaian language. The word reflects the fact that at the time of the birth of a second child, its elder brother or sister may become seriously ill and even die. The condition increases susceptibility to other diseases and is probably indirectly the cause of high infantile mortality from measles. Kwashiorkor is a result of the older child's being fed carbohydrate-rich but protein-poor foods at a time when, as we emphasized earlier, its relative protein requirements are far greater than that of an adult. By the age of four to six years this danger period is past. Where money to buy food is scarce, the well-being of the young could be ensured if the time between pregnancies were greater. Protein-energy malnutrition thus stems in part from social problems: the problems of how to ensure effective food distribution and of how to develop a widespread understanding of the nutritional needs of small children.

Malnutrition and agriculture

Problems of malnutrition cannot be dissociated from problems of agricultural productivity. There are two factors which reduce or keep low the supply of food. One is soil erosion; over-exploitation of land, and especially over-grazing by cattle, can result in vast areas becoming less and less productive. The second is the practice of shifting cultivation (p. 285) in which the natural fertility of the soil is exploited for a period and once this is temporarily exhausted, the area is left and a new area cleared for cultivation, so that at any time only a fraction of the area of potential agricultural land is being exploited. Further there are in many places complex problems of land tenure, with small scattered farm-holdings which prevent effective utilization of more modern, more sophisticated farming methods. There is one other factor which it is convenient to discuss here and which specifically affects cattle-raising and consequently the supply of protein.

Nagana

Over wide areas of the savanna, it is not easy or even possible to raise cattle as they die from the disease nagana. This disease is caused by various species of *Trypanosoma* and is distributed by several species of tsetse fly. It is similar in many ways to Rhodesian sleeping sickness, but while the latter occurs only in small isolated pockets, nagana is very widespread. Like the human disease, the cattle disease can be spread by *G. morsitans* and we will limit consideration to this particular species whose biology we have already discussed. Further, like those causing the human disease, the trypanosomes which affect cattle can survive also in game, so that the difficulty of the existence of reservoir hosts arises. From the viewpoint of control the two diseases have much in common, but while it is possible to reduce the incidence of Rhodesian sleeping sickness by encouraging a concentration of human beings in small towns, this is clearly not a practical solution with herds of cattle.

Chemicals are available both for prophylaxis and for cure. One of these, antrycide, was heralded in 1949 as a major contribution to the conquest of nagana: subsequently resistant strains of trypanosome have appeared, so that the drug has now only limited value. More serious is the fact that some of these strains, in becoming resistant to antrycide, have at the same time developed resistance to other available drugs. We have seen already comparable phenomena in the development of cross-resistance to insecticides (p. 306).

Although resistance makes chemical protection against nagana of limited value, such protection can be used where the abundance of tsetse is low, as well as to protect cattle moving through fly belts on their way to slaughter and also, during the peak of the dry season when tsetse numbers tend to fall and fodder is scarce, to extend the grazing area for cattle into lands which have not been cleared of fly. As in other cases of drug resistance, the careless use of drugs in too low a dose or neglect of regular treatment can make the problem more difficult; it is when the concentration of drugs in the blood falls to a fairly low level that drug-resistant strains can establish themselves in the cattle.

The fact that game serve as a reservoir for the trypanosomes has led to the idea that if all game could be eliminated from an area and the area itself protected from further invasion by both game and fly, then the land could be used for cattle ranching. Such a policy has been used in various areas. The area selected has first to be fenced to prevent reinvasion by game, and all bushes, trees and shrubs have then to be cleared around the perimeter to a depth of about 3 km to make a fly barrier. The success of such a measure can be seen from the results obtained at Shinyanga in Tanzania (Fig. 18.14). Bait cattle introduced into the area in 1951 did not contract nagana. The cost of this campaign, covering an area of 1 500 km^2 and involving the

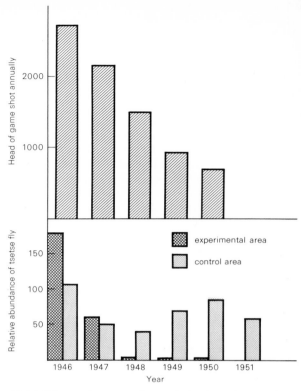

18.14 Effects of an experimental clearing of game from an area of 1 500 km^2 upon the relative abundance of tsetse fly (assessed by fly round technique). It is clear, when this area is compared with a control area, that game destruction can lead to eradication of tsetse fly. (Data from Potts and Jackson.)

destruction of over 8 000 game animals was, in 1950, about £20 per km^2. The selected location was however, such that only one game fence had to be erected and no clearance for fly barriers made. In less isolated areas, the initial cost would have been far higher and annual outlay would be needed to maintain both fences and barriers. Subsequent experience, in which use was made of the well-marked feeding preferences of *G. morsitans*, has shown that very effective control can be achieved by selective rather than total game destruction. As a first measure both elephant and buffalo were driven out of the area and thereafter shooting restricted to warthog, bushpig, kudu and bushbuck; other species such as zebra, impala, eland, roan and sable antelopes were not touched.

While such a policy has been successful in opening up many thousands of km^2 of fly-infested country to cattle ranching, it cannot be considered as a final solution, partly because there is a growing realization that game animals are themselves an important national asset and further that, in certain types of country, they may be more effective meat producers than cattle.

Two facts are of importance in relation to meat pro-

Game farming

18.15 N'dama cattle. These individuals are from a herd selected with the intention of obtaining a beast of greater size than the usual dwarf cattle but retaining resistance to trypanosomes.

duction in fly-infested areas. The first is that n'dama (Fig. 18.15) and other West African breeds of small cattle are more naturally resistant to the nagana trypanosomes than are the big zebu cattle. The second is that game animals infected by trypanosomes show no sign of the disease. These two facts suggest that there can exist among ruminants physiological mechanisms which provide protection against the disease and that an intensive programme of breeding might lead to the development of new types of cattle which, like the game, would be immune to nagana and yet have other desirable characteristics which fit them to be maximally productive in the areas where they are to live. This is a long-term measure but one which could probably be pressed more actively than at the present time.

The question of the exploitation of game rather than cattle as a source of protein has to be considered critically, not only from the viewpoint of its potential productivity, but also from that of the type of husbandry envisaged. It is possible to separate three distinct ideas:

a) Game are potentially more productive than cattle and it would be desirable to domesticate certain game animals rather than rely entirely upon traditional sources of meat.

b) Game are potentially more productive than cattle and it is therefore better policy to run game rather than cattle, or at least with cattle, on settled stock farms.

c) Game are not susceptible to nagana and, if managed, could provide a useful source of protein from large areas of pasture at present closed by tsetse fly to cattle and thus not exploited for meat production.

The first two ideas involve a disputed concept: that game are indeed more productive than cattle. We will first examine this argument. One way to approach the question is to ask what is the biomass of game and of cattle supported by similar sorts of pasture. Table 18.4 summarizes some of the data collected in recent years: it shows that the biomass of game varies from about 5 000 kg km^{-2} to about 30 000 kg km^{-2}. These differences are accounted for by two different factors. The high values are partly a consequence of high population densities of game with associated over-grazing: this can be seen from the different values obtained in various areas of the Ruwenzori National Park. Secondly, high values will arise where there are significant numbers of large ungulates such as elephant and hippopotamus in the population. From the viewpoint of meat production these slow-growing species with massive adults are of little value and thus high values of biomass due to an abundance of such beasts are of little relevance.

The lower values represent areas in which smaller, faster-growing game dominate. Here there are two things to notice. Firstly, that the biomass of game in such condi-

Table 18.4 Estimated biomass of ungulates in various localities in Africa (*Data from various sources*)

Locality	Type of habitat	Biomass ungulates (kg × 10³ km⁻²)
Virunga (Albert) National Park	short grass savanna	24·0
Ruwenzori (Queen Elizabeth) National Park	acacia savanna: heavy over-grazing	28·0–31·0
	acacia savanna: moderate over-grazing	12·0
	grassland: light grazing	9·8
Masai steppe: Nairobi National Park	grassland	*ca*. 5·0
Serengeti Game Reserve	grassland	12·8
Adjoining cattle herds	grassland	3·9
Acacia savanna with game		6·5–15·7
Acacia savanna with cattle		2·0–2·8
Cattle on stock farms	low-rainfall areas	7·8–8·8

Table 18.5 Growth rates (kg day⁻¹) of cattle and game (*Data from Talbot*)

Cattle	0·14
Wildebeest	0·18
Buffalo	0·26
Eland	0·30

tions is very similar to that of cattle on stock farms and, secondly, that it is markedly greater than that found for cattle using traditional herding methods.

Our concern is, however, not simply with the biomass but with the productivity and especially the food chain efficiency of game and cattle. In terms of production of young, game appear to be more productive. Wildebeest, topi and eland reproduce at two years old and the smaller gazelles when even younger, while the traditional type of cow does not breed until her third year. Furthermore the percentage pregnancies are higher with game animals, being about 80 percent in yearling springbok and 95 percent in wildebeest, compared with 50 to 60 percent in cattle. In comparable conditions of forage, growth rates of game are faster than those of cattle (Table 18.5). The quantity of meat obtainable from carcasses is of the same order of magnitude, but game meat is less fatty and therefore provides a richer potential source of protein.

On these criteria, it appears that while there is no evidence that game has any greater potential than cattle grown by intensive methods on stock farms, it does have a greater production potential than that of cattle ranched in the traditional manner. With this information, we can now return to consider the three ideas with which we started.

Our first problem relates to domestication: even if productivity were not markedly greater, would any advantages follow from domestication? One major consideration is water demand. In semi-arid areas in Kenya, eland survive drought at times when there are heavy losses of zebu cattle. Other game including Grant's gazelles and springbok are also better able to survive in semi-arid conditions than cattle. Thomson's gazelle has a higher water requirement but does less damage to areas immediately around water holes than do cattle, which commonly cause local erosion. Eland has in fact been domesticated (Fig. 18.16) and herds have been maintained in the U.S.S.R. since the beginning of the century. Of the three smaller animals, the springbok is farmed in Southern Africa and there have been successful trials of farming Thomson's gazelle in East Africa; neither species is, however, truly domesticated in the sense that the animals can be herded by a few men as can cattle. At present there is no economic pressure to develop this idea of domestication and in the semi-arid areas where it might be of particular value, it would in-

18.16 Tame eland being fed by hand.

volve a change in attitude of the herdsmen towards stock.

The second view, that game would be more productive than cattle on stock farms, does not appear to be well supported by available data. The most promising animal for such a purpose is the eland, but in fattening trials eland gained only about half as much weight daily as did cattle. Cattle excrete less urea daily, the urea retained being recycled to form protein; as a result eland require food of a higher protein content, while the efficiency of eland in utilizing the energy available in fodder is lower.

The third idea, that game could be harvested from areas which are at present closed by tsetse to cattle does offer the prospect of a greater supply of first-class protein and yet, except in a few isolated cases, it has not proved successful. One major difficulty is that such areas, because they are not agricultural country, are effectively uninhabited. As a result any animals killed for meat are far away from centres for processing, inspection and sale. Even if the carcasses are dressed where the animals are shot, the meat has to be transported long distances and if it is to be finally acceptable to the consumer, refrigerated transport may be necessary. All these increase the price of the meat and so far major undertakings of this nature have not proved economically attractive. There is one further problem: if such game populations are to be used to maximum effect as a source of meat, they must be skilfully managed and for this purpose a considerable number of men would be required. The animals are wild and have no owners; such labour would therefore work for wages. This is a very different way of life from that of the herdsman who owns his cattle and whose livelihood depends upon the way he tends the animals which are his personal property. At the present time at least, a change in attitude towards the work of animal husbandry such as this implies is not easily envisaged. Although there are major difficulties in such a scheme it may, nevertheless, prove more effective as a way of exploiting areas dominated by tsetse fly than to turn these lands slowly to open pasture for cattle, or to attempt to rid them of tsetse fly by some other means.

During this century our understanding of the causes of the major human diseases has vastly expanded. In some areas diseases such as malaria and smallpox which were once endemic have been completely conquered, although elsewhere they remain serious problems which lower the productive capacities of the inhabitants. The eradication of certain of these diseases lies within our power; in some cases there is lack of the necessary investment of manpower and money, but improvement in health is often hindered, sometimes by a lack of understanding on the part of peoples affected, sometimes in an unwillingness to change traditional ways of life. Most of these diseases affect the people of the towns as much as those of the villages, and with the rapid growth of urban populations new problems arise; in the next chapter we turn to consider the biological aspects of these issues.

Problems

1 Using Fig. 18.1 as a basis, prepare diagrammatic summaries of the relations between the life histories of the various parasites considered in this chapter and the methods of control which have been adopted.

2 Of two identical freshwater ponds, one was stocked with *Gambusia*. When the ponds were compared after some months, it was found that phytoplankton was far more abundant in that containing *Gambusia*. Suggest an explanation of this observation.

3 The tapeworm is a parasite of some importance in man. Using all the information available to you, suggest methods which might be used to control this disease.

4 How would you (a) determine the energy content of a sample of yam, (b) determine the daily energy requirement of a schoolboy?

5 What are likely to have been the consequences, in terms of human health, of the formation of the Volta Lake in Ghana? Explain the biological basis for each point you make.

6 Using the indexes to Books 1 and 2 assemble all the information you can upon
   (a) *Entamoeba histolytica*;
   (b) *Plasmodium* and its vector *Anopheles*;
   (c) *Trypanosoma* and its vectors, *Glossina* spp.;
   (d) *Schistosoma* and its vector snails;
   (e) *Onchocerca* and its vector, *Simulium*.
Prepare a full, illustrated account of the life histories, biology and methods of control of each parasite and, where relevant, the vectors.

7 The table below shows the amino-acid composition of beef protein and that of various plant crops.
(a) If you were responsible for agricultural policy, would you recommend extensive cultivation of any of these crops? What other data would you require? Give reasons for your proposals.

Amino-acid composition of various proteins, expressed as g 100g^{-1} protein (*Data from Doku and Mante*)

Amino-acid	Beef	Whole maize	Rice	Wheat protein	Soybean
Arginine	7·7	4·8	7·2	3·9	7·1
Cystine	1·3	1·5	1·4	1·9	1·9
Histidine	2·9	2·2	1·5	2·2	2·3
Isoleucine	6·3	4·0	5·1	3·7	4·7
Leucine	7·7	22·0	9·0	7·5	6·6
Lysine	8·1	2·0	3·2	2·0	5·8
Methionine	3·3	3·1	3·4	1·0	2·0
Phenylalanine	4·9	5·0	6·3	5·5	5·7
Threonine	4·6	3·7	3·9	2·7	4·0
Tryptophan	1·3	0·8	1·3	1·0	1·2
Tyrosine	3·4	5·5	5·6	3·8	4·1
Valine	5·8	5·0	6·4	4·2	4·2

(b) Soybean is a legume. Would there be any advantage in a policy of planting soybean and maize on alternate years? If so, why?

(c) Treated soybean has been used in place of cow's milk. Why should this make it an economically valuable crop?

(d) Soybean is grown successfully at the moment in fairly high latitudes. What problem might arise in attempting to use it as a crop in the tropics?

8 A goitre is a swelling of the thyroid gland. If there is a dietary deficiency of iodine, the gland swells; this condition is called 'simple goitre'. There is a second type of goitre due to malfunctioning of the endocrine system, leading to over-stimulation of the gland. What hormones are likely to be involved in a goitre of this type?

Bibliography

Revision reading

Hall, J. R.	*Senior Tropical Biology*, Longman, 1970, pp. 294–303
Mackean, D. G.	*Introduction to Biology*, tropical edition, Murray, 1969, Chap. 36
Stone, R. H., Cozens, A. B.	*New Biology for Tropical Schools*, Longman, 1969, pp. 51–7

Further reading

Boycott, S. A.	*Natural History of Infectious Disease*, Arnold, 1973
Cheng, T. C.	*Symbiosis*, Pegasus, 1970, Chap. 4
Goma, L. K. H.	*The Mosquito*, Hutchinson, 1966
Nash, T. A. M.	*Africa's Bane: the Tsetse Fly*, Collins, 1969
Welbourn, H.	*Nutrition in Tropical Countries*, Oxford University Press, 1963
Wilson, R. A.	*An Introduction to Parasitology*, Arnold, 1967
Alvarado, C. A., Bruce-Chwatt, L. J.	'Malaria', *Scientific American*, 1962, Vol. 206, pt. 5, p. 86
Gillie, R. B.	'Endemic Goitre', *Scientific American*, 1971, Offprint no. 1223
Harpstead, D. P.	'High Lysine Corn', *Scientific American*, 1971, Offprint no. 1223
Jones, J. C.	'The Sexual Life of a Mosquito', *Scientific American*, 1968, Offprint no. 1106
Rothschild, M.	'Fleas', *Scientific American*, 1965, Offprint no. 1027
Taylor, C. R.	'The Eland and the Oryx', *Scientific American*, 1969, Offprint no. 1131

19 Man in towns and cities

About 10 000 years ago, man settled for the first time in villages as cultivation of plants gradually replaced hunting and the gathering of wild fruits, seeds and tubers as a source of food. One such settlement was at Jericho in Palestine: here there is a constantly flowing spring of water which served as a focal point around which a succession of walled towns were built. The earliest settlers, although they cultivated wheats and barley, made no pottery; indeed, the site was inhabited for nearly 2 000 years before pottery-making first started. The mound which marks the site upon which successive villages and later towns were built reached a height of about 20 m. Such mounds or tels, formed from the remains of successive rebuildings of towns, have been well preserved in the Middle East. Elsewhere they are not so easy to recognize as they have been subjected to much greater erosion.

Small towns of perhaps 2 000 or so people present new biological problems; as the towns grow, these become more severe and today, where cities may contain several million people all aggregated in a relatively small area, we have a peculiar environment whose characteristics we must examine. In Africa south of the Sahara nearly 15 percent of the population now live in cities, and nearly half of these in cities of populations greater than 100 000. Moreover the rate of growth of the urban population is far more rapid than that of the population in the rural areas. For example, in Egypt between 1940 and 1960, the urban population increased by about 125 percent while the rural population increased only about 30 percent.

The urban ecosystem

We may, in very broad terms, say that a modern city is a man-made ecosystem which lacks both producers and decomposers. It is a vast aggregation of consumers who must be supplied with food, water and shelter, and whose biological waste products, whether these be incompletely eaten food, excreta or dead bodies, must be removed in some fashion. Clearly this is an over-simplification. In many places some of the inhabitants grow part of their food within the confines of the town—in small gardens, in hen-runs and so on; many draw part or all of their water supply from tanks storing rainwater. Furthermore, there remains almost always a scavenging fauna of ants, termites and cockroaches which remove small items of domestic waste, while larger scavengers such as dogs, vultures and even hyaenas are also to be found in cities. As development proceeds these become relatively less important, while non-biological waste products of human activity—newspapers, broken cups, basins, bottles, metal and plastic containers, old motor cars and lorries—become more abundant and must also be removed.

The town as an ecosystem has a second important feature which arises directly from the population density. We have already discussed the actions of a variety of density-dependent factors which serve as checks on population growth (p. 255); some of these affect natality, others mortality. It is an observed fact that the birth rates of the populations of industrialized cities tend to be lower than those of the rural areas, but whether or to what extent this is a direct biological effect of population density is uncertain: it could well be due to other, social influences like the realization that the children of smaller families are at an economic advantage in an urban environment, or the feeling that only a small family can live tolerably in the limited area and recreational facilities provided by a normal urban housing unit.

Urban mortality

Factors affecting mortality which arise from high population densities are more obvious: the most important of these is epidemic disease. Certain epidemic diseases are spread from person to person, either by direct contact or in the air. Measles is such a disease; in a dense population with no immunity the disease may spread very rapidly and cause high mortality. Early colonists from Europe spread the disease all over the earth and in many places large numbers of the local inhabitants died in epidemics which followed their first contact with Europeans. Influenza is another familiar disease of the same type which can rapidly spread in large urban areas. There is little in the design of cities which can protect the inhabitants from such epidemics.

There are other diseases, such as plague, which involve a vector. Plague is spread by fleas which normally are associated with the Black Rat, *Rattus rattus*. Here man can take action to control the disease by attempting to eliminate the normal host of the flea, as well as by designing housing and other town buildings so that they do not provide satisfactory living conditions for the rats.

Finally, diseases like typhoid and cholera are normally spread by drinking polluted water. The control of these, possibly the most serious of all urban diseases, depends upon effective methods of disposal of human excreta and upon the purification of water supplies used by the city dwellers. The ways in which these are effected we will discuss later in this chapter.

Essential needs of towns and cities

We turn now to consider the problems associated with the essential 'inputs' into a city ecosystem; of these the most important are foods and water.

Life in large towns and cities depends upon farmers producing more food than is required for their own immediate needs. It requires some type of transport system which allows the surplus food to be moved from the farms to the towns and commonly, at some point between the farmer-producer and the urban consumer, storage facilities which serve to smooth out seasonal variations in the supply of agricultural products. The production and storage of a food surplus are then the first biological problems which arise from human aggregations. We have already discussed many aspects of these in Chaps. 16 and 17.

The second necessary input is water. Water in cities is used partly for domestic purposes such as drinking, cooking, washing and for disposal of excreta as sewage. Depending upon the level of development, such usage may be less than 100 litres or as much as 1 000 litres per person daily. But manufacturing industry also requires water and the quantities of water required for some processes can be very great indeed (Table 19.1).

Table 19.1 Approximate quantity of water required for the production of one tonne of different industrial products (*Data from Morris*)

Product	kilolitres tonne^{-1}
Coke fuel (treated coal)	14
Beer	18
Steel	225
Aluminium	1 150
Synthetic rubber	2 225

Water supplies and water treatment

The water supplies to towns and cities are drawn sometimes from natural underground reservoirs, sometimes from lakes and rivers and sometimes from artificial reservoirs formed by damming river valleys. The chemical and biological characteristics of these waters differ and they are normally treated to make them suitable for domestic and industrial use. Even the process of water storage may pose an initial biological problem as the water carried into such reservoirs or lakes may be rich in algal nutrients, especially phosphates and nitrates. These nutrients may be derived from waste water discharges from other towns further up a river system or from surface run-off water flowing over agricultural land, especially if the land has been treated with fertilizer. When such water collects in a lake or reservoir there may result very heavy growths of algae forming 'blooms'. For example, one temperate reservoir holding about 35 million m^3 of water was estimated during such a bloom to contain 1 000 tonnes wet weight of algae, and using the water would have required the removal of 10 tonnes of this material daily. To prevent such events, water-supply reservoirs are treated with copper sulphate, but the copper ion must subsequently be removed before the water can be made available for general use.

All raw water supplies contain sediments which must be removed, while river, lake or reservoir water is likely to contain bacteria, including those which produce typhoid fever and bacillary dysentery, the cysts of *Entamoeba* (the causative agent of amoebic dysentery) and the infective stages of a number of parasites of man such as tapeworm and the nematodes guinea-worm, whip-worm and the big intestinal worm *Ascaris*. The cercariae of *Schistosoma* may occur as well as the causative agent of cholera, *Vibrio cholerae*.

Water supplies to cities are treated in a 'water works'. The water is initially filtered through fine wire mesh to remove any larger objects in suspension and then run into settlement tanks where it is allowed to stand for several days to permit non-colloidal material to settle. Then follows filtration treatment to remove bacteria: this can be done in two different ways.

a) In the 'rapid filtration' process the initial step is one of formation of a flocculent precipitate which traps any bacteria or other particles in the water. This precipitation requires the presence of calcium bicarbonate in the water and, unless the water is already 'hard', lime may be added. To the water is then added aluminium sulphate. This reacts with the calcium bicarbonate to form aluminium hydroxide as a flocculent precipitate.

$$Al_2(SO_4)_3 + 3Ca(HCO_3)_2 \rightarrow$$
$$3CaSO_4\downarrow + 2Al(OH)_3\downarrow + 6CO_2$$

Alternatively iron(II) sulphate may be used, with the formation of iron(III) hydroxide.

$$FeSO_4 + Ca(HCO_3)_2 \rightarrow Fe(HCO_3)_2 + CaSO_4\downarrow$$
$$Fe(HCO_3)_2 + 2Ca(OH)_2 \rightarrow$$
$$Fe(OH)_2 + 2CaCO_3\downarrow + 2H_2O$$
$$2Fe(OH)_2 + H_2O + \tfrac{1}{2}O_2 \rightarrow 2Fe(OH)_3\downarrow$$

This material is then filtered through sand in beds about 1 m deep. This removes the precipitates and also holds back bacteria, cysts, eggs and other potential infective agents. Such filter beds clog fairly rapidly and have to be cleaned by forcing water through them in the opposite direction to wash out the accumulated precipitate.

b) The 'slow filtration' process also uses sand beds of about 1 m depth. The filtration process here depends upon the fact that a growth of bacteria will develop over the surface of the sand; some of these bacteria secrete a gelatinous material which serves as a filter and has the further advantage that it adsorbs any copper ions that may have been added earlier to prevent algal blooms. Over this surface of bacteria and bacterial secretion a layer of diatoms may form which aids the process of oxygenation of the water, while beneath the sand surface both Protozoa and midge larvae crop the bacteria, so that an equilibrium is reached.

Following filtration, chemical softening of the water may be used if this is essential for industrial reasons; there is normally no necessity to soften water which is used simply for domestic supply. Then follow chlorination, as a further control over bacteria, and finally aeration. In exceptional circumstances it may be necessary to run the water through beds of activated charcoal to remove an unacceptable colour or taste.

Clearly such measures involve considerable capital outlay in engineering works and recurrent expenditure on chemicals, but if large numbers of people are to live within a limited area, the potential danger of the rapid spread of epidemic diseases like cholera is very great.

Air

There is a third necessary input, namely air. Until recently this has presented no very serious problems, but the growth of industrial activity and the increasing numbers of motor cars and lorries have altered this. Many factories have in the past been permitted to discharge, in an uncontrolled manner, waste gases which are potentially toxic. In cities in high latitudes the burning of coal for domestic heating also discharged into the air toxic products, especially oxides of sulphur, while the exhaust fumes of motor cars contain not only carbon monoxide but also carcinogenic (that is, cancer-producing) substances. There can thus be a problem of 'air pollution' which we will consider later (p. 377).

Disposal of waste

Let us now look at the other side of the balance sheet, namely the disposal of waste and excreta produced by urban consumers. Much waste material has in the past simply been left to decay naturally in dumps on land not required for other purposes. The material may simply be thrown there by the householder or be collected by some service provided by the municipal authorities. But the disposal of the waste of large industrial cities is more difficult, especially if it includes materials such as old motor cars which only slowly rust away or large quantities of glass or plastics which are not attacked by decomposing organisms.

Plastics can be disposed of with difficulty by incineration; old cars and other forms of metal scrap can be compressed so as to minimize their volume, and then dumped. It is only in the last few years that recycling indestructible waste materials such as aluminium cans and old cars has become economically conceivable.

There is a further waste which we must also note. Many industrial processes produce fluid wastes, effluents, which have commonly been discharged into rivers where they are attacked by decomposing organisms. Such wastes may, however, be toxic to many forms of life or cause deoxygenation of the water, so that significant stretches of rivers in and below cities may be devoid of plants and animals. This is one aspect of the problem of water pollution which we will consider further later (p. 378). The discharge of hot effluents from factories and power stations can also produce marked effects upon rivers.

Disposal of excreta

Of major biological interest and importance is the disposal of human excreta—urine and faeces. In large inland cities the essential problem is how to develop ways in which the normal processes of decomposition can go ahead as rapidly as possible and in as small an area as possible. Decomposition can occur in two ways: by anaerobic fermentation or by oxidation. Smaller sewage-disposal units like cesspits and septic tanks are essentially large fermentation chambers, while the more complicated 'sewage works' depends primarily upon the use of oxidative processes.

Cesspits and septic tanks

A cesspit is simply an excavated pit which should be 5 m or more in depth and preferably sited in well-drained soil. The processes of anaerobic fermentation break down the coarser material into smaller fragments and ultimately to water-soluble compounds which are carried together with fluid waste into the soil and there metabolized by soil-living bacteria. There is a slow accumulation of indigestible material at the bottom of the pit and in the course of time it may become necessary to fill the pit with earth and excavate a new one.

A septic tank is used in association with flush toilets. It may be a simple concrete tank in which anaerobic fermentation occurs, the waste water draining away into the soil, or it may be a combination of an anaerobic fermentation tank with an aerobic filter bed (Fig. 19.1). As anaerobic fermentation proceeds large volumes of gas such as methane are produced, while a mud-like deposit, sludge, forms at the bottom of the tank as well as a scum on the surface of the fluid. Periodically the sludge must be removed.

Where the output is poured over a filter, the final processes of decomposition depend upon the activity of aerobic bacteria which, for example, convert ammonia to nitrate. With these bacteria there develops a population

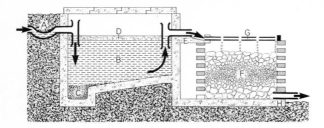

19.1 Vertical section of a septic tank with aerating filter bed. Sewage enters along pipe A, bent so as to produce a fluid seal to prevent the flow of gas backwards along the pipe. The sewage undergoes anaerobic fermentation at B, forming a sludge, C, and a scum D. Excess fluid flows out at E into an aerating filter formed of loosely packed stones, F, and enclosed in porous bricks to ensure a supply of air. The fluid is dispersed onto the stones from several perforated pipes, as shown at G, and flows slowly down over the stones. Here oxidation occurs and the fluid is discharged at H.

of consumers, especially Protozoa, so that an equilibrium density of bacterial population is reached, its size depending to a considerable extent upon the quantity of material passing through the tank.

Both cesspits and septic tanks are designed to deal with the waste production of individual housing units. Within towns the high population density usually requires that excreta are removed for central processing. Suitable vehicles may be used to collect material, commonly spoken of as 'night soil', from latrines, or there may be a system of sewage pipes which collect the sewage from a wide area.

Sewage farming

Methods of treatment vary. Night soil may be deposited on waste land away from the city. Such land may be opened up into a series of trenches 1·0 to 1·5 m deep into which the material is dumped. Each trench is then covered with earth and processes of anaerobic fermentation go ahead beneath the soil cover. Such land will, as a result, be richly fertilized and after a period may be used for the growth of crops; a fresh area of waste land has then to be opened for disposal of night soil.

An essentially similar method can be adopted for the disposal of water-borne sewage. The material collected is allowed to flood over a large area of waste land. The water evaporates and the solid excretory material slowly decomposes. This process, spoken of as 'sewage farming', has the disadvantage that large quantities of raw sewage are exposed and this presents the danger that disease organisms may be distributed from the sewage farm by flying insects. Furthermore, in countries where there is a dense population or where there are very large cities, the area of land required makes the procedure uneconomic, although

such land can ultimately be recovered and used for crop raising.

Disposal into rivers or the sea

Alternatively the raw sewage may be discharged directly into rivers or, in coastal towns, out to sea. The former procedure is clearly undesirable as the large discharge of organic matter results in the establishment of a massive bacterial population whose metabolic activity depletes the river water of oxygen, killing off most other organisms. As the water is carried towards the sea, the processes of fermentation proceed and the rich supply of nutrients offers conditions in which extensive algal growth can occur. As in a septic tank, anaerobic fermentation is replaced by oxidative processes; much of the nutrient is

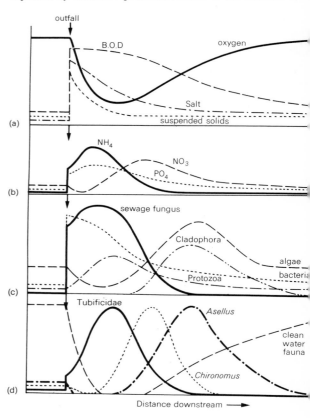

19.2 Diagrammatic representations of the changes along the length of a river below the point of discharge or outfall of an organic effluent such as raw sewage. In (a) the changes in oxygen content and suspended solids are shown, as well as that of the 'biochemical oxygen demand' (p. 348). (b) shows the changes in concentration of the major nutrients; note that the ammonium ion is replaced by nitrate and that the concentrations of both nitrate and phosphate slowly fall. (c) indicates the pattern of succession of micro-organisms and (d) that of the invertebrates. (After Hynes.)

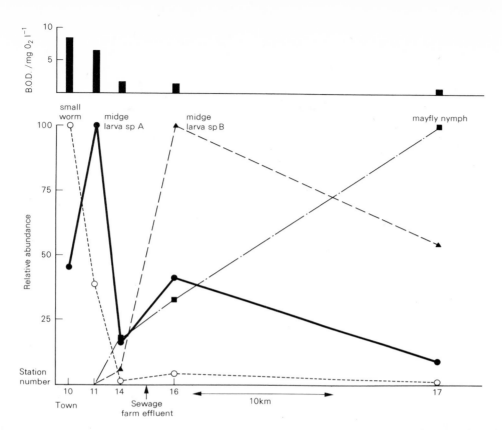

19.3 Changes in the biochemical oxygen demand and bottom fauna along about 30 km of river below the town of Estcourt in Natal, South Africa. Organic effluent from a fibreboard factory and a milk-processing works are discharged into the river just upstream to station 10. The process of 'self-purification' is almost complete after 30 km. Note that the effluent from a sewage farm located between stations 14 and 16 has less effect than the industrial effluent. (Data from Oliff.)

removed by the algae and then passed on to consumers so that finally, downstream, the normal river flora and fauna are found once more. Such a sequence of events is described as 'self-purification' (Figs. 19.2 and 19.3). The method, possibly acceptable where there is only a small community of people, is in general undesirable as it may make the river water useless for most purposes for many kilometres along the course of the river.

Discharge out to sea, where this is possible, is less evidently objectionable since, provided the discharge pipes end in a suitable place, the sewage is rapidly diluted. In practice, this method has often brought secondary difficulties as ignorance of the pattern of the local water currents in the sea has resulted in raw sewage being carried back to pollute the beaches.

Clearly it is desirable that the processes of fermentation and oxidation should be completed before the material is discharged into the river systems. This is particularly important in densely populated areas where the rivers may be used not only to dispose of the final products of sewage treatment but also as a source of drinking water. The

water itself is thus being recycled, and if such intensive usage is to be safe from the viewpoint of human health, it is essential that the discharge from sewage works should contain the minimum quantity of organic material, while the water-processing plants should be able to prevent entry of disease-causing or 'pathogenic' organisms into the water supply. It is alleged that where a series of large cities lies along the banks of a single river, the same water may have been drunk by several different people in succession on its way from the source of the river to the sea.

Stabilization ponds

The simplest method of sewage treatment within a fairly limited area is by the use of stabilization or oxidation ponds. These are particularly suitable in countries where there is abundant sunshine, as they depend for their success upon active growth of algae.

Before discussing the workings of this system it is desirable to be familiar with two of the methods used to assess the purity of the water output of a sewage works.

The first involves estimating the number of bacteria which might have originated from human faeces. One organism very abundant in faeces is the colon bacillus *Escherichia coli*, and the occurrence of more than a certain minimum number in water may be taken as indicating probable pollution with human faecal matter. One way in which its abundance is determined is to inoculate a series of tubes containing a sterile bacteriological medium with different volumes of the water to be tested. This is repeated several times, so that there will be several tubes each of which has been inoculated with the same volume of water. The medium used contains, among other things, lactose and an indicator. Immersed in the medium is a small inverted tube (Fig. 19.4). *E. coli*, if present, will metabolize the lactose and form lactic acid and carbon dioxide: the lactic acid will change the colour of the indicator and the gas will collect in the tube. The two events are taken to indicate the presence of an organism which is similar to or identical with *E. coli*. By noting the numbers of tubes in which fermentation has occurred, it is possible to determine the number of *E. coli*-like organisms per 100 cm³ of water. Since a count as low as 10 *E. coli* is considered to be an indication of faecal pollution, the volumes of the water samples used in such tests range from 50 cm³ downwards.

The second method involves the determination of the 'biochemical oxygen demand' (B.O.D.). The principle of its determination is simple. Two water samples are taken, and the oxygen content of one is determined immediately; the other bottle, tightly stoppered, is incubated in the dark at a constant temperature for a standard time, usually five days. At the end of this period the oxygen content of the water sample is determined. The difference in oxygen content (expressed as mg l⁻¹) is the 'five-day B.O.D.'. This provides an approximate measure of the quantity of substrate for aerobic organisms present in the water sample: the more substrate present, the smaller the quantity of oxygen which will remain. Clearly a large number of variables may influence the result. It is, however, a useful general index of water quality.

Stabilization ponds consist of a series of three shallow interconnecting ponds, each about 1·5 m deep. After passing through a coarse screen to remove solid matter, the sewage is run directly into the first pond. Provided the rate of addition of sewage (the loading) is not too great, biological changes occur which produce a dense population of algae. Initially bacteria and autotrophic Protozoa feed upon the available organic matter; this liberates nutrient salts which are then utilized by algae. Provided there is good sunlight, a dense suspension of algae will form and oxygen will be liberated. The oxygen allows the establishment of populations of various consumer organisms: bacterial-feeding Protozoa and small Crustacea, as well as larvae of insects such as midges. This material flows on slowly to a second pond where the process is carried further: bacterial-feeding consumers are more abundant and higher-order consumers such as dragon-fly larvae may appear. In the third pond animals such as mayfly nymphs, which are very intolerant of pollution, may be abundant, while fish can be introduced so that the organisms which are produced can be exploited as a source of food. The effectiveness of this procedure, which is equivalent to the events of self-purification in a river, can be seen from the data in Table 19.2. It depends upon allowing adequate time for the biological changes to occur, and to achieve satisfactory results it is generally necessary to ensure that the quantity of fluid added each day is about one-twentieth of the total volume of the first pond: this is expressed by saying that the pond has a twenty-day 'retention time'. Such ponds may thus occupy a large area. As a rule of thumb, a pond system of 1 ha can dispose of the sewage produced by 2500 people daily; in warm climates as in tropical Africa this area is probably less as the biological changes proceed more rapidly.

Of course, waste materials other than domestic sewage may also be discharged into the drains leading to the

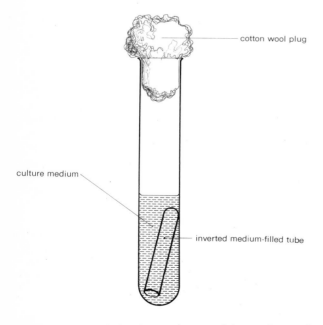

culture medium

cotton wool plug

inverted medium-filled tube

19.4 Bacteriological culture tube containing an inverted tube to detect the formation of gas.

Table 19.2 Composition of stabilization pond effluents (*After Stander*)

Effluent from	E. coli (organisms cm⁻³)	B.O.D. (mg l⁻¹)	Total nitrogen (mg l⁻¹)
Pond 1	10 000	58	26
Pond 2	85	21	12
Pond 3	5	18	4

sewage works. The total quantity of organic waste produced by various human activities, including industry, may be expressed in terms of the number of people who would produce an equivalent quantity of domestic sewage. Thus, for example, the waste produced in slaughtering a cow, if it were disposed of through sewage treatment, would be equivalent to that produced daily by 21 people, the waste in tanning the cow's hide to that of a further 18 people, while that in making 100 lbs of butter from the cow's milk would be equivalent to 34 people. Thus in assessing how great an area a community must set aside to treat its waste by a series of stabilization ponds, it is necessary to consider all the waste-producing activities. Some may produce materials which are very demanding in treatment; for example, the waste produced in the manufacture of a tonne of strawboard is equivalent to that produced daily by about 1 700 people.

Such stabilization ponds are excellently suited to the needs of small towns or large villages; there is little to go wrong and the water discharged into the rivers is clean, while with care the final pond can be used for fish production. In larger urban areas it may not be possible to devote so much land area to the processes of sewage disposal and more rapid methods of treatment are necessary. There are two systems commonly employed.

Filter beds

One system involves the use of filter beds (Fig. 19.5), somewhat similar to those used in association with a septic tank. The incoming sewage is first led into a large grit tank where heavy stony material settles rapidly to the bottom. This deposit is removed at intervals and dumped on waste land. The sewage then passes through coarse screens of about 10 cm and 2 cm mesh. These hold back lighter material, commonly of organic origin, which is removed and after passage through a mechanical disintegrator fed back into the raw sewage.

The filtered sewage then passes to a sedimentation tank where it is held for about ten hours. During this time the larger particles settle to form a 'sludge'. This sludge is removed every two to three months; it may be compressed to remove water and then be sold as fertilizer. The effluent from the sedimentation tank now passes to the sprinklers (Fig. 19.6), which consist of long arms arising from a slowly rotating central shaft. The arms are hollow and perforated with fine holes; the effluent from the sedimentation tanks is forced out along the arms, so that it emerges as a series of fine jets to fall onto a filter bed below. As a result of this process, the water reaching the surface of the filter bed has been partly oxygenated.

The filter bed consists of a circular structure made of porous bricks to ensure full aeration. The whole is filled with small stones to a depth of about 2 m and the effluent flows across the large surface area provided. About 3 l of effluent are spread over the surface of the stones of each

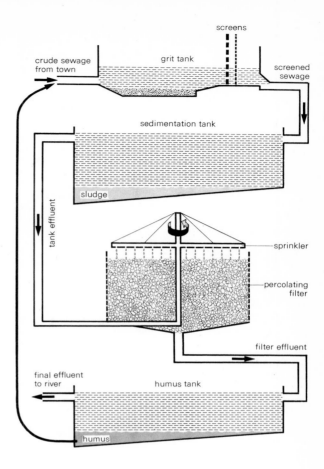

19.5 Schematic diagram of sewage treatment using percolating filters. For further explanation see text.

m³ of filter bed. When first brought into use such a filter effects little purification, but over the course of a few weeks a growth of bacteria and fungi becomes established. Many of these bacteria secrete a gelatinous matrix, while others, together with the fungi, grow in filaments so that the whole forms a fine meshwork. This is the basis of the filtering action, while both bacteria and fungi metabolize the organic material in the effluent. On the surface of the bed filamentous algae, and especially blue-green algae, become established. Upon this complex substrate grow Protozoa, especially ciliates, which feed upon the bacteria, and, by mucus secretion, possibly aid the clumping together of the bacteria in the effluent from the sedimentation tanks.

Were these processes to proceed alone, the surface of the filter would rapidly become choked. However larger consumers, including nematode worms, small oligochaetes and fly larvae (Fig. 19.7) establish themselves and these, by feeding upon the various organisms of the filter mat ensure that percolation can continue. Material is constantly being removed as the fly larvae pu-

19.6 Sprinkler beds in action. The arms rotate, spreading the fluid from the sedimentation tanks over the beds.

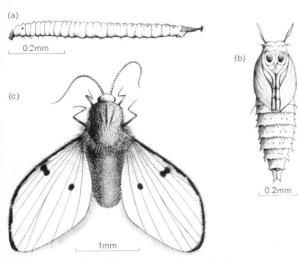

19.7 Among the midge larvae of filter beds are those of the moth-flies. (a) Larva, (b) pupa and (c) adult of *Psychoda*. Closely related to the moth-flies are the sand flies which have blood-sucking adults responsible from the transmission of a trypanosome which causes 'oriental sore'.

pate, emerge and fly away, while the remains of other organisms, together with cast larval skins, are slowly carried down through the filter bed into a second sedimentation tank below. Here, during a retention time of about four hours, further organic material—humus—settles out and the final effluent can be discharged into a river. The humus is removed weekly and returned to the inflow of crude sewage.

The advantage of this system is that the retention time of fluid in the filter beds is very short: the B.O.D. can fall from about 400 mg l^{-1} to 20 mg l^{-1} in a few hours. As a result the area occupied by the works is far less than that required by stabilization ponds; 1 ha is sufficient to meet the needs of about 25000 people, and with the use of high-rate filters, which have a lower efficiency but are readily brought into action, a value of 250000 people ha^{-1} may be achieved.

We have emphasized that the successful working of these filter beds depends upon the fact that the mat of bacteria, fungi and algae is being constantly destroyed, chiefly by the feeding activities of insect larvae. The whole complex within the filter forms a small ecosystem, with a charac-

350

teristic community of constant species composition over wide areas. One may wonder how a definite community so convenient to man came to be established within the relatively short time that this technology of sewage disposal has existed. The few species of insects which form the bulk of the fauna of the filter beds are found, together with a large number of other species, in muddy ponds in woodland habitats where there is a regular supply of organic matter from falling leaves. The fauna of the sewage filter beds thus represents a fragment of this far more diverse natural community. Many of the species from the natural community have specialized requirements for type of food and pupation site and these effectively exclude them from living successfully in filter beds, while slowly reproducing forms are at a disadvantage compared with the rapidly reproducing species characteristic of sewage works. The answer to our question then is that man has created a relatively uniform type of habitat; within this certain species can thrive, but the diversity of the fauna is slight compared with that found in the far more complex habitat in which these species naturally occur. Here, in a very different setting, we see a parallel to the simplification of the fauna characteristic of monocultures of agricultural crops.

The activated sludge process

The second technique, more elaborate in engineering requirements but even less demanding of space, is the 'activated sludge process' (Fig. 19.8). In this procedure the raw sewage is treated initially in the same way as with a filter bed, but the effluent from the sedimentation tanks is led into aeration tanks into which air is forced to ensure a process of aerobic breakdown. In a large sewage works the water may flow for a distance of more than 500 m along the aeration tank in which the retention time is about four to ten hours. The resulting effluent is led to further settling tanks where a sludge settles out. Part of this 'activated sludge' is returned to the aeration tank to be recycled. The rest of the sludge may be used directly as fertilizer or allowed to undergo a slow anaerobic fermentation, or 'digestion'. During this latter process methane is produced abundantly and may be used to supply power for the other operations within the sewage works. After digestion the residual sludge may also be sold as fertilizer.

What then is activated sludge and what are the biological events which accompany this process? Activated sludge consists of a matrix of bacterial and protozoal

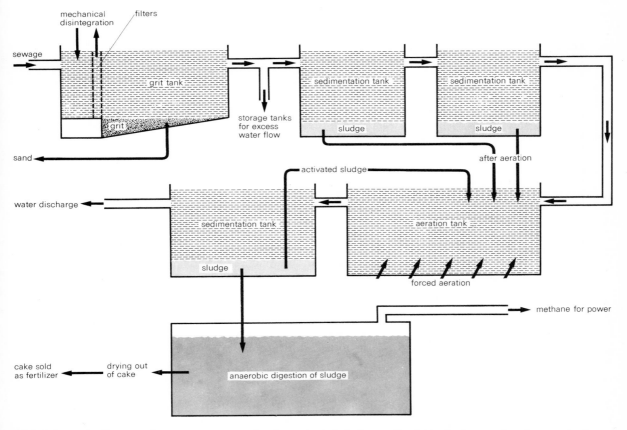

19.8 Schematic diagram of sewage treatment by the activated sludge method. For further explanation see text.

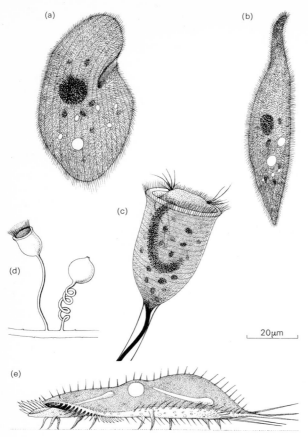

(a)

(b)

(c)

(d)

(e)

20µm

19.9 Ciliates associated with activated sludge. (a) *Colpidium* and (b) *Lionotus;* both are free-swimming forms. (c) *Vorticella,* a sessile ciliate found upon the flocs of sludge. The stalk contains a contractile fibre so that, as in (d), the animal may retract if disturbed. (e) *Stylonychia,* a ciliate which 'walks' on the surface of the flocs. The 'legs' are formed from fused cilia, and are called cirri. Among the rest of the fauna of sludge are *Amoeba, Arcella, Euglena, Peranema, Paramecium, Oxytricha* and *Carchesium* (Book 1 Figs. 18.1, 18.4, 18.5 and 18.7).

secretions in which both aerobic bacteria and bacterial-feeding Protozoa are included. These organisms are responsible for the metabolism of the organic material in the effluent from the sedimentation tank. The bacteria are acting as saprophytic decomposers; the Protozoa are primarily consumers feeding upon the bacteria (Fig. 19.9). The return of some of the activated sludge to the sedimentation tank serves to 'seed' the effluent with a large population of these organisms, so that once the fluid enters the aeration tanks the processes can be rapidly established; this initial seeding with the activated sludge allows the material to be maintained for a relatively short period in the aeration tanks. In this process the Protozoa play a key role: the mucus they secrete serves to agglutinate the bacteria into small clouds or 'flocs' of material which gradually coalesce to form the sludge.

The activated sludge process has two advantages over the sprinkler filter-bed system. It occupies even less land and, unlike the filter beds, does not depend for its effective working upon the presence of large populations of insect larvae which, when they emerge as adults, even though they are harmless, form a nuisance in homes in the immediate vicinity.

By these various techniques, designed to meet a variety of different densities of human population and pressure upon land surface, it is possible to speed the necessary process of decomposition and in this way enable large numbers of human beings to crowd together in a relatively small area without the constant threat of epidemic disease. It was indeed recurrent epidemics of cholera in London during the last century which first stimulated the development of effective methods of sewage disposal and water purification.

But the problem does not end there. While the organic content of the material is vastly reduced, the final effluent contains nutrient salts which have not been incorporated into either humus or sludge. These may be released into rivers and lakes and the resulting enrichment or eutrophication, particularly with phosphate ion, may lead to problems which we shall later discuss (p. 381).

Aspects of developing cities

These are some aspects of the biological problems which arise from man's tendency to aggregate in cities. City growth has in the past been relatively slow and as a result it was usually possible, by the gradual development of civic services, to meet the problems as they were recognized. The laying of drains and the building of satisfactory water supplies as well as houses did not lag too seriously behind expansion. Today in many developing countries, city growth has become very rapid: increasingly large numbers of people leave the countryside to 'try their luck' in the cities. As a result the civic services are often unable to expand sufficiently fast to meet the new demand; capital is not available for building new water-purification plants, new drainage systems, new housing estates and new sewage-disposal plants. Many of the newer, fast-growing cities are consequently characterized by large areas in which housing conditions are wretched, water supplies inadequate and sanitary facilities primitive. This is one reason why, if healthy urban living conditions are to be provided, the drift to the towns should be checked.

As city development proceeds, the activities of the urban consumers produce ever larger quantities of waste materials. The disposal of these becomes increasingly difficult, not simply because of the mass of material involved, but also because technological 'advance' results in new types of waste whose disposal presents new problems. This is the basis of urban pollution and is one aspect of the interrelations between man and his environment which we will shortly consider (p. 374).

Problems

1 Select some city in your country and, with the aid of a contour map, make proposals as to how the city should be supplied with water.
2 If a city is to be supplied with water from a river, what information will you require about the river? What difficulties might arise in maintaining a regular water supply and how might they be solved?
3 Any reservoir is filled from a 'catchment area'. If you were concerned with management of the catchment area, would you attempt to keep it free from trees or encourage the growing of woods and forest? Give reasons for your opinions.
4 Is there any advantage to be gained if the reservoirs of a city's water supply are stocked with fish which the local inhabitants are encouraged to catch? Are there any disadvantages? Give reasons for your opinions.
5 Compare the processes of decomposition in soil and in a sewage works.
6 Owing to some fault, the refilling of the aeration tank of an activated sludge works with fresh activated sludge was interrupted for a considerable time. Towards the end of this period, the contents of the tank which was 500 m long were sampled at intervals along its length. What would you expect to be the succession of organisms found, classifying the organisms by their modes of nutrition and methods of feeding?
7 (a) In designing a new city sewage works depending upon the use of activated sludge, the Design Engineer said that he considered that the only function of the aeration was to stir the fluid mixture and since this could be done more cheaply by a system of paddle blades, he proposed to design the works on this principle. Do you consider the Engineer's arguments are valid? Explain your reasoning.
(b) The City Council decided that it was essential to investigate the problem by full-scale experiment. You are the Chief Biologist attached to this investigation. Draw up a programme of study, indicating what is to be done, how it is to be done and why it should be done.
8 Any city requires a constant supply of food and water; it has also a heavy demand for energy and a need for recreational areas for the inhabitants. How do these requirements affect ecosystems which lie beyond the city's limits?

Bibliography
Revision reading

Daniel, F. *Health Science and Physiology for Tropical Schools*, Oxford University Press, 1966, Chap. 13

Further reading

_____ *Cities: a 'Scientific American' Book*, Penguin Books, 1967

Adams, R. M. 'The Origin of Cities', *Scientific American*, 1960, Offprint no. 606

Hirschorn, N., Greenough, W. B. 'Cholera', *Scientific American*, 1971, Vol. 225, pt. 2, p. 15

Greenberg, B. 'Flies and Disease', *Scientific American*, 1965, Offprint no. 1017

20 Man's numbers

The growth rate of any population of organisms is determined by the balance between additions due to natality together with immigration, and losses due to mortality together with emigration. Such considerations apply also to human populations. Our knowledge of the changes in human population numbers in recent years comes largely from the ten-yearly census made now in almost all countries. The first such population census in modern times was carried out in Sweden in 1749. In Africa a regular population census has been taken on Mauritius since 1851, but in most African countries such censuses have been taken regularly only since 1911 and completely reliable data on population changes in these countries are still meagre.

Census data in many countries are supported by the legal necessity of registering all births and deaths, and these data can be used to calculate the size of the population at any time. Such registration is still very incomplete in many African countries, making estimates of population change from one census to another inaccurate. The decennial census serves, of course, many other purposes in addition to a simple count of heads; it can provide information on the geographical distribution of people within a country or on patterns of employment, information about housing and so forth, thus making possible planning for future needs.

Patterns of population growth

Even with the rather unreliable data available to us from many countries, it is nevertheless possible to recognize that in almost all countries in the world there is a general tendency for the numbers of people to increase. Fig. 20.1 shows the population numbers for several countries for which there are reliable data running back over many years. In all of these the population is increasing, but at different rates: very slowly in Sweden, but very rapidly in Kenya and in France since 1950. While the normal trend is for population to increase, this did not apply to France between 1870 and 1946. During this time three wars with Germany were fought in France and these may have contributed to the lack of growth.

If you examine the data further, you will see that in England and Wales there was a very rapid increase in population during the nineteenth century, especially

between 1860 and 1910, and that subsequently this rate of increase has become less. Data for Algeria and Ghana show a different trend: the rate of population increase was low until relatively recently and then rose very considerably. Such countries today appear to be going through a pattern of population growth similar to that experienced in Britain in the first half of the last century and we must enquire what factors may be involved in these changes.

Changes in mortality

It is convenient to consider patterns of mortality before those of natality. This we can do by an examination of survivorship curves. Fig. 20.2 shows five such curves. One relates to Zaïre in 1950 and the other four to England and Wales at different times. In Zaïre in 1950 and in England and Wales in both 1845 and 1895, there was very heavy infantile mortality; one major difference between the survivorship curves for England and Wales in 1895 and in 1961 is that the number of deaths in the first year of life has sharply decreased. We can present these data in a

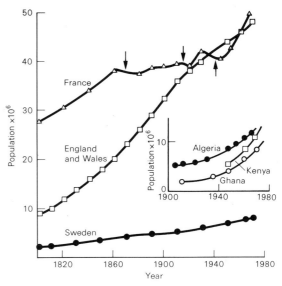

20.1 Changes in population of three European countries since 1800 and of three African countries for which reliable data are available. The arrows mark the dates of the three wars in which France fought Germany.

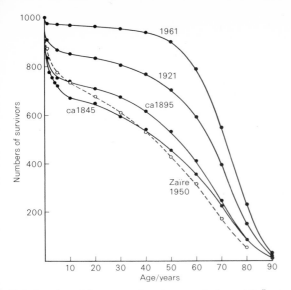

20.2 Survivorship curves for the population of Zaïre in 1950 and for England and Wales at different dates. Note the way in which the survivorship curve for Zaïre resembles that of England and Wales in 1845 and 1895, but that subsequently there has been a marked decrease in infantile mortality in England and Wales as well as a less marked decrease in mortality rate between the ages of 10 and 50. Maximum longevity has not significantly altered. The data are plotted on a linear, not a logarithmic scale.

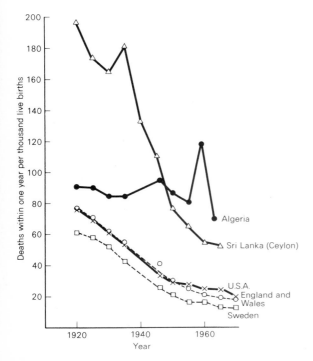

20.3 Infantile death rate for various countries since 1920.

different way. Infantile mortality can be expressed as the number of children dying within the first year of life for every 1 000 born, and Fig. 20.3 shows such information for a number of developed countries. It makes clear that one factor which has contributed to the growth of populations in recent years is the considerable increase in the chances of survival of any new-born baby; these values have now tended to level off, typically at an infantile death rate of about 20 per 1 000 live births.

This change has been due to better medical facilities and especially to improved control of infectious diseases; this is partly a result of the development of vaccines which give protection against the diseases of early childhood, but probably more important has been improved sanitation which has reduced deaths from such diseases as cholera and typhoid.

The same figure shows data relating to Algeria and Sri Lanka (Ceylon). Infantile mortality decreased dramatically in Sri Lanka after 1940 as a result of an intensive campaign against malaria.

The survivorship curves in Fig. 20.2 also show a second change which occurred in England and Wales between 1845 and 1961. The 1845 survivorship curve slopes downwards markedly after the age of 10 years, while in that for 1961 the slope is very slight until the individuals are far older. There is little difference in the age of the oldest members of the two populations, but a considerable difference in mean age. We can express this briefly by saying that while in 1845 half those born would have died before reaching the age of 44, by 1961 half could have expected to live to 72 years. Thus the members of this population are living longer; this tendency, also a product of greater medical skill and better health services, likewise causes the population to grow. The survivorship curve for Zaïre in 1950 shows that expectation of life was still low. Half the population of new-borns could have expected to be dead before reaching the age of 48. As medical services improve, this situation will change and with the change will go an increase in the numbers of the population. We may thus recognize two distinct factors in a changing pattern of mortality, both of which will increase the size of the population: decreased infantile death rate and a greater likelihood of survival during adult life.

Changes in natality

It is against these changing patterns of mortality that we may consider possible changes in natality. Increasing longevity has two potential effects upon natality: firstly, more girl children will survive to reproduce. Thus, using the data shown in Fig. 20.2, for every 1 000 girl children born in Zaïre in 1950, only about 700 could be expected to live long enough to give birth to at least one child; in England in 1961, the corresponding figure would be more than 970. Secondly, once a woman has reached reproductive age, her chance of survival throughout the full dura-

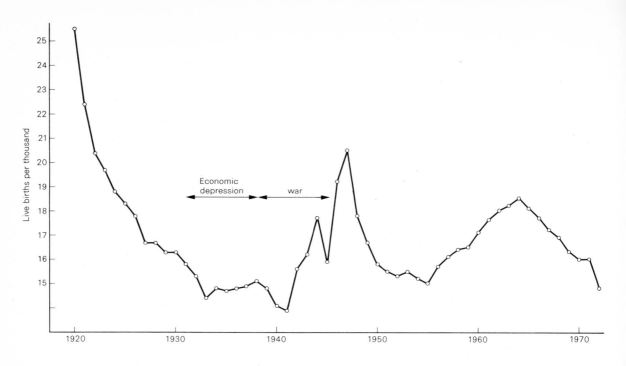

20.4 Annual birth rate (live births per 1 000 people) in England and Wales from 1920 to 1972. From 1931 until the outbreak of war in 1939, there was an economic depression with mass unemployment. At the end of that war, there was a characteristic high birth rate. This is also the explanation of the very high value for 1920, the earlier 'World War' having nominally ended in 1918, although British troops were still involved in fighting in various places up to 1921. After the war of 1939–45, economic conditions were poor, then improved and later became less satisfactory again. The falling birth rate from 1964 may be due partly to the wider use of more effective contraceptive measures and the sharp fall in 1972 may reflect the legalization of abortion. Such fluctuations in the birth rate make accurate prediction of future population numbers virtually impossible, as no trend has been held for more than a decade. During the period 1920–72 there would have been no growth of the population when the birth rate fell below about 14·0. At the present time the mean value for the birth rate in Africa is about 45·0. With present life expectation in Africa, the birth rate would have to fall to about 20·0 for the growth of the population to stop: this value will become lower as life expectation rises.

tion of her reproductive period has increased: as a result the number of children that might be born is greater. The way in which these changes actually affect natality in different human societies is more complex. Thus, for example, the average age of marriage has fallen in many developed countries and the average age of the mother at the birth of her first child has also decreased. This has not, however, led to an increase in the rate of population growth, since the size of a completed family has not risen: child-bearing starts when the woman is younger but stops at an earlier age than before. In fact, as indicated by annual data on birth rates, there is a highly irregular pattern of reproduction in many developed countries which is determined not by biological but by social and economic factors (Fig. 20.4).

Figs. 20.5a and 20.5b provide data showing how these various factors have affected population growth in England and Wales during the period of development, the 'Industrial Revolution', and in Sri Lanka as an example of a developing country for which there are data extending over many years.

If we take first the case of England and Wales, we see that between 1800 and 1870, both birth and death rates were fairly constant. The birth rate was markedly the higher so that, despite a high infantile mortality rate, the rate of population growth was relatively high, about 1·4 percent per annum. After 1870 the death rate started to fall sharply, as did the infantile mortality rate from 1900 onwards. There was, however, no corresponding increase in the rate of population growth as there was a greater fall in the birth rate than in the death rate. Thus, for example, while in 1901 births per thousand exceeded deaths by 11·5, in 1931 the difference was only 3·9 and in 1961, 4·3. The result was an actual fall in the rate of population growth to about 0·45 percent per annum.

Similar data for Sri Lanka, covering a shorter period of time, show a steady fall in death rate from 1922, while the infantile mortality rate started to fall sharply about 1940.

The birth rate has, however, fallen only slightly, so that the rate of population growth in the latter part of the period was about 3 percent per annum and the difference between birth and death rates, which was 9·6 in 1922, had risen to 24·2 in 1967.

In both countries there has been a marked fall in death rate. But in the developed country, this has been accompanied by a fall in birth rate so that there has been an actual fall in the rate of population increase; in the developing country decreased mortality has not been associated with a similar fall in birth rate, so that the rate of population growth has risen.

Future populations

These two cases illustrate a general situation in the world today, namely that rates of population increase are far higher in developing than in developed countries: Table 20.1 summarizes some of the data. If present population trends continue the population of the less-developed regions, which constitute at present about 70 percent of the total world population, will by the year 2000 have in-

creased to nearly 80 percent of the whole. Or, to express the matter in another way, while the present population of England and Wales will have doubled by the year 2110, that of Ghana will have doubled before the year 2000.

Such data are of immediate practical importance to people who are concerned with such matters as the extension of agriculture, the provision of urban employment opportunities and of sanitary, medical and educational services. It is clearly pointless to prepare plans on the basis of present population levels if in fact the numbers of people are increasing very rapidly. For this reason government planners, and as a secondary consequence those biological scientists concerned with food production and public health, are anxious to be able to forecast the likely population of a country at some future date.

There is a further aspect to the problem which is most easily seen by a study of bar charts showing the age-class composition of the populations of the United Kingdom, Sri Lanka and also Ghana (Fig. 20.6). We have already discussed how such bar charts are prepared (p. 261). The charts for Ghana and Sri Lanka are broadly similar and are characteristic of those for most developing countries.

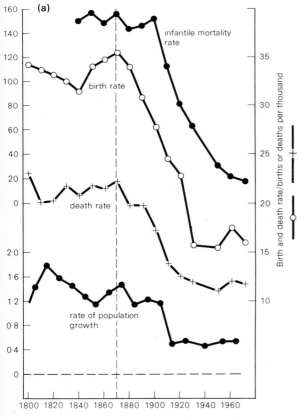

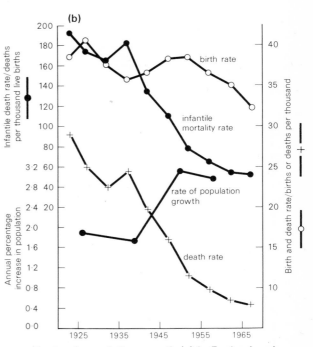

20.5 Changes in birth rate, infantile mortality rate, death rate and rate of population growth (a) in England and Wales between 1800 and 1970, and (b) in Sri Lanka between 1922 and 1967. Note that while in England and Wales the rate of population growth after 1870 tended to fall as a result of a decreasing birth rate, in Sri Lanka there has been an increase in the rate of population growth as both falling infantile mortality and general death rate have not been matched by a significant fall in the birth rate.

Table 20.1 Rates of growth and age composition of various human populations (*Data from various sources*)

	Birth rate per thousand (1970)	Annual rate of increase (1963–69) (%)	Approximate doubling time (years)	Percentage of population below 15 years of age
Developed countries				
Belgium	14·7	0·6	116	25
France	16·7	0·9	77	25
Holland	18·4	1·2	60	27
U.K.	16·2	0·6	116	24
U.S.A.	18·2	1·2	60	29
Developing countries				
Algeria	49·1	3·0	22	47
Ghana	46·6	2·7	26	45
Kenya	47·8	2·9	24	46
Tanzania	47·0	2·6	27	44
Zaïre	44·4	2·2	32	42
Zambia	49·8	3·1	21	45

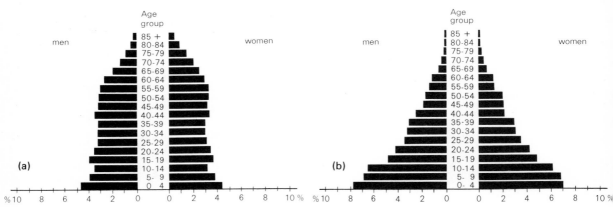

20.6 Age-class composition for (a) the United Kingdom, 1966, (b) Sri Lanka, 1963 and (c) Ghana 1960. Compare with Fig. 14.23(a).

The chart for the United Kingdom shows that the numbers of people in the different age groups are all very similar; in the two developing countries, however, there are many more people in the young age groups than in the older ones. This difference arises from the fact that in the two developing countries, unlike the United Kingdom, the birth rate has remained high. In Ghana in 1960, nearly 53 percent of the population was below the age of 20 (Table 20.1). As a result there is a heavy demand for schools and this must be met by the activity of the older people; they must increase their production of wealth to meet the needs both of the increasing public health services and of the growing educational services, while continuing to produce the necessary surplus to finance other types of development.

In time these large numbers of young people will themselves reach child-bearing age, so that the number of children may be expected to increase still more. Unless social attitudes towards child-bearing change, unless there is a decrease in the size of the completed family, we will have a positive feedback system in which ever-increasing numbers of young people are produced, themselves to give rise to still further, larger generations of children.

When this type of population expansion has run for many years, a second problem arises. During the early phases, there is an increase in the percentage of the population which is unproductive as a result of youth. At a later stage there is an increase in the proportion of the population which is unproductive as a result of old age. Thus about 8 percent of the population of the United Kingdom are over 65 years old, compared with less than 2 percent in Sri Lanka and Ghana. Unless there is some effective system of social security for the aged, they must depend for their living upon their younger relatives, so that the demands upon the productive section of the population steadily increase.

Population increase and food supply

A third consequence of an expanding population is the ever-increasing demand for food, both for the productive and the unproductive. Fig. 20.7 shows the change in food production per individual over fifteen years in different regions of the world. In the developing countries the increased production of food has only just kept pace with the growth in numbers of human beings: the quantity of food available per human being has remained very nearly the same throughout the period. We have seen that large numbers of people do not obtain sufficient food. Apart from local famines, there is widespread malnutrition and this situation has remained unchanged, despite much effort. To assess the extent of malnutrition on a world scale is difficult since the data for food supplies relate to particular countries. But within each country the available food is not uniformly distributed among the population: even in the affluent United States, a recent government survey showed that more than 10 percent of the population were malnourished. Present estimates suggest that about 10 percent of the world's population suffer from acute energy malnutrition and about 40 percent from protein deficiency. Since food production in the developing countries is increasing only just about as rapidly as their expanding populations, the proportion of the world's population which is malnourished has at best fallen only slightly; the actual number of individuals malnourished has greatly increased.

In 1963 the United Nations published estimates of the possible future population of the world making various reasonable assumptions about decreasing rates of mortality and using various values for the possible future patterns of birth rate. Fig. 20.8 summarizes three different levels of prediction. The lowest curve is based on the assumption that the birth rate will tend to fall markedly: even then decreasing mortality and the increasing population of individuals of reproductive age results, at best, in a

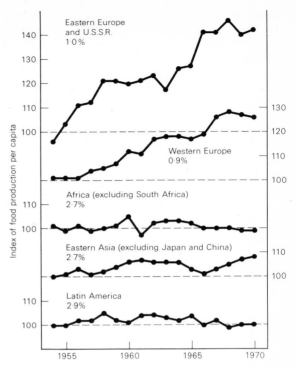

20.7 Increase in food production per head in different regions of the world, taking the average value for the period 1952–56 as 100. The percentage value by each area shows the rate of growth of population during 1971. Note that in the three developing regions food production per capita has not increased. In both Western and Eastern Europe, where the rate of population growth is relatively low, there have been increases of about 25 percent and 40 percent respectively.

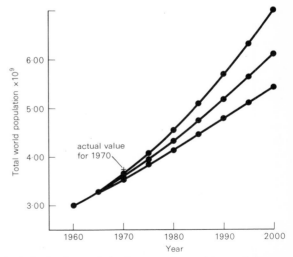

20.8 Projections of the increase in world population prepared by the United Nations in 1963 making various assumptions about changing patterns of birth rates. The estimated world population in 1970 was greater than the highest value predicted in 1963.

nearly constant rate of growth. The upper curve assumes that birth rates will fall only slowly. Actual world population in 1970 was about 3.71×10^9 people; the highest value predicted in 1963 was 3.66×10^9. Thus, at the moment, world population is growing faster than even the most extreme estimate of 1963.

The data suggest that the world population will probably double between 1960 and 2000, yet food production in the developing countries is increasing at a rate sufficient only to keep pace with the increase in population. We may ask what are the future prospects for the coming years.

Increasing food production

To increase food production in the developing countries there are two essential requirements: more extensive use of fertilizers and more water to allow greater productivity in areas of limited seasonal rainfall. The possibility also exists of opening up new land for agricultural production. Table 20.2 summarizes the estimated area of arable land under cultivation in different parts of the world in 1967.

Clearly the potential for expansion in Asia is small; in Africa it is still considerable. In general, however, the economic cost of increasing the area of arable land under cultivation is very great and more extensive exploitation of already developed land is possibly a better policy.

With present conventional methods of agriculture about one-third of the total arable land is lying fallow each year to permit the soil to regain some nutrients before re-cropping. In the forest areas of Africa where limited clearings are made and then abandoned after a few years, the proportion under fallow is still greater. But, with increasing population, the time which farmers can allow for regeneration of the soil becomes less and the quality of the soil decreases with more frequent exploitation.

The alternative is to avoid a fallow period: to use fertilizers or manure liberally to replace the nutrients which have been removed and, where conditions permit, to harvest two or even three crops each year. This has been achieved using fast-growing, high-yielding varieties of wheat in some parts of Asia, but its success depends on

Table 20.2 Estimates of land used or available for agriculture (*Data from U.S. President's Science Advisory Committee*)

Region	Percentage of potential arable land under cultivation (1965)	Unexploited arable land per capita (ha)
Europe	88	0·05
Asia	83	0·06
U.S.S.R.	64	0·55
North America	51	0·89
Africa	22	1·85
South America	11	3·06

adequate supplies not only of fertilizer but also of water: effective irrigation is essential.

To spread the use of this intensive agriculture to other areas requires effective policies of water management both in the construction of reservoirs and irrigation channels and for the protection from erosion of the soils in the area where the rain is first collected (p. 371).

Agriculture in arid lands

There are, furthermore, many areas where plants could grow or good grazing be provided but which remain unexploited or under-exploited owing to irregular rainfall or lack of water.

It has recently been discovered that mildly saline waters can be used for irrigation in regions where fresh water is lacking, provided the daily variation in temperature is considerable and the soil is loose and sandy. The water runs rapidly into the sand, coating the surface of the grains and producing a saturated atmosphere. At night, when soil temperature falls, the water vapour condenses on the root hairs of the plants and this salt-free water is taken up. Each fresh application of water washes out previous accumulations of salt as it flows freely into the deep layers of the soil.

Before highly saline water can be used, however, the salt must be removed from it. Two ways in which this can be done are by distillation, or by freezing the water and separating the crystals of pure ice from the remaining concentrated salt solution. Such procedures would be most useful in the coastal cities of arid regions, but their widespread use must await very considerable lowering of costs before they could be an economically viable proposition. Any desalination process involves considerable energy expenditure which is one reason why it is costly; moreover, since the installation must be near the sea, pumping stations would be needed to pipe the water inland, adding significantly to the cost of the recovered water.

FAO's 'Indicative World Plan'

The magnitude of the problem of feeding the world's expanding population is made clear in a study by the Food and Agricultural Organisation of the United Nations and published in 1962 as an 'Indicative World Plan for Agriculture'. This set out what would be required in agricultural development between 1962 and 1985 to ensure that there would be sufficient food to provide an adequate standard of nutrition for the expected world population in 1985. To achieve this objective the plan was partly based on the extensive use of high-yielding varieties of cereal crops, with their associated need for irrigation and fertilizer applications: the plan visualized a more-than-tenfold increase in utilization of fertilizer over the 23-year period. Nitrogenous fertilizer is especially important and to produce sufficient, heavy capital investment in nitrogen-fixation plants with their associated power supplies would be required. In practice difficulties of distribution arise, so that the cost of fertilizer delivered to a farmer may be so great as to make purchase uneconomic in terms of market prices of farm products. Further major 'inputs' foreseen were a more-than-tenfold increased use of herbicides and insecticides, a more-than-threefold increase in the use of agricultural machinery and a considerable increase in the areas of land under irrigation. The total annual investment in agriculture would have to increase more than fourfold and almost all of this would involve importation into the developing countries of commodities such as farm machinery, fertilizer and insecticide from the developed countries. To meet this expenditure the developing countries, unless they have reserves of mineral ores or oil required by the developed countries, would be dependent upon a growing market at a stable price of such crops as cocoa, coffee, rubber and tea. Thus both domestic agricultural production and agricultural production for export would have to rise.

Few of the requirements foreseen in the 'Indicative World Plan' have so far been fulfilled. The plan had, for example, envisaged a growth of 4 percent per annum in agricultural production in the developing countries; during the last decade the average annual growth rate has in fact been only 2·7 percent. Stress has therefore been laid by some biologists on the need to develop new methods of food production, especially of protein, to meet the ever-growing demand for food. These new, unconventional methods of agriculture are based upon two basic ideas. The first is that unicellular organisms grow more rapidly than do multicellular organisms and, further, that they can utilize a variety of industrial wastes as sources of carbon; the second is that much plant material not now exploited is in fact a rich potential source of protein if suitably treated.

Alternative sources of food

Micro-organisms

The high productive potential of micro-organisms can be illustrated by the fact that in the best possible conditions, the weight of live material in a bacterial culture will double every half-hour; in a yeast culture the time is about two hours, while photosynthetic algae will double their weight about every twelve hours. These rapid rates of growth can be contrasted with those of flowering plants. Let us suppose that 90 days are required for a sown maize grain to produce a plant yielding 500 grains. A photosynthetic alga could, theoretically, achieve a similar increase in 4·5 days. This high potential productivity has already been exploited commercially using yeasts, with waste materials such as coconut milk as sources of carbon. Various oil companies are seeking ways of making food from bacteria and yeasts grown on oil-refinery wastes. Studies upon the direct exploitation of sewage for the culture of algae have also been undertaken.

Two factors limit the potential efficiency of plant growth. The first is the fact that only a relatively small percentage of the total light falling upon a field of some crop actually strikes a site of photosynthetic activity and of this about 25 percent is reflected by the leaf surface. The second is that the concentration of carbon dioxide in the air is very low and, where illumination is adequate, it becomes the limiting factor for photosynthesis (Book 1 p. 95). These limitations could, in theory, be overcome by using cultures of unicellular algae provided with artificial illumination and with higher concentrations of carbon dioxide. Trials have been made in which cultures of the alga *Chlorella* were grown in permanently illuminated tanks into which waste carbon dioxide from some industrial process was pumped. While it has been found that continuous mass culturing in such conditions achieves high photosynthetic efficiency and that the product contains a large percentage of high-grade protein, the initial capital outlay required to establish the process on a commercial scale is, at least at present, prohibitively high.

Plant protein

The extraction of plant protein for human consumption has been attempted by two rather different techniques. The first is the relatively direct exploitation of material which is a by-product of the vegetable oil industry. Vegetable oils are extracted from soybeans, sesame, groundnuts and cotton-seed by pressure, and the residual 'cake' is rich in protein. Seedcake from groundnuts contains more than 50 percent protein, that from other sources slightly less. At the present time much of this material, if not thrown away, is used as fertilizer or as food for animals, commonly being exported to developed countries as feed for intensively reared pigs or hens. Since there is considerable loss of material between one step in a food chain and the next (p. 317), this process is wasteful, even where rearing is highly efficient. Furthermore, it involves the movement of protein from countries in which there is protein malnutrition to ones in which the protein content of the average diet is well above the minimum nutritional requirement. It has indeed been estimated that the protein content of the seedcake now produced in the world is sufficient to meet the protein requirements of about one-fifth of the world's population.

The second possibility is the extraction of protein from fresh leaves. This is technically feasible, and would allow exploitation of much green material produced by crops which goes to waste after harvesting. Such sources of protein are not limited to the leaves of commercial crops: there are many areas in the world which are unsuitable for conventional agriculture and which nevertheless support an abundance of vegetation. One extreme example is the Sudd in the White Nile (Book 1 p. 253). Exploitation of this growth as a source of leaf protein would have the additional beneficial effect of increasing the flow of water in the White Nile: it is estimated that at the present time about half the water entering the river above the Sudd is lost as a result of evapotranspiration there. Like the culture of *Chlorella*, this scheme is not economically viable at present. One field crop of potential value for leaf protein is alfalfa, which can yield as much as 2·5 tonnes of protein per ha and further provide fibre after extraction for use as cattle fodder. The economic practicality of such a scheme as a significant source of protein for the world's population has yet to be assessed.

Of these various proposals, only the use of seedcake as a source of human food has been widely adopted and is known to be an economically sound proposal. Thus, for example, a protein-rich flour-like material made from cotton seedcake and maize and called Incaparina has been available in Central America for the last decade; a similar type of material is manufactured in South Africa. Although both are very cheap, their use involves the introduction of a new item of diet to a large number of people and experience has shown that it is far from easy to get people of any culture or nationality to accept novel sources of food. Further work is therefore needed to find ways of making generally acceptable these products which could do much to improve the standard of human nutrition.

Population increase and cities

So far we have looked at the problem of the expanding human population purely from the viewpoint of providing an adequate supply of food. Census data show us a second trend of biological importance, namely that more and more people come to live in towns and cities. In the developed countries the majority of people live in cities: 80 percent in Holland and the United Kingdom, 70 percent in France and the United States. In the developing countries the proportion is far smaller: about 5 percent in Tanzania, 16 percent in Nigeria, 20 to 25 percent in Ghana, Zambia and Zaïre. But this percentage is increasing rapidly: thus in 1954 23 percent of the total population of Algeria lived in cities; by 1966 the proportion had risen to 40 percent. As the cities grow, not only do they take over arable land for building sites, but in developed countries increasing demands arise for land for other purposes. Experience shows that most human beings will not accept living in very dense communities if they can avoid it; where there is sufficient wealth to produce easy means of personal transport such as motor cars, a city will spread out over a very large area, with a ring of low population density surrounding the core of the city in which people work. Thus more land, commonly arable, is taken over for housing and also to provide road systems so that the inhabitants of these outer 'dormitory' areas can move easily into the central city core each day to work. In Africa the proportion of land occupied by large cities is still small compared with the arable land surface, but in many small, densely populated countries of Europe the potential for food production in terms of available land surface continues to fall. The high density of people can be maintained only by extensive imports of food as well as of raw materials to feed the factories.

Optimum population density

Such a situation has given rise to a debate as to what should be regarded as the 'optimum' population density. Thus, for example, the present population of England and Wales is over 45 million people, an overall density of 300 km^{-2}; many regard this as too high for a comfortable life. Certainly population densities are not unpleasantly high in much of Africa, but one point does require stressing. This is a matter which is sometimes referred to as the 'Netherlands fallacy'. The overall population density of Holland (the Netherlands) is rather more than 300 people km^{-2}, that of Africa as a whole slightly less than 10 km^{-2}: even that of the country with the highest population density on the continent, namely Rwanda, is only 130 km^{-2}. The high population density of Holland can be maintained only by very large imports of food and industrial raw materials. Thus although within Holland each person occupies, on the average, only about 300 m^2, nevertheless he is drawing his food and the raw materials for his work from a far larger area; his actual necessary living space is therefore much greater. One can express this in another way by saying that the human population supported by Africa is far greater than the human population actually living in Africa. It is unrealistic to expect that one could achieve over the whole of the inhabitable parts of Africa a population density as high as that of countries like Holland or Britain today.

Control of population growth

We have seen that in most developing countries food production is, at best, only just keeping pace with the increase in population numbers, and that these increases in population are due in part to a decrease in infantile and juvenile mortality. As a consequence there is a growing demand for educational services, themselves not immediately economically productive, and an increasing proportion of dependants in the population as a whole. Further, in many developing countries the present rate of population growth is of the same order of magnitude as that of the growth of material wealth. Thus, on the average, despite development, the standard of living is not improving. These relations have led many people to the view that if development is to bring better living conditions, it is necessary to reduce the rate of population growth.

Family planning

Before present medical and sanitary facilities became available, the population of Africa was probably almost constant, with high fertility counterbalanced by a high mortality. The mortality rate has decreased but the natality rate has not, so there is a rapid increase in population numbers, like that which occurred in most European countries during the last century. The subsequent fall in natality rate which led to a slackening of the rate of population growth in Europe was an undirected social adjustment to a new pattern of survival of children. There is a widely held view that the developing countries of the world cannot afford to allow such social adjustments to take their own course, but that, in the interest of more rapid development, people should be shown how they can reduce their fertility and be encouraged so to do.

This is a purely economic argument in favour of family planning. There are other arguments, possibly more immediately cogent. If one pregnancy follows another in rapid succession there is much evidence to suggest that for many women this is not only a severe burden but also adversely affects their health. The ability to control fertility also means that any increase in the size of a family can be related to its economic and social circumstances, so that proper attention and education can be given to all children.

The menstrual cycle

How then can human beings control their fertility? To answer this question we must first examine the pattern of ovulation in human females and the way in which ovulation is regulated. In all mammals there are two ovaries, attached to the dorsal body wall posterior to the kidneys and projecting into the body cavity; the human ovary is shaped like a bean, being about 3·5 cm in length, 2 cm in width and 1 cm thick. Immediately adjacent to each ovary is the internal opening of the oviduct. Each oviduct runs backwards to open into the sac-like uterus in which the embryo will develop (Fig. 20.9). The surface of the human ovary is covered with a single layer of peritoneal cells, the germinal epithelium. The mass of the ovary is formed of connective tissue. During development of the ovary in the foetus, egg cells migrate from an area near the ovary into this connective tissue, each egg cell becoming enclosed in a layer of cells derived from the germinal epithelium (Fig. 20.10). The egg cell and its enclosing cells form a 'follicle'. At birth there are about half a million follicles in each ovary; most of these will degenerate during the life of the individual.

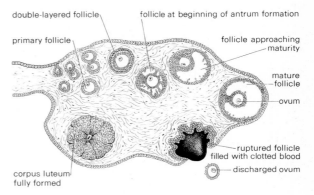

20.10 Diagrammatic section of an ovary showing the stages of maturation of a Graafian follicle and the formation of a corpus luteum. The stages follow in clockwise sequence.

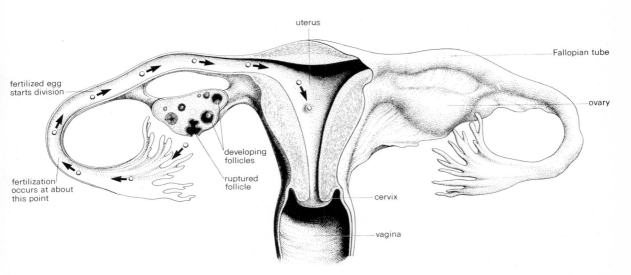

20.9 Diagram showing the relations of ovary, Fallopian tube or oviduct, uterus and vagina in a human female. The anatomical relations are shown on the right. On the left there is a diagrammatic section showing developing follicles within an ovary and the release of an ovum which is then passed down the Fallopian tube to the uterus. Fertilization normally occurs near the top of the Fallopian tube.

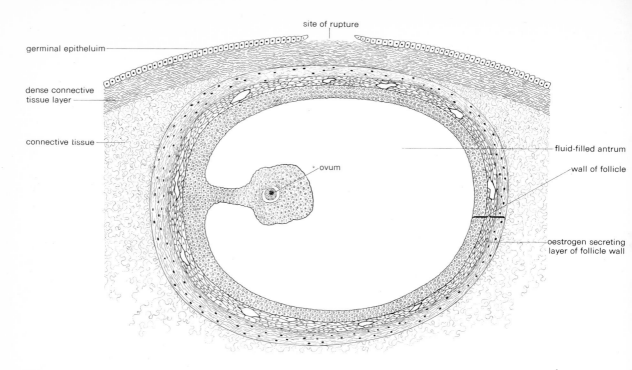

20.11 Detail of the structure of a mature Graafian follicle shortly before ovulation. (Modified from Freeman and Bracegirdle.)

Ovulation occurs in women about once every four weeks. Before ovulation a follicle develops very considerably to form a fluid-filled sac; usually only one follicle develops at a time. As follicular development proceeds the follicular cells surrounding the egg cell divide so as to form a thick envelope in which irregular spaces start to develop (Fig. 20.10). These spaces join together to form a single cavity, the antrum (Fig. 20.11). The developing or Graafian follicle moves towards the surface of the ovary and bulges outwards. The follicle wall then ruptures releasing the fluid in the follicle, while the egg and its coating of cells become free from the follicular wall and are shed from the ovary. At this time the internal opening of the oviduct is in close contact with the ovary. The internal surface of the oviduct is ciliated and the beating of the cilia drives fluid towards the uterus; by this means the egg is drawn into the oviduct and carried downwards to the uterus, partly by ciliary action, partly by a peristaltic action of the musculature of the oviduct.

When an egg has been shed, the cells lining the follicle grow rapidly, becoming filled with a lipid material which gives the structure a yellow colour; it is therefore known as a corpus luteum. About fourteen days after ovulation, if the egg has not been fertilized, the corpus luteum starts to degenerate, losing its fatty material and growing gradually smaller. Meanwhile another follicle starts to develop.

Correlated with these changes in the development of the ovarian follicle are changes in the structure of the uterine wall (Fig. 20.12). At the time follicular growth starts, the inner lining of the uterus, the endometrium, is a few millimetres thick; as follicular development proceeds it becomes thicker. Glands within the endometrium become actively secretory. These changes are described as 'progestational'. After ovulation the rate of endometrial growth decreases but the glands are more active and blood vessels become engorged with blood. As a result the whole tissue is swollen and in a suitable condition for the implantation of a fertilized egg. If implantation does not occur, degenerative changes set in about twelve days after ovulation, and about two days later the surface tissues of the endometrium break away with associated bleeding. This is the phenomenon we call menstruation. The flow of menstrual blood may continue for several days; the endometrium then reorganizes and starts a fresh cycle of development.

We thus have a cycle of events both in the ovary and in the endometrium which is normally repeated about every twenty-eight days. The onset of menstrual flow is a convenient point of reference and it has been found that ovulation most commonly occurs on the fourteenth or fifteenth day thereafter. There is, however, considerable variation between individuals in the length of the menstrual cycle; ovulation may occur earlier in the cycle than the fourteenth day and in some individuals the length of the cycle is variable. The egg takes three or four days to pass

OVARIAN FOLLICLES

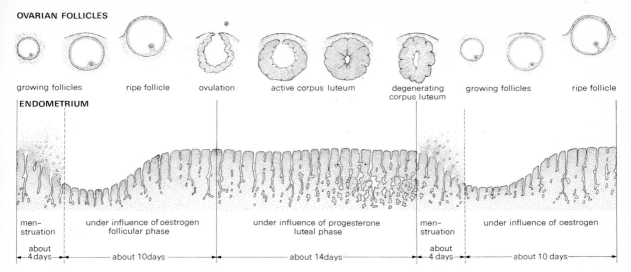

growing follicles   ripe follicle   ovulation   active corpus luteum   degenerating corpus luteum   growing follicles   ripe follicle

ENDOMETRIUM

| men-struction | under influence of oestrogen follicular phase | under influence of progesterone luteal phase | men-struction | under influence of oestrogen |
| about 4 days | about 10 days | about 14 days | about 4 days | about 10 days |

20.12 Correlation between ovarian and endometrial changes during the course of a menstrual cycle. Note that during the follicular phase there is a growth in thickness of the endometrium, while during the luteal phase there is marked development of endometrial glands. (After Corner.)

down the oviduct, but it can be fertilized only about 24 to 48 h after it has been shed. Fertilization therefore occurs towards the top of the oviduct.

The control of this cycle depends largely upon the activity of hormones released from the anterior lobe, the pars distalis, of the pituitary gland (Fig. 20.13 and 20.14). During the pre-ovulatory part of the cycle, the pituitary secretes follicle-stimulating hormone (FSH) which stimulates the growth of an already activated follicle. The hormone also stimulates certain cells in the wall of the follicle to secrete steroid hormones collectively called oestrogens. These oestrogens stimulate growth of the endometrium, and also act so as to reduce the rate of secretion of FSH from the pituitary and to stimulate the release of a second hormone called luteinizing hormone (LH). The fall in the concentration of FSH and the rise in that of LH causes release of the ovum. LH also causes the cells of the follicle to form the corpus luteum. The cells of the corpus luteum are stimulated to produce another steroid hormone called progesterone. In man this stimulation is due to the action of a pituitary hormone, but it is not clear whether this is LH or a different hormone, lactogenic hormone, which is also concerned with the formation of milk. Progesterone stimulates the further development of the uterine endometrium. About fourteen days after ovulation, secretion of the corpus luteum-stimulating hormone ceases; as a result secretion of progesterone also stops, and this is the immediate cause of the breakdown of the uterine endometrium in menstruation. As with FSH, the inhibition of the secretion of the corpus luteum-stimulating hormone is due to the effect of progesterone upon the secretory action of the pituitary. The secretion of these two hormones which act upon the gonad, the 'gonadotrophic hormones',

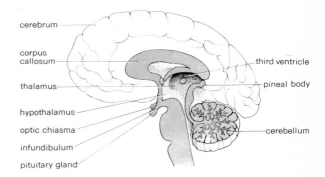

20.13 Diagrammatic section of the brain in the midline, that is, a 'sagittal section'. Note the pituitary gland projecting from the floor of the brain and connected to the hypothalamus by the infundibulum. The brain contains a number of cavities, the ventricles; the third ventricle lies immediately above the pituitary.

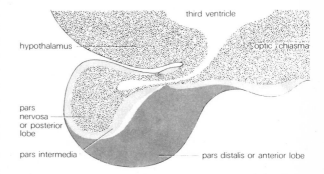

20.14 Diagrammatic sagittal section through the pituitary body of a primate, as seen from the right side.

365

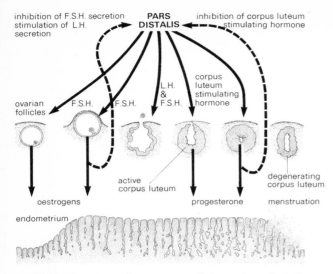

inhibition of F.S.H. secretion
stimulation of L.H.
secretion

PARS DISTALIS

inhibition of corpus luteum
stimulating hormone

ovarian follicles

F.S.H.   F.S.H.

L.H. & F.S.H.

corpus luteum stimulating hormone

oestrogens

active corpus luteum

progesterone

degenerating corpus luteum

menstruation

endometrium

20.15 Diagrammatic summary of the action of pituitary gonadotrophins and ovarian steroids during a menstrual cycle. Compare with Fig. 20.12. For further explanation see text.

is thus controlled by the action of the gonadial steroids whose synthesis they stimulate. These relations are summarized in Fig. 20.15.

How has this knowledge been used to provide man with methods of reducing fertility? Clearly any arrangement which prevents spermatozoa from reaching a newly shed egg will prevent its fertilization. This can be achieved mechanically either by covering the penis with a thin sheath so that ejaculated sperm do not enter the female genital tract, or by obstructing the opening between the vagina and the uterus, the cervix uteri, with some type of diaphragm so that the sperm cannot enter the uterus and can be washed out of the vagina before the diaphragm is removed.

Our knowledge of the biology of the reproductive cycle can be utilized more directly in reducing fertility by limiting coitus to those times within a menstrual cycle when fertilization is not likely to occur, that is, to the period of about ten days after the onset of menstrual flow and the period from the eighteenth day thereafter. Coitus is thus avoided during the week around the time ovulation is most likely to occur. This is spoken of as 'control by use of the safe period' and is acceptable to many people who regard other ways of preventing fertilization as unacceptable for ethical reasons. As we have said, the duration of the menstrual cycle varies considerably between individuals and the precise times of the 'safe' periods may have to be adjusted to the individual case. Some persons have very irregular menstrual cycles and there are attendant uncertainties associated with the use of this method in such cases. While limitation of coition to the safe period unquestionably reduces the chances of conception, it in no way precludes it.

We have also seen that the secretion of FSH is inhibited

by oestrogens and that of the corpus luteum-stimulating hormone by progesterone. These facts are exploited in the composition of 'contraceptive pills' which contain a mixture of oestrogens and progestins in sufficient quantity to inhibit the secretion of pituitary gonadotrophins and thus prevent the development of follicles to the point of ovulation. Such pills must be taken daily to be effective, normally from the fifth to the twenty-fifth day of a menstrual cycle.

There is one further type of contraceptive method, whose biological basis is still not clearly understood. This is the intra-uterine device (IUD) or loop; it consists of a thin, plastic-covered spring which is inserted into the cavity of the uterus; pregnancy is unlikely as long as the device remains in position. The IUD makes contact with the surface of the endometrium in many places, and its effect is probably due to some type of uterine reaction resulting from pressure on the endometrial wall. This reaction prevents the successful implantation of a fertilized ovum. Table 20.3 summarizes the relative effectiveness of these different methods in the control of pregnancy.

Female fertility may also be reduced through termination of pregnancy by abortion, that is, by destruction of the foetus; this is legally allowable in Great Britain, Japan and certain other countries. Modern methods of effecting abortion, if carried out in suitable conditions, have little associated danger; in less favourable circumstances abortion may be very dangerous.

So far no simple method of reducing male fertility has been found. Work is going ahead upon the development of a male contraceptive pill, which would make the spermatozoa incapable of fertilizing an egg. It is, however, possible by a relatively minor operation to make a man sterile by cutting the vasa deferentia which carry spermatozoa from the testes to the penis. This operation is now undertaken in some countries as a method of reducing fertility. The operation has no known effect upon the virility of the individual; it is, however, effectively irreversible. Attempts are being made to develop techniques by which, if needed, a man could regain his fertility.

Table 20.3 Effectiveness of different methods of controlling conception (*Data from Rhodes*)

Method of controlling conception	Relative failure rate
No control	100
'Safe period'	48
Penis sheath	28
Vaginal diaphragm	24
IUD	4
Contraceptive pill	1

Note: 'Relative failure rate' is here expressed as the number of pregnancies which would occur in a population using some particular method of control during a time when there would be 100 conceptions in an otherwise similar population using no control method.

Clearly the decision about the planning of a family and the way in which this might be effected is a personal matter between men and women. One can reasonably argue that this is a freedom of choice which all should be able to make and that no enforcement of contraception should be tolerated. In fact in the world today, the opposite is the position: while many governments encourage contraception, none enforce it, but several countries have laws which deny the individual freedom of choice and conscience in this matter by making contraception illegal.

It is especially important to recognize that sooner or later the growth of the human population must stop. This may happen as a result of the behaviour of individuals, assisted if they so desire by methods like the use of the contraceptive pill or the IUD which are the products of research. If mankind fails voluntarily to check the growth of his numbers, then sooner or later one of the many natural, density-dependent controls such as epidemics or famine will come into action. Perhaps before this there may be wars to obtain access to food. At the moment man's numbers and his food supply are in step. How long this will remain true we cannot tell. But no matter what technological developments are made, there is some upper limit to the quantity of food which can be produced. It would be ironic if the final result of modern medicine and technology were to be a world in which man, like his pre-agricultural forebears, had to devote almost all of his energies to obtaining food.

Such things lie still in the future. Nevertheless it is desirable to realize now that, while a family may enjoy complete freedom in determining its size, this freedom should be exercised in relation to a world of limited size and limited resources. A failure to consider the wider implications of other human activities has led to further problems of the relation between man and his environment and these we will consider in the next chapter.

Problems

1 If, in a country like the United Kingdom or Ghana, the birth rate dropped to a value equal to that of the mortality rate, would the population continue to increase in numbers?

2 If, in a country in which monogamy was legally enforced and there were no illegitimate births, each married couple had only two children, what would be the long-term effect upon the size of the population?

3 A dictator, anxious to control the growth of the population of his country, decided that no woman should be allowed to have more than three children. Two possible laws were considered. One ruled that all three children must be born before the woman was twenty-five years old; the other that at least five years must elapse between one birth and the next. Which would be the more effective check on population growth? Explain your reasoning.

4 In China, the government urges people to marry late as a contribution towards lowering the rate of population growth. What is the reasoning leading to this proposal? What other social attitude is necessary for its success?

5 Make a list of all the causes, other than old age, which lead to major loss of human life. State which are density-dependent and which density-independent, giving your reasons in each case.

6 Make a diagram summarizing the requirements for a high yield of food crops per unit area. How many of these involve the utilization of energy other than manpower? What sources of energy would you expect to be used in each case? How many of these energy sources can be regarded as renewable owing to the acquisition of energy from the sun?.

Bibliography
Further reading

Allison, A. (ed.) — *Population Control,* Penguin Books, 1970

Pirie, N. W. — *Food Resources, Conventional and Novel,* Penguin Books, 1969

Rhodes, P. — *Birth Control,* Oxford University Press, 1971

Youmans, W. B. — *Human Physiology,* Collier-Macmillan, 1962, Chaps. 36 and 37

Boerma, A. H. — 'A World Agricultural Plan', *Scientific American,* 1970, Offprint no. 1186

Boyko, H. — 'Salt-water Agriculture', *Scientific American,* 1967, Vol. 216, pt. 3, p. 89

Brown, L. R. — 'Human Food Production as a Process in the Biosphere', *Scientific American,* 1970, Offprint no. 1196

Champagnat, A. — 'Protein from Petrol', *Scientific American,* 1965, Offprint no. 1020

Coale, A. J. — 'The History of the Human Population', *Scientific American,* 1974, Vol. 231, pt. 3, p. 40

Csapo, A. — 'Progesterone', *Scientific American,* 1958, Offprint no. 163

Deevey, E. S. — 'The Human Population', *Scientific American,* 1960, Offprint no. 608

Demeny, P.	'The Populations of the Under-developed Countries', *Scientific American*, 1974, Vol. 231, pt. 3, p. 148
Freedman, R., Berelson, B.	'The Human Population', *Scientific American*, 1974, Vol. 231, pt. 3, p. 30
Frejka, T.	'The Prospects for a Stationary World Population', *Scientific American*, 1973, Offprint no. 683
Pinchot, G. B.	'Marine Farming', *Scientific American*, 1970, Offprint no. 1205
Pirie, N. W.	'Orthodox and Unorthodox Methods of Meeting World Food Needs', *Scientific American*, 1967, Offprint no. 1068
Segal, S. J.	'The Physiology of Human Reproduction', *Scientific American*, 1974, Vol. 231, pt. 3, p. 52
Scrimshaw, N. S.	'Food', *Scientific American*, 1963, Offprint no. 1153
Simpson, D.	'The Dimensions of World Poverty', *Scientific American*, 1968, Offprint no. 640
Taylor, C. E.	'Population Trends in an Indian Village', *Scientific American*, 1970, Offprint no. 1184
Tietze, C., Lewit, S.	'Abortion', *Scientific American*, 1969, Offprint no. 1129
Westoff, C. F.	'The Populations of the Developed Countries', *Scientific American*, 1974, Vol. 231, pt. 3, p. 108

21 Man's environment

Nearly all animals modify their habitats to some extent, but in 'natural' conditions the changes effected by animal activity during one season of a year will have been largely reversed before the season comes round again. Man is an exception: one of the characteristics of his activities is that he can make major changes to the environment and, further, take action to maintain these changes.

The impact of man on the environment

This relation between man and his environment is relatively new. The inhabitants of the forest zone might clear an area by burning and slashing, sow and harvest their crops for a few years until the soil was 'exhausted' and then move on. Regeneration of the forest would then commence and very many years pass before the area was reoccupied by man. No long-term changes were made to the whole environment; the forest dweller was in equilibrium with his environment. With the early development of agriculture in the savanna lands the situation was different. Former forest areas were cleared and then kept clear. Although short periods of fallow permitted the land to recover from the cropping of a harvest, man had begun permanently to modify the environment in his own interest.

We can, in some places, recognize this process of deforestation by a study of pollen grains in cores of mud from the bottoms of lakes (p. 61). Changes in pollen composition may reflect changing climatic conditions but recent changes indicating the replacement of forests by open land are commonly a result of the activity of man modifying his environment (Fig. 21.1).

By driving back the forest, man obtained more arable land for cultivation and, as he became more skilled in agriculture, the food supply and the population slowly grew. Agriculture requires good tools and gradually stone implements were replaced by iron ones. The demand for metal steadily increased and mines were opened to obtain iron and other ores. As industrial activity has increased in scale, these mines have greatly affected the landscape in many parts of the world. Useless slag has accumulated in artificial hills; 'opencast' mining, in which all the soil and rock above the ore is removed, has led to hills being cut away or new valleys excavated. The search for better sources of power than his own muscles led man first to destroy much woodland for fuel to drive simple machines, and then, as the scale of industrial development increased, to mine for coal and today to sink oil wells, lay pipelines, construct roads and build small towns in desert regions where few people previously lived. The need for power has led to the construction of vast dams like the Aswan dam in Egypt, the Kainji dam in Nigeria, the Volta dam in Ghana and the Kariba dam on the Zambesi. Artificial lakes covering thousands of square kilometres have thus been formed, with the result that large numbers of people have had to move to new homes; new opportunities for fisheries and transportation have been created as well as new problems from the spread of water-associated disease. Growing cities have added to the demand for water, so that small valleys have been drowned to form reservoirs, while areas of little or no agricultural value have been 'tamed' to provide recreational facilities for the city dwellers. Destruction of the natural forest has sometimes been followed by the planting of trees of value to man, often with a single species spreading as a uniform stand over thousands of hectares. Vast areas of land today are covered with conifers to supply the world with newspapers, magazines and books. Very many of these man-made changes have been such as to simplify the previously existing ecosystems and reduce the diversity of plant and animal life. Thus as man's numbers have increased, he has brought larger and larger areas of land under artificial control and, since his numbers increase ever more rapidly, the human pressure on the environment mounts. The surface of the earth is finite and thus those areas which have not yet been significantly affected by man's activities grow steadily less.

This is one aspect of man's impact upon his environment: but there is a second. As man has gained greater understanding of the nature of the world around him, he has turned this knowledge to his own uses in manufacturing commodities—motor cars and television sets, insecticides and artificial fertilizers—or in packaging natural products, such as ground-nuts and fruit juice, in containers made of metal or of synthetic materials, none of which is rapidly destroyed by the normal agents of decomposition. As cities have grown, so too has the quantity of their waste products so that more and more material is removed from the environment and redistributed into man-made accumulations of waste.

Percentage of total pollen grains

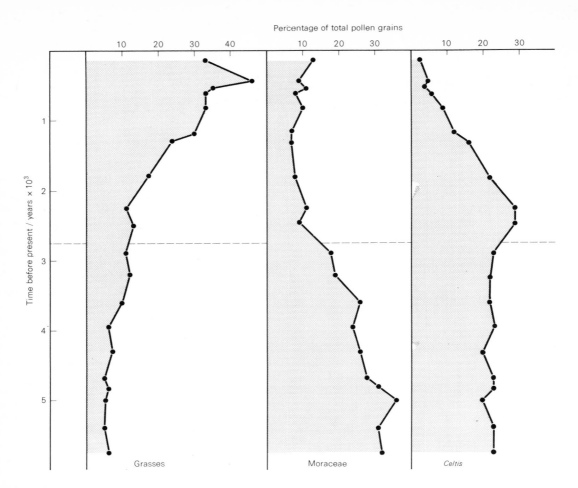

21.1 Analysis of pollen composition of cores taken from a site at the northern end of Lake Victoria. The time of deposition of different sections of the core was determined by the radiocarbon method (p. 466). The graph shows the percentage of pollen grains from grasses and from two taxonomic groups of woody plants characteristic of semi-deciduous forest. Note how about 2 750 years ago the proportion of pollen from forest trees started to decrease and that characteristic of grasses to increase. Archaeological evidence suggests that agriculture started in East Africa about 3 000–2 500 years ago and the changing composition of the pollen probably reflects deforestation by man rather than climatic change. (After Kendall.)

Such considerations have led to the view that there are two major ecological problems facing man today. The first is to find ways of checking or reversing the tendency towards ever-increasing simplification of the ecosystems with which man interferes; its solution may involve not only changes in agricultural practice in crop growing, in herd rearing or in opening up new land for agriculture but also the exclusion of some or all types of agricultural and industrial activity from certain areas, so as to prevent the destruction of their existing ecosystems. The second problem is how to reduce the rate at which possibly harmful chemicals and waste products are liberated into the environment. The first of these is the problem of conservation, the second that of pollution.

Conservation

Conservation of the environment is partly concerned with preventing or correcting environmental destruction caused by agricultural and industrial activity. We have already noted two effects of agricultural activity upon the environment.

Soil conservation

The first is soil erosion. In savanna, cattle herdsmen may let the sizes of herds grow until the carrying capacity of the land is exceeded and the soil becomes increasingly exposed because of over-grazing. The consequence is erosion of the soil surface, making the area even less able to support large herds of cattle. Erosion can also follow crop growing if bare, sloping surfaces are left from which the rains will wash the soils, or from which, in the dry season, wind will carry away the topsoil as a dust. The importance of this problem is illustrated by the fact that in 1934 it was estimated that 40 million hectares of arable land in the United States had been 'lost' as a result of erosion, that a further hundred million were seriously affected and that more than half of the total land surface of the country was eroded to some degree as a result of man's activities. Since that time there has been a growing realization that human agricultural activity can, if uncontrolled, lead to a destruction of the environment, making fertile areas barren; techniques have therefore been developed to 'conserve' the soil by preventing erosion (p. 292).

Deforestation and water conservation

The second problem which arises from agricultural activity is the destruction of forest and woodland. Forest regeneration is a slow process (p. 90), while increasing human populations result in the cutting down of larger and larger areas of forest to make land available for crop production. The consequences of this are more far-reaching than a simple loss of timber. Firstly, the exposed soil, once rich in organic matter, is now subject to leaching, so that its nutrients are carried away from the roots of plants. Secondly, the exposed soil is subject to erosion and, thirdly, the water supply is affected. Rivers and streams which provide towns and villages with water depend upon the existence of water reserves which are held in the ground and gradually drained away during the dry seasons. Where no such water-holding reserves or 'sponges' exist, the rivers flow only during and for a short time after the rains.

Such water reserves are commonly in forested areas. When rain falls on forest, the force of the drops is broken by the canopy, while dead leaves on the soil surface hinder run-off; moreover, the topsoil is porous because of worm and termite activity. Hence water percolates into the soil to give a water reserve which is released gradually into streams over a long period of time. Provided precipitation during the rains exceeds the annual evapotranspiration from the trees, reserves may be sufficient to ensure that streams flow throughout the dry season.

If, however, the forest cover is destroyed then, in the rains, surface run-off may remove a large proportion of the water, so that it runs directly into the rivers. The reserve is no longer effectively refilled and streams which once ran all the year round cease flowing a few weeks or months after the end of the rains. Some of these changes were demonstrated by an experiment in America in which all timber of mixed forest in a small watershed of 15·6 ha was felled during winter and left lying; the following summer the area was treated with herbicide to prevent regeneration. Events in this watershed were compared with those in neighbouring ones in which the forest was left un-disturbed. The felling had several striking consequences. Total run-off of water was more than 40 percent greater from the watershed that had been cleared of trees and the quantity of inorganic particulate matter in the water increased some ninefold as a result of erosion. At the same time the loss of nutrient salts was marked: the loss rate of potassium rose more than twentyfold and that of calcium tenfold, while other cations such as sodium and magnesium were also lost more rapidly. Loss of nitrate ion increased about fortyfold. Indeed the level of nitrate ion in the stream draining the watershed exceeded that permissible for drinking water in the United States.

Cutting down the forest thus affects soil nutrients, erosion and water supply. While deforestation can produce undesirable consequences, these are not immediately obvious to those responsible for the changes. It thus becomes necessary, as a matter of deliberate policy, both to conserve forests and also to re-establish them by reforestation.

Conservation of the fauna and flora

A further aspect of conservation relates to the threat of complete elimination of certain species of plants and animals as human agricultural and industrial activities expand. This has led to the suggestion that man should set aside areas to preserve particular habitats from extensive human interference or to preserve particular organisms from gradual extinction. Are there any reasons why this may be a desirable action? A wide variety of different reasons has in fact been proposed. One reason stems from the experience of the developed countries that many people living in cities enjoy an escape from the noise and hustle of city life into more peaceful surroundings. Areas suitable for recreation for city dwellers have therefore direct value in contributing to human enjoyment. In developed countries this need is met, with greater or less success, by increasing the area of undeveloped rural land owned by the State and kept for public use. The areas involved may be quite small or very large; the Yellowstone National Park in the United States covers nearly 9 000 km². Recreation is one attraction of the very large game reserves in East and Southern Africa such as the Tsavo National Park in Kenya with an area of more than 20 000 km², the Serengeti Park of about 15 000 km² in Tanzania and the Kruger National Park of 18 000 km² in South Africa. All bring tourists from overseas and thus contribute to the various national economies.

A second reason relates to the need to preserve rare plants and animals from extermination. Agricultural and industrial development destroys much of the local fauna and flora. While many of the species which thus become rarer may not appear to be of immediate use to man, we should remember that once a species has become extinct, it cannot, unlike a motor car or an aeroplane, be made again. It does not follow that because we have no use for a species today, future generations may not find it of value. Conservation is thus not merely a matter of sentimental attachment to wild plants and animals but essential if we take seriously our responsibility to the future.

Reserves of new natural products

This type of argument has two more immediate reasons for its support. Firstly, until the present century man depended almost exclusively upon the properties of natural products for his medicines. The first drug used to treat malaria effectively was quinine, extracted from the bark of the cinchona tree which grew in South America; the pain-reducing properties of an extract of the bark of the willow tree led to the isolation of salicylic acid, whose acetyl ester is the familiar aspirin. There may well exist many other naturally occurring drugs whose value has yet to be widely recognized. Research is indeed going ahead at present into the pharmacological bases of the traditional medicines of Asia and Africa. For example, species of the shrub *Rauvolfia* are used extensively by African and Indian herbalists. Analysis has shown these to contain a large number of alkaloids, one of which, reserpine, is now used in purified form throughout the world in the treatment of certain mental illnesses.

Reserves of new crop varieties

The second consideration relates to food crops. Man's food crops originated from wild plants and, by a process of selection, more useful varieties have been developed (p. 281). As selection proceeds the 'pool of variation' within a crop grows less. But the wild ancestors retain the potential of providing all sorts of characters which might be of value to man: they are a reserve in which new characteristics may be sought when needed. The preservation of the wild relatives of domesticated crops is thus of immediate practical importance.

The matter may be illustrated by reference to cocoa. One serious problem of cocoa production in Ghana, the world's largest producer, is a virus disease called swollen shoot. At the moment efforts are made to control the disease by destroying infected trees, but a more satisfactory solution would be the development of a variety of cocoa resistant to attack by the virus. For many years all cocoa grown in Ghana was derived from a very small number of beans imported from the island of Fernando Póo. Clearly the pool of heritable variety from such a small ancestral stock would be limited. In combating the disease, a search was made initially for local trees which might be resistant to the disease, but this met with no success. Other cultivated varieties of cocoa were subsequently imported from Brazil, the original home of cocoa. While these have valuable characteristics, they do not include effective resistance to swollen-shoot virus; other cocoa stocks are therefore being introduced to see whether they may not

contain the desired hereditary characteristic. New and useful heritable characteristics may yet be found in the wild ancestors of cocoa in the Amazonian forest. Attempts, however, have been made, and further plans developed, to cut out large areas of the Amazonian forest for replanting with monocultures of trees of immediate economic value for such undertakings as paper manufacture. If this is done, there is a definite possibility that potentially useful sources of heritable characteristics for other domestic crops will be lost.

To a limited extent this problem can be met by keeping collections of wild plants under artificial conditions. Like cocoa, the potato originates from South America and the Soviet geneticist Vavilov organized several expeditions to the Andes to collect, for cultivation, wild relatives of the potato as these wild plants might contain heritable characteristics valuable to the plant breeder. Such artificially cultivated plants tend, however, to be unintentionally selected for survival in botanical gardens or glasshouses; they therefore do not provide as valuable a reserve as those growing wild in their natural environment.

Similar concern has recently been voiced about maize. Maize itself (*Zea mays*) is not known in the wild state, but it can be crossed with a closely related weed called teosinte (*Zea mexicana*). Teosinte normally grows wild in maize fields in Central America and is a reserve in which desirable hereditary characters may be found. Increasingly sophisticated methods of cultivation are leading to its gradual elimination; its area of distribution is now only about half what it was at the beginning of the century. Furthermore, since cultivated maize can cross with teosinte, there is a flow of hereditary characteristics from the cultivated crop to the weed (Fig. 21.2). In any one area the type of maize grown is very uniform in its hereditary constitution, so that the reserve of characteristics in the teosinte tends to become increasingly diluted with those present in the cultivated varieties. For this reason, it is now urged that active steps be taken to protect and conserve this plant which, to the maize farmer, is nothing but a tiresome weed. These

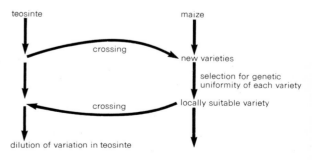

21.2 Diagram summarizing the relation between teosinte and maize as a source of potentially useful varieties for this crop. For further explanation, see text.

then are practical reasons for attempting to conserve as great a diversity of plant species as possible.

Conservation of insects

Broadly similar considerations apply to the preservation of the insect fauna. Many crop pests are species introduced from other areas, where they are naturally controlled by predators and parasites. Biological control depends upon locating these and introducing them to the place where their natural prey has become a pest (p. 300). Destruction of the natural environment and the simplification of the ecosystem by monoculture can lead to the loss of the reserves of potential biological control agents available to man.

Conservation of big game

The policy of conservation of big game animals is one which has attracted much attention, partly because the areas of land required are very great. In considering this matter, one point must be appreciated. Any conservation of organisms, even in an apparently undisturbed environment, is to a large degree artificial. This particularly applies to big game animals. Even the largest reserve will limit their movements and their traditional migrations are likely to be impeded. Attempts to run large herds of game in a limited area may result in numbers becoming greater than can be controlled by natural predators; there follows over-grazing and consequent destruction of the habitat. Such conserved areas cannot just be allowed to 'run wild'; they must be managed and the principles of management which we have already discussed (p. 318) apply or should be applied as strictly to reserves as to grazing lands.

This problem can be illustrated by reference to elephant in the vast Tsavo National Park in Kenya. This is an area of high, well-drained and arid land lying between Mount Kilimanjaro and the Indian Ocean. Unsuitable for agriculture, the area was declared a reserve in 1948. Elephant has always lived in this region, but in the past the herds migrated during the dry season to shaded and better-watered areas either inland or on the coast (Fig. 21.3). These dry-season retreats of the elephant herds have gradually been destroyed. The coastal forest has been replaced by plantations, and the inland forest cleared or turned to plantation agriculture. At the same time the migration routes have been cut by roads and railways as well as by settled farms and villages. Thus today the elephant herds are restricted to the Park.

Elephants require water: a bull elephant needs between 90 and 140 litres of water daily. The early management policy of the Park was to increase the available water supplies, so that the land could carry the elephants during the dry season. This readily available water has resulted in the elephant population's becoming far greater than the dry-season carrying capacity of the Park. Consequently

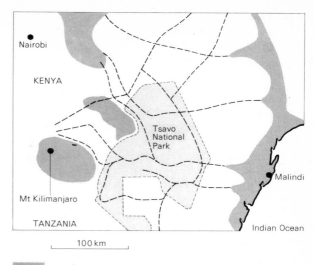

former dry season refuges

— — —· former migration routes

-------- boundary of Tsavo National Park

21.3 Tsavo National Park, showing the former dry-season refuges of the elephants and the migration routes they followed. Most of these areas have now been cultivated by man and the migration routes cut by roads and railways. The elephants are therefore restrained within an area which provides no typical dry-season habitats. (After Sikes.)

there has been steady destruction of trees and the over-grazing which follows over-stocking. Vast numbers of elephants died in the Park recently since their population had reached a crisis level. Two possibilities are now open. The first is to take no action, to hope that the population will fall to so low a level as to allow the animals to come into equilibrium with this unnaturally restricted habitat: this may well, however, simply lead to further destruction of the flora of the reserve. The other possibility is to follow a considered management policy, restricting the water supply and culling out elephants until their numbers are well below the present carrying capacity. Regeneration of the reserve could be achieved by deliberate control of the movements of herds, although this is likely to take many years. Positive management would moreover offer the potential of exploiting the herds as a source of meat and other materials: the present policy results only in periodic mortality which, when it occurs, is on so vast a scale as to make such exploitation impossible.

Conservation in the seas

Effective conservation coupled with scientific management can unquestionably go far to preserve the fauna and flora of the land from drastic elimination as a consequence of expanding human activity. A comparable problem might be thought to be unlikely to arise in the seas, where human

373

interference appears to be upon a relatively small scale. Nevertheless there has been in the past gross over-fishing in some areas and this continues today. Such over-fishing is unlikely permanently to endanger any species of fish and indeed past experience has shown that when the pressure of fishing effort is reduced, stocks usually recover in a few years (Fig. 21.4).

There is, however, one exception to this, namely the great whales (Mammalia: Cetacea). These are killed partly for their oil which is used for the manufacture of margarine and soap, and partly for their flesh which is used as meat, as protein supplement for domestic animals and as fertilizer. Both margarine and soap can be manufactured using other oils as starting materials. Since 1945 the whaling industry has expanded very rapidly in terms of size of whaling fleets, but production per unit effort has fallen sharply since about 1960 (Fig. 21.5). Scientific investigations undertaken at the request of the major whaling nations showed that the stocks of blue whale, the species mainly hunted, were being grossly over-exploited. In 1963 it was recommended that, to allow the populations to rebuild and thus ensure for the future a higher annual yield, fishing rates should be drastically curtailed for a number of years: otherwise the yield would continue to fall and the larger species of whale finally be exterminated. This advice was rejected by representatives of some of the major nations which have heavy capital investment in

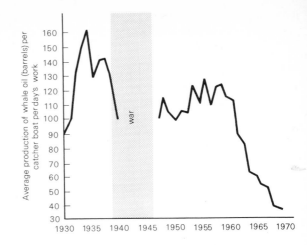

21.5 Decline in yield of whale oil per unit effort since 1960.

whaling boats or which, like Japan, are desperately in need of sources of protein to feed a large population living in a relatively small area. As a result the two largest whalebone whales, the Blue Whale and the Fin Whale, have been hunted nearly to complete extermination (Figs. 21.6a and 21.6b) and the same process of over-killing two other species, the Sei Whale (Fig. 21.6c) and the Sperm Whale, has now begun. Disregard for scientific advice favouring a policy of conservation has reduced the potential annual yield of blue whales from an estimated 6 000 per year to nothing. While one may regret the ignorance which led to the extermination of the dodo and the quagga, it is far harder to condone the actions of educated political and economic administrators who today disregard scientific advice.

These then are some of the practical reasons for attempting to conserve as great a diversity of organisms as possible. Certainly many people find great pleasure from observing wild mammals or wild birds, or from seeing hillsides gay with flowering plants, but the conservation of nature is not basically a matter of affording pleasure to a few, but of ensuring that the resources provided by the diversity of living organisms remain available for the practical needs of future generations.

Pollution

The problems of conservation stem from man's increasing modification of the environment to provide food and the raw materials for industry. Most of the problems of pollution may be regarded as the other aspect of human activity, namely the production of waste materials, some from food making, some from the disposal of human excreta, but increasingly those from industrial production and from the products of industry.

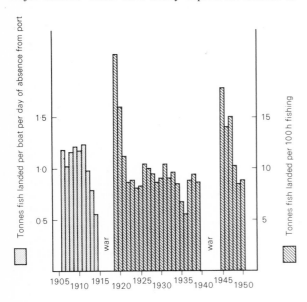

21.4 Fishing effort for haddock in the North Sea off Britain between 1905 and 1950. Note that the unit of fishing effort used after 1919 is different from that used between 1906 and 1914. During both wars fishing effectively ceased. The falling fish landings shortly before the first war may have been due to over-fishing. Note the high values of fish landings in the years immediately following each war, reflecting the ability of the stocks of fish to recover. (After Graham.)

374

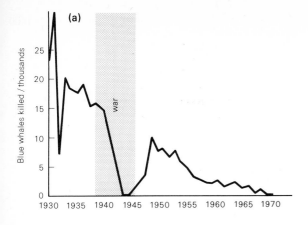

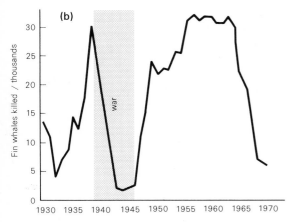

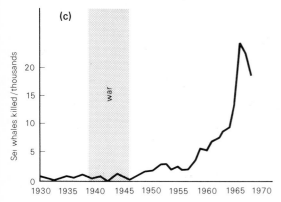

21.6 (a) The Blue Whale, the largest of the whales, has been so intensively hunted that is possible that the species may become finally extinct. Controlled hunting would have conserved the stocks and yielded about 6 000 whales a year. Certain of the major whaling nations refused to accept any effective limitations upon the catch rate. (b) As the stock of Blue Whales became exhausted, exploitation of the stocks of Fin Whales increased and these are now also rare. (c) More recently as the stock of Fin Whales has been depleted, the process of over-exploitation of Sei Whales has started.

In Africa, apart from the pollution of rivers with human waste materials and the waste discharges of factories, pollution is not generally a serious problem, but in the highly industrialized and often densely populated countries, this is not so: here pollution has become increasingly important. If pollution is a relatively minor problem in Africa, why should we trouble to discuss it here at some length? There are two rather different reasons. Firstly, some forms of pollution are not limited in their effects to the place where they originate. The most obvious example is that of radioactive fall-out from the atmospheric testing of atomic warheads. The radio-active products from such tests are widely distributed and can affect countries and peoples remote from the scene of the tests: it is for this reason that the governments of many developing countries are critical of such testing.

Secondly, many people believe that the developed countries were mistaken in allowing industry freely to discharge its waste products into the air, the rivers and the sea. While the ill effects of this policy have been felt only recently, the question arises as to whether, as industrial activity increases in the developing world, steps should not be taken to control industrial pollution from the outset. To understand the full implications of this issue, it is essential to know something of the characteristics of industrial pollution and of the possibilities for reducing it.

The practical study of pollution can arise in two very different ways. In one, it is possible to recognize some waste or other material which is being released into the environment in large quantities. It then becomes necessary to try to determine whether or not this material is having an undesirable effect upon the environment. This is not always easy to decide. It may be possible to recognize that some undesired change has occurred at the same time as the pollution was taking place, but it is essential to be able to show that this change was caused by the pollutant and not by some other environmental change. We shall shortly see how this difficulty can arise in considering the environmental effects of various persistent insecticides such as dieldrin and DDT.

In the second situation, some undesirable environmental or other change is observed and it is then necessary to attempt to identify the cause of the change. This also can be difficult, as it is not sufficient to be able to show that the two effects are correlated: there may be several other changes taking place which are also correlated with the undesirable change. Moreover, the undesirable effect may be due to several different factors acting together, no single factor being the 'cause'. This latter type of relationship is particularly well illustrated by studies on the causation of cancer of the lung. These we will describe, partly because of their medical and therefore human interest, partly because they show that lung cancer is particularly due to the cumulative action of air pollution and cigarette smoking, which has sometimes been described as personal pollution.

Pollution and lung cancer

About twenty years ago, studies of medical statistics in both the United States and Great Britain showed that while the death rate from many diseases such as pneumonia and tuberculosis had been steadily decreasing, the death rate from lung cancer was rising sharply. In both countries it increased nearly ten times between 1930 and 1960 (Fig. 21.7). There was an 'epidemic' of lung cancer and its causes had to be sought.

In 1935 observations made by two American surgeons suggested that the cause lay in the habit of cigarette smoking which had become increasingly common after 1920. Such a suggestion was not only unwelcome news to vast numbers of cigarette smokers but implied that a commercial product of enormous economic value was a dangerously toxic material. There were, however, many reasons for believing that the correlation which had been found between the incidence of lung cancer and the habit of cigarette smoking might not reflect a causal relation. It was possible that there had in fact been no real increase in the incidence of the disease but that it was more commonly recognized as a result of improved medical techniques, or that, because people were living longer, more survived to

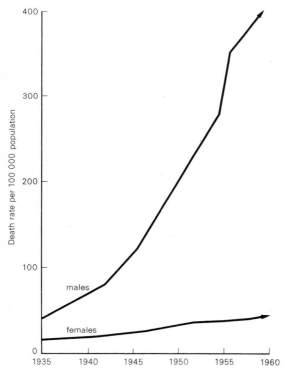

21.7 Death rates from lung cancer in the population between the ages of 65 and 74 in Britain between 1935 and 1960. Note that the rate of increase of the condition was very much more rapid in men than in women. The difference is due to the fact that cigarette smoking became a common habit among women only after about 1920.

Table 21.1 Death rates due to lung cancer per 100 000 people in England (*Data from Smith and Snyth*)

Population sampled	Characteristic	Death rate
(1958–64)		
General	Industrial city	295
General	Rural districts	132
(1951–61)		
Doctors (male)	Non-smokers	7
,,	1–14 cigarettes daily	57
,,	15–24 cigarettes daily	139
,,	> 24 cigarettes daily	227

Note that the difference between the death rates due to lung cancer of smokers and non-smokers is very much greater than the difference between the values for inhabitants of urban and rural areas. The smoking habit is of much greater importance as a causative agent than is urban air pollution.

display the condition, or that the disease was caused by an increase in cancer-producing materials discharged into the air from motor-car exhausts, since lung cancer was less common in rural than in urban populations (Table 21.1). Such arguments were not, however, in keeping with the fact which was presently recognized that lung cancer was far more common and increasing far more rapidly in men than in women (Fig. 21.7). It was further argued that cigarette smoking could not be the cause of the epidemic, since pipe and cigar smokers did not suffer significantly more from lung cancer than did people who did not smoke at all; furthermore, the disease was less common in American men who smoked very heavily than among men in Britain who smoked fewer cigarettes a day. It was subsequently shown, however, that both pipes and cigars trapped the cancer-producing or carcinogenic materials far more effectively than did cigarettes and that since the British smoked cigarettes to a shorter stub than did most Americans, the latter were partially protected from these materials by a greater 'filter' effect. Finally it was suggested that cigarette smoking was not the cause of lung cancer, but rather that people who were potentially more susceptible to lung cancer were also more inclined to take up cigarette smoking: that the alleged 'cause', smoking, was really the consequence of being a potential lung-cancer patient. We stressed earlier that correlations cannot be taken as evidence of cause: this fact formed the basis of the last argument in which, while accepting that there was a true correlation between the incidence of lung cancer and the habit of cigarette smoking, it was proposed that the causal relations were not that smoking leads to lung cancer, but rather that liability to lung cancer leads to smoking. To distinguish between these two possibilities would require a large and impractical social experiment. It is now generally accepted that cigarette smoking is indeed causally related to lung cancer and many governments have taken measures designed to reduce the incidence of cigarette smoking in their populations. But it is not the sole cause. As we mentioned, city dwellers are

Table 21.2 Effect of atmospheric sulphur dioxide level upon the growth of rye grass. The plants had been allowed to grow for 26 weeks before measurements were taken (*Data from Bell and Clough*)

SO_2 concentration (μg m^{-3})	Number of living leaves per plant	Leaf area (cm^2)	Dry weight of stubble (g)	Number of plants
9·0	85·6	417·2	0·48	144
191·0	47·3	203·6	0·22	144

more liable to the disease than are people who live in the country; this is because air pollution also plays some part in causing the condition: the disease might therefore be checked to some extent by reducing urban air pollution. To try to reduce the habit of cigarette smoking is, however, an easier and more practical step.

Industrial pollution: atmospheric pollution

In the developed countries, factories and power stations are usually concentrated in and around cities, while the cold climate necessitates that homes should be heated, commonly by the burning of coal. Coal burning for domestic purposes started in European cities about 1400 A.D.; by 1650 stocks of firewood had been nearly exhausted and

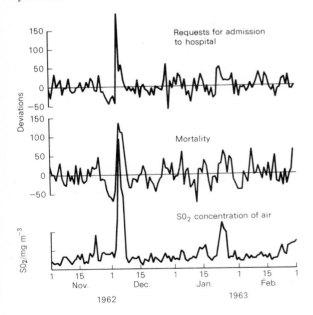

21.8 Changes during the winter months of 1962–63 in the level of air pollution in London measured as sulphur dioxide content of the air. Note how the sharp rise in the level of atmospheric pollution caused by abnormal conditions in early December resulted in an increase both in requests for admission to hospital and in the death rate. Both these latter values are expressed as the difference between the daily value and the mean value for the previous 15 days. (After Waller.)

coal was almost the only fuel used both in homes and for industry. The waste gases from coal burning were released into the atmosphere. These contain fine particulate matter as well as oxides of sulphur and nitrogen. The fine particles are on average about 0·1 μm in diameter but aggregate into clumps about 1 μm across. Such particles are, of course, readily inhaled and may irritate the respiratory surfaces. Fig. 21.8 makes it clear that both sickness, as shown by applications for admission to hospitals, and deaths can rise sharply when weather conditions lead to an abnormally high level of atmospheric pollution. Not only health, but also photosynthesis is adversely affected by air pollution. Oxides of sulphur, even in very low concentrations of 200 μg m^{-3}, can reduce the growth rate of many plants (Table 21.2), while fine particulate matter settling on leaves may block the stomata and cover the leaf surface with a thin layer of light-absorbing grime. In some places, gaseous industrial waste material may contain very fine particles of heavy metals, as well as sulphur dioxide; over a considerable area near such factories no plants may survive at all. Around copper-smelting works in the United States, for example, completely barren areas of 250 km^2 and more have been reported, while the vegetation was severely affected over a further area of 300 km^2. Lichens and mosses are particularly sensitive to the effects of air pollution, their abundance and number of species falling sharply as one moves from the countryside towards the centre of a large industrial city (Fig. 21.9). Comparable situations can occur in Africa. Thus, for example, ore roasting at the gold mines in Ghana has resulted in as much as 4 tonnes of arsenic(III) oxide being discharged daily in the smoke. In the immediate vicinity of the works, vegetation was found to contain 6000 parts arsenic per million dry weight and plants contained abnormally high concentrations even at 65 km from the area. Continuous exposure affected many of the workers and farmers with resulting physical weakness, headaches and defective vision.

Within the cities themselves, heavy road traffic adds to the extent of air pollution. One constituent of the exhaust gases of motor cars is carbon monoxide. This combines with haemoglobin to form carboxyhaemoglobin, a compound which is far more stable than oxyhaemoglobin, and as a result exposure to carbon monoxide reduces the oxygen-carrying capacity of the blood. In busy streets in some cities, local concentrations of carbon monoxide may build up to levels considerably higher than are acceptable

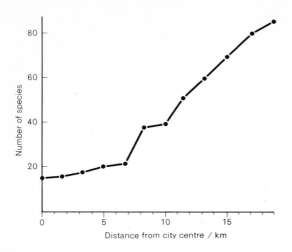

21.9 Numbers of species of mosses and lichens found at different distances from the centre of the industrial city of Newcastle in England. (After Gilbert.)

by legal health safety standards. While this may not be serious for the passer-by, it can have adverse effects on those who, like traffic policemen, are required to work for long periods in areas where traffic is dense. Furthermore, exhaust gases from cars contain carcinogenic compounds as well. These and other aspects of the industrial and domestic pollution of city air explain why lung cancer is more common in city dwellers than in countrymen (Table 21.1).

Effective techniques are available for the reduction of smoke emission from factories and especially from power stations. These methods, however, involve considerable expenditure and if enforced would lead to an increase in the cost of the product, especially of electricity, supplied to the consumer. British smoke abatement legislation illustrates what may be achieved: it resulted in a halving of industrial and domestic smoke emission between 1956 and 1966. Similarly, while techniques are being developed to reduce exhaust discharges from motor vehicles, these all lower the efficiency of the engine, increasing petrol consumption per kilometre. A major social problem of balance of advantage thus arises.

Oil pollution

Energy production as well as road and rail transport depend to a considerable extent upon the use of oil as fuel. Much of the world's oil is transported by tankers from developing countries to Europe and North America, and such tankers are a source of pollution in two distinct ways. The first arises from the wrecking of oil-laden tankers; this results in the release of vast quantities of crude oil, much of which may get carried ashore. For example, when an oil tanker was wrecked in 1971 near Cape Agulhas, the southernmost point of the African continent, more than

20 000 tonnes of crude oil escaped. The drift of oil onto the shore had marked effects upon the littoral animal community, but it is not possible to be sure whether these were due to the oil itself or to detergent sprayed about the wreck to disperse the oil. The effects were most marked in sheltered stretches of the coast where wave action was slight. Encrusting algae were killed, as were also sea urchins (Echinodermata), some species of limpet and periwinkles (Mollusca: Gastropoda), as well as two important food animals, a species of crayfish and a gastropod mollusc. Other limpet and periwinkle species as well as the barnacles (Arthropoda: Crustacea) were less affected. The present indications, from other areas where such events have occurred, is that the shore community slowly recovers: provided such incidents are rare, there is no lasting damage to the community.

The second type of pollution is less spectacular and its long-term effects uncertain. After tankers have discharged their cargoes, they wash out their tanks at sea. The waste oil floats, often as tarry lumps, which are then carried by wind action until thrown up on a shore: in some places long reaches of shore may be more or less permanently covered with an oily mess. Fig. 21.10 shows a length of beach in Ghana polluted in this way by discharge from tankers plying between the oilfields of the Persian Gulf and Europe. Such shore deposits, while unsightly, do not appear to cause any immediate economic loss, except where a town or village depends upon income from holiday-makers. Mineral oils, however, contain carcinogenic compounds, and shore-based fishermen constantly exposed to such pollution may therefore be at risk. Furthermore, these compounds might become incorporated into marine food webs, finally reaching man in fish. This is a possibility which has not yet been proved, but clearly it requires continuing study.

Such cumulative pollution of the shore is obvious. Misgivings have also been expressed as to whether the less obvious but steady accumulation of oil on the surface of the sea may not have gradual and undesired effects on marine life. It is, however, argued that since there has always been natural oil leakage from submarine deposits, the present additional load is unlikely to be important.

Pollution of rivers

River pollution is becoming increasingly widespread in developing countries. Sometimes this can occur because of the failure of factories sited on the banks of rivers to provide adequate and safe sanitary arrangements for its workers. Raw sewage is discharged directly into the rivers with danger to the health of villagers living further downstream and using river water directly for domestic purposes. Again factories in some towns have been allowed to discharge effluents rich in organic matter directly into relatively small rivers which are then converted into open sewers, making life unpleasant for those whose homes are

21.10 Oil pollution on a beach in Ghana. The black lines are formed of aggregations of tarry lumps carried onto the shore by wave action. The inset shows a close-up view of the deposits.

nearby. Here also control can be effected, although, as with the control of air pollution, it would involve increase in initial capital outlay. Once again the balance of social advantage between pollution and the cost of its control arises.

Pollution by synthetic chemicals

The chemicals released by industrial pollution are normally waste products. Different problems arise when substances deliberately released by man may be damaging to the environment and, in the long run, to man himself.

Experience over the last twenty-five years has strongly suggested that persistent insecticides, especially dieldrin and DDT, have damaging effects upon the fauna and thus upon the structure of different ecosystems. The third persistent insecticide, gamma-BHC, is more toxic to insects than DDT but less persistent: dieldrin combines high insect toxicity with long persistence. All three substances have low mammalian toxicities compared with some of the non-persistent organophosphorus insecticides such as parathion (Table 21.3).

Clearly the first consideration is whether DDT, the

Table 21.3 Toxicity of different insecticides to houseflies and rats, expressed as mg kg^{-1} body weight required to kill 50% of a sample of the population; this is spoken of as the Lethal Dose$_{50}$ or LD$_{50}$ (*After Busvine*)

Insecticide	Toxicity to houseflies	Toxicity to rats
Natural insecticides		
Pyrethrins	16·0	1 500
Chlorinated hydrocarbons		
DDT	18·0	150–800
Gamma-BHC	1·6	125–225
Dieldrin	1·0	50–87
Organophosphorus compounds		
Parathion	3·0	6–15
Malathion	50·0	1 400–5 800

most widely used insecticide, has any effects on man. The chlorinated hydrocarbons tend to accumulate in fatty tissues and the quantity of DDT found in human beings may be considerable. In 1964 mean concentrations were

379

found of 26 μg g^{-1} body fat of people living in New Delhi in India, 7·0 μg g^{-1} in the United States and 3·3 μg g^{-1} in ·the United Kingdom. Since the use of DDT has been curtailed or banned in the United States and the United Kingdom, levels in these countries have started to fall. Certainly there is no evidence that such concentrations of DDT are obviously toxic, but it is not known whether high concentrations have a mild debilitating effect, nor whether prolonged exposure to high levels of tissue DDT has any subsequent consequences. The individual who starts cigarette smoking at twenty years of age may not show lung cancer until thirty or more years later. High levels of tissue DDT have occurred in the general population now for only about twenty years.

DDT presents a further problem: it has been shown to affect the mechanism of inheritance of mice. We have no knowledge of such an action on man; but here also it is unlikely, in the absence of gross damage to the gonads, that this would be easily detected in human populations, particularly if prolonged exposure before reaching reproductive age is critical in determining the effect. There is thus clear wisdom in banning the use of a material potentially so harmful in countries where its use is not essential.

Despite its low mammalian toxicity, DDT is toxic to many other vertebrates. As early as 1946 it was shown that, in laboratory conditions, the dosage of DDT recommended for use in destroying mosquito larvae was lethal to young *Tilapia*. In breeding ponds the fish did survive, but a three-fold increase in the recommended dosage resulted in a 70 percent fish mortality within four days. Experience in the field showed that such levels of application were in fact frequently used.

DDT and dieldrin are toxic to birds also. Table 21.4 shows results of surveys of the bird population of a swamp habitat in north-eastern Nigeria where a single application of dieldrin was made using mistblowers during tsetse control operations: there was a dramatic fall in the abundance of insectivorous· birds with relatively little recovery after a year. Two fairly common species of insectivorous bird were possibly completely eliminated by the treatment, as may also have been the Lizard Buzzard which eats snakes. This slow recovery is different from common experience in the United States where destruction of small-

bird populations by dieldrin is followed by recovery within a year. It may be that the relative isolation of the specialized swamp habitat in Nigeria did not allow recolonization from the surrounding populations. Lasting destruction of insectivorous birds by repeated insecticide application to cotton crops in Chad has also been reported, including the elimination of species of importance to man in the control of insect pests.

Small insectivorous birds breed rapidly and, provided the application of insecticide is over limited areas only, their numbers may not be seriously reduced. They are, moreover, mostly second-order consumers, so that the quantity of insecticide they ingest will be fairly closely correlated with whatever may be applied for pest control. With birds of prey which feed on other vertebrates, the situation is different. We have seen that persistent insecticides become widely distributed in the environment and then accumulate in the tissues: thus a predator will, at each meal, acquire whatever insecticide has already accumulated in the tissues of its prey. This can lead to very high insecticide concentrations in the tissues of the high-order predators. Even if the dosage is not toxic to any individual specimen of their prey, it may become toxic to the predator.

Birds of prey are generally slow-breeding and although they may kill a limited number of young sheep or goats, they are in general useful since they feed mostly upon rodents which are destructive to crops. For this reason, and also, in developed countries, because such birds are now relatively rare, considerable concern was felt when it was found that the number of young successfully raised by these birds started to fall sharply at about the time the use of DDT became common. There is evidence that DDT affects thyroid function and the calcium metabolism of these animals. Upset of calcium metabolism is expressed in an abnormal thinness of the shells of their eggs, so that many are smashed while the birds are incubating them: Fig. 21.11 shows the observed correlation. This conclusion has not gone unchallenged. Museum collections were used to provide data for shell thickness in earlier years, and it was argued that these were not truly representative samples since collectors would tend to select for preservation those eggs which had the thickest shells. Data showing falls in population density were claimed to be due, not to insecti-

Table 21.4 Effect of a single dieldrin application in late November 1969 on the relative abundance of different types of bird observed in line transects before and after treatment, as well as a year later. Data from an unsprayed control area are also shown. All data are expressed relative to abundance in November 1969 (*After Koeman* et al.)

Type of bird	Dieldrin-treated area				Control area	
	Nov. '69	Dec. '69	Nov. '70	Dec. '70	1969	1970
Herbivorous	100	130	103	143	100	148
Carnivorous	100	98	98	106	100	119
Insectivorous	100	55	26	41	100	148

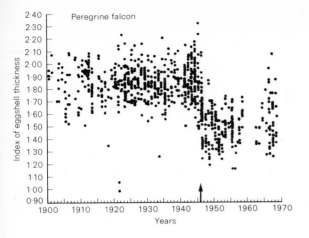

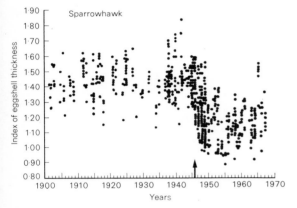

21.11 Eggshell thickness measurement of dated samples from two birds of prey in Britain. Note that in both cases characteristic thickness falls from about 1946 onwards when the persistent insecticides DDT and BHC first came into general use. Critical defenders of the use of persistent insecticides attribute these changes to some other unidentified cause. The recovery of eggshell thickness with the stopping of the use of dieldrin makes the 'other cause' explanation less readily acceptable. Alternative explanations cannot be completely excluded since, as with lung cancer and cigarette smoking, the data are limited to correlations.

cides, but to greater killing by farmers or to some other unidentified cause. As matters stood until recently such possibilities could not be excluded.

Fairly clear evidence that dieldrin has an adverse effect upon the reproduction of a bird of prey has now been obtained, as a consequence of the banning of its use in Britain. A decrease in population of the Golden Eagle had been observed in the West of Scotland where dieldrin was used as a sheep dip. The fall in population was associated with the characteristic eggshell thinning, but it might, however, have been due to an increase in the use of firearms by sheep farmers. In 1968 the use of dieldrin in sheep dips was prohibited by law and within four years the shells of the eagles' eggs returned to normal thickness and the birds began to breed successfully again. Of course, one could still argue that farmers used firearms less frequently in the period following the prohibition of the use of dieldrin, but this argument is now much less convincing.

Persistent insecticides have other effects upon the fauna. They influence the composition of the arthropod fauna of the soil (p. 304), and they may also reduce the population of earthworms, possibly checking rates of litter decomposition. It has further been suggested that they may, by action on the zooplankton, contribute to the process of eutrophication of freshwater, a phenomenon which we will next consider.

Eutrophication

Most of the water of a river is derived from rainwater which has passed through soil; most of the water of a lake usually comes from the rivers which supply it. While falling rain may normally contain some nitrogenous compounds, rainwater will subsequently leach from the soil further salts, including both phosphates and nitrates. In most lakes there is thus a gradual tendency for the concentrations of these ions to build up. Both are essential for the growth of planktonic algae and, as a result of their accumulation, the productive potential of a lake will increase: the lake becomes richer in nutrients, in algae, in primary consumers and in fish. Such a process of enrichment is spoken of as eutrophication. In natural conditions the change is likely to be slow and much of the nutrient material is incorporated in bottom deposits.

Any increase in the supply of nutrients is likely to increase the rate of eutrophication. If the number of villages along the banks of a river increases so that more waste material is added to the water, the flora and fauna of the river will become more productive; if the river runs into a lake, enrichment of the lake will take place more rapidly. If, in place of villages, towns are developing, the same process will occur as phosphate- and nitrate-rich water from sewage works is discharged into the rivers; the effect may be enhanced by extensive use of detergents which decompose with release of phosphate ion. If fertilizer is spread upon the land, some fraction will get carried into the waters of the drainage basin and further enhance the eutrophication. In developed countries, and especially in the United States, intensive feeding of stock produces large quantities of manure which is often disposed of without treatment, thus increasing the organic load and nutrient supplies in natural water systems.

In Africa there are many natural shallow lakes of high productivity; these are often described as 'eutrophic'. They yield an abundant supply of fish, as Lake Chilwa did in the past and promises to do again in the future (p. 112). In these lakes there appears to be a satisfactory balance between high concentrations of algae and high secondary productivity. This may be due to the fact that they are shallow and in some cases to the absence of marked seasonal phenomena, so that the nutrient balance within the lake ecosystem never departs markedly from an equilibrium value.

In deep temperate lakes there are marked seasonal changes and extreme eutrophication can lead to algal 'blooms' in which vast quantities of cells are produced. These presently die and, if washed ashore, produce an evil-smelling contamination. In temperate waters, productivity is low during the cold months of the winter (Fig. 21.12a). In early spring the surface waters become warm and form a distinct layer, the epilimnion, floating upon a cold water mass at about 4°C, the hypolimnion (Fig. 21.12b). The temperature gradient, the thermocline, between these two water masses is often very sharp and they do not mix. The phytoplankton in the surface water produces oxygen, but the water in the hypolimnion becomes depleted of oxygen. This condition is maintained throughout the summer, but as the surface waters cool in autumn and early winter, the whole water body is mixed and the hypolimnion is recharged with oxygen (Fig. 21.12c). Dead planktonic organisms and fish fall to the bottom and there decay, so that the bottom deposits are nutrient-rich. These nutrient salts are released into the hypolimnion during the summer when the oxygen concentration is low, so that when the autumnal mixing occurs, the surface waters are replenished with nutrients. These remain available to be exploited by the algae the following spring. Thus in the spring, there is typically a rapid growth of diatoms, followed later by green algae which, as the nutrients become depleted, are replaced by blue-green algae.

In lakes not subject to rapid enrichment, this seasonal cycle rarely results in excessive algal productivity. But in lakes fed by streams and sewers, where the waters are constantly being enriched with nitrates and phosphates, as well as with raw sewage, the surface waters will contain very high concentrations of nutrients at the time of the spring growth of diatoms. It is these conditions which result in dramatic algal blooms.

Such algal blooms are a source of considerable concern. Apart from the unpleasantness of their decay, they clog the filters of water-purification plants, they may produce unpleasant tastes in the water and some species of alga produce toxic materials which are lethal to fish. Since the industrialized countries are already faced with serious problems in providing adequate water for industrial purposes, this process of eutrophication has serious secondary consequences.

In Africa, eutrophication of lakes is not as yet a serious problem. The process of eutrophication may indeed have desirable results in leading to increased production of fish, although it may also lead to a fall in the yield of commercially valuable fish. Problems arising from the effects of eutrophication are not limited to lakes: experience in

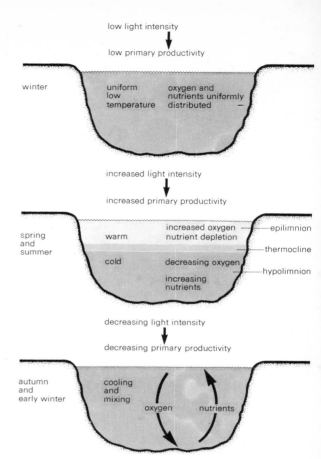

21.12 Diagrammatic summary of the annual cycle of changes in a temperate lake. Note that the nutrient supply in the epilimnion is normally the factor limiting the size of the population of algae. Once a thermocline is established, nutrient concentration tends to fall, both as a result of incorporation into organisms and of movement of dead organisms into the hypolimnion. Where there is nutrient-rich discharge from rivers, streams and sewers, this continues to supply the epilimnion throughout the spring and summer so that 'blooms' of algae may develop. At the same time, the resulting dead material leads to a far greater deoxygenation of the hypolimnion than would occur in the absence of a steady supply of nutrients.

rice growing in Bangladesh and elsewhere shows that the use of nutrient-enriched waters in irrigation systems can lead to serious difficulties when algal growths compete with crops for nutrients or block the flow of waters in irrigation canals. Like other natural resources, water must be exploited and managed with biological understanding, for the correct action to take will depend upon the local situation.

Military pollution

War is inevitably destructive, but until the present century its effects were limited. The development of high explosives and the use of massive artillery bombardments altered this situation. Intensive shelling of an area results in the formation of craters which may remain for more than fifty years, making difficult the use of farm machinery. During the war of 1939–45 the use of aircraft for intensive bombardment was developed. The selected targets were almost invariably cities, many of which were largely destroyed, partly as a direct result of high explosive and partly as a result of fire. The culmination of this type of warfare was the destruction of the Japanese cities of Hiroshima and Nagasaki by atomic bombs. Such bombardment had relatively little effect upon the environment, since the cities could be and were rebuilt.

The wars of south-east Asia have been of a different character. When the United States decided to provide military aid to the Government of South Vietnam, they were faced with the problem of dealing with an enemy whose main tactics consisted in ambush and the occupation and administration of rural areas. There was no 'front line' and no traditional military targets. One requirement was to deny the enemy cover from which he could mount ambushes, and another was to deny him food: the enemy was thus to be defeated by the destruction of the environment in the areas he held. To achieve this end, three methods were adopted: spraying from helicopters of defoliants to destroy tree cover together with the use of bulldozers to clear all vegetation from certain areas, the use of herbicides to destroy crops, and the use of concentrated high-altitude bombing of districts in which enemy forces might be present.

These operations were conducted on a vast scale. By the end of 1971 the U.S. Air Force had dropped twice the weight of high explosive it had used in the war of 1939–45. Spread over the whole area of South Vietnam, this would result on the average in only two bomb craters per hectare. The bombing was, however, concentrated in certain areas, so that a raid resulted in a dense pattern of craters, sometimes with an average separation of as little as 100 m. Such intensive bombardment can lead to rapid soil erosion, followed by the formation, in the type of soil found in Vietnam, of a hard, uncultivable surface. The bomb craters themselves became water-filled, providing breeding grounds for mosquitoes, while in many places irrigation systems required for rice cultivation were destroyed. Bombing of agricultural land and forest results not only in the formation of craters, but also in the spraying of the area with jagged pieces of iron. These may strike the trunks of trees, wounding them so that they become liable to fungal attack; moreover, such timber becomes difficult to exploit commercially as the fragments of metal break the teeth of saws. On agricultural land, the feet of draught-animals get cut by the bomb fragments and the wounds may prove fatal to the beasts. The use of defoliants and herbicides has less dramatic effects; but, like bombing, it exposes the soil to erosive action and kills or reduces the yield of trees like rubber, which is a major export of South Vietnam.

The consequences of this destruction can be accurately assessed only in the future. In deforested areas, a new savanna-type climax has been rapidly established but large areas of mangrove swamp, once important fishing grounds, show no signs of recovery. Since, moreover, one of the herbicides used is very persistent, large areas may remain denuded of plant cover for many years.

This type of military action can be regarded as concentrated and calculated pollution. But it represents merely an extreme case of what is occurring over the surface of the whole globe as a result of increasing industrialization and the increasing numbers of human beings. It is possible for industry to develop without having serious effects upon the ecosystem, but this requires foresight. The view is expressed that the developing countries cannot afford to worry about pollution, that they have little to gain from conservation and that the present problems of poverty and malnutrition are so great that the future consequences of actions taken today should not determine policy. To avoid pollution and to conserve the environment need not prevent development, but it may make certain types of development less rapid or more costly. While the task of the scientist is to inform society of the potential consequences of any course of action, the final decision as to which path to follow in this case, as in others, is a social issue, not a scientific one.

Problems

1 If over-exploited fish stocks are left undisturbed for a few years, they are likely to recover. This is not true of the stocks of whales. Why is there this difference?

2 The caption to Fig. 21.4 states that the fall in fish landings per unit effort between 1911 and 1914 may have been due to over-fishing. What alternative explanation might be put forward? Does the graph offer any support for the alternative interpretation?

3 Show how the fact that women did not become cigarette smokers to any significant extent before 1920 explains the differences between the curves shown in Fig. 21.7 for the incidence of lung cancer in men and women.

4. In a normal temperate lake there is an annual succession of algae starting with diatoms and ending with blue-greens. What characteristics of blue-greens make it possible for them to be especially abundant in the final phytoplankton community?

5 Make drawings to show how you would expect oxygen concentration and temperature to change with depth in the conditions illustrated in Figs. 21.12a, b and c.

6 In a certain area small farms were scattered among large areas of cotton plantation. Dieldrin was used extensively to control insect pests of the cotton; the introduction of these measures resulted in insect pests

becoming more abundant on the farmers' crops. Suggest a possible explanation for this event.

7 Eutrophication of natural waters is regarded in most developed countries as undesirable. Nevertheless schemes have been considered for deliberately adding fertilizer to certain African lakes. Explain this apparent contradiction.

8 You are Chief Scientific Adviser to your national government. Three new products requiring licence for import are (a) a herbicide, (b) a novel non-alcoholic drink and (c) an insecticide with highly specific action against the major pest of your country's most important food crop. There is reason to believe that the herbicide may have secondary and undesirable environmental effects, while the other two products may have slight carcinogenic activity. In all three cases, however, the evidence is open to alternative interpretations. What considerations would be involved in making recommendations to your government as to whether or not they should licence the import of each product?

9 One way in which man modifies his environment is by creating large artificial lakes. When these are formed, there may be very extensive growth of water-weed over their surfaces. What biological and economic disadvantages are likely to result from such an event? Are such weeds of any value at all?

Bibliography

Further reading

Mellanby, K.   *The Biology of Pollution*, Arnold, 1973

Stamp, L. D.   *Our Developing World*, Faber and Faber, 1968

Bormann, F. H., Likens, G. E.   'The Nutrient Cycles of an Ecosystem', *Scientific American*, 1970, Offprint no. 1202

Edwards, C. A.   'Soil Pollutants and Soil Animals', *Scientific American*, 1969, Offprint no. 1138

Hammond, E. C.   'The Effects of Smoking', *Scientific American*, 1962, Offprint no. 126

McVay, S.   'The Last of the Great Whales', *Scientific American*, 1966, Offprint no. 1046

Peakall, D. B.   'Pesticides and the Reproduction of Birds', *Scientific American*, 1970, Offprint no. 1174

Richards, P. W.   'The Tropical Rain Forest', *Scientific American*, 1973, Offprint no. 1286

Westing, A. H., Pfeiffer, E. W.   'The Cratering of Indochina', *Scientific American*, 1972, Offprint no. 1248

Woodwell, G. M.   'Toxic Substances and Ecological Cycles', *Scientific American*, 1967, Offprint no. 1066

Part 6
The origin of diversity—genetics and evolution

22 Variation and patterns of inheritance

When you look at the other members of your class, you have no difficulty in recognizing them as individuals. Each is different from the others in some details which allow you to tell them apart. Although they are all human beings, all members of the species *Homo sapiens*, they are nevertheless distinct. This phenomenon we describe by saying that there is variation between different individuals of the same species.

The variation between one human being and another may be relatively slight, involving differences in height, in the size of the head, the distance between the eyes, the size of the mouth and so on. But there are also much more striking differences, such as that between the dark skin of an African and the pale skin of a European, between the curly hair of an African and the long, straight hair of an Indian. Nor is this phenomenon of variation peculiar to man. A herdsman can usually tell one of his cows from another, even if they are all of the same breed. Further, just as there are marked differences between men of different races, so too there are very obvious differences between cattle of different breeds (Figs. 17.2 and 18.15); nevertheless they are all cattle.

This variation between individuals can also be easily recognized in the details of colour patterns of many invertebrate animals. If you collect several specimens of the giant snail, *Achatina*, you will find that there are obvious differences in the details of the brown markings on the shell between one individual and another. The same is true of the shapes and numbers of spots on the wings of individual butterflies of the same species, or of the patterns on the elytra of a beetle. Variation between individuals is found in all species, whether of plants or animals, although it may require experience or careful measurement to allow the differences to be recognized.

How does this variation come about? Clearly some of it arises during the lifetime of any individual. His skin may be cut, leaving a permanent scar, he may have lost a finger in an accident or he may have been ill when young so that his growth was stunted. But there is clearly more to it than this. The children of an African couple will have dark skins, those of a European pale skins. If a Fulani bull is mated with a Fulani cow, their calves are like their parents and very different from the calves of an n'dama bull and cow. Clearly some of the characteristics which distinguish individuals must be transmitted from parent to offspring,

that is to say, they are inherited. So we may ask: what types of variation can be inherited? What is the mechanism by which particular characteristics are transmitted from generation to generation?

Types of variation

If you examine a collection of cowpeas, *Vigna unguiculata*, you will notice that the flowers are either purple or white. If you examine very young plants you will find that some have red spots at the nodes, while others are uniformly green. These are examples of variation in which we can assign the individual specimens into one class or another: into the class of white flowers or of purple flowers, the class of red spot or no red spot.

Such a type of variation in which there are distinct categories is in no way peculiar to *Vigna*. Open your mouth slightly and stick out your tongue, and then try to shape it like a U (Fig. 22.1). Perhaps you can or maybe you can't. If the other members of your class try to do this,

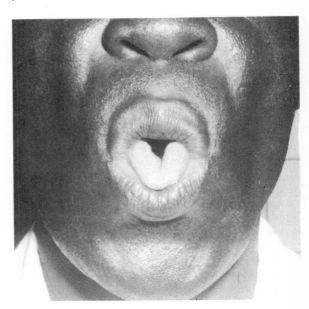

22.1 Tongue rolling. Not everyone is able to bend their tongue in this fashion. It is an example of discontinuous variation in man.

you will find that some can and others cannot, but there are no obvious intermediate gradations. Similarly, in the laboratory, you can test your ability to taste the bitter chemical phenylthiocarbamide in dilute solution. Some members of the class will be able to detect it in very low concentrations while others will find they can taste it only when the concentration is very high; again, there are no obvious intermediate gradations.

Discontinuous variations: blood groups

Variations of this sort, in which there are clearly defined contrasting characteristics, are described as 'discontinuous variations'. Sometimes it is possible to recognize more than two such contrasting characteristics. A very important example of this in man relates to what are called 'blood types'. If samples of blood are drawn from two individuals and the two samples are mixed, a rapid clumping or agglutination of the red corpuscles may or may not occur. Consider now two individuals, P and Q, whose bloods show this clumping reaction when mixed. If blood serum, the fluid which remains when blood has clotted, is prepared from the blood of, say P, and added to a drop of the whole blood of Q, then the clumping reaction may still be obtained. This response is attributed to the fact that the serum of the one individual contains 'anti-bodies' which react with substances called antigens on the red cells of the other individual who has a different type of blood (Book 1 p. 117).

Clearly this reaction between bloods is of great practical importance since, in a blood transfusion, one does not want to mix bloods that react together in this manner. The phenomenon was investigated about 1900 by an Austrian biologist, Karl Landsteiner. By examination of the reactions between the bloods of a large number of individuals, he was able to distinguish four distinct types of blood. Again, the variation is discontinuous, but in this case with more than a single pair of possible characteristics.

Landsteiner concluded that there are two distinct blood-cell antigens, which he called A and B. An individual's red cells may carry one or the other, or both, or neither. So we can describe a person as being respectively of blood group A or B or AB or, if he has neither antigen, of blood group O. Landsteiner further found that people with antigen A on their red cells invariably had anti-B antibody in their serum, that those of blood group B had anti-A antibody in the serum, while those of group O had both serum antibodies. Those of group AB had neither (Table 22.1): people of group AB obviously must lack both types of antibody, otherwise their own blood would agglutinate.

Let us look at the practical implications of these findings. If a patient is admitted to hospital for an operation, one thing which is done is to determine his blood group. The hospital has available samples of serum containing anti-A antibody and others containing anti-B antibody. By

Table 22.1 Red cell antigens and serum antibodies present in individuals of different blood groups

Blood group	Antigen on red cells	Antibody in serum
A	A	anti-B
B	B	anti-A
AB	A and B	none
O	None	anti-A and anti-B

mixing a drop of the patient's blood with a small quantity of each serum, his blood group can be quickly ascertained (Table 22.2). Assume that the patient is blood group O and requires a transfusion. If he is supplied with blood of any of the other groups, the antibodies in his serum will agglutinate the foreign corpuscles with serious consequences. Suppose the patient is group AB and we transfused blood of group O: the donor cells would not be agglutinated as they carry no antigen. We might expect a reaction between the antibodies in the donor serum and the red cells of the recipient, but in practice the donor serum is so rapidly diluted by the blood of the recipient that this is of little consequence. It could, of course, be completely avoided by suspending type O red cells in type AB serum: this is occasionally done, but is normally unnecessary. Table 22.3 sets out the possible transfusions which can be made and indicates which are safe. Type O blood can be accepted by a person of any blood group, and people of blood group O are therefore sometimes spoken of as 'universal donors'.

Table 22.2 Reactions of different types of blood with serum antibodies

Blood group of patient	Reaction with	
	anti-A antibody serum	anti-B antibody serum
A	Agglutination	No agglutination
B	No agglutination	Agglutination
AB	Agglutination	Agglutination
O	No agglutination	No agglutination

Table 22.3 Safe and unacceptable transfusions between individuals of different blood groups: + safe transfusion; − dangerous transfusion

Blood group of donor	Blood group of recipient			
	O	A	B	AB
O	+	+	+	+
A	−	+	−	+
B	−	−	+	+
AB	−	−	−	+

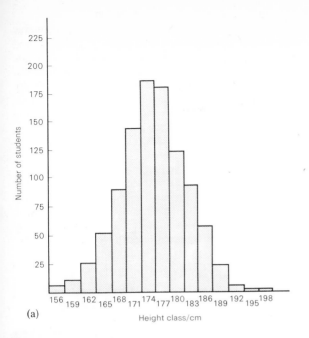

(a)

22.2 (a) Histogram showing the distribution of height among 1000 university students. The central value of each height class is indicated on the abscissa. Thus 156 implies a height class of 155–157 cm, 159 a class of 158–160 cm, and so on. (b) Histogram showing the distribution in weight of 2338 bean seeds grown in uniform conditions. The central value of each class is indicated on the abscissa. The weights of the original parent seeds all lay within the range 350–450 mg. Note that the spread of weight in the progeny is from a class of central value 100 mg to one of 800 mg.

(b)

Continuous variations

If you look round the class, it is immediately obvious that some characteristics like height are not discontinuous. A class is not clearly divisible into short students and tall ones. If you plotted the frequency of heights of a large number of adults, you would get a result something like Fig. 22.2a. It is possible that this is because different individuals have experienced different circumstances of nutrition, of health and so on; perhaps if everyone had been treated identically, then distinct size classes would appear. We cannot investigate the problem in this way with men, but we can do so with plants which can be grown from seeds in very uniform conditions. We find that the height of many different types of plants grown in uniform conditions shows a similar continuous range of sizes and that this is true also for other characteristics that we can measure, like the sizes or weights of seeds (Fig. 22.2b) or the number of seeds produced by each plant.

Variation of this sort is described as continuous variation. It is not restricted to characters like size or weight which are easily measured; for example human skin

colour shows continuous variation of pigmentation in both Africans and Europeans, although the average darkness of their skins is very different.

Inheritance and the gametes

We have described some aspects of the phenomenon of variation. We can now turn to our second question, namely the way in which characteristics are transmitted from one generation to another; how does an offspring inherit certain characteristics from its parents? In answering this question, we will also learn more about the causes of the variation we observe.

Living organisms arise from similar living things. They do not arise spontaneously; the start of a new organism usually involves the process of fertilization in which a nucleus from a pollen grain or a spermatozoon of an animal fuses with an ovum to form a zygote. Those characters which are inherited must be passed from parent to offspring through the process of fertilization. Sperm and ova are both single-celled gametes which do not of course display any of the characteristics of the developed organ-

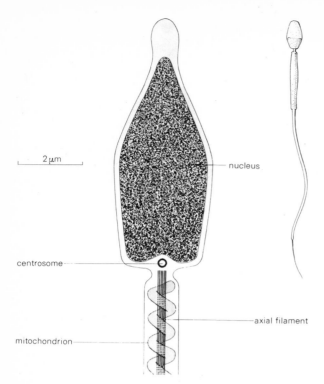

served in the meristematic tissue of a root tip. If the tissue is placed on a slide, flooded with a suitable stain, covered and then gently squashed, the cells spread out and can be studied. From an examination of a large number of cells, it is possible to reconstruct the sequence of events. More direct observations of the processes of cell division can be made on animal cells growing in tissue culture where the sequence of events can be seen and timed.

Mitosis

At the onset of division fine thread-like structures appear within the nuclear envelope. These can be stained with basic dyes and for this reason are called chromosomes (from the Greek words meaning 'colour' and 'body'); they are, of course, not coloured in the living cell. Later the chromosomes shorten and we find that they have slightly

22.3 A spermatozoon at right: it is formed of a head, a swollen middle piece and a thin tail. At left, detail of the structure of the head and middle piece. Only the axial filament extends into the tail.

ism, but the material from which the inherited characters arise must be present in the gametes. Any gamete consists of a plasma membrane, cytoplasm and a nucleus. In an egg, the bulk of the cell is formed of cytoplasm but apart from the tail there is little cytoplasm in a spermatozoon (Fig. 22.3), and in many species the tail is discarded at fertilization, only the head containing the nucleus penetrating the cytoplasm of the egg. It seems then reasonable to assume that it is something in the nucleus of the spermatozoon which carries the material which results in the appearance of paternal characteristics in an offspring. Since characteristics are usually transmitted equally from male or female parent, the same would apply to the nucleus of an ovum.

Cell division

Since an organism arises from repeated cell division, the study of this process may throw some light upon the manner in which 'instructions' concerning inherited characteristics are distributed in growing organisms. In a dividing cell, the nucleus divides first; subsequently the whole cell divides, so that each daughter nucleus comes to be associated with some of the cytoplasm of the parent cell. Both daughter cells grow and then the processes of division may be repeated. Such events may be easily ob-

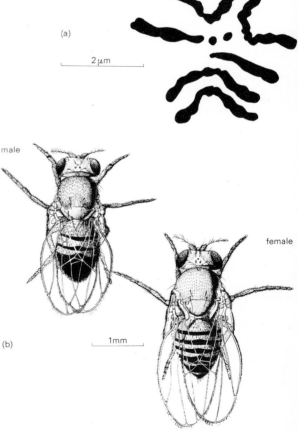

22.4 (a) Drawing of the shapes of the eight chromosomes of a female *Drosophila melanogaster* as seen in the metaphase of mitotic division of a brain cell. (b) Adult male and female *D. melanogaster*. Note the dark tip to the abdomen of the male; this is one characteristic used to distinguish the sexes.

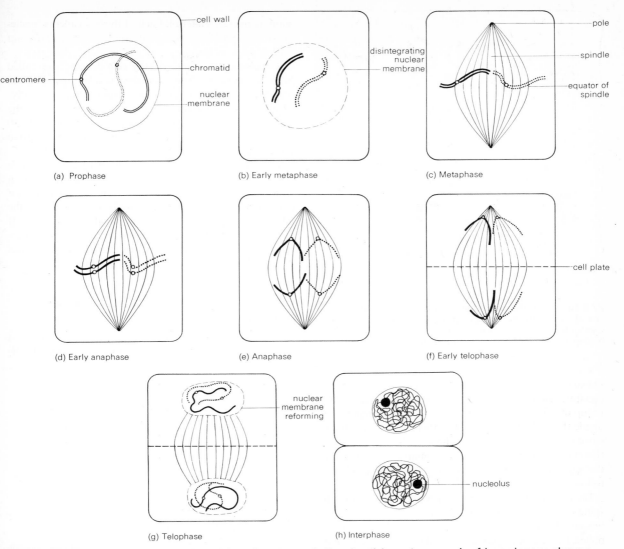

(a) Prophase

(b) Early metaphase

(c) Metaphase

(d) Early anaphase

(e) Anaphase

(f) Early telophase

(g) Telophase

(h) Interphase

22.5 Stages in the process of mitotic division of a plant cell. For simplicity only one pair of homologous chromosomes is shown.

different but characteristic shapes. Fig. 22.4a shows a drawing of the chromosomes of the female of the tiny fly *Drosophila* (Diptera) (Fig. 22.4b). You will notice that in a cell of this animal there are only 8 chromosomes, and further that, judging by their different shapes, there are two of each kind. The cells of many organisms have more chromosomes than those of *Drosophila*: there are 46 in man, 20 in maize but about 80 in a hen. In all species, the chromosomes are normally present as pairs, called homologous pairs.

As the division proceeds, the chromosomes become shorter and each can be seen to consist of two threads, each thread being called a chromatid (Fig. 22.5a). The two chromatids of a chromosome are held together by a structure called a centromere, which does not stain. The shortening of the chromatids continues and then the

nuclear membrane breaks down (Fig. 22.5b). This event is used to mark the end of the first stage of the process of nuclear division, the prophase, and the start of the next stage, the metaphase.

During prophase in an animal cell, two small structures called centrioles which lie together just outside the nuclear membrane start to separate, moving towards opposite ends of the cell. From each centriole there arise in the cytoplasm radiating filaments which form an 'aster' around each centriole, while in the region between the two centrioles the filaments form a 'spindle' which extends as the centrioles move apart (Fig. 22.6). There are no centrioles in the cells of the higher plants, and the spindle appears along the length of the cell shortly after the breakdown of the nuclear membrane (Fig. 22.5c).

The central region of the spindle is called its equator.

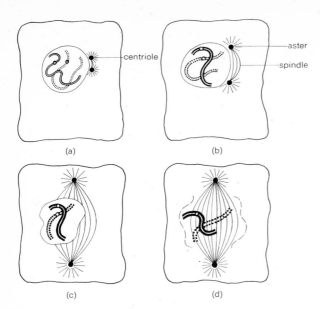

22.6 Stages in the prophase of mitosis of an animal cell showing the formation of a spindle and asters. Centrioles and asters do not occur in dividing cells of higher plants, nor are they found in all animal cells.

During metaphase the chromosomes move to this equator, each centromere becoming associated with a group of spindle fibres (Fig. 22.5c). The centromeres then divide (Fig. 22.5d), so that where there was originally one chromosome formed of two chromatids, there are now two chromosomes, each of one chromatid. The division of the centromeres is taken as the end of metaphase, which is followed by anaphase.

During anaphase the centromeres move apart along the spindle fibres with the arms of the chromatids trailing behind: the shape suggests that the centromeres are being pulled towards the poles of the cell (Fig. 22.5e). Usually towards the end of anaphase cytoplasmic division starts, in animal cells by a constriction of the plasma membrane at about the level of the spindle equator and in plant cells by the development of a cell plate. The end of the movements of the centromeres to the two poles of the dividing cell marks the end of anaphase which is followed by the final stage, the telophase (Figs. 22.5f and 22.5g).

During telophase the nuclear membranes start to re-form around each group of chromosomes; the chromosome threads elongate once more and presently can no longer be seen. In an animal cell, each centriole reduplicates itself, so that once again there is a pair in each cell. The cell has entered interphase. At the end of interphase, when the chromosomes reappear at the beginning of the next prophase, each consists once again of two chromatids: some process of reduplication of chromosome material occurs during the interphase. During interphase, examination of stained nuclei shows one or more concentrations of densely staining nuclear material. Each of these is called a 'nucleolus'. At prophase the nucleoli disappear, to reappear again during the telophase.

These nuclear events during cell division are called 'mitosis'; what we have described is a mitotic division. The relative times of the four stages differ markedly; prophase is the longest, taking about 55 percent of the total time; metaphase is the shortest and lasts only 10 percent of the time, while anaphase is slightly shorter than telophase.

From the viewpoint of our study of heredity, there is one essential point to note. A mitotic division is one in which each daughter cell receives one of each type of chromosome. The events are highly organized and the allocating of chromosomes to the daughter cells exact. If we assume that the two chromatids formed during interphase are identical, then it follows that the chromosomes of the two daughter nuclei are also the same.

Gamete formation and associated nuclear events

The events of nuclear division leading to the formation of gametes are different. In gamete formation in animals, the

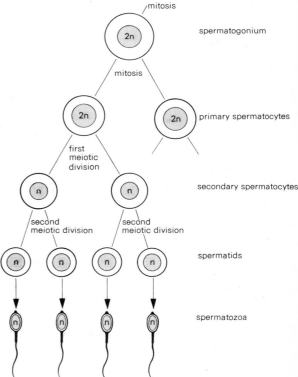

22.7 Diagrammatic summary of the stages leading to the formation of spermatozoa in a mammal. The number of chromosomes within each nucleus is indicated; note that the number is halved as a result of the first meiotic division.

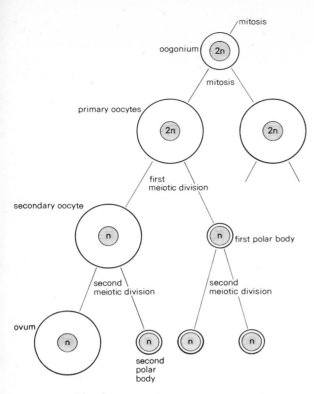

22.8 Diagrammatic summary of the stages leading to the formation of an ovum in a mammal.

The egg cell shed from the ovary of a female mammal is not a mature ovum, but a secondary oocyte. The first meiotic division occurs shortly before ovulation and the second meiotic division follows. This division does not, however, go beyond its metaphase and it is in this condition that the egg cell is liberated from the ovary. Only if fertilization occurs will the secondary meiotic division be completed and a mature ovum formed. Each oocyte shed is carried down the oviduct whose narrow initial section is called the Fallopian tube. It is here that fertilization normally occurs. Each oocyte is surrounded by a layer of cells derived from ovarian tissue and called the corona radiata: the spermatozoa must penetrate this layer of cells to reach the oocyte.

The events of meiotic division

How do the meiotic divisions differ from a mitotic division? At the start of the first meiotic prophase each chromosome has only a single chromatid thread (Fig. 22.9a). The chromosomes move around inside the nucleus until

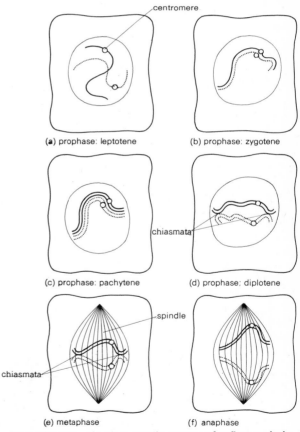

(a) prophase: leptotene
(b) prophase: zygotene
(c) prophase: pachytene
(d) prophase: diplotene
(e) metaphase
(f) anaphase

22.9 Diagram showing certain stages of a first meiotic division. For simplicity only one pair of homologous chromosomes is shown and details of changes in chromosome length have been omitted. There are several distinct stages in the prophase.

major events in the two sexes are also distinct. In a male mammal, adjacent to the walls of the tubules in the testes are large cells called spermatogonia. These cells divide mitotically and from their divisions there arises a different type of cell, which is called a primary spermatocyte. Each primary spermatocyte also divides, but the process of nuclear division differs from mitosis and is called a first meiotic division. The daughter cells of the primary spermatocytes are called secondary spermatocytes; they divide again to form spermatids which presently develop directly into spermatozoa (Fig. 22.7). The nuclear division of the secondary spermatocyte is broadly similar to a mitotic division, but nevertheless differs in detail and is called a secondary meiotic division. Note that each primary spermatocyte has given rise to four spermatozoa.

The events leading to the formation of an ovum (Fig. 22.8) are similar, but differ in detail. Corresponding to the spermatogonia are cells called oogonia. These give rise, by normal mitosis, to primary oocytes. There follows a first meiotic division, but the cytoplasmic division is unequal. One daughter cell, the first polar body, has almost no cytoplasm; the other, the secondary oocyte, has a great deal. The secondary oocyte now undergoes the second meiotic division; cytoplasmic division is again unequal so that a second polar body is formed as well as a large ovum. The polar bodies finally degenerate.

homologous chromosomes (p. 389) come to lie exactly side by side (Fig. 22.9b). Each chromatid thread then divides, so that there are four strands lying together (Fig. 22.9c). The centromeres of the homologous chromosomes next start to move apart, but the strands are not easily separated as one of the chromatid threads of one chromosome is attached to one of the chromatid threads of the other at one or more points called chiasmata (Fig. 22.9d). At this stage the nuclear membrane breaks down and prophase ends. The centromeres come to lie on the spindle, arranging themselves so that those of homologous chromosomes lie on opposite sides of the spindle equator; then, with the onset of anaphase, they start to move apart. The attachments between the threads at the chiasmata are released and the chromosomes are carried to the two poles of the cell (Fig. 22.9f).

If you follow the behaviour of the centromeres, you can readily see what has happened. Early in prophase, the centromeres of homologous chromosomes come to lie side by side and then later come to lie on either side of the spindle equator. Thus one centromere goes to one daughter cell and the other homologous centromere to the other daughter cell. Each daughter cell has received only one half of the centromeres present in the original cell. Further-

more, each has received one representative from each homologous pair of chromosomes. If there were $2n$ centromeres and thus $2n$ chromosomes in the original cell, there will be n in each daughter cell, although each of these chromosomes has two chromatid threads. $2n$ is called the diploid or zygotic number of chromosomes characteristic of the species being considered, while n is the haploid or gametic number.

At telophase in the first meiotic division the nuclear membrane may not reform and the chromosomes do not disappear. Cytoplasmic division takes place, and by the time the two daughter cells have separated, both are already in the prophase of the second meiotic division. Each chromosome has two chromatid threads, just as when they first appear in the prophase of a mitotic division. Metaphase follows and, as in mitosis, the centromeres alone divide, so that during the anaphase each chromosome has only one chromatid thread. Thus, just as in mitosis, each cell receives a complete set of chromosomes, but in this case only one of each kind: the haploid number of chromosomes is retained by each daughter cell formed in the telophase of the second meiotic division.

In this way each spermatozoon and each ovum is haploid and each contains one chromosome from each of the pairs present in the original spermatogonial or oogonial cells. At fertilization the nuclei of sperm and ovum fuse. The product of this fusion, called a zygote, contains once more the diploid number of chromosomes, one member of each homologous pair having come from the male parent and one from the female parent. As a result, the diploid number remains the same from generation to generation.

Gametogenesis in angiosperms

In a flowering plant, although the events of gametogenesis are different from those found in animals, the outcome is similar. The plant itself is a sporophyte and its cells are diploid. Within the microsporangium of the anthers, meristematic cells form microspore mother cells or microsporocytes; each of these undergoes two meiotic divisions to form four haploid microspores. Each microspore matures to form a pollen grain. A mitotic division then gives rise to one nucleus which forms the pollen-tube nucleus and a second, the generative nucleus, which divides again by mitosis to form two male gametes. In this fashion the three cells of the male gametophyte are formed (Fig. 22.10). One of the male gametes will fertilize the ovum, the other the polar nucleus which gives rise to the endosperm. Thus, in terms of transfer of nuclear material from one sporophyte generation to the next, each pollen grain contributes one haploid nucleus, so that in the process of fertilization, each pollen grain is functionally equivalent to an animal spermatozoon.

In a megasporangium the events are comparable. A diploid mother cell gives rise, as a result of two meiotic divisions, to four haploid megaspores. One of these en-

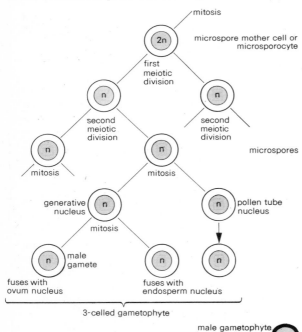

22.10 The pattern of nuclear divisions leading to the formation of a male gametophyte in a flowering plant. Note that there are no cell membranes separating the nuclei within the gametophyte.

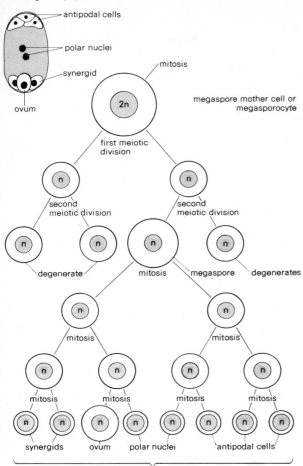

Female gametophyte

antipodal cells

polar nuclei

synergid

ovum

mitosis

megaspore mother cell or megasporocyte

2n

first meiotic division

n

n

second meiotic division

second meiotic division

n

n

n

n

degenerate

mitosis

megaspore

degenerates

n

n

mitosis

mitosis

n

n

n

n

mitosis

mitosis

mitosis

mitosis

n

n

n

n

n

n

n

n

synergids

ovum

polar nuclei

antipodal cells

8-celled gametophyte

22.11 The pattern of nuclear divisions leading to the formation of the female gametophyte in a flowering plant. The two polar nuclei share a common cytoplasm. They will fuse with one of the male gamete nuclei to form the triploid nucleus of the endosperm. The synergids and antipodal cells degenerate.

larges at the expense of the other three, in a manner recalling the formation of polar bodies in an animal. The resulting single, haploid megaspore then undergoes three mitotic divisions to form the eight cells of the female gametophyte (Fig. 22.11), only one of which differentiates into an ovum. At fertilization the fusion of the haploid nucleus from a pollen grain with the haploid nucleus of the ovum restores the diploid number of chromosomes which is characteristic of the sporophyte generation.

An hypothesis of heredity

With this information we may, as did the Austrian biologist August Weismann, suggest a provisional hypothesis

about the mechanism of inheritance. Weismann postulated that there was associated with the chromosomes some type of hereditary information and that the significance of a meiotic division was that it ensured that equal quantities of hereditary instructions were transmitted to the offspring from each parent. If we make this assumption, we may expect to find that the actual patterns of inheritance will reflect the behaviour of the chromosomes. Weismann lacked information upon these patterns and his theory therefore remained a speculation. At the beginning of this century, breeding experiments made the patterns clear; similar experiments had been carried out as early as 1865 by an Austrian monk, Gregor Mendel, but the significance of his findings had not then been appreciated. An American zoologist, W. S. Sutton, was led by his studies of meiosis in grasshoppers to a synthesis of the data from breeding experiments with the type of idea outlined by Weismann. It is thus necessary to see what is the nature of the patterns of inheritance.

Inheritance of discontinuous variations

We have already seen that inheritance is concerned with the characteristics of individuals, and that there may be either continuous or discontinuous variations of characteristics. Discontinuous variations in, which there are clear, contrasting characters are the easier to observe and we will therefore start with a study of two of these.

There is a garden flower called the four o'clock plant (*Mirabilis*, Book 1 Fig. 3.8). Seeds can be obtained which develop into plants with white flowers; other seeds will produce red-flowered plants. All the flowers of a plant grown from a single seed, however, are of the same colour. If we pollinate a white-flowered plant with pollen from another plant with white flowers, the seeds will develop into white-flowered plants and this process can be continued indefinitely. A corresponding result will be obtained with the red-flowered plants. This condition we describe by saying that, as far as flower colour is concerned, we have two true-breeding or pure lines or stocks.

If we pollinate a red flower with pollen from a white flower, the flowers of the next generation, which we will call the first filial or F_1 generation, are pink. If we do the experiment the other way round, that is using pollen from a red flower, the result is the same. Note that we have made two 'crosses' which we might write as W♂ × R♀ and R♂ × W♀. Such a pair of crosses is said to be 'reciprocal'.

We can explain such a result by assuming that the F_1 flowers have received hereditary information or instructions from both parents. What then happens if we fertilize one of the pink F_1 flowers with pollen taken from another F_1 flower to produce an F_2 generation? (This type of cross, between two members of the same generation, is spoken of as 'selfing'; it is possible to self F_2 generation individuals and so on.)

The observed result is that plants of the F_2 generation

carry flowers of three different colours: some plants have white flowers, some have pink and some have red. If we make a large number of crosses of this sort, we find that there are approximately equal numbers of red- and white-flowered plants, but twice as many plants bear pink flowers as red flowers. The different flower colours thus occur in the ratio of 1 white:2 pink:1 red. Note that this ratio becomes clear only if we make sufficient crosses to obtain a large number of plants.

Can we explain this result in terms of what we know about the behaviour of chromosomes? We have seen that at fertilization, one set of chromosomes is contributed to the zygote by each parent. Let us assume that on one particular chromosome in the nucleus of each cell of the red flowers there is some hereditary unit which we will call a 'gene', which 'causes' the production of red pigment. Each ovum will contain one such gene, but each mother cell will have contained two such genes, one on each of the two homologous chromosomes. The same reasoning applies to the white flowers: each gamete will contain a gene whose effect is that the flower is white, and each mother cell will have contained two such genes. Representing the 'white' gene by W and the 'red' gene by R, we can express this in symbolic form as follows:

	White flower	Red flower
Genes in mother cells (P_1)	W and W	R and R
Genes in gametes	All have W	All have R
Genes in zygote (F_1)		R and W

All the zygotes will be identical since, as far as these genes are concerned, all the gametes from each parent are identical. This conclusion agrees with our observation that all the F_1 flowers are pink.

What happens in gamete formation in an F_1 individual? In the first meiotic division in spore formation, the two chromosomes will separate, so that one cell will contain the R-bearing and the other the W-bearing chromosome. From the second meiotic division will come two cells each carrying R and two cells each carrying W. In the microsporangium, each of these cells will develop into a microspore and after two further mitotic divisions give rise to male gametes within the pollen grain. Each gamete will contain the same type of gene as the microspore from which it is derived and, as a result of the meiotic divisions, equal numbers of R-bearing and W-bearing microspores will have been formed (Fig. 22.12a). In each ovule, only one of the four cells formed by meiosis will develop into a megaspore, but which of the four cells develops is apparently a matter of chance; thus any one megaspore is as likely to contain the R gene as the W gene. Whichever gene is in the megaspore will be found also in the ovum.

As a result of these processes we have two types of male gamete, present in equal numbers, and two types of ovum, again in equal numbers. What will happen at fertilization? We can demonstrate this most easily by making a diagram (Fig. 22.12b) which shows the gametes and the resulting possible zygotes formed at fertilization.

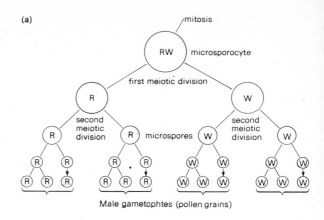

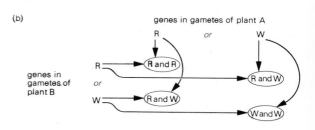

22.12 (a) The pattern of nuclear divisions and chromosome distribution in the formation of pollen grains from a microsporocyte which contains two homologous chromosomes, each carrying a different gene represented by R and W. Note that of the pollen grains formed, there are equal numbers containing each gene. (b) Diagram showing the gene compositions or genotypes of the possible types of zygotes, ringed, which could be produced in a cross between F_1 flowers. Note that each of these four types of zygote will be expected to occur with equal frequency in a large sample.

If you look at this diagram you will see that we have omitted a number of things which might at first sight seem important. Firstly, we have not indicated from which plant came the pollen. Since, however, the types of gamete and their relative proportions are the same for the two plants, A and B are fully interchangeable. Secondly, we have represented only the two types of gamete produced by each plant. This is because two is sufficient to indicate the proportions in which the two types would occur if we had a very large sample. Since the experimental result we are trying to explain relates to the proportions of different types of flowers in a large sample, this simplification is reasonable. You can see that if we took only, say, four ovules, then we might by chance have three R-containing ovules and only one W-containing one. The bigger the sample, the closer the ratio of R to W will come to unity.

We can simplify this diagram further, and simply write:

	Genes in gametes of A	
	R	W
R	RR	WR
W	RW	WW

Genes in gametes of B (left side, R and W rows)

Expected proportion of zygotes will be

$$RR:RW:WW = 1:2:1.$$

When we express it in this way, each zygote is formed from the fusion of the gamete shown at the top of each column with that shown at the left-hand end of the row. Of course there is no difference between RW and WR, since both are simply shorthand for R and W. We have also put in the bottom line a list of the expected zygotes and their relative proportions.

You will see that this table implies that, of the plants arising from these zygotes, we can expect about 25 percent to have two R-bearing chromosomes and to resemble the original red-flowered parent, 25 percent to have two W-bearing chromosomes and to resemble the original white-flowered parent, and 50 percent to have one R-bearing and one W-bearing chromosome, these plants resembling the pink-flowered F_1 parents. Our hypothesis is thus in keeping with our observations.

Not all crosses of parents with two such contrasting characters result in the F_1 progeny's being intermediate in appearance between the two parents; commonly the progeny resemble one parent only. Pea plants are of interest as they formed the material of the experiments of this sort made by Mendel: he observed whether the pea seeds were smooth or had a wrinkled surface, whether their cotyledons were green or yellow, whether the flowers of the plants were white or purple, and whether their stems were long or short. In his F_1, he found that the seeds were all round, their cotyledons all yellow, and in the plants the flowers all purple and the stems all long.

When he selfed the various F_1 plants, he obtained the following results:

itself if Sm is present. To express this idea we say that the action of the gene Sm is 'dominant' over that of Wr, or, more briefly, that Sm is dominant to Wr which is 'recessive'. Thus we may have a plant whose genetic make-up or genotype is SmWr, but whose appearance or phenotype is that of smooth seeds.

So we have the following situation:

Parental phenotypes	Smooth-seeded plant	Wrinkled-seeded plant
Genotypes of mother cells (P_1)	SmSm	WrWr
Genotypes of gametes	All Sm	All Wr
Genotypes of zygotes (F_1)		All SmWr

Given our assumption, all the seeds of the F_1 generation will be phenotypically smooth.

When we 'self' the F_1 plants, we will have the following:

Genotypes of mother cells (F_1)	All SmWr
Genotypes of gametes	50% Sm and 50% Wr

At fertilization, the genotypes of the zygotes will be determined as follows:

	Genotypes of gametes of plant A	
	Sm	Wr
Sm	SmSm	SmWr
Wr	SmWr	WrWr

Genotypes of gametes of plant B (left side, Sm and Wr rows)

Thus 25 percent of the seeds will have a genotype SmSm and these will be phenotypically smooth, 50 percent will have genotype SmWr and, according to our hypothesis of dominance, will also be phenotypically smooth, and 25 percent will have genotype WrWr and these will phenotypically be wrinkled.

It is convenient to have terms that distinguish between two individuals with identical alleles for a pair of contrast-

Seed shape	Colour of cotyledon	Colour of flowers	Length of stem
5474 smooth	6022 yellow	705 purple	787 tall
1850 wrinkled	2001 green	224 white	277 short
74·7% smooth	75·1% yellow	75·9% purple	74·0% tall

You will see that in each case the appearance of the F_1 parents reappeared in about 75 percent of the F_2 generation. Can we explain this in terms of our hypothesis?

Let us consider the case of seed shape and assume that it is controlled by two possible types of gene, Sm (for smooth) and Wr (for wrinkled). Such alternative genes we call alleles. We will further assume that when Sm is present, it shows itself completely in the plant; Wr cannot show

ing characters and ones which have two different alleles. The former are described as being homozygous, the latter as heterozygous. Thus in this example the P_1 individuals were both homozygous for their seed-shape characteristics, the F_1 were all heterozygous, while half the F_2 were homozygous, half were heterozygous.

While our hypothesis is in keeping with the observations, it would be desirable to make other crosses and see whether these also produce results which are in keeping with our expectations. One such is to cross F_1 plants with the parent stock; such a cross is spoken of as a 'backcross'. There are two possible backcrosses. If we backcross the heterozygous F_1 with the homozygous smooth-seeded parent, we will expect the following result:

	P_1 plant	F_1 plant
Genotypes of mother cells	SmSm	SmWr
Genotypes of gametes	All Sm	50% Sm and 50% Wr
Genotypes of zygotes	50% SmSm and 50% SmWr	

Phenotypically we will expect all the progeny to be smooth-seeded and this indeed is what we find.

The other backcross will be as follows:

	P_1 plant	F_1 plant
Genotypes of mother cells	WrWr	SmWr
Genotypes of gametes	All Wr	50% Sm and 50% Wr
Genotypes of zygotes	50% SmWr and 50% WrWr	

So in this case we would expect to find that about 50 percent of the progeny were smooth-seeded and 50 percent wrinkled. Experimental results closely agree with such an expectation.

The two cases we have so far considered in detail both concern plants. Experiments on animals give similar results. There have been very detailed studies on the fly *Drosophila* (Diptera) (Fig. 22.4) which has the advantages of being easily bred in the laboratory in small containers and of having a short generation time, so that the progeny of a cross can be studied about ten days after it has been made. Results from birds and mammals, including man, as well as from Protozoa such as *Paramecium* also support our hypothesis.

Inheritance in man: haemoglobin types

One important example of such inheritance patterns in man relates to the chemical composition of haemoglobin. The most common type of adult human haemoglobin is called haemoglobin A, but there is a second type of haemoglobin, haemoglobin S, which differs chemically from haemoglobin A. Each haemoglobin molecule is formed of two pairs of polypeptide chains. One chain, the α-chain, contains 141 amino-acid residues; the other, the β-chain, contains 146. The whole molecule, consisting of two α- and two β-chains, thus contains 574 amino-acid residues. Haemoglobin S differs from haemoglobin A in that at one position in each β-chain the amino-acid valine replaces glutamic acid. Individuals with haemoglobin S in their blood are found especially in a belt running across tropical Africa (Fig. 22.13) as well as among the Afro-American

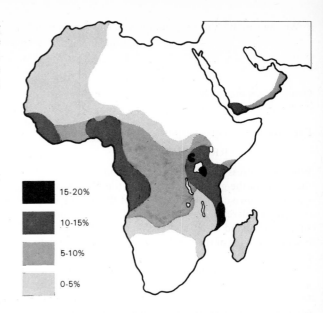

■	15–20%
▨	10–15%
▩	5–10%
░	0–5%

22.13 Distribution and frequency of occurrence in Africa of individuals whose blood contains haemoglobin S.

population of the United States. The presence of haemoglobin S confers some immunity to malaria but can have associated with it serious secondary illness. Its inheritance has been studied by examining the bloods of children, their parents and their grandparents. It has been found that each type of haemoglobin is associated with a specific gene, which determines the type of β-chain which is synthesized. Individuals may be homozygous for the gene for haemoglobin A and we can represent their genotype as $Hb^A Hb^A$, they may be heterozygous for the two genes and have a genotype $Hb^A Hb^S$, or they may be homozygous with a genotype $Hb^S Hb^S$. Furthermore, neither gene is dominant, so that an individual who is heterozygous, of genotype $Hb^A Hb^S$, will have both types of haemoglobin in the blood.

Individuals of genotype $Hb^S Hb^S$ can be easily identified if a sample of their blood is placed on a slide. While blood corpuscles containing haemoglobin A are circular discs, many of those of an individual with haemoglobin S will be shaped like a crescent or the blade of a sickle. The illness associated with the genotype $Hb^S Hb^S$ is therefore spoken of as 'sickle-cell anaemia' (Fig. 22.14).

Individuals homozygous for haemoglobin S are usually anaemic and the change in shape of the corpuscles may lead to obstruction of the blood capillaries. As a result the individual is unhealthy and may well die while still young. We will presently see (p. 496) why this tendency to severe ill-health occurs so frequently in African populations. Here we want to emphasize one point. It is possible not only to recognize individuals who are homozygous for haemoglobin S, but also the heterozygotes of genotype $Hb^A Hb^S$. If a drop of blood from such an individual is

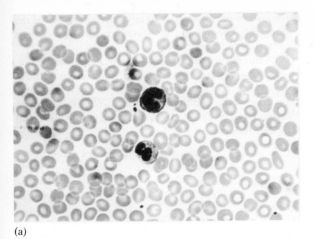

22.14 (a) Normal blood cells with haemoglobin A and **(b)** cells with haemoglobin S, in conditions of deoxygenation. Note the very abnormal shape of the latter cells.

placed on a slide and mixed with a chemical which absorbs oxygen, some of the cells will take on the sickle shape. We can easily see that if two such heterozygous individuals have children, some may be homozygous $Hb^S Hb^S$:

	Man	Woman
Parental genotype	$Hb^A Hb^S$	$Hb^A Hb^S$
Gametes	50% Hb^A; 50% Hb^S	50% Hb^A; 50% Hb^S

So at fertilization the progeny may be of the following possible genotypes:

		Paternal gametes	
		Hb^A	Hb^S
Maternal gametes	Hb^A	$Hb^A Hb^A$	$Hb^A Hb^S$
	Hb^S	$Hb^A Hb^S$	$Hb^S Hb^S$

Thus 25 percent of the possible F_1 genotypes will be homo-

zygous for haemoglobin S, that is to say that there is a 25 percent or 1 in 4 chance that any child may be of genotype $Hb^S Hb^S$. Note that we are dealing in terms of probability alone. It cannot be predicted that if there are four children, one, and only one, is going to have sickle-cell anaemia; none may or, on the other hand, two or three or all may have the condition. Since it is possible to determine beforehand the genotype of an individual parent, intending parents should, if possible, consult a clinic to find out whether they are indeed likely to have children with this disease. They will then at least be aware of what the future may hold.

Blood group inheritance

Inheritance of blood groups also follows this pattern, but with the complication that there are four different phenotypes: AB, A, B and O. Can we accommodate this within our hypothesis? Each of our examples so far has concerned only two alleles, which can give rise to three different genotypes and, depending on whether or not there is a dominance relation between these alleles, two or three phenotypes. To explain the facts of blood group inheritance we postulate the existence of three possible alleles. One, I^A, determines the formation of the A-antigen, one, I^B, determines the formation of B-antigen and the third, i, results in the formation of neither antigen. I^A is not dominant to I^B, nor I^B to I^A; an individual who is heterozygous for these two alleles will therefore produce both antigens and so belong to blood group AB. Both I^A and I^B can be regarded as dominant to i; as a result an individual of genotype $I^A i$ will produce A-antigen and be of blood group A, but individuals homozygous for I^A will also be of blood group A. Those homozygous for i will be of blood group O. The table below sets out the possible genotypes which can give rise to each of the four blood group phenotypes.

Blood group phenotype	Genotype
AB	$I^A I^B$
A	$I^A i$ or $I^A I^A$
B	$I^B i$ or $I^B I^B$
O	ii

Note that each individual can carry only two alleles: this follows from our assumption that alleles occur on homologous chromosomes and since, in a normal genotype, there is only a single pair of each set of homologous chromosomes, an individual can have only a single pair of homologous alleles.

Apart from its importance in blood transfusion, the pattern of inheritance of blood groups is sometimes used to settle legal cases involving disputed paternity. Let us take an example to see what sort of evidence might be led in a court. Suppose a child is blood group AB and its mother blood group A. The child's genotype will be $I^A I^B$ and the mother's either $I^A I^A$ or $I^A i$. Clearly the I^B

gene of the child must have come from its father. If the alleged father is, say, blood group O, it is highly unlikely that the child is his. If, however, he were blood group AB or B, the child could be his, but of course his paternity is not thereby proved: any other man with an I^B allele might equally well be the father. The evidence is therefore only negative, but has nevertheless been of value in certain cases in establishing that an allegation of paternity was not true.

Inheritance of two characters

So far we have considered only the inheritance of single characteristics. What happens if we consider two at once? What types of progeny appear, and can we account for observed results in terms of our hypothesis?

If, for example, we cross two pure lines of peas, one of which has smooth yellow seeds and the other wrinkled green seeds, we find that the F_1 seeds are all smooth and yellow. This clearly is in keeping with our hypothesis, since we have already postulated that the yellow seed-colour allele is dominant to that for green and that the allele for smooth seed is dominant to that for wrinkled. If now we 'self' the F_1, we get a number of different types of seed; some are, like those of the F_1, yellow and smooth, some are yellow and wrinkled, some green and smooth and some green and wrinkled. Can we explain such a result?

Let us assume that the alleles for seed colour are on one pair of homologous chromosomes and those for seed shape on another pair. Then we can write the parental genotypes of the two plants in the following way:

	Yellow,	Green,
	smooth-seeded	wrinkled-seeded
Parental phenotypes		
Parental genotypes	Y/Y S/S	y/y s/s
Genotypes of gametes	All Y S	All y s
Genotypes of zygotes (F_1)	All Y/y S/s	

Note that we have changed our notation in two ways. Firstly, to remind ourselves which is a dominant allele and which a recessive one, we have represented the dominant allele by a capital letter and the corresponding recessive by the same letter, but in small type. Thus y is the allele for green seed colour and s that for wrinkled seed. Secondly, to remember that we have postulated that the alleles for seed colour are on one pair of chromosomes and those for seed shape on another, we have joined each pair of alleles with an oblique line.

What would we expect to happen if we selfed the F_1? Firstly, we must ask what sorts of gamete each F_1 plant can produce. Each gamete will contain one of each type of chromosome: thus it may have a Y-carrying chromosome and either an S-carrying or an s-carrying chromosome, or it may have a y-carrying chromosome together with either an S- or an s-carrying chromosome. This follows from the fact that in gametogenesis it is a matter of chance which

chromosome of a pair goes to any particular pole of the dividing cell. The different, non-homologous chromosomes thus 'assort' independently.

With this information, using the same method as before, we can see what sorts of zygotes will be formed at fertilization and, further, deduce their phenotypes from our knowledge of the dominance relations. We will have four different types of gamete from each parent and the result will be as follows:

	Genotypes of gametes of parent A			
	YS	Ys	yS	ys
YS	Y/Y S/S	Y/Y S/s	Y/y S/S	Y/y S/s
Ys	Y/Y S/s	Y/Y s/s	Y/y S/s	Y/y s/s
yS	Y/y S/S	Y/y S/s	y/y S/S	y/y S/s
ys	Y/y S/s	Y/y s/s	y/y S/s	y/y s/s

(Genotypes of gametes of parent B: YS, Ys, yS, ys)

There are thus 16 different combinations, all equally possible. What will be their corresponding phenotypes and in what proportions will we expect them to appear?

All seeds with either a Y/Y or a Y/y genotype will be yellow and all those which also have an S/S or an S/s genotype will be smooth. If you count up, you will find that there are 9 such cases among the 16 possibilities. Extending this argument we can list all the possible phenotypes and then we get the following

Phenotype	Relative frequency
Yellow and smooth-seeded	9
Yellow and wrinkled-seeded	3
Green and smooth-seeded	3
Green and wrinkled-seeded	1

We can thus account in terms of our hypothesis for the four phenotypes observed in the F_2 derived from selfing the F_1 plants. Furthermore, the relative abundance of the different F_2 phenotypes agrees closely with our expectation of a relative frequency of 9:3:3:1. The actual results obtained by Mendel for such a cross were

Yellow and smooth	315
Yellow and wrinkled	101
Green and smooth	108
Green and wrinkled	32

which gives a relative frequency of 9·0:2·91:3·11:0·98.

If the two pairs of alleles are considered separately, each shows the expected relative frequency ratio of dominant to recessive phenotypes of 3:1.

The phenomenon of 'linkage'

Results such as this are not invariably found. Let us take

as an example two sets of characters found in *Drosophila*. One relates to wing length. There is an allele whose effect is to produce flies with very short wings compared with the normal long-winged flies (Fig. 22.15); this short-winged condition is called 'vestigial wing'. Flies which are similar in appearance to most specimens collected in the field are spoken of as 'wild-type', so the long wing is called the 'wild-type wing'. Crossing experiments show that the allele for vestigial wing is recessive to that for the wild type. Wild-type characters have no descriptive names other than 'wild-type' and so there is a convention that wild-type alleles are represented by a plus sign. Vestigial wing is a recessive character, so we represent it by vg and indicate the corresponding wild-type dominant by writing Vg^+.

The second character we will consider is 'black body'; the abdomen is markedly darker than in the wild type. In this case we have as possible alleles the wild-type B^+ and the black-body allele b.

By extrapolation from our previous example, we will expect that if we cross pure-bred wild-type flies with flies showing the characters black body and vestigial wing, all the F_1 progeny will be phenotypically wild-type. In practice, this is what we do find: for both characters the wild-type alleles are dominant. Further extrapolation indicates that we might expect that if we selfed the F_1, we would obtain four different F_2 phenotypes in the proportions of $9:3:3:1$. This expectation is not fulfilled. The overwhelming majority of the progeny are either wild-type or else have black bodies together with vestigial wings; in fact, about 75 percent of the progeny are of the wild type and about 25 percent have the phenotype of the two recessive characters, that is, they are 'double recessives'.

How can we accommodate these observations within our initial hypothesis? You will notice that the F_2 phenotypes occur in a 3:1 ratio. The two characters are behaving as if they were one, or at least as if they were 'linked' together. Such 'linkage' can be attributed to the occurrence of both

alleles on the same chromosome, with the result that in mitosis and meiosis the two wild-type alleles move about as one unit, the two recessive alleles as another.

We can represent the situation symbolically as follows:

	Wild-type parent	Double-recessive parent
Parental genotypes (P_1)	$\dfrac{B^+ \ Vg^+}{B^+ \ Vg^+}$	$\dfrac{b \ vg}{b \ vg}$
Genotypes of gametes	All $\underline{B^+ \ Vg^+}$	All $\underline{b \ vg}$
Genotypes of zygotes (F_1)	All $\dfrac{B^+ \ Vg^+}{b \ \ \ vg}$	

Note that we have introduced another convention: to remind ourselves that the alleles are both on the same chromosome, we have written down their symbols close together and inserted a bar to signify that they are 'linked'.

What will happen if we self the F_1? Our expectation can be represented as follows:

Genotypes of F_1 parent	$\dfrac{B^+ \ Vg^+}{b \ \ \ vg}$	$\dfrac{B^+ \ Vg^+}{b \ \ \ vg}$
Genotypes of gametes	$\underline{B^+ \ Vg^+}$ and $\underline{b \ vg}$	$\underline{B^+ \ Vg^+}$ and $\underline{b \ vg}$

At fertilization we will expect the following combinations of genotypes to occur:

		Genotypes of gametes of parent A	
		$B^+ \ Vg^+$	b vg
Genotypes of gametes of parent B	$\underline{B^+ \ Vg^+}$	$\dfrac{B^+ \ Vg^+}{B^+ \ Vg^+}$	$\dfrac{B^+ \ Vg^+}{b \ \ \ vg}$
	$\underline{b \ vg}$	$\dfrac{B^+ \ Vg^+}{b \ \ \ vg}$	$\dfrac{b \ vg}{b \ vg}$

and this is in keeping with our observation that about three-quarters of the progeny are phenotypically wild-type.

Linkage groups: a further test of the hypothesis

The foregoing result implies that the number of groups of linked characters should be the same as the number of observable chromosomes at the end of the second meiotic division, that is, the haploid number, since this is the number of different types of chromosome in the nucleus. The number of pairs of linked alleles will of course be much greater than this, since a pair A and B may occur on the same chromosome as another pair C and D. This is why we spoke of 'groups' of characters. Suppose that A and B as well as C and D are linked; if B and C are also

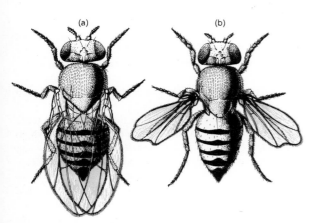

22.15 (a) Normal female *Drosophila melanogaster*. (b) A female showing the phenotype for vestigial wing.

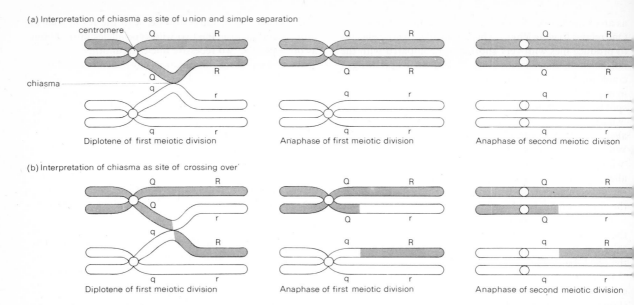

(a) Interpretation of chiasma as site of union and simple separation

centromere

Q   R

chiasma

Q   R

Diplotene of first meiotic division

Q   R

Anaphase of first meiotic division

Q   R

Anaphase of second meiotic divison

(b) Interpretation of chiasma as site of crossing over

Q   R

Diplotene of first meiotic division

Q   R

Anaphase of first meiotic division

Q   R

Anaphase of second meiotic division

22.16 Two interpretations of the structure of a chiasma. In (a) a chiasma is interpreted as being a simple adhesion of two chromatids which subsequently separate. After the anaphase of the second meiotic division, each pair of cells would contain identical chromosomes. In (b) a chiasma is interpreted as being a site of crossing-over so that after the anaphase of the second meiotic division the genetic composition of each of the four cells is different. Note that the shapes of the chromosomes in (a) and (b) are the same at each stage. With normal chromosomes it is impossible to determine which interpretation is correct.

linked, then all four alleles must be on the same chromosome and form a 'linkage group'.

Evidence for the presence of four linkage groups in *Drosophila melanogaster* has been produced by very extensive studies using specimens showing a wide variety of characters distinct from wild-type. Fig. 22.4 shows that in *D. melanogaster* the diploid number is 8; thus the haploid number is 4, a result again in keeping with our hypothesis that the genes are located on the chromosomes. This type of result has been obtained with other species of *Drosophila* which have a different haploid number. Thus *D. pseudoobscura* has a haploid number of 5 and correspondingly there are five linkage groups: similarly maize, with a haploid number of 10, proves to have ten linkage groups.

The exceptional individuals: crossing-over

In discussing the results of selfing the F_1 generation derived from wild-type flies and the double-recessive stock with black body and vestigial wing, we said that in the F_2 progeny 'the overwhelming majority of the progeny are either wild-type or else have black bodies and vestigial wings'. Among the F_2 progeny we do, however, find some flies that have wild-type body colour and vestigial wings, and also some which have wild-type wings but black bodies. Such individuals with a new combination of characters are called recombinants. We could explain such a result by

assuming that some type of exchange occurred between parts of homologous chromosomes, that is, that in the F_1 flies, a genotype $\dfrac{B^+ \, Vg^+}{b \ \ vg}$ can, in a limited number of cases, give rise by exchange to chromosomes which we can represent as $\underline{B^+ \, vg}$ and $\underline{b \, Vg^+}$. Is there any evidence for an event of this type?

You will remember that in the prophase of the first meiotic division homologous chromosomes come to lie side by side (Fig. 22.9); this stage of prophase is called zygotene. Each chromatid then reduplicates and the centromeres shortly start to move apart, a stage called diplotene. In diplotene it can be seen that two of the chromatid threads are joined together at one or more points forming 'chiasmata'. These chiasmata might be the physical expression of the exchange or 'crossing-over' which we have postulated. Can we find evidence for such an hypothesis?

What we are seeking is evidence that in diplotene there has been some exchange of chromatid material which should be observable during the following anaphase when the chromosomes have separated completely; but, as Fig. 22.16 shows, with any normal pair of chromosomes, we could not tell whether such an event had occurred or not as the chromosomes will stain uniformly along their lengths and we cannot distinguish a changed from an unchanged chromatid thread. Evidence would, however, be provided by a study of a pair of chromosomes which are

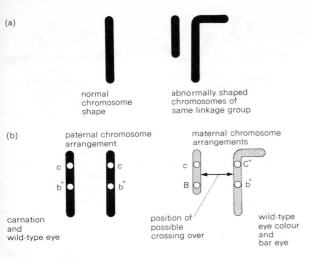

(a)

normal
chromosome
shape

abnormally shaped
chromosomes of
same linkage group

(b)

paternal chromosome
arrangement

maternal chromosome
arrangements

c — c

b⁺ — b⁺

carnation
and
wild-type eye

c — C⁺

B — b⁺

position of
possible
crossing over

wild-type
eye colour
and
bar eye

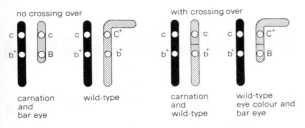

chromosomal arrangements of possible progeny

no crossing over

with crossing over

c — c   c — C⁺   c — c   c — C⁺

b⁺ — B   b⁺ — b⁺   b⁺ — b⁺   b⁻ — B

carnation
and
bar eye

wild-type

carnation
and
wild-type

wild-type
eye colour and
bar eye

22.17 (a) Shape of normal and abnormal chromosomes, all belonging to the same linkage group, used
to determine whether crossing-over observed in breeding experiments is associated with an exchange of material between homologous chromosomes. (b) Diagrammatic summary of a cross used to demonstrate
that crossing-over is in fact associated with exchange
of chromosomal material. Note that chromosomal
shapes of the four possible progeny are distinct, so
that it is possible to determine whether physical
changes in the chromosomes correlate with the actual
phenotypes of the progeny.

homologous, but in which one partner can be distinguished
from the other so that we could then recognize any
crossing-over by direct observation.

Convenient material for our purpose is provided by
homologous pairs, one member of which for one reason
or another is longer than the other. Fig. 22.17 shows two
such chromosomes compared with the homologous wild
type; one of the abnormal chromosomes is shorter and the
other has an arm attached to it. Both are distinct in shape.
In a particular stock of *Drosophila* there was a homologous
pair of chromosomes of these two different shapes and on
them were two 'marker' genes. One called 'bar' (B) changes
the shape of the eye (Fig. 22.18) and is dominant to the
wild-type allele (b⁺); the other, called 'carnation' (c),
affects eye colour and is recessive to the wild-type eye
colour (C⁺).

For simplicity's sake we will follow only what happens
when the females are crossed with males which are carrying carnation (c) as well as the wild-type allele for bar (b⁺)
(Fig. 22.17b). When there is no crossing-over, the progeny
will be either wild-type or else have carnation-coloured,
bar eyes. If crossing-over does occur, then the progeny
will have either carnation eyes of normal shape or bar eyes
of wild-type colour; moreover, the appearance of the
chromosomes in the two kinds of fly will be different.

Examination of the results of such crosses showed that
each type of fly had chromosomes of the expected appearance, providing evidence for the correctness of our hypothesis that the genetically observable phenomenon of
crossing-over is due to a physical rearrangement of
material between pairs of homologous chromosomes.

Chromosome maps

In our interpretation of crossing-over, we have assumed
that different genes are situated at definite sites or loci
along the length of a chromosome. Can we deduce any
further implications of this assumption and see whether
our deductions are supported by observation? Consider
the chromosomes shown in Fig. 22.19. We have inserted
the position of three pairs of alleles. If we assume that
crossing-over can occur at any place along the length of
the chromosome, then it will follow that, in suitable breeding experiments, crossing-over between A and c should
occur more frequently than between A and b. The frequency of crossing-over could thus give us some measure
of the 'distance' along the chromosome between different

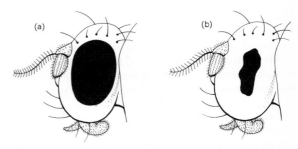

22.18 Lateral views of the head of *Drosophila* with (a)
wild-type eye and (b) bar eye.

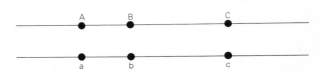

22.19 Diagram to explain the principle of construction
of a chromosome map. For further explanation see
text.

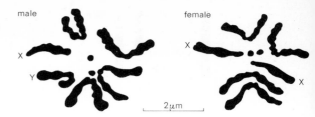

22.20 Map of the positions of known genes on a chromosome of *Aedes aegypti*. The characters are as follows: *dld*, resistance to dieldrin; *ix*, inter-sex; *bpd*, black pedicel (the base of antenna is black; that in the wild type is white); *y*, yellow larva (the wild type is grey); *s*, spotless abdomen (the wild-type abdomen has lateral patches of white), *DDT*, resistance to DDT.

loci, since the farther two loci are apart, the more frequently should they cross-over. Furthermore, if we measure in this way the 'distance' between A and b, B and c and also between A and c, then, provided our ideas are correct, we would expect to find that Ab + Bc = Ac.

Once we have found alleles for different characters in a species, we can by breeding experiments assign them to different linkage groups. By further experiments we can determine the frequency or 'cross-over value' between different loci of any linkage group and in this way test the validity of our deductions. Our expectations are fully confirmed by such experiments, which show us that the genes are arranged in a linear order along the length of the chromosomes. Furthermore, it is possible to make 'maps' of particular linkage groups, that is, 'maps' of the gene loci upon particular chromosomes, distances being expressed in 'map units' derived from measurements of cross-over values. Fig. 22.20 shows such a map for one chromosome of the mosquito *Aedes aegypti*.

The determination of sex

One of the most obvious examples of discontinuous variation is that in very many organisms the individuals belong to one sex or another. Moreover there are usually very nearly equal numbers of male and female individuals. We may ask whether the chromosomes of males differ in some way from those of females. In some dioecious plants, such as pawpaw, the chromosomes of the two sexes look identical when examined under the microscope; sex is determined in these cases by invisible differences in genes. In other organisms we can find more obvious differences in chromosome structure. Fig. 22.21 shows a drawing of the chromosomes of a male and a female of *Drosophila melanogaster*. It is clear that while there are four pairs of similarly shaped chromosomes in the female, there is one pair in the male in which the two chromosomes are of different shapes. Similarly, there are 23 pairs of chromosomes in human beings: in those of a woman the members of each pair resemble each other in shape, but those of a man include one pair in which one chromosome is markedly bigger than the other (Fig. 22.22). In both *D. melanogaster* and man, one of the chromosomes of the unequal male pair is similar in appearance to the two chromosomes of the corresponding pair found in the female. For con-

22.21 Metaphase chromosomes from brain cells of male and female *Drosophila*. Note that while the female has two identically shaped X chromosomes, the male has differently shaped X and Y chromosomes. The remaining chromosomes, or autosomes, of the two sexes are of similar shape.

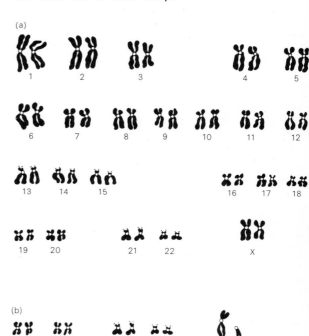

22.22 Drawings of the shapes of the 46 chromosomes of a human being as seen at metaphase. (a) The complete chromosome complement of a woman. Note that the two X chromosomes are almost identical in shape. (b) Chromosome pairs 19–22, X and Y of a man. Note the marked difference in shape of the X and Y chromosomes, and the similarity of the X chromosome of the male with that of the corresponding chromosomes of the female. A diagram showing a complete set of chromosomes as in (a) is called a karyotype.

venience of reference, the two chromosomes in the female are both designated X, as is the corresponding chromosome in the male; the distinctly different male chromosome is designated Y.

With this information, we can recognize that in meiosis, a female will produce gametes all of which carry an X chromosome and thus are identical. A male will, how-

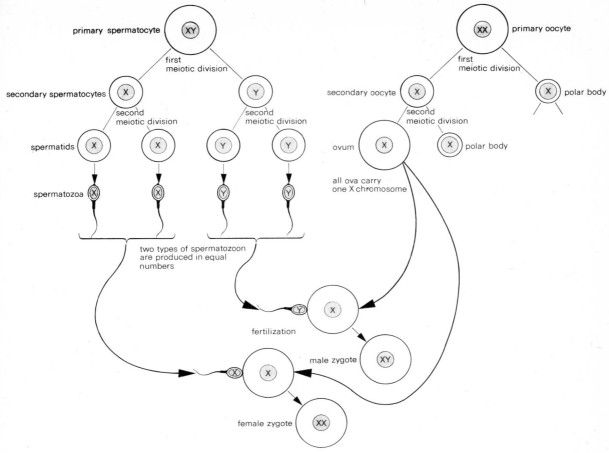

22.23 Diagram showing the manner in which the XX–XY arrangement of sex chromosomes will result, on the average, in the production of male and female offspring in equal proportions.

produce two different types of gamete, one carrying an X chromosome and one carrying a Y, and these two types should occur in equal numbers. That this conclusion is correct was demonstrated as long ago as 1891 when a German biologist H. Henking was able to show that one of the Hemiptera produced sperm some of which contained in the nucleus of the sperm head a visible chromosome, the X chromosome, which was absent from the nuclei of other sperm. In this particular species the effect was more obvious as there is no Y chromosome.

These facts are set out in a formal manner in Fig. 22.23; they imply that two types of zygote will be formed in equal numbers, one carrying two X chromosomes which we expect to be phenotypically female and one carrying an X and a Y which we expect to be phenotypically male. Thus we have an hypothesis which would account for the appearance of individuals of the two sexes in equal numbers.

In human beings there are two rare conditions: in the one there is an X chromosome which has no partner so

that the individual, who is phenotypically female, has a genotype XO; in the other there is an extra X chromosome and the individual, who is phenotypically male, has a genotype XXY. It would therefore seem that the Y chromosome has some male-determining gene or genes, while in the absence of the Y chromosome, provided at least one X chromosome is present, the individual becomes a female.

Sex linkage

It follows from these considerations that any recessive genes located on the X chromosome should invariably be expressed phenotypically in the male who has only a single X chromosome, but not invariably in the female, as the female may be heterozygous for the character.

Such characters have been recognized in human beings. One, which it is easy to detect, is red–green colour blindness, a condition in which the individual is unable to distinguish between the colours red and green. This is a rare condition in Africans but occurs in a small but significant

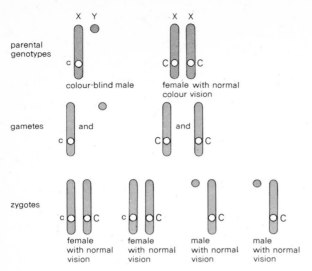

parental genotypes

X Y — colour-blind male (c)

X X — female with normal colour vision (C C)

gametes — c and ●

gametes — C and C

zygotes

c C — female with normal vision
c C — female with normal vision
C — male with normal vision
C — male with normal vision

22.24 Diagram showing the expected proportion of progeny of different phenotypes from the mating of a colour-blind man with a woman of normal colour vision. The allele for colour blindness c is recessive to C, that for normal colour vision.

parental genotypes

male with normal colour vision (C)

female with normal colour vision (C c)

gametes — C and ●

gametes — C and c

zygotes

C C — female with normal colour vision
C c — female with normal colour vision
C — male with normal colour vision
c — colour-blind male

22.25 Diagram showing the expected proportion of progeny from the mating of a male with normal colour vision and a female carrier of colour blindness.

percentage of Europeans. In towns this can be a handicap, as a red–green colour-blind individual cannot distinguish between a red and a green traffic light in the dark. Indeed in considering the suitability of applicants for certain types of employment, such as being an aeroplane pilot, it is normal to test the candidates' colour vision: applicants with defective colour vision will not be accepted for such jobs.

Let us look at some of the patterns of inheritance which we might expect in such cases. We will start by considering what happens if a colour-blind man is the father of several children by a woman with normal colour vision. We may set out our expectation as in Fig. 22.24 where we have drawn the chromosomes in diagrammatic form, so that we can distinguish the sex of the progeny easily. We would expect that from such a mating, all the children will have normal colour vision. This expectation is commonly but not invariably fulfilled; you will shortly see how exceptions can arise.

Let us first see what happens if one of the daughters of this family marries a man with normal colour vision. Our expectation is shown in Fig. 22.25. It implies that about half the boys from such a mating will be colour-blind, but all the girls will have normal colour vision. From a study of several generations in human families in which defective red–green colour vision is known to occur, we find our expectation is confirmed.

What might we expect to happen if another daughter from the first mating married a colour-blind man? The daughter is heterozygous for the alleles determining colour vision, a condition which we describe by saying that she is

a carrier of the gene, although the gene, being recessive, does not show up phenotypically. Our expectation is shown diagrammatically in Fig. 22.26. It is clear that from such a mating some of the daughters will be colour-blind; this is the exception we mentioned above. Since we cannot directly distinguish women who are colour-blind carriers from 'normal' women, some matings of women who have normal colour vision with colour-blind men may produce colour-blind daughters. Of course, if the father had normal colour vision, colour blindness would show only in the sons.

Such results would lead us to expect that colour-blind men should be far more common than colour-blind women, as the chance of a woman being homozygous for this relatively rare gene is slight. Such an expectation is fulfilled: in Europeans the relative frequency of male and female colour-blind individuals is about 16:1.

There are two other human sex-linked characteristics which are worth mention. The one relates to an enzyme called glucose-6-phosphate dehydrogenase, found in the red blood corpuscles of normal people. The recessive allele results in a deficiency of the enzyme. This condition, which is found in some parts of Africa, is serious, as treatment of such people with certain drugs, including at least one of the anti-malarial drugs, primaquine, can result in a break-up of a proportion of the red blood corpuscles and a resultant anaemia.

A second sex-linked characteristic is called haemophilia. In people with this condition the blood from a wound fails to clot quickly and there is thus a considerable danger of a fatal haemorrhage. Haemophilia occurred in both the

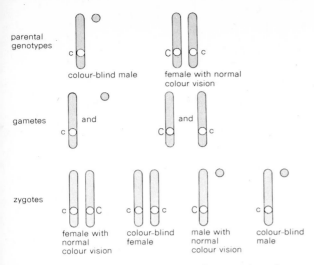

parental genotypes

colour-blind male   female with normal colour vision

gametes   and   and

zygotes

female with normal colour vision   colour-blind female   male with normal colour vision   colour-blind male

22.26 Diagram showing the expected proportion of progeny of different phenotypes from the mating of a colour-blind male with a female carrier of colour blindness. Compare this expectation with that shown in Fig. 22.24.

Russian and Spanish royal families and a study of the complex pattern of intermarriage among European royalty allows us to trace the passage of the gene back from generation to generation as far as Queen Victoria. Three of her daughters were carriers and by their marriages distributed the gene to other royal houses.

Sex determination in other organisms

It is sometimes convenient to distinguish the sex which has two identical sex chromosomes as the homogametic sex from that with two different sex chromosomes, the heterogametic sex. It can also be useful to be able to speak of all the other chromosomes collectively; they are referred to as the autosomes. Our discussion of sex linkage has shown us that recessive sex-linked characters are more frequent in the phenotype of the heterogametic than the homogametic sex. This is generally true even when, as in birds, butterflies and some fishes, the heterogametic sex is the female and not, as in mammals and Diptera, the male. Furthermore, it is important to realize that there can be interactions between the autosomes and the sex chromosomes: in *Drosophila*, for example, sex determination involves not only the X and Y chromosomes, but also the number of X chromosomes relative to the set of autosomes.

The Hymenoptera, including the ants, bees and wasps, have a specialized form of sex determination; the females are diploid and the males haploid. Meiosis is normal in females, but there is an abnormal meiosis in the males which allows for the production of haploid sperm. If an egg is fertilized, the zygote will be diploid and normally develop into a female; if it is not fertilized it will be haploid and develop into a male. A queen bee can control the sex of the offspring by determining whether or not an egg she is about to lay is fertilized. This control is so exercised by the queen that fertilized eggs are laid in worker and queen cells, but unfertilized eggs are laid in drone cells. It is probable that in bees a large number of alleles are concerned with sex determination and that individuals which are heterozygous for at least some of these alleles are female. A fully homozygous individual will however be male. Homozygous diploids are very rare, but the haploid drones are equivalent to homozygous individuals and thus they are male.

Continuous variation

So far we have considered the inheritance of contrasting characteristics. It is also necessary to seek an explanation of the phenomenon of continuous variation. Before attempting this, we will consider two further cases of contrasting characteristics which tell us more about possible patterns of gene action.

It sometimes happens that the crossing of two white-flowered plants may result in the production of an F_1 generation in which all the flowers are coloured. If the F_1 flowers are selfed then about 55 percent of the F_2 flowers are coloured and the rest are white. Such a result can be shown to be due to the presence of two sets of alleles belonging to different linkage groups. One pair are determinants of flower colour in which there is a simple dominance relationship between two alleles, say R and r; genotypes RR and Rr would yield coloured flowers and rr white flowers. The other pair of alleles (C and c) determine whether flower colour, even if genotypically represented by the alleles at the R locus, can express itself phenotypically. If the allelic pairs CC or Cc are present, then the genotype of the R locus will be expressed; if the genotype is cc, then the flowers will be white, even if the other pair of alleles is RR. To make the point clearer, we list below the nine possible genotypes and their phenotypic expression:

Genotypes	Phenotypes
C/C R/R C/C R/r C/c R/R C/c R/r	Coloured flowers
C/C r/r C/c r/r	White flowers, as a result of the presence of the r/r pair of alleles
c/c R/R c/c R/r	White flowers, as a result of the presence of the c/c pair of alleles
c/c r/r	White flowers, as a result of the presence of both c/c and r/r alleles

The interest of this example is that it shows that two

22.27 Different patterns of comb structure shown by cocks of various genotypes: (a) walnut (b) rose (c) pea (d) single.

independent pairs of alleles may both affect the expression of a single characteristic of the phenotype.

A rather more complex relation is found in connection with the shape of the comb of the cocks of certain breeds of domestic fowl (Fig. 22.27). In this case experiment shows that we are again dealing with two pairs of alleles (R and P) acting upon a single structure but the result of their interactions leads to a greater diversity of forms. The following genotypes and phenotypes can occur:

Genotype	Phenotype
R/R P/P ⎫ R/R P/p ⎪ R/r P/P ⎬ R/r P/p ⎭	All walnut
R/R p/p ⎫ R/r p/p ⎭	Both rose
r/r P/P ⎫ r/r P/p ⎭	Both pea
r/r p/p	Single

We can now turn to the problem of continuous variation, bearing in mind that different pairs of alleles can affect a single character. Let us postulate that the height of a plant above a certain minimum value m is determined by two sets of alleles, X or x, and Y or y. The recessive alleles have no action, but if one dominant gene is present the height is increased by one unit, if two are present by two units, and so on. If we cross a homozygous recessive plant which has a height m with a homozygous dominant plant which has a height of $m+4$ and then self the F_1, we will obtain progeny of the following heights and in the following proportions:

Height	m	$m+1$	$m+2$	$m+3$	$m+4$
Frequency	1	4	6	4	1

If instead we postulate three pairs of alleles X or x, Y or y and Z or z, we should obtain in the F_2:

Height	m	$m+1$	$m+2$	$m+3$	$m+4$	$m+5$	$m+6$
Frequency	1	6	15	20	15	6	1

If we postulate four pairs of alleles, the result would be:

Height	m	$m+1$	$m+2$	$m+3$	$m+4$
Frequency	1	8	28	56	70

Height	$m+5$	$m+6$	$m+7$	$m+8$
Frequency	56	28	8	1

Clearly we can extend this type of operation to an increasing number of pairs of alleles. As we do so, the number of possible height categories increases and increasingly the condition tends to resemble continuous variation. This idea can be modified in a variety of ways. We have postulated complete dominance, but we might also postulate that each member of a pair of alleles has a different intensity of effect. This would increase the number of possible categories. Although we have neglected completely the influence of minor environmental differences upon growth, it is possible to see how continuous variation could arise as a result of the action of several pairs of alleles all affecting the one character. It is clear that the analysis of continuous variation is far more complex than that of discontinuous variation. From breeding experiments, especially with maize plants, there is nevertheless evidence which is in keeping with the postulate that discontinuous variation is due to the action of multiple genes or 'polygenes', as such systems involving many pairs of alleles are called.

We have made one assumption, namely that the action of a gene in a heterozygote may be quantitatively only half that found in a homozygous dominant. Although this is not invariably true, such quantitative relations do occur. The first example we considered, namely that of flower colour in the four o'clock plant, is precisely such a case, less pigment being produced in the heterozygote than in the homozygous dominant. Table 22.4 provides another example: it shows that the vitamin A content of maize endosperm is proportional to the number of dominant Y genes which are present. Since endosperm is triploid, that is, it has three sets of chromosomes, data can be obtained for four different 'dosage' levels of the dominant gene.

Table 22.4 Vitamin A content of endosperm of maize seeds of different genotypes (*Data from Mangelsdorf*)

Genotype of endosperm	Relative vitamin A activity
yyy	0·02
Yyy	1·00
YYy	2·22
YYY	3·33

Note: The vitamin A activity of the different types of endosperm was determined by a biological assay depending upon the growth rate of rats. The values obtained were therefore in arbitrary units.

Environmental effects

We have hitherto assumed that there is individual variation due to minor differences in the effect on growth of the environment. Do we have any evidence that this is indeed so? Clearly were it not so, some continuous variations might be expressed as a series of distinct steps. The sort of evidence we need is provided by a series of experiments by the Danish geneticist Wilhelm Johannsen, who studied inheritance of seed weight in the bean, *Phaseolus vulgaris*. This plant is normally self-fertilizing and as a result the seeds of any one plant are homozygous for almost all loci. From an initial lot of 19 seeds, plants were grown and in each generation the heaviest and lightest seeds of each plant were used as material for the next generation (Fig. 22.28). Some of Johannsen's data, relating to the progeny of one of his initial plants, are shown in Table 22.5: over the years the difference in weight between the lightest and heaviest seeds chosen for further breeding was as great as 230 mg, but nevertheless the mean weight of progeny seeds produced from the heavy-seeded parents and the light-seeded parents differed by only 20 mg. Furthermore, average seed weight in the two lines alters in the same direction from year to year, reflecting varying

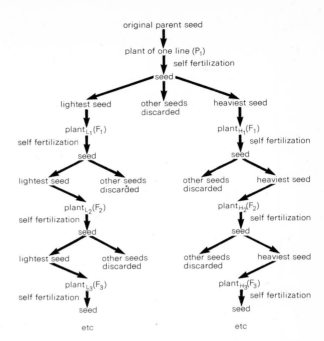

22.28 Diagram illustrating the principle of Johannsen's experiments on selection for seed weight in the self-fertilizing bean, *Phaseolus vulgaris*.

environmental conditions. These data show clearly that minor environmental influences can have a very considerable effect on the phenotypic expression of the genotype when we are dealing with characteristics which show continuous variation. They show further that our concept of a 'pure line' is valid since the mean weight of each group of seeds does not vary in a constant direction from year to year. Generations of plants of the same genotype have an effectively constant phenotype even though this may be modified by the changing environmental conditions from one year to another.

Table 22.5 Weights of seeds from bean plants over six generations, with selection for light and heavy seed weight in each generation (*Data from Johannsen*)

Year	Average weight (mg) of chosen parent seeds		Average weight (mg) of progeny seed from	
	Lighter seeds	Heavier seeds	Lighter seeds	Heavier seeds
1902	300	400	360	350
1903	250	420	400	410
1904	310	430	310	330
1905	270	390	380	390
1906	300	460	380	400
1907	240	470	370	370

The effect of genotype and environment on human characteristics

Such a conclusion leads to what is clearly a question of considerable interest, namely how far the characteristics of an individual human being are a product of his genetic make-up and how far a product of his environment. Deliberate breeding experiments upon human beings are clearly impossible, but nevertheless a relatively rare event does allow us to make some estimate of the importance of environment.

You will have met at some time two people who are 'twins', who were born of the same mother at the same time. Most twins develop from two quite separate eggs, each fertilized by a different spermatozoon. They are genetically distinct and may be of different sexes; as they grow up they resemble each other no more closely than do any other two children of the same father and mother. Children of the same parents are called siblings and most twins, despite their common birthday, are genetically siblings. They are spoken of as fraternal twins.

Far less frequently twins may arise in a different way. Shortly after fertilization the egg cell divides; each resulting cell is called a blastomere. If these two blastomeres should separate, each will develop independently and normally, resulting in twins which, derived originally from the same zygote, are genetically identical: they are described therefore as identical or monozygotic twins. They are of the same sex, look very similar as they grow up, have closely similar finger prints and so on. Identical twins have been studied and compared with fraternal twins, as this provides us with some measure of the relative effects of genotype and environment upon the individual. Table 22.6 summarizes results of one such study.

It can be seen immediately that in body structure both sets of identical twins resemble each other far more closely than do fraternal twins or siblings. In body weight, identical twins who have been living apart are as variable as siblings, which is perhaps to be expected since, as we are all aware, the type and quantity of food we eat markedly affects our weight. What is striking is that, when living together, and therefore presumably having a similar available diet, fraternal twins are more variable than identical twins. This suggests that there is in fact some genetical element in the determination of body weight.

Perhaps most interesting are the data in Table 22.6 relating to 'intelligence'. While we have no very clear idea as to what exactly is being measured by an 'intelligence test', within a single social class of a single cultural group such a test provides a measure of relative ability to respond correctly to various types of problem. Here you will note that the score difference between identical twins which have been reared apart and had therefore somewhat different educational and social experiences is almost as great as that for siblings and fraternal twins. Nevertheless the difference is less than that between fraternal twins who were reared together and therefore are likely to have had similar experiences. So it seems reasonable to conclude that there is some genetical influence upon whatever ability is being assessed by an intelligence test. The effect, however, seems to be slight compared with that of environmental influences.

The range of gene action

In the foregoing discussion, we have limited ourselves largely to very obvious phenotypic characters like flower colour or seed shape in plants, or wing length and eye colour in *Drosophila*. We have also mentioned differences in blood composition, such as the A-, B- and O-antigens upon red blood cells, in levels of enzyme activity such as the quantity of glucose-6-phosphate dehydrogenase in the blood and in details of protein structure such as those between haemoglobin A and haemoglobin S. But genes may have other types of action as well; they may affect the pathway of development, so that the resulting individual is structurally abnormal and, what is particularly important, genes can influence behaviour. We have seen that there is some evidence that an ability to score well in an intelligence test has some inherited component, but that

Table 22.6 Differences between pairs of identical and fraternal twins for various characteristics (*Data from Newman, Freeman and Holzinger*)

Character	Average pair differences			
	Identical twins reared together	*Identical twins reared apart*	*Fraternal twins reared together*	*Siblings of like sex*
Body height (cm)	1·7	1·8	4·4	4·5
Head length (mm)	2·9	2·2	6·2	—
Head width (mm)	2·8	2·9	4·2	—
Body weight (kg)	1·8	4·4	4·5	4·7
Intelligence quotient score	5·9	8·2	9·9	9·8
Size of sample	50 pairs	20 pairs	52 pairs	52 pairs

such ability is largely determined by the experiences of the individual. In animals with which it is possible to do breeding experiments, the effects of inheritance on behaviour are far more easily demonstrated. One particularly clear example is the calling song of adult male crickets (Orthoptera); the song serves to attract the female. The form of the song, and especially its rhythmic structure, is determined by a network of neurones in nerve ganglia in the thorax. Individuals of different genotypes produce different song patterns, and the differences are due to different patterns of nerve impulses being generated by the thoracic network. Indeed the output of particular, identifiable neurones within the network is different in individuals of different genotype. Here then we have a case of the structure and interconnections within the

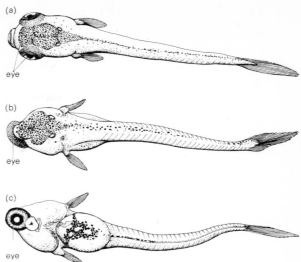

22.30 Effect of treatment of embryos of the top minnow with solutions containing an abnormally high concentration of magnesium ion. (a) Normal young fish seen from the dorsal surface. (b) Dorsal view of treated fish. (c) Ventral view of treated fish. Note that the treatment causes the fish to develop with a single median eye.

central nervous system being determined genetically and as a result affecting the motor activity or behaviour of the individual. The final output of the song-generating centre is not affected by normal environmental variables such as temperature, diet, crowding or season which impinge on an individual during development. Nor is it influenced by the individuals being able to hear during their development and maturation some different song; the song is not learnt by imitation of other singers.

In this particular instance the structural relations within the nervous system determined by the genes are almost completely unaffected by environmental influences. But genes never produce their effects entirely independently of the environment and commonly the phenotypic expression of the genotype will be affected by environmental factors. Thus, for example, genetically identical plants grown at different altitudes may differ markedly in form (Fig. 22.29). Similarly, to take a striking though unnatural example, if during the early developmental stages of some fishes, they are exposed to water containing an abnormally high concentration of magnesium chloride, they develop with a single median eye (Fig. 22.30); the abnormal environment has altered the 'normal', genetically determined pathway of development.

Further problems

If you reflect upon what we have been saying, you will notice that there is a seeming conflict of two ideas. The

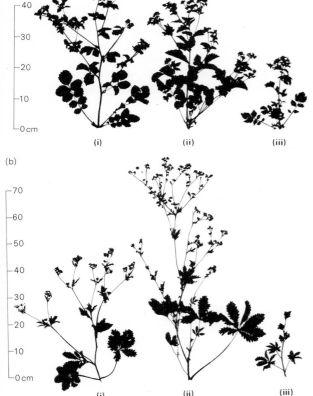

22.29 Effects of environment on the growth of plants with identical genotypes. (a) *Potentilla glandulosa.* These plants are vegetative offshoots of a single plant which was found growing in the wild in California at an altitude of 520 m. They were re-planted and allowed to grow for several years at the following altitudes: (i) 30 m (ii) 1 400 m (iii) 3050 m. (b) *Potentilla gracilis*, the parent plant was collected from 1 400 m. Offshoots (i), (ii) and (iii) were grown at the same altitudes as in (a). Note that in each case, plants grew best at the altitude closest to that of the original home. (After Clausen, Keck and Hiesey).

genotype of an individual is determined at the time of fertilization and the tissues of the organism which later develop all have an identical chromosome complement to that of the zygote: this stems from the description we have given of the nuclear events of mitosis. Nevertheless, in any higher organism, different tissues are built up from different cell types; these have 'differentiated' during development. If the genotype of a cell affects its activities, how are we to account for the fact that cells of the same genotype may nevertheless be very different? One possibility is that our initial assumption is incorrect and that the events of mitosis are more complex than we have so far assumed: we might, for example, postulate that there is some sorting out of different homologous chromosomes, so that the genotypes of different tissues are in fact different.

One simple way in which we can examine this matter is to ask whether already differentiated tissues can give rise to other types of differentiated cells or can produce only pre-existing cell types. The answer to this question is probably familiar: complete plants can be grown from parts or 'cuttings' of the stems of mature specimens. Similarly tubers, like yam, can give rise to complete plants. There is, however, the possibility that undifferentiated cells remain in the cutting or tuber and that in fact the new tissues arise from these. More satisfactory would be to destroy the nucleus of an unfertilized ovum, to replace it

by a nucleus from a differentiated cell, and to see if the product of such a nuclear transplantation develops into a normal individual. Such experiments (Fig. 22.31), using the eggs and differentiated midgut tissues of the Clawed Toad, *Xenopus*, have shown that ova containing nuclei taken from differentiated cells can indeed give rise to complete new individuals.

It thus seems that our initial assumption about the nature of events in mitosis is correct, that there is no sorting of chromosomes and that all the diploid nuclei of an individual are genetically equivalent. Nevertheless we have to seek some explanation of the phenomenon of differentiation. Research is going ahead on this problem at the present time and, so far, our detailed knowledge is largely restricted to events occurring in bacteria that are somewhat similar to differentiation. To understand these, we must enquire further into the chemical basis of the genes and how they produce their effects. This will take us into an area where polymeric molecules are of great significance, and in which studies on bacteria and viruses provide the major evidence for our conclusions.

There is a further and more practical reason why we desire to understand more about genes and the way in which they work. We have seen that all organisms are the products of an interaction between their genetical constitution and the totality of their environmental experience. If we have the ability to alter the genetical constitution of an organism, then we may be able to produce both plants and animals especially suited to man's needs. This has indeed been done: the high-yielding varieties of crop plants which form the basis of the 'Green Revolution' (p. 282) have been developed by measures taken deliberately to alter the genetic constitution of various parental stocks. To understand these procedures more clearly, it is also necessary to understand the chemical nature of the genes.

Problems

1 If two parents, both heterozygous for Hb^S have four children, what are the chances that none, one, two, three and all four children will be homozygous for Hb^S and have sickle-cell anaemia?

2 In tomato plants the normal type of leaf is called 'cut'. In some plants the leaves may be entire, which is spoken of as 'potato' (since the shape resembles that of the leaves of a potato plant). A cut-leafed plant was crossed with a potato-leafed plant. From the F_1 seeds 47 cut-leafed plants and 51 potato-leafed plants were obtained. When these cut-leafed plants were crossed with each other, 178 cut-leafed and 61 potato-leafed plants were obtained. When the potato-leafed plants were crossed together, all the plants obtained were potato-leafed. Which character is dominant? What were the genotypes of the original two plants?

3 Normal maize pollen stains blue when treated with iodine solution. There is a recessive allele which results

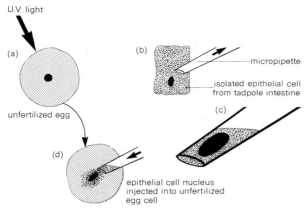

U.V. light

(a)

unfertilized egg

(b)

micropipette

isolated epithelial cell from tadpole intestine

(c)

(d)

epithelial cell nucleus injected into unfertilized egg cell

22.31 Nuclear transplantation experiment. (a) An unfertilized egg cell is irradiated with ultra-violet light, destroying the nucleus. (b) Epithelial cells from a tadpole intestine are separated; a micropipette is inserted into one cell. (c) The nucleus together with a small quantity of cytoplasm is removed. (d) The nucleus and surrounding cytoplasm are injected into the egg cell. Development proceeds and in a number of cases, when the operation was performed successfully, adult toads were obtained. A check on the origin of the nuclear material was possible, since the donor of the epithelial cell nucleus belonged to a strain of *Xenopus* in which each nucleus contained only one nucleolus, while the recipient egg cell came from a strain with two nucleoli in each nucleus. The nuclei of the adult tissues had only a single nucleolus.

in the pollen grains staining red, not blue. Pollen from a plant heterozygous for the alleles was spread on a slide and stained with iodine. Make a drawing to show what you would expect the preparation to look like under the microscope when there are ten pollen grains in the field. (The pollen grains are spherical.) Explain how you arrived at an opinion as to its appearance.

4 In a mongoose, brown coat colour **B** is dominant over grey coat colour **b** and short coat hair **S** is dominant over long coat hair **s**.

A brown, short-haired male was mated with a brown, long-haired female. In several litters, all their numerous progeny were either brown with short hair or brown with long hair.

The male was subsequently mated with a grey, short-haired female and the progeny of their litters were all short-haired, but either brown or grey.

What were the genotypes of the three parents? Show clearly how you arrived at your answer.

5 A man married twice. By his first wife he had two children whose blood groups were types B and O. He also had, by his second wife, two children of types AB and O. His first wife remarried a universal donor (type O) and their one child was type A. What were the genotypes of the man and his two wives? Show clearly how you arrived at your conclusions.

6 In tomatoes the gene for tall plant (T) is dominant to that for short plant (t). You have already determined in Problem 2 whether cut-leaf or potato-leaf is dominant. What ratios of phenotypes would you expect from

(a) a cross of homozygous tall, cut-leafed plants with short, potato-leafed plants?

(b) a cross between the progeny produced by cross (a)?

(c) a cross of homozygous tall, potato-leafed plants with short, cut-leafed plants?

(d) a cross between the progeny produced by cross (c)?

7 The fruit colour of tomatoes is determined by both skin colour and flesh colour. Skin colour is controlled by a pair of alleles Y (yellow) and y (colourless) and flesh colour by a pair of alleles R (red flesh) and r (yellow flesh). Final fruit colour will be determined by the combination of genes in different genotypes as follows:

R – Y –	red fruit	
R – yy	pink fruit	
rr Y –	yellow fruit	
rr yy	cream fruit	

(a) If a plant, homozygous for the red fruit genotype, is crossed with a plant carrying cream fruit, what will be the genotype and phenotype of the progeny?

(b) If the progeny of this cross is selfed, what will be the ratios of different genotypes and phenotypes of fruit colour in the F_2 plants?

(c) If a pink-fruit-bearing plant of genotype R/r y/y is crossed with a yellow-fruit-bearing plant of genotype r/r Y/y, what will be the ratios of different phenotypes of fruit colour in the progeny?

8 (a) A red-fruit-bearing tomato plant was crossed with a cream-fruit-bearing plant. The fruit colours of the progeny were 43 red, 38 pink, 39 yellow and 41 cream. What were the probable genotypes of the parents?

(b) A red-fruit-bearing tomato plant was crossed with a pink-fruit-bearing plant. The fruit colours of the progeny were 63 red and 23 yellow. What were the probable genotypes of the parents?

In both cases show how you arrived at your conclusions.

9 (a) A strain of *Drosophila* with dumpy wings **dp** and scarlet eyes **st** was crossed with a wild-type strain homozygous for both these characters. The progeny were backcrossed to the double-recessive parents. What would you expect to be the ratio of phenotypes from such a backcross?

(b) A strain of *Drosophila* with black body **b** and vestigial wings **vg** was crossed with a wild-type strain homozygous for both these characters. On backcrossing the F_1 flies to the double-recessive parents the following progeny were produced: 586 wild-type, 111 vestigial wings and grey (wild-type) body, 106 normal wings and black body, 465 vestigial wings and black body. What explanation would you offer for such a result?

10 Explain the technical value of backcrossing of F_1 progeny to recessive parents in genetical analysis.

11 Three *Drosophila* stocks carried the characters (i) black body **b** and purple eye **pr**, (ii) black body and vestigial wing **vg** and (iii) purple eye and vestigial wing. Each stock was crossed with a wild-type stock homozygous for these characters, and the F_1 progeny of each cross was then backcrossed to the double-recessive parent. The results of these backcrosses (expressed as percentages of different phenotypes) were as follows:.

(i) P_1 with black body and purple eye

Wild type	48·5
Black body and purple eye	45·5
Black body and normal eye	2·9
Grey body and purple eye	3·1

(ii) P_1 with black body and vestigial wing

Wild type	43·2
Black body and vestigial wing	38·3
Black body and normal wing	9·7
Grey body and vestigial wing	8·8

(iii) P_1 with purple eye and vestigial wing

Wild type	46·9
Purple eye and vestigial wing	40·8
Normal eye and vestigial wing	6·5
Purple eye and normal wing	5·8

What are the relative positions of these three alleles on the chromosome which carries them? Explain how you arrived at your conclusion.

12 How do you consider the data presented in Problem 11 might be used quantitatively?

13 Do chiasmata always form between the same loci in the prophase of a first meiotic division? Explain how you arrive at your answer.

14 In the prophase of a first meiotic division two chiasmata may sometimes be formed along the length of the same chromosome. What will be the effect of this phenomenon on (a) the identification of linkage groups and (b) the construction of chromosome maps?

15 A woman who was pregnant was very anxious to have a son. She consulted various people as to whether there were any steps which she could take to make certain that her baby would be a boy. One of these people gave her a medicine prepared from a secret recipe saying that if she drank that her baby would surely be a boy. Do you consider that a medicine is likely to be of value in ensuring that a foetus will be of one sex or the other? Give reasons for your opinion.

   If the woman drank the medicine, what are the chances that it would appear to 'have worked'?

16 A man and a woman, both of normal colour vision, had a colour-blind son Ali and two daughters, Bess and Ciss, both with normal vision. Ali had a daughter with normal colour vision; Bess had two sons, one colour-blind and the other with normal vision, and Ciss had five sons all with normal vision. What were the probable genotypes of the parents, their children and their grandchildren? Explain how you arrived at your conclusions.

17 In poultry, feather legs (F) is dominant over clean legs (f) and pea comb (P) over single comb (p).

   Two cocks, A and B, were bred with two hens, C and D. All four birds were feathered and pea-combed. Cock A produced offspring with both hens and all were feathered and pea-combed. Cock B mated with hen C produced progeny which were either feathered or clean, but all were pea-combed. With hen D, cock B produced progeny all of which were feathered but some were pea-combed and some single.

   What were the probable genotypes of the four birds? Set out the reasoning which led to your conclusions.

18 Show that the phenotypic ratio reported for the F_2 of a parental cross of

   X/X Y/Y Z/Z by x/x y/y z/z

given on p. 406 is correct.

19 On p. 398 we imply that in the first meiotic division any two pairs of homologous chromosomes will distribute themselves randomly between the two daughter cells. Suggest a possible way in which direct evidence for this conclusion might be obtained from a microscopic study of chromosomes.

20 While in most social bees, wasps and ants, whether a female becomes a queen or a worker is determined by nutrition, in the small stingless bees of the genus *Melipona*, there is genetic determination of caste: 25 per cent of females are genetically queens. The suggested mechanism is that caste is determined by two pairs of alleles, A and a, together with B and b, and that any individual heterozygous for both alleles is genetically a queen. Show that, regardless of the genotype of the male, 25 per cent of his female offspring will be genetically queens.

Bibliography
Further reading

Ashton, B. G.   *Genes, Chromosomes and Evolution*, Longman, 1967, Chaps. 1 to 4

Burns, G. W.   *The Science of Genetics*, Collier-Macmillan, 1969, Chaps. 1 to 4, 5–8, 10 and 11

Cove, D. J.   *Genetics*, Cambridge University Press, 1971, Chaps. 1, 2 and 3

George, W.   *Elementary Genetics*, Macmillan, 1965, Chaps. 1 to 6

Guerdon, J. B.   *Gene Expression During Cell Differentiation*, Oxford Biology Readers, Oxford University Press, 1973

John, B., Lewis, K. R.   *Somatic Cell Division*, Oxford Biology Readers, Oxford University Press, 1972

John, B., Lewis, K. R.   *The Meiotic Mechanism*, Oxford Biology Readers, Oxford University Press, 1973

Levine, R. P.   *Genetics*, Holt, Rinehart and Winston, 1965, Chaps. 3 to 7

Guerdon, J. B.   'Transplanted Nuclei and Cell Differentiation', *Scientific American*, 1968, Offprint no. 1128

McKusick, V. A.   'The Royal Haemophilia', *Scientific American*, 1965, Vol. 213, pt. 2, p. 88

McKusick, V. A.   'The Mapping of Human Chromosomes', *Scientific American*, 1971, Offprint no. 1220

Mazia, D.   'The Cell Cycle', Scientific American, 1974, Vol. 230, pt. 1, p. 54

23 The molecular basis of inheritance

In the last chapter we saw that there was good evidence that hereditary factors or genes are located on the chromosomes, but that a further understanding of the processes of heredity requires a knowledge of the nature of the genes and what they do within a cell. One starting point for such an enquiry is the question: what chemical substances are found in chromosomes? We could attempt to answer this question by studying the gross chemical composition of nuclei. This, however, does not tell us whether the substances we extract are specifically associated with the chromosomes, but with this knowledge we can devise specific staining methods for the chemicals we find and then use them to see which of these chemicals occur in the chromosomes of cells. This latter idea will already be familiar to you from the various tests used to determine the location of materials such as starch, fat or lignin in plant tissues.

The chemistry of cell nuclei

One easily obtainable source of material which consists of little other than cell nuclei is spermatozoa. The sperm of many species of freshwater fish can readily be obtained during the breeding season, by running one's fingers along the flanks of a male fish. This is spoken of as 'stripping' the fish and the dense sperm suspension is the 'milt'. Female fish can be stripped in a similar way and the technique is used for obtaining large quantities of young fish or 'fry' to stock reservoirs and fish ponds.

By the use of such material, it can be shown that sperm contain not only protein, but also certain chemicals called the nucleic acids which may constitute between 30 and 50 percent of the total dry weight. It can further be shown, by the use of specific staining techniques, that the chromosomes of eukaryote cells contain both protein and nucleic acids.

You are already familiar with the structure of proteins. The nucleic acids also prove to be very large polymeric molecules in which the repeating unit is a nucleotide, formed from a nitrogen-containing base combined with a sugar phosphate. Such a type of compound is already familiar since AMP, ADP and ATP are all nucleotides with the structure of

base—sugar—phosphate

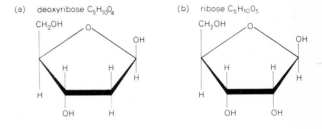

23.1

In the nucleic acids, such units are joined together to form polymeric chains in the following fashion:

base—sugar—phosphate

base—sugar—phosphate

base—sugar—phosphate

Further analysis shows that the sugar in the nucleotides of the major type of nucleic acid in sperm is a pentose, deoxyribose (Fig. 23.1a), which is related to the pentose sugar ribose (Fig. 23.1b), a constituent of ATP, but which has one less oxygen atom than ribose. It will form deoxyribonucleotides, in contrast to AMP or ATP which are ribonucleotides. The nucleic acid polymer is called a deoxyribonucleic acid, commonly abbreviated to DNA.

There are four different types of nitrogenous base in DNA. Two are purines, compounds related to uric acid, and two pyrimidines (Fig. 23.2). The two purines are adenine and guanine. The two pyrimidines are cytosine and thymine; their six-membered rings are clearly related to the corresponding rings of the purines.

The chemical nature of a gene

The question now arises as to whether the 'material' of a gene is either of these two constituents of a chromosome, the protein and the DNA, or whether perhaps a gene is a complex of both substances. The first clear evidence relating to this problem came from studies made in 1944 by O. T. Avery, C. M. Macleod and M. McCarty, three

413

adenine

cytosine

guanine

thymine

23.2

American scientists who were investigating a phenomenon found in bacteria and called 'transformation'. This effect was originally demonstrated by F. Griffith in *Pneumococcus*, the bacterium which causes pneumonia. Griffith had cultures not only of the normal, disease-causing or virulent type of *Pneumococcus*, but also of another strain which is not virulent and is rapidly destroyed by phagocytes if injected into a mammal. When grown on agar plates these two strains of *Pneumococcus* form colonies of markedly different appearance. The virulent strain produces large colonies with a smooth, shiny surface and is therefore designated S (for smooth), while the non-virulent strain forms very small colonies with a rough, matt surface and is therefore designated R (for rough).

Griffith made the following observations:

a) If living, strain S bacteria were injected into mice, the mice died and strain S bacteria could be cultured from their heart blood.

b) If living, strain R bacteria were injected, the mice survived; no strain R bacteria could be cultured from them.

c) If strain S bacteria were first killed by heat treatment and then injected into mice, the mice survived and no *Pneumococcus* could be obtained from them.

d) If living strain R and heat-killed strain S bacteria were both injected into a mouse, the mouse died and live strain S could be recovered from the heart blood.

Clearly some material from the dead, heat-treated, strain S bacteria had modified, or 'transformed', the strain R bacteria. This might be due simply to the activation of a gene already present, but since such modified bacteria continue, when cultured, to form smooth colonies, their genetic mechanism must have been permanently altered in some fashion. A few years later it was shown that the same effect could be obtained without using mice. If living,

strain R bacteria were cultured *in vitro* with heat-killed, strain S bacteria, transformation still occurred.

Avery and his co-workers set out to identify the material in heat-killed, strain S bacteria which brought about the transformation. They fractionated the transforming material, and were able to show that the active fraction was deoxyribonucleic acid. The fraction ceased to be active if it was first treated with the enzyme deoxyribonucleotidase (DNAase) which hydrolyses DNA.

Such a result tells us only that DNA is a transforming principle. Avery and his co-workers then went on to show that the R to S transformation of *Pneumococcus* could be effected only by DNA extracted from *Pneumococcus* cells; DNA from other sources such as yeast was inactive. Since that time many other examples of bacterial transformation have been studied and these confirm the finding of Avery and his colleagues that transforming agents are composed of DNA.

A very different type of experiment leading to the same conclusion utilized the colon bacillus *Escherichia coli* and a virus or bacteriophage which attacks the bacillus, reproducing within the bacterial cell whose walls ultimately break down liberating the newly synthesized 'phage particles'.

This experiment concerns T2 phage, which has a com-

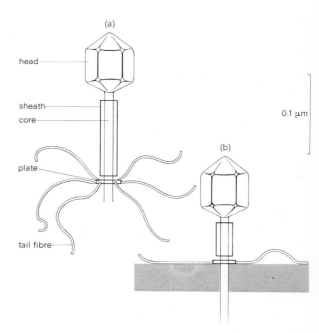

23.3 Diagram of a T-type bacteriophage. (a) The free phage particle. (b) The particle becomes attached to the wall of a bacterium by the tail fibres. The protein of the sheath then contracts and the core is driven through the wall of the bacterium. DNA contained within the head capsule passes down the core into the cytoplasm of the bacterial cell.

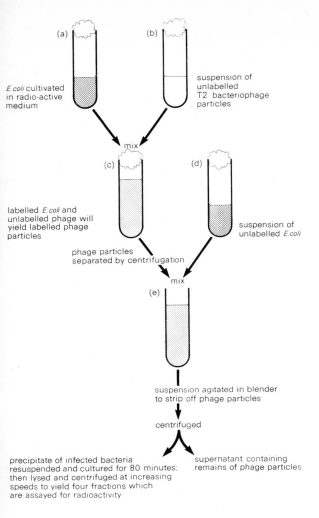

(a) E. coli cultivated in radio-active medium

(b) suspension of unlabelled T2 bacteriophage particles

mix

(c) labelled E.coli and unlabelled phage will yield labelled phage particles

phage particles separated by centrifugation

(d) suspension of unlabelled E.coli

mix

(e) suspension agitated in blender to strip off phage particles

centrifuged

precipitate of infected bacteria resuspended and cultured for 80 minutes; then lysed and centrifuged at increasing speeds to yield four fractions which are assayed for radioactivity

supernatant containing remains of phage particles

23.4 Principle of experiment to determine whether both protein and DNA or only the latter are injected into a bacterial cell when infected by T2 phage. Suspensions (a) and (b) are mixed to produce phage particles labelled either with ^{32}P or ^{35}S. These particles are separated by differential centrifugation and then mixed with (d). Almost immediately the suspension is agitated to strip off the phage particles from the bacterial walls; the mixture is then centrifuged to collect the infected bacteria which, after a period to allow growth of new phage particles, are lysed, separated into fractions by differential centrifugation and then assayed for radioactive content.

plex structure (Fig. 23.3; see also Book 1 Fig. 19.24). The outer covering of the head, the tail and the tail fibres consist of protein and within the head capsule is a long single strand of DNA. When a cell of E. coli is attacked by T2

phage, the phage particles become attached to the bacterial cell wall by the tail fibres, the sheath protein of the tail contracts, driving the core of the sheath through the bacterial cell wall, and the contents of the head capsule pass down the hollow core into the bacterial cell. Phage reproduction then occurs within the cell: thus the material injected into the cell contains the genetic information for making new phage particles. The problem is to determine whether the only material injected is DNA, or whether protein is also injected. If only DNA is injected, then we have further evidence that this material can transmit heritable information to new organisms.

To decide between these alternatives, use was made of the fact that sulphur atoms occur in amino-acids and therefore in protein, but not in DNA, while DNA contains a great deal of phosphorus which is not present in protein. By growing E. coli in culture media containing either $KH_2{}^{32}PO_4$ or $Mg^{35}SO_4$, it was possible to obtain bacteria either with protein labelled with the radioisotope ^{35}S or with nucleic acids labelled with the radioisotope ^{32}P (Fig. 23.4).

If such cultures were infected with T2 phage, phage particles with either S-labelled protein or P-labelled DNA could be obtained. Such labelled particles were then added to suspensions of unlabelled E. coli and after a few minutes, the bacteria were collected by centrifugation. They were then suspended in clean medium and 'churned' in a high-speed mixing device called a Waring blender; this has the effect of detaching the phage particles which remain attached to the bacterial cell wall. The bacterial cells were centrifuged once again, washed and resuspended in medium. After 80 minutes, during which time the phage reproduced, the bacteria were lysed to release the phage and the suspension centrifuged into four fractions. The content of radioactive sulphur or phosphorus in each fraction was then determined. In the fraction containing the phage particles about 30 percent of the original ^{32}P was recovered, but less than 1 percent of the original ^{35}S (Fig. 23.5).

The reverse experiment has also been performed. It is possible to remove the DNA from T2-phage particles by suspending them first in a 3M solution of potassium chloride and then pouring this suspension into a very large volume of water. The resulting particles, now lacking DNA, will still attach themselves to the cell walls of E. coli, but they fail to produce any infection.

From these and other experiments with bacteria and virus particles, there is much evidence that the basic genetic material is DNA. With eukaryotic cells, the evidence is as yet indirect. It is possible to show, by measuring the light absorption of suitably stained nuclei, that the quantity of DNA in a cell doubles during the interphase of mitosis (Fig. 23.6). Similarly, if we compare the DNA content of the nuclei of spermatozoa and of red blood cells, we find that the latter contain almost twice as much as the former (Table 23.1).

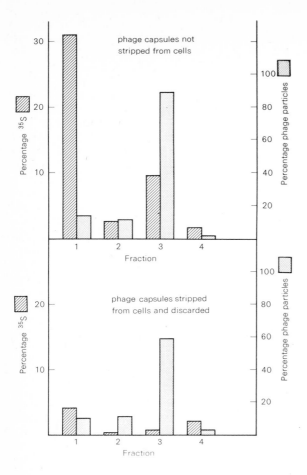

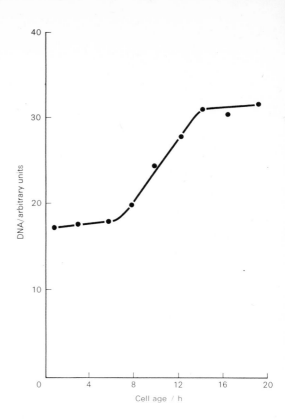

23.6 Graph showing the DNA content at intervals after the start of interphase of mouse cells growing in tissue culture. The DNA is estimated by staining the cells specifically for DNA and then measuring the quantity of stain photometrically. Each point represents mean values for 40 or more cells.

23.5 Results obtained from the type of experiment outlined in Fig. 23.4. The bar charts compare the percentages of the initial total quantity of ^{35}S remaining in four fractions collected at the final stage in Fig. 23.4. In the upper chart, the step of removing the attached phage particles by treatment with a blender was omitted. Fraction 1 is largely bacterial cell walls; these are heavily labelled in the upper bar chart owing to the presence of attached phage bodies. Phage particles are mostly brought down in fraction 3 which has almost no associated radioactivity in the lower chart; this implies that almost none of the protein present in the infecting phage particles (Fig. 23.4c) is present in the phage progeny. It follows from these data that less than 1 percent of the protein present in the original phage particles has been transmitted to the newly formed particles and that it is therefore unlikely that genetical information is transmitted as protein.

Table 23.1 Quantity of DNA in sperm and erythrocyte nuclei of different species expressed as mg $\times 10^{-9}$ per nucleus

	Sperm	Erythrocytes
Carp (fish)	1·64	3·49
Toad	3·70	7·33
Man	3·25	7·30

Note: Although mature human erythrocytes have no nuclei, their developing stages, found in bone marrow, are nucleate.

The characteristics of gene action

To recognize that DNA is the material of the genes does not, however, tell us anything about the nature of gene action. To understand this, it is necessary to examine the effects of various alleles and see whether we can produce a plausible hypothesis as to what the genes may be doing. We have indeed already seen one example in which it is possible to describe in chemical terms the difference between the actions of one allele and another: haemoglobin S differs from haemoglobin A by the substitution of one amino-acid for another in the β-chain of the molecule. It

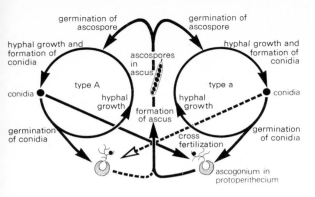

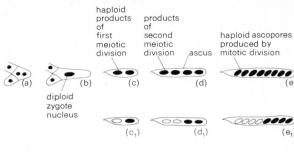

23.7 Life cycle of *Neurospora*. Two distinct 'mating types', A and a, occur. Both can be cultured indefinitely from hyphae. Protoperithecia may be formed and these can be 'fertilized' by conidia of the opposite mating type. A conidium settles on one of the hair-like trichogynes which project from each protoperithecium and its nucleus passes into the protoperithecium. Several mitotic divisions of nuclei from both sources then follow, followed by fusion to produce several zygote nuclei each of which gives rise to an ascus.

23.8 Stages in the development of an ascus. In (c_1)–(e_1) the products of the first nuclear division are shown as a black and a white nucleus. Note the way in which the arrangement of subsequent divisions results in the formation of two groups, each of four ascospores: the four ascospores of a group are all usually identical with respect to any one allele, since they are derived from a single haploid nucleus formed by the first meiotic division.

might then be that in other cases also the DNA is concerned with the synthesis of particular proteins.

A study of rare alleles in the mould *Neurospora* (Ascomycetes) has been of particular importance. The vegetative stages of this mould are haploid, so that the complications of dominance relations which occur in diploid organisms do not arise: if an allele is present its effect will be manifest.

The life cycle of *Neurospora* is shown in Fig. 23.7. There are two distinct strains of the mould, types A and a. Both can form female organs called ascogonia. If these two strains are grown together a process of fusion occurs, as in fertilization, between nuclei derived from a conidium of one mating type and those of an ascogonium of the other type. Note that this 'mating' will occur only between moulds of different types: type A moulds of different strains grown together will not show mating. Fusion to form zygote nuclei is followed immediately by two meiotic divisions, which restore the haploid number, and by a further mitotic division of all the daughter cells. During the meiotic divisions, the nuclei are enclosed in a long single cell, the ascus. Owing to the shape of the ascus, the products of the meiotic and mitotic divisions are kept in a straight line. As a result the four cells in one half of the ascus are derived from one daughter cell of the first meiotic division and those in the other half, from the other daughter cell (Fig. 23.8). As development proceeds the products of these divisions, the ascospores, become surrounded by heavy spore walls which allow each

to be manipulated separately and used as a founder cell for a new hyphal culture.

Using various experimental techniques which we will discuss later (p. 440) conidia were produced which might be expected to contain rare alleles. Such conidia were used to fertilize a 'wild-type' culture of the opposite mating type. Each resulting ascospore was then isolated in a separate culture medium. Wild-type *Neurospora* will grow in a so-called 'minimal medium' containing only sucrose, the vitamin biotin, and certain inorganic salts including nitrate. The wild-type mould is able to synthesize from these precursors amino-acids and thus protein, as well as necessary vitamin compounds such as riboflavin, thiamine and so on. Any ascospore unable to synthesize one or more of these compounds cannot grow on minimal medium.

The ascospores were first isolated into a 'complete' medium which contained amino-acids from hydrolysed protein as well as yeast and malt extract to provide vitamins. Thus even if a spore were deficient in the ability to synthesize one of these compounds, it could nevertheless obtain it from the complete medium. Conidia from each of such cultures were then subcultured into four different media (Fig. 23.9):

a) the complete medium;
b) the minimal medium;
c) the minimal medium enriched with amino-acids;
d) the minimal medium enriched with vitamins.

If the mould grew in minimal medium, then its synthetic

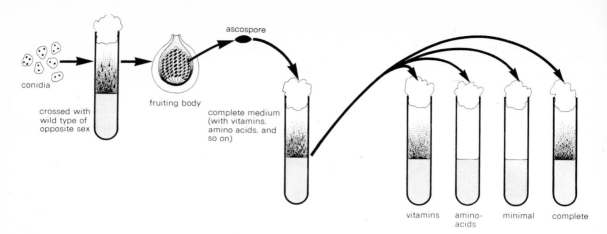

23.9 Diagram showing the procedure used to detect strains of *Neurospora* deficient in different synthetic abilities. For further explanation, see text. The strain illustrated is deficient in ability to synthesize one of the vitamins.

ability did not differ from that of wild-type mould. If, however, it failed to grow in minimal medium but grew in one of the enriched media, say (c), then it lacked an ability to synthesize some amino-acid. The strain could meanwhile continue to be grown in the complete medium.

By further subculturing into minimal media enriched with particular amino-acids, it was possible to determine the precise nature of the deficiency in synthetic ability which characterized any particular strain. Some results of one such study are shown in Table 23.2. These three amino-acids are known to be linked in the following synthetic chain leading to the formation of arginine

$$\xrightarrow{(1)} \text{ornithine} \xrightarrow{(2)} \text{citrulline} \xrightarrow{(3)} \text{arginine}$$

where (1), (2) and (3) represent different enzymes catalyzing the changes.

Examination of the data in Table 23.2 shows that provided strain 21502 was supplied with orthithine, it grew; in the absence of ornithine there was no significant growth and so we may conclude that some event prior to ornithine synthesis and corresponding to step (1) was failing to occur. In strain 30300, while addition of citrulline

permitted growth, there was little growth on addition of ornithine; thus it seems reasonable to assume that this strain fails to produce the enzyme system necessary for the conversion of ornithine to citrulline. By similar reasoning strain 36703 lacks the necessary enzymes for step (3).

Many other similar experiments using other moulds and also bacteria have yielded results which can be interpreted as implying that the action of 'wild-type' genes is to direct the synthesis of particular enzymes and that the alleles isolated by the procedures we have described are characterized by a failure to synthesize some specific enzyme.

The actions of many other types of allele can be interpreted in the same way. Thus, for example, in some varieties of the Cape primrose, *Streptocarpus*, blue flowers are dominant to pink: the difference depends upon a single gene. The structural skeletons of the two flower pigments are shown in Fig. 23.10; they differ only in the presence of two extra —OCH$_3$ groups in one of the two pigments. We may postulate that the dominant allele causes the production of some enzyme responsible for this addition and that the enzyme is absent in the pink flowers. Similar conclusions can be drawn from a study of the different types of eye colour found in *Drosophila*.

Table 23.2 Growth of different strains of *Neurospora* on minimal medium with different amino-acids added (*Data from Srb and Horowitz*)

Strain number	Dry weight (mg) of mycelium after 5 days growth in minimal medium supplemented by 0·005 mM of			
	Nothing	Ornithine	Citrulline	Arginine
21502	0·9	29·2	37·6	37·2
30300	1·0	0·8	34·1	37·6
36703	0·0	0·0	0·0	20·4

pink pigment

blue pigment

For simplicity only three groupings are shown; these show the only differences between the two pigments.

23.10

This view also provides us with an explanation of certain types of hereditary disease in man. One such condition, spoken of as phenylketonuria, is due to the accumulation of a very high level of phenylpyruvic acid and phenylalanine in the blood; as much as 1 g of phenylalanine may be excreted each day. The condition is serious as the phenylpyruvic acid prevents normal development of the brain, leading to severe mental retardation. If diagnosed at birth, the effect can be countered by keeping the affected child for some years on a diet low in phenylalanine. The condition stems from an inability to convert phenylalanine to tyrosine (Fig. 23.11). Once again it can be postulated that there is a failure to synthesize an enzyme, in this case that required for the conversion of phenylalanine to tyrosine.

In many of these and in other cases, it has been shown that, as we have postulated, enzymatic material is in fact absent. In yet other instances, as in that of haemoglobin synthesis, different alleles have been shown to produce proteins of different chemical composition. The conclusion from all such experiments is that the normal result of gene activity is the synthesis of some specific protein which may or may not be an enzyme.

The examples which have been analysed all relate to biochemical changes in which some product or its absence can be detected. Some anatomical differences can also be explained in terms of enzyme-controlled processes. For example, the difference between round and wrinkled pea seeds is related directly to starch synthesis; the greater quantity of starch synthesized by the seeds of plants carrying the genes for 'round' fills out the seed coat which otherwise is shrivelled or 'wrinkled'. We still have no clear idea, however, of the nature of the mechanism controlling the development of other characteristics, such as 'bar' and 'wild-type' eye in *Drosophila*. This reflects the fact that an understanding of causal factors which underlie the patterns of development of different organisms is still largely lacking, but it is generally assumed that in these cases also the determining action of any gene relates to protein synthesis.

The nature of dominance

This general idea provides us with some insight into the phenomenon of dominance. If we postulate that there are two alleles A and a, one of which directs the synthesis of an enzyme, but the other does not, then, a phenotype A/a will not be recognizably different from one whose genotype is A/A, provided the presence of only one A gene in the genotype is sufficient to ensure the production of an adequate quantity of enzyme to synthesize its metabolic product. This type of relation will explain why, for example, in man the allele for brown eye colour is dominant to that for blue eye colour, a condition in which the brown pigment is not formed: in the heterozygote sufficient enzyme for the synthesis of brown pigment is formed in the cells of the iris.

If, however, the quantity of protein synthesized determines the quantity of product, then we will not find a dominance relationship, but rather one in which the quantity of product is proportional to the number of active genes present. Such a case we have already described in connection with the quantity of vitamin A in the endosperm of maize (p. 406). Similar reasoning explains why, in the four o'clock plant, homozygous flowers of genotype R/R are red, while those which are heterozygous and of genotype R/W are the more dilute colour pink (p.393).

This interpretation allows us also to understand why it is that an individual who is heterozygous for Hb^A and Hb^S has both types of haemoglobin in his blood cells. If both genes in the heterozygote are actively directing the synthesis of their characteristic protein, then both proteins will occur in the phenotype. By the same reasoning we can understand why it is possible to have four different phenotypes of the ABO blood group system.

By extension of this idea we can comprehend the type of result we described on p. 405 in connection with flower colour. Here we said that two sets of alleles were involved. If one, C, was present in either the homozygous or heterozygous condition, then the flower would be coloured, provided a second allele, R, at a different locus was also present, again either in heterozygous or homozygous form. This case is basically similar to that of arginine biosynthesis discussed above. If we assume that the chain of biosynthesis of the flower pigment runs

$$\text{colourless precursor A} \xrightarrow{(1)} \text{colourless precursor B} \xrightarrow{(2)} \text{pigment}$$

then we may postulate that the gene C produces an enzyme

23.11

which converts precursor A into precursor B in step (1). In the homozygous recessive, c/c, no active enzyme is produced and hence no pigment can be produced since precursor B will not be formed. Similarly the gene R can be regarded as determining the production of the enzyme necessary for step (2) in the biosynthesis of the pigment. In the homozygote of genotype r/r, no pigment will be produced even if the plant is homozygous for the gene C.

Such results lead us to a further question. If, in some haploid organism, the presence of a gene results in the failure of production of an enzyme, does this gene cause the production of an enzymatically inactive protein or is no protein produced at all? The answer to this question can be illustrated by results from experiments upon the synthesis of the enzyme tryptophan synthetase in *Neurospora*. The enzyme can catalyse the reaction

$$\text{indoleglycerol phosphate} + \text{serine} \rightarrow \text{tryptophan}$$

The structures of the compounds are omitted as they are irrelevant to our argument.

Several strains of *Neurospora* not capable of catalysing this reaction have been isolated. If such strains produce a protein which is, for some reason, incomplete as an enzyme, then it should be possible to detect the presence of such a substance. This is done as follows: the purified enzyme from the 'wild-type' mould is injected into the blood stream of a rabbit. The rabbit will respond to the presence of the foreign protein by producing an antibody which will react with the enzyme antigen: the product of this antigen–antibody reaction is inactive as an enzyme. We know from other experiments that antibodies react with proteins which are closely similar in structure to the antigens which originally stimulated their synthesis. Thus, if an enzymatically inactive but otherwise similar protein is produced by these strains of *Neurospora*, it also will react with the antibody.

Extracts are made from the various *Neurospora* strains, following the same procedure as that used to isolate the enzyme. To each extract is now added sufficient of the antibody from the rabbit serum to react with the antigen-like protein if it is present. The two precursors of tryptophan and also the enzyme extracted from wild-type mould are then added and the reaction mixture presently tested for the presence of tryptophan.

If a protein resembling the enzyme is present it will combine with and inactivate the antibody. Added enzyme will be free to react with the substrates and tryptophan will be synthesized. If, however, no such protein is present the antibody will react with the added enzyme and inactivate it; as a result no tryptophan will be synthesized (Fig. 23.12).

When such experiments are carried out they give what may seem a surprising result. Most strains produce a material which will combine with the antibody, but some do not; in other words, some strains are producing a

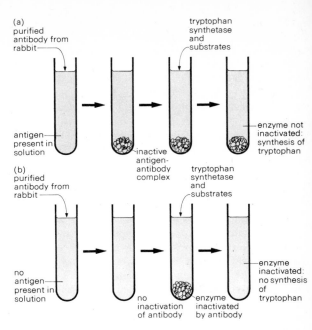

23.12 Diagram outlining experimental procedure used to test for the presence of protein antigenically similar to *Neurospora* tryptophan synthetase. For further explanation, see text.

Reaction 1 indoleglycerol phosphate + serine ⟶ tryptophan
Reaction 2 indole + serine ⟶ tryptophan
Reaction 3 indoleglycerol phosphate ⟶ indole

23.13 Reactions catalysed by tryptophane synthetase.

protein similar to the enzyme tryptophan synthetase, while others are not. Thus, although phenotypically the alleles of the different strains are similar, the synthetic activities they direct may differ.

We can carry this analysis one step further. Tryptophan synthetase catalyses the three distinct reactions shown in Fig. 23.13. If we test the protein products that are inactive in catalysing reaction 1 with the precursors of reactions 2 or 3, we find some which will catalyse reaction 2 but not reactions 1 or 3 and others which will catalyse reaction 3 but not 1 or 2. Thus these strains can produce different proteins whose only common character is that they cannot catalyse reaction 1. To understand how this situation can arise, it is necessary to comprehend the events of protein synthesis which we will now outline.

Protein synthesis

It is convenient to start by describing a second type of nucleic acid, one which is found mainly in the cytoplasm of eukaryote cells; DNA is found chiefly in the nucleus. This nucleic acid differs in composition from DNA in two ways. Firstly, it contains ribose in place of deoxyribose: it is therefore called ribonucleic acid, which is abbreviated to RNA. Secondly, thymine is replaced by a different pyrimidine, uracil, which lacks the methyl group found in thymine. Several different types of RNA are found in the cytoplasm, each playing a different role in the processes of protein synthesis.

The importance of RNA in protein synthesis is suggested by the photographs of bacteria reproduced in Fig. 23.14. These are of unstained bacteria photographed by ultra-violet light of a wavelength of 257 nm. Light of this wavelength is absorbed strongly by nucleic acids, but only slightly by protein. The first photograph was taken from cells 18 hours after the start of a new culture. At this time there is little cell division and the cells are spoken of as being in the 'lag' phase. Fig. 23.14b shows cells from the same culture somewhat later. Active cell division has still not started, but the cells are absorbing the ultra-violet light more strongly. Finally in Fig. 23.14c, we see cells at the beginning of the period of active cell division when the population density is increasing rapidly and synthesis of new protein is at its height. Correlated with the active

protein synthesis there is now a great deal of nucleic acid in each cell. Special staining methods can be used to show that this is RNA.

Protein synthesis *in vitro*

It is possible to break cells up gently and then, by centrifuging the resulting suspension of fragments at different speeds, to separate different cell organelles. With a fairly low centrifugal force, nuclei and fragments of plasma membrane are brought down, a rather greater force separates the mitochondria, while with still more rapid centrifugation a fraction is obtained which was originally described as containing 'microsomes'. If a radioisotope-labelled amino-acid is injected into the blood stream of a guinea pig and after some time the animal is killed, the pancreas removed and the cells broken up and fractionated in this way, most of the radioactive label is found in protein associated with the microsome fraction. This suggests that it is this material which is particularly associated with protein synthesis (Fig. 23.15a). Similar results can be obtained *in vitro* by first disrupting the cells

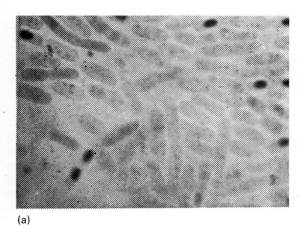

(a)

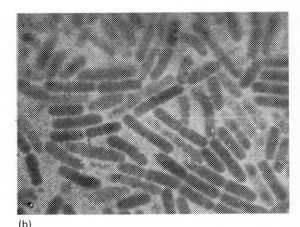

(b)

(c)

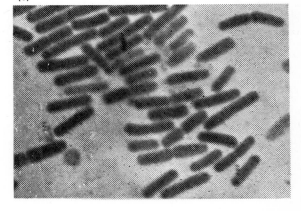

23.14 Unstained bacteria taken from cultures at different times after inoculation and photographed by ultra-violet light. The presence of nucleic acid is shown by the absorption of the light, producing a dark image of the bacterial cells. (a) After 18 h culture; (b) middle of the lag phase before rapid cell division has started; (c) the beginning of the period of rapid cell division.

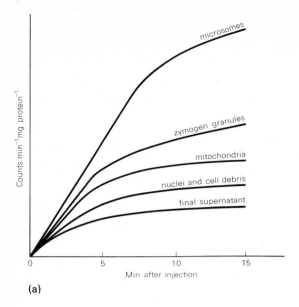

(a)

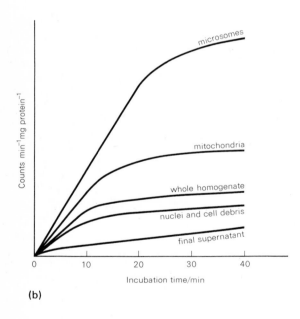

(b)

23.15 (a) Distribution of radioactivity in fractions of pancreas cells at intervals after injection of labelled amino-acids into the experimental animals. Thus the incorporation of the amino-acids is taking place *in vivo*. Note that the label accumulates most and most rapidly in the microsomal fraction. (b) A similar experiment but starting with disrupted rat-liver cells. Note that there is incorporation of the radioactive label in the protein, showing synthesis to be occurring *in vitro* and, further, that here also the synthesis of protein is mainly associated with the microsomal fraction.

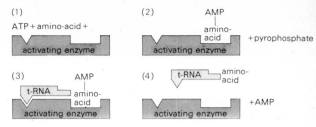

23.16 Diagrammatic representation of the reactions leading to the combination of an amino-acid with t-RNA. (1) and (2): an amino-acid-activating enzyme complex is synthesized with the formation of AMP from ATP. (3) t-RNA combines with this complex and a t-RNA–amino-acid complex is formed which (4) dissociates from the enzyme.

and then adding radioisotope-labelled amino-acids to the suspensions (Fig. 23.15b). Thus proteins can be synthesized in a mixture of the components of disrupted cells.

Transfer RNA

Once the possibility of protein synthesis *in vitro* had been demonstrated, the stages in this process could be elucidated by biochemical methods. Such studies have shown that, as an initial event in the incorporation of an amino-acid into a protein, each amino-acid combines, in a series of reactions, with a type of RNA of low molecular weight which is spoken of as transfer RNA or t–RNA (Fig. 23.16). There are many different sorts of t–RNA in a cell, each being able to combine with only one type of amino-acid.

Here it is convenient to introduce a technical term used in much of this type of research. RNA particles of different molecular weight may be separated by ultracentrifugation and the speed with which they sediment is measured in a unit, the 'sedimentation coefficient', which is expressed in svedbergs, (abbreviated to S) and named after the Swedish biochemist who first developed the ultracentrifuge. Particles which sediment rapidly will have high S values; smaller particles which sediment less readily lower S values. Note that the S value is influenced by the shape of the molecule and is not directly a measure of molecular weight. The t-RNAs have sedimentation constants of about 4S, and with 75 to 80 nucleotides in the molecule, a molecular weight of about 25 000 daltons.

Microsomes and ribosomes

Examination with the electron microscope of the cytoplasm of a protein-secreting cell, such as one from the pancreas, shows it to contain a complex system of membranes, the endoplasmic reticulum (Fig. 23.17). Upon these membranes are small spherical structures called ribosomes. Not all endoplasmic reticulum carries ribosomes and not all ribosomes lie on the membranes of an

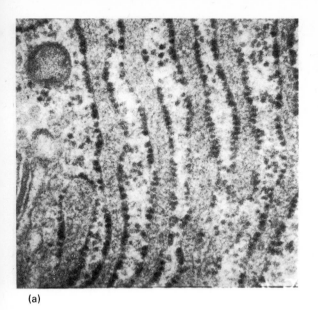

(a)

(b)

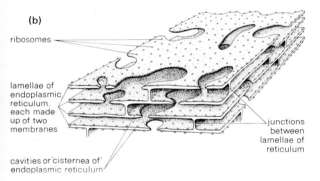

ribosomes

lamellae of
endoplasmic
reticulum,
each made
up of two
membranes

junctions
between
lamellae of
reticulum

cavities or cisternea of
endoplasmic reticulum

23.17 (a) Electron micrograph showing the membranes of the endoplasmic reticulum with associated ribosomes: these are the black dots, each being about 18 nm in diameter. (b) Diagram showing a three-dimensional reconstruction of the endoplasmic reticulum.

endoplasmic reticulum. 'Microsomes' consist of broken fragments of endoplasmic reticulum in the form of membranes to which ribosomes are attached. The membranes can be dispersed by the addition of bile salt, so that a pellet of ribosomes alone can be collected by centrifugation. *In vitro* experiments show that the ribosomes, in the absence of the membranes, can bring about protein synthesis.

Each ribosome is a double unit of about 18 nm diameter and consists of a smaller and a larger particle united together. These particles may be dissociated; in bacteria the smaller has a sedimentation coefficient of about 30S and a molecular weight of about 0.9×10^6 daltons and the larger a sedimentation coefficient of about 50S and a molecular weight of about 1.8×10^6 daltons. The sedimentation coefficient of the combined particles is about

70S. In eukaryote cells, the particles are slightly larger: 40 and 60S particles combine to form 80S units. Chemical analysis shows that both particles are formed from protein and RNA. Such RNA is referred to as ribosome-RNA or r-RNA. The RNA in each particle is a single giant molecule; that in the smaller particle has a sedimentation coefficient of 16S and that in the larger one of 23S. There are about twenty different protein molecules specifically associated with the small particle and about thirty with the bigger; some of these have been shown to have enzymic activity.

Messenger RNA

At this stage it is possible to erect a number of hypotheses about protein synthesis. We might, for example, postulate that the t-RNA molecules with their associated amino-acids react in some fashion with the ribosomes and that different types of protein are assembled on different types of ribosome. Experiment shows that this is not so. No protein synthesis occurs in a mixture consisting only of amino-acids, ribosomes, t-RNA, a source of ATP and the activating enzymes for the amino-acids, unless the addition is made of the supernatant fluid which remains after the ribosomes have been removed by centrifugation. Clearly some further material is involved in these reactions. This proves to be a further type of RNA, which is now spoken of as 'messenger' RNA or m-RNA.

A clear demonstration of the role of m-RNA in protein synthesis comes from experiments using oocytes of the Clawed Toad, *Xenopus* (Book 1 Fig. 21.16), and the immature red blood cells of a rabbit. These blood cells are still nucleated and retain the ability to synthesize haemoglobin. The red cells were disrupted and, after centrifuging to remove nuclei, cell membranes and mitochondria, the RNA was extracted from the resulting supernatant fluid. This RNA was then centrifuged and separated into fractions of 4, 5, 9, 16 and 28S. A small quantity of one of the fractions was injected into the cytoplasm of an oocyte of *Xenopus* together with some haemin, a precursor of the non-protein, iron-carrying part of the haemoglobin molecule. The oocyte was also supplied with a radioisotope-labelled amino-acid to allow identification of newly synthesized protein. This process was then repeated with the other fractions. After six hours the oocytes were disrupted and the cell suspension centrifuged. The contents of the supernatant fluid were examined by chromatography to see whether there had been any synthesis of haemoglobin and whether this haemoglobin was rabbit haemoglobin or toad haemoglobin, which are chemically slightly different.

It was found that haemoglobin had been synthesized by the eggs injected with the 9S fraction and that it was chemically indistinguishable from rabbit haemoglobin; it did not occur in controls or in any of the oocytes injected with other RNA fractions (Fig. 23.18). Thus the 9S RNA

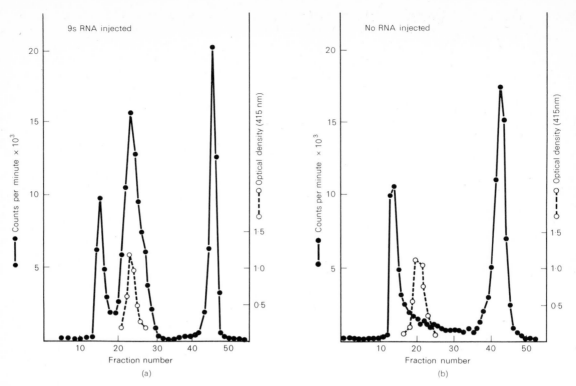

23.18 (a) Oocytes of *Xenopus* were injected with rabbit 9S RNA and haemin and cultured for six hours with radioactive histidine. The oocytes were then homogenized in a solution containing a small quantity of unlabelled rabbit haemoglobin. The homogenate was then run through a chromatographic column to separate the proteins; more than 50 separate fractions were collected. Each was assayed for radioactivity and photometrically for haemoglobin. (b) A similar experiment, but without the 9S RNA. Note that in (a), between fractions 20 and 30, there is a peak of radioactivity which is not represented in (b). This corresponds to a protein synthesized only in the presence of 9S RNA. The open circles record colorimeter measurements of the absorption due to the added haemoglobin. Note that this is also to be found between fractions 20 and 30, correlating with the peak of radioactivity and providing evidence that the labelled protein detected in (a) but absent in (b) is rabbit haemoglobin.

fraction obtained from the cytoplasm of the immature rabbit blood cells was able to 'instruct' the cytoplasm of the *Xenopus* oocytes to synthesize rabbit haemoglobin; it fulfilled the role of 'messenger' which we postulated. Indeed synthesis of the new, although foreign, protein occurred about 100 times more rapidly in *Xenopus* cytoplasm than in disrupted cell suspensions. From these experiments it is clear that one function of m-RNA is to direct the synthesis of specific proteins and indeed it has proved possible to use synthetic ribonucleic acids to direct the production of quite unnatural proteins *in vitro*. It follows also that ribosomes are not specific in their actions: toad ribosomes can be used to synthesize a mammalian protein.

We have summarized our conclusions thus far in Fig. 23.19 but we have still to learn how these different constituents are linked together. Before we can understand this we must look further at the structure of DNA, as this will show us an important general property of the nucleic acids.

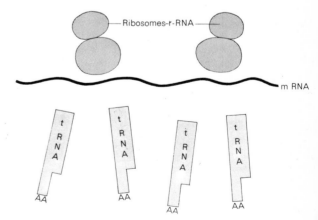

23.19 Diagram showing the three different types of RNA found in the cytoplasm and concerned in protein synthesis. Understanding of the interrelations of these units depends upon a knowledge of the rules of base pairing first elucidated for DNA.

Table 23.3 Molar proportions of bases, relative to adenine as 10, in DNA from various sources (*Data from Davidson*)

Source of DNA	Adenine (A)	Guanine (G)	Cytosine (C)	Thymine (T)	Total purines	Total pyrimidines	A/T	G/C
Calf thymus gland	10·0	7·6	8·0	9·8	17·6	17·8	1·02	0·95
Calf kidney	10·0	7·9	7·8	10·0	17·9	17·8	1·00	1·01
Rat bone marrow	10·0	7·5	7·5	9·9	17·5	17·4	1·01	1·00
Herring sperm	10·0	8·0	8·2	9·9	18·0	18·1	1·01	0·98

* The thymus is a glandular structure just anterior to the heart. It produces cells which are liberated into the blood stream and are concerned in the formation of antibodies.

The structure of DNA

Chemical analysis of DNA has shown that there are three regularities in its composition. These are:

a) the total number of purine bases per mole is equal to the total number of pyrimidine bases per mole;

b) the ratio of adenine to thymine is unity;

c) the ratio of guanine to cytosine is also unity.

Such data are shown in Table 23.3; they imply that the molecule must be, in some fashion, highly organized. The resolution of its structure has come from research by two English crystallographers, Rosalind Franklin and Maurice Wilkins, as well as by an American biologist, James Watson, working with an English physicist, Francis Crick. Watson and Crick approached the problem primarily by molecular model building and their ideas depended for experimental proof upon the X-ray crystallographic studies of Franklin and Wilkins.

The Watson–Crick model has two features. Firstly, the molecule is not a single linear polymer, but consists of two polymeric strands which are twisted to form a double helix (Fig. 23.20). The backbone of each of these strands is formed of the chain of deoxyribose and phosphate groupings, while the bases project inwards towards the axis of the helix. These are represented in Fig. 23.20 by bars joining one strand with the other.

The crystallographic evidence showed the molecule to be a long regular uniform fibre of about 2 nm diameter. If this condition is to be satisfied, then the bases must be arranged so that any purine base on one strand is opposite a pyrimidine base on the other; if two purines were adjacent at one point and two pyrimidines at another, the diameter of the fibre would vary markedly along its length, and this would conflict with the evidence from X-ray crystallography. More specifically it is necessary for adenine to be partnered by thymine and guanine by cytosine (Fig. 23.21). The whole structure, untwisted so as to appear in a single plane, is illustrated in Fig. 23.22. Such a structure is in conformity with the results of the chemical analyses of base composition. Since each purine unit is paired with a pyrimidine unit, it follows that the total number of purine bases per mole will equal the total

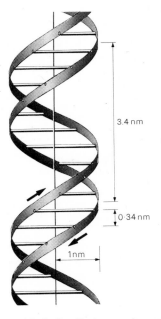

23.20 Model of a double helix. Each strand represents the sugar–phosphate backbone of a DNA polymer. The bars represent the bases which are arranged in pairs along the length of the molecule. The arrows indicate that the two strands are orientated in opposite directions. Compare Fig. 23.27.

number of pyrimidine bases. Since adenine (A) is paired with thymine (T), the ratio of the two bases will be unity; the same applies to guanine (G) and cytosine (C).

These relations are spoken of as the 'rules of base pairing', namely that A goes with T and G with C. One consequence of this rule is that if we write down a sequence of bases representing one strand of a DNA molecule, such as –A–T–G–A–C–T–, then it follows that the sequence of bases in the other strand must run –T–A–C–T–G–A–. Any pair of bases or sequences of bases which conform to the rules of base pairing are spoken of as being complementary.

There is much evidence that if two complementary series of bases occur, either in two different regions of a single nucleic acid polymer or in two different polymeric

425

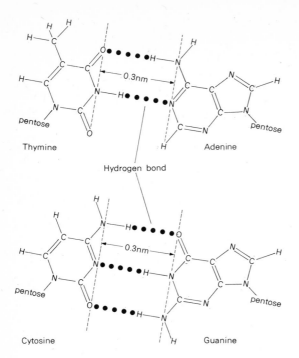

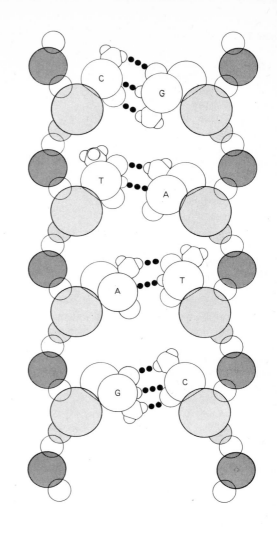

23.21 Details of the arrangement of bonding between complementary purines and pyrimidines in DNA. The spacings represent correct interatomic distances. Note that the distance between the two pairs of complementary bases is the same. Any attempt to replace cytosine by thymine, while preserving the rest of the arrangement, including the orientation of the pentose bonds, permits the formation of only a single hydrogen bond and, further, brings two keto-groups together which will disrupt the spacing.

molecules, these will tend to join together, being held by hydrogen bonds in a similar fashion to that found in the double strand of DNA (Fig. 23.21).

The base pairings of RNAs

Unlike DNA, RNA does not show regularities of base composition. This is part of the evidence for the view that it is a single-stranded, linear polymer. It is nevertheless possible to envisage that two molecules of RNA, in which a limited region of one is complementary to a limited region in the other, will bind together. Thus we may postulate that if some length of an m-RNA strand has a base sequence which is complementary to a base sequence in a t-RNA molecule, the two will tend to unite. We can extend this hypothesis and recognize that if a sequence of bases in a strand of m-RNA correspond to the complementary sequences of several different t-RNA molecules, then, because each t-RNA molecule is specific for a parti-

23.22 Diagram showing the arrangement of the two chains of the double helix if they were straightened and seen in a single plane. Such a drawing distorts the spatial relations but may assist in understanding the arrangement of the molecules.

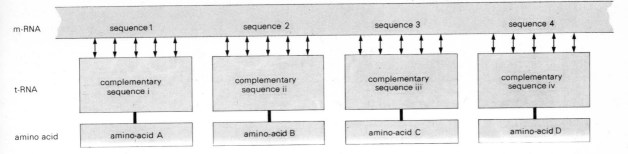

23.23 Formal diagram to show how a set of base sequences in a strand of m-RNA, by pairing with different t-RNA molecules, could order a sequence of amino-acids. The double-headed arrows represent hydrogen bonds between the complementary sequences in m-RNA and t-RNA.

cular amino-acid, the sequence of bases in the m-RNA would be equivalent to a particular sequence of amino-acids (Fig. 23.23). Such a process of relating a linear sequence of nucleotide bases to a linear series of amino-acids is akin to translating a sentence in one language like French into another like English, and is indeed spoken of as 'translation'.

The RNA 'language'

We arrive thus at the view that the sequence of amino-acids in a protein can be 'represented' by a sequence of bases in m-RNA. Clearly one question of interest is to ask: how many bases are required to represent or 'specify' a particular amino-acid? Analysis shows that the number of different amino-acids which occur in known proteins is 20; other amino-acids are found in both plants and animals, but they are not constituents of proteins. We therefore require a set of base sequences which will distinguish between at least 20 different objects and we have at our disposal four different bases which we can use in any order within a sequence. Clearly four single bases cannot represent 20 different amino-acids. If the sequence were of two bases, then the maximum number of combinations would be 4×4 or 16, which is still too few. With three bases we would have a choice of $4 \times 4 \times 4$ or 64 possible combinations, which is more than sufficient for our purpose. So the most economical hypothesis is that three bases in sequence can specify an amino-acid.

There are two features to this idea. We require only 20 combinations and yet appear to have 64. The accepted view is, firstly, that the length of a sequence of bases or 'codon' specifying a particular amino-acid is indeed three and, secondly, that several codons may specify the same amino-acid; for example, there are in m-RNA six different codons all specifying the amino-acid leucine, four specifying alanine but only two for histidine. We describe this situation in which several codons have the same 'meaning' by saying that the 'code' is 'degenerate'.

Reading the message

Allowing that three bases constitute a codon, that is that there is a 'triplet code', we may ask further how the code is read. Consider a length of m-RNA in which there is a sequence U–U–G–A–C–U–G–A–G. This might be read in at least two ways. In one, each successive group of three bases constitutes a codon; our nine bases would constitute three codons. Another possibility is that the code 'overlaps'; that is, UUG forms the first codon, UGA the second, GAC the third and so on. The evidence favours the first possibility. Two of the reasons are these. Firstly, if we postulate an overlapping code, any one codon will limit the possible sequence of immediately adjacent amino-acids. Thus, if we have an amino-acid coded by ACG, which is the codon for threonine, then this amino-acid must be preceded by one whose codon reads ?AC and be succeeded by one whose codon will read CG?. ?AC allows us a choice of four different amino-acids but CG? will be arginine since CGA, CGC, CGG and CGU all code for arginine; this is a reflection of the degeneracy of the code. We would thus expect that in all proteins arginine would be found immediately adjacent to threonine. A study of amino-acid sequences does not, however, reveal this regularity; since the prediction which follows from the hypothesis is not fulfilled, the hypothesis cannot be valid. Secondly, let us consider the result of changing one base in an m-RNA sequence: this can be achieved experimentally. If there is a non-overlapping code, the change will produce a difference between the original and the modified protein of one amino-acid only; this is what we find naturally in the case of haemoglobin A and haemoglobin S in which glutamic acid, coded in m-RNA as AUG, is replaced by valine, coded as UUG. If, however, there is an overlapping code, then a single base change could result in a change of two or even three consecutive amino-acids. Such a condition is not met, while changes of the type to be expected to result from a non-overlapping code are common.

427

It is not possible here to summarize the various steps in the investigations which have led to the determination of the amino-acid equivalent of the different possible sequences of the triplet code. In recent years, however, the actual sequences of bases in considerable lengths of the nucleic acid molecules of two bacteriophage particles have been determined: these nucleic acids ultimately direct the synthesis of certain proteins of known amino-acid sequence. It is found that the two sequences, of nucleic acid bases and of amino-acids in the proteins, correspond to our hypothesis that the code is non-overlapping and degenerate, and that each codon is formed of three bases. Furthermore, this work has confirmed the relations between different triplets and particular amino-acids which had been deduced from earlier experiments.

The role of the ribosomes

With these ideas in mind, we can now return to the problem of the relations between t-RNA, m-RNA and the ribosomes. One of the most striking observations has been that if cells are disrupted and centrifuged, the ribosome-containing fraction includes not only 70S, 50S and 30S particles but much heavier particles as well. Examination of these under the electron microscope shows them to consist of long thin strands with ribosomes attached at intervals along their length. The most reasonable interpretation is that each strand is a molecule of m-RNA and that, for the purposes of protein synthesis, the ribosomes are attached to the m-RNA.

This concept has been elaborated into a hypothetical picture of protein synthesis of the type shown in Fig. 23.24. At the onset of the synthetic process the two subparticles of a ribosome become attached to one end of the m-RNA molecule. There is evidence that this starting point carries a special codon for a particular amino-acid which is subsequently removed from the completed protein. Each type of t-RNA molecule is visualized as having in its structure three bases which are complementary to a codon of the m-RNA: such a complementary triplet on t-RNA is called an anti-codon. If, for example, the m-RNA codon is CAU, then the corresponding t-RNA anticodon will be GUA. On each ribosome there are two 'binding sites' at which t-RNA molecules can attach; which t-RNA molecules attach is determined by the m-RNA. Once two such molecules are in place, the enzymes associated with the ribosomes synthesize a peptide bond between the two amino-acids. This alters the stereochemical situation; the leading t-RNA molecule becomes free and the second moves into the position originally occupied by the first, carrying with it the m-RNA strand, as a consequence of the codon-anticodon link. This brings the next codon in the sequence in line with the empty t-RNA binding site which is then occupied by an appropriate t-RNA molecule with its associated amino-acid. Another peptide link is synthesized and the process is repeated, the developing protein chain remaining attached to a t-RNA molecule. In this way there is a regular movement of each ribosome along any m-RNA strand to which it is attached. Finally, the m-RNA molecule terminates in a codon which corresponds to no

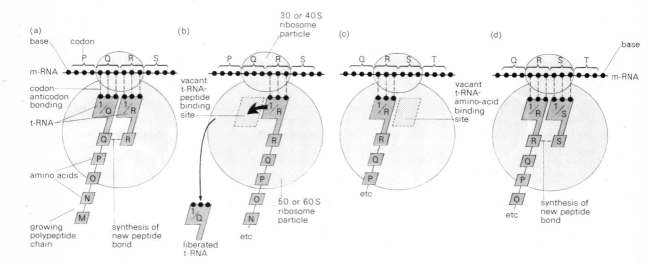

23.24 Diagram showing the possible events during the synthesis of a polypeptide chain. (a) There are two binding sites on the larger ribosome particle. One binds a t-RNA–polypeptide complex and the other a t-RNA–amino-acid compound. (b) After the synthesis of a new peptide bond, the polypeptide chain is liberated from the left-hand t-RNA molecule which then leaves the binding site. The right-hand t-RNA molecule then moves to the t-RNA–polypeptide binding site, carrying the m-RNA strand with it. (c) This frees the t-RNA–amino-acid binding site. (d) A new t-RNA–amino-acid compound occupies the vacant site and a fresh peptide bond will be synthesized.
The symbols such as 1/Q, 1/R on the t-RNA should be read as 'anticodon to Q', 'anticodon to R', and so on.

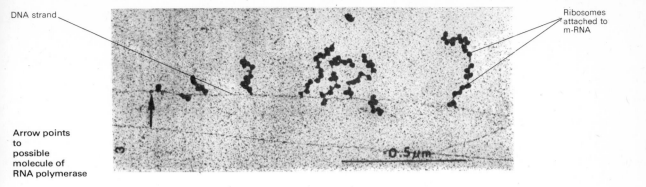

DNA strand

Ribosomes
attached to
m-RNA

Arrow points
to
possible
molecule of
RNA polymerase

0.5μm

23.25 Electron micrograph of a DNA strand from a disrupted bacterial cell. m-RNA strands, still being synthesized, have already attached to them ribosome particles which will be translating the m-RNA. Polypeptide molecules will not appear with the technique employed in making this photograph.

amino-acid. This is a 'signal' saying 'end synthesis'. There are three such terminating codons, UAA, UAG and UGA. They are commonly referred to by the misleading term 'nonsense codons', although they are not, of course, devoid of 'sense' or 'meaning', but represent a very definite message in the code.

The origin of m-RNA

This leaves us with two further questions. One, which is clearly of central importance to our original problem of the nature of the gene and its actions, is the origin of the various types of m-RNA. In a eukaryote cell, protein synthesis occurs mostly in the cytoplasm under the direction of the molecules of m-RNA. But the genes, which we believe to be the ultimate source of 'information' on the amino-acid sequences in the various proteins, lie on the chromosomes within the nucleus. The most reasonable hypothesis is, therefore, that each m-RNA strand is synthesized within the nucleus and, if the protein for which it codes is synthesized in the cytoplasm, the m-RNA molecule passes through the nuclear membrane into the cytoplasm.

It is possible to extend the concept of base pairing to the synthesis of m-RNA. We may visualize the base sequence of the DNA molecule as organizing along its length complementary sequences of ribonucleotides as determined by the rules of base pairing. Thus what is originally a sequence or 'sentence' in DNA is 'rewritten' in RNA; this process is therefore referred to as 'transcription'. Then a strand of m-RNA is synthesized by the action of a special RNA-synthesizing enzyme, DNA-dependent RNA-polymerase; this enzyme synthesizes RNA only in the presence of DNA, hence its name. Electron micrographs of nucleic acid material from disrupted bacterial cells do indeed show us

the whole process (Fig. 23.25). The long, relatively straight strand is a molecule of DNA. Along its length arise chains of m-RNA, those to the right being longer than those further to the left, as they were synthesized earlier; ribosomes have already become attached to the newly formed chains of m-RNA. Such a picture would not be found with material from a eukaryote cell as the ribosomes are mainly in the cytoplasm and not in the nucleus.

This concept presents two problems: one is the way in which a molecule of the RNA-polymerase 'knows' where to start the process of synthesis of m-RNA. The probable answer to this we will describe shortly (p. 434). The second concerns the action of RNA-polymerase. Some local process must occur at the site of m-RNA synthesis to separate the bases of the DNA one from another, so that they are free to pair with complementary ribonucleotides. This is presumably an aspect of the activity of the enzyme, but the details of the mechanism are not yet known. In Fig. 23.26 is a diagram of the sort of event which may occur during the synthesis of a molecule of m-RNA. You will see that only one strand of the DNA is being copied. Fig. 23.27a shows a very short length of two complementary stands of DNA. We have inserted the accepted numbering of two of the carbon atoms in the pentose molecules. Note that while on the left each sugar is linked to phosphate by carbon 3′ above and by that numbered 5′ below as you move down the page, those on the right are arranged in the opposite sense. The RNA-polymerase transcribes only one of the two DNA chains, namely that which we designate as 3′ → 5′; the other strand is not copied. It must not, however, be assumed that the genes from which the m-RNA molecules are transcribed all lie on one strand and that the other is always inactive. There is evidence that, as illustrated in Fig. 23.27b, two neighbouring genes may lie on different strands.

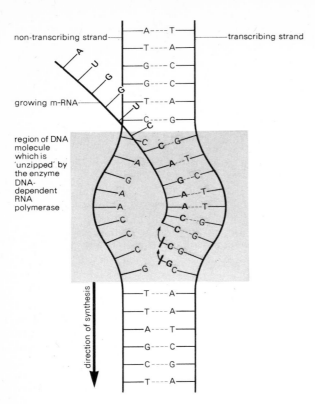

non-transcribing strand — transcribing strand

growing m-RNA

region of DNA molecule which is 'unzipped' by the enzyme DNA-dependent RNA polymerase

direction of synthesis

23.26 Diagram showing the possible action of DNA-dependent RNA-polymerase. The enzyme is visualized as separating or 'unzipping' locally the bonds uniting the base pairs of the DNA molecule so that those of one strand can serve as a 'template' on which to assemble a strand of m-RNA.

The origin of ribosomes

Finally we may ask what is the origin of the ribosomes. Studies using brief exposure of cells to radioisotope-labelled bases allow us to follow the pathways of synthesis of the ribosomal particles as well as their locations within the cell. These show that precursors of the ribosomal particles are first synthesized within the nucleus of a eukaryote cell in close association with the nucleolus. The DNA of the nucleolus may therefore be the site of the genes which specify the base sequences of the precursors of r-RNA. These precursor molecules then pass through the nuclear membrane and in the cytoplasm of the cell undergo various modifications, including the addition of their specific proteins, to result in the formation of 40S and 60S ribosomal particles. t-RNA is also synthesized from the chromosomal material associated with the nucleolus.

This brief sketch provides some insight into the events which link the genes, formed of DNA, with the amino-acids which will be incorporated into specific proteins.

Fig. 23.28 summarizes in diagrammatic form the events believed to occur in a eukaryote cell.

The role of the endoplasmic reticulum and the Golgi apparatus

We may mention briefly one further detail. Ribosomes freed from the membrane of the endoplasmic reticulum are able to synthesize protein *in vitro*. What then is the role of the reticular membrane within the cell? A survey of eukaryote cell structure shows that a rough endoplasmic reticulum, that is one covered with ribosomes (Fig. 22.17a), occurs typically in cells which are either secreting protein or accumulating it in some reserve form. This suggests that

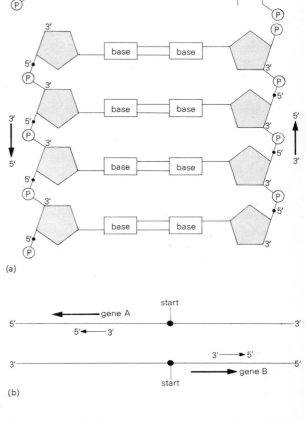

23.27 (a) Detailed structural arrangement of phosphate (P) and pentose residues in the two complementary strands of DNA. (b) DNA strands are read in the direction 3' → 5'. While, as a result, only one strand of the double helix will be transcribed, both strands may carry genes which will be read in opposite directions.

the reticulum is concerned with 'collecting' the products of the synthesis of certain proteins. Experiments have been made in which pancreatic cells of guinea pigs were exposed to injected amino-acids marked with a radioactive label. The tissue was fixed after different time intervals and the position of the labelled molecules detected by autoradiography. In this technique a tissue labelled with radioactive material is brought into close contact with a photographic plate. The technique may be applied to whole structures (Book 1 Fig. 8.7) or to histological sections. In the latter case, the section is flooded with photographic emulsion and the position of the radioactive atoms within cells can be determined by a study of the tracks left in the emulsion by ionizing particles. Study of a series of such preparations showed that the radioactive atoms were incorporated in newly synthesized protein on the endoplasmic reticulum within five minutes. The protein is believed to pass from the ribosomes through the membrane of the reticulum into the cavities or the cisternae (Fig. 23.17b), and to be transported through smooth endoplasmic reticulum, that is reticulum lacking ribosomes, to a cytoplasmic structure called the Golgi apparatus where the radioisotope appears after about twenty minutes. There it is concentrated into vacuoles to form secretory zymogen granules, in which the label appeared after about one hour.

The molecular basis of chromosome replication

The conclusions we have reached are that a gene is formed of a polymeric molecule of DNA and, by extension, that any chromosome must consist at least in part of a long molecule of DNA. In bacteria and bacteriophages, there is little protein associated with the DNA molecules and by suitable treatment the entire molecules can be extracted and their length determined by examination with the

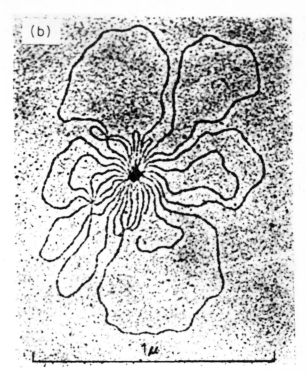

23.29 Electron micrograph of the DNA molecule normally contained within the capsule of a bacteriophage particle. The dark structure near the centre of the loops of DNA is the capsule.

electron microscope. Fig. 23.29 shows a bacteriophage from which the DNA has been extruded. The total length of this molecule is about 17 μm. The DNA in T2 phage is a single molecule nearly 50 μm in length. The length of the DNA molecules of bacteria may be much greater: *Escherichia coli*, for example, has a single chromosome which contains about 6×10^6 nucleotides and is more than 1 mm in length. In eukaryote cells the chromosomes are a complex of protein and nucleic acid; while treatment of the chromosomes of certain types of cell with protein-digesting enzymes does not disrupt the continuity of the threads, treatment with an enzyme which hydrolyses DNA does break up the structure. This finding is in keeping with the postulate that the molecular structure giving continuity to a chromosome is DNA.

One of the properties we have postulated as characteristic of chromosomes is that during the interphase of mitosis, each produces an exact copy of itself. Does the structure of DNA cast any light upon how this may come about? We have already seen that if we know the sequence of the bases in any polynucleotide, we can write down the complementary sequence as defined by the laws of base pairing (p. 425). This allows us to visualize two possible ways in which a DNA molecule could replicate. The one is that a complete second molecule is formed along the length of the first, the required nucleotides being ordered

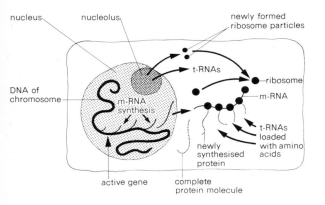

23.28 Schematic representation of the probable events of protein synthesis in a eukaryote cell showing how a nuclear gene determines the synthesis of a specific protein in the cytoplasm.

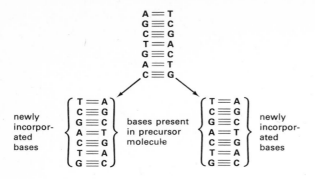

23.30 The concept of semi-conservative DNA replication.

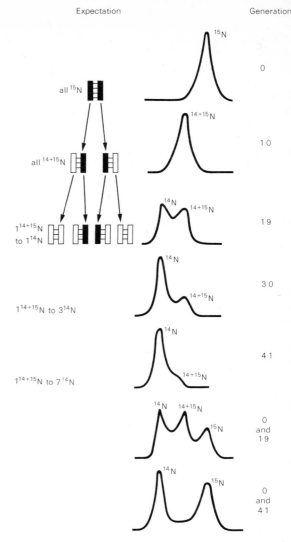

along the length of the double helix and then, by enzyme activity, linked into two polymeric chains. Such a possible method of replication is called 'conservative', since the original molecule remains intact. The other possibility is that the two chains of a double helix separate and each then serves as a pattern or 'template' for the synthesis of a new complete molecule of DNA. As a result of the rules of base pairing, the two daughter molecules will be identical (Fig. 23.30). Such a possible method of replication is called 'semi-conservative' since each new molecule includes, or has conserved, half of the parent molecule.

Using a technique called density-gradient centrifugation, it is possible to separate molecules of DNA of differing isotopic composition; if, for example, *Escherichia coli* is grown in a medium containing [^{15}N]ammonium chloride, the DNA synthesized can by this technique be distinguished from that of cells grown in a medium with [^{14}N]ammonium chloride. This possibility was exploited by two American biochemists, M. S. Meselson and F. W. Stahl, to determine whether chromosome reduplication is conservative or semi-conservative. Their technique was to grow the bacteria for more than ten generations in a medium containing nitrogen-15. At the end of this period more than 95 percent of the nitrogen-14 in the bacteria had been replaced by nitrogen-15. The medium was then abruptly changed to one containing [^{14}N]ammonium chloride. Any new nitrogenous bases synthesized would contain nitrogen-14 rather than nitrogen-15.

If replication were conservative, then after some generations we would have two types of DNA; one heavily labelled with nitrogen-15, the other containing none. If, however, replication is semi-conservative we would expect to find molecules of mixed isotopic composition, containing equal proportions of nitrogen-14 and nitrogen-15, although with growth these would form a smaller and smaller proportion of the entire population.

The results obtained are shown in Fig. 23.31. It is clear that three types of DNA, differing in isotopic composition, are found and we may thus conclude that the normal pattern of replication is semi-conservative. The interest and importance of the finding is that it shows the way in

23.31 Evidence for the semi-conservative replication of DNA. Bacteria grown in medium containing ^{15}NH$_4$Cl are cultured and then transferred to medium containing ^{14}NH$_4$Cl. Samples are withdrawn at intervals, the DNA extracted and then fractionated by density-gradient centrifugation. After centrifuging, the gradient is photographed in ultra-violet light (compare Fig. 23.14) and the intensity of absorption measured along the gradient by a photometer. Each graph shows the curve of photometer readings. The column on the right shows the number of generations from the start of culturing in normal medium. The data on the left show the expected isotopic composition of the DNA if semi-conservative replication occurred. If replication were conservative there should be two peaks in the first new generation. The two bottom curves come from mixtures to allow alignment of the ^{14}N and $^{14+15}$N peaks against the original ^{15}N peak. The upper of these curves shows clearly the presence of three types of DNA of different isotopic composition.

which the rules of base pairing coupled with the double-stranded nature of the DNA molecule act together to ensure a constancy of chemical composition of the chromosomes from one cell division to the next.

Control of gene activity: enzyme induction

We mentioned earlier the paradox that in a higher organism, although all the cells of an individual have an identical set of genes or 'genome', nevertheless different cells are structurally and functionally distinct. We concluded that there must exist, at the level of the individual cell, some type of control which determines whether a particular gene does or does not produce its normal product, which we now know probably to be m-RNA.

What we wish to study, if we are to elucidate the mechanism of control of gene action, is a system in which some gene can be active in certain circumstances but not in others. Examples of this type of phenomenon are provided by various strains of *Escherichia coli*. If these bacteria are cultured in the presence of certain sugars such as lactose, the cells are found to contain an enzyme, β-galactosidase, necessary for the metabolism of lactose. If such cells are subcultured into a medium which contains glucose but not lactose, synthesis of β-galactosidase ceases; if the cells are returned to a medium containing lactose, synthesis of the enzyme is resumed. The simplest hypothesis to account for such a phenomenon is to assume that the activity of the gene concerned with the enzyme's production is controlled in some fashion by the presence of its substrate. This process is called 'enzyme induction'.

A control of the opposite sort is also found. If the bacterium is cultured in a medium containing a complete supply of amino-acids, it utilizes these exclusively for the synthesis of new proteins and other materials. If, however, certain of these amino-acids are omitted from the culture medium, the bacterial cells are found to contain enzymes which can synthesize the missing amino-acids from simpler precursors; in the presence of these amino-acids, no such enzymes are produced. Thus, in this case, the presence of a particular metabolite inhibits in some manner the activity of those genes concerned with relevant enzyme synthesis.

From an ecological viewpoint, controls of this character are clearly of adaptive value. *E. coli* is an organism whose available food supply will be affected by the nature of the food eaten by its host at any particular time; thus an energy source like lactose may be available at some times but not at others. Since *E. coli* can also live outside the alimentary tract of animals, it must also be able to exploit relatively simple materials likely to be available in, say, natural waters. If, however, a source of amino-acids is immediately available, there is a saving of energy, not only by exploiting this source but also in ceasing to synthesize enzymes not immediately required for metabolic purposes.

The control of β-galactosidase synthesis has been particularly closely studied. Induction of new enzyme synthesis is a very rapid process, starting, at 37°C, within three minutes of the addition of lactose; synthesis of the enzyme stops equally rapidly once the inducer is removed. In terms of our hypothesis this second observation implies that the m-RNA coding for the enzyme is rapidly destroyed.

Not all strains of *E. coli* show this phenomenon of induction of β-galactosidase. In some the enzyme is constantly synthesized, regardless of whether the substrate is present or not. Experiments show that these strains are genetically different from 'inducible strains' and that the difference depends upon a gene locus remote from that concerned with β-galactosidase synthesis. It thus seems that the control of gene activity effected by lactose depends upon what occurs at this second locus: to express this we will call it the 'regulator' locus. One hypothesis which we can erect is that in an inducible strain the regulator locus produces an m-RNA which directs the synthesis of a protein, repressor protein, which inhibits or represses the activity of the locus at which the m-RNA for β-galactosidase is synthesized (Fig. 23.32a). In those strains in which the enzyme is always present, we may suppose that the regulator gene is not able to direct the synthesis of such a protein (Fig. 23.32b). We would thus expect the active regulator gene from an inducible strain to behave in a dominant manner to the inactive gene of a non-inducible, or 'constitutive', strain. This expectation is in agreement with experimental observation.

How then does the inducer work? One possibility is that

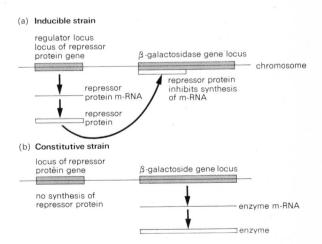

(a) **Inducible strain**

(b) **Constitutive strain**

23.32 Diagram to illustrate the difference believed to exist between an inducible and a constitutive strain of bacterium. In the latter, enzyme synthesis will occur whether an inducer is present or not. In the former, the absence of an inducer results in repressor protein inhibiting the activity of the gene locus directing enzyme synthesis.

it combines with the repressor protein and this alters the shape of the protein molecule; the changed protein can then no longer act as an inhibitor and consequently synthesis of m-RNA can proceed at the β-galactosidase locus. This hypothesis is summarized in Fig. 23.33. You will see that it includes 'structural genes'; these are the genes which synthesize those m-RNAs that are translated into proteins used by the cell in metabolism. It is necessary to include a controlling unit, the operator, which must have certain chemical characteristics that allow it to bind with repressor protein. We have added a further unit, the promotor, for which there is also genetic evidence which we cannot elaborate here; this is considered to be the site at which DNA-dependent RNA-polymerase (p. 429) first binds before starting to move along the DNA strand to synthesize m-RNA.

The operon

A unit of operator-promotor and one or more associated structural genes directing protein synthesis is called an operon. Since both operator and promotor form part of the DNA helix of the chromosome, they will be inherited and thus have certain of the properties we have attributed to genes. In some bacteria and viruses a single promotor–operator complex controls the activity of several structural genes which are arranged in sequence. The proteins synthesized by such a sequence are frequently involved in a common metabolic pathway. Thus, for example, there are ten enzymes concerned in the synthesis of the amino-acid histidine from its precursor, a phosphorylated pentose sugar. In the bacterium *Salmonella* all the structural genes for these enzymes belong to a single operon, but chromosome mapping shows that the order of the genes along the length of the operon is not that of the sequence in which they act during histidine synthesis. All ten enzymes will react as a unit if the operator is repressed.

Fig. 23.34 shows a second, very similar scheme in which an operon becomes active in the absence of a particular substance, as for example some amino-acid. In this circumstance, we postulate that the shape of the repressor protein is such that it cannot normally bind with the operator. If, however, the relevant amino-acid is present, this combines with the repressor protein, so altering its conformation that it can now bind at the operator site and thus inhibit the synthesis of m-RNA.

This hypothesis answers a question we raised earlier, namely: how does a molecule of DNA-dependent RNA-polymerase recognize where it should start the process of m-RNA synthesis and distinguish one strand of a double helix from the other? The answer is that this is determined by promotor regions. To bind RNA-polymerase, any promotor must have some specific conformation of nucleotide bases, although we still do not know what this may be. The complementary strand of the double helix will not have this pattern and thus RNA-polymerase bind-

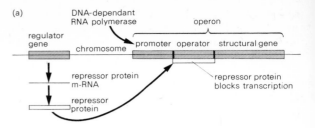

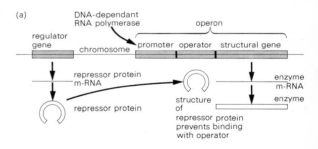

23.33 Diagram to illustrate the possible action of an inducer which, by combining with repressor protein, modifies its structure so that it can no longer bind with the operator; the RNA-polymerase can then transcribe the structural gene. (a) No inducer present: transcription blocked; (b) inducer present: structural gene transcribed. Note that the large cross-hatched genes are drawn this way simply for clarity: a bacterial chromosome has an almost uniform diameter.

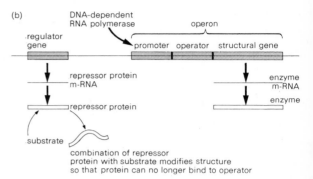

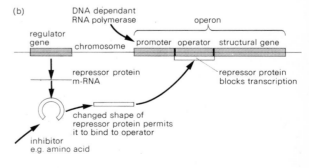

23.34 As Fig. 23.32, but showing how an operon may be inhibited by a substrate.

434

ing will occur on only one of the two strands. As we have already noted, there is no *a priori* reason to believe that all promotor sites and structural genes lie on one strand over the entire length of the DNA molecule of a chromosome.

There is much indirect evidence for this hypothesis of the mechanism of control of gene action, and no experimental results which cannot be accommodated within the hypothesis have so far been found. A protein with the properties of a repressor for the operon which includes the structural gene for β-galactosidase has been isolated from *E. coli*. Whether the hypothesis is applicable also to the control of gene action in eukaryote cells is not known. A

phenomenon described as 'puffing' can be observed in the chromosomes of certain insects (Fig. 23.35); it is believed that these 'puffs' reflect the local accumulation of structural gene products. What is of interest is that the distribution of these 'puffs' along the lengths of the chromosomes alters during development and can be changed if the cells are treated with insect hormones (Fig. 23.36). This clearly is a phenomenon somewhat similar to that of enzyme induction in bacteria, but the underlying biochemical mechanisms have still to be elucidated.

Finally we may consider briefly the control of the rates of synthetic processes within cells. Fig. 23.37 shows a

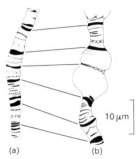

(a) (b)

10 μm

23.35 The chromosomes of certain cells of various flies such as *Drosophila* have abnormally big chromosomes (see p. 441) which stain with a pattern of bands. The pattern is constant and can be used to identify particular regions of a chromosome. (a) A normal chromosome. (b) The same region at a different stage of development including the formation of a swollen area or 'puff'. Puffs are believed to be due to very active elaboration of gene products.

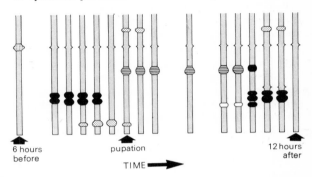

6 hours before pupation 12 hours after

TIME ➡

23.36 Changes in the pattern of 'puffs' in one region of a chromosome of *Drosophila* from six hours before pupation until twelve hours after. It is assumed that the presence of puffs corresponds to the positions of genes which are active. Thus during the time around pupation different genes become active. The length of chromosome illustrated is equal to about 12 map units.

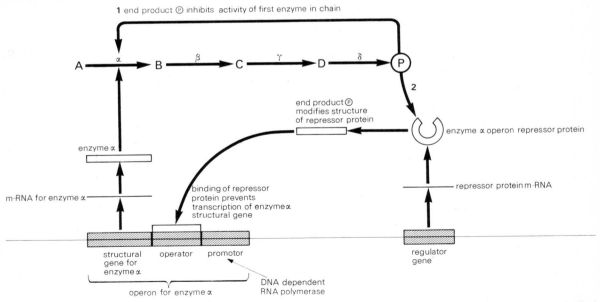

23.37 Two possible mechanisms by which the quantity of product P formed from a precursor A may be controlled. (1) There is a direct feedback inhibition in which P inactivates the enzyme α by combining with it and thus inhibiting further synthesis. (2) The product modifies the structure of a repressor protein so that it can bind with the operator of the operon whose structural gene determines the m-RNA for the enzyme α.

sequence of synthetic steps, each dependent upon an enzyme. What is required is that the quantity of the final product P should determine the rate of its own formation, so that less is produced as its concentration rises. Experiment shows that this may occur by the end-product inhibiting the activity of the enzyme involved in the first link of the metabolic chain; for example, in some organisms the synthesis of tryptophan is controlled in this way. Alternatively the end-product may inhibit its own formation by its effect upon the operon which includes the structural gene concerned in the synthesis of the first enzyme of the chain; the end-product possibly modifies the shape of the repressor protein specific for that operon, allowing it to bind with the operator and thus inhibit transcription of further m-RNA.

We have so far seen something of the characteristics of inheritance, of the concept of genes as the controlling units and of the chemical nature of these genes. We have also seen that different alleles can be found at homologous loci upon chromosomes. We can now turn to the problem of what may be the difference between two alleles and ask how the operons of two alleles may differ. This leads us to the problem of how these differences may have arisen and the possibility that we can in some way artificially produce new alleles which may be of value to man.

Problems

1 A particular plant occurs in two true-breeding varieties, one having white flowers and the other purple. When crossed all the F_1 plants have purple flowers. If an F_1 plant is backcrossed to a white-flowered plant, the progeny consist of blue-, purple-, red- and white-flowered plants in almost equal numbers. How would you account for such a result?

2 In a different plant there occur two true-breeding varieties, one having white flowers and the other red. If these are crossed the F_1 progeny are all purple-flowered. When these were selfed, the F_2 progeny consisted of 181 plants carrying purple flowers, 63 red and 81 white. How would you account for this result?

3 In yet another plant, true-breeding red-flowered individuals were crossed with true-breeding white. All the F_1 were purple. On selfing, 107 plants of the progeny of the F_2 carried purple flowers, 37 blue, 35 red and 75 white. How would you account for this result?

4 (a) In Fig. 23.8a the two nuclei which fuse to form the zygote nucleus (b) were different. One carried the gene P and the other its allele Q. Make a series of drawings showing the stages of the distribution of the chromosomes carrying these alleles during the formation of the eight ascospores in the mature ascus, showing particularly pachytene (see Fig. 22.9) of the prophase of the first meiotic division, and the anaphases of all three divisions.

(b) Suppose that the gene P produces red ascospores,

the gene Q blue ascospores. Make a drawing of a mature perithecium or 'fruiting' body showing four asci, colouring in the ascospores appropriately.

5 In the previous problem you will have found that the order of the alleles of the ascospores within a mature ascus runs

$$P P P P Q Q Q Q$$

Examination of a large number of asci showed that the following sequences also occurred:

$$P\ P\ Q\ Q\ P\ P\ Q\ Q$$
$$Q\ Q\ P\ P\ P\ P\ Q\ Q$$
$$P\ P\ Q\ Q\ Q\ Q\ P\ P$$
$$Q\ Q\ P\ P\ Q\ Q\ P\ P$$

although they were far less common. How would you explain this phenomenon? What would you expect to be the relative frequency of occurrence of the four types?

6 Two strains of *Neurospora* both of which required arginine for growth were crossed. Of 96 ascospores tested, 24 were able to grow on minimal medium. How would you explain such a result? What will be the expected distribution along the asci examined of ascospores capable of growing on minimal media?

7 *Neurospora* does not normally require the vitamin thiamine. Three strains of *Neurospora* were isolated which required the vitamin for growth. One strain (A) grew if the thiamine was replaced by a substance called thiazole; one strain (B) grew if the thiamine was replaced by a pyrimidine, while the last strain required both thiazole and the pyrimidine for growth. The molecular weight of thiamine is considerably greater than that of the other two compounds. What conclusions can you draw about the synthesis of thiamine by *Neurospora*? Assuming the need for thiamine is due to different enzyme deficiencies, show which enzymes are lacking in each strain. If there were a fourth (D) which required thiamine, but would not grow in the presence of both thiazole and pyrimidine, what would you conclude?

8 Part of one strand of a DNA molecule was found to have the following sequence

$$3'-G-C-C-T-A-G-A-T-C-5'$$

(a) What is the sequence of the complementary strand?

(b) The promotor lies to the left. What will be the sequence of m-RNA transcribed from this segment of DNA?

(c) Assume that the nine bases represent three codons. What will be the anticodon sequences of the corresponding t-RNA molecules?

9 On p. 433, we said, 'We would thus expect the active regulator gene to behave in a dominant manner to the

inactive gene of the non-inducible, or "constitutive", strain.' Explain the reasons for this expectation.

10 If 23 percent of the bases of the isolated, purified DNA of a bacterium were adenine, what will be the percentage of each of the other bases?

11 You have now made a complete survey of the most important aspects of cell function. Using the index of both volumes of this work, gather all the information together, summarizing the data in three ways: (a) by one or more drawings showing the characteristic structures or organelles to be found in any cell; (b) by making notes on the functions of these different structures and (c) by making notes summarizing the evidence which has led to conclusions about the functions of the different types of organelle.

Bibliography

Further reading

Ashton, B. G.	*Genes, Chromosomes and Evolution*, Longman, 1967, Chap. 10
Bonner, D. M., Mills, S. E.	*Heredity*, Prentice-Hall, 1964, Chaps. 1 to 5
Burns, G. W.	*The Science of Genetics*, Collier-Macmillan, 1969, Chaps. 14 to 17
Debusk, A. G.	*Molecular Genetics*, Collier-Macmillan, 1968, Chaps. 1, 2, 3 and 5
Cove, D. J.	*Genetics*, Cambridge University Press, 1971, Chaps. 4, 5, 9 to 12
George, W.	*Elementary Genetics*, Macmillan, 1965, Chaps. 9, 10 and 11
Levine, R. P.	*Genetics*, Holt, Rinehart and Winston, 1965, Chaps. 1, 2 and 11
Baserga, R., Kisieleski, W. E.	'Autobiographies of Cells', *Scientific American*, 1963, Offprint no. 165
Beermann, W., Clever, U.	'Chromosome Puffs', *Scientific American*, 1964, Offprint no. 180
Bragg, L.	'X-ray Crystallography', *Scientific American*, 1968, Offprint no. 325
Brown, D. D.	'The Isolation of Genes', *Scientific American*, 1973, Offprint no. 1278
Changeux, J. P.	'The Control of Biochemical Reactions', *Scientific American*, 1965, Offprint no. 1008
Clark, B. F. C., Marcker, K. A.	'How Proteins Start', *Scientific American*, 1968, Offprint no. 1092
Clowes, R. C.	'The Molecule of Infectious Drug Resistance', *Scientific American*, 1973, Offprint no. 1269
Crick, F. H. C.	'The Genetic Code I', *Scientific American*, 1962, Offprint no. 123
Crick, F. H. C.	'The Genetic Code III', *Scientific American*, 1966, Offprint no. 1052
Davidson, E. H.	'Hormones and Genes', *Scientific American*, 1965, Offprint no. 1013
Hurwitz, J., Furth, J. J.	'Messenger RNA', *Scientific American*, 1962, Offprint no. 119·
Miller, O. L.	'The Visualization of Genes in Action', *Scientific American*, 1973, Offprint no. 1267
Neutra, M., Lebloud, C. P.	'The Golgi Apparatus', *Scientific American*, 1969, Offprint no. 1134
Nirenberg, M. W.	'The Genetic Code II', *Scientific American*, 1963, Offprint no. 153
Nomura, M.	'Ribosomes', *Scientific American*, 1969, Offprint no. 1157
Oster, G.	'Density Gradients', *Scientific American*, 1965, Offprint no. 299
Ptashne, M.,	'Genetic Repressors', *Scientific American*, 1970, Offprint no. 1179
Rich, A.	'Polyribosomes', *Scientific American*, 1963, Offprint no. 171
Ruddle, F. H., Kucherlapati, R. S.	'Hybrid Cells and Human Genes', *Scientific American*, 1974, Vol. 231, pt. 1, p. 36
Yanofsky, C.	'Gene Structure and Protein Structure', *Scientific American*, 1967, Offprint no. 1074

24 Alleles and the sources of variation

In the previous chapter we considered data relating to the activity of different alleles recessive to the structural gene which directs the synthesis of the enzyme tryptophan synthetase (p. 420 and Fig. 23.12). We saw that different proteins were produced by different recessive alleles and that, in some cases, no detectable protein was produced at all. Can we explain findings of this sort in terms of the ideas we have subsequently developed?

Let us consider a hypothetical case in which a structural gene directs the synthesis of an enzyme. We will suppose that the gene may occur as any one of four phenotypically distinct alleles, A, B, C and D. These have the following characteristics:

Allele A: full enzymic activity;

Allele B: no enzymic activity, but a protein closely similar to the enzyme is present;

Allele C: activity of the enzyme is less than that found with allele A;

Allele D: no protein similar to the enzyme is present.

We know further that the activity of an enzyme depends upon the presence in its protein molecule of an active or 'binding' site (Book 1 p. 37). The activity of this binding site depends upon its having the correct amino-acid sequence.

If we assume that there has been a change in one of the nucleotide bases in the DNA of the structural gene, then the enzyme molecule synthesized under the direction of the m-RNA formed may, at some point, have one amino-acid replaced by another. Given this assumption we can postulate that the absence of enzyme activity of the protein synthesized by allele B is due to a single base substitution in that region of the structural gene which specifies the amino-acid sequence of the binding site. This could result in some change in the shape or 'conformation' of the enzyme molecule in that region so that all enzymic activity is lost, even though a protein closely similar in other ways to the original enzyme might be synthesized.

We can similarly postulate that allele C results from a base substitution which, while not totally inactivating the enzymic binding site, reduced its affinity for the substrate. As a result fewer substrate molecules would bind per unit time and the rate of the enzymic reaction would be lowered.

We can thus explain the differences in enzyme activity shown by the proteins synthesized in the presence of the three alleles A, B and C with the hypothesis that the base

sequences of their structural genes are different; as a result the m-RNA molecules which are synthesized direct the formation of slightly different and functionally distinct proteins. We have already seen such a difference in a single amino-acid in the β-chains of haemoglobin A and haemoglobin S, and that this difference is the result of a difference of one nucleotide base between the two alleles (p. 427). There are many other types of human haemoglobin differing similarly by one amino-acid from the sequence found in haemoglobin A (Fig. 24.1). A similar analysis of 11 alleles of tryptophan synthetase from *Neurospora* showed that each was characterized by a difference in one amino-acid from that found in the wild-type sequence. Moreover, in some cases distinct alleles were formed by different amino-acids occurring at the same point in the protein chain. Thus amino-acid number 210 of the wild-type sequence is glycine; in one allele, strain A23, it had been replaced by arginine and in another, strain 46, by glutamic acid.

How can we account for the case, as with allele D, in which no antigenically detectable protein is formed? Retaining our idea that the differences between alleles can be due to a difference in base pairs in the DNA, we can recognize the following possibilities (Fig. 24.2):

a) A 'nonsense' or terminating codon occurs very early in the m-RNA sequence produced by the structural gene, so that only a few amino-acids are joined together before a ribosome disengages from the m-RNA. Such an oligopep-

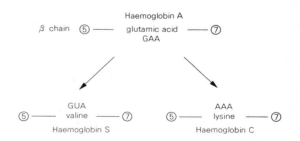

24.1 Base changes in the same codon can yield different alleles. Glutamic acid occurs as amino-acid 6 in the β-chain of haemoglobin A. A single base change in the m-RNA codon yields either haemoglobin S or haemoglobin C, depending on its position.

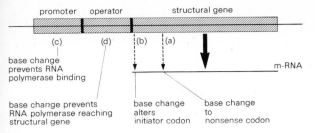

base change
prevents RNA
polymerase binding

base change prevents
RNA polymerase reaching
structural gene

base change
alters
initiator codon

base change
to
nonsense codon

24.2 Possible loci in an operon of base changes which might result in a failure to synthesize a protein.

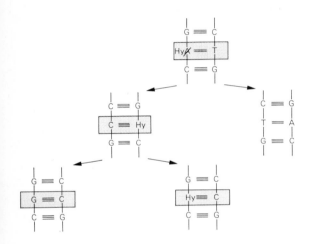

24.3 Treatment of DNA with nitrous acid can change the amine binding group of adenine into a keto-group, yielding hypoxanthine, which forms a hydrogen bond with the amine group of cytosine. Hypoxanthine thus acts like guanine and an A = T base pair will be replaced by G ≡ C.

tide is unlikely to give a detectable antigenic response and will have no enzymic action.

b) A base difference occurs in the initiator codon so that there is a failure of any ribosomes to bind to the m-RNA. As a result, no translation will occur at all.

c) A base difference in the promotor alters its properties, so that it will no longer bind RNA-polymerase and thus no m-RNA is synthesized.

d) A base change occurs in the operator gene which in some manner prevents the RNA-polymerase from moving from the promotor to the structural gene, so that m-RNA synthesis cannot occur.

There is thus the possibility of the occurrence of several alleles, all characterized by a failure to produce any recognizable protein, but differing among themselves.

Mutation

If our hypothesis is correct in suggesting that a change in a nucleotide base will convert one allele into another, then it should follow that such changes might be produced artificially by exposing cells to chemical reagents which react with the bases.

One such chemical is nitrous acid. This reacts with $-NH_2$ groups and so can, for example, convert adenine into another base, hypoxanthine. This latter, during replication, acts not like adenine but like guanine so that a base pair which was originally A—T will, after several replications, be replaced by G—C (Fig. 24.3). Experiment shows that new alleles are in fact produced when suspensions of a wild-type strain of a bacterium are treated with very dilute nitrous acid. Such alleles which have arisen from some different precursor are spoken of as 'mutations' and a chemical with an action like that of nitrous acid is said to be 'mutagenic'. A number of different chemical mutagens are known and their action is essentially similar to that of nitrous acid. If our hypothesis of the nature of the mutagenic mechanism of nitrous acid is correct, then it should not only be possible to effect a change of the form allele A→allele B by exposing cells carrying the A allele to the reagents, but also to produce the reverse change of allele B→allele A by the same mechanism. Such changes have been demonstrated and the occurrence of such 'reversions' is evidence that this type of mutation arises from events at the molecular level. Furthermore, a mutation produced by one chemical mutagen of this type can be reversed by a different chemical mutagen: the effect is thus not specific to the reagent used.

Very different is the action of chemicals called acridines. Their mutagenic effects, which are shown particularly by bacteriophage during active replication, cannot be reversed by mutagens such as nitrous acid; they can, however, be reversed by further treatment with acridine. This has led to the suggestion that acridines can act on the DNA molecule either by removing or by adding a pair of bases. The effect of such a deletion is illustrated by a hypothetical example in Fig. 24.4. If a single base is removed from a codon, all subsequent bases may still be translated as triplets, but the resulting protein will be different. If, as a result of a second treatment with the mutagen, a base is inserted close to the original deletion, a new protein closely similar to the original will be produced. If this new protein, which differs from the wild-type protein only in two amino-acid changes, is functionally similar to the wild-type protein, then a reversion of phenotype will have occurred. Mutations of this type which involve a displacement of the triplets are described as 'frame shift' mutations.

Mutagenesis by physical agents

Mutations may also be produced by ultra-violet light and ionizing radiation such as X-rays and the high-velocity electrons of β-rays.

24.4 Effect of a single base deletion from DNA on the amino-acid sequence of the protein synthesized. For clarity the individual triplets are spaced out.

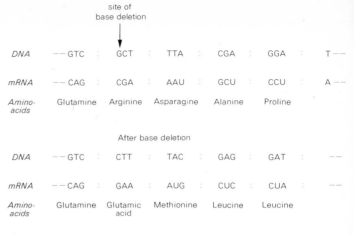

site of
base deletion
↓

DNA	——GTC	GCT	TTA	CGA	GGA	T——
mRNA	——CAG	CGA	AAU	GCU	CCU	A——
Amino-acids	Glutamine	Arginine	Asparagine	Alanine	Proline	

After base deletion

DNA	——GTC	CTT	TAC	GAG	GAT	——
mRNA	——CAG	GAA	AUG	CUC	CUA	——
Amino-acids	Glutamine	Glutamic acid	Methionine	Leucine	Leucine	

Ultra-violet radiation is an effective mutagenic agent for unicellular organisms, bacteria and viruses. For example, in discussing evidence as to the nature of gene action, we said that certain experiments on *Neurospora* depended upon the isolation of rare alleles (p. 417): these alleles were in fact produced by irradiation of conidia with ultra-violet light. As ultra-violet light is absorbed by tissues, it has little or no action on the gametes of higher animals since the radiation does not reach the gonads. In studying the relative efficiency of ultra-violet light of different wavelengths, it has been found that it has its greatest action at that wavelength at which DNA absorption is at its maximum. This suggests that the action of ultra-violet light is directly upon the DNA molecule and that it produces alterations in base composition.

Certain of the actions of X-radiation may possibly be indirect, arising from the local formation of hydrogen peroxide which is known to be a mutagenic chemical. But, in eukaryote organisms, many of the mutagenic actions of X-rays arise from physical breakage of the chromosome strands. The effects we observe are not due simply to local changes in nucleotide bases. The simplest case to consider is that of a chromosome in, say, the prophase of the first meiotic division. If the chromatid thread is broken, the part associated with the centromere will behave normally during the following meiotic division and subsequently. The fragment lacking a centromere will, however, be distributed at random between the nuclei during cell divisions and fail to reduplicate (Fig. 24.5). The loss of such a chromosome fragment will result in the loss of structural genes. If such a loss occurs in the first meiotic division and the deficiency involves only a short length of the chromosome, the deficient gamete may survive. A zygote produced from such a gamete and a normal gamete carrying recessive alleles in the region of the deficiency will result in the expression of the recessive allele in the progeny. A homozygous deficiency is usually not viable. It has, for example, been possible to produce maize plants in which one pair of homologous chromosomes both lack the ter-

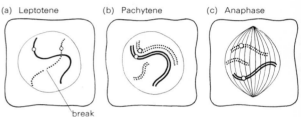

(a) Leptotene   (b) Pachytene   (c) Anaphase

break

24.5 If (a) a chromatid breaks in leptotene (Fig. 22.9), a fragment, lacking a centromere, will (c) fail to attach to the spindle in anaphase and produce a terminal deletion. If the fragment is lost, this invariably results in the death of the cell with the damaged chromosome.

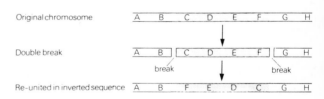

Original chromosome | A | B | C | D | E | F | G | H |

↓

Double break | A | B | C | D | E | F | G | H |
break   break

↓

Re-united in inverted sequence | A | B | F | E | D | C | G | H |

24.6 A double break in a chromosome may result in an 'inversion' if the segment is reversed before repair. The letters are an arbitrary convention to indicate a sequence of regions along the length of a chromosome.

minal region, but such plants fail to synthesize chlorophyll and soon die.

One characteristic of chromosomes is that if there are two broken ends, these tend to join together. As a result, if two breaks occur, the whole chromosome may reunite, but with part of its length reversed (Fig. 24.6). Such a change in chromosome structure is called an inversion. In our present ignorance of the molecular structure of eukaryote chromosomes, we cannot describe the exact molecular effects of such breakages and fusions. By extrapolation

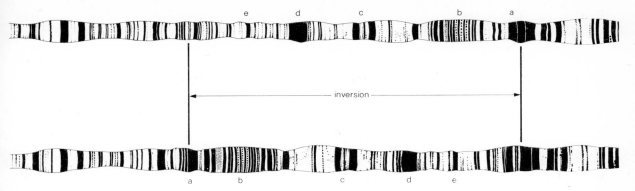

24.7 Part of the length of two homologous salivary gland chromosomes of *Drosophila*. Note the way in which the banding pattern, as indicated by the letters, shows the presence of an inverted region.

from what we know of bacterial chromosomes we might expect that at the points of breakage, the two operons will be disrupted and if the breaks occur within structural genes, not only will new types of m-RNA be produced, but previous control patterns will be altered. This is, however, completely speculative.

How is it possible to recognize such a change within a chromosome? One of the many characteristics that make *Drosophila* a very suitable organism for genetical studies is that it has, in the cells of its salivary glands, chromosomes which are in a permanent prophase of mitosis. Moreover, these chromosomes do not consist ·of two chromatids joined to a centromere, but of 1 024 chromatids packed together to form a single strand. Thus the chromosomes are both long and of considerable diameter. Furthermore, along the length of each chromosome there is an uneven pattern of banding so that, by close inspection of the pattern, particular lengths of chromosome may be identified. In this way, inversions may be recognized (Fig. 24.7); there is, however, another method. In the prophase of meiosis, homologous chromosomes come to lie together, homologous regions of the two chromosomes lying side by side. If there has been an inversion in one chromosome, then clearly such pairing cannot occur along the full length of the two chromosomes. Nevertheless the chromosomes do arrange themselves so as to achieve the maximum degree of pairing that is mechanically possible and, if the inverted region is long, a characteristic loop-like structure will appear during the prophase pairing (Fig. 24.8a). The salivary gland chromosomes of *Drosophila* show a similar pairing, so that homologous chromosomes lie together along their lengths, and as a result inversions may be easily recognized by the loops they produce. Fig. 24.8b shows the detail of such a loop in a pair of *Drosophila* chromosomes; the difference in banding patterns at the origin of the loop can be easily seen. Other types of rearrangements have been recognized in this way and these too can produce phenotypic effects. Thus double breaks can result in three further types of change in chromosome structure. In one a portion

(a)

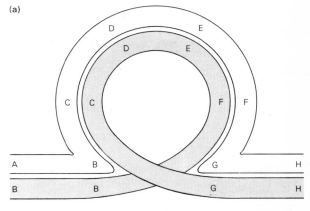

(b)

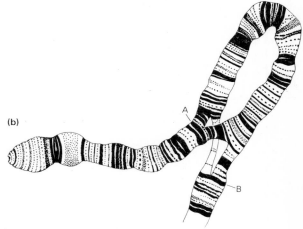

24.8 (a) Diagram showing how a loop can form when homologous chromosomes pair as in the zygotene of a first meiotic division. (b) Drawing of an inversion loop in a salivary gland chromosome of *Drosophila*. In these chromosomes homologous regions are closely paired, so that the two chromosomes appear as a single strand. The inversion runs from A to B, but by loop formation homologous regions, recognized by their banding patterns, are brought together.

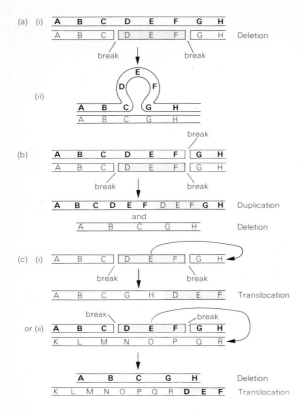

24.9 (a) (i) A double break within a chromosome may result in loss of material. (ii) Deletions will produce loops in paired homologous chromosomes, but they differ in detail from the loops produced by inversions. (b) A double break in one chromosome and at least one break in the homologous member of a pair may lead to the formation of repeated regions along the length of a chromosome. Such duplications will produce loop structures similar in appearance to (a) (ii) at pairing. (c) A double break in a chromosome may result in the fragment attaching to the end either (i) of the same chromosome or (ii) of a non-homologous chromosome.

of the chromosome is lost, not from the end, but from the middle (Fig. 24.9a); this is spoken of as a deletion. The second is the opposite, namely the incorporation of a fragment deleted from one chromosome into the structure of another, so that two identical lengths are formed; this is spoken of as a duplication (Fig. 24.9b). Finally a segment may be excised and then attached, either to the chromosome from which it originated, or to some other chromosome. Such changes are called 'translocations' (Fig. 24.9c).

We used such gross changes in chromosomal shape to elucidate the events of crossing-over (p. 401). In the experiment described, one of the chromosomes was abnormally short because of a terminal deletion; the detached fragment was, in this case, joined to a different chromo-

some. The other chromosome was peculiar as it had attached to it a fragment from another chromosome; it was thus formed by a translocation.

Polyploidy

All these different types of change which can find expression in the phenotype are mutations. There is one other important change which can occur and which will affect the phenotype of a eukaryote organism. In a mitotic division of a plant cell, no cell plate may form at metaphase and all the chromosomes can become included in one nucleus. The cell now has $4n$ rather than $2n$ chromosomes and is called a tetraploid. Such events may occur at different times during the life cycle of an organism, so that completely tetraploid individuals can arise. Moreover other 'mistakes' of a similar character can occur so that individuals with $6n$ or $8n$ or more, as well as with $3n$, $5n$ and $7n$ sets of chromosomes have been found. All these are collectively described as polyploids. They are more common in plants than in animals.

The cells of polyploid individuals are commonly slightly larger than those of diploids, and, among plants, the specimens are often more vigorous. Polyploids offer a number of advantages to the plant breeder; it is therefore of importance to be able to produce them artificially. This is done by the use of a chemical called colchicine which inhibits spindle formation at metaphase, thus making the formation of polyploid cells more probable.

Variation in natural populations

We have seen that two distinct types of mutation may lead to the formation of new alleles. One type, involving a change in the base sequence of DNA, is often spoken of as a point mutation. Such mutations can sometimes be quickly recognized by the presence of new types of protein with different physical properties from those of the 'wild-type' protein. Thus, in Fig. 24.10 we show a short length of the β-chains of haemoglobin A, of haemoglobin S and also of a third type, haemoglobin C, in which lysine replaces the glutamic acid found in haemoglobin A. We have also inserted the charges associated with these amino-acid residues. You will note that while, over this sequence of eight amino-acid residues, HbA has no net charge, HbS has an excess positive charge and HbC a still greater excess positive charge. As a result these three proteins can be separated by electrophoresis. Such a technique has been used to study whether point mutation alleles are to be found in natural populations. The results of such investigations show that differences commonly occur between individuals as far as functionally similar protein molecules are concerned. In some populations one type of, say, a specific enzyme may be very common and all others very rare. In other cases we find that several different functionally similar proteins are common within a single population

Type of haemoglobin									Net charge
A	Valine⊕	Histidine	Leucine	Threonine	Proline	Glutamic acid⊖	Glutamic acid⊖	Lysine⊕	nil
S	Valine⊕	Histidine	Leucine	Threonine	Proline	Valine	Glutamic acid⊖	Lysine⊕	⊕
C	Valine⊕	Histidine	Leucine	Threonine	Proline	Lysine⊕	Glutamic acid⊖	Lysine⊕	⊕⊕

24.10 The sequence of the first eight amino-acids in the β-chain of three different types of human haemoglobin. The net charge on each of the three types is different, permitting their separation by electrophoresis.

and that as a result, in terms of this particular protein, many distinct types of individuals occur. Point mutations are thus not laboratory artifacts, but are part of the sources of variation between individuals in any natural population.

The second type of variation arises as a consequence of disruption of the integrity of a chromosome. It has been found, particularly from a study of naturally occurring populations of *Drosophila* in which these structural changes are fairly easily recognized, that chromosomal rearrangements also constitute a source of the variation among the members of a population. Thus study of the incidence of some particular inversion will show that it occurs in some individuals and not in others.

Mutation in nature

Both these types of variation in the structure of the hereditary material contribute to the phenotypic variation which we encounter within the members of any population of a species; the processes of sexual reproduction, together with crossing-over, serve to 'shuffle' these variations so that the offspring of any cross in nature differ one from another. Mutations of different sorts can be produced by ionizing radiations; the genetic apparatus of all organisms is constantly exposed to such radiation which, reaching the earth from space, causes mutations to occur 'naturally', although there may be other environmental factors which are also mutagenic. Human activity has, of course, increased the abundance of such agents. Exposure to ionizing radiation has increased, partly as a result of 'fall-out' from the military testing of atomic warheads, slightly as a result of release of radioactive waste from nuclear power plants, but most especially from the use in medicine of X-rays as a diagnostic method, together with various types of radiotherapeutic measures. Thus natural background radiation constitutes only 56 percent of the total radiation to which the average American citizen is exposed annually: of the rest 40 percent stems from medical uses of various sorts. Mutagenic chemicals may also be released into the environment; thus one of the herbicides extensively used by the U.S. Air Force in Vietnam was found to contain a mutagenic chemical. Nevertheless, at any single gene locus, recognizable mutations are relatively rare events; in laboratory stocks they may occur in one of every 50 000 to 500 000 gametes. Each individual gamete, however, carries many thousand genes, and the probability that any zygote will contain a mutation is therefore quite high. As a result mutation provides new alleles to the pool of variation.

This knowledge has been exploited by plant breeders. In seeking mutations which can be of value for man's cultivated crops, one method adopted is to expose large numbers of plants to ionizing radiations from an artificial source and in this manner increase the rate of occurrence of new alleles. This technique is one facet of the plant-breeding programme which led to the development of the high-yielding strains of wheat and rice whose introduction has been described as a 'Green Revolution'. Improvements of wheat yields in irrigated lands have been especially impressive; in the Punjab in India, yield per ha increased by 75 percent between 1965 and 1970.

Variation between populations

If samples of discrete populations of some species are collected in different localities and compared, they commonly differ in the frequency with which particular genes occur. This is very obvious in man and is the origin of the phenomenon of biological races. The same sort of thing can be seen in other organisms, sometimes over quite a short distance. To take one very striking example, the frequency of occurrence of a particular chromosomal inversion in *Drosophila funebris* was determined for a number of samples collected at different localities in and around the city of Moscow. In central Moscow, 88 percent of the individuals carried the inversion, away from the centre 56 percent and in the suburbs 12 percent, while 20 km away from the city only 2 percent showed the trait. Here then the quantity of variation within a species itself varies. How can we explain this phenomenon and what is its significance? We will return to these two problems in the next chapter.

Problems

1 The codons for glycine are GGU, GGC, GGA and GGG. Amino-acid number 210 in the wild type of tryptophan synthetase of *Neurospora* is glycine. In strain 46, this is replaced by glutamic acid for which the codons are GAA and GAG. In strain A23 the glycine is replaced by arginine. What can you deduce about the probable codons for arginine?

2 Most mutations produced by artificial means are reces-

443

sive and very many are deleterious or lethal in a homozygote. Suggest reasons why this may be the case.

3 A deletion is not usually lethal in a heterozygote, but an individual which is homozygous with the same deletion in both chromosomes of a homologous pair does not usually survive. Why?

4 In a plant, red flower colour is dominant to white. A number of seeds from a red-flowered plant were irradiated and the resulting plants, all with red flowers, were crossed with white-flowered plants. The seeds from individual plants were kept separate when sown. In some cases all the seeds developed into red-flowered plants, but in others about half the plants carried red flowers and half white. Suggest two interpretations of this phenomenon.

5 When the F_1 white-flowered plants produced by the crosses described in Problem 4 were backcrossed to the red-flowered parent, much of the seed proved to be sterile, but those plants which developed had red flowers. These plants, when selfed, produced red- and white-flowered progeny in a ratio of almost 3:1. Do these facts allow you to distinguish between your two hypotheses? Explain your reasoning.

Bibliography

Further reading

Ashton, B. G.   *Genes, Chromosomes and Evolution*, Longman, 1967, Chap. 5

Burns, G. W.   *The Science of Genetics*, Collier-Macmillan, 1969, Chap. 12

Cove, D. J.   *Genetics*, Cambridge University Press, 1971, Chap. 5

Debusk, A. G.   *Molecular Genetics*, Collier-Macmillan, 1968, Chap. 4

George, W.   *Elementary Genetics*, Macmillan, 1965, Chap. 7

Levine, R. P.   *Genetics*, Holt, Rinehart and Winston, 1965, Chap. 10

Sigurbjörnsson, B.   'Induced Mutations in Plants', *Scientific American*, 1971, Offprint no. 1210

25 The interaction between variation and environment

In discussing the origins of agriculture, and especially of crops, (p. 280f) we said that man has been able to 'improve' the qualities of various plants by a process of selection. We will now analyse this idea in greater detail, considering as an example the changes which have taken place in maize cobs (Fig. 16.3). In the course of time the cobs and the individual maize grains have become larger. We attributed these changes to the fact that the maize farmers chose to use the largest grains as seed for each harvest, or at least did not choose the smallest; either way, they were exercising some selection of the grains used for the following harvest.

A character which shows continuous variation, as does the size of maize grains, is typically determined genetically by a large number of genes whose collective action partly determines the phenotype (p. 406). For any polygenic character, there will be a large number of different genotypes present in a natural population, and the processes of random mating lead to a distribution curve which is roughly bell-shaped, like that for the heights of students in Fig. 22.2a. The smallest individuals are likely to have a large number of genes for shortness, the largest a large number for tallness. We cannot be more definite than that because environmental factors will also have some influence (Table 22.6).

Reverting now to maize, if we reject each year the smallest seeds as not worth replanting, then we will start a gradual process of elimination of genes for smallness and a gradual accumulation of genes for large size; the average size of the grains will thus tend to increase slowly from harvest to harvest. At the same time any mutations which result in larger grain size will tend to be preserved and thus the maximum size of grain will slowly increase. In this way man, as a selective consumer, has gradually changed maize so that modern cultivated maize bears little obvious resemblance to the earliest known maize plants. The same story can be told of wheat and other domestic crops.

Sometimes this process of human selection can bring about changes which affect the whole appearance of the organism. Fig. 25.1 shows a series of photographs of different breeds of dog. Some are tiny, some very big; some have very short hair, some very long; some have long snouts, others almost no snout at all. If we did not know that they are in fact all one species of animal, we would put them into several different species, possibly into a number of different genera. These various breeds of dog were produced by human selection, usually to do particular types of work. Sheepdogs help shepherds herd sheep, alsatians guard one's home, terriers dig out and kill rats, pointers and setters assist men shooting birds; even the 'sausage dog' was originally selected to help hunt badgers, fairly large carnivores which live during the day in burrows.

One can draw a rough analogy between this process of selection leading to different breeds of dog and the history of the motor car. Fig. 25.2 shows an early motor car and a horse-drawn vehicle of about the same date. It is clear that the engineers designing the motor car had done relatively little beyond replacing the horse by an internal-combustion engine. But the buyers of motor cars needed vehicles to do different types of work, and these needs the engineers attempted to meet; different firms put different patterns of car upon the market and the buyers 'selected' those which they found most suitable and most reliable for their particular requirements. As a result of both engineering skill and customer selection, motor cars have, over nearly a century, greatly changed in appearance. Today they scarcely resemble horse-drawn vehicles in any way, but there is a wide variety of specialized types from saloon cars and Land-Rovers to tractors and bulldozers, all depending upon the use of internal-combustion engines.

By these processes of selection, exploiting both the naturally existing variety of genotypes and the relevant mutations which occur from time to time, man has been able to produce very many different types of domesticated plants and animals. It seems unlikely that the first steps were taken with any concept of selection in mind, but today plant and animal breeders seek out new sources of variation which may be suitable for producing still better varieties of crops and herds. New variation is also deliberately induced by treating organisms with chemicals and ionizing radiation to induce mutation.

Insecticide resistance

Sometimes man, by changing the environment, unintentionally brings about changes in the populations within it. This is what has happened with the development of resistance to insecticides. 'Resistance' usually depends upon biochemical reactions which, by modifying the insecticide,

(a)

(b)

(c)

(d)

(e)

(f)

25.1 Breeds of dog. The ancestors of the dogs were wolves; domestication of different species of wolf possibly occurred independently in various parts of the world. (a) Two Alsatian dogs: originally a sheep and watch dog but now widely used as a police dog, it is closely similar to a wolf in build. (b) An Old English Sheepdog, used for herding sheep: note the shorter muzzle and the long coat with hair almost covering the eyes. (c) A Borzoi, used originally for hunting wolves: note the very elongated snout, slender body and long legs suitable for running very fast after its prey. (d) The face of a bulldog, a breed originally used for attacking bulls for 'sport': the absence of a muzzle allowed the dog to bite and grip the nose or flanks of a bull while still being able to breathe. The sport of bull-baiting is now illegal in most countries. (e) A Dachshund or badger-hound, used for driving badgers from their underground lairs: the short legs and the very short coat allowed the dog to move freely through the tunnel systems excavated by badgers. (f) A Chihuahua and a Corgi in snow: the black Chihuahua is fullgrown and an example of a 'toy-dog'. The Corgi is used as a watchdog and to herd cattle in rough country.

(a)

(b)

(c)

(d)

(e)

(f)

25.2 The 'evolution' of motor car design. (a) A horse and cart. (b) A Daimler car of 1886. Note its close similarity to a horse cart with high wheels fitted with wooden spokes and solid tyres. The driver's seat is very high; in a horse cart he had to be able to see over the back of the horse and this has not been modified although there was now no horse. The 3 h.p. engine was at the back. (c) A Peugeot of 1902. The one cylinder engine is now at the front. The wheels are lower and fitted with rubber tyres but the driver's seat is still very high so that a step, the running board, was needed. The step and mud guards were arranged as a single unit. (d) A Rolls-Royce of 1907 with a six cylinder, 40 h.p. engine. The running board is still present and the tyres narrow. (e) A 1935 Bentley. This closely resembles a modern car, but the running board and mud guards are still separate from the main body work. The resemblance to a horse-drawn cart has otherwise been completely lost. (f) A modern car: a 1974 Lotus. The body is now a single unit with no separate running boards or mudguards; improved radiator design allows the front of the bonnet to be lower so that wind resistance can be reduced by a stream-lined body shape.

make it less toxic or quite harmless. For example, the first observed case of resistance to a synthetic insecticide was that of houseflies to DDT. Resistant houseflies contain an enzyme which removes one of the chlorine atoms from DDT, turning it into a harmless compound. The synthesis of this enzyme depends upon a single gene which confers some resistance in the heterozygote. Even if the gene was originally rare in the population, both homozygous and heterozygous individuals would clearly have a far greater chance of survival in the presence of DDT than individuals which did not carry the gene, especially in places where the DDT concentration is only slightly greater than the normal lethal level. Within the fly population of any area the greater chance of resistant flies surviving to breed results in a higher proportion of individuals of the next generation carrying the genes for resistance; finally almost the whole population would become resistant. Thus man, by introducing a novel chemical into the environment of the flies, set in train a series of events leading to a change in the most common genotype of the flies. There are other genes which also enhance the resistance of houseflies to DDT; where these occur in a local population, they will be selected in a similar way. If one of these genes should arise by mutation in some population in which it was not originally present, then it is likely to be preserved and increase in frequency within that population. In fact the genotypes of DDT-resistant flies from different places are not identical, but the events resulting in the development of resistance have been similar.

We may take our argument one step further. Where resistance to any insecticide depends upon several genes, the more effective the insecticide the fewer the generations which will be needed before the resistance becomes obvious. A very effective insecticide may kill off a large percentage of the population, but those individuals that survive to breed will have genes which confer high resistance, so that there will be a rapid increase in the proportion of resistant genotypes within the population. This type of effect we have already illustrated by reference to the time taken by the Blue Tick, *Boophilus*, to become resistant to various insecticides (p. 305).

Man can thus change the genotypes of organisms, either directly by deliberate selection of the parents of succeeding generations or by modifying the environment. We have given other instances of this latter type of effect such as the development of malaria parasites resistant to anti-malarial drugs (p. 329). Similarly certain bacteria have become resistant to sulphonamide drugs and also to antibiotics, rats have become resistant to a chemical poison which had been used successfully for many years to control these pests and, at least in the laboratory, weeds resistant to herbicides have been produced.

Classification

Such man-made changes are clearly of great practical im-

portance both in agriculture and in medicine, but they have a wider biological interest as they may exemplify a more general process constantly at work in the world around us. In Book 1 chaps. 17 to 19 we described the variety of organisms that exists today and showed that it is possible to build up a system of classification; this depends upon the fact that in any locality there is generally a number of closely similar individuals which freely interbreed: these are all members of one species. We said further that we could group together closely similar species into units we call genera, the genera into families and so on (Book 1 p. 155ff).

Such categories are built up on the basis of differing degrees of similarity of structure. The fact that organisms can be classified in this fashion raises the question: why? Why is it that animals with habits as different as those of a giraffe, a whale and a bat should all have in common a large number of anatomical and physiological characters which we describe as typical of the class Mammalia? Would it not be more reasonable to expect that all marine vertebrates would be similar in structure, that all flying vertebrates would have identical adaptations? Why, despite their great differences in mode of life, are there many structural similarities between fishes, frogs, snakes and birds which allow us to describe them all as 'vertebrates'?

The existence of these common patterns of organization presents a problem which has been pondered by biologists for several hundred years. Two main types of hypothesis have been erected to explain these facts. The first is that all living organisms were created at some time in the past and the wisdom of the creator determined that there should be various sorts of mammal, of bird, of reptile and so on, and also that each of these groups should have certain characteristics in common.

The alternative hypothesis sees the similarity of structure as resulting from a genetical relationship. This hypothesis postulates that over the course of time organisms have changed and that the changes have tended to produce greater diversity. If we picture a population of a species at time t_0, then partly as a consequence of the natural diversity of niches within the biosphere, this species will have diversified to form several separate species by time t_1 (Fig. 25.3). If we were living at such a time we would have united these species within a genus. At some later time t_2, the process will have gone further: some of the older species will have become extinct and the process of diversification gone so far that, were we then alive, we would have assigned the descendent populations to distinct genera. At some still later time we would find it convenient to separate the genera into different families, that is groups of genera which, because of their common ancestry, still had certain characteristics in common. This process, carried on over long periods of time, could lead to the types of interrelationships between organisms that make it possible to construct a classificatory system.

This hypothesis involves a process of gradual change

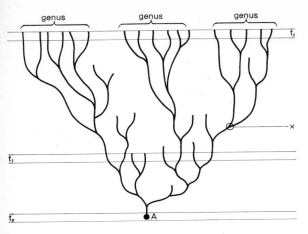

25.3 Diagram showing how increasing adaptive divergence from an ancestral species A at time t_0 might lead to the existence of several different species of the same genus by time t_1 and several different genera by time t_2. For explanation of X, see text p. 452.

which is called 'evolution'. It does not postulate any unusual types of event, as do various creation hypotheses, and so it may be examined by the normal methods of scientific enquiry. The evolutionary hypothesis depends upon two major postulates: firstly, that the genotypes of organisms may change with time and, secondly, that these changes result in diversification.

We have already seen that genotypes can change with time, and that in certain cases this has been due to a process of selection. If selection acts also upon wild populations of organisms, it provides a way in which change might occur. But this is not the only possible hypothesis: the French biologist Lamarck considered that the changes were a consequence of the activities of the organisms themselves.

The Lamarckian hypothesis

Lamarck, who lived at the beginning of the last century, believed that evolution occurred and that there were two things which brought about evolutionary change. Firstly, he believed that characteristics acquired during the life of an organism could be inherited by the progeny. Thus, if a young man developed powerful muscles from constant practice at weightlifting, his children would be born with more powerful muscles than those of his twin brother who was a bank clerk and seldom took physical exercise. But if changes in an animal are a result of its activities, then unless it constantly undertakes new forms of activity, it will remain the same. So Lamarck also postulated that there was an inner drive in animals always leading them to try new things. Those whose bodily form was suitably modified as a result of their activities transmitted these changes to their offspring which were thus slightly different from their

parents and, motivated by the same inner drive, took the process a step further.

This is a reasonable hypothesis, but it is not valid. Many attempts have been made to find experimental evidence for the inheritance of characteristics acquired during the life of an individual and they have all failed to do so. Our knowledge of the genetic mechanisms of inheritance has been gained only since the beginning of the present century and there is no evidence that the things which organisms do affect the genotype of their germ cells. Certainly mutations can occur, but not in a direction specifically related to the activities of the organisms.

Lamarck's hypothesis of the cause of evolutionary change, like the phlogiston theory of combustion, provides an explanation of many facts, but it involves an assumption which is in conflict with certain observations. We must therefore discard the hypothesis.

Selection

If we reject Lamarck's hypothesis, we are left with the idea that the changes we postulate are due to the action of selection. This is the idea originally proposed by Charles Darwin and Alfred Russel Wallace; it is often called the Theory of Natural Selection, to distinguish the process from the artificial selection made by man of his domestic plants and animals. On this view, the development or evolution of resistance to insecticides is an example of natural selection, even though it is a consequence of human activity.

Let us first examine the basic assumptions of this theory as it is understood today. Firstly, it assumes that within any one species, there is variation among individuals; this we have seen to be true (p. 385ff). Secondly, it assumes that at least part of this variation is heritable; this also we have seen to be true. Thirdly, it assumes that in all species of organism some individuals die before reaching sexual maturity; this also we have seen to be true (p. 252ff). Further, it assumes that individuals carrying certain genotypes are more likely to be eliminated during this early mortality than others; this we have so far only assumed. Lastly, it is necessary to be able to identify some advantage which is gained from the change, that is a 'selective advantage', as well as some agent which will produce a differential mortality leading to the greater chance of survival of those individuals which have the selective advantage.

Such an argument is sometimes said to be completely circular, in that those individuals which enjoy a selective advantage are those which survive and that the thing which ensures their survival is their selective advantage. In abstract terms the objection appears to be logical, but in particular cases where some specific character is involved, it has often been possible to recognize wherein the advantage lies and why it should lead to survival. This is obvious

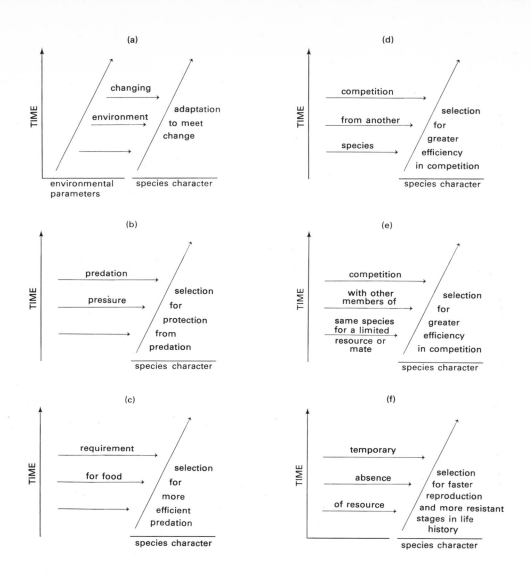

25.4 Diagram summarizing various types of selective force which might result in adaptive changes in organisms.

in, for instance, the evolution of DDT resistance in houseflies.

We must further consider in what circumstances selection may act. One of these (Fig. 25.4a) is some environmental change which leads to differential mortality, for example the situation which leads to the development of resistance to insecticides or drugs. But any change which results in an organism's achieving greater protection from its predators also has survival value (Fig. 24.4b). Equally there is selective advantage in any changes which result in a predator's being better able to find, or for that matter digest, its prey (Fig. 25.4c). Thus, quite independently of any environmental change, the existence of a food web will lead to selection resulting in change. Such evolution

resulting from interaction between predator and prey is often described as 'co-evolution'. Similarly, competition between any two species for the same environmental resource (Fig. 25.4d) is likely to lead to change in both, since there will be a selective advantage to both in competing more effectively. Even a single species, if its numbers are varying around the carrying capacity of its habitat, tends to change, as the individual members of the population are competing with each other for whatever resource is limiting (Fig. 25.4e). This is true also for species which reproduce rapidly while some transient resource, like a food crop, is abundantly available (Fig. 25.4f): those individuals with a relatively high reproductive rate, short life cycle or a highly adapted resistant stage have a greater chance of survival until the next crop becomes available, and thus be more likely to transmit their genes to future generations. Here too, as a result of intraspecific competition, change may occur.

The Peppered Moth, *Biston*

Clearly these different types of selection may interact: for instance, some modification to the environment may lead to an alteration in predator–prey relations which can result in change. One example of a man-made environmental change which resulted in an altered relation between predator and prey has been very closely studied; it relates to the Peppered Moth, *Biston betularia*, which occurs in Great Britain. It is necessary first to explain why a moth should have been chosen for study. If we are to follow changes within a species, it is essential that we should have a record of the appearance or structure of the species over a fairly long period of time and furthermore that the samples of the population available for study should be fairly big. For a long time there have been amateurs in Britain who have collected moths and butterflies and many of these collections have been preserved in museums. Comparative study of collections made at different times can readily give us information about changes in the colour and patterns of the wings. Such studies have shown that at the beginning of the last century, before the industrial development of Britain, specimens of *Biston* had wings with a broken pattern of light and dark brown patches. In 1848 a single specimen was collected in the city of Manchester with almost black wings. Black-winged moths or 'melanics' became increasingly abundant in the local population and by 1895 about 98 percent of the moths in the city had black wings. Black-winged moths started to appear in other industrial cities as well, but the lighter-coloured or typical form remained common in some country areas. The problem was to understand how this change in phenotype had occurred and whether it was in fact due to natural selection. It seemed likely that the events related in some fashion to the growth of industry and the first hypothesis investigated was that the wing colour of the adults was affected by the fact that the caterpillars, feeding on soot-covered leaves, absorbed unusually large quantities of lead and manganese salts. Carefully planned experiments showed that this hypothesis was not correct and further produced evidence that the black wing colour depended upon the presence of a gene which was dominant to the allele of the light-coloured type.

A second hypothesis took as its starting point the fact that the wing pattern of typical *Biston* is an example of cryptic coloration (p. 163). If the adult moths with brown wings come to rest upon lichen-covered tree trunks, the patterning on their wings blends with the background. But lichens fail to survive in areas where there is heavy air pollution (p. 377), and any moth with wings of the typical pattern is conspicuous when resting on a lichen-free and often soot-blackened tree trunk. Further, the melanic moths are far better concealed there, although they are very obvious when resting upon the trunks of lichen-covered trees.

These ideas led to the suggestion that the selective advantage of the observed change related to concealment of the adult moths from bird predators. It was thus necessary to see whether in fact such differential predation occurred. As we emphasized on p.449, while we might postulate that there was differential mortality among individuals of different genotypes, we have so far given no clear evidence for this; the study of *Biston* provided an opportunity to examine the validity of this assumption. Two sets of experiments were conducted. In the first series equal numbers of typical and melanic moths were released in a city garden and watched during the day. At intervals, more moths were released to ensure that the numbers of the two types available remained almost equal. During two days of observation 43 typical moths had been eaten, but only 15 melanics. The same experiment repeated in a pollution-free country area gave the opposite result: during the course of several days of observation 164 melanics were eaten by birds, but only 26 typical moths.

These experiments provide evidence not only that differential mortality can occur, but also that birds can act as differential predators of the two colour forms of the moth; they are, however, open to the objection that the situation was somewhat artificial. Further experiments

25.5 Typical and melanic specimens of *Biston* at rest on a soot-blackened tree trunk.

were undertaken in which large numbers of moths, marked with small spots of paint on the lower surface of the wing, were released and then subsequently recaptured by the use either of a light trap (p. 240) or by using females as bait (p. 308). Such an experiment was first carried out in a city area. The results obtained are summarized in Table 25.1. The results of this experiment confirm our expectations, but are not critical since the melanics might be more easily recaptured than the typical individuals. When the experiment was repeated in the country, the opposite result was obtained which implies that the difference originally observed cannot be attributed to ease of trapping but must relate to survival.

Here we have sufficient evidence to attribute this change to the action of natural selection. There is inherited variation within the population and there is differential mortality, while the selective advantage enjoyed by one or other form is appropriate concealing coloration and the selective agent is predation by birds.

The response of *Biston* to industrial pollution is not unique. In England alone at least 15 other species of moth have also produced melanic forms and similar events have occurred both in Europe and the United States. Presumably the causes have been similar, but they have not been examined in detail.

One feature of the history of the melanic form of *Biston* in England is that the melanic gene spread outwards from the area in which it first became established. *Biston* can fly more than two kilometres in a single night; as a result, the melanic gene could spread through the population and, since it is dominant, dark-coloured moths rapidly became abundant. We have already seen (Fig. 16.32) a somewhat comparable case, the spread of BHC-resistant capsids through the cocoa-growing area of Nigeria.

Biston shows us a further characteristic which we have to consider. Within an industrial city, the melanic forms are at an advantage and the local population will be almost

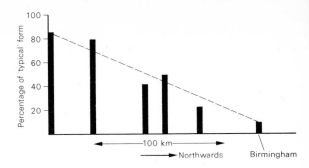

25.6 Graph showing the percentage of patterned or 'typical' *Biston* in populations at different distances on a line running approximately due south from the industrial city of Birmingham in England. (Data from Kettlewell).

100 percent melanics, the typical moths being almost entirely absent. In rural districts the reverse is the case, but there is no sharp boundary zone. The further from the industrial areas, the less the pollution and correspondingly the smaller the percentage of melanics within the population (Fig. 25.6). This observation is comparable to the case of the abundance of a chromosome inversion in *Drosophila funebris* which we described on p. 443: the further from the centre of Moscow, the less common the inversion. We do not know what is the significant environmental factor affecting the fly in this way, but we can now understand why such a distribution of a chromosomal change may be encountered.

These results show that our postulates concerning natural selection as a possible cause of change in organisms are reasonable, and that, as a result of the various pressures we suggested on p. 450, selection acting upon a number of different characteristics of a species could lead to changes such that two samples of the population taken at two well-separated times might be found sufficiently distinct as to be classified as two different species.

Diversification

In Fig. 25.3, however, we made an additional assumption, namely that, as at X, a single species may in some fashion give rise to two separate species. We have reason to believe that this process is normally so slow as not to be observable; we can, however, ask what are the circumstances in which it might occur, and what sort of intermediate stages would we expect to find while it is taking place.

Fig. 25.6 shows that there can be a gradual change in the relative abundance of two phenotypes as we move from one sort of environmental situation to another; such a gradient is spoken of as a cline. Fig. 25.7 expresses this idea in diagrammatic form; at a time t_1 the populations at either end of the cline become separated by some type of

Table 25.1 Differential predation rates of two varieties of *Biston* by birds in city and country (*Data from Kettlewell*)

Release and recapture experiments near the city of Birmingham:

	'typical'	melanic
Number of specimens released	64	154
Number of specimens recaptured	16	82
% of specimens recaptured	25·0	53·2

Similar experiments in pollution-free country:

	'typical'	melanic
Number of specimens released	496	473
Number of specimens recaptured	62	30
% of specimens recaptured	12·5	6·3

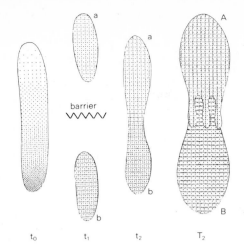

25.7 Diagram showing the possible process of sub-speciation and speciation. At time t_0 a population of a single species is widely distributed along some type of environmental gradient. As a result a cline is established; this is indicated by the density of stippling. At time t_1 some barrier divides the previously single population into two separate breeding populations, a and b. The differences between these populations becomes more obvious after 'gene flow' between them has been prevented by the barrier. At time t_2, the barrier is removed and the two populations may interbreed at the boundary, the individuals being intermediate in appearance. Alternatively, at time T_2, when the populations come again into contact they will no longer interbreed: two separate species A and B have formed.

barrier to their free movement. We now have two separate populations, each subject to selection in the two different areas they inhabit. They will tend increasingly to diverge. If at a time t_2 the barrier is removed, the two populations can come in contact once again. In this new circumstance

the individuals of both populations may tend to prefer their previous habitat; some interbreeding may, however, occur. If we take samples of the two populations at places away from the boundary zone, the members of one population will be clearly different from those of the other. Nevertheless since they can interbreed, we would not regard them as belonging to different species; we may describe the situation by saying that they belong to different subspecies.

Let us now assume that the barrier remains in place for a far longer time. Differences between the two populations will continue to accumulate and if, after a time T_2, the barrier is broken down, the two populations may well no longer interbreed. We have now what we would describe as two separate species, neither of which resembles the original species. In this fashion we can picture what might be the events leading to divergent speciation. We can test the validity of this idea to some degree by seeing whether the stages we have postulated do indeed occur in natural conditions.

Subspecies

We have already met various examples of subspecies: they include those of the elephant (p. 69) and the buffalo (p. 69) as well as the deermouse *Peromyscus* (p. 28). In the latter case we have also seen that in artificial conditions each subspecies tends to prefer its characteristic habitat, an assumption that we have just made. This is probably true also of the subspecies of elephant and buffalo although, this has not been tested experimentally.

Each of these three cases concerns a pair of subspecies, one of which is typically found in forest and the other in more open country. What happens at the boundary? Fig. 25.8 shows the recorded distribution of museum specimens of buffalo from the region to the west of Lake Victoria, including part of the Congo forest. You will see

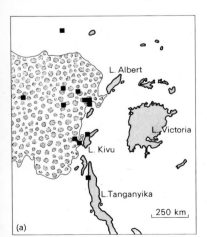

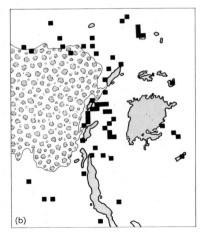

25.8 Recorded distribution between the Congo forest and the eastern savanna of (a) short-horned forest subspecies, (b) long-horned savanna subspecies and (c) intermediates, of lthe buffalo, *Syncerus*. (After Grubb).

that specimens with horn lengths less than 50 cm have been collected almost exclusively within the forest and those with horn lengths greater than 70 cm in the savanna, but that along the forest–savanna boundary a number of specimens intermediate in character have been found. It is clear that animals of this type might occur if there is breeding between members of the forest and savanna populations, since it is very probable that horn length is a polygenic character and that the hybrids from two extreme populations will be intermediate in this particular character. This is the type of relation between populations which we have shown diagrammatically at t_2 in Fig. 25.7.

The forest and savanna buffaloes differ in a number of other characteristics. We do not yet know their adaptive significance, but it seems reasonable to assume that these differences relate functionally to the differences between the two environments.

In this example the forest–savanna boundary appears to act as a partial barrier, preventing free mixing of the two populations. This is certainly true today, but it seems likely that some other, more effective barrier originally divided the parent populations; what that barrier may have been we do not know for certain.

A different type of barrier, and one which we can recognize today, has been responsible for the formation of two subspecies of the forest-living Blue Monkey, *Cercopithecus mitis*, found widely distributed in East Africa. The Great Rift Valley in Kenya runs from north to south, to the west of Nairobi; it is about 60 km across, its floor lying 1 000 m or more below the surrounding country. To east and west is forest country in which *C. mitis* occurs, but the valley itself is very dry thorn scrub. Comparison of specimens from both sides of the valley shows that the colour patterns of the hair coat are distinct. To the west the general coloration of the coat is a dark grey with a well-marked band of black running across the shoulders. To the east, the general coloration has a distinct reddish hue; there is no black band across the shoulders, but a well-marked collar of white hair around the throat. Such differences would normally be sufficient to suggest that we are dealing with two distinct species. This is, however, not so. At the southern end of the Rift Valley, in northern Tanzania, a belt of forest joins the eastern and western forest blocks, and in this area intermediate forms are found. So we regard the two populations of *C. mitis* living on the two sides of the Rift Valley as belonging to different subspecies, since they can interbreed where the environmental conditions allow them to come in contact. Here also we have the situation represented diagrammatically in Fig. 25.7 at t_2. Whether contact between the two populations was ever completely broken, we do not know. While the narrow bridge of forest which joins them today may have been broken at some time in the past, it is also possible that the connection is so limited as to reduce the 'flow' of genes between the two populations sufficiently to allow each population to evolve almost completely independently.

Species

The final stage in the process we have postulated can be illustrated by two other forest-living populations of *Cercopithecus*, this time from West Africa. These populations represent distinct species. One, *C. campbelli*, ranges from Ghana westwards to Senegal, the other, *C. mona*, from Ghana eastwards to Cameroun. *C. mona* can be distinguished from *C. campbelli* by the presence of bands of white hair around the eyes and of two patches of white hair at the base of the tail; they differ also in their typical calls. The differences between these two species are not obviously greater than those which distinguish the eastern and western populations of *C. mitis* in Kenya. Nevertheless, where these two populations overlap, as they do near the southern end of the Volta Lake in Ghana, no intermediates are found: they are therefore regarded as separate species.

The West African forest is broken by an area of savanna spoken of as the Dahomey gap (Fig. 25.9); *C. campbelli* is found typically to the west of the gap, *C. mona* to the east. There is reason to believe that in the past the Dahomey gap was more arid than it is today and would have been country, like the Rift Valley, in which *Cercopithecus* could not live. In more recent times conditions have become less

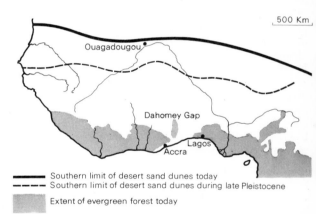

25.9 Map of West Africa. The stippled area shows the extent of evergreen forest today. Note the way in which the savanna extends southwards to the sea in the area lying between Lagos and Accra. This is the Dahomey gap. The heavy line near the upper margin shows the southern limit of moving desert sand-dunes today. In the late Pleistocene the desert extended further south as indicated by the finer broken line: the evidence for this is the occurrence of desert sands in the northern savanna zone. At that time the Dahomey gap must have been wider than it is today as the climate was more arid. The gap thus formed a more effective barrier to migration of forest animals from east to west or west to east. This barrier is believed to have been responsible for the evolution of two distinct species of *Cercopithecus* in the two forest regions.

harsh and some forest has been re-established so that the two populations have been free to spread and live together. They were, however, separated for a sufficient length of time to have become differentiated into separate species.

The examples of the buffalo and *Cercopithecus* concern two different situations. The two subspecies of buffalo live in two distinct biomes and it seems likely that major environmental differences have led to accumulation of different alleles of adaptive value. The populations of monkeys, however, occupy broadly similar habitats and we cannot ascribe the differences between them to obvious environmental factors.

Specific and subspecific characters

This raises the question of whether the differences in hair coloration of the two species or subspecies of *Cercopithecus* are of any selective value, or whether the process of differentiation is in fact a result of selection. There are three distinct points which have to be considered here. Firstly, it is relatively easy to describe differences, but to recognize, and still more to demonstrate, their possible selective value is far more difficult, and requires detailed knowledge of the habits of the species within their natural environment as well as laborious experimentation. As research has gone ahead, however, many characteristics originally regarded as of no adaptive importance have later been shown to have survival value. One example is that of secondary plant substances whose significance has been clearly recognized only within the last decade (p. 140). While it may be difficult to demonstrate the adaptive significance of the differences between two subspecies, it is of course even more difficult to prove that they have no survival value at all.

The second point relates to gene action. We have seen how a structural gene directs the synthesis of a specific protein (p. 416) and in the cases we considered, this protein was commonly an enzyme involved in a well-known metabolic pathway. There is, however, evidence that some genes may have more than one phenotypic consequence. For example, laboratory studies on the effect of different alleles on the fertility of *Drosophila* have shown that the eye–colour allele 'eosin' increases the fertility of females, as do various other genes affecting eye colour; on the other hand, the alleles for 'black body' and 'vestigial wing' reduce fertility. A similar phenomenon has been demonstrated in the Scarlet Tiger Moth (Fig. 9.15b), which displays three different wing patterns controlled by a single pair of alleles, the two homozygotes and the heterozygote all differing in detail. These alleles affect not only wing pattern, but also both survival during the early larval stages and fertility. Thus a character, such as wing pattern or eye colour, which may appear to have no adaptive significance, can be an incidental expression of the presence of a gene whose other actions are those upon which selec-

tion is operating. Such an effect is well illustrated by the study of the number of spots upon the wings of the Meadow Brown Butterfly, *Maniola*. For many years, a population of this species on a small island consisted largely of individuals either with no spots (about 30 percent of the population) or two spots on the wings. The area in which this population lived was isolated and grazed by cattle. The cattle were later removed; the grass rapidly grew tall and various herbs became more abundant. With this change there was a change in the relative proportions of individuals of different wing pattern: the two-spotted pattern became markedly more common, the form with no spots relatively rare. While it seems unlikely that there was any direct relation between the wing pattern and the change in the habitat, wing pattern is easily observed and its change can be simply recorded. The less obvious changes upon which selection is actually operating may go unnoticed.

Thus without very detailed genetic and physiological analysis, it is not possible to say whether or not some character, such as the presence of dark hairs across the shoulders of one of the two subspecies of *C. mitis*, may be closely associated with some other which is of direct adaptive value. Consideration of only those phenotypic characters used by taxonomists to separate species or subspecies may lead us to the possibly mistaken conclusion that the alleles of which they are an expression have no survival value.

Lastly, it cannot be excluded that the character has indeed no survival value. If within a very small population there should appear a mutation which is not deleterious, there is a possibility that the gene may, by chance, spread within the population. For this to occur, the population must, however, have been reduced to very small numbers and subsequently have remained isolated. While this is a theoretical possibility and has indeed been demonstrated in laboratory populations of *Drosophila*, it has never been clearly shown to be of importance in natural populations of plants or animals, except possibly in those found on islands far away from the mainland.

The Galapagos finches

One example of the processes of speciation in which the adaptive significance of the differences between certain species can be recognized is provided by a group of small birds, the finches of the Galapagos Islands. These islands form a small, isolated archipelago which lies on the Equator about 800 km west of South America; a study of their bird fauna suggests that they have been repeatedly colonized from the neighbouring continent. Table 25.2 summarizes the closeness of taxonomic relation of different island birds to those which occur on the mainland. It shows that a wide variety of different degrees of relation exists and is most easily understood if we assume that the cuckoo has only recently become established, the martin at some earlier

Table 25.2 Relation of certain Galapagos birds, other than finches, with those in South America (*Data from Lack*)

Coccyzus melacoryphus (cuckoo)	same species
Progne modesta modesta (martin)	different subspecies
Myiarchus magnirostus (Tyrant Flycatcher)	different species
Nesomimus trifasciatus (mockingbird)	different genus

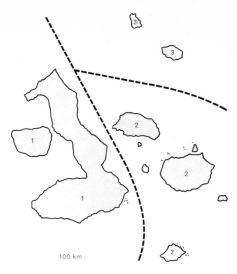

25.11 Distribution of three subspecies of the finch *Camarhynchus psittacula* in the central island group of the Galapagos archipelago.

date and so on. On this basis, the ancestors of the finches must have colonized the islands a very long time ago, as there are on the islands thirteen different but fairly closely related species divided into three genera. The close relation between the different species suggests that they have evolved from a single small population.

In one genus, *Geospiza*, there are three species, all of which live together in the arid, coastal zone of the central islands of the group. All three species are seed-eaters and differ only in body size and the strength of the bill (Fig. 25.10). Despite these relatively slight differences, the species do not interbreed.

These observations raise two questions. Firstly, how did three such closely similar species arise? We have suggested that the finches are probably all derived from a single flock which arrived at the islands a long time ago. We can visualize the early population having been scattered among the islands of the central group and there developing into separate species with slight differences in the types of food they eat. Such differences might well have arisen from differences in the relative abundance of different sorts of food on the different islands. As a result of subsequent migration, the species came again in contact. By this time, however, they could no longer interbreed and their different feeding habits would become further differentiated as a result of interspecific competition. Another genus of finch, *Camarhynchus*, shows today the kind of distribution which we have suggested might have been shown by *Geospiza* in the past. Each of the three subspecies of *Camarhynchus psittacula* occupies at present a distinct group of the central islands (Fig. 25.11).

The second question is whether the differences in beak size, the main character which distinguishes these three

species of *Geospiza*, are adaptive. That the three species have rather different feeding habits can be seen from analysis of their stomach contents. The two larger and stronger-billed species will take large, hard seeds which are rejected by the smallest species. The smallest species and the intermediate one both feed on grass seed. The three species are thus not in complete competition for the available food resources and the character which makes this possible is beak size; it can thus be seen as an adaptation which now permits the co-existence of three very similar species of a single genus.

In sum, the results of studies on the distribution of closely related species and subspecies are in keeping with our postulate about the formation of new species by the divergence of two isolated populations derived from a single stock. But the further step, that of showing that the easily observable differences between populations are the result of differential selection, is not easy without very detailed studies and these have so far been made on only a very few species.

Barriers to reproduction

There are two other matters which this account of the possible origin of new species requires us to consider. The first relates to the evolution of barriers to successful reproduction between two populations which have been isolated and which are evolving under different selection pressures. When the two populations meet again, three different relationships may arise. Firstly, they may interbreed and produce offspring, but because of differences in parental genotypes such offspring may either be of low fertility or actually sterile. Secondly, individuals may mate

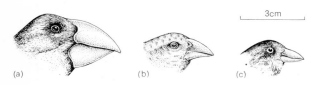

(a)	(b)	(c)	3cm

25.10 Differences in bill size of three seed-eating species of the finch *Geospiza* which occur together on certain islands of the Galapagos archipelago.

456

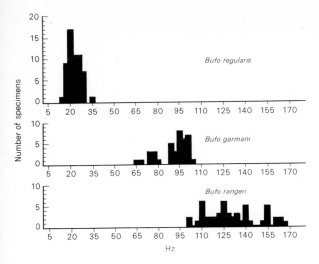

25.12 Differences between pulse rates of the calls of three species of *Bufo* which occur together at Pretoria in the Transvaal. (After Passmore).

but because of the differences in parental genotypes the matings themselves are sterile. In some animals, such as the insects, individuals from different populations may attempt to copulate but because of changes in the structure of their external genitalia, successful mating is mechanically impossible. As we shall shortly see, the continuing action of selection will tend to decrease the probability of all such matings.

The third possibility is that the barrier depends upon differences in behaviours associated with mating. For example, there may be differences in mating calls, as in closely related species of *Bufo* (Fig. 25.12); among the insects there may be different responses to sex-attractant pheromones or differences in the pheromones secreted. The mating barrier may also be due to a difference in breeding season, or simply to a tendency for the two populations to occupy different habitats when they occur together.

Why should selection tend to reduce interbreeding between two distinct populations? We have already pointed out that the offspring of such matings have a low fertility or may be sterile. Now mating in most terrestrial animals depends upon each partner's reacting to sensory stimulation from the other. Consider two individuals A_1 and A_2 from one population, A. If A_1 reacts most readily to sensory stimulation from members of his own population group, while A_2 reacts more strongly to those of another population group B, then because of the greater chance of survival of offspring of a mating $A_1 \times A_n$ than of those of a mating $A_2 \times B_n$, there will be a tendency for genes favouring sensory responses leading to $A_x \times A_y$ matings to spread through the A population and those for $B_x \times B_y$ matings to spread through the B population.

In this situation, any features which tend to emphasize the differences between A and B will have selective value, so that we may expect the populations to diverge increasingly in certain features specifically associated with courtship and mating.

Sexual selection

For the same reason, if two closely related species come to live together there will be a tendency for selection to increase those differences between them which are connected with courtship and mating. A similar tendency may occur between the sexes of a species which breeds annually. If early breeding enhances the chances of survival of the young, then those individuals whose genotypes result in early mating are most likely to contribute to the 'gene pool' of the future populations. In animals such as birds whose courtship may be of considerable importance, any male whose appearance especially rouses responses from a female is more likely to be successful in early mating. The same argument will apply, though possibly with lesser importance, to the female. As a result we find in some bird species, such as peacocks, what we ourselves might consider to be excessive emphasis upon the ornamentation of male plumage. Once we appreciate that this can arise as a result of differential selection between males for early mating, we can enjoy the beauty of many birds without feeling that the exuberance of their plumage is incomprehensible.

Types of barrier

The second matter we must consider is the types of barrier which can serve to separate two populations into independent units. We have already mentioned one: the presence of a strip of one biome separating two areas of some other biome. There are other natural barriers. For terrestrial animals with poor powers of dispersal, such as weakly flying butterflies, the enlargement of a major river system may act as a barrier. Long mountain ranges may act as barriers since they have a different vegetation from the valleys on either side, while species which during times of cooler climate have spread over wide areas may become restricted to isolated mountains if the mean temperature rises. A very different type of barrier to the movement of terrestrial organisms is the sea. Where oceanic islands are close to the mainland, they may be frequently invaded (p. 113). If they are remote, as are the Galapagos, invasion is relatively rare. Obviously, barriers which completely prevent the spread of one species may nevertheless be readily crossed by some other.

For aquatic organisms, many lakes can be regarded as 'islands of water' and they contain their particular species and subspecies. We have already mentioned (p. 112) a species of *Tilapia* which is found only in Lake Chilwa in Malaŵi and in another immediately adjacent lake. Similarly the very isolated Lake Bosomtwi in Ghana has a species of *Tilapia* not found elsewhere. In the big lakes the situation is more striking. *Tilapia* belongs to a family of fishes called the cichlids: there are nearly 130 different species of this family in Lake Victoria and of these only three occur elsewhere.

We can get some information from the study of lake fishes as to how rapidly new species can arise. Adjacent to Lake Victoria lies Lake Nabugabo. Geological evidence shows that about 4000 years ago this lake became separated from Victoria by a sandbar. Today it contains five species of cichlids found nowhere else; these must have evolved within this isolated water body. This is a striking example of the way in which new species may evolve by the separation of single populations into two isolated ones.

Polyploidy

The types of barrier between populations which we have so far considered are all mechanical or behavioural. But a different kind of barrier, a genetical barrier, arises in the case of a polyploid individual. If among a diploid population of a plant species, a tetraploid individual occurs, it will be genetically isolated from the diploid parent stock. Should the situation be favourable, more tetraploid individuals may arise by vegetative reproduction or by self-fertilization of the plant. As a result a tetraploid population will co-exist with a diploid population, but they will not interbreed. Within such co-existing populations there may be competition between diploids and tetraploids. If the tetraploids have an advantage, a completely tetraploid local population will arise, and this has the potential of diverging from the parent stock represented by other, diploid populations.

The early stages of such differentiation are possibly to be recognized in an English plant, *Galium palustre*, commonly called the Marsh Bedstraw. In England there are both diploid and tetraploid populations; the diploids occur in damp localities which dry out during the summer, and the tetraploids in places which remain moist throughout the year.

That such an event may be of general importance, especially in the evolution of plants, is shown by a study of haploid chromosome numbers in various families. Thus, for example, among the Labiatae, which includes many aromatic herbs such as *Ocimum* species, the most common gametic number is 16, while there are several species with a gametic number around 8, suggesting that this was the primitive haploid number of the family. Among species with many more chromosomes, gametic numbers of 24 and 32 are common, while there is a single species with a value of 51 which was perhaps originally hexaploid.

In animals, this process of incipient speciation by polyploidy is much rarer than in plants: it is most common among hermaphrodites such as the flatworms, earthworms, leeches and gastropod snails. One important example is provided by the snail *Bulinus*. The basic haploid number,

18, is found in *B. tropicus* and *B. natalensis*, neither of which is a vector of *Schistosoma*. The species which acts as a vector, *B. truncatus*, is a tetraploid, while in Ethiopia are found hexaploid and octaploid *Bulinus* which differ so slightly from *B. truncatus* that they are regarded as all belonging to the same species. The populations of hexaploids and octaploids are ecologically separate from those of the tetraploids and are found at altitudes above 2000 m. This is paralleled by plants in West Africa where polyploid populations of certain species are found in montane habitats. In these species, as with the Marsh Bedstraw, polyploidy not only provides a barrier to interbreeding between populations, but populations of different ploidy have distinct ecological preferences which may, in time, lead to the development of morphological characteristics which would allow their assignment to different species by a taxonomist.

Hybridization

There is one other, very different way by which new species can arise, namely by hybridization between existing species. Such hybrids are usually sterile, but since many species of plant can reproduce vegetatively, the hybrid may be able to maintain itself. Should specimens of the hybrid double their chromosome number so as to become polyploid (p. 442), the new plants may be able to reproduce sexually once more. The details of such an event in a maritime grass *Spartina* are summarized in Fig. 25.13.

Such hybrid polyploids are especially common among domesticated plants. The most primitive wheat has a zygotic number of 14, but the commercial wheats in use today have zygotic numbers of either 28 or 42. That is they are tetraploids or hexaploids. It is believed that the tetraploid wheats, used for making such products as macaroni, arose from a cross between the original diploid wheat and a wild grass, followed by a doubling of the chromosome number to form a fertile hybrid, just as with *Spartina*. A similar event, again involving a wild grass, probably gave rise to the hexaploid wheats which are used in the manufacture of flour for bread. It will be clear from what we

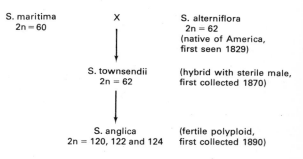

25.13 Diagram showing the origin in Britain of *Spartina anglica* from the sterile hybrid *Spartina townsendii*. *S. maritima* was the original native species.

have already said that new species formed by hybridization and subsequent achievement of polyploidy will have considerable selective potential, since the reserve of variation within the genotype is greatly increased.

The evolution of higher categories

In Fig. 25.3, we suggested that the existence of taxonomic categories was due to the divergent nature of the process of speciation. In this way we may visualize members of a group of species becoming sufficiently distinct to warrant their separation into genera while different genera, following the same pattern, will evolve into distinct families. Such a process can be pictured as having occurred on the Galapagos archipelago to give rise to the three genera of finch which we find there today. But a different pattern of events may be recognized, namely one involving the acquisition either of a single character, possibly by mutation, or of a novel functional system by more gradual modification of a pre-existing one. If either provides the population, or the species, with very considerable selective advantage, it may be able to occupy a wide range of habitats from which it was previously excluded by competition. The processes of speciation would then proceed again.

One example of such a phenomenon is provided by plants of the family Cruciferae, the cabbage family, all of which are characterized by the possession of mustard oils which provide them with considerable protection against potential consumers. We can visualize this as happening initially in a single step and this new potential then permitting the occupation of a variety of habitats in which speciation could proceed. A more complex example of such a 'success story' is provided by the conversion of the gas bladder of fishes from a lung to a hydrostatic organ, the swimbladder. The highly specialized organ that we know today may have evolved relatively slowly, but at some stage in that process it provided the ancestral teleosts with sufficient selective advantage to allow them to occupy a large number of habitats which they had not previously penetrated: with this went the evolution of new species, new genera and new families. We may speak of such critical changes as the evolution of 'key characteristics'.

If you review the characteristics of the major classes and phyla of animals described in Book 1 chap. 18, you will be able to recognize, as we stressed in the opening paragraphs, that these largely reflect different methods of locomotion and feeding and that the two are interrelated. The evolution of key characteristics can be regarded as producing this type of end result. A slight change in a method of locomotion, if it has selective advantage, will become amplified since each increase in efficiency will not only enhance survival, but place the organisms into different competitive relations with others, offering them the possibility of occupying a variety of new environments. If such a process occurred repeatedly, it would result in the formation of patterns of organization which serve as the basis for the erection of higher categories within the classificatory system.

This is as far as we can take the argument that the hypothesis of natural selection would lead to a process of evolutionary diversification. A vast amount of investigation remains to be done to test fully whether the characteristics of present-day populations, subspecies, species and so on do in fact fully conform to the expectations which follow from the hypothesis. Few experimental studies of the problem have yet been carried out, but where any detailed analysis of the changes in natural populations and of their genetic basis have been made, these have been found to be in keeping with the concept of natural selection.

We can, however, approach the matter in a different way and ask whether the postulate of an evolutionary process has any other, less direct consequences which we might expect to be able to observe in the world around us. The possibility of erecting a system of classification can be seen as a consequence of evolution, but the form which it has actually taken is not an obvious, inevitable outcome. There are, however, other effects which follow more directly from the postulate of evolution. These we will now consider and see whether our expectations are fulfilled.

Problems

1 How would you attempt to determine whether there is a difference in resistance to some insecticide between populations of *Anopheles gambiae* collected in the north and south of your country?

2 In the light-trap experiment with *Biston*, why were the identifying paint spots put on the lower surface of the wing?

3 In England in 1952 legislation was introduced controlling the quantity of smoke which could be emitted by factories. A sample of 760 *Biston* collected between 1952 and 1964 in the city of Manchester in England were all melanics. Subsequently between 1966 and 1969 a further 972 specimens were collected and of these 25 were light-coloured. What tentative conclusion might be drawn from these observations concerning the relative 'fitness for survival' of the two colour forms?

4 In Fig. 25.7 we started with a cline and then erected a barrier to divide the original population into two. To account for divergent speciation, is the initial assumption of a cline within the population necessary?

5 Selection would be expected to reduce the extent of variation within a species. Populations of species do nevertheless show considerable variation in particular characters. How would you attempt to explain this contradiction?

6 There are three ecological 'rules' which apply to homeotherms. These are (a) Allen's rule: the size of body appendages, such as the ears of mammals, are relatively greater in low than in high latitudes; (b) Bergmann's rule: body size tends to be greater in

high than in low latitudes; (c) Gloger's rule: pigmentation of hair or feathers is less in arid than in humid regions.

What do you consider may be the physiological or biological explanation of these generalizations? Are they in keeping with the concept of selection? If so, explain how.

7 Which would you regard as 'key characteristics' (p. 459) in the evolution of the various classes of terrestrial vertebrates from an ancestral population of air-breathing fishes?

8 Explain briefly why crossing between populations of diploid and tetraploid individuals results in sterile offspring.

9 Given the postulate that species arise by adaptive divergence, as suggested in Fig. 25.3, what would you expect to be the simplest resulting patterns and how would this express itself in a taxonomic system? Why is a more complex system found necessary to classify existing animals?

10 Complete determinations of the amino-acid sequences in homologous protein molecules from different animals have been made. One can assess the number of changes which have occurred over geological time by comparing the composition of such proteins from, say, a fish and a mammal. Such studies show that there are marked differences between the molecules of haemoglobin, fewer between molecules of cytochrome c, while histone IV, a protein associated with the DNA of the chromosomes, has changed only very slightly. If such differences represent the rate of 'molecular evolution', suggest why these three molecules may have evolved at such different rates.

11 We stated on p. 449 that we had presented no evidence of differential predation of members of a single species in natural conditions. There are, however, in Chapter 9 two experimental results which suggest that such a phenomenon is likely to occur: summarize these. How do they differ from the situation found in *Biston*?

12 The following data relate to the bird faunas of four small islands in the Gulf of Guinea. 'Endemic' means that the species is found only in that locality (or island) and nowhere else. Suggest an evolutionary interpretation of the observations.

13 In many hermaphrodite animals, such as snails and flatworms, there are complicated anatomical arrangements which reduce the probability of self-fertilization. What may be the selective advantage of cross-fertilization?

14 On p. 372, we stated that wild plants grown in artificial conditions 'tend to be selected and do not provide as valuable a reserve (of variation) as those which grow wild in their natural environment'. Why should this be?

15 Suggest the design of an experiment by which one might attempt to test the Lamarckian hypothesis of the inheritance of an acquired character. What precautions are needed in the conduct of such an experiment?

16 On p. 450 we listed six possible types of selective force which might cause a change in the phenotype of a species. Are all these as applicable to plants as to animals? Explain how you came to your conclusions.

17 On p. 457 we stated that some geographical barriers which 'completely prevent the spread of one species may be readily crossed by some other'. Make a list of possible types of geographical barrier and suggest examples of animals which could and which could not cross each type of barrier.

18 A ladybird is a small beetle which commonly feeds on aphids. The species *Adalia bipunctata* occurs in two forms: in one form, the hard fore-wings or elytra are coloured red with two black spots (the 'typical' form) and in the other the elytra are black with two red spots (the melanic form). Both forms or 'morphs' may occur in the same locality. The difference in coloration has been shown to depend upon a single pair of alleles. The animals are *not* preyed upon by birds.

(a) Specimens of the two morphs were chilled to 0°C for 30 min and then exposed for 12 min to the light of a 100 watt incandescent lamp. The locomotor activity (expressed in special units) was measured at intervals; the results obtained are summarized in the following table

Temperature (°C)	Locomotor activity	
	Typical morphs	Melanic morphs
5·0	8·8	33·4
7·5	51·0	67·0

Island	Fernando Póo	Principé	São Tomé	Annobon
Area (km²)	2000	126	1000	15
Distance from nearest mainland (km)	35	220	280	340
Number of endemic species	1	5	13	1
Percentage of endemic species in total bird fauna	0·7	19	33	14

Suggest an interpretation of these results.

(b) The relative abundance of melanics in different localities was compared with the number of hours of mean annual sunshine. The data obtained were as follows

Range of hours of sunshine	Percentage of melanic morphs in population
< 1 100	87
1 100–1 200	70
1 201–1 300	61
1 301–1 400	32
1 401–1 500	10
1 501–1 600	8
> 1 600	2

(i) Present these data as a histogram.
(ii) What do you consider the data imply in terms of selective advantage?
(iii) What do you consider might be the biological mechanisms at work to produce these results?

(c) Breeding experiments show the melanic allele to be dominant to that for the 'typical' red form. What further conclusion does this finding suggest?

19 (a) Darwin considered that the existence among social insects such as ants of specialized, sterile workers was strong evidence against the Lamarckian theory of the mechanism of evolutionary change. What do you consider may have been his argument?

(b) Suggest how the existence of such castes could be accounted for by the Darwinian theory of natural selection.

20 On p. 449, we said that one of the basic assumptions of the theory of natural selection is that 'in all species of organism some individuals die before reaching sexual maturity'. This statement is unnecessarily narrow, but both easy to understand and easy to demonstrate as true. Suggest a more general formulation of the assumption. What further type of event is included by this new formulation? How would you attempt to see whether such events occurred in natural populations?

Bibliography

Further reading

Ashton, B. G.	*Genes, Chromosomes and Evolution*, Longman, 1967, Chap. 7
Dowdeswell, W. H.	*The Mechanism of Evolution*, Heinemann, 1963
Ford, E. B.	*Evolution Studied by Experiment and Observation*, Oxford Biology Readers, Oxford University Press, 1973
Hamilton, T. H.	*Process and Pattern in Evolution*, Collier-Macmillan, 1967
Ross, H. H.	*Understanding Evolution*, Prentice-Hall, 1966
Savage, J. M.	*Evolution*, Holt, Rinehart and Winston, 1969
Stebbins, G. L.	*Processes of Organic Evolution*, Prentice-Hall, 1971
Wallace, B.	*Population Genetics*, BSCS Pamphlet no. 12, Heath, 1964
Wallace, B., Srb, A. M.	*Adaptation*, Prentice-Hall, 1964
Bennet-Clark, H. C., Ewing, A. W.	'The Love-song of the Fruit Fly', *Scientific American*, 1970, Offprint no. 1183
Bishop, J. A., Cook, L. M.	'Moths, Melanism and Clean Air' *Scientific American*, 1975, Vol. 232, pt. 1, p. 90
Kettlewell, H. B. D.	'Darwin's Missing Evidence', *Scientific American*, 1959, Offprint no. 842
Lack, D.	'Darwin's Finches', *Scientific American*, 1953, Offprint no. 22

26 The consequences of natural selection

In the previous chapter we attempted to show that the existence of genetic variation within a population will lead to change as a result of the tendency for differential mortality between different genotypes. A further examination of this process of selection led us to the idea that in the course of time living organisms have 'evolved' and we saw that some of the phenomena which we can observe today could be regarded as stages in the evolution of new species. We further saw that, by an extension of these ideas, we can account for the fact that it is possible to erect a system of classification of organisms.

We also suggested that the idea that organisms have changed with time provides a rational explanation of various other observed phenomena. We can turn this argument around, and say that if a number of natural phenomena can be explained by assuming that there has been a process of evolution, this constitutes support for the hypothesis itself. We will therefore review various biological phenomena and see whether they may collectively be regarded as consequences of a process of organic evolution.

Fossils

Man has long been surprised to discover the shells of marine snails and bivalves buried deep in the soil on hills well away from the sea and to find, sometimes while mining, bones which do not belong to any known animal. Very large bones, which we know today to be those of elephant-like animals, were once regarded as evidence of former giants and one specimen of a large amphibian dug up in Switzerland in 1726 was described by its pious discoverer as the remains of a man drowned in Noah's Flood! Such remains of dead organisms we call fossils; their study is called palaeontology.

That we should occasionally find buried the remains of dead animals need not surprise us. If, however, there has been an evolutionary process, then we would expect certain features to characterize these remains, namely:
a) that some would be of types of organism which existed in the past but which are no longer alive today;
b) that the species of organisms which existed in the past were different from those which occur today;
c) that the older the deposits from which the fossils come, the greater would be the differences between the organisms whose remains are found and those which exist today;

d) that each type of organism, whether extinct or still existing, should have appeared for the first time in deposits of some particular age, that is, that there has not simply been a steady impoverishment of the fauna and flora over the course of time;
e) that it should be possible to follow changes over the course of time leading from extinct animals to ones which are still alive today; and
f) that remains of types of organism intermediate in structure between taxonomic categories should be found.

Fossilization

Before turning to consider the evidence itself it is desirable to understand something of the nature of fossils and of the conditions which lead to their preservation.

Perhaps the most remarkable fossils ever discovered are the complete remains of animals which have been preserved in 'deep freeze' in the permanently frozen soils of northern Siberia and Alaska. Such frozen specimens include animals called mammoths (Fig. 26.1), related to the elephants, and a species of rhinoceros with a thick hairy coat. Neither animal exists today.

Preservation in this way is rare and most fossils consist of the skeletal parts of animals—bones and shells—in which, as the organic material has decomposed, it has been slowly replaced by calcareous or siliceous minerals, so that the 'bone' has turned to 'stone' and thus been preserved.

26.1 A restoration of the woolly mammoth. The tusks were 3 to 4 m in length and the hairs 20 to 30 cm long.

The wood of trees is sometimes preserved in a similar way.

Sometimes the organism has fallen upon a soft mud surface; the mud has then slowly been mineralized without distortion so that a thin impression of the original specimen remains. This is a very rare phenomenon, but what little we know about extinct soft-bodied animals such as worms and jellyfish depends upon the chance of finding such casts in shale (Fig. 26.2a). Impressions of leaves may be formed in the same way (Fig. 26.2b). Coal deposits have been formed largely from plant material and are often associated with abundant fossil plants.

Apart from curious specimens like the 'deep-frozen' mammoth from the Arctic, have we any reason to believe that stony fossils really represent the remains of animals which once existed? For a long time the palaeontologists had evidence from fossils of a group of fishes, the coelacanths, which had been abundant about 250 million years ago. They differed markedly both from the present-day cartilaginous and bony fishes and also from the lungfishes. Although their skeletal structure was well known, it was assumed that these fishes had become totally extinct about 70 million years ago. It was therefore a great surprise and of great interest when a specimen belonging to this group was caught in 1938 by fishermen off the port of East London in South Africa. Intensive search has shown that this fish, *Latimeria* (Fig. 26.3), occurs mainly around the Comoro Islands to the north of Madagascar; as many as a dozen specimens have now been collected. Examination of the structure of *Latimeria* has fully confirmed the validity of the conclusions drawn from a study of the fossil material. From such evidence we may reasonably conclude that the bony fossils do indeed represent the remains of organisms which once existed.

(a)

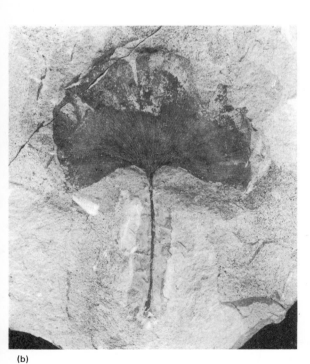

(b)

26.2 Photographs of fossil impressions. (a) A cast of an extinct polychaete worm. The specimen which is about 4 cm long, was found in Australia in a rock of late pre-Cambrian age. (b) A fossil leaf of *Gingko biloba*.

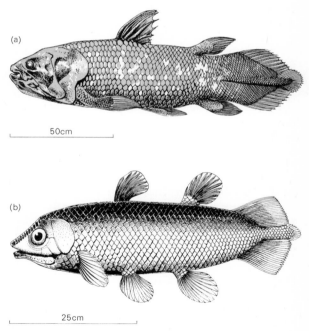

(a)

50cm

(b)

25cm

26.3 (a) A drawing of the coelacanth, *Latimeria*. (b) Drawing based on a reconstruction of a coelacanth made in 1891 from fossil material. Note the similarities, such as the details of the tail, between (a) and (b), remembering that *Latimeria* was not found until 1938 and that these fishes are not of the same genus.

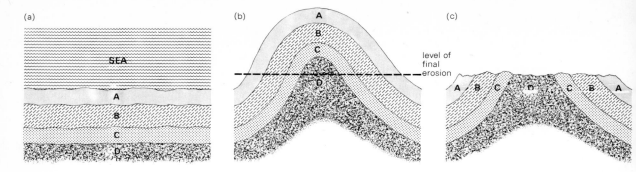

26.4 Diagram showing in highly simplified form the way in which (a) marine deposits may, in being pushed upwards during mountain-building movements, (b) become folded and, how, (c) with subsequent erosion different deposits are exposed. The arrangement of the exposed sediments A, B, C, D reflects the sequence of their deposition.

It is essential to appreciate that the chance of any organism being fossilized is very slight. Dead plants are usually quickly decomposed by soil organisms. The shells of dead, marine, littoral gastropods and bivalves are usually smashed to pieces by wave action, as examination of a sample of coarse sand under a hand lens will show. In deeper water the shells slowly dissolve, so that the chances of preservation are relatively small. Dead fish are usually eaten by scavengers and only those specimens which are rapidly buried are likely to be preserved. Very similar considerations apply to the remains of terrestrial animals: the overwhelming majority are destroyed by scavengers and decomposers, so that fossilization here also is rare, depending largely upon the animal's being buried immediately after death and in soils which are not so acidic as to dissolve the bone. We must not therefore expect to be able to find complete skeletons of all the vertebrates that may have existed in the past. Not only are the chances of fossilization low, but the places where it does occur will represent only a part of the habitats available at any time. Moreover there are many indications that the earliest forms of many groups were very small, so that the likelihood of finding their remains is very slight indeed. For example, the earliest fossil remains of mammals, dating from about 100 million years ago, are mostly teeth and fragments of jaws; these all come from very small animals, mostly no bigger than mice.

Dating fossil remains

One obvious question is: how is it possible to make statements about the ages of fossils, or at least of the rocks in which they occur? During the history of the earth there has been constant erosion of the land surface and the eroded material has been carried into the sea or into large inland lakes. During the course of time this erosion has been offset by processes of mountain building which have often resulted in the forcing upwards of large areas of the sea floor to form part of the land. In some places lateral move-

ments of the earth's crust have folded these layers of sediment. By fresh erosion the different layers are exposed (Fig. 26.4); a study of the relations between these sedimentary layers in different places has allowed geologists to determine the relative ages of sediments. In this way a sequence has been built up, different layers commonly being identified by characteristic fossils they contain. Such studies have led to the recognition of different geological periods (Fig. 26.5); these are convenient reference divisions in the evolutionary history of the earth, but must not be thought of as a set of completely distinct layers, each separated from the next by some sharp discontinuity. Thus, for example, in Britain the oldest rock formations containing abundant fossils are referred to as Cambrian, the next oldest as Ordovician; as a result of particular local geological events, these two deposits are distinct. In North America however, events were different and there no discontinuity is found between Cambrian and Ordovician rocks.

Useful as is the establishment of such a sequence, it tells us nothing about the ages of the deposits. Reliable dating depends upon the use of the fact that different radioactive elements 'decay' at different rates. Each has a characteristic 'half-life', the time during which half the material originally present will have undergone radioactive disintegration. This provides us with a method of measuring time. We will illustrate the principles by reference to two methods, one of which is used for dating relatively recent biological material and one which is applicable to certain types of rock.

Dating by radioactive carbon

The method applicable to organic remains depends upon the fact that high-energy cosmic radiation entering the earth's atmosphere turns a small proportion of nitrogen atoms into radioactive carbon atoms of atomic number 14. Carbon-14 (^{14}C) has a half-life of about 5700 years, so that, if the cosmic-ray bombardment stopped, the concen-

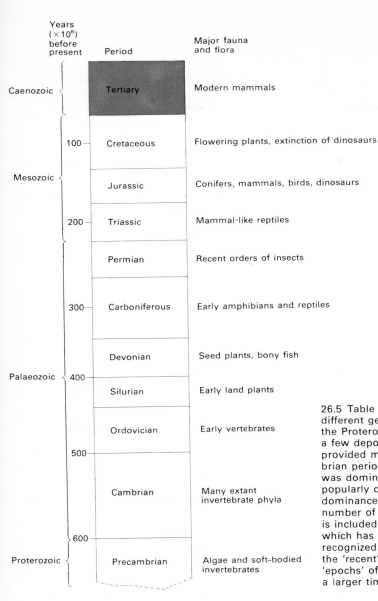

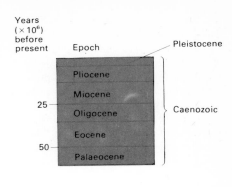

Years ($\times 10^6$) before present	Period	Major fauna and flora
Caenozoic	Tertiary	Modern mammals
100	Cretaceous	Flowering plants, extinction of dinosaurs
Mesozoic — Jurassic	Jurassic	Conifers, mammals, birds, dinosaurs
200	Triassic	Mammal-like reptiles
	Permian	Recent orders of insects
300	Carboniferous	Early amphibians and reptiles
	Devonian	Seed plants, bony fish
Palaeozoic 400	Silurian	Early land plants
	Ordovician	Early vertebrates
500	Cambrian	Many extant invertebrate phyla
600		
Proterozoic	Precambrian	Algae and soft-bodied invertebrates

Years ($\times 10^6$) before present	Epoch	
	Pliocene	Pleistocene
25	Miocene	
	Oligocene	Caenozoic
50	Eocene	
	Palaeocene	

26.5 Table showing the major geological periods. Four different geological 'eras' are recognized. The rocks of the Proterozoic are relatively poor in large fossils, but a few deposits have been found recently which have provided much detail of marine life before the Cambrian period. The Mesozoic is the time when the land was dominated by very large reptiles including those popularly called dinosaurs. The Caenozoic is the era of dominance of mammals. Each era is divided into a number of periods. The greater part of the Caenozoic is included in the Tertiary, but a Quaternary period, which has witnessed the emergence of man, is also recognized. This includes the Pleistocene epoch and the 'recent'. The Tertiary is divided into a number of 'epochs' of which the details are shown on the right at a larger time scale.

tration of ^{14}C in the atmosphere would slowly fall. In fact there is an equilibrium between the removal of radio-carbon atoms by radioactive decay and the formation of new ones, an equilibrium which results in the presence of a very low but measurable quantity of ^{14}C in the atmosphere.

During the processes of photosynthesis, plants fix carbon atoms, including both the stable ^{12}C and the radioactive ^{14}C isotopes. Within the plant, the ^{14}C gradually decays to ^{12}C. The proportion of ^{14}C in all living plants is the same, since they have taken their carbon from the atmosphere; but when a plant dies carbon fixation ceases, and the ^{14}C level starts to fall. If in a sample of a long-dead plant, say some wood from the tomb of a king of ancient Egypt, the proportion of ^{14}C is half that occurring in

present-day plants, we can conclude that the wood was probably produced by a tree about 5700 years ago. Thus, by determining the concentration of ^{14}C in samples of pre-served plant materials, including fragments from lake sediments (p. 370), we can tell how long ago the material died. By this technique we can date organic remains as far back as about 100000 years. Older material cannot be dated in this way since ultimately the concentration of ^{14}C becomes too small to measure.

Dating by potassium/argon ratios

A second method of dating depends upon the fact that all naturally occurring potassium contains a very small

465

quantity of the radioactive isotope ^{40}K, which decays to form calcium and argon. The half-life of ^{40}K is fairly long, $1·3 \times 10^9$ years, so that this method can be used for dating materials which are too old to be dated by the radiocarbon technique. Imagine a volcanic eruption: as the hot lava flows over the country any gases will be driven off by the high temperature. As the lava cools, it forms a solid mass, impermeable to gases, but containing some small quantity of potassium salts. With time the ^{40}K decays, liberating argon which is trapped within the stone. A sample of such rock can be analysed for both its total argon and ^{40}K content in the laboratory. The ratio $^{40}K/Ar$ will then be a measure of the time since the lava was deposited: the lower the ratio, the older the lava. In many parts of East Africa lava beds resulting from different major volcanic eruptions have been identified. Any undisturbed fossil material lying between two such beds must be older than the more recent upper layer of lava but younger than the lower layer. In favourable conditions it is thus possible to put a fairly narrow date range upon the material sealed below the upper layer. Similar procedures using radioisotopes of greater half-life allow us to extend dating back still further in time.

The fossil record

Although fossils provide us with a very incomplete record of life in the past, it is possible to recognize the types of event we would expect to have occurred had there been an evolutionary process. On the basis of the number of fossil specimens, a quantitative estimate can be made of the probable abundance at different times of individuals of the larger taxonomic groupings. If we do this we find evidence of a changing ecological scene. Fig. 26.6 shows in very simplified form the geological history of certain groups of plants and animals.

Cephalopods

As a representative of the marine invertebrates, we show the history of the Cephalopoda, the class of the phylum Mollusca that includes squids and the octopus (Book 1 Fig. 18.47). One living cephalopod, *Nautilus*, has an external shell; this is different from that of the snails in that it contains a series of transverse partitions or septa. The body of the animal fills the last chamber (Fig. 26.7). Such septate shells first appeared in the latter part of the Cam-

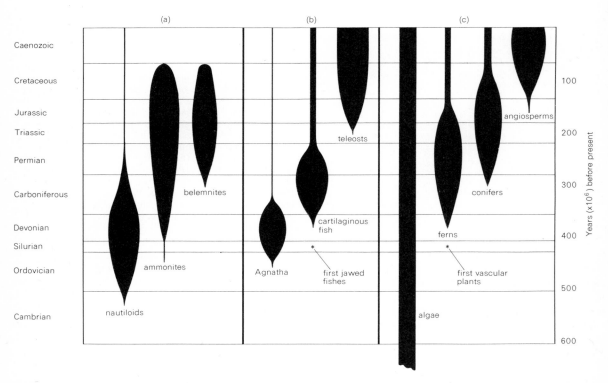

26.6 Diagrammatic representation of the succession of forms of (a) cephalopods, (b) fishes and (c) plants in the fossil record. Only certain groups are shown; many other taxa have been omitted for clarity. The width of each block indicates the relative abundance of the different taxa at different times on an arbitrary scale and omitting much detail; it serves only to show the times of first and last appearance in the fossil record and the time of maximum abundance.

466

brian (Fig. 26.6a) and become increasingly abundant at a later date. It is possible to distinguish two types of shell. In one group, the nautiloids, the septa are gently curved while the surface of the shell is smooth and lacks any complex patterning (Fig. 26.8a): this is the type that appeared first, that became very abundant during the Ordovician, and that is still represented by *Nautilus*. The other group, the ammonites, had wrinkled septa, while the surface of the shell had complex patterning and sculpturing (Fig. 26.8b). Such shells first appeared in the Ordovician and became increasingly abundant while the numbers of the nautiloids grew less. Squids and cuttlefish differ from *Nautilus* in having an internal shell. The earliest shells of this type appear in Carboniferous deposits; one large group with such shells, the belemnites, became extinct together with the ammonites towards the end of the Cretaceous. Here then is evidence of new types of organism coming into existence and also of groups becoming extinct.

Fishes

The same sort of picture (Fig. 26.6b) emerges when we study the fishes. The earliest fossil fishes are found in the late Ordovician rocks and become abundant in the Silurian and Devonian. These fish were characterized by the fact that, like modern lampreys and hagfish (Book 1 p. 215), they had no jaws. Fossils of jawed fishes are first found in rocks of upper Silurian age, but fossils showing the characteristics of modern bony fish, the teleosts, do not appear until the late Triassic and become increasingly abundant and diverse right up to the most modern deposits.

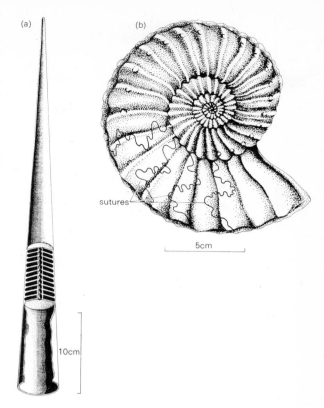

26.8 (a) The shell of an extinct, uncoiled nautiloid. Note the simple arrangement of the septa. (b) The shell of an extinct ammonite. Note the heavy sculpturing on the outside of the shell. The suture lines reflect the complicated foldings of the septa, a character whose functional significance is not understood.

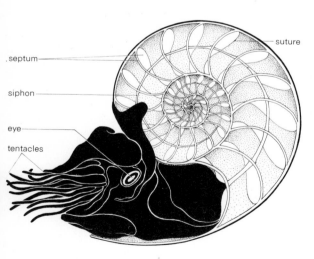

26.7 Diagram of the structure of *Nautilus* within its shell. The animal is shown as if whole, but the shell has been cut open, slightly to the left of the mid-line, so as to show its internal arrangement. The chambers of the shell are largely air-filled, so the shell acts as a float. The shell may be about 15 cm or more in diameter.

Plants

This sort of pattern can be recognized also among the plants (Fig. 26.6c). Fossil algae are found long before the start of the Cambrian (p. 502), but the earliest indications of terrestrial plant life are provided by remains of vascular plants from the late Silurian. Ferns appeared in the Devonian, as did large gymnosperm trees. Conifers appeared for the first time towards the end of the Carboniferous, but the angiosperms arose far later, probably some time during the Jurassic, becoming very abundant from the late Cretaceous onwards.

Tetrapods

The earliest tetrapod fossils appear in the very late Devonian. Structurally they resemble a group of fishes related to the coelacanths (p. 463). These were the earliest amphibians; they became very abundant during the Carboniferous and Permian but were rare by the Jurassic.

26.9 (a) A reconstruction of *Eryops,* an extinct amphibian found in the lower Permian. The animal reached about 3 m in length. (b) A reconstruction of *Seymouria,* a vertebrate showing both amphibian and reptilian anatomical characteristics. The body length reached about 50 cm.

Some of these were relatively big animals with heavy, flattened heads and short legs, hardly holding the body clear of the ground (Fig. 26.9a). Fossils identified as reptiles first appear in the upper Carboniferous, birds and mammals in the Jurassic.

Fossils intermediate between major taxa

We have no problem in distinguishing between an extant amphibian and an extant reptile. Their skins are different in texture; amphibians typically lay their eggs in water and reptiles usually lay a yolky egg with a leathery eggshell. Furthermore, the reptilian embryo lies in an amniotic cavity and has an allantois, just like the embryo of a bird (Book 1 Fig. 25.13). None of these characteristics can be seen in fossils: how then can we decide whether a fossil is that of an amphibian or a reptile? By comparing the skeletons of living reptiles with those of fossils, we can build up a sequence of changes with time which leads us from present-day reptiles back to the early tetrapods. In the same way we can construct a sequence from the fishes which gave rise to the Amphibia, through early Amphibia which we recognize by their limbs, to more advanced Amphibia. Somewhere these two sequences should meet and in the lower Permian we find fossils of individuals with a mixture of characters: some typical of earlier amphibians, some of later reptiles. This is the case, for example, with a fossil called *Seymouria* (Fig. 26.9b) whose remains were found in Texas. The skull of *Seymouria*

contains, just behind the eye, a bone which occurs in the skulls of the early Amphibia but not in those of the Reptilia; further, the palate of *Seymouria* is typical of an amphibian. The toes of reptiles have more bones than have those of the early amphibians and *Seymouria* has typically reptilian toes; similarly the shape of the neural arch of its vertebrae is that characteristic of many early Reptilia but not of Amphibia. In this fossil we have an example of what we would expect to find if reptiles evolved from amphibians, namely the existence of animals which are intermediate in structure between one major grouping and another.

Intermediates between reptiles and birds also exist. The earliest known bird is called *Archaeopteryx*; only three specimens have been discovered. It is unquestionably a bird, as the imprint of feathers can be seen on the fossils (Fig. 26.10). Its skeleton is, however, very similar to those of a group of fossil reptiles called the Ornithischia, many of which were bipedal (Fig. 26.12). The reptilian features of the skeleton of *Archaeopteryx* can be seen in Fig. 26.11: there is a long tail, long fingers very different from the

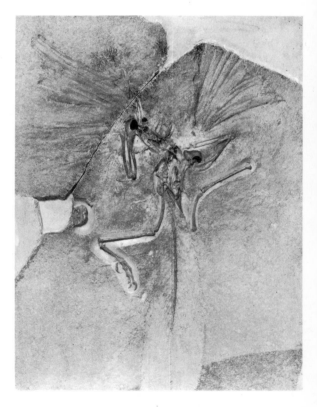

26.10 Photograph of one of the fossil specimens of *Archaeopteryx.* All three specimens have been found in deposits which probably lay at the bottoms of lakes. It is suggested that the birds were drowned in very stormy weather and rapidly covered with mud before any significant decay occurred. The long tail with its associated vertebral column may be easily recognized.

arrangement in the wing of a modern bird, while the breast bone, which is very large in most birds to provide an origin for the flight muscles, is not significantly developed in *Archaeopteryx*. Unlike extant birds, *Archaeopteryx* had teeth, while the long bones, which in extant birds are hollow, are solid in *Archaeopteryx*. Here again we have the sort of transitional form which we might expect to find if the birds had arisen by a process of evolution from one of the now-extinct groups of reptiles.

As a last example, we will take the origin of mammals; the fossils of Africa have contributed considerably to our understanding of this problem. The earliest unquestionable remains of mammals are jaw fragments and teeth from the middle Jurassic. But reptiles showing mammal-like characteristics occur in the Permian and Triassic. One of these, *Cynognathus* (Fig. 26.13), shows a number of familiar mammalian characteristics. The teeth are differentiated into incisors, canines and cheek teeth and the last are cusped, although not in the mammalian pattern; there is a secondary palate forming a roof to the mouth, but the lower jaw, unlike that of a mammal, is formed of several bones. At the back of the skull, articulating with the atlas

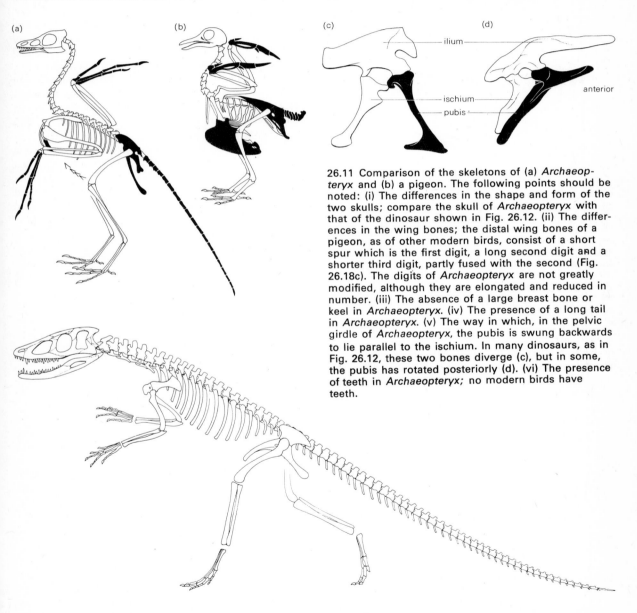

26.11 Comparison of the skeletons of (a) *Archaeopteryx* and (b) a pigeon. The following points should be noted: (i) The differences in the shape and form of the two skulls; compare the skull of *Archaeopteryx* with that of the dinosaur shown in Fig. 26.12. (ii) The differences in the wing bones; the distal wing bones of a pigeon, as of other modern birds, consist of a short spur which is the first digit, a long second digit and a shorter third digit, partly fused with the second (Fig. 26.18c). The digits of *Archaeopteryx* are not greatly modified, although they are elongated and reduced in number. (iii) The absence of a large breast bone or keel in *Archaeopteryx*. (iv) The presence of a long tail in *Archaeopteryx*. (v) The way in which, in the pelvic girdle of *Archaeopteryx*, the pubis is swung backwards to lie parallel to the ischium. In many dinosaurs, as in Fig. 26.12, these two bones diverge (c), but in some, the pubis has rotated posteriorly (d). (vi) The presence of teeth in *Archaeopteryx*; no modern birds have teeth.

26.12 Skeleton of a bipedal dinosaur from the upper Triassic. The animal was about 1.3 m in length.

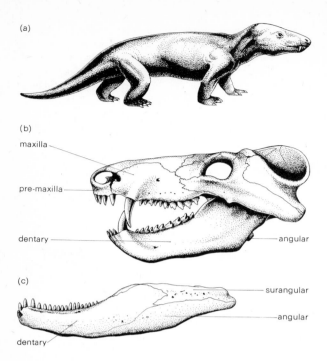

(a)

(b)

maxilla

pre-maxilla

dentary

angular

(c)

surangular

angular

dentary

26.13 (a) Reconstruction of the mammal-like reptile, *Cynognathus*. The animal was about 2·0 m in length. (b) Drawing of the skull of *Cynognathus*. It is about 0·5 m long. Note the differentiation of the teeth and the fact that the dentary forms almost the whole of the lower jaw. Other lower jaw bones are found on the inner surface. (c) Drawing of the lower jaw of a primitive reptile for comparison with that of *Cynognathus*. Note that three bones are found on the outer surface of the lower jaw.

vertebra, are two occipital condyles as in a mammal, while in a typical reptile there is a single median condyle. The toes retain the reptilian arrangement of bones in which, starting from the thumb, there are 2, 3, 4, 5 and 3 bones in succeeding fingers; in a mammal the arrangement is, as you can see in your own hand, 2, 3, 3, 3, 3. Thus, while the skull shows a mixture of typically reptilian and mammalian characteristics, the foot is reptilian. In other related reptiles the skull retains reptilian characteristics, while the toe bones are typically mammalian. This is the sort of result which we might expect if closely similar selective pressures were acting on a number of related groups of animals at the same time. Such pressures might favour a number of different adaptations, but not all would necessarily appear at the same time in different groups.

The evolution of the horse

We have so far attempted to show that organisms which existed in the past were different from those we know today, that the fossil record shows us both new patterns of organization appearing and others becoming extinct and that there are organisms which are intermediate in structure between major taxonomic groupings. We have still to provide an example of a pattern of steady change leading from some extinct ancestor to an organism which is alive today. For this we require a very extensive collection of fossils, such as are provided by the ancestors of the horse, whose evolution took place in North America. By a comparison of material from increasingly ancient geological strata, it is possible to trace back the evolution of the present-day horse, *Equus*, to its ancestor in the Eocene, more than 50 million years ago. There we find a small animal, commonly known as 'eohippus', standing about 0·5 m at the shoulder, with four toes on each front foot and three on the hind, and with cheek teeth which have a low crown. Connecting eohippus and *Equus* are at least seven different genera, while there are also fossil remains of many other horse-like animals. From a study more especially of their teeth, we know that the latter were not ancestral to our present-day horse.

As Fig. 26.14 shows, the evolution of the horse has been associated with two major structural changes. The first relates to the teeth. The high-crowned teeth of the later horses were adapted for feeding on highly abrasive food which wears down the teeth relatively rapidly; they were grazers, feeding upon grass. But the early ancestors of the horse had low-crowned teeth unsuitable for grazing and they probably fed upon the soft leaves of shrubs; that is, they were browsers. The second change relates to the reduction in the number of toes. These two changes occurred quite independently.

What the drawings in Fig. 26.14 do not show is that the change from a low- to a high-crowned tooth was a relatively rapid process and that associated with it went a change in the structure of the foot from one in which the main impact in running was taken by a fleshy pad behind the toes to one in which the impact was taken by the middle toe itself (Fig. 26.15). Both changes have been associated with the probability that the area of open grassland increased very greatly during the early Miocene and offered a valuable resource to be exploited by a fast-running herbivore with suitable grinding teeth. What we would stress is that where, as in the case of the horses, there is a fairly extensive fossil record, it is possible to recognize a series of gradual evolutionary stages leading to an organism extant today.

Before leaving discussion of the fossil evidence for evolutionary change, we wish to emphasize once again that, from the nature of the process of fossilization, the fossil record is bound to be very incomplete. Thus, the absence of fossils intermediate between group A and group B does not exclude the possibility that group A is in fact ancestral to group B. We have to base our conclusions upon the evidence which *is* available. It is not reasonable, as demanded by certain critics of the concept of evolution,

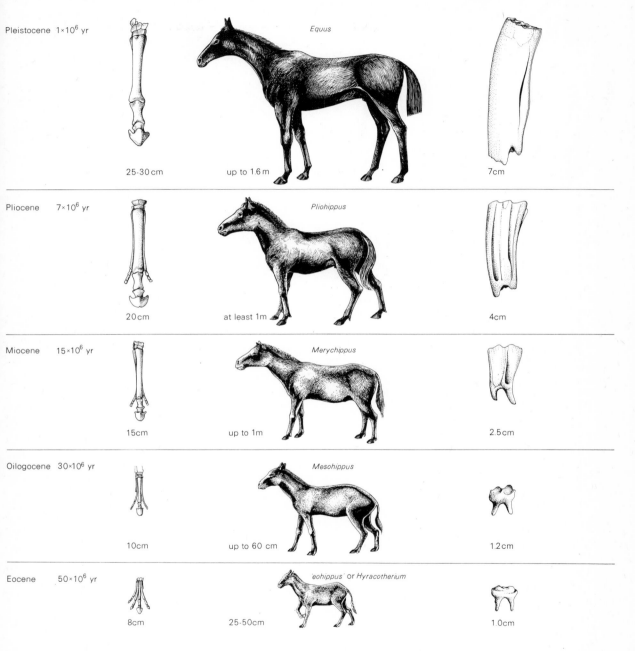

Pleistocene 1×10⁶ yr — 25-30 cm — *Equus* — up to 1.6 m — 7 cm

Pliocene 7×10⁶ yr — 20 cm — *Pliohippus* — at least 1 m — 4 cm

Miocene 15×10⁶ yr — 15 cm — *Merychippus* — up to 1 m — 2.5 cm

Oilogocene 30×10⁶ yr — 10 cm — *Mesohippus* — up to 60 cm — 1.2 cm

Eocene 50×10⁶ yr — 8 cm — 'eohippus' or *Hyracotherium* — 25-50 cm — 1.0 cm

26.14 Diagrammatic summary of the evolutionary pathway from 'eohippus' to *Equus*. It is important to realize that each genus included many different species. On the left is shown the geological epoch in which the genus occurred, together with the time of ending of each period expressed in years before present. In the next column can be seen the major features of the right fore foot; its approximate length is indicated. In the central column are drawings of reconstructions of the different genera; the approximate height at shoulder is shown. On the right are drawings of molar teeth in side view together with their approximate length.

471

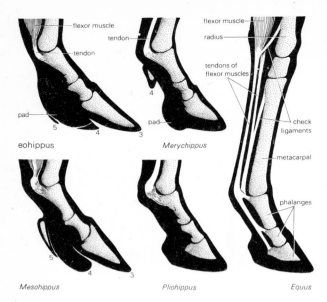

26.15 Drawings of the probable structure of the fore-limbs of the ancestors of the horse. The drawings show the shaft of the bones of the third digit of the left fore-foot as they might appear in dissection. Many structures present in the foot have been omitted for clarity. In eohippus and *Mesohippus*, the toes are supported by a pad which is reduced in *Merychippus* and absent in *Pliohippus*. Note the check ligaments in the leg of *Equus*. There are two flexor muscles; the tendons of both are shown, but only one of the muscles is drawn. If the tendons are pulled, they will stretch the muscles until the check ligaments become taut. The ligaments serve to protect the muscles from being torn by too great extension of the toes. (After Camp and Smith).

to expect large numbers of transitional fossils normally to be discovered. Indeed the criticism reflects an ignorance of the nature of the evidence and is one which would not be voiced by anyone who comprehended the types of event which lead to fossilization.

Adaptive radiation

While some types of evolutionary change may fit organisms better to survive in the environment in which they live or may adapt them, as with the ancestors of the horse, to a changing environment, we might expect that other changes might also provide certain organisms with exceptional competitive advantages over others.

An analogy may help you to understand the possible consequences of such an event. Until the beginning of the last century, men depended upon horses or oxen for transport over land, upon oars or sails for transport on the sea. With the invention of the steam engine, new methods of transport appeared, including railways to supplement horse-drawn carts and carriages, while steam vessels fairly

quickly replaced the older, less efficient sailing boats. During this century another invention, the internal-combustion engine, led to the replacement of horses and horse-drawn carriages by motor cycles and motor cars, of horse-drawn ploughs by tractors, of steam engines on the railways by diesel engines, and at the same time allowed man to move into new environments with aeroplanes and submarines. A single technical advance has been followed by the development of a wide variety of specialized types of engine to fulfil different purposes. To stretch the analogy we might speak of the internal-combustion engine as having occupied a variety of different social and ecological niches.

In the same fashion, an evolutionary change providing exceptional competitive advantage to some group of organisms might be expected to enable them successfully to invade a wide variety of habitats and to become adapted to these by increasing specialization of structure and function. This is indeed a recognized phenomenon; it is described as 'adaptive radiation'. For example, in the evolution of the terrestrial vertebrates, two highly important events led to such radiations. One was the evolution of a type of embryonic development which no longer required eggs to be laid in water; this represented the major advantage of the reptiles over the amphibia. The second was the development of homeothermy, which occurred twice: in the evolution of the birds and also in the line leading to the mammals. The full exploitation of homeothermy represented a major advantage of the mammals over the reptiles which had been the dominant land vertebrates throughout the Mesozoic. You will recognize that such adaptive radiation depends upon the evolution of what we described earlier as 'key characteristics' (p. 459).

When we study the patterns of adaptation of the mammals, we see that they have come to fill a vast variety of niches (Fig. 26.16); the marsupials have shown a similar but less extensive radiation to that of the eutherian mammals (p. 117). It is possible to see a similar radiation among the reptiles during the long ages when they were the dominant vertebrates (Fig. 26.17). Our figure is a gross over-simplification of events spread over more than one hundred million years, as there were in fact several such radiations. The point which we would stress is that this phenomenon which we can recognize among the extant mammals and, from a study of the fossil record, see as a result of a radiation from an ancestral stock, is what we might expect as a consequence of an evolutionary process.

Homology and analogy

One of the facts which impressed the anatomists at the beginning of the last century was that the same patterns of bones occurred in widely different vertebrates, serving widely different purposes. The limb bones of a jumping frog, a running horse, a flying bird, a swimming whale

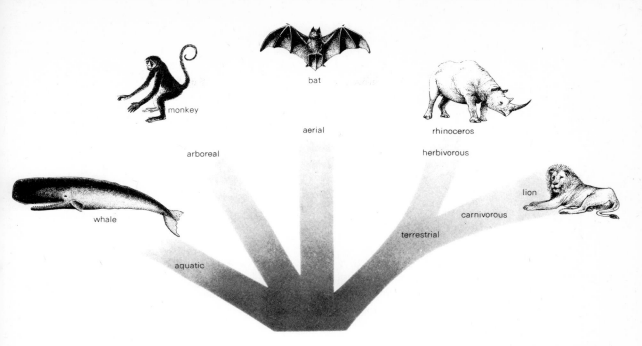

26.16 An example of adaptive radiation among the eutherian or true placental mammals. Familiar animals occupy very different niches, although they all retain the common characteristics which define the Eutheria.

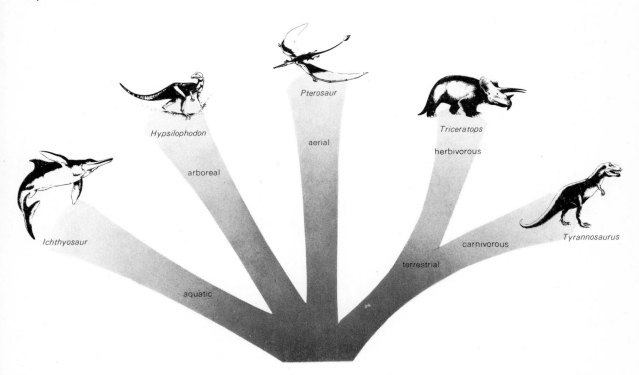

26.17 Examples of adaptive radiation among the Mesozoic reptiles. The ichthyosaurs were marine and reached a length of 10 m, but were typically about 3 m in length. *Hypsilophodon* was about 1·5 m in length and may have climbed trees. The pterosaurs had gliding, but probably not flapping flight; the body was usually less than 1 m in length, and members of one genus in which the body was not much larger had a wing span of about 8 m. *Triceratops* reached a length of about 8 m, while the overall length of *Tyrannosaurus* was about 16 m.

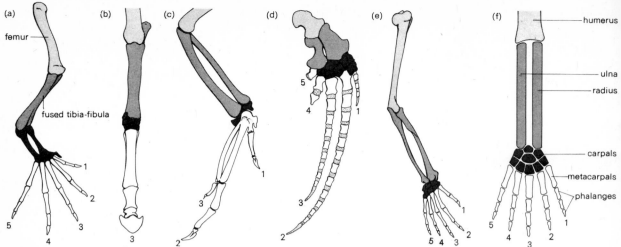

26.18 Comparison of the structure of (a) the right hind limb of a frog and the right fore limbs of (b) a horse, (c) a bird, (d) a whale and (e) a man. (f) shows the common pattern to which all these structures may be referred.

and a man all conform to the same basic pattern (Fig. 26.18). This relation they described by saying that corresponding bones in these different structures were 'homologous'. Such homology is what we would expect if there had been an evolutionary process. The earliest land vertebrates evolved a type of walking limb whose pattern of bones was itself largely determined by the structure of the fins of their ancestors. This limb pattern, which we call pentadactyl, has remained typical of all terrestrial vertebrates, but with every radiation among the vertebrates specializations have arisen. Thus, if we compare the detailed anatomy of the wing bones of the extinct flying reptiles, the pterodactyls, with those of birds and of bats, we find that each is very distinct (Fig. 26.19); each had a particular 'starting point' from a different ancestral form and the precise circumstances in which selection for flight occurred resulted in structurally different end-results. Nevertheless the bony elements on which the three types of wings are built are those of the pentadactyl limb.

We can thus understand, if we accept the concept of evolutionary change, the phenomena of structural homology. The 'plans' recognized by the early anatomists are a reflection of a single 'starting point' which was the foundation of subsequent evolutionary change.

The opposite situation may also arise. If the 'starting points' are structurally different, then the details of

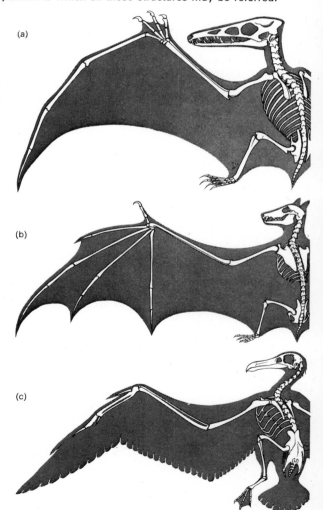

26.19 Comparison of the wing structure of (a) a pterodactyl, an extinct flying reptile, (b) a bat (c) a bird. The main support for the wing of the pterodactyl is from the fifth digit, that of the bat from digits two to five and that of the bird from digit three (compare Fig. 26.18c). Both the pterodactyl and the bat have membranous wings and, unlike that of the bird, the hind limb is included in the wing structure.

structures with the same function will be different. Insects are flying arthropods, and their wings arise from out-pushings of the wall of the thorax, not from modified limbs; there is no anatomical similarity between insect wings and those of flying vertebrates. This situation we describe by saying that the two types of wing are 'analogous'—having the same function—but not 'homologous' for, as we have seen, this term implies structural similarity which can be interpreted in evolutionary terms as some degree of common ancestry.

Embryonic development

The development of any organism is a complex and integrated process. Any change early in the process is likely to upset this integration and result in the failure of the embryo to develop. Changes which find their expression late in development are more likely to be viable. We might therefore expect early development to be a very conservative process, changing far less during the process of evolution than does the final adult form. This conclusion explains certain facts concerning the structure of vertebrate embryos to which attention was first drawn by the German embryologist von Baer in 1828. Von Baer emphasized that the early stages of all vertebrate embryos are very similar and that they come to differ one from another increasingly as development proceeds. For example, Fig. 26.20 shows comparable stages of development of a fish, a bird and a man. There are two features of interest. Immediately behind the head of the fish can be seen the gill slits; in a comparable position in the bird and man there are furrows. These are described as 'gill clefts': a detailed study of their structure and especially of their embryonic blood vessels shows that these clefts are homologous with the gill slits. The second feature is that the human embryo has a short tail. The occurrence of such structures is in keeping with our earlier suggestion that if there has been an evolutionary process, embryonic development will be less subject to change than adult structure. Change certainly does occur —gill clefts never open into the pharynx as do gill slits— but the broad pattern of early development of a fish is repeated by a mammal.

Another example of this sort of phenomenon is the similarity of structure and mode of formation of the embryonic membranes, the chorion and amnion, and of the allantois, in a chick and a pig (Book 1 p. 312ff). If we accept what we have learnt from the study of the fossil record, namely that both birds and mammals have evolved from reptilian ancestors and recall that these same structures are present also in the eggs of reptiles, the similarity of developmental pattern becomes comprehensible as another example of the conservatism of embryonic development. Here too there can be modification: while the amniotic cavity of the pig is formed in a manner very closely similar to that of a hen, in human development the amnion cavity forms in a more direct fashion as a split between different tissue layers.

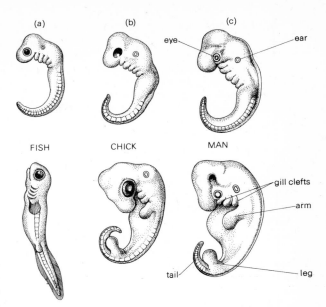

26.20 Comparison of the structure of the early embryos of (a) a fish, (b) a chick and (c) a man. Note the close similarity in appearance of all three at the early stage of development and between the chick and the human embryo at a later stage.

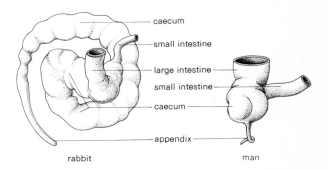

26.21 Drawings comparing the structure of the caecum and appendix of a rabbit and a man. Note that while both structures are well developed in the rabbit they are vestigial in man.

Vestigial structures

If you look again at Fig. 26.14, you will see that in the Miocene the second and fourth digits of the ancestors of the horse became very short and might be regarded as functionless remnants of earlier structures which once played a significant role in running. A large number of structures are known which are small in size in some species while large in others. The caecum and vermiform appendix in man are homologous with corresponding structures in a rabbit (Fig. 26.21). In the rabbit the caecum has a clear function in cellulose digestion (Book 1 p. 105); whether the human appendix has any significant function is not certain. Such structures were described by the early anatomists as 'vestigial' and they were assumed to be functionless. We could interpret their decreased size in evolutionary terms if we suppose that structures which have become functionless will not be maintained by any selective agent and that hereditary changes which lead to their reduction in size can therefore persist. By chance such structures might then tend gradually to be eliminated.

When we come to look more closely at so-called 'vestigial' structures, we often find that it is in fact possible to ascribe functions to them in their reduced condition. Where this is so, their size is under the control of selective forces and not merely a matter of chance. The complete disappearance of a structure may similarly depend upon selection. An example of such an alternative interpretation, inevitably speculative, is provided by a consideration of the toes at various stages in the evolution of the horse. The horse comes from an ancestor which was small and essentially digitigrade (Book 1 p. 139) although the toes were supported upon a fleshy pad (Fig. 26.15). Selection appears to have favoured both increased size and increased speed; we cannot be certain why but it is clear that the two are related since greater size would lead to a longer stride. Increase in leg length was achieved partly by an elongation of the metacarpals and metatarsals. The whole foot became essentially a single shaft of bone; nevertheless the second and fourth digits were retained (Fig. 26.22). It is probable that these, though reduced in size, were still functional. During evolution from a digitigrade type of foot found in eohippus to the unguligrade foot found in *Merychippus*, the pad of the foot became increasingly reduced (Fig. 26.15). As the foot struck the ground, the

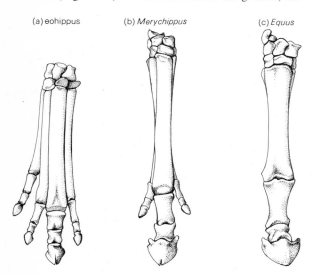

(a) eohippus   (b) *Merychippus*   (c) *Equus*

26.22 Details of the structure of the right foot of (a) eohippus, (b) *Merychippus* and (c) *Equus*. Note that in the latter two genera the foot is effectively formed of a single bony shaft.

toes would tend to be bent upwards. If this movement were allowed to go too far the muscle flexing the toe would be torn. It is likely that the small lateral hooves served to check this bending movement and that they were assisted by the action of 'check' ligaments attached to the tendons of the flexor muscles. This condition persisted for a very long time, probably about 20 million years, and was not modified until the early Pliocene. In the genus *Pliohippus* we find some species with the two lateral digits and others without. The loss of lateral digits occurred within a relatively short time. It has been suggested that this change, which occurred in only one of the four genera of horse-like animals known to be extant at that time, depended upon an increase in the strength of the check ligaments. This made the 'stopping' action of the lateral toes unnecessary, as the ligaments were now strong enough to prevent tearing of the flexor muscle. Further, the lateral toes may always have been liable to damage which could result in reduced efficiency of running. Thus, rather than a haphazard disappearance of a structure which was no longer functional, there may have been a constant selection pressure for the elimination of the lateral toes, but this could express itself only when the check ligaments were sufficiently developed.

Biochemical evolution

Elimination need not be limited to structures. One biochemical characteristic of consumers is that they lack various synthetic mechanisms found among producers: as a result the food of consumers must contain certain 'essential' amino-acids and lipids, as well as various vitamins (Book 1 p. 152). This can be regarded as the consequence of the loss of certain genes which were no longer 'essential' since the enzymes whose synthesis they directed were not required. Here indeed chance may have played a role; this is suggested by the fact (Table 26.1) that different, closely related flagellates lack different enzymes required for the biosynthesis of the vitamin thiamine. You will recognize the parallel here with experimentally induced mutant forms of *Neurospora* (p. 417). But whereas wild *Neurospora* has a full complement of these enzymes, the different flagellate species are able to survive in nature although lacking one or more. We might regard these species as extant organisms which still show some of the stages which occurred in the evolution of the requirement general among the Metazoa for vitamin B_1.

Phylogeny

We have earlier suggested (p. 448) that we may regard the classificatory system of the taxonomists as a result of an evolutionary process. Taxa such as orders in the animal kingdom can often be seen as representing the consequences of radiations following upon the evolution of some

Table 26.1 Pathway of biosynthesis of thiamine and the occurrence of different enzymes in various species of flagellate (*Modified from Lwoff*)

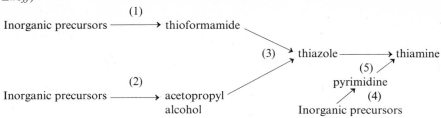

Enzyme	Polytoma obtusum	Polytoma ocellatum	Polytomella caeca	Strigomonas oncopelti
(1) Thioformidase	+	−	−	−
(2) Acetopropylase	+	−	−	−
(3) Thiazolase	+	−	−	−
(4) Pyrimidinase	+	+	−	−
(5) Thiaminase	+	+	+	−

key characteristic which offered great competitive advantage. This key characteristic would be diagnostic of the class or subclass to which the orders belonged. Thus the orders of the eutherian mammals reflect a radiation based on a placental pattern of reproduction in a homeotherm, both characteristics of the subclass. At the level of phyla, key characteristics largely relate to major differences in methods of feeding and locomotion (Book 1 chap. 18). We can thus think of the classificatory system as the reflection of an historical process, the process described as phylogenesis. After the general acceptance by biologists of the concept of evolution, much effort was dedicated to attempting to trace the 'phylogenies' of different organisms. We have considered the phylogeny of the horse; here we are on fairly secure ground as there is a relatively abundant fossil record. As our knowledge of vertebrate palaeontology grows, our ideas about vertebrate phylogeny change in detail, but the broad outlines now appear to be reasonably certain. With the invertebrates and most groups of plants the picture is completely different. The fossil record is meagre and most phylogeny is an exercise in ingenious speculation. This is not to say that such speculation is unproductive; it frequently suggests lines of research which themselves prove fruitful. Nevertheless such schemes are speculative and, unless critically examined, can give a misleading impression of certainty. For this reason, since such critical discussion cannot be elaborated here, we have deliberately omitted presenting any such phylogeny.

There is, however, one group, the Class Flagellata, which deserves brief mention. In considering these organisms we drew attention (Book 1 p. 188) to the diversity of nutritional types found within the class, and suggested that this was perhaps a reflection of their relatively unspecialized structure. The group, however, may also be regarded as approximating to the organizational level at which con-

sumers first evolved from producers; the other classes of Protozoa may have evolved from heterotrophic flagellates. This is not to imply that any living species of, say, ciliate evolved from any living species of flagellate or that the living flagellates belong to species which have persisted unchanged since the separation of consumers from producers.

Cell structure and function

If it is true that consumers evolved from producers and that both were initially very closely related unicellular organisms, then the physiology of these organisms must have been very similar, apart from the presence in some of photosynthetic organelles, and so too would have been their genetic mechanisms. We might therefore expect to find in their descendants biochemical evidence for common ancestry in the form of common metabolic pathways and mechanisms of protein synthesis. This is precisely what we do find. In both plants and animals the processes of oxidation yield ATP and the chemical events of this oxidative phosphorylation are very similar; cytochrome pigments concerned in the final stages are found in both plants and animals. Also, as we have already seen in Chaps. 22 and 23, the processes of nuclear division in plants and animals are closely similar as are those associated with gene action. In both types of organism the fundamental genetic material is DNA, which in both is transcribed to m-RNA, and in both the m-RNA is translated by a process involving t-RNAs and ribosomes; moreover the m-RNA code is the same in both.

This argument can be extended further; the biochemical genetical mechanisms of the bacteria are the same as those of plants and animals, while aerobic bacteria synthesize ATP by pathways very similar to those found in plants and

477

animals. This strongly suggests that all living organisms, whether bacteria, viruses, plants or animals, have a common origin. We will consider the wider implications of this idea in Chap. 28.

Persistent types of organization

The suggestion that extant flagellates may be similar to their remote ancestors raises the question of why it is that certain types of organization which we might consider to be 'primitive' still exist today. There are two aspects to this matter. If you look back at Fig. 26.6 you will see that the earliest type of fishes, the jawless fishes, are still represented by a small number of species. What was once a highly diverse group has persisted, but the living Agnatha are all specialized ectoparasitic predators; the extinct agnaths, which were filter feeders and lived in a variety of habitats, appear to have been unable to compete with the jawed fishes, and only a few atypical, specialized species have remained. The same is broadly true of the Amphibia. The large terrestrial Amphibia (Fig. 26.9a) were unable to compete effectively with the reptiles; the living terrestrial Amphibia are almost all Anura, frogs and toads, with a highly specialized method of locomotion and elaborate defence mechanisms against predation. Once again the living representatives are atypical of the group at the height of its radiation.

But we may also ask: why are there still Protozoa? The answer to this question surely is: why not? The Protozoa, as small, mainly bacteria-feeding consumers are well adapted to the types of niche they occupy and their unicellular organization allows them very rapidly to exploit any food resource which may be available. The same type of argument can be developed in relation to other organisms: for example, the bryophytes and ferns are well adapted both physiologically and by their life cycles to existence in forests (p. 52). In short, any type of organism which can survive, will survive. Nevertheless there have been extinctions and replacements in the past which we do not and probably will never understand. It is not known why, for example, the highly successful trilobites (Fig. 28.7) became extinct in the Permian, nor why in a relatively brief space of time the highly diverse reptilian fauna which dominated the earth during the Triassic and Jurassic ceased to exist; why, on a more modest scale, the horse which had evolved primarily in North America became extinct on the American continent towards the end of the Pleistocene, or why in the early Pleistocene many large African mammals such as those whose reconstructions are shown in Fig. 26.23 also became extinct.

Geographical distribution

The extinction of the horse in its evolutionary 'homeland' raises another question. If *Equus* evolved in America, how is it possible for horses to have occurred all over the Old

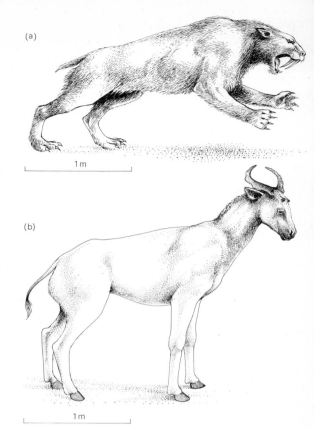

26.23 Reconstructions of two African mammals which became extinct in the early Pleistocene. (a) A sabre-toothed cat. (b) A browsing herbivore related to the giraffe.

World? We know, for example, that zebras and other horses, including the three-toed *Stylohipparion*, existed in Africa during the Pleistocene. Other similar questions may be asked. Why is it that the nearest relative of the North African and Asian camels, the llama (Fig. 26.24), occurs in the Andes on the west of South America? Why is it that marsupials are abundant in Australia and, apart from a few species in America, are found nowhere else? Why is it that the same genera of fossil reptiles occur both in southern Africa and in Brazil in South America?

If we postulate that evolution has occurred, then we must attempt to explain how members of these various groups of animals could have migrated from their places of origin in one continent to other distant continents. Our theories have to take account not only of biological, but also geological history. There are two quite distinct types of geological circumstance which may be used to account for these distributions. One is the occurrence of temporary 'land bridges'. The Isthmus of Panama which joins North and South America is an example. It is less than 50 km across at its narrowest. The geological evidence suggests that although this land bridge existed in the Mesozoic it

(a)

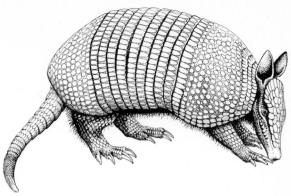

26.25 An armadillo, *Dasypus*. Body length is about 65 cm. This is a representative of one of the mammalian orders which evolved in South America and are found only on the American continent.

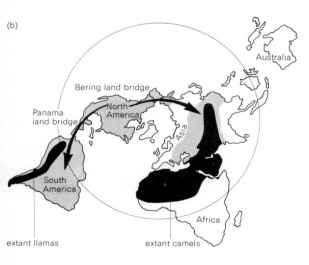

(b)

26.24 (a) The llama, *Lama glama*; the animal is about 1·2 m high at the shoulder. (b) Map of the world as seen in polar projection. The present distribution of the camels and llamas is indicated by solid black and the distribution of fossil members of the family Camelidae by stippling. The family probably originated in North America and crossed into Asia by the Bering land bridge before the Pliocene, while they spread into South America across the Panama land bridge during the Pleistocene. (After Matthew).

was broken in the late Cretaceous and only re-established as a result of movements of the earth's crust in the late Pliocene. The mammalian fauna of South America was thus completely isolated from that of North America for about 60 to 70 million years. A study of the fossils shows that the Pliocene mammalian faunas of the two Americas were quite distinct, but that in the Pleistocene, mammals formerly restricted to North America appeared in South America, while a few South American mammals, such as the armadillo (Fig. 26.25), reached North America. Armadillos are members of an order of mammals which is restricted to the New World, and which evolved in South America.

North America is separated today from the Old World; the nearest approach is at the Bering Strait which is less than 100 km wide at its narrowest point. There is geological evidence that at different times during the past there has been a land bridge across the strait, linking Asia to North America. It is believed that the ancestors of the horse moved across such a land bridge from North America into the Old World. This bridge seems to have been broken and remade several times as there is fossil evidence of separate migrations of horse ancestors into the Old World. A genus related to *Mesohippus* moved into Asia during the Miocene, while the ancestor of *Stylohipparion* migrated during the early Pliocene. The bridge, broken in the middle Pliocene, re-formed during the Pleistocene to provide a route for invasion of the Old World by the newly evolved genus *Equus*; once established in Asia, there were no barriers to its migration over the whole of the Old World land mass.

The Bering Strait may also have been the route by which the ancestors of the camel entered Asia from North America during the late Miocene, while the ancestors of the llama entered South America after the re-forming of the Isthmus of Panama at the end of the Pliocene. In keeping with this picture we find that in North America there are

479

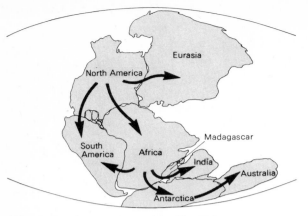

(a) Permian: monotremes and marsupials widespread.

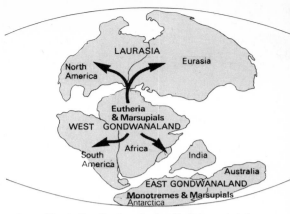

(b) End of Triassic: East Gondwanaland and India separate before evolution of eutherian mammals.

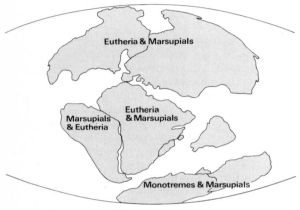

(c) End of Jurassic: South America begins to separate from Africa with fauna of marsupials and early Eutheria.

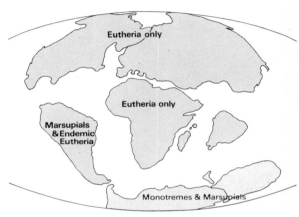

(d) End of Cretaceous: Madagascar separates from Africa with eutherian fauna which evolves in isolation.

26.26 Maps showing the probable arrangement of the continents (a) during the Permian, (b) at the end of the Triassic, (c) at the end of the Jurassic and (d) at the end of the Cretaceous. The geological evidence suggests that the continental masses had been separated before the Permian and then had moved together to form the super-continent of Pangaea. The possible stages of evolution of the mammalian fauna are indicated on the maps. Note that Antarctica and Australia separated from Gondwanaland during the Triassic, taking with them a fauna of monotremes and marsupials, but eutherian mammals had not yet evolved. By the end of the Cretaceous, South America had separated from Africa and took a fauna of marsupials and early eutherian mammals which radiated to give South America its peculiar families of eutherian mammals. Later India became joined to the Asiatic land mass and was colonized by eutherian mammals from the north, while Madagascar, which has a peculiar mammalian fauna, separated from Africa during the Cretaceous. (After Fooden).

abundant fossils of forms which are ancestral to both the camels and the llamas. The Proboscidia, the order today represented only by the elephants, present a picture of movement in the opposite direction. They originated in Africa in the late Eocene and by the Miocene were widespread not only in the Old World but also in North America, spreading into South America during the Pleistocene once the Panama land bridge had been re-established.

A second, more dramatic type of geological change has also occurred. There is now a considerable body of evidence that the major continental land masses have not always occupied their present positions and that during the Permian they formed a single extensive continent, referred to as Pangaea. This subsequently broke up into a northern and a southern continent, called Laurasia and Gondwanaland respectively (Fig. 26.26). Gondwanaland included all the southern continents, but by the end of the Triassic the future Australia, Antarctica and India had separated from Africa and South America. In keeping with this view is the fact that fossil beds of the middle Triassic in southern Africa and South America contain the same genera of reptiles. In one locality in Brazil, remains of reptiles belonging to 16 different genera have been found and of these 14 also occur in South Africa. Similarly fossil plants and also reptiles of lower Triassic age from India and southern Africa are closely similar, as are those of the same age recently found in Antarctica. Furthermore, in an arc roughly corresponding to the present valley of the River Indus, the Triassic deposits are marine, having accumulated before the Indian subcontinent had become part of the Asiatic land mass.

Such geological changes provide us with an understanding of the present distribution of the various types of mammal. It seems reasonable to assume that the egg-laying monotremes evolved before the marsupials and that the true placental mammals, the Eutheria, evolved still later. The suggestion is that the Eutheria had not yet evolved at the time Gondwanaland split. Australia and Antarctica thus carried away a mammalian fauna composed only of monotremes and marsupials; later during the Triassic, early eutherians evolved and when the South American land mass separated from Africa, probably during the early Jurassic, it carried away not only marsupials but early placentals which there radiated to form the completely distinct mammalian fauna characteristic of South America during the Eocene. When contact was established with North America much later, one of the marsupials migrated north.

Thus, by combining the geological history of the earth with our knowledge from the fossil record of past faunas and floras, the present distribution of organisms can be largely understood. Much detail still has to be filled in and, since the fossil record is incomplete, certain points may remain obscure. We can, however, see that the two processes of geological and evolutionary change together provide a rational basis for explaining many presently observable facts of plant and animal distribution.

Rates of evolutionary change

People who are not biologists sometimes say that they cannot accept the idea of evolutionary change because they cannot see it taking place. Before considering the wider implications of this view in terms of scientific method, it is desirable to examine briefly the problem of rates of change.

During the present century the Blue Tick, *Boophilus* (Arachnida), has become resistant to three different insecticides and the rate at which resistance spread through the population was greater the more effective the insecticide (p. 305): that is to say, the greater the selective pressure, the greater the rate of change. Arsenic-resistant ticks clearly have, from the viewpoint of survival, a great advantage over those which are not resistant; nevertheless, it took nearly the full duration of a man's working life for the effect of this selection to become sufficiently marked to be noticeable to the farmers. Similarly, although there are clear advantages for *Biston* to be melanic in industrial cities, the spread of melanism was fairly slow and would probably have gone unnoticed longer had not butterfly

collecting been a popular hobby. But these changes could also be observed because they occurred in response to an abnormally drastic environmental change; that is to say, the selective pressure for change in a particular direction was unusually high. If, however, the selective advantage between the extremes of the natural variation is less, then the changes will be spread over many generations: the less the difference, the greater the number of generations. This is the reason why most evolutionary changes are not obviously recognizable; they occur far too slowly.

Three more points require emphasis. First, so long as some genetically determined phenotypes have selective advantage over others which also occur within the population, there will be change: this change may be extremely slow but it will nevertheless occur.

Secondly, organisms show variation in a very large number of characters; as a result these will all tend to show change during the course of time. Thus, for example, during the 12 million years between the first fossils we assign to *Merychippus* and those we assign to the earliest specimens of *Pliohippus*, there were changes not only in the teeth and limb bones but also, as the fossils show, in the size of the animal and in the size and proportions of its skull and its brain (Fig. 26.27). At different times the changes occurred at different rates. Thus there was fairly strong selection for high-crowned teeth during the Miocene, while there was far weaker selection leading to a strengthening of the hoof ligaments. Not until this process had proceeded for a very long time did the situation arise which permitted loss of the lateral toes. But lack of lateral toes appears to have had considerable advantage as this event took place fairly rapidly during the Pliocene. Throughout the Miocene lateral toes were probably also, by themselves, disadvantageous but selection was acting upon the limb structure as a whole and, in this case, one change depended upon another taking place first. In a final

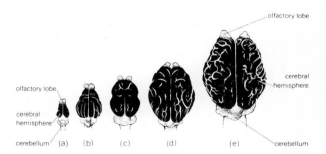

26.27 It is possible to obtain information about the shapes of the brains of extinct animals by making casts of the insides of their skulls. The drawings show the appearance of the brain of different genera of horse. Note not only the increasing size of the brain but the relatively greater size of the cerebral hemispheres compared with the cerebellum in the more recent genera. (a) eohippus, (b) *Mesohippus*, (c) *Merychippus*, (d) *Pliohippus*, (e) *Equus*. (After Simpson).

analysis, selection works on the whole organism, not upon isolated structures or functions, convenient though it may be to treat them separately. This is, of course, the reason why there is co-ordination between the different structures of any organism; lack of co-ordination would be selectively disadvantageous.

The third point relates to taxonomy. With the type of gradual change which we believe would result from the action of natural selection, there should be no clear taxonomic boundaries. Where there is a full fossil record spreading over a fairly long period of time, this is precisely what is found. It is easy to distinguish a late specimen of *Pliohippus* from an early specimen of *Merychippus*. But the decision as to whether a specimen collected from about the Miocene–Pliocene boundary belongs to one genus or the other becomes arbitrary: there are no sharp discontinuities. Similar considerations apply to divisions of genera into species.

Scientific hypotheses

We have seen that if we postulate that there has been a process of evolutionary change, then a very large number of different observations become explicable in terms of a single concept. This is a very important aspect of scientific argument. If you turn to your chemistry textbook, you will find that this is the type of argument which led Dalton to propose the atomic theory. He found that a number of quantitative relations were most easily explicable in terms of the single concept of atomism.

Some people reject the idea of an evolutionary process on the grounds that it cannot be seen to be taking place. But no one has ever 'seen' an atom, although we do have electron micrographs of large molecules. Seeing may be believing, but many scientific ideas are accepted and acted upon without the objects or the phenomena they postulate ever having been 'seen'. For many years men believed that the earth was flat and that if one could walk or sail far enough one would come to the edge. Even in this century some people have clung to this view although there has long been a very considerable body of evidence that the earth is approximately spherical, and ships and aircraft are navigated on this assumption. But only recently has it become possible for men to get sufficiently far away from the earth's surface to be able to see directly that the planet is spherical. Similarly it has long been believed that the sun, not the earth, is the central body of the solar system, a conclusion based upon the fact that very large numbers of astronomical observations find their simplest explanation if we make this assumption. If we assume, as did the ancients, that the earth is the centre of the solar system, highly complex additional assumptions are necessary to explain the observed movements of the other planets. Yet no one has ever 'seen' by direct observation that the sun is indeed the central object of the solar system.

In these three cases final observational proof requires an ability to 'see' an object which is very minute or to move vast distances away from the surface of the earth. Similar difficulties arise if we wish to 'see' any process of slow change. In all cases where there is no method of making direct observations, whether examining the postulate of the existence of atoms, electrons or atomic nuclei, of a heliocentric solar system or of an evolutionary process, the method adopted by scientists is to seek the simplest explanation which is in agreement with the known facts. It is possible to have alternative theories; these must, if they are to be scientific, be able to provide equally rational explanations of the available data. If it becomes apparent that one theory provides a less simple and less comprehensive explanation, perhaps being less able to accommodate new data, then it will be abandoned in favour of the other; thus the phlogiston theory of combustion was replaced by the oxidation theory as a result of the observations of Lavoisier. Just as it is possible, should the evidence require it, that we may one day abandon the theory that the sun is the centre of our solar system, so too the present theory of evolution by natural selection may one day be abandoned, but only in favour of a rational alternative hypothesis which provides a more comprehensive explanation of the phenomena we have discussed. It must be appreciated that what is called an 'argument from ignorance' carries little weight. To reject a theory simply because there are certain facts which it does not explain is not the method followed by science; thus although we do not know, for example, how the angiosperms evolved from gymnosperms, we would not be justified in rejecting the theory of evolution because of our ignorance on this point. As we have already stressed, there are good reasons for expecting gaps in the fossil record.

Is there a plan in evolution?

The overwhelming majority of contemporary biologists accept the concept of evolutionary change and the vast majority the idea of natural selection. Such numbers prove nothing: the validity of a scientific argument is not based upon a democratic process and this is not our point. What we wish to emphasize is that some biologists believe that in the evolutionary process they can recognize a 'plan'.

'Design' in nature

We will discuss first the problem of the 'detailed plan of design' of organisms. In several chapters in Book 1, especially those dealing with the structure and function of a producer and a consumer, we sometimes looked at questions from the viewpoint of efficiency of design. This should not be taken as meaning that we must postulate the existence of some biological engineer 'designing' different organisms. The facts can be interpreted as a result of natural selection, since organs and biochemical processes of greater efficiency tend to displace those of lesser efficiency. It can, however, be profitable in looking at structure and function to ask not simply the question 'why, in functional terms, is this organ constructed in this manner?', but also the question 'if I were building a structure to fulfil this function, what points would I have to consider?' This latter question has frequently led to the recognition of the functional significance of different organizational forms, when simple structural observation has not evoked the same understanding. Thus, in Problem 7 of Chap. 23 in Book 1, we asked you to work out the consequences of certain patterns of blood flow in a complex of blood vessels in which arterial and venous blood are brought into very close contact. Such structures were recognized by anatomists and described as 'retia mirabilia' (meaning 'wonderful nets'); they occur in a variety of organ systems in various vertebrates. But their functional significance came from an appreciation of their similarity in design to the heat exchangers in power stations. Many retia do act as heat exchangers, but they may have other roles. There is a rete associated with the oxygen-secreting gland of the teleost swimbladder (Fig. 6.10), which acts as an oxygen exchanger: just as a 'heat exchanger' rete in some birds and mammals serves to prevent heat loss from the body, so the rete associated with the gas gland serves to prevent loss of oxygen from the swimbladder.

It should not, moreover, be assumed that organisms are invariably constructed to the 'best' possible design. The structure of the eye of a squid is closely similar to that of any vertebrate such as a mammal (Fig. 26.28). Although the Cephalopoda have no evolutionary relationship to the vertebrates, it is no surprise that selection should have resulted in the evolution of two similar mechanisms; such a phenomenon is spoken of as convergence. If you look at Fig. 26.28 you will notice one difference. While the sensitive elements of the retina of a squid are directed towards the incident light and the nerve fibres come away from the back of the retina, in a vertebrate the nerve fibres pass through the retina and spread over its surface; the sensory elements are actually facing away from the incident light. The place where the optic nerve enters the eye is called the blind spot. Certainly this curious arrangement works efficiently, but it is not the way in which an engineer would design an eye: his design would resemble a cephalopod's eye. We can indeed understand the form of the vertebrate retina in terms of the evolutionary history of the vertebrate eye; to elaborate on this point would, however, take us too far from our main theme.

A second example is provided by the arrangement of the wings of insects. A single pair of wings is the most efficient arrangement for flapping flight. In most insect orders there are, however, two pairs of wings. In some orders, such as Hemiptera, Lepidoptera and Hymenoptera, there are various mechanical arrangements (Book 1 Fig. 18.66) to ensure that the two wings on each side move together. The different sorts of mechanism suggest that these have evolved independently. The original 'design' of a flying

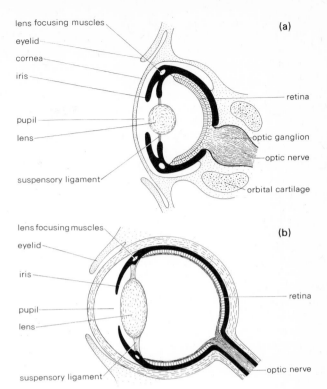

26.28 Comparison of the structure of the eye of (a) a squid (Mollusca: Cephalopoda) and (b) that of a mammal. In the squid the retinal cells receive their innervation from the outer surface. In vertebrates the nerve fibres pass through the retinal layer and form an inner covering through which light must pass to reach the retinal cells.

insect was thus not the most efficient aerodynamic system.

Teleology

There is one other aspect to this issue of 'design'. In Book 1, in considering the adaptations of organisms to different environments, we spoke of the 'problems' which these present as habitats. We further wrote about 'solutions' to these problems; indeed many biologists today will write 'the organism solved this problem by . . .'. But they do not mean to imply that the organism pondered about the matter, presently thought of a satisfactory solution and then evolved in a suitable direction. They invariably mean that selection resulted in the evolution of new species possessing some functional arrangement which better fitted them for survival. The 'problem' was a selective force acting upon the organisms: the solution the consequence of differential survival. The words 'design', 'problem' and 'solution' are here being used as convenient shorthand expressions, and are not to be taken as implying the operation of intelligence.

To write about either 'design' or 'problem solving' implies that there is an 'end in view'. Most biologists who accept natural selection as the mechanism of evolution would reject the idea that selection operates with any 'end' in view. All that happens is that certain genotypes have greater survival value than others. The idea that processes are guided in a particular direction by 'goals' or 'ends' rather than by earlier and present events, is described by philosophers as 'teleology'. The outcome of the process of selection, when one can look backwards in time, appears to have been directed teleologically. But this does not mean that there was any real 'goal' in the evolutionary events; they were determined simply by survival in a competitive situation.

Some biologists have nevertheless believed that the results of evolution can only be explained if there is a directive force in the evolutionary process, and that selection works constantly in one direction. Such a view was once put forward to explain the evolution of the extinct cephalopods and especially of the increasingly complex patterns upon the shells of ammonites (Fig. 26.8). This idea does nothing, in fact, other than use different words to describe phenomena we do not understand. Moreover our knowledge of the evolutionary history of different groups of animals shows that the pathway of evolution is not always straight; it can sometimes 'double back' upon itself. This is easily recognized in the history of the gastropod snails. Originally aquatic animals, some became terrestrial. In terrestrial snails the respiratory surface is a lung-like vascularization of the wall of the mantle cavity (Book 1 Fig. 18.44); the gills have been lost. Nevertheless there are a number of aquatic snails which have lung-like respiratory organs rather than gills. The simplest interpretation of this circumstance is that the ancestors of these species were terrestrial and that they have become aquatic once again; many other details of their anatomy are in keeping with this hypothesis. In such cases we can hardly speak of evolution having a single direction. We can, however, suggest that the ancestors of those snails which are secondarily aquatic failed to become adequately adapted to meet the stress of water loss on land and that those individuals whose behaviour tended to take them back to aquatic environments were able to leave successors; other populations either became more fully adapted to terrestrial life or else became extinct.

Man as the goal of evolution

We must finally consider the view that the principal goal of evolutionary history has been the emergence of man and that, as a conscious organism with an appreciation of beauty and ugliness, of right and wrong, of good and evil, he is not only completely different from other animals, but could not be simply the product of a selective process. Some biologists take this view. Others deny it, holding that the hypothesis is as yet unnecessary to explain the facts, while admitting that we do not have a complete understanding of man's mental evolution. One guiding principle of scientific method is that a more complex working hypothesis is less acceptable than a simpler one. In this instance, the hypothesis of 'purpose' is the more complicated and in other fields of science would not be regarded as acceptable. But many men believe that in some way they are different, and certainly because one hypothesis is more complex than another, it is not thereby proved to be false. There are no criteria by which we can take a decision, as the observable facts are open to either interpretation.

The practical significance of natural selection

When the idea of natural selection was originally put forward in 1859, it met with very great opposition from some biologists and many laymen. Since that time agriculturalists have depended increasingly upon carefully planned feats of 'genetic engineering' to produce new and desirable varieties. Much of this depends upon the application of the ideas of selection. More recently man has encountered new problems which have arisen as consequences of selection and these have made more difficult his struggle against pests, parasites and other disease-causing organisms. In the future, it is imperative that the idea of selection be always to the fore in devising new methods of control. Selection is thus a reality which applied biologists must heed; it is a concept which can no longer be rejected as an academic, unlikely and possibly unpalatable idea. In its wider context it provides us with a rational interpretation of a vast array of observable facts, although there remain many that we still do not understand and may indeed never be able to understand because we cannot travel backwards in time. The concept of evolution through natural selection is a unifying hypothesis which fulfils all the criteria required of scientific hypotheses. The fact that large numbers of observations are in agreement with its implications suggests that it is highly likely to be correct; but this is not a final proof. Such a 'proof' can never be forthcoming; we cannot 'prove' electrons any more than we can 'prove' evolution, but both hypotheses are in keeping with what we can observe in the world around us.

Problems

1 The following observations were made by the authors in Ghana at the time of writing this book:
   (a) Traffic on the road keeps to the left.
   (b) High Court judges wear wigs, as do barristers pleading in court.
   (c) In the markets coins which are clearly stamped 'five pesewas' and 'ten pesewas' are often referred to as 'sixpence' and 'shilling'.
   (d) The members of many church choirs wear curious, rectangular, flat-topped hats with a tassel hanging down one side.

(e) Most official business is conducted in a language called English.

(f) A popular national sport is called 'Association Football'.

Suggest a single hypothesis to explain these observations. Do you consider your hypothesis is (i) valid and (ii) proved? Compare your procedure with that adopted in the present chapter in considering the possibility that there has been an evolutionary process.

2 On p. 462 is a list of six features which should be demonstrable from the fossil record if evolution has occurred. Give one example of each.

3 In a tadpole the hind limbs develop before the fore limbs. Does this lead us to conclude that the ancestors of the Amphibia evolved originally as bipeds and later evolved fore limbs? What alternative explanation can you offer for the facts?

4 In mammals there is a 'secondary palate' forming the roof of the mouth cavity; as a result a mammal can chew its food and breathe at the same time. Except in the crocodiles, there is no secondary palate in the present-day reptiles. Fossils of terrestrial reptiles with secondary palates have been found and it has been suggested that this is evidence that they may have been 'warm-blooded'. What do you consider may be the argument in favour of this view? Suggest a functional reason why crocodiles have a secondary palate.

5 In most snakes there is neither a pectoral nor a pelvic girdle. In the python, however, there is a 'vestigial' pelvic girdle to which is articulated a femur and two other tiny bones. This appendage ends in a well-developed claw on the outside of the body; this claw is more strongly developed in males than in females. In a related American species the femur has been shown to be supplied with several muscles which are innervated. Discuss these observations in relation to the concept of 'vestigial organs'.

6 Outline how a vascular rete may act so as to prevent loss of oxygen from the swimbladder of a bony fish.

7 By reference to Table 26.1 determine which are the simplest precursors of thiamine which must be added to cultures of (a) *Polytoma ocellatum* and (b) *Polytomella caeca* to ensure growth.

Bibliography

Further reading

Auffenberg, W.	*Present Problems About the Past*, BSCS Pamphlet no. 6, Heath, 1963
Dowdeswell, W. H.	*The Mechanism of Evolution*, Heinemann, 1963, Chap. 5
Neill, W. T.	*Biogeography*, BSCS Pamphlet no. 18, Heath, 1964
Stebbins, G. L.	*Processes of Organic Evolution*, Prentice-Hall, 1971, Chap. 7
Colbert, E. H.	'The Ancestors of Mammals', *Scientific American*, 1949, Offprint no. 806
Deevey, E. S.	'Radiocarbon Dating', *Scientific American*, 1952, Offprint no. 811
Deevey, E. S.	'Living Records of the Ice Age', *Scientific American*, 1949, Offprint no. 834
Glaessner, M. F.	'Pre-cambrian Animals', *Scientific American*, 1961, Offprint no. 837
Millot, J.	'The Coelacanth', *Scientific American*, 1955, Offprint no. 831
Newell, N. D.	'Crises in the History of Life', *Scientific American*, 1963, Offprint no. 867
Seilacher, A.	'Fossil Behavior', *Scientific American*, 1967, Offprint no. 872

Geological history

Dietz, R. S., Holden, J. C.	'The breakup of Pangaea', *Scientific American*, 1970, Offprint no. 892
Hallam, A.	'Continental Drift and the Fossil Record', *Scientific American*, 1972, Offprint no. 903
Hurley, P. M.	'The Confirmation of Continental Drift', *Scientific American*, 1968, Offprint no. 874
Kurtén, B.	'Continental Drift and Evolution', *Scientific American*, 1969, Offprint no. 877
McKenzie, D. P., Sclater, J. G.	'The Evolution of the Indian Ocean', *Scientific American*, 1973, Offprint no. 908
Valentine, J. W., Moores, E. M.	'Plate Tectonics and the History of Life in the Oceans', *Scientific American*, 1974, Vol. 230, pt. 4, p. 80
Wilson, J. T.	'Continental Drift', *Scientific American*, 1963, Offprint no. 868

27 The evolution of man

If all other living organisms have evolved, then it is reasonable to assume that man is as much a product of the evolutionary process as any other animal. In tracing man's evolutionary origins we rely, as with other vertebrate groups, largely upon fossils and, as has become clear in the last thirty years, the fossils of man's ancestors are mostly to be found in Africa.

The Primates

If we are to trace man's origins, the first question we have to consider is to which other mammals man is most closely related. Man belongs to the order Primates which includes monkeys and apes, as well as the pottos and the bush babies. The basic anatomical characteristics of the order relate to the tree-living habit which is typical of the group. Firstly both hands and feet typically have flat nails, which are modified claws (Fig. 27.1). Primate climbing depends upon grasping the branches of trees with hands or feet, not upon using claws as do other tree-climbing mammals such as the squirrels (Rodentia), the domestic cat, leopard and palm-civets (Carnivora) and the pangolins (Pholidota) (Book 1 Fig. 18.81a). A second feature of primate structure correlated with their methods of climbing is that in the hand the first digit or thumb is separated from the other fingers, so that it can be swung around to grip a branch: in most Primates the same arrangement is found in the toes of the foot. In all Primates the eyes are directed forward to allow for binocular vision, the snout is small, the number of young in a litter is commonly only one and there is usually only a single pair of mammae or breasts, just behind the pectoral girdle and not posterior as in a cow.

Among the Primates there are four major families: the Old World Monkeys (Cercopithecidae) which are found in Africa and Asia, the New World Monkeys (Cebidae) of South America, the apes (Pongidae), represented today by the gorilla and the chimpanzee in Africa and the gibbons and orang-utan in Asia, and the Hominidae of which man is the only extant species.

The Old World Monkeys, apes and man have a number of characteristics in common which distinguish them from the rest of the Primates. The eye is enclosed in a complete bony socket, the brain is relatively large and the young are carried by the mother, not deposited in the nest. The Hominidae and the apes lack tails, and also have other structural similarities; they are more closely related to each other than to the monkeys.

The differences between apes and man

A complete account of human evolution should trace our ancestry back to the origins of the earliest primates but what interests us most is the later stages: when, how and why did man become different from the Pongidae? how far back in time must we go to find a common ancestor? We must therefore begin by asking in what ways man differs from the Pongidae. Skeletal characters are especially important since we are going to have to deal with fossils, and only bones and teeth are normally preserved as fossils. Almost all the major skeletal differences are correlated, directly or indirectly, with locomotion. Man habitually walks upright on his hind legs: he is a biped. Apes, although capable of walking on two legs, usually support themselves on their knuckles when they do so; but they are more expert climbers than we are and often swing themselves from branch to branch by their arms in a way we cannot do, a mode of progression known as brachiation.

In man the hind limb is very much longer than the fore and the foot is very different in structure from the hand. The foot has become a purely locomotory organ: the big toe lies parallel with the others and cannot be used in grasping, as can an ape's (Fig. 27.2). The hand, freed from locomotory duties, has become adapted as a purely manipulative organ. The finger bones or phalanges are straight, not slightly curved like those of an ape; the thumb is relatively large and its muscles and articulations so arranged that we can bring the tip of the thumb into contact with the

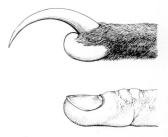

27.1 Comparison of a claw and a nail. The claw is the more primitive type of horny structure at the tip of a mammalian finger. Flat nails are characteristic of most primates and correlate with the habit of grasping branches in climbing trees.

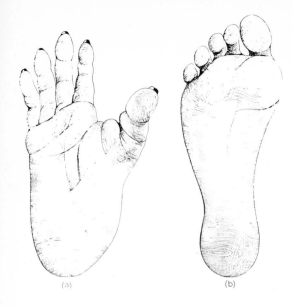

27.2 Comparison of the feet of (a) a chimpanzee and (b) a man. The big toe of the chimpanzee is separated from the other digits and highly mobile.

tip of any of the four fingers (Fig. 27.3). This means that we can not only grasp an object between the flexed fingers and the palm of the hand, as we do when we wish to apply maximum force; we can also hold it between the thumb and the tips of one or more fingers, as we do when we require fine control rather than power.

The human hind leg is orientated almost in line with the backbone, whereas in a typical quadruped it lies approximately at right angles to the backbone and in an ape the angle is only slightly greater. This change in orientation implies big alterations in the lines of action of the muscles moving the femur and consequently major changes in the shape of the pelvis from which these muscles originate (Fig. 27.4). Since, moreover, bipedal balance is very different from quadrupedal, the curvature of the backbone is altered from the normal quadrupedal 'convex upward' condition.

An animal's eyes must look where it is going and the

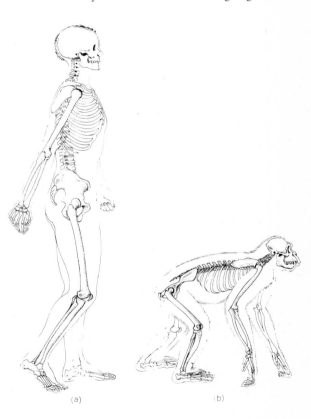

27.4 Comparison of the structure and posture of (a) a man and (b) a chimpanzee. Note how in man the hind leg and backbone are almost in a straight line and the neck vertebrae are parallel to the front of the face. In the chimpanzee, the vertebral column is almost at a right angle to the femur and the cervical vertebrae are nearly at right angles to the face, so that the foramen magnum opens near the back rather than the base of the skull. Note also the marked difference in shape of the pelvic girdles.

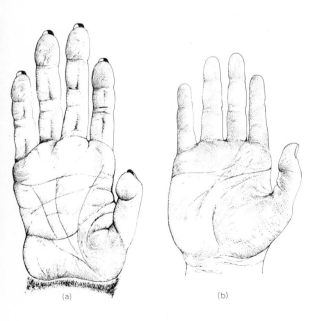

27.3 Comparison of the hands of (a) a chimpanzee and (b) a man. Note the relatively greater length of the human thumb.

487

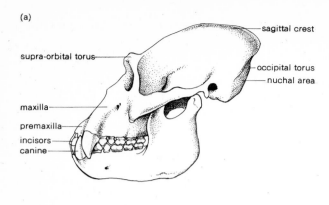

(a)

sagittal crest

supra-orbital torus

occipital torus
nuchal area

maxilla

premaxilla

incisors
canine

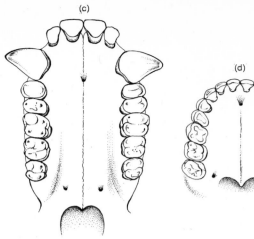

(c)

(d)

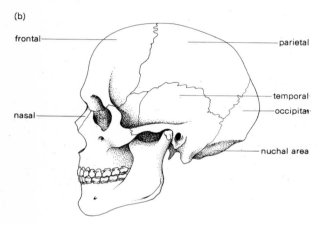

(b)

frontal

parietal

temporal
occipital

nasal

nuchal area

27.5 Comparison of the skulls of (a) a gorilla and (b) a man. In man the braincase is larger, while that of the gorilla forms a strong bony sagittal crest to provide an adequate area of origin of the temporalis muscle moving the lower jaw (compare with that of a dog: Book 1 Fig. 10.11a). The powerful canine teeth and large cheek teeth result in the formation of a snout which is missing in man whose teeth are relatively smaller. The nuchal area is for the insertion of muscles which raise the head. Note that it is larger in the gorilla and faces backwards, not downwards as in man: the difference reflects the relation of the normal position of the head to the long axis of the body. (c) and (d) compare the arrangement of the teeth in the upper jaw of a gorilla and a man. Note that the teeth of the gorilla are arranged in a Π, with the incisors forming a row which is at right angles to the line formed by the cheek teeth. In man the tooth row, the dental arcade, is rounded like a ∩. Note also that the tooth row of the gorilla is not continuous. There is a diastema between the incisors and canines to accommodate the canines of the lower jaw.

orientation of a biped's skull on its backbone must therefore be altered. In man the eyes look out at right angles to the backbone, in a quadruped more nearly parallel. This means that if we place a human skull with the eye sockets directed forwards, the opening through which the spinal cord passes, the foramen magnum, will face almost directly downwards, instead of partly backwards. Thus a skull alone can indicate whether its owner was bipedal or not.

The braincase of man is extremely large, the snout reduced and the jaws relatively small. The canines are no longer than the other teeth, and there is therefore no need for any diastema permitting them to interlock when the mouth is closed; thus, unlike that of the apes, the arch of the teeth, the dental arcade, is smoothly rounded without any gaps between teeth (Fig. 27.5).

All of these features are reflections of bipedalism, although the form of the skull and teeth is linked only indirectly. A skilled manipulative hand can take over many

of the jobs which other mammals must do with their teeth. Fruit can be plucked or animals caught and killed with the hands, or with tools or weapons held in the hand; the food can be broken or cut up into pieces small enough to be put into the mouth. Weapons may also be used in fighting; there is thus no need for large canine teeth or a long snout to accommodate them. A large brain is of no use in itself; what matters is the complexity of behaviour which it can produce; ideas are of no selective value unless they can somehow be translated into action. Clearly the types of complex action made possible by a manipulative hand are vastly greater than those of which any other animal is capable. The manipulative hand is the organ that translates the brain's ideas into actions and in this way the ideas, and by extension the brain which produces them, become subject to the forces of natural selection.

One human characteristic distinguishing man from apes is his reduced body hair. Of this there can be no fossil record, but the reduction suggests that man must have originated in a warm tropical climate, otherwise he could hardly have afforded to dispense with his insulating coat. It was the products of hand and brain—fire, clothing, strong shelters against inclement weather—that ultimately allowed him to spread not only into temperate but even into arctic regions.

Human behaviour

Apart from these bodily characteristics, man differs from the apes in two very striking aspects of behaviour. Apes occasionally make use of simple tools; they may crack nuts with a stone or use a bunch of leaves as a sponge to sop up water or to wipe dirt from their bodies. They may pull termites out of a log with a twig, even shaping the tool by pulling off any leaves or side branches; but the amount of workmanship involved is slight and the resulting tool not worth keeping for future use. Man, on the other hand, continually uses tools or the products of tools in his daily life; the care and skill that goes into their manufacture may be very great and they are rarely discarded once their immediate purpose has been served. Behaviour, of course, does not fossilize, but the results of behaviour may be preserved. During his evolution man began to use stone for the manufacture of tools. Many such tools survive and their characteristics—the skill required to make them and the diversity of types shown—may tell us something about their makers.

The second difference is that man has articulate language; he produces words, not simply noises. Apes, like other mammals, have a number of vocal signals but these do not constitute an abstract symbolic language in which particular sound patterns stand for particular objects, actions or ideas. Man certainly has comparable vocal signals—cries of pain, of horror, of surprise, laughter and weeping. These do not have to be learnt and are much the same in all cultures but, in addition, we have true language which is learnt and which differs from one culture to another. This language makes possible a complexity of social interactions and hence a social organization vastly more intricate than exists in any ape society. It also greatly increases the ease with which any skills developed or discoveries made by one generation can be handed on to the next.

The fossil record

With these differences in mind, we may now ask the question: what can palaeontology, the study of fossils, tell us about how man came to have his own peculiar characteristics? We cannot expect to find a very detailed record of the whole of our past history. When most animals die they are eaten or rot to pieces without becoming buried in conditions likely to lead to fossilization. Of those specimens that are preserved, many are disarticulated and frag-

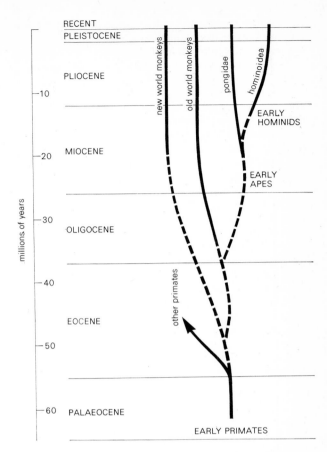

27.6 Schematic drawing showing the various divisions of the Caenozoic era and the approximate time of separation of the major groupings of the Primates. Broken lines indicate an incomplete fossil record. The earliest primates probably arose from the same stem that gave rise to the Insectivora during the Cretaceous, the last period of the Mesozoic.

mented bones, and of these only the most durable parts remain. Teeth are the hardest and most resistant structures and lower jaws are also strongly built. Many finds therefore consist of isolated teeth, teeth attached to small fragments of jaws or complete lower jaws; skulls or parts of skulls may survive, but limbs and vertebrae are fragile and therefore rarely found. Despite these limitations, it has been possible to piece together considerable parts of the story of man's evolution and every year new discoveries are made which gradually help to fill in the gaps and make the picture more complete.

Fossil primates can be found right back to the beginning of the Caenozoic era, some 70 million years ago, but the first recognizably ape-like fossil comes from the lower Miocene, roughly 20 million years ago (Fig. 27.6). This was a rather small, lightly built creature, somewhat monkey-like in general appearance. The limb bones, however, show that it must have been able to swing itself from branch to branch as apes do and the details of the cusp patterns on the teeth are ape-like, rather than monkey-like. From this beginning, there followed in the later Miocene a radiation of large, large-brained, forest-dwelling brachiating primates—the first apes, classified in a family of their own, the Dryopithecinae. These early apes flourished about 14 million years ago, both in Africa and in India. Among these is one genus *Ramapithecus*, which has been found on both continents. It may have been markedly different from the other dryopithecines, its distinguishing features being a reduced snout with small incisor and canine teeth and a rounded dental arcade (Fig. 27.7). If this reconstruction of the remains is correct, there must have been something special in the mode of life of *Ramapithecus*. It seems most likely that it fed on some type of food which could be plucked with the hands and put into the mouth. The same features are characteristic of human dentition, so the distinction between *Ramapithecus* and the other dryopithecines may reflect the beginning of the separation of the hominid and pongid lines. Unfortunately *Ramapithecus* is known only from jaw fragments. There is no skull from which we might judge the position of the foramen magnum or make an estimate of brain size, and there are no limb bones. We therefore know nothing of the posture or mode of locomotion of *Ramapithecus*. If, however, the animal habitually sat while eating, this may well have initiated

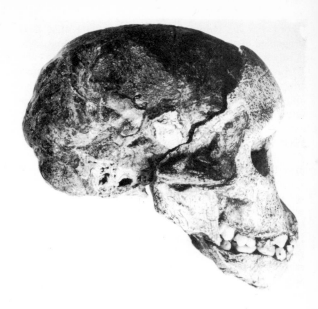

27.8 The skull of a young australopithecine found by Raymond Dart at Taung in 1925. Dart concluded that the skull was that of a hominid although it had many pongid features, including a well-developed snout and small brain; the dentition was however characteristic of the Hominidae and not the Pongidae. Very many specimens of *Australopithecus africanus* have been excavated since that time.

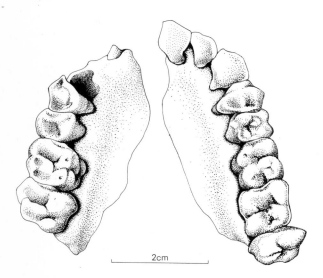

2cm

27.7 The upper jaw fragments of *Ramapithecus* and a suggested reconstruction of the palate. These fossils are about 14 million years old, that is, they are late Miocene and may be early hominids. In the absence of parts of the skeleton other than the jaws and teeth, this conclusion cannot be regarded as unquestionable. The teeth are lower-crowned than those characteristic of the apes and it is suggested that there was no specialized canine and no diastema, so that the dental arcade was smooth. The correctness of this reconstruction has, however, recently been questioned and the palate may have been typically pongid.

changes in the muscles of the back in adaptation to holding the spine vertical and these, in turn, might have paved the way for the subsequent development of bipedalism.

The australopithecines

From here onwards there is a big gap in the human fossil record, a gap of some 10 or 11 million years, from the upper Miocene to the upper Pliocene. To understand the next part of the story, however, we must go just a little further and consider the hominids of the lower Pleistocene. The first to be discovered, and the ones for which the material is most complete, are from deposits in southern Africa. The original find, a juvenile skull (Fig. 27.8), came in 1925 from Taung and subsequent material from Makapan in the northern Transvaal and from Sterkfontein and Swartkrans, a little further south, not far from Johannesburg (Fig. 27.9). The material includes skulls (Fig. 27.10), jaws, pelvic girdles, some fragments of limb bones and an almost perfect vertebral column.

The first specimens found were skulls which, apart from a relatively large braincase, small jaws and man-like characteristics of the dentition as a whole (Fig. 27.11), also showed from the position of the foramen magnum that their owners must have been bipedal. This deduction was subsequently substantiated when pelvic girdles (Fig.

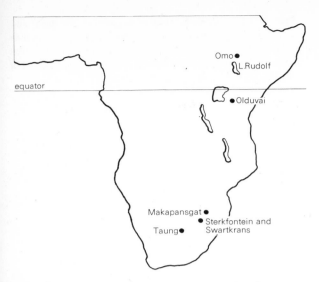

27.9 Map showing the position of the major sites where fossil hominids have been excavated in Africa.

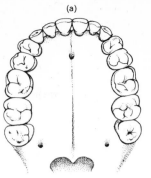
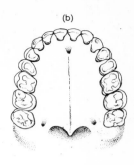

27.11 Comparison of the dental arcades of (a) *Australopithecus* and (b) *Homo sapiens*. Compare with Figs. 27.5c and 27.5d. Note that *Australopithecus* shows the hominid features of a rounded arcade with no specialization of the canines and no diastema. Its resemblance to the suggested arrangement of the dentition of *Ramapithecus* (Fig. 27.7) can also be recognized. Detailed comparison depends upon the structure of the cusps of the teeth: here too there are close similarities between *Australopithecus* and *Homo*.

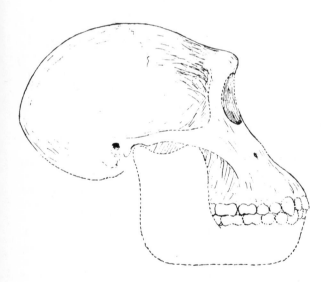

27.10 *Australopithecus africanus:* Robert Broom's drawing of the skull of an elderly female. Note the marked snout. No teeth remained with this specimen.

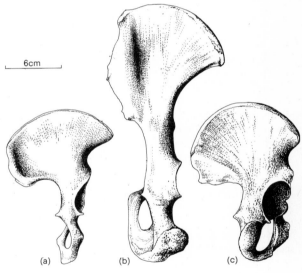

27.12 Comparison of the pelvic girdles of (a) *Australopithecus*, (b) a chimpanzee and (c) *Homo sapiens*. As can be seen in Fig. 27.4, the shapes of the pelvic girdles of man and chimpanzee are very different and relate to the mode of walking. The girdle of *Australopithecus* is very similar to that of man, reflecting the fact that it also walked upright. (After Broom).

27.12) and limb fragments were discovered. The Taung specimen was named *Australopithecus africanus* and further remains of this species were later found at Sterkfontein and at Makapan. At Swartkrans a rather similar creature came to light, but it was possibly a different species. It was a larger animal, with heavier jaws, massive cheek teeth and powerful jaw muscles, but it too was clearly bipedal (Fig. 27.13). This form was accorded the rank of a separate genus and named *Paranthropus robustus*. J. T. Robinson has interpreted the differences in the skulls as

491

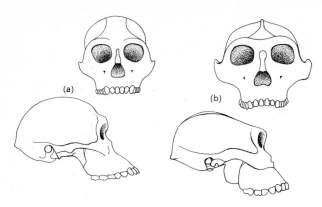

27.13 Diagram comparing the forms of skull of (a) *Australopithecus* and (b) *Paranthropus*. Note the development of a sagittal crest on the skull of *Paranthropus* which correlates with its heavier jaw structure.

Table 27.1 Estimated cranial capacities of apes and hominids. It is not legitimate to compare apes with hominids unless account is taken of body size. *Australopithecus* was about the size of a chimpanzee, *Paranthropus* that of a gorilla (*Data from Holloway*)

Species	Cranial capacity (cm³)
Chimpanzee (*Pan*)	mean: 397
Australopithecus africanus	range: 428–485; mean: 442
Gorilla	mean: 498
Paranthropus robustus	mean: 530
Homo habilis	mean: 657
Homo erectus (from Java)	range: 775–900
Homo erectus (from Pekin)	range: 850–1 300; mean: 1 075
Homo sapiens	range: 1 300–2 000; mean: 1 350

indicating different feeding habits: *Paranthropus* was considered to be a specialized vegetarian, eating hard seeds, roots, tubers and so forth, all of which require considerable grinding; *Australopithecus* was a more omnivorous creature. On *a priori* grounds one would expect some such difference, for the two forms existed side by side for at least a million years. Such co-existence could hardly have been possible had they been in direct competition for exactly the same types of food (p.270). Many later workers have placed these two in the single genus *Australopithecus*, while some prefer to regard *Australopithecus africanus* as being a member of the genus *Homo*. To make clear the distinction between the various hominids, we have retained the name *Paranthropus*, while *A. africanus* and *P. robustus* are collectively described as 'australopithecines', a term with no taxonomic implications.

Homo habilis and the definition of *Homo*

Subsequent work in East Africa has brought to light many specimens of both types from deposits of which the most important are at Olduvai (Tanzania), Omo (Ethiopia) and East Rudolf (Kenya). The deposits at Olduvai, however, produced something further. Along with a species of *Paranthropus* are other specimens which, although very like *Australopithecus africanus*, differ in having a quite unusually large braincase (Table 27.1). This at once raises a difficult problem: by what criteria should we decide whether a hominid is sufficiently advanced to be placed in the same genus as ourselves, *Homo*? Clearly to qualify as man, he must be a true biped and possess a hand with a highly mobile thumb which can be brought into contact with each of the other fingers of the hand; this is spoken of as a fully opposable thumb. But what further characters should be included? Brain volume is the one most com-

monly used and various authorities have set the threshold required for inclusion within *Homo* at about 700 cm³. Some anatomists have attempted to produce a list of other characters but most of those concerning the skull simply reflect the possession of a brain which is large in relation to the size of the jaws. On the basis of these characters, one of the Olduvai hominids has been placed in the genus *Homo*, with the specific name of *habilis*. *Homo habilis* remains are found as far back as the earliest Olduvai level, dated at 1·8 million years ago.

Early tools

Man has, of course, been defined not only on anatomical features but on behavioural ones: man is the 'tool-making animal'. This definition, however, is not as helpful as it might seem. Firstly, finding hominid bones together with tools does not necessarily prove that the hominid made the tools, nor does finding bones of a hominid without tools prove that that hominid was incapable of making tools. Moreover, if living apes make simple tools from twigs, we would expect a complete gradation in time from the casual use of a stone to smash open a nut, a tortoise or a skull left over from a lion's kill to the manufacture of highly complex and diverse implements. Simple stone tools do occur at Olduvai, together with *Homo habilis* remains, but they are also found at Sterkfontein where *Australopithecus africanus* is the only known hominid. While the presence of tools cannot therefore be taken as proof of the existence of *Homo*, they do indicate the presence of a hominid very considerably more skilled at tool making than any ape. A more interesting question is to ask what the tools are like, or what they might have been used for. The most striking thing about these early tools is that considerable care has been taken to produce a sharp

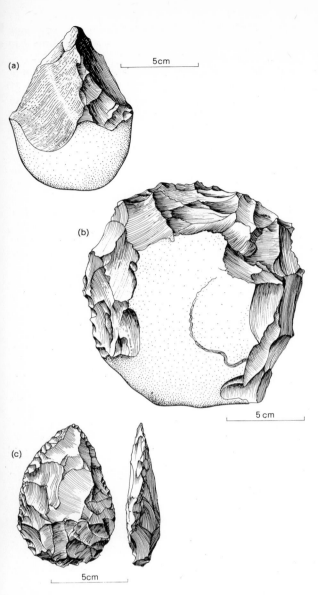

27.14 A rough 'pebble tool' from Olduvai. Such tools vary in size from about 3 to 12 cm in diameter. They may have been made by *Australopithecus* or by *Homo habilis*. (b) A stone tool from Pekin made by *Homo erectus* and showing an advance in technique on the pebble tool. (c) A hand-axe from a site in Kenya occupied about 70000 years ago by *Homo sapiens*.

lopes. Since chimpanzees kill and eat smaller animals, this is not very surprising. It is easy to imagine a gradual sequence from the occasional killing of some much smaller and weaker animal to true hunting, and, since the large Carnivora will scavenge on each other's kills when they get the chance, early man very likely did so as well.

Some hand and foot bones found at Olduvai very probably belong to *Homo habilis*. The foot bones are clearly those of a biped: the big toe is in line with the rest and details of the other bones indicate an arched foot of essentially human type as opposed to the flat foot of an ape. The finger bones, although not as straight as those of modern man, are less curved than those of apes. Unfortunately the thumb bones are missing but, judging from the shape of the facet with which the thumb articulated, the thumb was not quite as mobile as that of modern man but must have been stronger and more divergent than that of an ape. *Homo habilis* therefore appears to have had rather less manual skill than ourselves but considerably more than any ape; there is no difficulty in believing that the Olduvai tools could have been fashioned by his hand.

The origin of *Homo*

The deposits at East Rudolf go back in time somewhat further than those of Olduvai. From these too have come remains of two sorts of hominid. One is a heavy-jawed *Paranthropus*, the other a more lightly built creature with many resemblances to *Australopithecus*. The even older Omo deposits were laid down between 2 and 3 million years ago and here again are a *Paranthropus* and a lightly built form identified provisionally as *Australopithecus*. *Paranthropus* thus runs through all the deposits from about 2·5 million years ago at Omo to 750000 years ago, at Peninj, not far from Olduvai. *Australopithecus* occurs from Omo to Makapan, that is, from approximately 2·5 to 1·5 million years ago. But with material from deposits more than two million years old, it becomes increasingly difficult to decide whether particular specimens are fossils of an advanced *Australopithecus* or an early *Homo*. This suggests that while *Paranthropus* and *Australopithecus* are distinct as far back as we can trace them, some 2·5 million years ago in the upper Pliocene *Homo* started to separate from *Australopithecus*. Even among the early Pleistocene representatives it is by no means easy to say where we should draw the line between the two genera. Such difficulties are, of course, exactly what one must expect if evolutionary change has occurred. The phylogenetic relationships suggested by these facts are shown in Figure 27.15.

Unfortunately we cannot take the two lineages back in time and link them with *Ramapithecus*, although such a derivation is the most reasonable hypothesis we can make at present. The only actual link between *Ramapithecus* and the upper Pliocene hominids is a single tooth, showing intermediate characteristics. This comes from the Ngorora

cutting edge on one side (Fig. 27.14). It is difficult to imagine their being used to gather or process vegetable foods; they look much more suitable for skinning animals and cutting up meat. They strongly suggest that their makers were living, at least in part, on animal foods, a supposition borne out by the presence in the same deposits of numerous bones, mainly those of medium-sized ante-

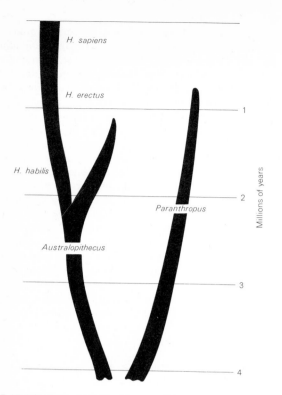

27.15 Diagram showing the possible relations between *Homo*, *Australopithecus* and *Paranthropus*. About 2·5 million years ago there were two related hominids in Africa: one 'Australopithecus' is almost certainly, ancestral to modern man; the other 'Paranthropus' occupied a different ecological niche and became extinct. While there are differences of opinion about nomenclature, there is agreement upon this point.

formation in northern Kenya and is dated at 10 million years ago.

The evolution of the genus *Homo*

Moving forwards in time from the early to the middle Pleistocene, the story is much clearer. The advances that were characteristic of *Homo habilis* are carried further. Half a million years ago a larger species of *Homo* was in existence and had become widely distributed throughout the Old World; his brain was both absolutely and relatively larger and his facial proportions were much more human. Remains of this type of man, *Homo erectus*, have been found in Java, China, Europe and Africa; possibly the earliest specimen is a single fragmentary skull from Swartkrans but the finds at Choukoutien, near Pekin in China, are in many ways the most interesting. Dated at half a million years ago, this is the earliest known occurrence of man in an area with really cold winters. There is abundant evidence that 'Pekin man' knew the use of fire, and numerous charred animal bones suggest that he may have roasted his meat. The animal bones show that he was

a hunter and the tools found with his remains show more skilled workmanship and greater diversity of form than those associated with *Homo habilis* (Fig. 27.14).

Although considerably more advanced than the men of the early Pleistocene, *Homo erectus* is still primitive by comparison with modern *H. sapiens*. The brain is not so large and the forehead low and receding. The jaws and their associated muscles are large and, correlated with this, the skull is strengthened above the eyes by a bony thickening, forming a distinct brow ridge (Fig. 27.16). Nevertheless evolution from *H. erectus* to *H. sapiens* involves a continuation of the same evolutionary trends that were obvious from the beginning of the Pleistocene. These reflect increasing skill of the hands and increasing dependence on the tools produced by them. Wherever we can study appropriate sequences of deposits, we can trace the emergence of modern *sapiens*-type man during the latter part of the Pleistocene.

Language

At some stage in this process articulate language must have made its appearance. The ability to talk and to understand language involves special areas in the forebrain, one linked with the motor-control areas for the organs of speech—the larynx, tongue, palate and lips—and one with the receiving area from the ear. These areas are larger in man than in any other species; unfortunately they do not make a sufficiently distinctive mark on the inner surface of a skull for us to be able to identify them and judge their

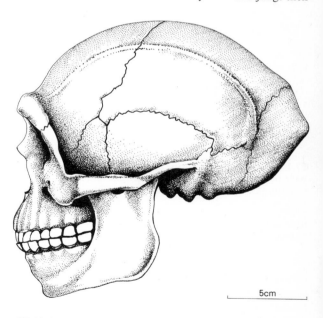

27.16 Drawing of the skull of a female *Homo erectus* from Pekin. Note that the profile of the skull is very much like that of modern man, but there are very heavy brow ridges.

size in fossils. When speech began can therefore only be guessed. It is clear, however, that once the making of complex tools had started, adequate communication between individuals would become increasingly desirable and the more complex co-operation which it permitted increasingly worthwhile: in other words, the selective pressure for improved intraspecific communication would be very high. Whether *H. habilis* could talk or not is questionable; it is difficult to imagine that *H. erectus* did not have some form of language. Speech, however, like tool-making, must have had a history and fully developed languages could not have sprung suddenly into existence. It therefore seems likely that the evolution of true language was going on throughout much of the lower Pleistocene.

Man today

Modern *Homo sapiens* is world-wide in distribution but, like other widely ranging species, he shows local differentiation. We commonly describe the different types of man as representing different 'races', a term also employed by taxonomists to describe populations of animals whose distinguishing features are not sufficiently great to warrant treating them as subspecies.

If our ideas about selection are correct, then we should be able to recognize racial differences in man as adaptive. At the moment this is true only to a limited extent. Let us first examine how far racial differences can be related to the environment. The most obvious is in degree of skin pigmentation. There is evidence that the incidence of cancer of the skin is correlated with exposure to ultra-violet radiation. Its incidence in white Americans living at latitude 41°N is only a quarter of that of a comparable population living at 32°N, while its incidence in Europeans living in South Africa is very much greater than in the 'Cape-coloureds' who have pigmented skins. The same is found when incidence among Afro-Americans is compared with that among white Americans, as well as with the 'native' and European immigrant population of the Argentine. Thus we can recognize a very direct adaptive value of skin pigmentation.

This raises the question of why there should be races found living at high latitudes which are devoid of pigmentation. It has been suggested that absence of skin pigmentation relates to the need for vitamin D. Apart from any taken with the food, this vitamin is synthesized in the skin by the action of ultra-violet light upon certain steroids. In the tropics and subtropics the quantity of ultra-violet light normally available is probably sufficient to supply the body's needs for the vitamin. But at higher latitudes, especially in winter, it is desirable to be able to absorb as much ultra-violet light as possible. The loss of skin pigment of the pale-skinned races may be a response to this need, and indeed there is evidence that Afro-American children living in New York are more inclined

to suffer from vitamin D deficiency than white children living in the same conditions.

A second obvious racial difference is that of body size and build. This is probably directly related to thermal regulation. The short, broad build of the eskimo, who live in the north of Canada, minimizes heat loss, which will be considerable in tall, slender people, like many of those living immediately south of the Sahara.

But there are other racial differences, such as the curly hair of the African compared with the lank hair of the European and Indian. The significance of these, if it is adaptive, eludes us. Even within a racial 'group' there are differences in the quantity of body hair; for example, Africans who live in the south of the continent have very markedly less body hair than those who live in West Africa.

There is a second aspect of racial adaptation which we have to consider, namely the relation between the different races of man and their biotic environment, most especially parasites and their vectors. The relevant racial differences of which we have the greatest knowledge relate to blood proteins, partly because blood is the one human tissue that can be sampled almost painlessly and without making any visible scar. Some of these we have discussed in Chap. 22. The ABO system of blood antigens has been very extensively studied. The relative frequencies with which different blood-group types occur in different populations show remarkable variations, even within a 'race'. Table 27.2 summarizes some of these data. The biological significance of most of these differences is still obscure, but some are understandable in terms of history. For example, among the Basque people who live in the north-west of Spain the relative frequency of the ABO blood groups is markedly different from that of other Spaniards. Furthermore, the

Table 27.2 Relative frequencies (%) of I^A, I^B and i genes which determine the ABO blood-group system (*Data from various sources*)

	I^A	I^B	i
People in Africa:			
Nuer of the Sudan	16	13	71
South African Bantu	19	12	69
Hottentots	27	23	50
Bushmen	20	2	78
Pygmies	23	22	55
Other countries or peoples:			
Chinese (Pekin)	19	25	56
Bulgaria	33	13	54
East Germany	28	12	60
West Germany	24	5	71
Basques	24	1	75
Southern Spain	24	11	65
Algeria	24	13	63

Basque language is totally different from the other European languages, almost all of which, despite their differences, have much in common both in grammar and in the sound of the common words. The Basque language is thought to be a relic of one which was once widespread and was displaced, possibly as a result of migrations from the east similar to the southward migration of the Bantu people some hundreds of years ago. Such movements of peoples, together with resulting genetic mixtures due to intermarriage, will clearly confuse any picture of the adaptive value of the ABO blood-group system. Nevertheless there are certain fragments of evidence which suggest that in the past the different antigens may have had different adaptive values. For example, people of blood group A are significantly more susceptible to smallpox than those of other blood groups and the same sort of relation is found between blood group AB and Rhodesian sleeping sickness. On the other hand people of blood group O are preferred as hosts by *Anopheles gambiae*.

These observations suggest that the occurrence of different genes affecting blood composition may have been influenced in the past by selective forces, but it is now far harder to recognize these factors owing to extensive migrations of peoples, especially in the Old World.

There is, however, one known blood condition which is directly related to one type of malaria fever, caused by one species of *Plasmodium*: this is the occurrence of haemoglobin S (p. 396). People who are homozygous Hb^S/Hb^S suffer from sickle-cell anaemia and those who are heterozygous Hb^A/Hb^S have what is described as 'sickle-cell trait', which is not normally accompanied by clinical symptoms. The question immediately arises as to why natural selection has not weeded out the Hb^S gene; why is it carried by 20 percent of the people living in southern Ghana, and by 40 percent of those living in some parts of Uganda?

The answer is that when people who are heterozygous Hb^A/Hb^S are infected with *Plasmodium falciparum*, their attacks of fever are less acute than those experienced by people who are homozygous Hb^A/Hb^A. This is especially true of young children who thus receive protection during the period before they are old enough to have acquired some level of immunity.

In the past, when no very effective steps could be taken to prevent or cure malaria, the heterozygotes were at a selective advantage compared to the other two genotypes and the Hb^S gene therefore became established in populations living in places where *P. falciparum* was common. If the Hb^S gene in the heterozygote conferred advantage, then it was inevitable that individuals homozygous for Hb^S and having sickle-cell anaemia would be produced; the superior immunity of the heterozygotes was 'bought' at the 'expense' of the high probability that these homozygous recessives would die young. Where malaria was less common, those who were homozygous Hb^A/Hb^A were at a relatively smaller disadvantage; in this circumstance the proportion of such individuals was greater in the population.

In the absence of *P. falciparum*, the heterozygotes enjoyed no advantage over those homozygous for haemoglobin A and if no medical treatment were available for children homozygous for haemoglobin S, we would expect the frequency of haemoglobin S in the population to fall over the course of time. This is what has happened among some of the Afro-American populations and also in the African population of two former Dutch colonies in South America. In one, Surinam, *P. falciparum* occurs, and about 20 percent of the African population are heterozygous for haemoglobin S, a proportion close to that found in West Africa today. In Curaçao, where there is no *P. falciparum*, only about 5 percent of the African population are heterozygous Hb^A/Hb^S.

At the beginning of this century it was estimated that about half the deaths of human beings were attributable directly or indirectly to malaria: it was by far the most lethal of all diseases. It is therefore to be expected that any genes providing even some measure of protection against malaria would tend to be selected. The gene for haemoglobin S is not unique. That for haemoglobin C may have a somewhat similar action; individuals of genotype Hb^C/Hb^C are also anaemic and in the past would have been likely to die young. The same consideration probably applies to the condition of glucose-6-phosphate dehydrogenase deficiency (p. 404).

These results show us that some characteristics which have distinguished different human races and populations in the past were of selective value; as far as others are concerned we are still ignorant. Moreover, certain characteristics, such as different patterns of hair growth, may be the product of sexual selection and in this circumstance we cannot expect to find adaptive significance.

Today, as human beings tend to move increasingly from one place to another, we may expect the genetic picture to become ever more confused; but for a wide variety of reasons, some social, some political, the present differentiation of races is likely to persist in the future. It is clear that at least some of the characteristics which distinguish the different races are adaptive. These differences cannot be graded as 'superior' or 'inferior' since they relate to, and have been the basis of, human survival in different environments in the past. If it is meaningless to assign qualities of relative worth to adaptations to meet different environmental situations, it is equally meaningless to attempt to deny the existence of racial differences. The deeper our understanding of the biological significance of these differences, the greater will be our ability to make the most, not the worst, of the wide range of potentials, both physical and cultural, of our species.

Problems

1 Two characteristics of the Primates are (a) binocular vision and (b) the pectoral position of the mammae. Why are these considered to be adaptations to a tree-climbing habit?

2 From an inspection of Fig. 27.5c where would you expect the diastema to be on the lower jaw of a gorilla?

3 It has been suggested that retreat of the forest was a key environmental event which led to the evolution of man, driving him to living in the savanna. Do you regard this as a satisfactory hypothesis?

4 Pekin man probably made fire. How do you think he might have done this?

5 In 1912 some bones were excavated in southern England which were regarded at that time as being representative of a very primitive hominid. Subsequently they were shown to be forgeries which had been deliberately buried so that they might be 'discovered'. The remains suggested that the 'animal' had a large brain and also powerful ape-like jaws and teeth. The remains were in fact part of the fossilized brain case of a specimen of *Homo sapiens* and the broken jaw of an orang-utan, stained to give the appearance of fossilization, together with some artificially abraded and stained ape teeth. Such a combination of characters is now regarded as unlikely in any ancestral hominid. Why?

6 The incidence of colour blindness is markedly greater in the populations of industrialized countries than among peoples who still depend largely upon food gathering in forests. Suggest a possible interpretation of this observation.

7 The gene Hb^S is found in the peoples who live in Mauritania and Mali. It becomes more common to the south and east. Malaria due to *P. falciparum* is said not to extend north of the latitude of Dakar in West Africa. What hypotheses might explain this distribution of the Hb^S gene?

8 The data in Table 27.2 show that there is evidence of an east–west cline in the frequency of the I^B gene, which is exceedingly rare among the Basques. What hypotheses might account for such a distribution?

Bibliography

Further reading

Day, M. H. *The Fossil History of Man*, Oxford University Press, 1972

Napier, J. R. *Primates and their Adaptations*, Oxford University Press, 1972

Oakley, K. P. *Man, the Tool Maker*, British Museum (Natural History), 1950

Pilbeam, D. *The Evolution of Man*, Thames and Hudson, 1970

Tattersall, I. *Man's Ancestors*, Murray, 1970

Allison, A. C. 'Sickle Cells and Evolution', *Scientific American*, 1956, Offprint no. 1065

Andrew, R. J. 'The Origins of Facial Expressions', *Scientific American*, 1965, Offprint no. 627

Broom, R. 'The Ape-men', *Scientific American*, 1949, Offprint no. 832

Holloway, R. L. 'The Casts of Fossil Hominid Brains', *Scientific American*, 1974, Vol. 231, pt. 1, p. 106

Howells, W. W. '*Homo erectus*', *Scientific American*, 1966, Offprint no. 630

Krogman, W. M. 'The Scars of Human Evolution', *Scientific American*, 1967, Offprint no. 636

Loomis, W. F. 'Rickets', *Scientific American*, 1970, Offprint no. 1207

Napier, J. R. 'The Evolution of the Hand', *Scientific American*, 1962, Offprint no. 140

Napier, J. R. 'The Antiquity of Human Walking', *Scientific American*, 1967, Offprint no. 1070

Simons, E. L. 'The Early Relatives of Man', *Scientific American*, 1964, Offprint no. 622

Simons, E. L. 'The Earliest Apes', *Scientific American*, 1967, Offprint no. 636

28 The origin of life

If we accept the idea that the animals and plants which occur upon the earth today have evolved from other forms, then it follows that if we could travel back far enough in time, we would meet the first organisms from which all others have arisen. It follows also that these 'first organisms' must also have had an origin and have arisen from some inanimate system.

Such a statement contains various assumptions which we should examine. Firstly, it implies that living organisms had, at some time in the past, a unique origin. Is it not possible, however, that completely new forms of life are constantly arising even today? This question is one which has long interested people and was the subject of debate and experiment until less than 100 years ago. The view was once held that, if suitable conditions were provided, quite complex organisms would be spontaneously generated.

Thus, for example, the chemist van Helmont (1577–1644), who studied carbon dioxide and invented the word 'gas', stated that if one placed wheat grains and a dirty shirt in an open vessel and left it undisturbed for three weeks, at the end of that time mice would have been spontaneously generated as a result of the action of human sweat upon the wheat grains. Such an idea seems crude, but there was uncertainty about smaller organisms: did not decaying fish spontaneously generate maggots?

That this was not so was shown in a series of experiments by the Italian biologist, Francesco Redi (1629–79). He demonstrated that if fish or meat was left in an open container, maggots soon appeared, but if the container were corked, or even covered with fine netting, although the fish and meat decayed, there were no maggots.

A new problem arose with the invention of the microscope. Van Leeuwenhoek (1632–1723) was the first person to observe Protozoa and bacteria. Here was a level of simple organization which might well be spontaneously generated, even if mice and fly maggots were not. This view was partly shown to be false by another Italian biologist, Spallanzani (1729–99), who prepared glass tubes containing nutrient broth, sealed them, and then heated them for an hour. After a few days, the tubes were opened. No microscopic organisms could be seen. Spallanzani concluded that the heating had killed any organisms that had been there originally and that no new ones had been spontaneously generated. But his experiments were open to the objection that by sealing the tubes he had excluded oxygen and this had prevented the action of the 'vital force' necessary for spontaneous generation.

There the matter rested until 1864 when the French biologist Pasteur carried out a series of critical experiments which met the objection which had been raised to Spallanzani's work. The essential feature of Pasteur's work was the use of a long-necked flask. This was filled with a nutrient broth. The neck was then drawn out into a long curved capillary (Fig. 28.1) and the material in the flask allowed to boil vigorously for several minutes until steam issued freely through the open end of the neck. The flask was then allowed to cool. Oxygen was not now excluded, but still no putrefaction occurred. This is because any bacteria carried in with the air as the flask cooled would be killed by contact with the hot culture medium, or be trapped in the twisted neck. If, however, the neck of the flask was cut to expose the broth to contamination by micro-organisms in the air, fermentation soon started.

Biogenesis

These results of Pasteur's were taken as decisive evidence for the theory of 'biogenesis', namely that all living organisms have arisen from other living organisms. This is, however, not what they show: Pasteur demonstrated only that the sterile nutrient media which he used would

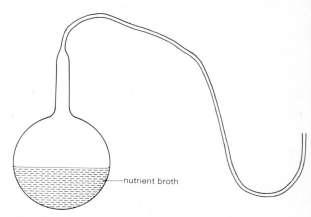

—nutrient broth

28.1 Sketch to show the pattern of flask used by Pasteur to demonstrate that no micro-organisms developed in sterile media with full access to air.

not, in the conditions prevailing in a glass flask, give rise to any organisms which were either visible with a microscope or capable of fermenting the chemicals in the broth. This is not the same as the wider generalization, which may be an unjustified extrapolation from a special case.

The question remains as to how living organisms first arose. It is possible to envisage three different types of answer to the problem of the origin of life. The first is that the original living organisms arose on the earth as a result of some completely unique event which involved divine intervention. Such a theory postulates the action of forces other than those which normally exist in the world around us. Scientific hypotheses are constructed on the assumption that events are the consequences of forces which are constantly at work. The hypothesis of an act of 'special creation' is therefore not open to scientific investigation. This is not to say that the hypothesis is necessarily false: only that, by its very nature, it excludes further study. From the purely scientific viewpoint, such an hypothesis is of no immediate value: the positive question is whether we can see how life might have originated without divine intervention. Even if we could construct a fully plausible account of how this might have occurred, it does not constitute proof that this is what did occur. Clearly, it is impossible to make dogmatic statements about events which took place more than three thousand million years ago.

The second type of hypothesis suggests that life did not originate on the earth, but in some other part of the universe and that primitive living organisms were brought to the earth initially on meteorites. This hypothesis has the limitation of simply moving the question into some other setting for, if we accept it, we are left with the problem of how life first arose in some other part of the universe. We cannot categorically exclude this hypothesis, but we can make some attempt to assess its probability by asking whether it is likely that any living organism at all resembling existing organisms could have survived upon a meteorite to land on the surface of the earth.

There are many different types of meteorite. Some, believed to be fragments from other bodies within the solar system, are of a stony nature. Examination of the chemical composition and structure of these suggests that they have not been subjected to very high temperatures since the time of their formation and they could therefore have served as 'vehicles' to bring very simple living organisms to earth. Indeed the claim was made at one time that the remains of such organisms could be seen. It is now generally accepted that these 'organisms' are either tiny aggregations of inorganic mineral material or pollen grains of terrestrial origin. Such meteorites do, however, contain various carbon compounds. Assuming that these do not arise from contamination after impact, their presence suggests that organic molecules can be formed in parts of the solar system other than the earth. Indeed, recently collected samples of moon rock contain traces of amino-acids. These meteorite chemicals, however, have certain characteristics suggesting that they have not originated from the synthetic activity of living organisms, at least as we know them.

The remaining hypothesis is that life originated as a result of the action of normal physical and chemical agencies on earth. This hypothesis, unlike the two others, is open to investigation and has been examined by biochemists in recent years. The results of such investigations and their limitations we will now consider.

Abiogenesis and the primitive atmosphere

If by some extraordinary event all living organisms were destroyed, the earth's atmosphere would gradually be depleted of oxygen. This would result from various natural causes: the most obvious is that of volcanic eruption in which reactive elements such as sulphur are thrown out. These combine with oxygen to form stable oxides and, in the course of time, the oxygen at present in the atmosphere would become permanently immobilized in this form. This idea leads us to the important conclusion that the oxygen now in the atmosphere is the product of photosynthetic activity and that before there were any living organisms the atmosphere of the earth was different.

Our first task, then, is to enquire what may have been the composition of such an atmosphere. The atmosphere of Venus is largely carbon dioxide, and carbon dioxide also occurs in the thin atmosphere of Mars; spectroscopic examination shows the atmospheres of the outer planets, Jupiter and Saturn, to be composed largely of hydrogen, ammonia, methane and water as ice. Such observations have led to the hypothesis that the primitive atmosphere of the earth resembled that of the outer planets, and to the question whether organic compounds could be formed by the action of natural forces in such conditions.

Experiments to examine this question were first made in 1953 by an American chemist, Stanley Miller. The principle of his apparatus is shown in Fig. 28.2. The apparatus is filled with a mixture of gases presumed to be similar to the primitive atmosphere of the earth. The spark discharge can be regarded as supplying energy equivalent to that made available from a lightning stroke. Examination of the products formed after about 100 hours showed them to include glycine, alanine, aspartic acid and glutamic acid as well as a large number of other organic compounds. The experiment demonstrated that amino-acids could be formed from compounds that might have been present in the primitive atmosphere of the earth.

Many experiments, similar in principle to Miller's, have been made since, often using other sources of energy such as ultra-violet light or other high-energy radiation or bombardment with elementary particles. Many other compounds of biological interest have been produced, including purines and pyrimidine bases and a far wider range of amino-acids, including some, such as phenylalanine,

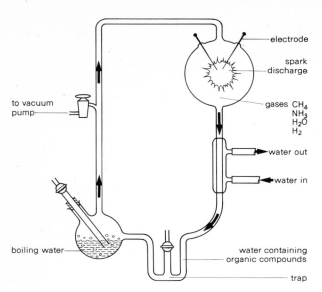

28.2 Diagram showing the principle of the apparatus used by Miller to effect organic syntheses in an atmosphere which may resemble that of the earth before life orginated. The apparatus is filled with a gas mixture. There is a constant movement of water vapour arising from the heated flask and condensing in the trap below. Energy for synthesis is provided by the spark discharge which can be regarded as equivalent in action to lightning strikes.

which contain a benzene ring, together with fatty acids, sugars and even porphyrins.

The characteristic building blocks of living organisms could thus have arisen in conditions in which there were no living organisms. Today such compounds would be rapidly absorbed or broken down by bacteria and fungi, but when there were no living organisms their quantity might be expected to increase steadily with time.

The formation of polymers

A major characteristic of the molecules of living organisms is that very many are polymers and it is reasonable to assume that polymeric molecules had to exist before any organisms could have been formed. The production of such molecules must have been preceded by the formation of local concentrations of simpler organic molecules, and various suggestions have been put forward as to the mechanisms which might effect such concentrations. It has been suggested that this occurred on the clays of estuarine deposits, as these provide a large surface for adsorption and possibly for the arrangement of molecules into monomolecular sheets. There are also various views as to how the actual polymerization may have taken place. One which is

supported by very striking experiments assumes that polymerization occurred in dry, hot conditions, such as might have arisen in dry tidal pools exposed to sunlight. Certainly protein-like polymers can be produced in the laboratory by heating mixtures of amino-acids to 75°C or higher. What is more remarkable is that if these polymers are extracted with hot water and the extract is allowed to cool, the material forms microscopic spheres (Fig. 28.3) which when sectioned and examined under the electron microscope prove to be built of a double layer of material (Fig. 28.4). It does not of course follow that these struc-

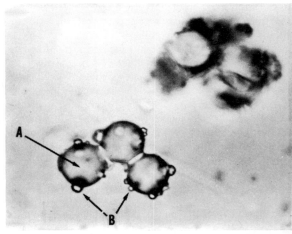

28.3 Microspheres (A) formed by hot-water extraction of heat-polymerized amino-acids. These specimens had been left in the extract and had started to form buds (B). The microspheres usually range in size between 1 and 5 μm. (From Fox).

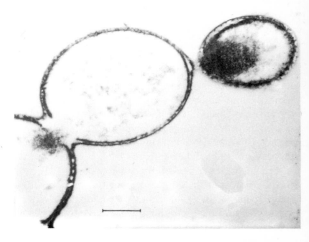

28.4 Electron micrograph of microspheres in section. Note the double structure of the membrane. Although this resembles the double protein layer of the cell membrane, there are no lipids in the microspheres and the resemblance may have no significance. (From Fox).

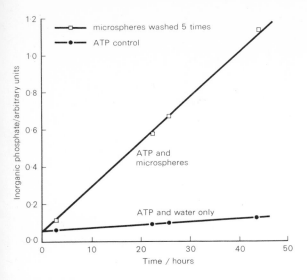

28.5. ATPase activity of microspheres, measured by the release of phosphate (in arbitrary units). The microspheres were washed several times and the supernatant liquid showed no catalytic activity; this was found only in association with the microspheres. (After Fox).

tures represent 'protocells', but clearly a definite, if low, order of structural complexity can be produced abiotically.

These protein-like polymers, if prepared in the presence of a zinc salt, show another interesting property. The enzyme ATPase contains zinc and the ability of the artificial zinc-containing microspheres to catalyse ATP hydrolysis was tested. Fig. 28.5 shows the results obtained: this material evidently has a slight but definite catalytic activity.

While it is possible in the laboratory to produce a very wide variety of complex organic molecules by the use of physical sources of energy in the synthesis, one essential feature of all known biological systems is the direction by a nucleic acid polymer of the sequence of amino-acids incorporated in a protein chain. While nucleic acid polymers can be produced abiotically, we lack successful laboratory experiments showing how links between nucleic acids and protein polymers might first have been established and further, equally important, how one nucleic acid polymer could serve as a template for the formation of another: as yet we can only speculate. Both of these steps may have involved the type of 'protoenzymic' action seen in the zinc-containing microspheres. A further enzymatic requirement is needed for a proto-organism, namely one which allows it to exploit in some fashion the organic compounds in the environment as a source of energy for organic synthesis. These, the absolute minimum requirements to produce a functional organism with the potential of reproducing, are summarized in Fig. 28.6.

If such minimum requirements can be satisfied, even at

a very low order of efficiency, by protein-like molecules replicated on a nucleic acid template, then there will be an accumulation of protein and nucleic acid molecules within the protocell. But the protocell must reproduce. One peculiarity of the microspheres is that they bud and that, placed in a solution of proteinoid, these buds will grow in mass. The mechanism of this phenomenon is still not understood, but it demonstrates that a simple type of 'reproductive' increase is possible.

If we assume—and this is pure speculation—that some process similar to the budding of microspheres was the first type of reproduction, then, in our very simple organisms, we have the necessary conditions for the operation of selection, as the molecules transmitted to the buds will be the same as those of the parent microsphere. If mutational events occur, some types may reproduce more rapidly than others. A proportion of such proto-organisms will be destroyed by natural events and their chemical content set free to provide 'food' for others. We can, in this fashion, visualize selection leading over long periods of time to more efficient enzyme systems, an increase in the size of the genome leading to the potential for producing new types of enzyme and so on. Once established the process of becoming more complex probably became more rapid.

Crises in the history of life

Such 'organisms' were saprophytic, depending upon the natural processes of abiological synthesis for their energy supply. These processes are slow and undirected, and clearly no further advance could be made until a more

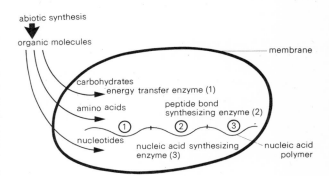

28.6 Scheme to show the absolute minimal structural and enzymatic equipment for a self-replicating heterotrophic protocell. It is assumed that the membrane can grow and bud without specialized structural features as do Fox's microspheres (Fig. 28.3). ①, ② and ③ are the 'genes' corresponding to the three protoenzymes. It is possible to visualize the protoenzymes being incorporated in the structure of the membrane as the protocell grows. Later specialization of such an event might be a step towards the formation of various cell organelles.

501

abundant source of energy could be tapped. We may suppose that at some time photosynthetic metabolic pathways developed. These, even if initially very inefficient, would have conferred selective advantage over those protobionts which had not evolved this ability.

Photosynthesis is basically a process in which light energy is used for the reduction of carbon dioxide. In green plants the reducing agent is water, but some photosynthetic bacteria use other substances, such as organic acids, as hydrogen donors. In highly simplified form we may write the two reactions as follows

$$2AH_2 + CO_2 \rightarrow CH_2O + 2A + H_2O \text{ (photosynthetic bacteria)}$$

$$2OH_2 + CO_2 \rightarrow CH_2O + O_2 + H_2O \text{ (green plants)}$$

Note that oxygen is liberated only when water is used as a hydrogen donor. It seems probable that primitive photosynthetic processes depended upon hydrogen donors other than water.

Only efficient photosynthesis may be expected to exploit the most energy-rich radiation available. If our ideas about the primitive terrestrial atmosphere are correct, ultraviolet light would have reached the surface of the earth, and such short-wavelength light may have been used initially. The evolution of increasingly efficient photosynthetic processes ultimately led to the replacement of organic acids and similar substances as hydrogen acceptors by the readily available water. This would have resulted in the release of oxygen. In the upper atmosphere oxygen is converted to ozone which filters out the very short ultraviolet waves. As this change occurred, not only may there have been a change in photosynthetic metabolism, since high-energy, short-wavelength radiations were no longer available, but there would have been selection for organisms which possessed new metabolic pathways to exploit the oxygen. The less efficient anaerobic metabolism would have been replaced by more efficient aerobic metabolism.

Beyond this we are upon more certain ground as we can assume that metabolically these photosynthetic and aerobic organisms had much in common with algae.

The fossil record

What light does the fossil record throw upon these problems? Animals with calcareous skeletons, whether they are vertebrates or molluscs, leave a well-defined fossil record; the earliest known chordates are to be found in the Ordovician rocks which are less than 500 million years or 0.50 aeons old (an aeon is a period of 10^9 years). Molluscs start to become abundant in the upper Cambrian, but in the lowest Cambrian deposits, which are about 0.57 aeons old the remains are mainly those of soft-bodied animals such as sponges, coelenterates and annelid

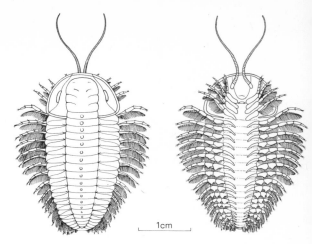

28.7 A trilobite, a representative of a completely extinct group of marine arthropods.

worms, as well as types of animal which carried an exoskeleton of calcareous plates and may be related to the echinoderms. There are also remains of an extinct group of marine arthropods, the Trilobita (Fig. 28.7).

Fossil-bearing strata of still earlier, Precambrian, deposits are rare. In central Australia impressions of soft-bodied animals, including coelenterates and annelids, have been found in marine sediments dating back to about 0.65 aeons. Traces of higher animals have not so far been found in rocks older than these, but in such ancient rocks there is evidence for the existence of algae and bacteria. Single-celled organisms believed to be eukaryotes are to be found in rocks of 1.0 aeons old and may occur in rocks as old as 1.3 aeons; there is certainly no trace of these in still earlier rocks 1.9 aeons old. Fossils which resemble blue-green algae have been found in rocks as old as 2.0 aeons, while in rocks dated to 3.1 aeons remains of bacteria and larger organisms which may be prokaryote algae have been found (Fig. 28.9). Complex layered formations formed by photosynthetic organisms and known as stromatolites date from about 2.8 aeons. Very similar formations have been found growing today and photosynthetic bacteria play a significant role in the formation of these. There is, however, no reason to believe that the fossil stromatolites liberated oxygen; they contain the remains of filamentous organisms but this growth form may well have evolved before the use of water as a hydrogen acceptor in photosynthesis. Nevertheless such a photosynthetic mechanism must have evolved before about 2.0 aeons ago, as the presence of oxidized sediments shows oxygen to have become abundant by that time.

Fossil chemicals

Conclusions based upon the interpretation of minute fossil structures, often only a few micrometres in diameter, are inevitably uncertain. But evidence for the existence of living organisms can be sought in a different way. If fossilized plant material such as coal is extracted by various organic solvents, it can be shown to contain considerable quantities of 'fossil' organic chemicals. The same technique has been applied to specimens of Precambrian rocks. These also contain small quantities of organic compounds which, there is reason to believe, belong to the original sediments and are not due to later infiltration.

We have suggested that abiotic synthesis of a wide variety of organic chemicals could have occurred. If we detect such chemicals in ancient rocks, can we decide whether they were formed in this way or are the product of the synthetic activity of living organisms? To answer this question, we will consider as an example the isoprenoid phytane (Fig. 28.8) which occurs attached to the metalloporphyrin fraction of chlorophyll (Book 1 Fig. 9.6). This has an empirical formula $C_{20}H_{42}$. Such an empirical formula clearly indicates a very large number of possible isomers: calculation shows there to be more than 350 000. But only three of these isomers are normally derived from living material. If the 'fossil' isoprenoids were the products of abiotic synthesis, we might reasonably expect that a considerable number of different isomers would occur. In the Precambrian rocks whose organic chemical contents have been examined, the isoprenoids which occur are those found in present-day organisms and include phytane. These include rocks of 3·2 aeons old, as well as those which contain what are believed to be fossil bacteria and algae; the two lines of evidence thus support one another.

The presence of 'fossil' phytane in such ancient rocks is not, however, evidence that oxygen-forming photosynthetic processes occurred as long ago as 3·0 aeons. As well as chlorophyll, there are other compounds of biological importance that are isoprenoid derivatives, and these might have been the precursors of the phytane.

The time scale of evolution

Geophysical evidence suggests that the age of our planet is about 4·7 aeons. For about one-ninth of that time there have been vertebrates on the planet, while Metazoa have existed for about one-sixth of the time (Fig. 28.9). During the remaining five-sixths we can picture firstly a cooling and stabilization of the earth, succeeded by a long period of perhaps an aeon during which there was a gradual accumulation of organic compounds as a result of abiotic synthesis, resulting in what has been described as the 'primitive soup'. This was followed by an aeon during which there was a slow evolution of primitive organisms cul-

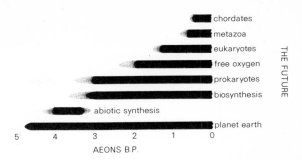

28.9 Summary of the possible succession of major events during the evolution of life upon our planet. An aeon is a period of 10^9 years and B.P. is short for 'before present'.

minating in the appearance of the first oxygen-producing autotrophs. Maybe as long as a further aeon elapsed before the evolution of eukaryote cells. After that time the process of evolution leading to increasing complexity of structure became more rapid.

If this reconstruction of past events is broadly correct, the very early stages of the evolution of cellular organization took place very slowly. These are precisely the events which we find most difficult to understand since we can now study only the highly complex end-result of biochemical evolution: there is no evidence, even in the most general terms, of the detailed sequence of changes which resulted in the elaborately integrated machinery of any surviving cell. What we can conclude is that it is possible to visualize a series of events, depending upon the action of normal physical and chemical forces, which could have given rise to living organisms. Beyond this we cannot go. There can be no positive evidence as to what did happen, regardless of what we choose to postulate may have occurred.

If we can tentatively reconstruct the past, we may also attempt to see ahead into the future. This is a far from idle occupation as man is altering his environment at an ever-increasing pace. The consequences of this we will briefly examine in our final chapter.

Problems

1 Pasteur used the absence of fermentation of nutrient broth as evidence that no micro-organisms were spontaneously generated in the conditions of his experiments. Is there any class of organism which might have been formed in such conditions but which would not be detected in this way?

2 Accepting the scheme shown in Fig. 28.9 as correct, would any present-day organisms be able to survive if they were put in an environment such as existed (a) 2·0 aeons, (b) 2·5 aeons, (c) 3·0 aeons and (d) 3·5 aeons ago?

28.8 Skeletal formula of the isoprenoid phytane.

If so, which types of organism would you expect to be able to survive?

3 Material is today 'recycled' in the biosphere as a result of the decomposing activity of organisms like bacteria. Would you expect to have found organisms playing such a role on our planet 2·5 aeons ago?

4 Oxygen-requiring bacteria are grown in pure culture in laboratories today. How have the procedures used by Pasteur in his experiments with flasks been adapted to the need of a bacteriological laboratory to store sterile media?

5 A space-fiction story has described a peculiar organism whose tissues contained silicon rather than carbon. Why did the author select silicon as the element suitable for a completely new type of organism?

6 The genetic code is, as far as known, the same for all organisms occurring on the earth today. Does this necessarily imply that they all had a common ancestor?

7 Fig. 28.6 claims to summarize the 'minimum requirements' for a self-reproducing organism. Once these requirements are satisfied we can say the organism is 'alive'. Would you consider virus particles to be living organisms? Give your reasons.

8 It has been suggested that the evolution of the first consumers resulted in an acceleration of the rate of evolutionary change. Suggest why this might have been the case.

9 The basic equation of photosynthetic activity shows that for each molecule of carbon dioxide taken up, one molecule of oxygen is released. This quantity of oxygen is sufficient to reconvert the fixed carbon to carbon dioxide when the plant is broken down by decomposers, or in life by respiration. There is thus no seeming gain of oxygen from photosynthesis. Nevertheless it is suggested that photosynthesis, using water as a hydrogen donor, resulted in an accumulation of oxygen in the atmosphere. How do you consider this contradiction might be resolved?

Bibliography

Further reading

Bernal, J. D., Synge, A.
The Origin of Life, Oxford University Press, 1972

Keosian, J.
The Origin of Life, Chapman and Hall, 1965

Young, R. S., Ponnamperuma, C.
Early Evolution of Life, BSCS Pamphlet no. 11, Heath, 1964

Barghoorn, E. S.
'The Oldest Fossils', *Scientific American*, 1971, Offprint no. 895

Echlin, P.
'The Blue-green Algae', *Scientific American*, 1966, Offprint no. 1044

Eglinton, G. Calvin, M.
'Chemical Fossils', *Scientific American*, 1967, Offprint no. 308

Glaessner, M. F.
'Pre-Cambrian Animals', *Scientific American*, 1961, Offprint no. 837

Morowitz, H. J., Tourtellotte, M. E.
'The Smallest Living Cells', *Scientific American*, 1962, Offprint no. 1005

Part 7
Looking ahead

29 Ecology and the future of man

Man has always recognized that there are certain features of his environment which limit his freedom of action. It is not possible to 'defy the law of gravity' and walk over the edge of a cliff without the certainty of falling; it is not possible to thrust one's hand into a fire without the high probability of being burnt. Man has also long known that there are certain biological facts which he must respect: that to eat certain fruits may lead to death, that the bite of certain kinds of snake will kill. But other biological facts also significant for his survival he has come to appreciate only relatively recently. The connection between mosquitoes and malaria has been known for less than 100 years, as has that between aquatic snails and schistosomiasis. The need to include certain vitamins in the diet is also quite recent knowledge, as is the need for effective sanitation to keep city-dwellers free from epidemic diseases. Survival thus depends upon knowledge. We are coming increasingly to realize that a knowledge of isolated facts is not sufficient; it is necessary to understand interrelationships also. Thus we might attempt to get rid of the snails which spread *Schistosoma* by adding poisonous molluscicides to the water in which they live. Before doing this, we should first consider the possible effects on other fauna and the likely consequences of their destruction on food fishes which also live in the water. In Chap. 16 we described numerous attempts to tackle problems in isolation which merely led to the appearance of other, sometimes worse problems.

In other words, it is desirable to consider biological facts in the context of their ecological background. One of the aims of ecology is to understand the structure of communities, how these communities are built up into a series of trophic levels, and how the numbers of organisms at each level are regulated. This view of the biological world places central emphasis upon the whole ecosystem as the natural unit of biological activity. Man's activities alter ecosystems. Just as we cannot, without risk, neglect the fact of gravity, so too in our relations with the biological world, we cannot, without risk, modify the environment with total disregard for the structural relations of ecosystems. It is sometimes objected that too much emphasis is placed on the dangers of meddling with ecosystems. Sceptics will point out that the history of civilization has been a story of the increasing replacement of relatively non-productive communities with man-made farms, woodlands and pastures, and that, by trial and error, farmers and fishermen all over the world have developed techniques which allow them to obtain food indefinitely from their 'managed ecosystems'. They will point to the great achievements of modern agriculture and medicine—the 'Green Revolution' and the large-scale elimination of malaria—as evidences of man's success in changing his environment.

It is true that, in the past, ecosystems have been modified, but this has been a fairly gradual process, involving trial and error mainly on a relatively small scale. The recent upsurge in modern technology has meant that huge areas are being drastically altered at great speed, often with no clear knowledge of what the long-term effects are likely to be. The destruction of the forests of Vietnam (p. 383) is a particularly frightening example of this phenomenon. The greater the magnitude of any operation the more imperative it is that the possible biological consequences on affected ecosystems should be carefully considered.

We have drawn attention to many instances where such disregard for ecological considerations has led to disaster. We have stressed the problems which follow from over-grazing or over-fishing, from over-exploitation of savanna lands with resulting major erosion, from destruction of normal agencies regulating population numbers.

We have seen, (p. 287), the costly failure of the 'Ground-nuts Scheme' which was launched with inadequate knowledge of the ecology of the area it was intended to develop. Before large areas are flooded by the construction of dams and hydroelectric installations to obtain urgently needed supplies of power, the possible side-effects should receive consideration. These may include the spread of water-borne disease like schistosomiasis, the resettlement of the former occupants of the flooded area requiring the opening of new lands for cultivation and possibly new agricultural techniques, changes in the pattern of river flow with disruption of the lives of those who live below the dam and perhaps alteration of the pattern of coastal erosion, so that whole villages may have to be abandoned.

Such examples underline our point that in developing Africa, where major schemes with biological consequences are becoming increasingly common, it is essential to have the fullest possible comprehension of the workings of the relevant ecosystems and that intelligent decisions cannot be taken in the absence of such information.

But there is a second way in which we may look at the biological world, a way which emphasizes the individual organism rather than the ecosystem. We started Book 2 by discussing the concept of autecology, by asking: how do organisms establish themselves in particular habitats? We can regard the phenomena we described as being concerned with ensuring that organisms reach habitats in which they find the resources necessary for their survival. In Chap. 6, for example, we saw that, for an animal community, it is the available flora which constitutes its basic resource, on which it depends for living space and food. This exploitation of the biological resources within a community has led to the phenomenon of co-evolution—the evolution of adaptation to one another shown by members of a food web—and to the repeating patterns of parasitism and other types of close interrelation between organisms which live together. Particularly important is the idea that it is the resources available to an organism which regulate its population size at a value close to the carrying capacity of its habitat. The numbers of human beings are now increasing at the rate of about 2 percent per annum: that is, in an exponential manner. If we accept that man must ultimately be subject to the same ecological rules that apply to other organisms, we are faced with the question of what may be the carrying capacity of the planet for human beings.

The environmental resources exploited by organisms other than man are characteristically renewable; such resources are never completely used up. A carnivore exploits the resource provided by its prey, but the prey normally re-establishes its numbers year after year. The prey in its turn may exploit some primary producer, but

again, the populations of these organisms are regularly replenished. The producer depends upon a supply of sunlight, which for all practical purposes represents a permanent resource of energy, and upon nutrients supplied partly by mineralization during decomposition, partly by the slow weathering of rock. In a natural ecosystem, such as a tropical forest, relatively little matter leaves the ecosystem; most of it is recycled and what is removed is replaced by the natural processes of soil formation.

This balance between utilization of resources and their replacement is one of the 'rules' of survival which has been observed by organisms for hundreds of millions of years. Most resources are renewable; a few seemingly non-renewable resources, such as weathered rock, are exploited so slowly that their removal is offset by geological processes. Man has also existed by these rules for many thousands of years: even when he destroyed areas of forest to plant his crops, he soon moved on and the abandoned clearing became reforested. Today the situation is very different. To maintain the high rate of production from agricultural lands needed to feed the human population, resources which are not renewable are being exploited. Coal and oil are both used as sources of power to manufacture tractors; oil is used as a raw material for the manufacture of insecticides. Tractors consist of metals, including complex alloys, derived from ores dug out of the earth. The coal or oil once burnt cannot be recovered; the tractor once worn out will corrode away.

Man's way of life today depends upon the exploitation of such non-renewable resources; the rate of their exploitation, like the human population, is increasing exponentially (Fig. 29.1) while the stocks are not unlimited. Table 29.1 provides estimates of the approximate date at which

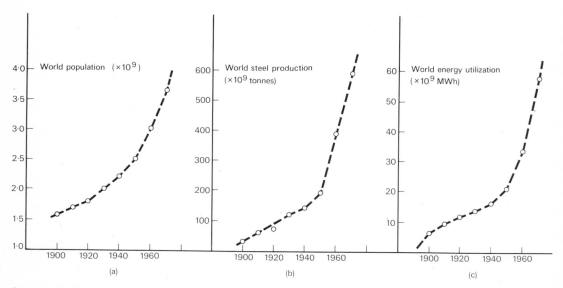

29.1 Graphs showing the growth of (a) world population (b) world steel production, (c) world energy utilization, since the beginning of the century (from various sources).

Table 29.1 Estimated dates of exhaustion of stocks of particular metal ores using present extraction techniques (*Data from various sources*)

Metal	Year
Lead	1987
Zinc	1988
Gold	1989
Silver	1990
Platinum	1990
Tin	1992
Copper	2010
Tungsten	2010
Molybdenum	2060
Nickel	2095
Cobalt	2120
Manganese	2125
Aluminium	2140
Iron	2500

the stocks of different metals now extensively used by industry will be exhausted: with present extraction techniques the world reserves of some of these are not sufficient to last even until the end of the century.

These figures have another aspect. The present consumption of these non-renewable resources is very unevenly distributed among the peoples of the world. The rich nations are major users of these limited materials; the poorer nations use relatively little. For example, at present rates of consumption the total probable world resources of oil are sufficient to meet man's needs for more than a century; but today nearly half of the world's production is consumed by the United States, whose population amounts to less than 7 percent of the total population of the world. If a sudden increase in prosperity were to permit all the peoples of the world to use oil as rapidly as do the inhabitants of the United States, the probable oil stocks of the world would be completely exhausted within about thirty years.

Such considerations show us that, in ecological terms, modern man is totally different from other organisms, as he has developed a way of life dependent upon the use of non-renewable resources. Their exploitation obviously cannot continue indefinitely and yet the steadily growing human population and the steadily increasing demand for manufactured articles results in an ever-increasing rate of utilization of these dwindling resources.

Man has ceased to be in 'equilibrium' with his environment and it is clear that some type of change must lie ahead. Some people believe that human ingenuity will always be capable of finding new resources as the older ones become exhausted. They point to the vast supplies of iron and aluminium in the soil, to mineral deposits on the sea bed, and to the possible use of water as fuel for power generators employing the principle of nuclear fusion. Such optimists look forward to an indefinite period of increasing material prosperity. Others consider that any such new technologies, if indeed they could be developed, would be so much more expensive than existing methods based on high-grade ores and fuels that they could not provide a satisfactory substitute.

Our point is that an understanding of basic ecological ideas allows us to comprehend why man may be regarded as having reached the threshold of a crisis and that this crisis stems from the fact that man has used his intelligence to exploit the resources of our planet, but has taken no heed of the consequences of his acts. Ecology cannot tell us how, in historical terms, man will meet this problem. It does suggest that one solution, and possibly the only solution, lies in finding a totally different pattern of living, of different aspirations and ideas as to what constitutes the 'good life'.

Man differs from other animals in his manual skill, which allows him to make objects not only of utility but of beauty, and in his ability to communicate complex ideas in speech, not only for practical ends but to delight the imagination. It is these abilities, both of creating and enjoying, which make man unique. If to be fully human is to make maximum use of these abilities, it does not follow that the present pattern of human life is the only possible one. In far simpler material circumstances man produced works which afforded him great pleasure in both their creation and their subsequent enjoyment. While good health, good housing, good food are essential before all else, there is no reason to believe that man can exercise his unique gifts only if he possesses the vast number of material objects which have come to be widely regarded as 'essential'. It is desirable to consider for what end such things are 'essential' and whether the end itself can be justified in terms of being fully human.

Index

Page references in **bold type** are to figures or diagrams, including chemical formulae, which relate to the word indexed. Page references in *italics* lead to definitions or explanations of terms or topics. In many cases the meaning of a term is made clear in a figure; in such cases reference may be in **bold type** only. 'f' after a page reference means that the subject is treated on the following page as well; 'ff' means that it is treated on two or more of the following pages. 'spp.' after a generic name means that there are several species in the genus.

Ant-lion *See* Neuroptera
Antelope *See* Ungulate
Antibiotics 448; use for amoebic
  dysentery 327; in animal
  husbandry 317 *See* Drugs
Antibody *386*, 420
Anticodon *See* Codon
Anticrypsis *177*
Antidorcas (Springbok) *See*
  Ungulate
Antigen *386*, 420
Antrum cavity of ovary **363**, **364**
Ape (Mammalia, Primates,
  Pongidae) 7; differences from
  man 486f; fossil 490 *See*
  Chimpanzee, Gorilla,
  Ramapithicus
Aphid *See* Hemiptera Homoptera
Aplysia (Sea slug) *See* Gastropoda
Arabia 43
Arachnida 72, 73 *See* Camel spider,
  Mite, Scorpion, Spider, Tick
Araneus See Spider
Archaeopteryx (Aves) **468**, **469**
Ardeola See Cattle Egret
Argiope See Spider
Arid areas, agriculture in 360
Armadillo (Mammalia, Edentata)
  479
Arsenic(III)oxide 303, 305, 377
Ascogonia **417**
Ascorbic acid *See* Vitamin C
Ascospore **417**
Ascus **417**
Aspirin 372
Associations 209ff, 230ff
Aster *389*, **390**
Atlas mountains 59
Atmosphere, of Earth 499f; of
  planets 499
Australopithecus (Mammalia,
  Primates) **490**, **491**, **492**, **494**
Autecology *1*, 36
Autolysis *128*
Autoradiography 431
Autosome **402**
Avena See Oats
Avery, Oswald Theodore (1877–
  1955), American biochemist 413
Aves *See* Bird
Avicennia (Mangrove) 87, 95
Awns of grasses, as dispersal aids 9
Axonopus compressus (Carpet grass)
  1

Baboon (*Papio*) *See* Monkey
Backcross *396*
Bacteria 73, 218, 477, 502;
  cellulose-digesting in cattle 193;
  in termites 193; nitrogen fixing
  224; in soil 126; resistance 448
  See Escherichia coli, Nitrifying
  bacteria
Bacteriophage **414**, 415, **431**, 439
Baer, Karl Ernst von (1792–1876),
  German zoologist 475
Bag-worm (*Cryptothelia junodi*) *See*
  Moth

Balanus (Barnacle) *See* Crustacea
Bambarra groundnut (*Voandzeia
  subterranea*) 283, 284, 285
Banana (*Musa*) 280, 283, 285, 312;
  introduction to Africa 284;
  Panama disease 295, 296
Baobab tree (*Adansonia digitata*)
  283; seed **285**
Barbus (Minnow) *See* Fish
Barley (*Hordeum vulgare*) 280, 343
Barnacle *See* Crustacea
Barrier 453f; genetical 458; types of
  457; to reproduction 456
Bary, Anton de (1831–1892),
  German biologist 212
Basal area, of trees 82
Base pairing 425f, 433
Base substitution 438
Bat (Mammalia, Chiroptera) 30, 49,
  65, 448; coloration 163;
  coexistence of species 272; fruit-
  eating 66, 104, 178; insectivorous
  178ff; wing **474**
Bates, Henry Walter (1825–1892),
  British zoologist 161
Bauxite 124
Bean 224, 289, 336f; *Phaseolus
  vulgaris* 407; soy 361
Beating 240
Bee bread *201*
Bee (Insecta, Hymenoptera),
  Bumble 150f, 204: Honey (*Apis
  mellifera*) 155, 171, 198ff; activity
  patterns 199; castes 198;
  determination of 203; characters
  198; cell construction 198; colony
  foundation 203; colour vision
  146f, **149**; dances 201f, **202**;
  drone *198*, 204; fertilization 204;
  flower constancy 149; forager
  recruitment 201; glands 199; hive
  odour 206; honey stomach **200**;
  mouthparts **200**; nectar **200**; nests
  198, **199**; polarized light 202f;
  queen cell 198, **199**, 203; queen
  substance *203*; sense of smell
  146; sex determination 405;
  training 146ff; trophallaxis 206:
  Solitary 204: Stingless 171, **204**:
  Wood-boring **161**
Beetle (Insecta, Coleoptera) 75,
  108, 109, 127, 131, **132**, 154,
  160, 170, 225, 305, 308; feeding
  response 147; larvae 75 127, 132,
  227: Ambrosia **219**, 231:
  Bombadier **156**: *Chrysomela
  gamellata* 268, 302: Colorado
  Potato (*Leptinotarsa decemlineata*)
  143: Dung (*Scarabaeus*) **76**, 109,
  132: Eucalyptus Snout weevil
  301: Flour (*Tribolium*) **257**, 312;
  competition between species 270f;
  with Meal Moth 273; effect of
  population density 256, **257**:
  Khapra (*Trogoderma granarium*)
  312: Ladybird 210 212:
  Lasioderma **248**: Rhinoceros
  (*Oryctes*) 132, 299, 300: *Rodolia*

304: Rove (Staphylinidae) **132**,
  225, **226**
Behaviour, and habitat selection,
  21ff; inheritance of 408f;
  oviposition 18f; territorial 31f
Belemnite *See* Cephalopod
Bering Strait **479**
Berlinia grandiflora, in fringing
  forest 81
Beta-galactosidase 433, 435
BHC (Benzene hexachloride) 304ff,
  309, 312f, 330, 379
Bilharzia *See* Schistosomiasis
Biochemical Oxygen Demand
  (B.O.D.) *348*
Biogenesis *498*
Biological control 304, 306f, 373;
  examples 301f, 333; limitations
  301; principle 300f
Biomass, in forest and savanna 56;
  and productivity 277; pyramid of
  233, 274f
Biomes *36*; of Africa 36, **37**;
  productivity of 277
Biotin 221
Bird 30, 66, 100, 110, 154, 163,
  165, 320, 405, 448, 451, 475;
  effects of insecticides 303f, 380f;
  fauna of Zaïre 66; of Galapagos
  Islands 455f, **456**; food
  preference 187; fossil record **468**,
  469; insectivorous 66, 106;
  migration 106; pair formation
  189; parental care 189; territory
  259; warning calls **173**; wing of
  469, **474**: Bishop (several genera)
  189: Bulbul (several genera) 159,
  189: Button quail (*Turnix*) 189:
  Buzzard (several genera) 115,
  380: Cape Raven (*Corvulter
  albicollis*) 154: Cape Wren-
  warbler (*Pinia maculosa*) **32**:
  Drongo (several genera) 159,
  162: Eagle, crowned
  (*Stephanoaetus coronatus*) 189;
  golden (*Aquila chrysaetus*) 381:
  Falcon (several genera) 171:
  Flycatcher (several genera) 162,
  265: Galapagos finches (several
  genera) 455, **456**: Glossy Starling
  (*Lamprocolius nitens*) 110, 189:
  Hamerkop (*Scopus umbretta*) 189:
  Hawk (*Accipiter* spp.) 171, 177:
  Heron, European (*Ardea* spp.)
  30: Hoopoe (*Upupa africana*)
  158, 159: Hornbill (several
  genera) 158, 159: Myna, Indian
  (*Acridotheres tristis*) 113; Pigeon
  (*Columba livia*) 171: Red-billed
  Ox-pecker (*Buphagus
  erythrorhynchus*) 209: Seagull
  (*Larus* spp.) 154: Shrike (several
  genera) 32, 162: Sparrow (*Passer*
  spp.) 29, 161: Spur-winged plover
  (*Hoplopterus spinosus*) 209:
  Sunbird (several genera) 189;
  Orange-breasted (*Anthobaphes
  violacea*) 189: Vulture (several

Maize (*contd*)
rust diseases **285**, 295; southern corn leaf-blight 296

Malagasy Republic **43**; Madagascar **480**

Malapterurus electricus (Electric catfish) *See* Fish

Malaria 217, 244, 372, 396; drug treatment **329**; eradication campaign 328ff, 355; parasite *See Plasmodium*; Vector *See* Mosquito, *Anopheles*

Malathion 303, 308, 312

Malaŵi 108, 109, 111, 301; Lake 108, **109**

Mali 106

Malnutrition 326, 334ff, 359; kwashiorkor *337*; protein-energy 337; marasmus *337*

Mammal 65, 100, 405, 448; adaptive radiation **472**; age determination 250; eye **483**; and fire 110f; fossil record 468f; pair formation 189; parental care 189f; reptilian origin 469, **470** *See* Aardvark, Armadillo, Bat, Carnivora, *Dendrohyrax*, Elephant, Hare, Insectivora, Mammoth, Marsupial, Pangolin, Primates, Rabbit, Rodentia, Ungulate, Whale

Mammoth (*Mammuthus primigenius* and other species: Mammalia, (Proboscidea) **462**

Man, body build 497; Bushman 280; chromosomes **402**; community 190; differences from apes 486f; diseases 325f, 495; effect on environment 369ff; embryo **475**; evolution 486ff; as goal of evolution 484; growth 320; hair 488, 495; hands 486, **487**; inheritance 396f, 408, 419; language 494f; limb 486, **487**, **491**; nutrition 334ff; parasites 326f, 495; Pigmy 280; races 495f; skin pigmentation 495; skull 478, **488**; society 192; speech 489, 494f; teeth **488**, **491**; tool making 489, **492**, 493; *See Homo*, Population, human

Mandrill (*Mandrillus sphinx*) *See* Monkey

Mangrove 383 *See Avicennia*, *Rhizophora*

Manihot esculenta See Cassava

Man-made lake *See* Lake, man-made

Mantid (Insecta, Dictyoptera) 64, 110, 168f, 177, 185; Praying (*Mantis religiosa*), colour change 166

Manure 287f, 322, 326; green 289

Map, chromosome 401f, **402**; units *402*

Marasmus *337*

Marriage, age of, effect on population growth, 356

Marsh Bedstraw (*Galium palustre*), diploid and tetraploid populations, 458

Marsupials, geographical distribution 478, **480**; life forms 117

Mating, call, of *Bufo* **457**; type, of *Neurospora*, **412**

Mauritius 43, 115

Mayfly (Insecta, Ephemeroptera) 99, 100, 190; habitat selection by nymphs 25, **26**

Mbuga 59

Meadow Brown Butterfly (*Maniola jurtina*) *See* Butterfly

Mealy bug (Insecta, Hemiptera Homoptera) 15: of cocoa, *Planococcoides njalensis* 212, 297; *Stictococcus sjostedti* 212: of coffee, *Planococcus kenyae* 301, 304, 306: of citrus, *Planococcus citri* 210

Measles 343

Medium, culture, complete *417*; minimum *417*

Meerkat (*Suricata suricatta*) *See* Carnivora

Megaphanerophyte *56*

Megasporangium 392

Megaspore 392, **393**

Meiosis **391**, 392ff, 400, **440**, 443

Melanin 167

Melanocytes **167**

Meloidogyne incognita (Root-knot nematode) *See* Nematode

Mendel, Gregor Johann (1822–1884), Austrian biologist 393, 395, 398

Menstruation 364, **365**, **366**

Merozoite, of *Plasmodium* 215

Meselson Matthew Stanley (1930–), American biochemist 432

Mesofauna, of soil *72*

Mesophanerophyte *56*

Messenger RNA *See* Ribonucleic acid

Metabolic rate, relation with body size 274

Metabolism, evolution of 477, 502

Metaphase **389**, **391**, 442

MHWN (Mean high water neap tides) **271**

MHWS (Mean high water spring tides) 27, **271**

Microclimate, measurement of 20f

Microfilaria (Nematoda) 214, *333*

Microhabitat *20*, 117

Micro-organisms, as source of food 361

Microphanerophyte *56*

Microscope, inverted 234, **235**

Microsome *421*, 423

Microsphere **500**, **501**

Microspore 392

Microsporocyte 392

Migration, of army worm (*Spodoptera*) 258; birds 106, 259; Driver ants (*Dorylus*) 197, **198**, 258; locusts 106f, **107**, 258;

Quelea 107, **108**, 258; tsetse fly (*Glossina*) 108, **109**; ungulates 16, 105, **106**; diurnal 102f; seasonal 105f; vertical, by fish 102, mosquitoes **104**, plankton 102, **103**

Migratory locust (*Locusta migratoria*) *See* Locust

Miller, Stanley Lloyd (1930–), American chemist 499, 500

Millet 280, 312; bulrush (*Pennisetum americanum*) **282**, 283: finger (*Eleusine coracana*) **283**: wild and cultivated 281, **282**

Millet grain-midge (*Geromyia*) *See* Diptera

Millettia thonningii 7; dispersal **8**

Millipede (Arthropoda, Diplopoda) 71, 72, 73, 75, 127, 128, 155; *Habrodesmus* 73; *Spirostreptus* 73

Milt, of fish *413*

Mimicry *160*f, **226**; Batesian *161*; Müllerian *161*

Minerals in human diet 335ff; structure of 120f

Mining, impact on environment 369

Minnow. *See* Fish

Miombo 59 *See* Savanna, Guinea

Mirabilis (Four O'Clock plant) 393, 419

Miracidium larva (Platyhelminthes, Trematoda) **218**; of *Schistosoma* 26, 327

Mistletoe *See Loranthus*

Mite (Arachnida, Acari) 72, 109, 129, 130, 131, 225, 305; food 73, 131; population cycles 268, **269**: Citrus Red 307: Citrus Rust 308

Mitosis 388f, **389**, **390**, 415, 416

Mitragyna, in flood plain savanna **81**, in swamp forest 85

MLWS (Mean low water spring tides) 27, **271**

Mole Game Reserve *See* Game reserve

Mole rat (*Cryptomys* and other genera) *See* Rodentia

Mollusca 502 *See* Cephalopoda, Gastropoda, Lamellibranchia

Molluscicide *327*

Mona monkey (*Cercopithecus mona*) *See Cercopithecus*

Monarch butterfly (*Danaus plexippus*) *See* Butterfly

Monkey (Mammalia, Primates) 7, 66; coexistence of species 67, 272: Baboon (*Papio* spp.) 237: Colobus, Black and White (*Colobus polykomos*) 67; Olive (*C. verus*) 67; Red (*C. badius*) 67: Drill (*Mandrillus leucophaeus*) 67; Mandrill (*Mandrillus sphinx*) 67, **68**: White-crowned Mangabey (*Cercocebus torquatus*) 67 *See also* *Cercopithecus*

Monoculture 286, 294, 298

Monophagous *147*

Monsoon, and West African rains 41

519

also Flower, Green revolution
Plantain (*Musa*) 283, 336
Plasmodiophora, germination 147
Plasmodium (Protozoa, Sporozoa) 15, **215**, 329f; *P. falciparum*, 496; *P. vivax* 215
Platyhelminthes, flatworms 71, 99 *See* Fluke, Miracidium, *Schistosoma*, Tapeworm
Pleistocene, climatic changes 59
Plutella maculipennis See Moth
Pluvial period *60*
Pneumatophore, of swamp trees **85**, **86**
Pneumococcus, 414; S and R strains 414
Poecilogale albinucha (African weasel) *See* Carnivora
Poikilocerus (Insecta, Orthoptera) *See* Grasshopper
Point quadrat *See* Quadrat
Polar body, **391**
Polistes spp. (Social wasp: Insecta, Hymenoptera) *See* Wasp
Pollen **61**, 465; analysis 61, 369, **370**; collection by bees 200f, **201**; formation of **392**
Pollination 85; attraction of insects 148ff; and cauliflory 49; and senses of insects 145ff; by pseudocopulation *150*, **151**
Pollution, of air 345, **377**; of rivers **346**, **347**, 378; of sea shore 347, 378, **379**; estimation of water pollution 348; industrial 377, **378**; military 383; oil 378, **379**
Polychaeta 15, 218, 225, **463**; lugworm (*Arenicola*) 187
Polygene *406*, 445
Polymer, abiotic synthesis 500f
Polyphagous *147*
Polyploidy *442*, 458
Pond, fish 322; sampling methods 238f; stabilization 347
Pongidae *See* Ape
Poppy (*Papaver sominiferum* and other species), coexistence of species 271; population density and maturation **258**
Population, age composition 241; control *265*, 299; cycles 268ff; interactions between species 265ff; peak 259ff, 266; regulation *256*, 265ff *See also* Population density, Population growth, Population, human
Population density *1*, *110*, 233ff; estimation of bottom fauna 238; of fish 236, 261; of freshwaters 238f; of insects 240f; of mosquitoes 241f; of parasites 244; of plankton 234; of rocky shores 238; of terrestrial plants 239f; of terrestrial vertebrates 243f; of tsetse fly 241; capture-recapture techniques 237; changes with time 246ff; edge effect 265ff; effect on mortality 254f; on

natality 256; migration 258f
Population growth, effect of density-dependent mortality 255f; prediction of 259f; rates of 246f
Population, human 354ff, 369; of Algeria **354**; of cities 343; of Ghana **354**; of Kenya **354**; age composition **358**; survivorship **252**, **355**; and food supply 261, 359f, **359**; growth rates **249**, 354, **357**; effect of age structure 358; family size 356; natality 356; practical importance of 357; control of growth 362ff; optimum 362; predictions 261, 359f, 359
Porcupine (*Hystrix* and other genera) *See* Rodentia
Porifera *See* Sponge
Potamogeton, fruit **11**; germination 11
Potassium 288, 292; fertilizer 290
Potassium/Argon ratio, for dating fossils 465f
Potato (*Solanum tuberosum*) 143, 283, 372
Potato cyst nematode (*Globodera rostochiensis*) *See* Nematoda
Potto (*Perodicticus potto*: Mammalia, Primates) 67
Prawn *See* Crustacea
Predation, differential 451; pressure 266, 268, 450; escape from 268f; protection from by chemicals 154f, concealment 163f, group formation 170f, mechanical means 153
Predator 268, 451; adaptations 177f
Pregnancy 363f; protein requirements 336
Prey 268; protection from predators 153ff, 183 *See* Predation
Prickly pear (*Opuntia*), control 302; thorns **138**, 141, 145
Primaquine **329**, 404
Primary productivity *275*; of aquatic macrophytes 275; forest 276; land plants 275f; phytoplankton 275; sea 103; measurement 275; net value *275*, 276
Primates (Mammalia) 163, 486ff; characters 486; families 486; fossil 489f *See also* Ape, *Australopithecus*, Bush-baby, *Cercopithecus*, Chimpanzee, Gorilla, *Homo*, Man, Monkey, *Paranthropus*, Potto, *Ramapithecus*
Procrypsis 177
Producers, association with consumers 219f; with decomposers 221f; relations with consumers 187
Productivity 361; and biomass 277; of different biomes 277; of coral algae 220; of game animals 339f; and growth rate 275, 319ff *See* Primary productivity
Profile diagram, of forest *44*, **44**; of

savanna types **56**
Progesterone 365, **366**
Promotor, genetic **434**, **435**, **439**
Propagules 2, 3, **5**
Prophase, of nuclear division **389**, **390**, **391**, 441
Prophylaxis *329*
Propolis *199*
Protection, from predation, by group formation 170f; strategies 174f *See* Predation
Protein, -energy malnutrition 337; first class 317, *336*; food content 323, 335; plant, as food source 361; requirements of children 336; of mothers 336; vegetable 336; synthesis 440ff, **428**, **431**, 479, **500**; control of 435f; repressor 433
Proteroglyph snake *185*, **185**
Protobiont 502
Protoperithecium **417**
Protozoa 73, 319, 478; counting in soil **127**, 128; in termite gut 131 *See* Amoeba, Ciliophora, *Entamoeba*, Flagellata, *Plasmodium*, Rhizopoda, *Trypanosoma*
Psammophis phillipsii (Olive grass snake) *See* Snake
Pseudarthria 18
Pseudocopulation, with orchids *150*, **151**
Psychoda (Mothfly) *See* Diptera
Pteridophyte, spores of 5
Pterocarpus santalinoides, water dispersal 5, **6**
Pterodactyl **474**
Puccinia 295
Pueraria 294
Pupalia, dispersal of **6**
Pure line, in breeding *393*, 407
Purine *413*, **414**
Pyramid, of biomass *See* Biomass; of energy *See* Energy; of numbers *See* Numbers
Pyrethrin 303, 329
Pyrethrum (*Chrysanthemum cinerariaefolium*) *143*
Pyrimidine *413*, **414**, 421
Python spp. *See* Snake

Quadrat, frame 1; point, for cover assessment **89**; for sampling hydrophytes 238f
Quagga (*Equus quagga*) *See* Ungulate
Quarantine, reasons for 302f
Queen substance *203*, 205, 206
Quelea quelea (Black-faced Dioch: Aves) **107**, 189; migration **108**, 258; mortality **256**
Quinine 329, 372

r See Intrinsic rate of increase
R_0 *See* Net reproductive rate
Rabbit, European (*Oryctolagus cuniculus*: Mammalia,